MODELLING AND CONTROL IN BIOMEDICAL SYSTEMS 2006
(including Biological Systems)

A Proceedings volume from the 6th IFAC Symposium,
Reims, France,
20 – 22 September 2006

Edited by

DAVID DAGAN FENG

Biomedical and Multimedia Information Technology (BMIT) Group,
School of Information Technologies, The University of Sydney, Australia, and
Department of Electronic and Information Engineering,
The Hong Kong Polytechnic University, Hong Kong

OLIVIER DUBOIS

CReSTIC Research Centre, University of Reims Champagne Ardenne,
Reims, France

JANAN ZAYTOON

CReSTIC Research Centre, University of Reims Champagne Ardenne,
Reims, France

and

EWART CARSON

Centre for Health Informatics, City University,
London, UK

Published for the
International Federation of Automatic Control
By
ELSEVIER LTD

Elsevier
The Boulevard, Langford Lane, Kidlington, Oxford OX5 1GB, UK
30 Corporate Drive, Suite 400, Burlington, MA 01803, USA

First edition 2006

British Library Cataloguing in Publication Data
A catalogue record for this book is available from the British Library

Library of Congress Cataloging-in-Publication Data
A catalog record for this book is available from the Library of Congress

ISBN–13: 978-0-08-044530-4
ISBN–10: 0-08-044530-6

Tranferred to Digital Printing, 2010

Printed and bound in the United Kingdom

PREFACE

As one of the most prestigious international events of IFAC (International Federation of Automatic Control), the 6th IFAC Symposium on Modelling and Control in Biomedical Systems (including Biological Systems) was held in Reims, France, from 20-22 August 2006. This Symposium was organised by the University of Reims Champagne Ardenne and the Société de l'Electricité, de l'Electronique et des TIC (SEE). It was sponsored by IFAC Technical Committee on Biomedical System Modelling and Control and co-sponsored by the International Union of Physical and Engineering Sciences in Medicine (IUPESM), the Institute of Electrical and Electronic Engineers, Engineering in Medicine and Biology Society (IEEE-EMBS), the International Measurement Confederation (IMEKO), the GDR MACS research network of CNRS, the Société Française de Génie Biologique et Médical (SFGBM), the Centre de Recherche en STIC (CReSTIC) of the University of Reims, the French Ministry of Research, The Region Champagne Ardenne, The City of Reims, and the Department of Marne.

Previous Symposia in this prominent theme took place in Venice, Italy in 1988, Galveston, USA in 1994, Warwick, UK in 1997, Karlsburg/Greifswald, Germany in 2000, and Melbourne, Australia in 2003. Being multi and inter-disciplinary in nature, the 2006 Symposium has attracted practitioners in engineering, information technology, mathematics, medicine and biology, and other related disciplines, with authors from 24 countries.

Further to the review process, 96 papers were accepted from the 128 contributions that were received. Besides the abstracts of the four plenary lectures, this volume contains the 92 papers that were presented by their authors at the Symposium. The published papers are coming from France, UK, Italy, USA, Germany, Portugal, New Zealand, Poland, Canada, Brazil, Mexico, Denmark, Australia, HKSAR, China, Czech Republic, Switzerland, Turkey, Romania, Uruguay, Algeria, Ireland, Hungary, and Indonesia.

In order to accommodate the large number of high-quality papers presented in the single-track sessions of the Symposium, short oral presentations at the platform plus poster presentation and discussion with the attendees before the posters were the main methods used during this symposium for attendees to exchange ideas. In addition, we have selected 20 papers, in most cases one paper per country or region, for longer oral presentations. However, both groups of papers possess the same high quality in spite of their difference in mode of presentation.

The papers included two invited keynote presentations given by internationally prominent and well-recognised research leaders: Claudio Cobelli, whose talk is titled "Dynamic modelling in diabetes: from whole body to genes"; and Irving J. Bigio, whose talk is titled "Elastic scattering spectroscopy for non-invasive detection of cancer". Two prestigious industrial speakers were also invited to give keynote presentations: Terry O'Brien from LIDCO, whose talk is titled "LIDCO: From the laboratory to protocolized goal directed therapy"; and Lorenzo Quinzio of Philips, whose talk is titled "Clinical decision support in monitoring and information systems".

The editors are grateful to the members of the IPC and the outside reviewers for their valuable contribution to the selection process and for their help in keeping high the standards of the MCBMS. We also wish to express our sincere thanks to the members of the Organising Committee for their precious help. In particular, we thank the authors and all those who have assisted us by acting as scientific or financial sponsor or cosponsor.

We hope that this volume will be a valuable source of information on the state of the art in Modelling and Control in Biomedical Systems.

The editors

David Dagan Feng, Olivier Dubois, Janan Zaytoon, and Ewart Carson

6th IFAC SYMPOSIUM ON MODELLING AND CONTROL IN BIOMEDICAL SYSTEMS (including Biological Systems) 2006

Sponsored by

International Federation of Automatic Control (IFAC)
Technical Committee on Modelling and Control of Biomedical Systems (TC 8.2)

Co-Sponsored by

IEEE/EMB - Institute of Electrical & Electronic Engineers, Engineering in Medicine & Biology Society
IMEKO - International Measurement Confederation
IUPESM - International Union of Physical & Engineering Sciences in Medicine
SFGBM - Société Française de Génie Biologique et Médicale
GDR MACS of CNRS
French Ministry of Education, Research & Technology
University of Reims Champagne Ardenne
Region Champagne Ardenne
City of Reims
Department of Marne

International Program Committee (IPC)

Honorary Chairman: Ewart Carson (UK)

Chairmen: D. Feng (AU & HK) and J. Zaytoon (F)

Lissan Afilal (FR)	Etienne Colle (FR)	Patrice Laquerriere (FR)	Joerg Raisch (DE)
Steen Andreassen (DK)	Jacques Duchêne (FR)	Swamy Laxminarayan (US)	Yannick Remion (FR)
Er-Wei Bai (US)	Aydan Erkmen (TR)	François Xavier Lepoutre	Christian Roux (FR)
Jing Bai (PRC)	Neil D. Evans (UK)	(FR)	Su Ruan (FR)
Jean-Yves Boire (FR)	Keith R. Godfrey (UK)	William S. Levine (US)	Maria Ruano (PT)
Noël Bonnet (FR)	Philippe Gorce (FR)	Derek Linkens (UK)	Michel Sorine (FR)
Tom W. Cai (AU)	Da-Wei Gu (UK)	Nigel Lovell (AU)	Fuchuan Sun (PRC)
Daniel U. Campo-Delgado (MX)	Kevin Guelton (FR)	Mahdi Mahfouf (UK)	Jasjit Suri (US)
Jean-Philippe Cassar (FR)	Thierry-Marie Guerra (FR)	Noureddine Manamanni (FR)	Karl Thomaseth (IT)
Christine Cavaro-Ménard (FR)	Per Hagander (SE)	Michel Manfait (FR)	Tatsuo Togawa (JP)
Guy Cazuguel (FR)	Randall A. Hawkins (US)	Catherine Marque (FR)	Xiuying Wang (AU)
J. Geoffrey Chase (NZ)	Martin Hexamer (DE)	Teresa Mendonça (PT)	Didier Wolf (FR)
Kewei Chen (US)	Henry S.C. Huang (US)	Saïd Moughamir (FR)	Koon-Pong Wong (HK)
Sirong Chen (HK)	Helmut Hutten (AT)	Carlos Pedreira (BR)	Liang-Chih Wu (TW)
Howard J. Chizeck (US)	Hidehiro Iida (JP)	Philippe Poignet (FR)	Tian-ge Zhuang (PRC)
Claudio Cobelli (IT)	Adriaan A. Lammertsma (NL)	Fabio Previdi (IT)	
		Alain Pruski (FR)	

Other Referees

H. Alonso	M. Farina	T. Lotz	P. Rocco
C. Azevedo Coste	M. Ferrarin	M. Lovera	A. Sala
P. Castiglioni	S. Garatti	H. Magalhães	R. Salbert
T. Chen	C. Garnier	S. Micallef	M. Sayed-Mouchaweh
V. Chen	D. Guiraud	G. Millon	T. Schauer
F. Delmotte	C. E. Hann	N. O. Negard	N. Seguy
S. Delprat	W. Holderbaum	F. Nicolier	W. Spinelli
C. Diack	P. Hoppenot	C. Nunes	R. Taïar
J. L. Diez	J. Lauber	F. Ollivier	M. Tanelli
K. Djabella	S. Lebonvallet	J. Pedro Gaivão	Q. Zhang
D. Elvia Palacios	J. Li	G. Pillonetto	

Organized by

SEE and the *Centre de Recherche en STIC* (CReSTIC) of Reims University

National Organizing Committee (NOC)

Chair: J. Zaytoon

Vice-Chairs : Lissan Afilal, Kevin Guelton, Noureddine Manamanni, Saïd Moughamir

Industrial Vice-Chair : François Fourchet

V. Carré-Ménétrier	F. Gellot	S. Lecasse	R. Taïar
O. Chevrier	K. Guelton	L. Lucas	
E. Desjardin	A. Hamzaoui	O. Nocent	
O. Dubois	R. Huez	B. Riera	

CONTENTS

BIOMEDICAL FUNCTIONAL IMAGING

BIOMEDICAL SYSTEM CONTROL

DYNAMIC MODELING IN DIABETES: FROM WHOLE BODY TO GENES

Claudio Cobelli

Department of Information Engineering,
University of Padova, Italy

Abstract: Diabetes is one of the major chronic diseases such that, together with its complications it can account for more than 10% of national healthcare expenditure. Mathematical modeling can enhance understanding of this disease in quantitative terms and is becoming an increasingly important aid in diagnosis, prognosis and in the planning of therapy. Mathematical modeling in relation to carbohydrate metabolism and diabetes has a long history stretching back some 45 years. Initially modeling has focused on the dynamics of glucose and insulin and their interactions, principally at the whole body and organ levels. However, over recent years the scope of mathematical modeling in relation to diabetes has seen dramatic expansion such that it is now being applied across the spectrum from populations of patients (public health) to the molecular level. This paper will explore recent developments of mathematical modeling in our laboratory across this ever increasing spectrum. Ingredients will include models to assess, at whole body, the efficacy of homeostatic control and system fluxes and, at organ level, unit processes in skeletal muscle, a key target tissue. To do so both whole body as well as regional tracer experiments, these last employing Positron Emission Tomography, will be discussed not only to understand the physiology but also the pathophysiology of glucose metabolism, like obesity and diabetes. Microarray technology offers an important tool to understand how genes change expression and interact as a consequence of external/internal stimuli. Dynamic stimulus/response experiments can provide time series expression data from which regulatory networks can be obtained by reverse engineering, and this is illustrated for insulin stimulation of muscle rat cells. Recent technological advances in diabetes include more reliable subcutaneous glucose sensors: interpretation and clinical use of continuous glucose monitoring time series data can be powered by dynamic modeling, in particular we show how critical hypoglycemic events can be predicted ahead in time. Finally, the importance of dynamic modeling in an important diabetes health care problem is discussed by showing its use in conjunction with gait analysis for preventing diabetic foot complications. *Copyright © 2006 IFAC*

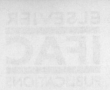

ELSEVIER
IFAC
PUBLICATIONS

LIDCO – FROM THE LABORATORY TO PROTOCOLIZED GOAL DIRECTED THERAPY

Terry O'Brien

CEO LiDCO Group Plc
Research Fellow Dept. of Applied Physiology St Thomas' Hospital, London

Abstract: A new generation of cardiovascular monitors, fueled by data from non or minimally invasive sensors, employing algorithms that model the cardiovascular system combined with user interfaces that facilitate decision support and protocolization of care are entering a new era where the costs and risks of applying the technology are going to be far outweighed by the clinical, human and financial returns. *Copyright © 2006 IFAC*

Keywords: Cardiovascular modelling, monitoring, critical care, visualization, protocol, oxygen delivery.

1. INTRODUCTION

LiDCO Group Plc is based in London and was founded in the early 1990's by Dr Terry O'Brien and Dr David Band in collaboration with the United Dental and Medical Schools of St Thomas' and Guys Hospitals (now King's College, London.) Since that time, the Group has developed inventions within the cardiovascular monitoring field. LiDCO's products have been extensively validated and demonstrated to reduce the hospital stay of high risk surgery patients by twelve days - saving £4,800 per patient treated. Extrapolated to the whole of the UK this would equate to a saving of £500 million per annum for the National Health Service.

LiDCO applies a multi-disciplinary combination of physiological expertise, sensor and computing technology to monitor and display the relationship between linked physiological variables. The transformation of raw physiological data into useable information and then specific treatment protocols that can improve clinical outcome has been a key objective throughout the development of the Company's products. LiDCO's principal products are a sensor/in vivo diagnostic product (the LiDCO System) and a continuous waveform analysis algorithm (the PulseCO System) housed in a platform monitoring product (the LiDCO*plus* Hemodynamic Monitor), which when used together provide a range of data concerning the performance of a patient's heart, blood volume and systemic oxygen delivery.

Our financing strategy was two stage, firstly to partner with our host Medical School for the start-up and pre product registration / product development phase. The funding of salaries, intellectual property development and all of the running costs were paid for though raising funds - seed capital from founders, followed by early corporate marketing license fees payments and private individuals. In this phase in total the Company raised £9.25 million. LiDCO Group became a Plc in July 2001 when it floated on the Alternative Investment Market (AIM, London) raising £15 million. Subsequent to the Aim listing we raised an additional £5 million - these funds were used for sales expansion purposes. In summary, to bring the technology to the international market has cost £29 million and taken more than ten years.

2. LIDCO'S TECHNOLOGY

Monitoring of the key cardiovascular parameters - blood pressure, cardiac output (blood flow in litres / minute) and oxygen delivery (total oxygen in mls / minute/ body surface area) - can provide a practical, early warning of cardiovascular change and adverse events in surgery and critical care patients. Improved care in this high-risk group should reduce the incidence of adverse events in hospitals and thereby reduce costs. The current market leader for the measurement of cardiac output and oxygen delivery is the highly invasive, thermodilution pulmonary artery catheter (PAC). Thermodilution derived cardiac output is the measurement of blood flow using a cold injection of an isotonic solution into the right atrium of the heart and the measurement via a thermister of the subsequent temperature change in the pulmonary artery. In addition to the risks of this technique, there are problems with the interpretation of this complex data set in the hospital acute care setting. Thus, despite being available for more than 30 years, the therapeutic value of the PAC has yet to be established and its use has been restricted to a small number of patients who could benefit from these measurements.

The LiDCO™*plus* is a cardiovascular monitor, providing continuous, reliable and accurate assessment of the hemodynamic status of critical care and surgery patients. This is achieved by running two proprietary algorithms: a continuous arterial waveform analysis system (PulseCO™) coupled to a single point lithium indicator dilution calibration system (LiDCO™). The design objective of the LiDCO™*plus* Monitor was to develop a novel platform monitor that would provide an easily interpretable user interface displaying real time: blood pressure, pre load (fluid management), cardiac output/oxygen delivery and after load (peripheral resistance) parameters. The technical innovation of the LiDCO technology is both in the method of using lithium as an intra vascular marker substance to accurately measure cardiac output and the design and clinical application of the lithium ion-selective electrode. The lithium method is at least as accurate a measurement of cardiac output as the older and more invasive PAC approach, but with the advantages of being simple and quick to set-up by a nurse or doctor, with no complications associated with its use. The LiDCO*plus* Monitor user interfaces are designed to simplify the setting and achievement of individualized target cardiovascular parameters in the acute care setting. The user, often a nurse, should be helped by interaction with the monitor interface to achieve the target by the appropriate administration of fluids and inotropic drugs and then with decision support to maintain the patient to the required target.

3. GOAL-DIRECTED THERAPY (GDT) AND IMPROVING OUTCOMES

Goal-directed therapy is a general term used to describe the use of pre-set cardiac output and oxygen delivery levels to guide intravenous fluid and inotropic drug therapy. GDT has not yet been introduced into routine practice. The principal reason for this is the limited availability of intensive care unit (ICU) facilities and staff coupled to safety concerns regarding the use of the invasive PAC to measure cardiac output. Clearly, LiDCO's minimally invasive technology could be used to implement GDT by nursing staff in risk patients after major general surgery. Therefore, a study was undertaken to assess the effect of post-operative GDT on complication rates and duration of hospital stay in high-risk general surgical patients (Pearse *et al.*, 2005). This was a randomised controlled study conducted in the adult ICU at St George's Hospital, London. Patients were assigned to GDT (62 patients) or control group (60 patients) by computer-generated random sequence. Patients in the control group were administered intravenous colloid solution to achieve a sustained increase in central venous pressure (CVP) of at least 2 mmHg for 20 minutes. GDT patients received intravenous colloid solution to achieve a sustained rise in stroke volume (amount of blood in each heart beat; cardiac output = stroke volume x heart rate) of at least 10% for 20 minutes. The GDT group also received an inotrope (dopexamine) if the targeted oxygen delivery index (DO_2I is oxygen delivery per square meter of body surface area) did not reach 600 ml min^{-1} m^{-2} with intravenous fluid alone.

The GDT group achieved significantly greater levels of oxygen delivery in the first 8 hours after surgery. Fewer patients developed complications in the GDT group (27 patients (44%) versus 41 patients (68%). The total number of complications per patient was also lower in the GDT group (0.7 per patient (SD 0.9) versus 1.5 per patient (SD 1.5); $p = 0.002$). The reduction in the number of post-operative complications in the GDT group was associated with a reduction in mean duration of hospital stay by 12 days (17.5 days versus 29.5 days, 41% reduction (95% confidence intervals 0 to 81); $p = 0.001$).

4. CONCLUSIONS

This is the first study to investigate the effects of post-operative GDT in high-risk patients undergoing major general surgery. The effect of the GDT protocol was to reduce the number of patients developing complications and shorten the hospital stay in comparison with a protocol designed to reflect standard care. LiDCO's technology uniquely provides real-time measurement of the absolute level of oxygen delivery, minimally invasively, without the need for insertion of an invasive catheter into a major artery or the heart. Using this technology to apply a nurse led GDT protocol to high-risk surgery patients reduced total hospital stay by an average of 12 days saving £4,800 per patient treated. Implementation of a similar strategy in other hospitals across the UK National Health System could result in estimated savings of £500 million annually. This GDT protocol has now become a standard of care at this hospital and is targeted to save the hospital £2 million pounds per year in bed days. The next generation of more cardiovascular monitors, coupled to treatment protocols, can dramatically reduce complications and hospital stay in risk surgery patients.

REFERENCES

Pearse, R, Dawson, D, Fawcett, J, Rhodes, A, Grounds, M, Bennett, D. (2005). Early goal directed therapy following major surgery reduces complications and duration of hospital stay. A randomised controlled trial. *Critical Care*, **9**: 687 –693.

ELASTIC SCATTERING SPECTROSCOPY FOR NONINVASIVE DETECTION OF CANCER

Irving J Bigio

*Departments of Biomedical Engineering, Electrical & Computer Engineering,
and Physics, Boston University*

Abstract: Optical spectroscopy mediated by fibre-optic probes can be used to perform
noninvasive, or minimally-invasive, real-time assessment of tissue pathology *in-situ*. The
most common approaches have been based on UV-induced fluorescence spectroscopy
and Raman spectroscopy, which are assumed to be responsive to biochemical changes in
cells. On the other hand, our method of elastic-scattering spectroscopy (ESS) is sensitive
to the sub-cellular architectural changes, such as nuclear grade or nuclear to cytoplasm
ratio, mitochondrial size and density, etc., which correlate with features used in
histological assessment. The ESS method senses those morphology changes in a semi-
quantitative manner, without actually imaging the microscopic structure. To aid in the
design of optical probes and the understanding of the resulting spectroscopic signals,
modelling of photon scattering and migration in tissue is carried out using Mie theory and
Monte Carlo simulations. Clinical demonstrations of ESS have been conducted in a
variety of organ sites, and promising results have been obtained. Larger-scale clinical
studies are now starting. *Copyright © 2006 IFAC*

ELASTIC SCATTERING SPECTROSCOPY FOR NONINVASIVE DETECTION OF CANCER

Irving Itzkan

Department of Biomedical Engineering, Newton, MA & Cambridge Opto-system
and Physics, Boston University

Abstract. Optical spectroscopy mediated by fiber-optic probes can be used to extract information quantitatively in situ, yielding the assessment of tissue pathology in vivo. The most common techniques have been based on UV-induced fluorescence spectroscopy and Raman spectroscopy, which are expected to be diagnostic of biochemical changes in cells. On the other hand, our method of elastic-scattering spectroscopy (ESS) makes the in situ subcellular architectural changes, such as nuclear grade or nuclear to cytoplasm ratio, mitochondrial size and density, etc., which correlate with features used in histological assessment. The ESS method senses these morphology changes in a different manner, without actually imaging the microscopic structure. By use of the proper choice of optical probes and the concentration of the scattered spectroscopic signals, quantitation of photon scattering and migration in tissue is carried out using Mie theory and Monte Carlo simulations. Clinical demonstration of ESS have been performed for a variety of organ sites, and promising results have been obtained. Larger scale clinical studies are now underway.

CLINICAL DECISION SUPPORT IN MONITORING AND INFORMATION SYSTEMS

Lorenzo Quinzio, MD

Philips Medical Systems Böblingen GmbH, Germany

Abstract: *Antidote to information overload:* Clinical decision support systems offer built-in intelligence to assist healthcare teams with the many tasks that demand cross-referencing and analysis of clinical information. Thus patient monitors, clinical measurements and clinical information systems may be an antidote to information overload and may help clinicians to develop a coherent picture of their patient's status. On a practical level, clinicians should implement clinical decision support systems that provide decision support automatically as part of clinician workflow, deliver decision support at the time and location of decision making, provide actionable recommendations, and use a computer to generate the decision support. The technical tools are invented, now we have to tailor them to meet the clinical users' needs. *Copyright © 2006 IFAC*

Keywords: Decision support system, information systems,

1. WHY IS THERE A NEED FOR CLINICAL DECISION SUPPORT?

Patient safety is universally recognized as the most important clinical topic in healthcare today. On the opposite the hospitals are struggling with limited resources and increasing patient acuity. Worldwide governments are trying to find solutions that enable a high standard of care without the price tag attached. Medical advancements allow people to live longer, often with the consequences of multiple chronic illnesses and a lengthened recovery period. Even more in some countries there is a shortage of clinicians, leaving nursing positions in hospitals unfilled. This leads to inexperienced and unqualified staff even in the critical care areas.

To address these deficiencies in care, healthcare organisations are increasingly turning to Clinical Decision Support Systems (CDSS), which provide clinicians with patient-specific assessments or recommendations to aid clinical decision making. CDSS have shown promise for reducing medical errors and improving patient care (Kawamoto et al, 2005).

2. WHAT IS CLINICAL DECISION SUPPORT?

Clinical Decision Support (CDS) refers broadly to providing clinicians with clinical knowledge and patient-related information, intelligently filtered or presented at appropriate times, to enhance patient care. They vary greatly in their complexity, function and application. Clinical knowledge of interest could range from simple facts and relationships to best practices for managing patients with specific disease states (HIMMS, 2006).

To be used in the clinical routine decision support systems often are designed as computer applications. They can simplify access to data needed to make decisions (Overview), assist in establishing a diagnosis and in entering appropriate orders (Review), provide reminders and prompts at the time of a patient encounter, and generate alerts or reminders when new patterns in patient data are recognized (Clinical Advisories).

Decision support systems that present patient-specific recommendations in a form that can save clinicians time have been shown to be highly effective, sustainable tools for changing clinician behaviour (Payne, 2000). Furthermore they can be used to check criteria and compliance of appropriate guidelines. To fulfil these requirements clinical decision support can be integrated into existing computer-based systems to provide decision support automatically as part of clinician workflow. Thus they could be implemented a) into diagnostic devices like the patient monitoring and b) into a documentation system like a computer based clinical information system.

Important criteria for a clinically useful CDSS are:
• Data actively used drawn from existing sources
• System improves clinical practice
• Knowledge based on best evidence
• Knowledge fully covers problem
• Clinician can control system
• The system is easy to use
• The system can be configured and updated
• The decisions made are transparent

3. CLINICAL DECISION SUPPORT IN MONITORING

Modern patient monitors like the Philips IntelliVue have built-in clinical decision support tools that reflect clinical thought processes. Clinical decision support tools built directly into patient monitors range from multi-parameter event detection and alarming (Advisories) to sophisticated graphic displays of real-time and trended data (ST Map and Horizon Trends).

A central Information Center is the heart of the Patient Monitoring Network, combining the real-time monitoring surveillance of a central station with sophisticated clinical analysis tools. The Information Center provides matchless surveillance – complete waveforms, alarms, and numerics – of networked monitors and telemetry systems. A suite of Clinical Review Applications on the Information Center provides a coherent environment for analyzing patients' complete monitoring records from the past 96 hours. A range of carefully chosen, consistently applied display techniques makes it easier to discern physiological patterns or correlate different parameters.

3.1 Overview - A better overview with ST Map

Changes in the ST segment of an electrocardiograph tracing, for example, can indicate myocardial ischemia, or less-than-normal blood flow to the heart. The graphical display of ST Map (Fig. 1) is designed around the clinician and displays a mind's-eye view of ST segment changes, with the goal of helping clinicians recognize patterns and track patient progress more easily.

3.2 Review - Smart review with Horizon Trend

Trends have in the past been used to look at patient data retrospectively. Trends allow:

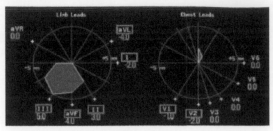

Fig. 1. Comprehensive Overview with ST Map in acute phase: ST Elevation (III; aVF, II) and ST Depression (aVL, I, V1, V2).

• Graphical representation of the patients status over a time period
• Allows for easy recognition of changes in patient status
• Layout can be organized to reflect a clinical scenario

By combining parameters on the display (Fig. 2), clinicians are assisted in their cognitive process of pattern recognition. For each parameter a baseline or target value can be set by the end user. Either the current value or a target value can be monitored for the patient. A scale can be selected to detect the baseline deviations. The arrow indicates as a Trend indicator how the patient's value has changed in the preceding ten minutes.

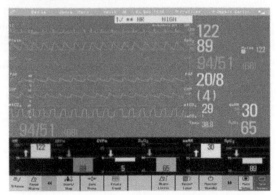

Fig. 2. The Horizon view clearly demonstrates that patient's condition is moving towards the targeted goals of therapy. Clinicians are alerted to changes that could lead to an adverse event for the patient (e.g., "back to sleep" and potential for airway obstruction).

3.3 Clinical Advisories with Advanced Event Surveillance

Events are electronic records of episodes in the patients' condition. They are used to drive alert notification to assist with protocol compliance. An Event is generated with at least one or up to four different monitoring parameters e.g. heart rate, blood pressure, respiration rate or temperature.

Advanced Event Surveillance (Fig. 3) allows clinicians to enter protocol requirements (e.g., for sepsis bundle) and let them be notified when they are met.

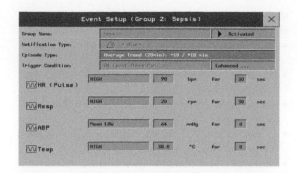

Fig. 3. Advanced Event Surveillance for heart rate, respiration rate, blood pressure and temperature.

4. CLINICAL DECISION SUPPORT IN INFORMATION SYSTEMS

Information management systems are used every day in intensive care units, operating rooms, and obstetrical departments. All are optimized for their environments, and have key qualities, including the integration of clinical decision support systems:

o Automated data acquisition from patient monitors and scores of other bedside devices, which saves charting time and reduces transcription errors.

o Open databases for comprehensive longitudinal reporting and data analysis, which supports regulatory compliance efforts, quality improvement initiatives, and research

o HL7 data exchange capabilities , to facilitate interaction with other hospital systems (e.g., HIS, LIS, pharmacy).

o Networking and remote access capabilities, to facilitate consults and information sharing among all caregivers.

4.1 Overview - Patient Summary

Clinical Information systems are able to support the workflow by enhancing the clinical work with comprehensive documentation that focuses on significant information. Once entered automatically or manually into the system, the instant availability of patient information not only helps to automate discharge or transfer documentation, it also makes it easier to provide a patient summary as a global overview for example for shift changes.

4.2 Review - problem-oriented data flowsheets

In addition to quick overviews, a flexible data review is provided with problem-oriented data flowsheets and documentation forms. This time-scalable flowsheets present patient data that has already been documented in a different context. For example a haemodynamic review shows a combination of vital signs, cardiovascular medication and laboratory data, that refer to the stability of the circulation system. A review for infection monitoring presents certain laboratory results, vital parameter like temperature and microbiological findings. Overall the user can configure decision-support flowsheets to display patient information for specific purposes (Fig. 4).

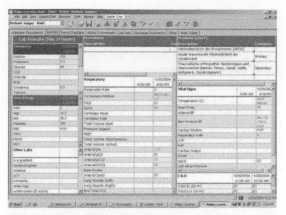

Fig. 4. The Patient summary provides a quick overview of the patient's status for easier handoffs between shifts, caregivers, etc.

4.3 Clinical advisories

Reminders, alerts and advisories draw on all the data in the chart – labs, monitoring, calculations, etc. – to provide early warning of potentially serious conditions. The available data for clinical advisories contains:

• Patient monitoring data
• Third-party devices (bedside monitors, ventilators, infusion pumps, etc.)
• Images (ultrasound, x-ray, CT, MR)
• Lab results (blood tests, urinalysis)
• Pharmacy – drug/drug interactions, dosing guidelines, Computer Physician Order Entry (CPOE), Medical Administration Record (MAR).
• Patient demographics and medical histories (e.g. ADT, microbiology)
• Documentation of patient care process, e.g. assessments and interventions

A significantly important component of this strategy is a real-time rules-based engine (Fig. 5). Integrating the aggregate patient data from the CIS and physiological measurements from the Clinical Network, this dynamic engine can trigger alerts and advisories and provide notification to the caregivers in case of any clinical significant changes, e.g. with pager or in-house phone.

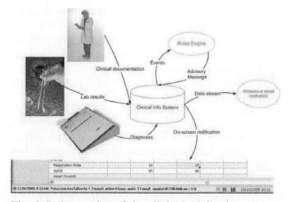

Fig. 5. Rules engine of the clinical advisories.

CDSS can be customized to help to implement clinical guidelines and protocols. It synthesizes elements from multiple data sources and present them in clinically relevant ways to help care teams make well-informed treatment choices at the point of care. With a comprehensive, longitudinal clinical database, one can track the effectiveness of new guidelines, mine patient data for trends, and substantially increase the hospital's efficiency in complying with regulatory bodies.

The guidelines for recognizing and treating sepsis put forward by the international Surviving Sepsis Campaign, for instance, call on caregivers to monitor and manage a number of parameters from many different sources, including urine output, central venous pressure, glucose levels, and blood cultures. Since CareVue Chart automatically receives lab results as well as data from patient monitors and other bedside devices, it is uniquely positioned to deliver early warnings and help nurses evaluate a patient's response to therapy.

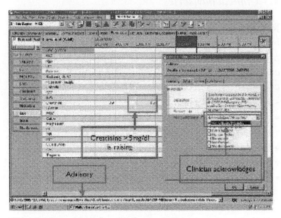

Fig. 6. Example of a clinical advisory.

5. DISCUSSION

From a technical point of view, clinical decision support systems have achieved a phase of maturity, but concerning the actual use in clinical settings, CDSS's are still in their infancy. Overall it seems that the tools are invented, but that we need to change the daily habits.

The importance of Clinical Advisories is well accepted. They help the care team by quickly identifying situations to which the team may need to respond and thus save time to treat. CDSS can effectively implement guidelines by giving patient specific recommendations at points of care. Clinical decision support can measurably improve the quality, safety and cost-effectiveness of patient care (Osheroff, 2005)

Regarding the clinical use, Garg et al. (2005) who reviewed one hundred trials that evaluated the effect of a CDSS, formulate some important issues for CDSS implementation. They include CDSS user acceptance, workflow integration, compatibility with legacy applications, system maturity, and upgrade availability.

In addition Kawamoto et al (2005) analysed 70 randomised controlled trials identifying features

strongly associated with a decision support system's ability to improve clinical practice:

- Automatic provision of decision support as part of clinician workflow
- Provision of decision support at the time and location of decision making
- Provision of recommendations rather than just assessments
- Computer based decision support, e.g. workflow integration into an electronic medical record
- Improved practitioners performance associated with CDSSs that automatically prompt users compared with requiring users to activate the system

In conclusion to make the clinicians more familiar with CDSS and to make such systems more successful accepted medical standards like guidelines should be implemented, to be used in daily practice. A targeted approach of decision support may prove to be better and more effective than a blanket one (Atreja et al 2004). A smart integration into the clinical workflow seems to be crucial.

6. ANTIDOTE TO INFORMATION OVERLOAD

Clinical decision support systems offer built-in intelligence to assist healthcare teams with the many tasks that demand cross-referencing and analysis of clinical information. Thus patient monitors, clinical measurements and clinical information systems may be an antidote to information overload and may help clinicians to develop a coherent picture of their patient's status. The technical tools are invented, now we have to tailor them to meet the clinical users' needs.

REFERENCES

Atreja A, Mehta N, Jain A, Harris CM. (2004) Computer alerts for potassium testing: Resisting the Temptation of a blanket approach *JAMIA* 2004 Sep-Oct;11 (**5**):433-4

Garg AX, Adhikari NK, McDonald H, Rosas-Arellano MP, Devereaux PJ, Beyene J, Sam J, Haynes RB. (2005) Effects of Computerized Clinical Decision Support Systems on Practitioner Performance and Patient Outcomes: A Systematic Review, *JAMA*; Vol **293**, No. 10, 1223-38

HIMMS Website (2006)http://www.himss.org/asp/to pics_clinicalDecision.asp).

Kawamoto K, Houlihan CA, Balas EA, Lobach DF (2005) Improving clinical practice using clinical decision support systems: a systematic review of trials to identify features critical to success *BMJ*; March 2005;**330** (7494):765

Osheroff JA, Pifer EA, Teich JM, Sittig DF, Jenders RA (2005) Improving Outcomes with Clinical Decision Support: An Implementer's Guide, *HIMSS Publishing*, 2005, ISBN: 0-9761277-2-5

Payne TH (2000) Computer Decision Support Systems, *Chest* **118**:47-52

ACOUSTO-OPTIC IMAGING TECHNIQUES FOR OPTICAL DIAGNOSIS

M. Lesaffre[a]**, F. Jean**[a]**, A. Funke**[a]**, P. Santos**[a]**, M. Atlan**[a]**, B.C. Forget**[a]**, E. Bossy**[a]**,
F. Ramaz[a]**, A.C. Boccara**[a]**, M. Gross**[b]**, P. Delaye**[c]**, G. Roosen**[c]

*[a] Laboratoire d'Optique, Ecole Supérieure de Physique et
de Chimie Industrielles de la Ville de Paris, CNRS UPRA0005,
Université Pierre et Marie Curie,
10 rue Vauquelin F-75231 Paris cedex 05
[b] Laboratoire Kastler-Brossel, UMR 8552 (ENS, CNRS, UMPC),
Ecole Normale Supérieure, 10 rue Lhomond F-75231 Paris cedex 05
[c] Laboratoire Charles Fabry de l'Institut
d'Optique, Unite Mixte de recherche du Centre National de la
Recherche Scientifique, de l'Institut d'Optique et de l'Univeristé
Paris-Sud, Bat 503, Centre Scientifique d'Orsay F-91403 Orsay
Cedex*

Abstract: The combination of light and ultrasound to measure optical properties through thick and highly scattering media is a tantalizing approach for \emph{in vivo} imaging. This is partly due to the ballistic nature of ultrasound in biological tissue and thus the well-defined localization of the signal with a mm^3 resolution. Optics can reveal echography-silent tumors by monitoring the wavelength of the laser source and thus measuring the optical absorption linked to *oxy-* or *deoxy-hemoglobin*. The coherent nature linked to the acousto-optic effect allows interferometric measurements. A difficulty arises from the speckle nature of the light to analyze, and two techniques with a high *etendue* are available at present in order to eliminate speckle blurring. They use either a CCD-camera that treats independently each grain of speckle, or a large area single detector and a photorefractive crystal that adapts the wavefront of the reference beam to the speckle output pattern. *Copyright © 2006 IFAC*

Keywords: Coherence imaging, Light propagation in tissues, Turbid media, Holography, Holographic interferometry, Turbid media.

1. INTRODUCTION

The transmission of light through some *cm* of biological tissue is weak, but still measurable with sensitive detectors and appropriate data post-treatment. This is essentially true for the red and near infrared region (typically between *600-1000 nm*), and thus it is possible to send light inside the human body. From a practical point of view, many difficulties have to be overcome because of the weakness of the signal and the high level of multiple light scattering. But still, optical images within thick tissues could be obtained in a near future. The last two decades have seen the emergence of different

methods in order to collect the small *flux* crossing thick tissues and to analyze it to obtain images of organs. One of these directions couples optics and acoustics with two approaches: the former consists of *tagging* photons crossing a small volume of the media with an ultrasound beam. Compared to pure optical techniques like Diffuse Optical Tomography (Gibson, *et al.*, 2005), this technique offers a higher resolution (e.g *mm³*) thus close to the one obtained with conventional echography. The basis of acousto-optic imaging has been first proposed by François Micheron and Daniel Dolphi (Dolfi, *et al.*, 1989), who looked for alternative solutions to *X-ray mammographies*, whose innocuity was subject to discussion. Though a patent has been deposited in 1987, the concept of imagery had been forgotten for a decade. More recently, a few teams have engaged on research in this field (Wang, *et al.*, 1995; Leutz, *et al.*,1995; Wang, 2001; Kempe, *et al.*, 1997; Lévêque, *et al.*, 1999; Lev, *et al.*, 2003). At present, we are developing experiments where the signal is recorded by holographic processes (Gross, *et a.*., 2003; Ramaz, *et al.*, 2004). This is a promising technique since it significantly improves the sensitivity of detection (Atlan, *et al.*, 2005; Murray, *et al.*, 2004; Gross, *et al.*, 2005). We will see in the following paragraphs the principle of the techniques, and what kind of images can be obtained. Let us first detail the principle of acousto-optics imaging: it consists to illuminate the tissues or the organ and to detect the output *flux*. Such light is of low intensity; moreover, because of multiple scattering, its structure essentially consists in many waves that have followed random paths through the media. This is due to microstructures in the tissue (cells, intracellular organites, collagen fibers,...) that perturb the propagation of light when the distance becomes larger than roughly *50μm*, which corresponds to the typical length between two scattering events. When the propagation length becomes larger than *1mm*, the scattering events are so numerous that it is not possible any more to know the initial direction and polarization of an incoming photon. When light is produced by a laser, it is possible to work with a coherent wave, whose phase and wavelength are well defined in space and time, and thus optical waves scattered by the tissues can still keep trace of this coherence state. But in which form? This is an interference pattern, detectable for example on a screen put close to the organ under study. Since the different waves have followed many different paths, their relative phases on the screen differ significantly from one point to another. The resulting intensity distribution is called speckle. This is an interference pattern appearing granular and disordered, with many bright and dark spots. Laser users are familiar of this phenomenon, easily seen with a laser pointer directed on a sheet of paper, for example: the different points of the rough surface scatter light and constitute an ensemble of secondary, but dephased sources, whose interference produces speckle.

The speckle nature of the output light linked to the media is an inherent difficulty. We will see that an appropriate treatment allows to measure selectively waves that have crossed the region subjected to the ultrasound. We use acoustic waves at *2MHz*, which corresponds to a wavelength of *0.7mm* within biological tissues, containing essentially water. A short ultrasonic pulse (*1μs*) can be focused in a volume of *1mm³*. At this frequency, the ultrasonic wave is weakly absorbed by the biological media, and exhibits a ballistic propagation.

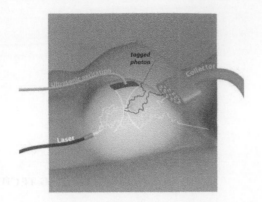

Fig. 1. Illustration of acousto-optic imaging in thick biological tissues.

2. TAGGING LIGHT WITH THE ULTRASOUND

Why do we apply ultrasound in the region of interest? Because the US modulates the *phase* of the optical waves that cross this region by creating periodically a compression or a dilatation of the medium; the microstructures of the tissue vibrate at the same frequency as the US. Since they scatter optical waves, the optical paths (the phases) of these waves are modulated periodically. In addition to the frequency of the laser ω_L, it appears within the optical waves new frequencies, so called sidebands. The main components correspond to the laser frequency shifted from plus or minus the US frequency (e.g $\omega_L + \omega_{US}$). The light exiting the media contains thus three frequency components. The dominant contribution corresponds to $\omega = \omega_L$: it is related to the diffused photons (*e.g untagged*), that have not experienced the effect of ultrasound. The photons associated to the sidebands, much more scarce, result from the interaction between light and the US; they are called *tagged photons*.

The principle of acousto-optics imaging stands as follows: in order to obtain optical information about the region of interest, one has to detect selectively the photons tagged by the ultrasound. The image is built-up by scanning the US over the organ. Conveniently, such a scan is already done along one direction when an ultrasonic pulse is used: the small vibrating region moves at the sound velocity and thus the choice of the temporal window of detection determines the position of the acoustic zone at this time (the propagation time of light is negligible even for random paths that reach up to ten times the sample thickness).

As a consequence, the small zone affected by the US can be viewed as a source of tagged photons, thus a small virtual source that explores the medium and moves at the ultrasound velocity. Supposed we detect the *tagged photons* at different times $t_1, t_2, ..$ the insonified region is located respectively at $R_1, R_2, ...,$ whose position is calculated from the velocity of sound in the medium (e.g *1500 m.s⁻¹* for water), as shown in Fig.2. At $t = t_1$, the photons from zone R_1 reaches the detector. The *flux* coming from this region depends essentially on optical properties of the medium; the more it absorbs, the weaker is the signal. Optical absorption generally has a spectral dependence. If measurements are done at many wavelengths, one can determine the nature of tissues and thus properties that are interesting from a medical point of view, such as the vascularization level or the degree of oxydation of hemoglobin.

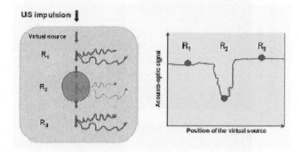

Fig. 2. Axial localization of the acousto-optic signal with an ultrasonic pulse

3. PHOTONS SELECTED BY INTERFERENCES

How is it possible to select the *tagged photons* from those that have not crossed the ultrasonic volume? Since the US frequency is very small compared to the optical one (a few $10^6 Hz$ compared to $3.10^{13} Hz$), the frequency difference between the three components is too small to be separated with an optical filter. The solution is then to analyze the speckle pattern produced by each of these fields, which are *not* correlated. One possibility is to measure on a CCD camera the interference between the signal and a reference beam at frequency $\omega_L + \omega_{US}$: since such detectors have a long response time, only the tagged photons at $\omega_L + \omega_{US}$ will be able to produce an interference signal stable enough to be detected. The other interference terms vary too fast for the CCD, and the latter can only record their average *flux*. In other words, the speckle that corresponds to frequencies other than $\omega_L + \omega_{US}$ are blurred. The CCD camera is an ensemble of micro-detectors (pixels); in order to avoid averaging effects due to the speckle, the optical conjugation is adjusted so that a speckle grain matches the size of a single pixel of the camera. In these experiments, the CCD does not provide an ordinary image, but is considered as a multi-detector matrix, and thus improves the signal to noise ratio.

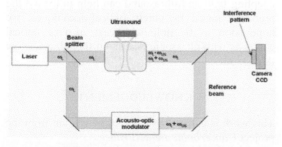

Fig. 3. Interferometric selection of the tagged-photons

In the experimental setup, a laser source (frequency ω_L) is divided into two beams (see Fig.3). One of the beam illuminates the sample that is subjected to the ultrasound. The second one (reference beam) is shifted in frequency with acousto-optic modulators such that its frequency equals one class of the *tagged photons*, e.g $\omega_L + \omega_{US}$ or $\omega_L - \omega_{US}$. A second beam-splitter recombines on the CCD the reference beam and the photons coming from the sample in order to measure the interference pattern. The summation of the intensities measured on each pixel gives the *flux* of the *tagged photons*. In fact, such a setup can give more information than the *flux* because it records the interference pattern *at a time* on all the pixels of the CCD, and this for different phase states of the reference: such a configuration determines entirely the amplitude and the phase of the optical field. The richness of this information permits to filter the noise components and thus control the quality of measurements.

4. A FASTER DETECTION WITH SELF-ADAPTIVE WAVEFRONT HOLOGRAPHY

The use of CCD cameras can be puzzling, depending on experimental situations. The amount of information required to realize an image is significant (more than a *GB*). The transfer of data and their treatment can be time consuming, which is prohibited if *real-time* measurement is required. An even more fundamental difficulty is due to *in vivo* motions of tissues, or blood circulation, because the fast variation of the phase of the photons blurs the speckle field on a time-scales between *0.1-1ms*. This phenomenon is generally called *speckle decorrelation*, and an acquisition time longer than this decorrelation reduces the signal to noise ratio of the detection. Under these conditions, the use of CCD's is not always appropriate, because acquisition rates hardly exceed a few *kHz*, the holographic technique that we develop gets rid of the camera and uses a single-element detector with a large area of $1cm^2$, but still with a fast response. An efficient *flux* collection and a fast acquisition are thus possible. This technique has initially been used to characterize vibrational modes on rough surfaces; we have adapted it for acousto-optics imagery (Delaye, *et al.*, 2000; Campagne, *et al.*, 2001).

As in the previous setup, the laser frequency is shifted in order to produce a reference beam with the same frequency as the *tagged photons*. The object beam (speckle) and the reference beam are then recombined in a photorefractive crystal (see Fig.4). In such materials, the refractive index varies from one point to another as a function of the local light intensity (Yeh). The interference pattern of the two waves is recorded within the volume of the crystal via the spatial modulation of the refractive index, and thus a hologram is built. As the crystal takes a time of about *1/10ms* to build a hologram, it records selectively the hologram of the *tagged* photons, whose temporal variation is slow.

The signal is extracted as followings : as in conventional holography, the reference is diffracted by the hologram, and produces in output a wave that is the exact replica (amplitude and phase) of the object wave coming from the *tagged photons* : at the output of the photorefractive crystal stand two waves closely related. Their interference produces a signal that is detectable with a mono-element detector, *in real-time*. This configuration has the advantage to be rapid, relatively cheap, and requiring a limited data treatment, since a single position of the ultrasound requires a single measurement.

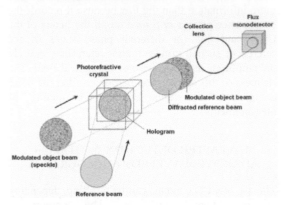

Fig. 4. Principle of self-adaptive wavefront holography

5. CONCLUSION

Another approach, somewhat inverse to the acousto-optic imagery, is based on the photo-acoustic effect. In this mode, a short laser pulse (*e.g 1ns*) is emitted and propagates through the scattering tissue. The light produces a local heating at position where it is absorbed. This heating generates a pressure wave, or rather a shock wave, that propagates in all directions at the velocity of sound. The detection of the acoustic signal created by the laser pulse is detected with many ultrasonic transducers positioned close to the region of interest and it is possible to construct a photo-acoustic image of the optical absorption of the tissue (Wang, 2003-2004}. Photo-acoustic techniques appear to be promising, especially for imaging small animals, a situation where the thickness of organs is reduced. In addition, the photo-acoustic signal can be used to simulate *non invasively* a local acoustic emitter, dedicated to hyperthermal therapy using a phase conjugate acoustic technique.

Which images can be obtained with acousto-optic methods? The technique needs further improvements, and first images are of low details compared to the ones obtained by X-rays tomographies or MRI. Up to now the aim was to establish the feasibility of the principle and to evaluate its potential. We have performed tomographic images on phantoms models approaching the optical properties of human tissues (e.g turkey breast or calibrated scattering gels of thicknesses in the range of *2-4cm* containing absorbing inclusions). One of the experiments

consisted of a turkey breast of which a region has been overheated by an intense ultrasonic beam (hyperthermal therapy). The acousto-optic image, obtained with a few hundreds of points, reveals clearly the heated zone (Fig. 5).

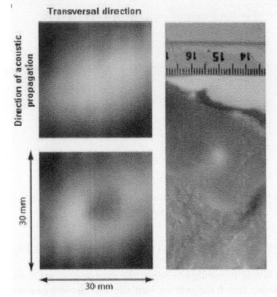

Fig. 5. Evidence of an acousto-optic contrast after hyperthermal heating.

Though the acousto-optic method has been shown feasable, much work remains to be done in order to obtain images suited for medical diagnosis. Some clinical tests will be undertaken in the next months on female breasts, an organ well suited for this technique. The technique can be improved in many ways can be brought to the technique, for example by automation of the data acquisition, but one of main the difficulties remains the weakness of the signal. If coupled however, with other imagery techniques, acousto-optic tomography should reveal itself as useful to diagnosis as it gives access to information on the optical properties of tissues (color, absorption and scattering coefficient), which is impossible to obtain with X-rays, echography or MRI imaging techniques.

Seeing through highly scattering media such as biological tissues is still a goal difficult to reach. The main reason being that the scattering is heterogeneous which makes the inverse problem very complex. Here we have tried to demonstrate that coupling light and ultrasound can help to bypass the problems raised by purely optical techniques: we hope soon to be able to reveal *in vivo* optical contrasts with ultrasonic resolution though a few *cm* thick tissues.

ACKNOWLEDGEMENTS

This work is currently supported by a grant from the project *Cancéropôle Ile-de-France*.

REFERENCES

Atlan M., B.C. Forget, F. Ramaz, A.C. Boccara, and M. Gross (2005). Pulsed acousto-optic imaging in dynamic scattering media with heterodyne parallel speckle detection, *Opt. Lett.* **30**(11), 1360-1362.

Campagne B., A. Blouin, L. Pujol, J.P. Montchalin (2001). Compact and fast response ultrasonic detection device based on two-wave mixing in a gallium arsenide photorefractive crystal, *Rev. Sc. Inst.* **72** 5, 2478-2482 (2001).

Delaye P., S. de Rossi, G. Roosen (2000). High amplitude vibrations detection on rough surfaces using a photorefractive velocimeter, *Opt. and Las. in Eng.* **33**, 335-347.

Dolfi D. and F. Micheron (1989). Imaging process and system for transillumination with photon frequency marking, *International Patent WO 98/00278(1989).*

Gibson, A.P., J.C. Hebden and S.R. Arridge (2005). Recent advances in diffuse optical imaging. *Phys. Med. Biol* **50**, pp. 1-43.

Kempe M., M. Larionov, D. Zaslavsky, and A. Z. Genack (1997). Acousto-optic tomography with multiple scattered light, *J. Opt. Soc. Am. B* **14**, 1151-1158.

Gross M., P. Goy, and M. Al-Koussa (2003), Shot-noise detection of ultrasound-tagged photons in ultrasound-modulated optical imaging, *Opt. Lett.* **28**, 24.

Gross M. , F. Ramaz, B.C. Forget, M. Atlan, A.C. Boccara, P.Delaye, and G. Roosen (2005). Theoretical description of the photorefractive detection of the ultrasound modulated photons in scattering media, *Opt. Exp.***13**(18), 7097-7112.

Leutz W. and G. Maret (1995). Ultrasonic modulation of multiply scattered light, *Physica B* **204**, 14.

Lev A. and B. Sfez (2003). In vivo demonstration of ultrasound-modulated light technique, *J. Opt. Soc. Am. A* **20**(12), 2347-2354.

Lévêque S., A. C. Boccara, M. Lebec, and H. Saint-Jalmes (1999). Ultrasonic tagging of photon paths in scattering media: parallel speckle modulation processing, *Opt. Lett.* **24** (3), 181.

Murray T.W., L. Sui, G. Maguluri, R.A. Roy, A. Nieva, Blonigen F., and C.A. DiMarzio (2004). Detection of ultrasound-modulated photons in diffuse media using the photorefractive effect, *Opt. Lett.* **29**(21), 2509.

Ramaz F., B. C. Forget, M. Atlan, A. C. Boccara, M. Gross, P. Delaye, and G. Roosen (2004). Photorefractive detection of tagged photons in ultrasound modulated optical tomography of thick biological tissues, *Opt. Exp.* **12**(22), 5469-5474.

Wang L. (2001). Mechanisms of ultrasonic modulation of multiply scattered coherent light: a analytic model, *Phys. Rev. Lett.* **87**, 1.

Wang L.H, S.L. Jacques and X. Zhao (1995) Continuous wave ultrasonic modulation of scattered light to image objcets in turbid media, *Opt. Lett.* **20**, 629.

Wang L.V. (2003-2004)., Ultrasound-mediated biophotonic imaging : a review of acousto-optical tomography and photo-acoustic tomography, *Disease Markers*, **19**, 123-128.

P. Yeh. *Introduction to Photorefractive Nonlinear Optics*, Wiley eds, ISBN: 0-471-58692-7.

IMPROVEMENT OF THE CONTRAST IN CANCER DETECTION BY AUTOFLUORESCENCE BRONCHOSCOPY USING A NARROW SPECTRAL VIOLET EXCITATION : A PRELIMINARY STUDY

Blaise Lovisa[1], Tanja Gabrecht[1], Snezana Andrejevic[2], Pierre Grosjean[2], Alexandre Radu[2], Philippe Monnier[2], Bernd-Claus Weber[3], Hubert van den Bergh[1], Georges Wagnières[*1]

[1] *Swiss Federal Institute of Technology (EPFL), Laboratory of Photomedicine, 1015 Lausanne, Switzerland*
[2] *The CHUV University Hospital, ENT Department, CH-1011 Lausanne, Switzerland*
[3] *Richard Wolf Endoscopes GmbH, D-75438 Knittlingen, Germany*

Abstract: Autofluorescence (AF) bronchoscopy is a useful tool for early cancer detection. However the mechanisms involved in this diagnosis procedure are poorly understood. We present a clinical autofluorescence imaging study to assess the depth of the principal contrast mechanisms within the bronchial tissue comparing a narrowband (superficial) and broadband (penetrating) violet excitation. Knowledge of this parameter is crucial for the optimization of the spectral and optical design of clinical diagnostic AF imaging devices. An intensity contrast improvement was observed with the narrowband excitation, suggesting that the heme absorption plays a key role in the AF contrast mechanism. *Copyright © 2006 IFAC*

Keywords: medical systems, intensity contrast enhancement, autofluorescence imaging, bronchial cancer, clinical study.

1. INTRODUCTION

Bronchial carcinoma is the leading cause of cancer deaths in the world with the highest incidence rate in North America and Europe. Most of the lesions are diagnosed at an advanced stage, which explains the very small 5-years survival rate corresponding to this condition (Jemal, *et al.*, 2004). Thus, improved techniques for detection of early lesions are urgently needed. Bronchoscopy is the only established method that allows detection, localization and definitive histological diagnosis of endobronchial lesions.

*Georges Wagnières, Swiss Federal Institute of Technology (EPFL), Station 6, Building CH, 1015 Lausanne, Switzerland, Tel. +41216933120, Fax +41216935110, e-mail: georges.wagnieres@epfl.ch

Conventional white-light bronchoscopy (WLB) has nevertheless important diagnostic limitation; the most important being its small sensitivity for early cancerous and pre-cancerous lesions (Hirsch, *et al.*, 2001). Therefore, one promising approach to overcome this limitation is based on the imaging of the tissue autofluorescence (AF) (Goujon, *et al.*, 2003; Wagnières, *et al.*, 2003). While WLB detects mostly minimal alterations of the tissues, autofluorescence bronchoscopy (AFB) exploits the spectral differences and intensity contrasts between normal and early cancerous tissues. More precisely, the spectral contrast in AFB is based on the decrease in the green spectral region of the tissue AF intensity of the spectrum for (pre-)cancerous lesions compared to healthy tissue under violet excitation (Hung, *et al.*, 1991; Wagnières, *et al.*, 2003; Zellweger, *et al.*, 2001b). Such contrasts can be visualized with the help of specific endoscopic imaging devices (Wagnières, *et al.*, 1998).

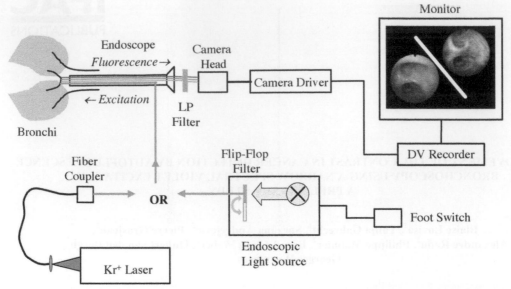

Fig. 1. The fluorescence imaging setup consisting of a filtered endoscopic light source and a filtered endoscopic camera. Light from the Kr+ laser can be coupled into the endoscope instead of the light from the endoscopic light.

Numerous clinical studies have demonstrated that AFB is about twice more sensitive than WLB for the detection of bronchial CIS and dysplasia (Goujon, *et al.*, 2003; Häußinger, *et al.*, 2005; Lam, *et al.*, 1998; Pierard, *et al.*, 2001; Sutedja, *et al.*, 2001; Wagnières, *et al.*, 2003). However, this high sensitivity comes along with a limited specificity (Wagnières, *et al.*, 2003). Although the mechanisms underlying the tumor/healthy contrasts are poorly understood at the present time, it is likely that the decrease of hemoglobin concentration in the sub-mucosa plays a significant role. This statement is supported by the study reported by (Zellweger, *et al.*, 2001b). In an extensive spectral study of the bronchial tissue AF, it demonstrated that the best contrasts between healthy and (pre-)malignant tissues on one hand, and meta- and hyperplasia vs. (pre-) malignant lesions on the other hand, are observed with an excitation spectral domain much smaller (410nm,FWHM 3nm), than usually used in AFB (typically 430nm, FWHM 40nm). Therefore, the preliminary study described here aims to investigate the influence of the excitation spectrum bandwidth on the contrast with imaging AFB. More precisely, we report the contrast improvement between a broadband filtered light source from the DAFE system (Richard Wolf Endoscopes GmbH, Germany) and a line shape excitation from a Krypton laser.

2. MATERIALS AND METHODS

2.1 Imaging System

In this study, we compared AF images obtained with a broad- and a narrowband excitation light source, as illustrated schematically in Figure 1.

The diagnostic autofluorescence endoscopic imaging system (DAFE) basically consists of a filtered endoscopic light source and a camera driver unit. An IR filtered 300W Xenon lamp (Richard Wolf Endoscopes GmbH, Germany) was used as a broadband excitation source. It is equipped with a flip-flop filter holder, allowing the operator to switch easily between white and violet excitation light, this light being delivered to the bronchoscope optics via a liquid light guide. The violet excitation filter has a central transmission wavelength at 430nm with a FWHM of 40nm.

Light from a Krypton (Kr+) laser (Spectra Physics Type 171) was used as the narrowband excitation. This light was injected into a $400\mu m$ optical quartz fiber and coupled into the liquid light guide mentioned above using a custom made fiber coupler. The latter allows the operator to change the injection angle, which can be useful to homogenize the illumination on the bronchi. The Kr+ laser was used in the multi-line mode (407nm, 413nm) with a maximal output power of 2.5W. However, due to the limited transmission of the light guide, the power of the violet light was about 150 mW with both excitation sources.

The white light and the AF images are detected in both setups by a 3 CCD endoscopic camera (Richard Wolf Endoscopes GmbH, Germany) clipped to the endoscopic optics. The zoom objective of the camera was equipped with a 475nm cut-on long pass filter, in order to reject all violet excitation light. The system can be used with conventional rigid optics or fibro-endoscope. The images are visualized on a monitor and tape- recorded on a digital video (DV) recorder.

2.2 Endoscopic procedure

All 3 patients participating in the study had known bronchial lesions which had been identified previously by AF bronchoscopy with the DAFE

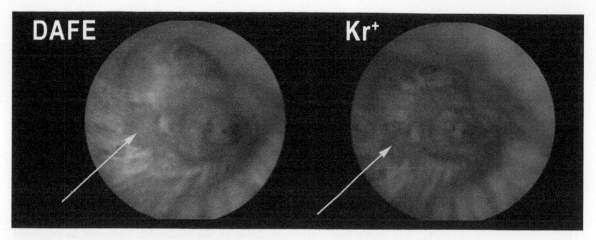

system in a former examination. The lesions were first examined under conventional white light (WL) illumination, and then with the broadband DAFE excitation. Eventually, the DAFE light source was replaced by the Krypton laser, and the same lesions were examined. At the end of each site observation, one biopsy per site was taken to perform a histopathological analysis of the site. All the examinations were performed under total anesthesia using rigid optics. The whole procedure was captured by the endoscopic camera and tape-recorded on the DV recorder.

2.3 Image analysis

Image analysis was performed offline in order to compute the green channel intensity ratio between the lesion and the surrounding healthy tissue. Still images from the DV recording were digitized via the IEEE1394 port of a portable PC. Several analysis zones (typically 3) were selected per biopsied site to

Fig. 2. Green color channel of an image showing the intermediate bronchus excited with the broadband (DAFE) and the narrowband (Kr+) excitations. Arrows show a pre-cancerous lesion with sharp intensity decrease.

accommodate the geometry artifacts resulting from different angles of view, distance between probe and tissue and position of the endoscope within the bronchi. Zones were classified according to their visual appearance on the image. Selection criteria for a lesion were an AF+ zone in the region of the later-taken biopsy and presence of no blood, whereas a healthy lesions has no suspect appearance. All the pixels intensity values were background-subtracted and gamma-corrected. The resulting green-to-green ratio is given by $(G_t/G_h) = (G_{tumor}) / (G_{healthy})$. Consequently, a high contrast between a lesion and healthy tissue is associated with a small ratio.

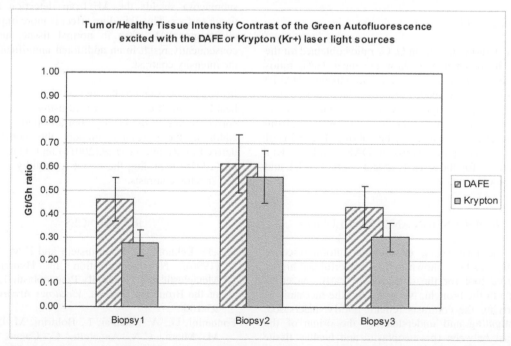

Fig. 3. Tumor vs. Healthy Tissue Intensity Contrast of the Green Autofluorescence excited with the DAFE or Krypton (Kr+) laser sources. The errors bars show the error resulting from the image analysis procedure (±20%)

Suspect sites under violet excitation were classified as autofluorescence positive (AF+), whereas unsuspicious sites were labeled AF-. According to (Gabrecht, *et al.*, 2005a), the errors related to this image analysis procedure were estimated by computing and comparing the intensity level values and ratios from multiple AF+ and AF- zones selected arbitrarily within a sample image. They were in the order of ±10% for the intensity and ±20% for the intensity ratios. The errors related to the image analysis procedure

3. RESULTS

Three patients undergoing pre-therapeutic or therapeutic panendoscopy were included in the study. A total of 3 positive lesions were examined alternatively with the broadband and the narrowband excitation. Each lesion was AF+ in both excitation modes, but hardly visible under WL illumination. Two biopsies (1 and 3) were graded as CIS, and biopsy 2 was graded as severe dysplasia.

3.1 Visual results

Figure 2 depicts the green channel images of the AF images obtained with the broadband (DAFE) and line-shape (Kr+) excitation light. It shows two lesions on the spur and the inner wall of the intermediate bronchus. A distinct intensity decrease (i.e. contrast) in the lesion areas compared to the normal surrounding tissues is clearly distinguishable. For each site, the intensity decrease of the green AF is more marked with the Kr+ laser than with the broadband excitation.

3.2 Image analysis

Figure 3 shows the mean G_t/G_h ratios obtained on the tree. The hatched bars show the mean G_t/G_h ratios per site obtained with the broadband (DAFE) excitation source, while the plain bars show ratios obtained with the line-shape (Kr+) excitation source. The error bars represent the 20% error resulting from the image analysis as described above. The ratios of the G_t/G_h compared between DAFE and the Kr+ excitations for the sites 1, 2 and 3 are 1.7, 1.1 and 1.4, respectively.

4. DISCUSSION AND CONCLUSION

Over the past years, endoscopic autofluorescence imaging has been shown to be a powerful and highly sensitive tool for the detection of early cancerous lesions in the bronchi. Nevertheless, the mechanisms underlying the contrasts remain poorly understood. Investigating and understanding the origin of the contrast between (pre)neoplastic and healthy tissue will allow an optimization of the available devices. Spectrofluorometric *in vivo* studies conducted by (Qu, *et al.*, 1995) and (Zellweger, *et al.*, 2001a;

Zellweger, *et al.*, 2001b) have shown a sharp intensity decrease in the green part of the AF spectrum on tumoral lesions relative to normal tissues. These results are also in good agreement with the G_t/G_h ratios computed in our study, which are smaller than 1. As shown in Figure 3, our preliminary study suggests that a better intensity contrast between healthy tissues and lesions is achieved with the narrowband excitation. Indeed, the average G_t/G_h ratio is 1.4 ± 0.3. This is in reasonable agreement with the mean ratios adapted from Zellweger's data (G_t/G_h=1.6).

Since only the ratio of the green AF was computed, we can not assess whether the spectral contrast is modified by the bandwidth. However, as suggested by (Gabrecht, *et al.*, 2005b), the bandwidth of the excitation light has no detectable influence on the spectral contrast, i.e. the intensity ratio between the red and green channels.

The better contrasts obtained with the narrowband excitation suggests that the concentration of blood in the tissue can be regarded as a key factor underlying these contrast mechanisms. Indeed, the Kr+ laser light is centered on 410nm, which corresponds to the absorption peak of hemoglobin. The morphometric studies from (Fisseler-Eckhoff, *et al.*, 1996) and (Fontanini, *et al.*, 1999) showed an increase in the microvessel density (MVD) in the (pre)neoplastic bronchial tissues, the increase of MVD preferentially occuring in the vicinity of the basement membrane. Hence, the blood concentration is higher in/under the abnormal tissue than in its healthy surrounding tissue. Due to the light absorption properties of blood, the Kr+ excitation light will be strongly absorbed by the tissue blood in the superior layers of the submucosa. Moreover, the tissue blood in the submucosa shields the AF from detection at the tissue surface. This shielding effect is more important in (pre)neoplastic than in normal tissue and will consequently result in an additional amplification of the intensity contrast.

In conclusion, our results suggest that the tumor to healthy contrast can be improved using an excitation corresponding to the hemoglobin absoption peak. In addition, these results support the conclusions derived by Zellweger *et al.*(2001b) and Gabrecht *et al.* (2005b) regarding the tumor to healthy intensity and spectral contrasts.

REFERENCES

Fisseler-Eckhoff, A., D. Rothstein and K.M. Müller (1996). Neavascularization in Hyperplastic, Metaplastic and Potentially Preneoplastic Lesions of the Bronchial Mucosa, *Virchows Archiv*, **429**, 95-100

Fontanini, G., A. Calcinai, L. Boldrini, M. Lucchi, M. Mussi, C.A. Angeletti, C. Cagno, M.A. Tognetti and F. Basolo (1999). Modulation of Neoangiogenesis in Bronchial Preneoplastic Lesions, *Oncol Rep*, **6**, 813-817

Gabrecht, T., A. Radu, P. Grosjean, B.C. Weber, G. Reichle, L. Freitag, P. Monnier, H. van Den Bergh and G. Wagnières (2005a). Improvement of the Specificity of Cancer Detection by Autofluorescence Imaging in the Tracheo-Bronchial Tree Using Backscattered Violet Light, *submitted*,

Gabrecht, T., P. Uehlinger, S. Andrejevic, P. Grosjean, A. Radu, P. Monnier, B. Weber, H. Van Den Bergh and G. Wagnières (2005b). Influence of the Excitation Wavelength on the Tumor-to-Healthy Contrast in Autofluorescence Bronchoscopy - a Comprehensive Study, *Proceedings of SPIE - The International Society for Optical Engineering*, **5862**, 1-6

Goujon, D., M. Zellweger, H. Van Den Bergh, G. Wagnières, A. Radu, P. Grosjean, P. Monnier and B.C. Weber (2003). In Vivo Autofluorescence Imaging of Early Cancers in the Human Tracheobronchial Tree with a Spectrally Optimized System, *Journal of Biomedical Optics*, **8**, 17-25

Häußinger, K., F. Stanzel, M. Kohlhäufl, H. Becker, F. Herth, A. Kreuzer, B. Schmidt, J. Strausz, S. Cavaliere, K.M. Müller, R.M. Huber, U. Pichlmeier and C.T. Bolliger (2005). Autofluorescence Bronchoscopy with White Light Bronchoscopy Compared with White Light Bronchoscopy Alone for the Detection of Precancerous Lesions: A European Randomised Controlled Multicentre Trial, *Thorax*, **60**, 496-503

Hirsch, F.R., S.A. Prindiville, Y.E. Miller, W.A. Franklin, E.C. Dempsey, J.R. Murphy, Bunn P.A, Jr. and T.C. Kennedy (2001). Fluorescence Versus White-Light Bronchoscopy for Detection of Preneoplastic Lesions: A Randomized Study, *Journal of the National Cancer Institute*, **93**, 1385-1391

Hung, J., S. Lam, J. LeRiche and B. Palcic (1991). Autofluorescence of Normal and Malignant Bronchial Tissue, *Lasers in Surgery and Medicine*, **11**, 99-105

Jemal, A., L.X. Clegg, E. Ward, L.A.G. Ries, X. Wu, P.M. Jamison, P.A. Wingo, H.L. Howe, R.N. Anderson and B.K. Edwards (2004). Annual Report to the Nation on the Status of Cancer, 1975-2001, with a Special Feature Regarding Survival, *Cancer*, **101**, 3-27

Lam, S., T. Kennedy, Y.E. Miller, M. Unger, D. Gelmont, V. Rusch, B. Gipe, D. Howard, J.C. LeRiche, A. Coldman and A.F. Gazdar (1998). Localization of Bronchial Intraepithelial Neoplastic Lesions by Fluorescence Bronchoscopy, *Chest*, **113**, 696-702

Pierard, P., B. Martin, J.-M. Verdebout, J. Faber, M. Richez, J.-P. Sculier and V. Ninane (2001). Fluorescence Bronchoscopy in High-Risk Patients - a Comparison of Life and Pentay Systems, *J Bronchology*, **8**, 254-259

Qu, J., C.E. MacAulay, S. Lam and B. Palcic (1995). Laser-Induced Fluorescence Spectroscopy at Endoscopy: Tissue Optics, Monte Carlo Modeling, and in Vivo Measurements, *Optical Engineering*, **34**, 3334-3343

Sutedja, T.G., H. Codrington, E.K. Risse, R.H. Breuer, J.C. Van Mourik, R.P. Golding and P.E. Postmus (2001). Autofluorescence Bronchoscopy Improves Staging of Radiographically Occult Lung Cancer and Has an Impact on Therapeutic Strategy, *Chest*, **120**, 1327-1332

Wagnières, G., A. McWilliams and S. Lam (2003). Lung Cancer Imaging with Fluorescence Endoscopy, *Handbook of Biomedical Fluorescence*, 361-396

Wagnières, G.A., W.M. Star and B.C. Wilson (1998). In Vivo Fluorescence Spectroscopy and Imaging for Oncological Applications, *Photochemistry and Photobiology*, **68**, 603-632

Zellweger, M., D. Goujon, R. Conde, M. Forrer, H. Van den Bergh and G. Wagnières (2001a). Absolute Autofluorescence Spectra of Human Healthy, Metaplastic, and Early Cancerous Bronchial Tissue in Vivo, *Applied Optics*, **40**, 3784-3791

Zellweger, M., D. Goujon, H. Van Den Bergh, G. Wagnières, P. Grosjean and P. Monnier (2001b). In Vivo Autofluorescence Spectroscopy of Human Bronchial Tissue to Optimize the Detection and Imaging of Early Cancers, *Journal of Biomedical Optics*, **6**, 41-51

FUZZY CLUSTERING ON ABDOMINAL MRI FOR ADIPOSE TISSUE QUANTIFICATION

Vincent Roullier *,**,[1] **Christine Cavaro-Ménard** *
Christophe Aubé *** **Guillaume Calmon** **

* *LISA UPRES-EA 4014, Angers, France*
** *GE Healthcare, Department of Radiology, Velizy, France*
*** *Angers Hospital, Medical Imaging Department, Angers, France*

Abstract: In this paper, we present an automatic and reliable segmentation to quantify intra-abdominal to subcutaneous adipose tissue ratio, in metabolic syndrome diagnosis. We use dual echo Magnetic Resonance (MR) images acquired in phase and out of phase. The segmentation is provided by two fuzzy algorithms: fuzzy generalized clustering and fuzzy connectedness algorithm. A result validation is performed with a comparison of expert results with purpose-made software results. *Copyright © 2006*

Keywords: image processing, medical applications, MRI, fuzzy algorithms, classification, robust performance, reliability evaluation.

1. INTRODUCTION

Medical image computing has revolutionized the field of medicine by providing new methods to extract specific medical informations. Image segmentation is one of the most important steps as preprocessing of many image data analysis. Image processing can help radiologists in diagnosis, treatment planning, as well as treatment delivery. The main goal of the segmentation process is to divide an image into regions that have strong correlation with objects or areas of the real world depicted in the image. Medical images are *fuzzy* by nature, they can be considered as a composition of different signal intensities providing from: different specific tissues, noise, blurring, background variations, partial voluming and certain acquisition-specific effects (e.g. surface coil intensity falls off in MR imaging).

The metabolic syndrome is found in more than one quarter of all adults over the age of 40 years. Its presence greatly increases the risk of developing *cardiovascular disease*, *kidney disease*, and *diabetes*. The accumulation of intra abdominal adipose tissue is at least in part responsible for the development of the metabolic syndrome. Intra-peritoneal adipose tissue represents 10 to 15% of total adipose tissue in lean subject. Criteria of metabolic syndrome are based on biological and morphological measure and particuliarly of the waist circumference. Circumference depends on intra peritoneal and subcutaneous adipose tissue surfaces. We propose to study this fat distribution to prevent risk accurated by the metabolic syndrome. The visceral adipose tissue to subcutaneous adipose tissue ratio is a useful marker

---

[1] PhD financed by GE Healthcare

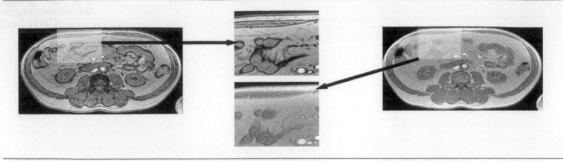

Fig. 1. On the left, the out of phase slice, on the right, in phase slice. In the middle, a zoom of any parts of images

of this disease (Positano *et al.*, 2004) . In clinical pratice, this measurment requires a long and tedious manual segmentation by radiologists and can not be use routinely. Positano *et al.* (Positano *et al.*, 2004) proposed a method based on fuzzy algorithm and active contour models to quantify the surfaces of visceral and subcutaneous adipose tissue. Results are good for subcutaneous fat but take into account some internal organs (as kidney, colon and aorta that don't contains fat) in the visceral fat. In fact, active contour model is not adapted to segment visceral fat because of all internal organ that are complex to be taken into account. The method described in (Poll *et al.*, 2003) used a specific acquisition. They suppressed the peak of the water and threshold the result. This method is rapid but requires radiologist intervention to discriminate visceral fat to subcutaneous fat and include non fat pixels because their intensity are close to fat intensity. After discussion with expert, we decide that radiologist intervention is important but not before or during the process. The process must be automatic. In fact, this intervention has to allowed just as the end as verification and/or modification.

In this paper, we present the material used and the acquisition parameters. Next, we describe the two fuzzy algorithms. In the third section, we present results and validation of our process. We conclude and present the perspectives in the fourth section.

2. MATERIAL

2.1 Patients

There were 37 patients (28 men and 9 women) included in this study, median age 59.7 years, range 42 to 73 years, median weight 94.13 kg, range 66 to 126 kg, median Body Mass Index (BMI) 33.4 kg/m^2, range 24.3 to 41.3 kg/m^2. These patients are over weighted and have metabolic syndrome.

2.2 Acquisition

MR Imaging was performed in all patients using standard technique. In brief, patients were examined suspine using a static 1,5 Tesla machine and flexible phases array surface coil wrapped around the patients abdomen (Signa Excite and 8 body phase array coil - GE Healthcare - Milwaukee). Axial T1-weighted gradient echo in-phase and out-of-phase examinations were performed at level L3 vertebrae. All the examinations were performed in breath hold to avoid motion artefact. The acquisition parameters as FOV are selected according to the patient morphology. The images are presented in the Fig. 1.

In the following section, we present our automatic segmentation process based on two algorithms : fuzzy clustering and fuzzy connected.

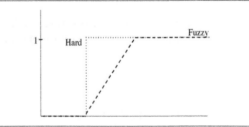

Fig. 2. Dot line represents hard truth and dash line represents partial truth.

3. ALGORITHMS

3.1 Fuzzy Logic

As we explain in introduction, the MR images are fuzzy by nature because each pixel involves the signal intensity received from a volume element of the patient by the coil. The use of algorithms based on fuzzy logic is then justified by the nature of MR images. The fuzzy logic is an expansion of the *boolean logic* dealing by the concept of the **partial truth**. Whereas the classical logic holds that statement can be expressed only in binary terms (0 or 1, black or white, yes or no), fuzzy logic replaces the boolean truth values with degrees of truth (see Fig. 2).

3.2 Fuzzy clustering based on objective function

Fuzzy clustering methods are based on the definition of an objective function. The objective function assigns a quality or error to each cluster arrangement. This quality is based on the distance between data and typical attributs of cluster (i.e. prototypes).

Prototype based algorithm can be divided into two categories: probabilistic and possibilistic approaches. Each approach owns a particular objective function family.

3.2.1. Clustering problem
The aim of clustering is to create from initial dataset a partition that underlines the structure of this dataset. The clustering problem is stated as follow :

- Let $Y = y_1, y_2, \ldots, y_n$ be the dataset to be partitioned. Each of the $y_{i=1..n}$ is defined as a p-dimensional vector $y_i = (y_{i_1}, \ldots, y_{i_p})$.
- Let c be the wished number of classes.
- Let $U = (u_{ik})$ be a $c \times n$ matrix where u_{ik} is the membership of point y_k in class i.
- Let $V = v_1, v_2, \ldots, v_c$ be the c prototypes resulting of clustering algorithm. These cluster prototypes are p-dimensional points.
- Let m be the fuzzy index, $m \in]1, +\infty[$.

The probabilist fuzzy partition, considers that for each point the sum of all the memberships should be equal to 1. The Possibilistic c-Means algorithm was proposed by Krishnapuram (Krishnapuram, 1993) to alleviate the influence of outlier by relaxing this constraint. The clustering problem depends on the objective function used $J(Y, U, V)$ define according to Y, the data set we want to cluster, U, the membership matrix and V the prototype matrix. The solution that minimize the objective function is given by an iterative algorithm presented in algorithm 1 and supply the optimal solution of the problem.

Algorithm 1 Iterative resolution of the minimization of objective function

---
Require: m, U_0, V_0, ε, $n \leftarrow 0$
  while $|V_{n+1} - V_n| > \varepsilon$ **do**
    $U_{n+1} \leftarrow f(U_n)$
    {f: membership update function}
    $V_{n+1} \leftarrow g(V_n)$
    {g: prototype update function}
    $n \leftarrow n + 1$
  end while

Some objective functions (fuzzy or possibilist) and differents approaches have been proposed in lit-

terature as Bezdek (Bezdek, 1981). We propose in this paper using generalized objective function presented by M. Menard (Ménard and Eboueya, 2001) including Tsallis information (Tsallis, 2000). Tsallis information allows to spread centroid more than classical objective function. This particularity is important in our algorithm to easily connect fat classified region and non fat classified region with the second algorithm. Now, we present the generalized objective function.

3.2.2. A probabilistic generalized function family
We must minimize the following probabilistic generalized objective function (Eq. 1):

$$J(U,V;Y) = \sum_{i=1}^{c} \sum_{k=1}^{n} u_{ik}^m d^2(y_k, v_i)$$
$$+ \frac{1}{\lambda(m-1)} \sum_{i=1}^{c} \sum_{k=1}^{n} u_{ik}^m \qquad (1)$$
$$- \frac{1}{\lambda} \sum_{k=1}^{n} \gamma_k (\sum_{i=1}^{c} u_{ik} - 1)$$

The first term is the mean square term, equivalent to the Bezdek objective function presented in (Bezdek, 1981) The second term defines Tsallis entropy when $\sum_{i=1}^{c} u_{ik} = 1$.

The mimisation of Eq. 1 gives Tsallis normalized distribution (Eq. 2):

$$u_{ik} = \frac{1}{Z_m} [1 + \lambda(m-1) d^2(y_k, v_i)]^{-\frac{1}{m-1}} \qquad (2)$$

where $Z_m = \sum_{j=1}^{c} [1 + \lambda(m-1) d^2(y_k, v_j)]^{-\frac{1}{m-1}}$. The prototype update equation can be written as (Eq. 3):

$$v_i = \frac{\sum_{k=1}^{n} u_{ik}^m y_k}{\sum_{k=1}^{n} u_{ik}^m} \qquad (3)$$

The probabilistic generalized algorithm is called Probabilistic Generalized c-Means (FGcM).

3.2.3. A possibilistic generalized function family
If the probabilistic one $\sum_{k=1}^{n} \gamma_k (\sum_{i=1}^{c} u_{ik} - 1)$ is replaced by the possibilistic constraint term $\frac{1}{\lambda} \sum_{k=1}^{n} u_{ik}$.

The functional that we obtained is the following (Eq. 4):

$$J(U,V;Y) = \sum_{i=1}^{c} \sum_{k=1}^{n} u_{ik}^m d^2(y_k, v_i)$$
$$+ \frac{1}{\lambda(m-1)} \sum_{i=1}^{c} \sum_{k=1}^{n} [u_{ik}^m - u_{ik}] \qquad (4)$$
$$- \frac{1}{\lambda} \sum_{i=1}^{c} \sum_{k=1}^{n} u_{ik}.$$

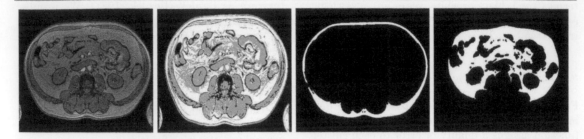

Fig. 3. Example of result. Left to right : the out of phase image, the classified image, the automatic segmentation of the subcutaneous fat, the automatic segmentation of intra-abdominal fat.

The second term is the Tsallis entropy. The last term is the possibilistic constrain.

The membership update function is then the following (Eq. 5):

$$u_{ik} = \frac{1}{[1 + \lambda(m-1)d^2(y_k, v_i)]^{\frac{1}{m-1}}} \quad (5)$$

The prototype update function is given by (Eq. 6):

$$v_i = \frac{\sum_{k=1}^{n} u_{ik}^m y_k}{\sum_{k=1}^{n} u_{ik}^m} \quad (6)$$

The possibilistic generalized algorithm is called Possibilistic Generalized c-Means (PGcM).

In our algorithm, we used successively FGcM and PGcM algorithms. First, we used the FGcM algorithm because the probabilistic constrain gives us prototypes with more regularity. Then we initialize the PGcM algorithm with the previously found prototype. To be stable, the PGcM algorithm needs to be initialized near the real prototype.

After classification process, we applie the fuzzy connectedness algorithm on classification results.

3.3 Fuzzy Connectedness Problem

The Fuzzy Connected Image Segmentation framework developed by Udupa (Udupa and Samarasekera, 1996) assigns fuzzy affinity measurment to each object we want to connect. The affinity between two given pixels (or voxels) in an image (or a volume) is defined as a combined weighted function of the degree of coordinate space adjacency, the degree of intensity space adjacency, and the degree of intensity gradient space adjacency. The goal of this step is to define the specific intensity patterns attached to the object of interest.

We defines the connectedness problem as follow :

- A binary scene over a fuzzy digital space $(\mathbb{Z}^n, \alpha)$ is a pair $\xi = (C, f)$, where C is a n-dimensional array of spatial elements (pixels or voxels) and f is a function whose domain is C (called the scene domain), and whose range is a subset of the closed interval $[0, 1]$.

- A reflexive and symetric fuzzy relation μ_k in C that measure the affinity or two pixels.

In the following section, we call c and d the image locations of two pixels in the image, and c the fixed point of the studied region.

We define in C the fuzzy affinity k as follow (Eq. 7):

$$\begin{aligned} k &= \{((c,d), \mu_k(c,d) | (c,d) \in C\} \\ \mu_k &: C \times C \to [0,1] \\ \mu_k(c,c) &= 1, \ \forall c \in C \\ \mu_k(c,d) &= \mu_k(d,c), \ \forall (c,d) \in C. \end{aligned} \quad (7)$$

The general form of μ_k can be written as follows (Eq. 8):

$$\begin{aligned} \mu_k(c,d) &= h(\mu_\alpha(c,d), \mu_\psi(c,d), \mu_\phi(c,d), c, d) \\ & \forall (c,d) \in C, \end{aligned}$$

where:

- $\mu_\alpha(c,d)$ represents the degree of coordinate space adjacency of c and d,
- μ_ψ represents the degree of intensity space adjacency of c and d,
- μ_ϕ represents the degree of intensity gradient space adjacency of c and d.

We define the fuzzy k-connectedness K as a fuzzy relation in C, where:

- $\mu_k(c,d)$ is the strength of the strongest path between c and d,
- the strength of a path is the smallest affinity along the path.

In a generic implementation of a fuzzy connectedness for (Eq. 8), we used (Eq. ??):

$$\mu_k(c,d) = h(\mu_\alpha(c,d), f(c), f(d), c, d), \quad (8)$$

where:

- $\mu_\alpha(c,d)$ is an adjacency function based on the distance of two pixels,
- $f(c)$ and $f(d)$ are the intensity of pixels c and d, respectively.

In this general form, $\mu_k(c,d)$ is shift-variant. In other words, it depends on the location of pixels c and d.

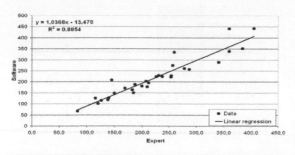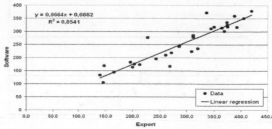

Fig. 4. Comparison between results obtained by radiologist and by the algorithm. Left : Subcutaneous fat, Right Visceral fat

We used a more specific and shift-invariant definition for a fuzzy affinity was introduced in (Eq. 9)

$$\mu_k(c,d) = \mu_\alpha(c,d)[w_1 h_1(f(c), f(d)) + w_2 h_2(f(c), f(d))], \quad (9)$$
$$\mu_k(c,c) = 1,$$

where, $\mu_k(c,d)$ is a linear combination of $h_1(f(c), f(d))$ and $h_2(f(c), f(d))$, with $w_1 + w_2 = 1$. The three features taken into consideration are: the adjacency between the pixels $\mu_\alpha(c,d)$, the intensity of the pixels $h_1(f(c), f(d))$, and the gradient of the pixels $h_2(f(c), f(d))$.

The adjacency function $\mu_\alpha(c,d)$ is assumed to be a hard adjacency relation, such that:

$$\mu_\alpha(c,d) = \begin{cases} 1 & if \ \sqrt{\sum_i(c_i - d_i)^2} \leq 1 \\ 0 & otherwise, \end{cases} \quad (10)$$

where $c_i (0 \leq i \leq n)$ are the pixel coordinates in n dimensions. The functions h_1 and h_2 are Gaussian functions of $\frac{1}{2}(f(c) + f(d))$ and $|f(c) - f(d)|$, respectively, such that:

$$h_1(f(c), f(d)) = exp-\frac{1}{2}[\frac{\frac{1}{2}(f(c)+f(d))-m_1}{s_1}]^2$$
$$h_2(f(c), f(d)) = exp-\frac{1}{2}[\frac{(|f(c)-f(d)|)-m_2}{s_2}]^2 \quad (11)$$

where m_1 and s_1 are the mean intensity and standard deviation of the intensity of the sample region and m_2 and s_2 are the mean and standard deviation of the gradient of the sample region.

4. RESULTS

To separate the fat from the rest, we perform a classification with three prototypes show in Fig. 3 (background, fat, and the rest (organ, muscles, ...). Final results are presented in Fig. 3.

4.1 Validation

The validation of this method was in two steps. We began by inter- and intra-observer analysis of the viseral and subcutaneous of the sufaces obtained by manual segmentation. The observers are two radiologists (MD-PhD and MD) and segment

manually the slice on the advantage workstation (GE Healthcare - AW 2.0) installed in the hospital. We observed a good correlation(Tab. 1, 2) with a good reproductability ($P < 0.05$).

Table 1. Correlation coefficient of inter-expert segmentation. R1 VAT and R1 SAT (respectively R2 VAT and R2 SAT) represent respectively the result of the manual visceral and subcutaneous adipose tissue segmentation of the radiologist 1 (respectively 2).

	R1 SAT	R1 VAT
R2 SAT	0.96	XXX
R2 VAT	XXX	0.94

Table 2. Correlation coefficient of the intra-expert segmentation. R1 VAT1 and R1 SAT1 (respectively R1 VAT2 and R1 SAT2) represent respectively the result of the manual visceral and subcutaneous adipose tissue segmentation of the radiologist at the date number 1 (respectively 2) .

	R1 SAT 1	R1 VAT 1
R1 SAT 2	0.96	XXX
R1 VAT 2	XXX	0.95

Comparison between quantification of subcutaneous fat using purpose-made software and manual segmentation by radiologist showed an excellent correlation (R^2=0.89, P<0.05) (Fig. 4).

Automatic quantification of intra-abdominal fat correlated with manual segmentation (Fig. 4) shows a good correlation (R^2=0.85 , P<0.05). The difference is explained by the presence of structures like aorta, intestine or colon in peritoneum.

Bland and Altman tests showed that results between the two segmentation (manual and automatic) are coherent for the two computed segmentation (Fig. 5).

We excluded four patients from this study because their breath hold (during the examination) was not controled, the body was not entire covered or the image post-reconstruction failed (Fig. 6).

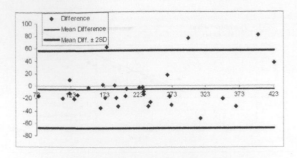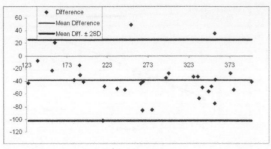

Fig. 5. Bland and Altman statistic test: Left, Subcutanerous fat and right, visceral fat

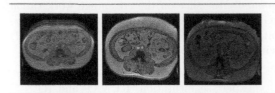

Fig. 6. Sample of exclude patients: Left to Right : breath artefact, non entire body cover, reconstruction error.

In this case, the automatic process gave results but those ones were absurds. We need to propose a graphical user interface to allow radiologist to segment and correct results.

5. CONCLUSION AND PERSPECTIVES

5.1 Conclusion

In this paper, we propose an automatic, reliable and non-invasive method to quantify abdominal fat and to quantify a marker of the metabolic syndrome.

The coefficient of correlation between automatic and manual measurments is comparable to inter- and intra- observer variability for the subcutaneous fat, and acceptable but not as good for intra-abdominal fat.

This evaluation confirms the choice of fuzzy logic that is adapted to the nature of our images. More over the process needs only few seconds (whereas active contour models need long computer time).

5.2 Perspectives

Futures developments could improve these results by taking into account inhomogeneity of the signal intensity. We can reduce the inhomogeneity by using a new protocol that corrects the intensity with a pre-calibration. We can also include inhomogeneity correction in the FGcM algorithm. in phase image are not use in this algorithm but radiologist use it to discriminate fat from region not fat. We could add these images in the classification process.

REFERENCES

Bezdek, J.C. (1981). *Pattern Recognition with Fuzzy Objective Function Algorithms*. Plenum Press,New York.

Krishnapuram, R. (1993). A possibilistic approach to clustering. *IEEE Trans. Fuzzy Systems*.

Ménard, Michel and Michel Eboueya (2001). Extreme physical information and objective functions in fuzzy clustering. *Fuzzy Sets and Systems*.

Poll, L.W., H.J. Wittsack, J.A. Koch, R. Willers, M. Cohnen, C. Kapitza, L. Heinemann and U. Mödder (2003). A rapid and reliable semi-automated method for measurment of total abdominal fat volumes using magnetic resonance imaging. *Magnetic Resonance Imaging*.

Positano, V., A. Gastaldelli, A.M. Sironi, M.F. Santarelli, M. Lombardi and L. Landini (2004). An accurate and robust method for unsupervised assessment of abdominal fat by mri. *Journal of Magnetic Resonance Imaging*.

Tsallis, C. (2000). Entropic nonextensivity: a possible measure of complexity. *Fractal*.

Udupa, Jayaram K. and Supun Samarasekera (1996). Fuzzy connectedness and object definition: Theory, algorithms, and applications in image segmentation. *Graphical Models and Image Processing* **58**(3), pp. 246–261.

RETINAL ANGIOGRAM REGISTRATION BY ESTIMATION OF DISTRIBUTION ALGORITHM

Johann Dréo * **Jean-Claude Nunes** **
Pierre Truchetet * **Patrick Siarry** *

* *Université Paris XII, Val de Marne, Laboratoire Image*
Signaux et Systèmes Intelligents (E.A. 3956), 61 avenue
du Général de Gaulle, 94010 Créteil CEDEX
** *Université Rennes 1, Laboratoire Traitement du Signal*
et de l'Image (UMR INSERM 642), Campus de Beaulieu,
Bâtiment 22 35042 Rennes CEDEX

Abstract: Retinal fundus photographs are employed as standard diagnostic tools in ophthalmology. We employ optimization techniques for registration of retinal angiograms, using non-linear pre-processing (Wiener filtering and morphological gradient) and computation of a similarity criterion. The present work makes a comparison between different optimization techniques, namely the *optical flow* minimization method, the *Nelder-Mead* local search, the *CEDA* and *CHEDA* metaheuristics. The impact of the resolution and median filtering of gradient image is studied and the robustness of the approaches is tested through experimental studies, performed on ICG angiographies. Our proposed method has shown interesting results, especially for high resolution registration problems. *Copyright © 2006 IFAC*

Keywords: Image registration, optimization, meta-heuristic, image processing, biomedical images.

1. INTRODUCTION

Registration is an important tool for solving many medical image analysis problems. Many common minimization strategies have been applied to image registration problems, such as exhaustive search, gradient descent, simplex method, simulated annealing, genetic algorithms and Powell's minimization (Ritter et al., 1999; Jenkinson and Smith, 2001).

In most cases, the registration is performed in two steps: image processing and optimization of a similarity criterion. The image processing step aims at improving the image quality and extracting the relevant information required to perform the optimization step. The optimization step, in term, must find the optimal shift according to an objective function, describing the quality of the registration. The optimization step is often carried out by implementing mathematical optimization methods, that are generally only suitable for local optimization and may fail to find a global optimum.

As the image processing and the calculation of the objective function are time consuming, global optimization methods such as metaheuristics, that require more evaluations, are often avoided in favour of local optimization methods, that need less time to find an optimum. But, when dealing with complex problems involving local optima, the use of global optimization algorithms can be successful (Jenkinson and Smith, 2001).

Combinations of temporal images or different image modalities are frequently used in order to help physicians in their diagnosis. During any angiographic sequence, there will inevitably be eye movements and it is essential that this phenomenon be corrected prior to the application of quantitative analysis. The use of the registration methods has become an important tool for computer-assisted diagnosis and therapy. The registration process permits the generation of deformation fields that reflect the transformation of an image in a realistic way with respect to the given anatomy. The goal of the present work was to improve analysis quality in various applications of ophthalmology by improving angiogram registration.

This paper presents registration of the retinal angiograms using a metaheuristic as a global optimization method and is composed of five more sections. It firstly examines the registration problem and the image processing methods used (Section 2) and then introduces the optimization tools (Section 3), mainly an *IDEA* metaheuristic. Results are presented in Section 4 and an elaborated discussion is presented in Section 5. Finally, conclusion makes up the last section.

2. REGISTRATION OF RETINAL ANGIOGRAMS

Rigourous experimentations have shown that our earlier proposed method in (Nunes et al., 2004), based on a local search is not sufficiently robust (only 30% in indocyanine green angiograms) in case of strong inter-image variations. In the majority of the previously published works on automatic registration of the retinal images (Berger et al., 1999; Can and Stewart, 1999; Hampson and Pesquet, 2000; Mukhopadhyay and Chanda, 2001; Pinz et al., 1998; Ritter et al., 1999; Simo and de Ves, 2001; Zana and Klein, 1999), it was assumed that the extraction of the features or the landmarks are known *a priori*. However, in late phase, the retinal angiogram images are characterized by poor local contrast. The proposed method can overcome the problems associated with detection in the vascular structures. This article presents an algorithm for the automatic iconic registration of fluorescein and indocyanine green angiograms which is based on non-linear processing, summing of pixel-wise squared differences and optimization techniques.

2.1 Retinal angiography images

Normally, series of ocular fundus images are obtained through fluorescein and/or ICG angiography. Both of these tests are useful for evaluating the retinal and choroidal circulation and in the diagnosis and treatment approaches for many retinal diseases such as Age Related Macular Degeneration (ARMD), Cyto-Megalo-Virus Retinitis (CMVR) and Diabetic Retinopathy (DR) (Richard et al., 1998).

This technique consists of an injection of fluorescein or ICG in the arm's cubital vein, followed by the observation of its distribution along retinal vessels at certain time instants. Retinal angiography (up to 36 frames) (Richard et al., 1998) is usually divided into three phases, early, mid and late. It thus provides the ability to visualize vascular or choroidal structures, and possibly detect existing diseases.

The vessels are the only significant visible structures (Richard et al., 1998) in all the images used in angiographic registration. However, variations in local intensity can give rise to many difficulties, namely non-uniform background of the image, poor local contrast, eye movements, various kinds of noises, and the presence of blood vessels having non-connected endings, due to local intensity variations.

2.2 Image preprocessing

The filtering stage or noise reduction allows a more robust registration of the images. The first stage namely Wiener filtering attempts to obtain edge-preserving filtering of the vascular structure, to permit angiographic registration. Since during angiography there are intensity variations of the retinal structures, we computed the registration transform from gradient images (morphological gradient) and not from original images.

2.3 Image registration

The registration of the retinal images is required to recognize and quantify vascular retinopathies and choroïdopathies like in DR, CMVR and ARMD. Automated registration of the retinal images enables accurate comparisons between the images and equips to automate the calculation of the changes for both the lesions and the normal anatomic structures.

Mostly classical search strategies have been used in motion analysis and image registration problems (Bangham et al., 1996; Hart and Goldbaum, 1994; Irani et al., 1994; Kim et al., 2001; Odobez and Bouthemy, 1994; Zhang and Blum, 2001).

One common approach in most of these strategies is the application of a multiresolution method (Odobez and Bouthemy, 1994; Zhang and Blum, 2001) based on optical flow, where the search is performed at increasingly higher resolutions. An important area of use of medical image registration is for retinal images (Berger et al., 1999). In order to perform the reliable registration of the retinal images, feature extraction is generally employed (Berger et al., 1999). Moreover, presence of low local contrast and noise makes the detection of vascular structure difficult. However, there exists no registration method for ICG angiograms. We proposed an iconic registration method based on the optical flow (Nunes et al., 2004), but it is not robust enough in the case of ICG images. This method can be suitably applied only in the case of the fluorescein images.

2.4 Method proposed for the registration

2.4.1. Registration method   An overview of several registration algorithms can be found in (Brown, 1992; Maintz and Viergerver, 1998; Hill et al., 2001). We propose to compute only the translation transform since it is more significant and more delicate to be obtained.

The proposed algorithm can be summarized in five steps:

- Wiener filtering of the original image,
- morphological gradient computing,
- median filtering (optional step),
- computing the similarity measurement (summing of absolute intensity differences) between the two images under the current transform,
- and global optimization of similarity criteria.

Thus, before transform computing, a non-linear pre-processing is performed.

Over the last few years, intensity-based (or iconic) techniques have been applied to a number of registration problems. Their basic principle is to maximize a criterion measuring the intensity similarity of corresponding pixels.

The similarity measurement is the calculation used to judge the closeness between two images under the current transformation. In (Roche et al., 1999), Roche *et al.* demonstrated what are the assumptions made corresponding to a number of popular similarity measurements in order to better understand their use, and finally how to choose a method which is the most appropriate one for a given class of problems. The sum of squared intensity differences (SSD), the sum of absolute intensity differences (SAD) (Yu et al., 1989), cross-correlation (Cideciyan et al., 1992), entropy of the difference image, etc. are easy to compute and often afford simple minimization techniques. Many Computer Vision algorithms employ the sum of pixel-wise squared differences between the pair of images as a statistical measurement of similarity. (Roche et al., 1999).

3. OPTIMIZATION TOOLS

An optimization problem can be defined as a problem in which the aim is to find the best of all possible solutions. More formally, find a solution in the search space which has the minimum (or maximum) value of the objective function. In the case of the registration problem, the objective function must describe how good is a registration between two images. We will therefore consider the similarity function and the set of the feasible image shifts respectively as the objective function and the moves within the search space.

Many different automatic registration methods have been proposed to date, and almost all of them share a common mathematical framework, *i.e.* optimizing a cost function. It has been demonstrated (Nunes et al., 2004) that in case of ICG angiograms the use of optical flow together with the standard multiresolution approach is not sufficient to find the global minimum, reliably.

One can potentially employ several optimization techniques that are available in practice. One of the most widely used categories is the category of the local search algorithms like gradient descent, iterated descent, simplex methods and so on. These methods can efficiently solve simple optimization problems with only one optimum. When dealing with more difficult problems, with local optima, global search algorithms are often used, especially metaheuristics, like evolutionary algorithms, simulated annealing or ant colony algorithms. The advantage of local search algorithms is their rapidity, but their main drawback is that they can get easily trapped in local optima.

In this paper we have tested three methods, a simplex local search algorithm called the Nelder-Mead Search (*NMS* (Nelder and Mead, 1965)), an estimation of distribution algorithm (*CEDA*, (Bengoetxea et al., 2002)) and an hybrid of these two algorithms (*CHEDA*) (Dréo, 2004), for the problem under consideration.

Estimation of distribution algorithms are populationnal metaheuristics where an explicit probability distribution is used for computing the transistion between two iterations.

3.1 Objective function and parameter setting

The base of the objective function used to describe the problem is the similarity criterion, previously described in the section **??**. The function is defined as $f : N \rightarrow R$ to be minimized.

The *CEDA* and *CHEDA* algorithms are used with default parameter values (selection ratio: 0.5). The number of points is set to 100 and the allowed maximum number of iterations for the simplex, in the *CHEDA* algorithm, set to 10. The stopping criterion used is a limit of evaluation number. In this paper, the upper limit is fixed to 2000 calls to the objective function. The *NMS* algorithm uses default parameter values. The algorithm stops if the current step length is smaller than 10^{-8} or if it has reached the limit of evaluation number.

4. RESULTS

All angiographic images used in this paper were digitized from the video signal output at a resolution of 1024×1024 pixels and with a quantization of 8 bits per pixel. The algorithms have been tested on different resolutions from 10% to 100% of the original image size, and with or without additional median filtering of the gradient image.

4.1 Preliminary tests

In order to comprehend the behaviour of the optimization algorithm and to test its consistency for the problem, we used a simple registration problem where the global optimum is known (Figure 1).

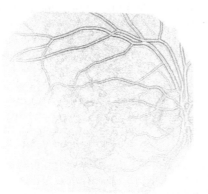

Fig. 1. Simple registration problem used.

Classical mathematical optimization techniques require less computation time when performing a registration at low resolutions. However, when dealing with a high resolution problem, the time taken can drastically increase. On the contrary, the computation time used by the metaheuristic

remains almost unchanged for different resolutions.

4.2 Robustness

In order to test the robustness of the methods, we have performed 20 tests on the same simple registration problem. Generally classical local optimization methods used in registration of angiograms are employed for low resolution problems. As high resolution images carry more informations, we have tested the impact of resolution on the efficiency of the metaheuristic. Moreover, the additional median filtering is often used to improve the optimization test. However since it is the computation time which is of prime concern for this problem, we have tested its real impact when using the metaheuristics for the optimization step.

The additional filtering is only relevant for high resolutions. The standard deviation is a good measure of the robustness of the algorithm, as it is a measure of the number of bad registrations, *i.e.* the greater the standard deviation is, more times the algorithm fails to find a good registration.

The *NMS* algorithm used alone can find optimal positions, with standard deviation increasing with resolution, whereas the *EDA* algorithms show very little variations in their efficiencies (Figure 2).

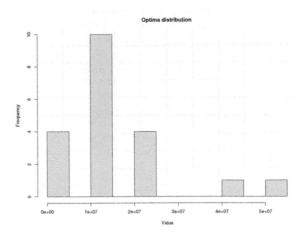

Fig. 2. Distribution of the optima for the CHEDA algorithm.

4.3 Test case

According to the results of the robustness tests, we have tested the metaheuristic for a high resolution (100% of the original image size) without additional median filtering. We have used a set of 4 angiograms, performing 20 optimizations on each image.

The metaheuristics could not determine the precise global optimum for all the runs. Indeed, if they always find an approaching value for the ideal registration, they can lack in determining the accurate shift values.

The *CHEDA* metaheuristic can achieve better robustness than *CEDA* method, which is also better than the *NMS* local search used alone. However, there can still be some problems in accurate registration, where a translational motion is not sufficient to represent the real transform. In spite of having a good dominant registration, there can be a residual error at the periphery of the angiogram.

5. DISCUSSION

Our results demonstrate that using a metaheuristic for the optimization step of the registration of angiograms can be very useful when dealing with high resolution images. Indeed, the main advantage of the optimization methods presented in this paper lies in their constant evaluation cost. With classical methods like the optical flow, the time cost of the optimization drastically increases with the resolution. This is not the case for the methods presented above, as the number of evaluations remains constant with variations in the resolution. This feature of metaheuristics is due to their sampling operated on the objective function, which is not dependent on the way the problem is calculated but depends on the way the algorithm behaves.

However, the computation time still remains a critical constraint and our result shows that for high resolutions, employing an additional median filtering is not an advantage as it decreases the robustness and increases the computation time. Our notion is that one should try to avoid too many additional filtering steps as this may filter out some of the relevant informations presented to the metaheuristic, and thus decrease its ability to find the global optimum.

The *NMS* method shows the same advantage as the metaheuristic from the point of view of computation time, as its performance remains almost unchanged with increase in resolution. However, our results show that the robustness of this local search decreases when optimizing high resolution problems. This is due to the existence of local optima that can trap the local search. Indeed, this problem is often encountered in classical local optimization algorithms used in registration and is solved by a multi-resolution approach. But such approaches are highly time consuming, and the use of a metaheuristic solves the problem posed by local optima without drastically increasing the computation time.

The problem of the peripheral error is less significant compared to the dominant translation, which is most difficult to be obtained. This problem cannot be solved through a rigid approach. Indeed, an elastic registration method can be used to correct this residual transform, as shown in (Nunes et al., 2004).

6. CONCLUSION

Registration is an important issue in many applications concerning medical image analysis, as motion correction and multimodal fusion. Because of eye movements during the angiographic acquisition, a registering stage of angiographic frames is necessary to improve the quantitative analysis of the retinal pathologies. The superposition of the images will allow direct comparison with the previous images, and this can be favourably utilized to judge the progress of the disease.

However, angiographic data can vary considerably in intensity (*e.g.* the grey levels of the blood vessels vary from dark to bright in the angiographic phases) and intensity based registration algorithms are hence unsuitable for this purpose. The optimization techniques used are especially adapted for high resolution problems where more classical techniques cannot be favourably used due to the excessive time requirement. The metaheuristics are proved to have a better robustness than a local search algorithm and can achieve good qualitative registrations.

Future evolves are intended to test these algorithms on more complex problems involving more parameters, such as affine registration, elastical registration or multi-resolution methods where the low time cost characteristic of metaheuristics should be a decisive factor. Furthermore, the methods can be better adapted to the problem, with the use of a tuned initial step or a more powerful similarity criterion, like mutual information. The authors wish to pursue these research directions in near future.

ACKNOWLEDGEMENTS

The authors also wish to thank Centre Hospitalier Intercommunal of Créteil (CHIC) for providing a large number of retinal angiographic images, and for partially supporting this work.

REFERENCES

J. A. Bangham, R. Harvey, and P. D. Ling. Morphological scale-space preserving transforms in many dimensions. *J. Electronic Imaging*, 5:283–299, 1996.

E. Bengoetxea, T. Miquélez, P. Larrañaga, and J. A. Lozano. *Estimation of Distribution Algorithms, A New Tool for Evolutionary Computation*, chapter Experimental Results in Function Optimization with EDAs in Continuous Domain, pages 181–194. Genetic Algorithms and Evolutionary Computation. Kluwer Academic Publishers, 2002.

J. W. Berger, M. E. Leventon, N. Hata, W. Wells, and R. Kinikis. Design considerations for a computer-vision-enabled ophtalmic augmented reality environment. *Lectures Notes in Computer Science*, 1205:399–410, 1999.

L. G. Brown. A survey of image registration techniques. *ACM Comput. Surveys*, 24:325–376, 1992.

A. Can and C. V. Stewart. Robust hierarchical algorithm for constructing a mosaic from images of the curved human retina. In *IEEE Conf. on Computer Vision and Pattern Recognition*, volume 22, 1999.

A. V. Cideciyan, S. G. Jacobson, C. M. Kemp, R. W. Knighton, and J. H. Nagel. Registration of high resolution images of the retina. In *SPIE: Medical Imaging VI: Image Processing*, volume 1652, pages 310–322, 1992.

J. Dréo. *Adaptation de la méthode des colonies de fourmis pour l'optimisation en variables continues. Application en génie biomédical.* PhD thesis, Université Paris 12 Val de Marne, 13 December 2004.

F. J. Hampson and J. C. Pesquet. Motion estimation in the presence of illumination variations. *Signal Processing: Image Communication*, 16:373–381, 2000.

W. E. Hart and M. H. Goldbaum. Registering retinal images using automatically selected control point pairs. In *IEEE International Conference on Image Processing*, 1994.

D. L. G. Hill, P. G. Batchelor, M. Holden, and D. J. Hawkes. Medical Image Registration. *Physics in Medicine and Biology*, 46:1–45, 2001.

M. Irani, B. Rousso, and S. Peleg. Computing occluding and transparent motion. *IJCV*, 12:5–16, 1994.

M. Jenkinson and S. Smith. A global optimisation method for robust affine registration of brain images. *Medical Image Analysis*, 5:143–156, 2001.

M. Kim, J. C. Jeon, J. S. Kwak, M. H. Lee, and C. Ahn. Moving object segmentation in video sequences by user interaction and automatic object tracking. *Image and Vision Computing*, 19:245–260, 2001.

J. B. A. Maintz and M. A. Viergerver. A survey of medical image registration. *Med. Image Anal.*, 2:1–36, 1998.

S. Mukhopadhyay and B. Chanda. Fusion of 2D grayscale images using multiscale morphology. *Pattern Recognition*, 34:606–619, 2001.

J. A. Nelder and R. Mead. A simplex method for function minimization. *Computer Journal*, 7:308–313, 1965.

J. C. Nunes, Y. Bouaoune, E. Deléchelle, and P. Bunel. A multiscale elastic registration scheme for retinal angiograms. *Computer Vision and Images Understanding*, 2004.

J. M. Odobez and P. Bouthemy. Robust multi-resolution estimation of parametric motion models applied to complex scenes. Technical Report 788, IRISA, 1994.

A. Pinz, S. Bernögger, P. Datlinger, and A. Kruger. Mapping the human retina. *IEEE Trans. on Med. Imag.*, 17:606–619, 1998.

G. Richard, G. Soubrane, and L. A. Yannuzzi. Fluorescein and ICG angiography. *Thieme*, 1998.

N. Ritter, R. Owens, J. Cooper, R. H. Eikelboom, and P. P. V. Saarloos. Registration of stereo and temporal images of the retina. *IEEE Trans. On Medical Imaging*, 18:404–418, 1999.

A. Roche, G. Malandain, N. Ayache, and S. Prima. Towards a better comprehension of similarity measures used in medical image registration. In *MICCAI*, 1999.

A. Simo and E. de Ves. Segmentation of macular fluorescein angiographies, a statistical approach. *Pattern Recognition*, 34:795–809, 2001.

J. J.-H. Yu, B.-N. Hung, and C.-L. Liou. Fast algorithm for digital retinal image alignment. In *IEEE Ann. Int. Conf. Engineering Medicine Biology Society, Images Twenty-First Century*, volume 2, pages 374–375, 1989.

F. Zana and J. C. Klein. A multimodal registration algorithm of eye fundus images using vessels detection and Hough transform. *IEEE Trans. on Medical Imaging*, 18:419–458, 1999.

Z. Zhang and R. S. Blum. A hybrid image registration technique for a digital camera image fusion application. *Information fusion*, 2:135–149, 2001.

AUTOMATIC MULTIMODAL REGISTRATION OF GATED CARDIAC PET, CT AND MR SEQUENCES

Xavier Baty [*,1] **Christine Cavaro-Ménard** [*]
Jean-Jacques Le Jeune [**]

* LISA UPRES-EA 4014 62, av. Notre Dame du Lac
49000 Angers
** Pôle Imagerie, Centre Hospitalier Universitaire
4, rue Larrey 49000 Angers

Abstract: In this paper, we present an automatic multimodal registration method applied to gated PET, CT and MR images. CT images acquired on the same device as the PET ones are used to merge the anatomical MR and functional PET images. The registration process is divided in two steps: a 3D structure registration and a grey-levels registration. This approach enables global then local transformations. The structure registration uses a 3D biventricular heart model initialized on CT and MR data to define an optimal rigid transform. This global registration is then refined with the grey-levels step based on mutual information and free form deformations. *Copyright © 2006 IFAC*

Keywords: Image registration, Medical applications, Cardiac sequences

1. INTRODUCTION

Cardiovascular diseases, in particular cardiac insufficiency, are exponential growing diseases. The different therapeutic options include chemicals drugs, revascularization surgery or heart transplant. Non-invasive evaluation of cardiac function is a major point for diagnosis and follow up of ischemic diseases in order to choose and adapt the better treatment. The complementary natures of Magnetic Resonance (MR) and Positron Emission Tomography (PET) imaging provide to cardiologists significant information about myocardial viability evaluation after infarction. In one hand, PET imaging is a gold standard for ventricle function evaluation and in the other hand, MR imaging gives a detailed anatomical image and is also a reference method for evaluating the both ventricle function (left and right). X-ray Computed Tomography (CT)

imaging is a very high detailed anatomical modality and can also give complementary information about the coronary artery tree. Thus, registration and merging of these images lead to a more informative image.

In cardiac viability studies, a mental registration of the information from different imaging modalities is routinely performed by clinicians. Automatic registration, based on image processing, is therefore expected to offer better accuracy, reproducibility and to save time. Registration of cardiac images is a complex problem because of the mixed motions of the heart and the thorax structures. Moreover, as compared to the registration of brain images, the heart exhibits much fewer accurate anatomical landmarks and the images are usually acquired with lower resolution. A review of cardiac image registration approaches can be found in (Makela *et al.*, 2002). Anyway, these methods used a transmission PET image where we use a more detailed CT image. Moreover, theses methods only merge av-

---
[1] PhD financed by General Electric Healthcare.

erage PET images to end-diastole MR images since they don't use gated PET data.

We present an automatic method to register MR, PET and CT images gated to Electrocardiogram (ECG). Registration is the first step before image merging. We use a registration framework introduced in (Camara Rey, 2003): Anatomical information are incorporated into the registration process. The registration is divided in two steps. The first one is a 3D structure registration. The rigid transformation thus obtained initializes the second step that is a grey-level based registration. In our application, this approach is necessary because images are gated to ECG. It leads to a great amount of data. The 3D structure registration uses a 3D biventricular heart model that allows to reduce the computing time during the grey levels registration by reducing the deformation space. Thus, we take into account anatomical information.

In the following section, we present more precisely images modalities used for this application. Next, we describe the automatic registration method. The fourth section shows the results that we comment.

2. MULTIMODAL IMAGING OF THE HEART

The left ventricle ensures alone 80% of the cardiac function. Radiologists are then interested in the follow up of this part of the heart. and use a lot of different views to observe human body. For our application, we use two of them (short axis and axial directions) represented on Figure 1.

2.1 PET imaging

Positron Emission Tomography (PET) is a nuclear medical imaging technique which produces images of functional processes in the imaged organ. ^{18}F-FDG emission PET is used for studies about myocardial viability. The spatial resolution of PET images (about 3-4 mm) is low compared to MRI or CT (about 1 mm) and so don't allow a precise location of tissues alterations. CT images are now used to perform attenuation correction because of better resolution compares to a transmission PET image.

2.2 CT imaging

X-ray Computed Tomography (CT) is a medical imaging method with a very good spatial and temporal resolution. Because of this, the CT offers very good anatomical images. In heart imaging, CT images don't provide any functional information, but registered and merged to a PET image lead to a functional and anatomical image.

2.3 MR imaging

Magnetic Resonance Imaging is used to distinguish pathologic tissue (such as a tumor) from normal tissue. While CT provides good spatial resolution, MRI provides comparable resolution with far better contrast resolution. In heart imaging, MRI is used to study the myocardial perfusion and viability and permits the calculus of ventricular function parameters such as left ventricle fraction ejection, end diastolic and end systolic volumes or left ventricle mass.

2.4 Image acquisitions

All images used in this study were acquired in the Angers Hospital. PET-CT data were scanned on a General Electric Discovery ST. MR data were scanned on a 1,5 T General Electric Signa Horizon LX 9.1. The images are gated to ECG. Acquisition parameters are given in table 1. The General Electric Advantage Workstation device registers and merges directly PET and CT images. It also reformats the acquired axial slices to short axis slices.

	PET	CT	MR
Size	128×128	512×512	256×256
Number of Slices	47	335	12
Slice Thickness	3,27 mm	1,2 mm	8 mm
Field of View	circular 50 cm	circular 50 cm	rectangular 460×345 mm^2
Slice View	axial	axial	short axis

Table 1. Acquisition parameters for PET, CT and MR images.

3. AUTOMATIC CARDIAC REGISTRATION

In viability studies, mental registration of the information from theses different imaging modalities is routinely performed by clinicians. Automatic registration is expected to provide more informative images and to save time by assuring accuracy and better repeatability.

Bases of image registration can be found in (Brown, 1992; Glasbey and Mardia, 1998). For medical image registration, more information can be found in (Maintz and Viergever, 1998; Thompson and Toga, 1998; Thompson and Toga, 2000; Hill et al., 2001; Pluim et al., 2003). Image registration between source image (noted S) and target image (noted T) consists in the determination of the optimal transformation φ_θ that leads $S^\varphi := \varphi(S)$ similar to T (Brown, 1992) :

$$\hat{\varphi} = \arg \max_{\theta} C(S^{\varphi_\theta}, T) \qquad (1)$$

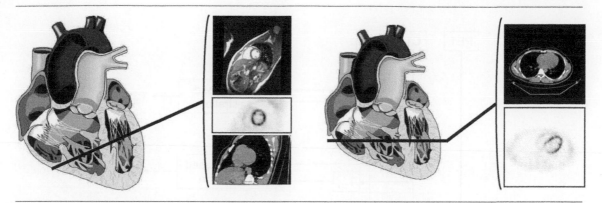

Fig. 1. Localization of the slices - Left: Short Axis slices of MR, PET and CT (from high to low) Right: Axial slices of CT and PET (from high to low).

The transformation is defined by the vector of parameters θ over a space depending of the chosen transformation. Image registration can be break down into three main components (Ruckert, 2001) :

- a similarity metric between the images to register that evaluates the quality of the registration accuracy by comparing the transformed source image to the target one,
- a transformation method that will be optimal when an extremum of the similarity criterion is reached (minimum or maximum depending of the optimization implementation),
- an optimization scheme in order to improve the transformation in accordance with the evolution of the similarity metric.

The choice of these components is driven by the features used to guide the registration. Registration methods can be classified in two classes depending on the features to register :

- *Structures features* are points, lines or surfaces extracted from the images. The features must be homologous reference structures present in the images to register. These features can be external landmarks or anatomical references. Anatomical references are often obtained by using segmentation that constitutes the first step of these registration methods. Next, the optimal transformation between the features is computed; i.e. the one that provides the better alignment of the segmented corresponding features. Finally, the transformation is extended (mainly by interpolation) and applied to the whole image. One of the main advantage of this method is the reduction of the amount of data involved in the registration. Then, the computational cost of registration is reduced.
- Methods based on the *grey-levels* take into account the whole data contained in the images. The registration is lead by the evolution of the similarity metric computed between the transformed image and the target image. The optimization step adjusts the transform parameters

in order to maximize the similarity of the images. The absence of segmentation and the robustness to the variations of input images make this approach attractive. An evident drawback is that the computing time can be considerable and can be a limit to a clinical routine application. An initialization near the solution is also needed because of problems of local extrema (especially in multi-modal case).

3.1 Developed scheme

Our application consists to register and to merge gated PET and MR heart sequences via CT images. The complex nature of the heart prevents the use of a direct registration. Moreover, no assumption of relation between the pixels intensity can be made. (Makela *et al.*, 2002) obtained good results using a transmission PET image as a link between the emission PET images and the MR ones. Here we use CT images as link because new acquisition device allows to acquire quasi simultaneously CT and PET images and because CT images have better spatial and temporal resolution than transmission PET images. Then we need ti define the transformation that registers CT and MR images. Knowing this transformation, we can apply it to PET images (registered to CT during acquisition) in order to have PET images registered to MR images. The global scheme of this registration process is represented on the synoptic diagram on figure 2.

3.1.1. 3D structure alignment The 3D structure alignment is the first step of our process. To perform a global registration (applied on the whole image), we choose a *rigid transformation* that is composed of translations, rotations, scaling or projection. We construct a 3D biventricular heart model based on the work of (Makela *et al.*, 2002) and (Pham, 2002). This model is deformed to fit with the CT data in one hand and the MR data in the other hand. The deformation is performed with an active deformation method

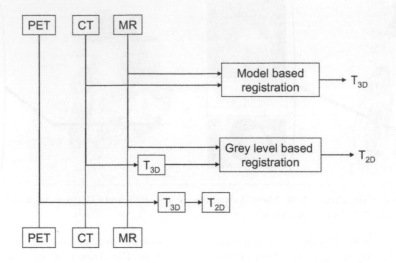

Fig. 2. Global scheme of the registration process. First CT data are registered to MR using a heart model. Using the obtained transformation a grey level based registration is performed. Finally the two transformations are applied on the PET data.

based on a 3D gradient vector flow (GVF) (Xu and Prince, 1998). Then, we use an Iterative Closest Point algorithm (ICP) (Besl and McKay, 1992) to register the two models. This algorithm is based on calculus of a distance between controls points and minimizes this distance by least-square approximation.

3.1.2. Grey levels registration The grey levels registration step assures the local registration (where the applied transformations depend on local similarities). Registration methods using voxels similarity based measures rely on iterative transformations of the source image to map the target image at convergence. Generally, local transformations have more degrees of freedom than the rigid ones. Classical transformations are Radial Basis Function (Ruprecht and Muller, 1995) and Free Form Deformations (FFD) (Sederberg and Parry, 1986). In our work, we use Free Form Deformations that model the transformation by linear composition of spline basis functions. Deformations are obtained by tuning an underlying mesh of control points regularly placed upon the image to transform. The control points displacements are interpolated to obtain a smooth and continuous C^2 transformation. The advantage of spline basis is its limited support that leads to controlled local deformations contrary to radial basis function that uses a sparse grid of control points and an infinite support.

In order to take into account all of the structures inside the images, we perform a multi-resolution decomposition. From the images to register (S and T), it consists in building two pyramids of images by recursive filtering (mostly gaussian). At the top of the pyramids, low-scale images can be registered. The obtained transformation is upsampled to initialize the registration at the next level of the pyramids. It permits a global to local approach of registration.

For similarity criterion based on grey-levels information the following assumption is made: it exists a kind of dependency between the intensities of the two images to register. Therefore the choice of the similarity criterion is a critical step for the design of registration algorithm. A trade-off must be taken between accuracy of results versus robustness and computation time. The dependency is modeled as a relation between the grey levels of the images to register. Functional relation is adapted to the case of monomodal registration. In a multimodal case, a functional relation is difficult (almost impossible) to model and criteria used are often based on the joint histogram of the images. In the case of statistical only relation between the images, the optimal criterion is the mutual information (Roche *et al.*, 2000) introduced by (Viola and Wells, 1995). This criterion is well suited for multimodal registration. The algorithm we developed includes mutual information as similarity criterion and a free form deformation transform associated to a multiresolution framework (by recursive gaussian filtering) to reduce the computation time.

3.1.3. Optimization method The optimal parameters of the transformation are defined using an optimization algorithm. Transformations with high degree of freedom excludes the use of *extensive* researches over the parameters space. Thus, *iterative* search is used in order to find a global extremum for the similarity metric. These methods can be divided in two classes whether it needs or not the use of the derivatives of the cost function to optimize. The Simplex and Powell's methods do not need the derivatives. So they require less computing time but are more sensitive to local extrema. Gradient descents, Marquardt-Levenberg or Gauss-Newton methods require the computation of the hessian matrix. These methods are less sensible to local extrema. The choice is again a trade-off between accuracy of result and computing time. These optimization algorithms (and many more) are described in (Press *et al.*, 1992). As we have to tune a number of parameters depending of the FFD grid size, we use a modified version of the Limited memory Broyden, Fletcher, Goldfarb and Shannon minimization that allows to specify bounds for the parameters in a large search space (Byrd *et al.*, 1997).

3.2 Temporal registration

Our application needs the registration of short axis PET images on MR images for 16 frames, that is to say 192 registrations. This prevents a clinical routine application if the process is not optimized. Knowing the MR-CT grey levels transformation $\mathcal{F}$ for frame F (noted $\mathcal{F}_F$) we initialize the registration for frame $F + 1$ (noted $\mathcal{F}_{F+1}$) as the sum of $\mathcal{F}_F$ and $\mathcal{G}_{F,F+1}$ where $\mathcal{G}_{F,F+1}$ is the transformation resulting of the monomodality temporal registration between the MR slice at frame F and the same MR slice at frame $F + 1$ as described on figure 4.

4. RESULTS AND COMMENTS

4.1 Structure alignment

The heart model has been constructed by segmenting heart contours on MR images from a healthy patient. From the contours a 3D model is constructed (see figure 3) using the softwares Nuages [2] and GHS3D [3].

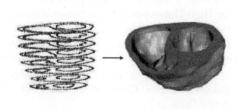

Fig. 3. Construction of the heart template

The model is initialized on the target MR data and the same is done for the CT data. The initialization

[2] www-sop.inria.fr/prisme/personnel/geiger/geiger.html
[3] www-rocq1.inria.fr/gamma/ghs3D/ghs.html

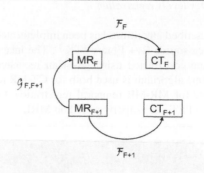

Fig. 4. Knowing the MR-CT grey level transformation $\mathcal{F}$ for frame F (noted $\mathcal{F}_F$) we initialize the registration for frame $F + 1$ (noted $\mathcal{F}_{F+1}$) as the sum of $\mathcal{F}_F$ and $\mathcal{G}_{F,F+1}$ where $\mathcal{G}_{F,F+1}$ is the transformation resulting of the monomodality temporal registration between the MR slice at frame F and the same MR slice at frame $F + 1$

is simply done by indicating the center of the cardiac cavity to the software. Then Gradient Vector Flow forces are computed in order to attract the contours of the model to the contours of the heart. The 3D model is deformed using the Finite Element Method described in (Pham, 2002). An ICP algorithm is then performed to obtain the global transform that maps CT space to MR space.

The structure alignment guided by the constructed heart template permits the scaling and the global alignment of the structure. The global transformation that register the two models is a composition of translation and rotation. Since the CT and PET sequences are reformatted to a short axis view the rotation is almost nil. The figure 5 shows the results of the global registration between MRI and CT models. Next, the grey level registration step allow a local registration.

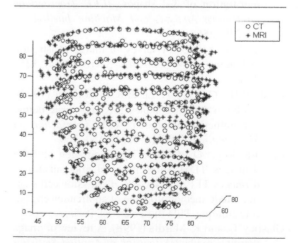

Fig. 5. Result of rigid registration between the CT and MRI models

4.2 Grey levels registration

The described algorithms has been implemented using the open-source C++ library ITK [4]. The image pyramids are constructed using gaussian recursive filter. The same algorithm is used both for CT-MR registration and for MR-MR temporal registration. Figure 6 shows a PET slice superimposed on MRI.

Fig. 6. Result of the grey levels registration

5. CONCLUSION

We present an automatic method to register mutimodal cardiac series. The use of 3D structure registration based on a heart model avoids manual intervention for segmentation and provides a global transformation. The grey levels registration step based on free form deformations and mutual information ensures the taking into account of the local deformations. The temporal registration process is speed up by initializing registration with a composition of the previous temporal registration and the temporal registration between two consecutive MR images. The whole process is designed to be as robust and fast as possible, but clinical evaluation must be done before clinical use

REFERENCES

Besl, P.J. and N.D. McKay (1992). A method for registration of 3-d shapes. *IEEE Transactions on Pattern Analysis and Machine Intelligence* **14**, 239–256.

Brown, L. G. (1992). A survey of image registration techniques. *ACM Computing Surveys* **24**(4), 325–376.

Byrd, R.H., C. Zhu, P. Lu and J. Nocedal (1997). L bfgs b fortran routines for large scale bound constrained optimization. *ACM Transaction on Mathematical Software* **23**(4), 550–560.

Camara Rey, O. (2003). Recalage non linéaire d'images TDM, thoraciques et abdominales et d'images TEP, au FDG-18, d'émission corps entier: étude méthodologique et application en routine clinique. PhD thesis. ENST Paris.

Glasbey, C. and K. Mardia (1998). A review of image warping methods. *Journal of Applied Statistics* **25**, 155–171.

Hill, D. L. G., P. G. Batchelor, M. Holden and D. J. Hawkes (2001). Medical image registration. *Physics in Medicine and Biology*.

Maintz, J.A. and M.A. Viergever (1998). A survey of medical registration. *Medical Image Analysis* **2**(1), 1–36.

Makela, T.J., P. Clarysse, O. Sipilä, N. Pauna, Q. C. Pham, T. Katila and I. E. Magnin (2002). A review of cardiac image registration methods. *IEEE Transactions on Medical Imaging* **21**(9), 1011–1021.

Pham, Q. C. (2002). Segmentation et mise en correspondance en imagerie cardiaque multimodale conduites par un modèle anatomique bi-cavités du cœur. PhD thesis. Institut National Polytechnique, Grenoble.

Pluim, J., J. A. Maintz and M. A. Viergever (2003). Mutual information based registration of medical images: a survey. *IEEE Transactions on Medical Imaging* **22**(8), 986–1004.

Press, W.H., S.A. Teukolsky, W.T. Vetterling and B.P. Flannery (1992). Numerical recipies in C. *Cambridge University Press*.

Roche, A., G. Malandain and N. Ayache (2000). Unifying maximum likelihood approaches in medical image registration. *International Journal of Imaging Systems and Technology: Special Issue on 3D Imaging* **11**(1), 71–80.

Ruckert, D. (2001). *Medical Image Registration*. Chap. Non-rigid registration: Techniques and applications. chapter 13, pp. 281–302. Hajnal J. V., Hill D. L. G., and Hawkes D. J. Editions CRC Press.

Ruprecht, D. and H. Muller (1995). Image warping with scattered data interpolation. *IEEE Computer Graphics and Applications* **15**(2), 37–43.

Sederberg, T. W. and S. R. Parry (1986). Free-form deformation of solid geometric models. *Proceedings of the 13th annual conference on Computer Graphics and Interactive Techniques* **20**, 151 – 160.

Thompson, P. M. and A. W. Toga (1998). *Brain Warping*. Chap. Anatomically-Driven Strategies for High-Dimensional Brain Image Warping and Pathology Detection, pp. 311–336. Toga A.W. Editor Academic Press.

Thompson, P. M. and A. W. Toga (2000). *Handbook of Medical Imaging: Processing and Analysis I*. Bankman Editor. Chap. 36, pp. 569–601. Academic Press.

Viola, P. and P. Wells (1995). Alignement by maximisation of mutual information. *Proceedings of ICCV 1995, Boston MA* pp. 15–23.

Xu, C. and J. Prince (1998). Snakes, shapes, and gradient vector flow. *IEEE Transactions on Image Processing* **7**, 359–369.

[4] www.itk.org

DIFFUSE REFLECTANCE SPECTROSCOPY MONTE-CARLO MODELING: ELONGATED ARTERIAL TISSUES OPTICAL PROPERTIES

Emilie Péry *,*** **Walter C.P.M. Blondel** *,**
Cédric Thomas *,** **Jacques Didelon** ***
François Guillemin *,**,***

* *Centre de Recherche en Automatique de Nancy,*
UMR 7039 CNRS - INPL - UHP
54516 Vandoeuvre-Lès-Nancy Cedex, France
** *Université Henry Poincaré Nancy 1,*
54000 Nancy, France
*** *Centre Alexis Vautrin,*
54511 Vandoeuvre-Lès-Nancy Cedex, France

Abstract: Optical methods, such as reflectance and fluorescence spectroscopy, have shown the potential to characterize biological tissues. The goal of this study is to simulate the steady-state light transport in arterial tissues with optical parameters found in the literature, then to deduce optical properties of tissues through optimization and finally to experimentally verify Monte-Carlo modeling of steady-state diffuse reflectance. The optical properties found are roughly in the same order of magnitude than the optical parameters found in the literature and the results indicate that the simulated results agree reasonably well with the experimentally measured results. *Copyright © 2006 IFAC*

Keywords: Monte Carlo simulation, photon transport, optical properties, optimization problems, reflectance spectroscopy.

1. INTRODUCTION

Optical methods can be used to characterize biological tissues non-invasively. By taking simultaneously spectral readings and by correlating data from various types of method (autofluorescence, diffuse reflectance...), the differentiation degree between various types of biological tissues can be increased through the complementarity of collected information (Bigio and Mourant, 1997), (Georgakoudi *et al.*, 2001).

Light-tissue interactions may be modeled through statistical simulation methods (i. e. Monte Carlo algorithm) which aims to simulate the random walk of photons inside biological tissue. It pro-

vides a very flexible technique for investigating light propagation in tissues and has been widely used for nearly two decades (Metropolis and Ulam, 1949), (Wilson and Adam, 1983). Monte Carlo simulation has been developped to solve various physical problems besides laser-tissue interactions. This type of statistic simulation is well adapted to calculate light transmission and reflectance following absorption and diffusion in complex and multilayered structures such as the biological tissues and to solve the problem of identifying the optical properties of each layer.

In our previous studies (Choserot *et al.*, 2005), (Péry *et al.*, 2005), we used autofluorescence and elastic scattering spectroscopies to show the existence of a correlation between optical properties (spectra) and rheological properties (stress - strain characteristics) of artery rings before and after cryopreservation. The study presented here extends the experimental work through a Monte Carlo simulation.

Based on Monte Carlo algorithms already developped and published in the literature (Prahl *et al.*, 1989), (Wang *et al.*, 1995), and (Liu *et al.*, 2003), we have developed a simulation program of steady-state light transport in arterial tissues with specific features : like multiple distances of reflectance fibers (corresponding to the geometry of our probe), broad band of visible wavelength excitation and emission with $10nm$ sampling step. Each photon launched is propagated using the optical properties of the layers at the specific excitation wavelength. Actually, simulations developed in the literature rather use monochromatic light sources than broad band spectrum sources. Considering the whole wavelength range from 600 to 800 nm should allow to better characterize the optical contribution of the different layer constituents.

In this work, we compare optical parameters obtained by simulation to various strain states with optical parameters found in the literature.

2. MATERIALS AND METHODS

Segments of carotid arteries were harvested from four young pigs weighing between 20 and 30 kg, following a potassium injection. Each pig carotid artery segment was cut in 4 rings of about 4 mm in length: 16 rings in total. Diffuse reflectance spectra were measured for each ring in a water bath at first, just after excision and then after a one-month cryopreservation (Metropolis and Ulam, 1996) at different elongations (Choserot *et al.*, 2005).

2.1 Measurements

An uniaxial mechanical testing device was used for stretching the rings and measuring the circumferential elongation and the corresponding force.Circumferential stresses were calculated for large strains. Rings were stretched from 0% to 70% by 10% steps.

Simultaneously, in order to measure optical characteristics of the artery samples under test, an elastic scattering spectroscope was developed for recording spatially resolved diffuse reflectance spectra mainly between 600 and 800 nm at two distances between illumination and acquisition fibers: 0.53 mm and 1.74 mm.
The light source combined three LEDs covering

600 to 800 nm and a specific seven fiber optic probe (200 mm core diameter each) was used for the experiments. The probe positionning was adjusted with a specific device to come in gentle contact with the upper surface of the arterial tissue during tests.
This device used an USB2000 spectrometer (Ocean Optics, France; pixel resolution≈0.32 nm) connected to a computer and a specifically developed software to collect, process and store diffuse reflectance spectra for each strain applied.

2.2 Modeling

GENERAL PARAMETERS: The trajectories of the photons were simulated in the 600 nm to 800 nm wavelength band, considering a semi-infinite medium with three layers corresponding to the adventice, the media and the intima layers of the arterial tissue. The program calculates the energy quantities deposited with each event in each layer according to absorption and scattering coefficients $\mu_a^i(\lambda)$ and $\mu_s^i(\lambda)$. Three coordinate systems can be used in the Monte Carlo simulation at the same time. A cartesian coordinate system is used to trace photon movements; a cylindrical coordinate system to score internal photon absorption as a function of r and z, where r and z are, respectively, the radial and axial coordinates of the cylindrical coordinate system and finally, a spherical coordinate system to sample the propagation direction change of a photon.

Each layer is described by the following parameters: a thickness e, an absorption coefficient μ_a (cm^{-1}), a scattering coefficient μ_s (cm^{-1}), a refractive index n, and an anisotropy factor g (see Fig. 1). The refractive index of the ambient medium above the tissue n_1 was the one of air. The ambient medium below the tissue was an isotonic NaCl solution for which $n_2 = 1.33$. n^i, μ_a^i, μ_s^i, g^i are respectively the refractive index, the absorption coefficients, the scattering coefficients, and the anisotropy factors for the adventice ($i = A$), the media ($i = M$) and the intima ($i = I$). The tissue layers are parallel to each other.

Configuration parameters of the software include illumination and collection fiber geometries, three-dimensional light distribution in tissue multiple layers, and wavelength resolution.

We determined the experimental values of the various parameters to be used in our model like the respective thickness of the three layers of the arteries according to the histological cuts realized and images of each ring.

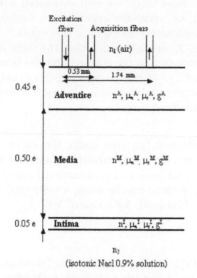

Fig. 1. Schematic representation of the three-layers model used to simulate light transport in an arterial tissue. e is the total thickness of the artery wall and n^i, μ_a^i, μ_s^i, g^i are respectively the refractive index, the absorption coefficients, the scattering coefficients, and the anisotropy factors for the adventice ($i = A$), the media ($i = M$) and the intima ($i = I$). n_1 and n_2 are the refractive index of surrounding medium, i.e. air ($n_1 = 1$) and isotonic NaCl ($n_2 = 1.33$).

The numerical values used in our simulation for the optical parameters of the intima, the media, the adventice (Table 1) and the refractive indices (Table 2) for arterial tissue were based on a combination of few references from the literature (See Ref. 1: (Cheong *et al.*, 1990) and Ref. 2: (Muller and Roggan, 1995)).

Table 1. Values of optical parameters for arterial tissue chosen from the literature and implemented in our simulation program (Ref. 1: (Cheong *et al.*, 1990), and Ref. 2: (Muller and Roggan, 1995)).

Description	λ (nm)	μ_a (cm^{-1})	μ_s (cm^{-1})	g	Ref
Intima	476	14.8	237	0.81	1
	580	8.9	183	0.81	1
	600	4	178	0.81	1
	633	3.6	171	0.85	1
	1064	2.3	165	0.97	2
Media	476	7.3	410	0.89	1
	580	4.8	331	0.9	1
	600	2.5	323	0.89	1
	633	2.3	310	0.9	1
	1064	1	634	0.96	2
Adventice	476	18.1	267	0.74	1
	580	11.3	217	0.77	1
	600	6.1	211	0.78	1
	633	5.8	195	0.81	1
	1064	2	484	0.97	2

Table 2. Values of the refractive index for arterial tissue (Ref. 2: (Muller and Roggan, 1995)).

Description	λ (nm)	n	Ref
Intima	456-1064	1.39	2
Media	456-1064	1.38	2
Adventice	456-1064	1.36	2

In order to work over a broad-band spectrum (between 600 and 800 nm), we have interpolated the five values found in the literature to determine values for the other wavelengths (20 values), one value each 10 nm. Ten million photons were launched in each simulation at random uniformly distributed locations over the diameter of the excitation fiber, i. e. 1.5 millions photons per wavelength.

SIMULATING PHOTON PROPAGATION: Step 1, the photon are injected orthogonally into the tissue at the origin and thrown from a random position in the fiber diameter. The photons emitted by the source (parameters corresponding to the light source used in our experiments) are launched with a random trajectory and are included in the surface of the emission fiber. When the photon is launched, some specular reflectance will occur if there is a refractive-index-mismatched interface between the tissue and the ambient medium. If the refractive indices of the outside medium and the tissue are n_1 and n_A respectively, then the specular reflectance, R_{sp}, is expressed by the relation 1:

$$R_{sp} = \frac{(n_1 - n_A)^2}{(n_1 + n_A)^2} \tag{1}$$

Step 2, if photons hit an interface between two layers (all-or-none method), either they are completely refracted ($n_i < n_t$ where n_i and n_t are the refractive indices of the incident and transmitted layers), or they are completely reflected ($n_i > n_t$ and $a_t > a_c$ where a_t corresponds to the angle of transmission and a_c the critical angle), or the two cases are possible ($n_i > n_t$ and $a_t < a_c$) according to the reflective coefficient. This reflective coefficient, $R(a_i)$, is calculated by Fresnel's formulas (cf. equation 2):

$$R(a_i) = \frac{1}{2}\left[\frac{\sin^2(a_i - a_t)}{\sin^2(a_i + a_t)} + \frac{\tan^2(a_i - a_t)}{\tan^2(a_i + a_t)}\right], \tag{2}$$

where a_i is the angle of incidence, and a_t the angle of transmission.

At each step, the energy deposited with each event is recorded and cumulated in each voxel, for all photons.

Step 3, when a photon is scattered, the probability distribution of the deflection angle θ is described by the scattering phase function (Henyey and Greenstein, 1941):

$$p(\cos\theta) = \frac{1}{2}\frac{1-g^2}{(1+g^2-2g\cos\theta)^{3/2}} \qquad (3)$$

Step 4, photons can terminate in three differents ways. After a photon travels, it can be counted out of the tissue by reflection or transmission. Through diffuse reflection, some photons can be collected in the diffuse reception fibers. Finally, when the energy left for a photon still in the tissue is less than a threshold value, a chance of surviving is given following the Russian roulette technique (Hendricks and Booth, 1985).

3. RESULTS AND DISCUSSION

3.1 Experimental results

We compute the mean of the elastic scattering spectra collected on each channel (channel 1: 0.53 mm and channel 2: 1.74 mm) for three different strains applied to the samples. The resulting spectrum is shown in Fig. 2.

These results show us that the global intensity of spectra decreases as strains rise. These variations are less marked for channel 2 than for channel 1. The longer course that the photons must carry out between excitation fibers of the channel 2 and the reception fiber, implies more absorption by the arterial tissue, which results in a lower total intensity second group of spectra (channel 2). The spectra resulting from scattered photons

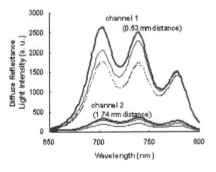

Fig. 2. Experimental results of diffuse reflectance (mean of spectra of every artery ring) for strains of 0% (full line), 30% (fine line) and 60% (dotted line) at 0.53 mm (channel 1) and 1.74 mm (channel 2) excitation-reception distances.

coming from the excitation channel 1 thus seem to be good indicators of the differences in optical behavior and in mechanical state of deformation of the samples tested. Intensity variations of the

diffuse reflectance are well correlated with elongation, i.e. structure organization modifications, thus with artery mechanical properties.

In Fig. 2, we also notice that the light intensity corresponding to the diffused photons issued from channel 2 (1.74 mm emission distance) only varies very slightly with strains for fresh as well as for cryopreserved rings.

We calculate the area under the curve for each spectrum, for each imposed strain and for each channel for fresh and cryopreserved artery and we compare these results using a statistical Student T-test (Table 3), for a risk of 5%.

Table 3. Statistical results (Student T-test) comparing of elastic scattering for the channel 1 (0.53 mm). NS means Non-Significant Difference with H_0 accepted (H_0: null hypothesis) and DS means Significant Difference with H_0 rejected.

	T_{calc}	T	
Intra pigs: fresh	0.11	2.45	NS
(sample's number = 8)			
Intra pigs: cryopreserved	0.22	2.45	NS
(sample's number = 8)			
Intra fresh and cryopreserved	2.34	2.14	DS
(sample's number = 16)			

Looking at results for channel 1 (0.53 mm emission distance), we observe there is no significant difference between stretched fresh rings and between cryopreserved rings whereas there are significant differences between the two population fresh and cryopreserved rings. Similar results (not shown) are obtained for channel 2 (1.74 mm emission distance).

3.2 Simulation and optimization results

SIMULATION WITH PARAMETERS FOUND IN THE LITERATURE. Tables 1, 2: Comparing Fig. 2 and 3, we can notice that we obtain the same variations for the channel 2, i.e. the global intensity of spectra decreases as strains rise. But for the channel 1, the variations are opposite. Indeed, the propagation of light is influenced by fondamental or microscopic optical properties, in particular absorption μ_a and scattering μ_s coefficients, refractive index n and anisotropy factor g.

By looking more precisely at the optical parameters, especially μ_s and in particular the values at 1064 nm, we can observe that μ_s decreases between 400 nm and 633 nm before increasing

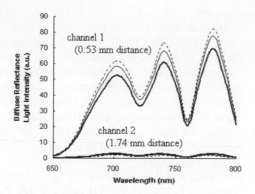

Fig. 3. Simulation results (mean of spectra of every artery ring) of diffuse reflectance spectra for strains of 0% (full line), 30% (fine line) and 60% (dotted line) at 0.53 mm (channel 1) and 1.74 mm (channel 2) excitation-reception distances.

considerably at 1024 nm. Our interpolation between 633 nm and 800 nm takes into account this last value at 1064 nm. It could affect our simulation results.

OPTIMIZATION OF OPTICAL PARAMETERS. Therefore, we decided to go through an identification process (experimental optimization of the optical parameters μ_a and μ_s for our experiments). We decided to keep the values of n (the influence of this parameter is small, but it can push the solution away from the optimum) and g as found in the literature. We searched for the values of each optical parameter for each wavelength, which minimize the error function (cf. equation 4).

$$Error(\lambda) = \sum_{\lambda} |S_m(\lambda) - S(\lambda)|^2 \qquad (4)$$

with $S_m(\lambda)$ the measured diffuse reflectance spectra and $S(\lambda)$ the simulated diffuse reflectance spectra.

Examples of values minimizing our error function are given in Tables 4 and 5 for two typical wavelength peaks of our excitation.

Table 4. Values of optical parameters for 0% strain.

Description	λ (nm)	μ_a (cm^{-1})	μ_s (cm^{-1})
Media	740	1.7	375
	780	1.7	375
Adventice	740	1.3	200
	780	1.5	207

Comparing Tables 1, 4 and 5, we can see that our optical parameters are roughly in the same order of magnitude than those found in the literature.

Table 5. Values of optical parameters for 0%, 30% and 60% strain at $\lambda = 780$ nm.

Description	Strain (%)	μ_a (cm^{-1})	μ_s (cm^{-1})
Media	0	1.7	375
	30	1.8	367
	60	1.5	393
Adventice	0	1.5	207
	30	2.5	193
	60	3.6	220

When strain rises, μ_a decreases and μ_s increases in the media, whereas in the adventice μ_a increases and μ_s seems more constant (about 5% variation max). Results seem to indicate that in average, the media, respectively the adventice, is less, respectively more, absorbed.

SIMULATION WITH OUR VALUES. We simulate the diffuse reflectance spectra for every artery ring (cf. Fig. 4). We can see that we obtain the same variations for the two channels.

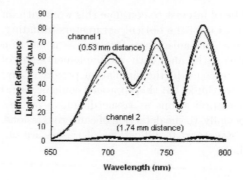

Fig. 4. Simulation results of diffuse reflectance spectra for strains of 0% (full line), 30% (fine line) and 60% (dotted line) at 0.53 mm (channel 1) and 1.74 mm (channel 2) excitation-reception distances.

In order to verify the difference between fresh and cryopreserved arteries, we use a statistical Student T-test over simulated spectra (Table 6).

Table 6. Simulation results (Student T-test) for the channel 1 (0.53 mm).

	T_{calc}	T	
Intra pigs: fresh	1.45	2.45	NS
(sample's number = 8)			
Intra pigs: cryopreserved	0.97	2.45	NS
(sample's number = 8)			
Intra fresh and cryopreserved	2.29	2.14	DS
(sample's number = 16)			

We can notice that for results of both experiments and simulations, the global intensity of spectra decreases as strains rise and these variations are less marked for channel 2 than for channel 1. However, a more important level of diffuse reflectance light intensity can be observed in simulation in the red wavelength range.

4. CONCLUSION

This study highlights the existence of a correlation between rheological and optical properties of arteries before and after cryopreservation, through experimental measurements and simulation. Our simulation program takes into account absorption and diffusion of light over a broad band spectrum (600 nm - 800 nm). Few values of optical parameters are available in the literature for the artery ring and these values were deduced from different experimental conditions. That's why, the variations of spectra are opposite for the channel 1 with these parameters. So, the characterization of the optical parameters (μ_a, μ_s, and g) is very important to find the same simulated diffuse reflectance spectra than those found experimentally.

It will be of interest to continue this work with an optimization of the optical parameters including, this time, the anisotropy factor g as a function of wavelength, and with an implementation of the fluorescence in the simulation program. And finally, we think that this approach could be useful to other applications as tissue diagnosis *in vivo*, and specially, to the detection of cancerous lesions, where structural modifications of tissues are observed.

5. ACKNOWLEDGEMENTS

The Authors gratefully acknowledge the "Région Lorraine" and the "Ligue Contre Le Cancer (CD52, CD54)" for their financial support.

REFERENCES

Bigio, I.J. and J.R. Mourant (1997). Ultraviolet and visible spectroscopies for tissue diagnostics: fluorescence spectroscopy and elastic-scattering spectroscopy. *Phys. Med. Biol.* **42**, 803–814.

Cheong, W.F., S.A. Prahl and A.J. Welch (1990). A Review of the Optical Properties of Biological Tissues. *IEEE J. Quantum Electron.* **26**, 2166–2185.

Choserot, C., E. Péry, J.C. Goebel, D. Dumas, J. Didelon, J.F. Stoltz and W.C.P.M. Blondel (2005). Experimental Comparison between Autofluorescence Spectra of constrained Fresh and Cryopreserved Arteries. *Clin. Hemorheol. Microcirc.* **33**, 235–242.

Georgakoudi, I., B.C. Jacobson, J. Van Dam, V. Backman, M.B. Wallace, M.G. Muller, Q. Zhang, K. Badizadegan, D. Sun, G.A. Thomas andL.T. Perelman and M.S. Feld (2001). Fluorescence, reflectance, and light-scattering spectroscopy for evaluating dysplasia in patients with barrett's esophagus. *Gastroenterology* **120**, 1620–1629.

Hendricks, J.S. and T.E. Booth (1985). MCNP variance reduction overview. *Lect. Notes Phys.* **240**, 83–92.

Henyey, L.G. and J.L. Greenstein (1941). Diffuse radiation in the galaxy. *Astrophys. J.* **93**, 70–83.

Liu, Q., C. Zhu and N. Ramanujam (2003). Experimental validation of Monte Carlo modeling of fluorescence in tissues in the UV-visible spectrum. *J. Biomed. Optics* **8**, 223–236.

Metropolis, N. and S. Ulam (1949). The Monte Carlo method. *J. Am. Statistical Association* **44**, 335–341.

Metropolis, N. and S. Ulam (1996). Effects of cryopreservation on the viscoelastic properties of human arteries. *Ann. Chir. Vasc.* **10**, 262–272.

Muller, G. and A. Roggan (1995). Laser-Induced Interstitial Thermotherapy. Vol. PM 25. Bellingham, WA.

Prahl, S.A., M. Keijzer, S.L. Jacques and A.J. Welch (1989). A Monte Carlo Model of Light Propagation in Tissue. Vol. IS 5. pp. 102–111.

Péry, E., W.C.P.M. Blondel, J.C. Goebel, J. Didelon and F. Guillemin (2005). Spectral (optical) and mechanical responses of fresh and cryopreserved issued arteries. Vol. 5695. Bellingham, WA.

Wang, L., S.L. Jacques and L. Zheng (1995). MCML - Monte Carlo modelling of light transport in multi-layered tissues'. *Computer Methods and Programs in Biomedicine* **47**, 131–146.

Wilson, B.C. and G. Adam (1983). A Monte Carlo model for the absorption and flux distribution of light in tissue. *Med. Phys.* **10**, 824–830.

THREE-DIMENTIONAL COHERENT OPTICAL DIFFRACTION TOMOGRAPHY OF TRANSPARENT LIVING SAMPLES

**Bertrand Simon[†], Matthieu Debailleul[†], Vincent Georges[†]
Olivier Haeberlé[†] and Vincent Lauer[‡]**

[†]*Laboratory MIPS, IUT Mulhouse, 61 rue Albert Camus, 68093 Mulhouse Cedex France*
[‡]*Lauer Optique et Traitement du Signal, 1 Villa de Beauté, 94130 Nogent/Marne, France*

Abstract: We present a technique to image living transparent specimens in 3-D, based on coherent optical diffraction microscopy. The sample is successively illuminated by a series of plane waves having different directions. Each scattered wave is recorded by phase-shifting interferometry and a Fourier representation of the object is reconstructed. The specimen, first recorded in Fourier space, is then reconstructed in the object space. This technique permits a 3-D reconstruction of the complex index of refraction distribution, with a resolution of the order on a quarter of the wavelength. *Copyright © 2006 IFAC*

Keywords: Microscopes, Image Reconstruction, Fourier Optics, Tomography, 3D-Domain

1. INTRODUCTION

The fluorescence microscope is the instrument of choice in biology, because of its unique capabilities for 3-D imaging of living specimens, and thanks to the development of specific fluorescent dyes, which permit to study precise cellular structures or functions. However, the resolution is still limited compared to scanning electronic microscopy or near-field techniques. This has motivated many works to improve the resolution, speed of acquisition, or depth of observation.

Fluorescent techniques however present the possible limitation that one has to label the specimen. The dye may experience bleaching during the acquisition, or induce phototoxicity into the specimen. In some cases, it is therefore preferable not to have to tag the specimen with fluorescent chemicals.

The observation of transparent or quasi-transparent specimens is however difficult, especially in 3-D, for two reasons. First, the low contrast does not permit to identify intracellular structures. Secondly, transmission microscopes suffer from a bad resolution along the optical axis, because of the presence of a so-called "missing-cone" in the Optical Transfer Function (OTF). As a consequence, while the resolution in the (x,y)-plane is often sufficient, the image presents a strong deformation along the optical axis (z-axis).

In order to improve the ability of transmission microscopes to detect small, quasi-transparent structures, the phase contrast microscope and the differential phase contrast or Nomarski microscope have been invented. While very successful, these apparatus suffer from the fact that a pseudo-contrast and/or pseudo-relief are recorded. For morphologic studies, the obtained images are often convincing. However, these microscopes all use an incoherent source to build a transmitted image of biological objects. This image is 2-D only, and to obtain a 3-D image, the technique of optical sectioning is used, which requires a translation of the specimen with respect to the microscope objective. The intensity in the image is linked to the absorption and the index of refraction of the specimen, but in a complex manner. As a consequence, the intensity cannot be directly related to a physical quantity of the observed object.

We have developed a technique based on coherent optical diffraction, which permits to image transparent specimens in three-dimensions and presents two advantages. It both permits a higher resolution and allows recording of the complex index of refraction distribution into the specimen. From these data, various representation of the specimen can then be computed.

2. PRINCIPLE

The wave diffracted by a weakly scattering object, when illuminated by a parallel coherent light beam, can be recorded in both amplitude and phase. In the Born approximation, it is then possible from this recorded wave to reconstruct a two-dimensional, spherical subset of the three-dimensional frequency representation of the weakly scattering object. Using a series of illumination beams having different directions, different subsets of the object's three-dimensional frequency representation can be reconstructed. The corresponding equations of diffraction tomography were originally established by Wolf (Wolf 1969) for scalar fields.

Figure 1 shows the principle of diffraction tomography, compared to holography. In the Born model, at first order and in the scalar approximation, diffraction is interpreted as a Fourier transformation (Born.and Wolf, 1991). In the Fourier plane, one then records Fourier components of the object index of refraction distribution. The set of Fourier components, which can be recorded, is limited by the numerical aperture (NA) of the microscope objective used in the detection system (Fig. 1(a)). For the sake of clarity, Figure 1 depicts a 2-D, (v_x-v_z) representation only. In three dimensions, the set of detected waves corresponds to a cap of the Ewald sphere, limited by the detection numerical aperture.

The radius of the Ewald sphere in the Fourier space is linked to the wavevector $k=2\pi/\lambda$, where λ is the wavelength of observation.

The idea of diffraction tomography is to increase the set of Fourier components, which can be recorded, by illuminating the sample with successive waves having different angles of incidence (Fig. 1(b)). Holography can in this sense be considered as a special case of coherent diffraction tomography with no angular scanning of the illumination wave.

The detection system and the specimen are fixed. As a consequence, when illuminating the specimen with waves having different incidences, one records different sets of Fourier components, which have to be correctly reassigned in the Fourier space, as shown by Figure 1(c). To properly reassign these components, one has first to record both the phase and amplitude, then to precisely measure the actual shift in the 3-D Fourier space between each set. Ideally, this shift is zero for a purely rotational system, but in practice, a dephasing may appear. When using a large set of illumination angles, the well-known butterfly shaped support of the Optical Transfer Function appears (Fig. 1(d)).

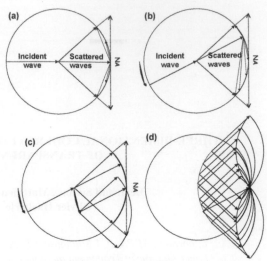

Fig. 1. Principle of coherent diffraction tomography. Construction of the set of detected waves.

The most straightforward method to record both the phase and amplitude of the scattered wave is phase-shifting holography. However, when successive illumination beams of different directions are used, it is generally not possible to control the relative phase of these beams. As a consequence, each scattered wave detected by phase shifting holography is affected by a non-controlled phase shift, which does not allow reconstruction of the object's three-dimensional representation.

We have developed a measurement-oriented approach to diffraction tomography (Lauer, 2002), taking into account not only the scattered wave and the illuminating wave, but also the reference wave and the phase relations between these three waves, giving a more complete description of the field than previous implementations of this apparatus (Devaney and Schatzberg, 1992)

This has permitted to successfully use phase shifting holography with successive illumination beams with different directions, as originally suggested by Wolf (Wolf, 1969). This is made possible by an accurate compensation of the non-controlled phase shifts, which itself results from a complete frequency-space analysis of the image acquisition method.

Figure 2 explains why the resolution in coherent diffraction tomography is expected to be better than for a classical transmission microscope using incoherent illumination. For the sake of simplicity, a one-dimensional only sketch is given. When using incoherent illumination, under many angles of incidence (role of the condenser in a microscope), the detection bandwidth is limited from $-2NA/\lambda$ to $+2NA/\lambda$ in the Fourier space, but higher frequencies are strongly attenuated (dotted line).

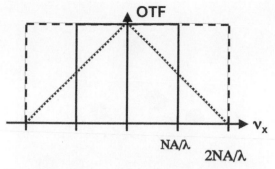

Fig. 2. Comparison of Optical Transfer Functions for incoherent transmission microscopy (dotted line), holographic microscopy (solid line), and coherent diffraction tomography (dashed line).

In holographic microscopy, the detection bandwidth is more limited from $-NA/\lambda$ to $+NA/\lambda$ in the Fourier space. However, these frequencies are detected without attenuation, the transfer function being constant over this interval (solid line).

In coherent diffraction tomography, the detection bandwidth is increased by angular scanning of the illumination wave. If the condenser has the same numerical aperture than the objective, one obtains the same detection bandwidth from $-2NA/\lambda$ to $+2NA/\lambda$ in the Fourier space, but with constant transmission, thanks to the use of coherent illumination (dashed line). As a consequence, the ability to detect small details is strongly increased by the better optical transfer function of the tomographic microscope, despite the fact that it has the same frequency support than classical transmission microscopes.

3. IMPLEMENTATION

The prototype of the microscope (Lauer, 2002) is shown in Fig. 3. In order to measure the diffracted function directly in the Fourier space, we have built a prototype in which the CCD sensor is in a Fourier plane, so that each pixel of that sensor corresponds to a given spatial frequency of the diffracted wave leaving the observed sample.

A polarized HeNe laser generates a coherent beam, which is divided by a beamsplitter into an illumination beam and a reference beam. This illumination beam is focused on the object focal plane of the aplanatic-, achromatic condenser (NA=1.4), passes through the condenser and leaves it as a plane wave illuminating the object. The direction of this illuminating plane wave can be controlled by modifying the orientation of the tilting mirror: a slight tilt of the mirror generates a large angular variation of the plane wave illuminating the object. The wave scattered by the object passes through the microscope objective (NA=1.4), as well as the non-scattered part of the illuminating wave.

An intermediate image is produced and spatially filtered by the image diaphragm. Spatial filtering by the image diaphragm limits the size of the observed part of the object, which in turn avoids undersampling on the CCD sensor placed in a Fourier plane. The wave then passes through lenses to reach the CCD sensor so that a plane wave originating from the object forms a point on the CCD sensor.

This point corresponds to the actual spatial shift of the illuminating beam, which is used to reassign the detected frequencies in the Fourier space.

The reference wave is virtually centred on the centre of the image diaphragm and coincides with a wave originating from a centred point source within the observed sample. The piezoelectric mirror is used to shift the phase of the reference beam. The two-level liquid crystal attenuator is a fast-switching device based on a polarization rotator and a polarizer. It serves to modify the intensity of the illumination beam in real time, during image acquisition. By combining various images corresponding to different attenuations, the system's dynamics can be considerably improved. The microscope also comprises a dedicated computer and appropriate electronics to control the piezoelectric mirror, the tilting mirror and the two-level attenuator, to grab the data acquired by the CCD, and to compute a three-dimensional representation of the observed sample.

4. RESULTS

Figure 4 shows typical recorded data in the Fourier space. Each set of three phase-shifted holograms permits to obtain a different sphere cap in the 3-D Fourier space.

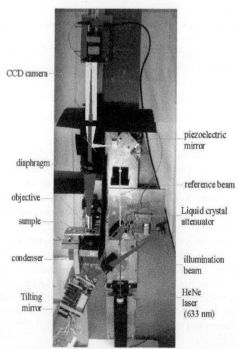

Fig. 3. Photograph of the tomographic microscope. The current prototype works only in transmission.

Fig. 4. 3-D frequency representation of the observed specimen. Top : (v_x-v_y) cut, bottom : (v_x-v_z) cut.

In the (v_x-v_y) plane, these portions of spheres appear as circles, as can be noticed on Fig. 4 top. Figure 4 bottom shows a cut along the (v_x-v_z) plane.

As the current prototype only works in transmission, the 3-D optical transfer function suffers from the presence of a so-called missing-cone of undetected frequencies. As a consequence, the resolution along the z-axis will be lower than in the x-y plane, and the detection of structures presenting variations along the z-axis only will be more difficult.

Figure 5 shows the reconstructed object in image space, after performing a 3-D Fourier transform of the frequency data set of Fig. 4.

The radial lines visible in Fig. 4 top correspond to the limits of the diaphragm clearly visible on Fig. 5. In this image, an extended depth of field representation is given, obtained by averaging the real part of the complex index of refraction along the vertical direction. This data set presents both a large field of view and a high resolution.

One advantage of our system is that different representation of the same specimen can directly be given from the same 3-D recorded data set: maximum intensity projection, extended depth of field, optical sectioning. Figure 6 shows a single yeast from Fig. 5 with different representations. Fig. 6(a) shows a horizontal section through the middle of the yeast. The thick cellular membrane is visible. From this image, the lateral resolution can be estimated better than 200 nm (the Abbe criterion giving 226 nm for an incoherent transmission microscope). Fig 6(b) displays a horizontal section through the middle of the vacuole, which shows sharp limits but no thick membrane.

Fig 6(c) shows a maximum value projection from a series of (x-y) sections. Previously unnoticed organelles are now visible.

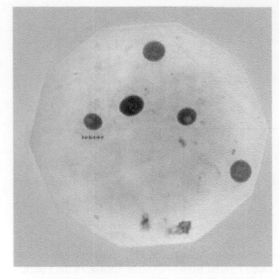

Fig. 5. Specimen (yeast culture) reconstructed in the spatial domain from a Fourier transform of the frequency representation given in Fig. 4 (extended depth of field representation). Scale bar : 5 μm (under the foremost left cell).

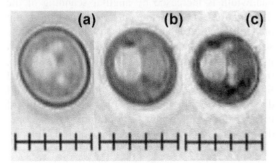

Fig. 6. Different representations of the same yeast. (a) :section through the middle of the yeast. (b) :section through the vacuole. (c) : maximum intensity projection. Scale bar : 5 μm.

Fig. 7. Vertical section of the yeast depicted in Fig. 6. Scale bar : 5 μm.

The acquired data set actually being a 3-D one, one can also reconstruct (x-z) sections of the specimen, as shown on Fig. 7. However, as explained previously, the resolution is clearly much lower along the z-axis, and stronger deformations and blur can be noticed.

There exists other 3-D microscopy imaging techniques, like for example Confocal Laser Scanning Microscopy (CLSM) or Electron Microscopy Tomography (EMT) (Leapman *et al.*,

2004). In terms of resolution, our instrument has similar or better lateral performances than the confocal microscope and lower performances along the vertical axis (because of the missing-cone), and much lower than EMT.

We however would like to emphasize, that it gives access to another physical quantity (after proper calibration): the optical index of refraction distribution within the specimen.

Confocal Laser Scanning Microscopy is based on fluorescence, so gives a fluorescence distribution image, which requires a specimen labelling procedure, while our method might be used on unstained specimens.

Electron Microscopy Tomography gives another contrast: the specimen electron absorption, but its big disadvantage compared to our method is that the observation is incompatible with life specimens, because of the sample preparation, while our method works on living samples.

5. CONCLUSIONS

We have developed a coherent diffraction tomographic microscopy technique, which permits three-dimensional imaging of transparent living specimens. Our prototype permits a better lateral resolution than the optical transmission microscope working with incoherent light.

Because the built prototype only works in transmission, it however presents similar limitations in terms of resolution along the optical axis. In principle, one can however complete the detection of the diffracted wave in order to also record its reflected component, which should greatly improve the resolution along the optical axis too.

We are now working on an improved version of this instrument, to combine fluorescence microscopy with tomographic microscopy, by modifying a commercial fluorescence microscope. In a second step, we intend to combine reflection tomography with transmission tomography, in order to greatly improve the axial resolution.

This technique permits to record the complex index of refraction distribution into the observed specimen. Then, different rendering of the specimen can easily be computed (optical sectioning, maximum intensity projection, extended depth of field) from data directly connected to physical quantities, the real part of the refraction index describing the refraction properties of the specimen, while the imaginary part describes the absorption of light by the specimen. Coherent diffraction tomography may therefore facilitate the study of unprepared specimen, by providing access for the biologists to physical parameters not yet available by other microscopy techniques.

REFERENCES

Born, M. and Wolf, E. (1991) *Principles of Optics* Pergamon Press.

Devaney, A.J. and Schatzberg, A. (1992) The coherent optical tomographic microscope. *SPIE Proc.* **1767**, 62-71.

Lauer, V. (2002) New approach to optical diffraction tomography yielding a vector equation of diffraction tomography and a novel tomographic microscope. *J. Microscopy* **205**, 165-176.

Leapman, R.D. *et al.* (2004), Three-dimensional distributions of elements in biological samples by energy-filtered electron tomography. *Ultramicr.* **100**, 115-125.

Wolf, E. (1969) Three-dimensional structure determination of semitransparent objects from holographic data. *Opt. Comm.* **1**, 153–156.

ELSEVIER
IFAC
PUBLICATIONS

A PORTABLE RAMAN PROBE FOR IN VIVO PATHOLOGICAL TISSUES CHARACTERISATION

Olivier Piot[1], Ali Tfayli[1], Sylvain Rubin[2], Franck Bonnier[1], Ganesh Sockalingum[1],
Sylvie Derancourt[3], Philippe Bernard[3], Michel Manfait[1]

[1]Unité MéDIAN UMR6142, Université de Reims Champagne-Ardenne, 51 rue Cognacq Jay, 51096 Reims cedex, France.
[2]Service de Chirurgie Thoracique et Cardio-vasculaire, CHU Robert Debré, rue du Général Koenig, 51100 Reims, France.
[3]Service de Dermatologie, CHU Robert Debré, rue du Général Koenig, 51100 Reims, France.

Abstract: Measuring Raman spectra of patient tissues, rapidly, in vivo and in real time, and allowing immediate diagnosis are challenges that have to be reached for a future clinical development of optical techniques. We present here examples of Raman spectra collected with a portable system on skin lesions and aortic tissues. Performances, but also limitations and required improvements of such a system will be discussed. Copyrigh©2006 IFAC

Keywords: optical spectroscopy, optical fibre, medical systems, spectral analysis, diagnosis, discriminate analysis.

1. INTRODUCTION

Vibrational spectroscopies, infrared absorption and Raman scattering, permit to characterize biological tissues at the microstructural and molecular level. Their potential for diagnosing various pathologies has been reported in several studies. Many in vitro investigations were carried out to differentiate cancerous from benign tissues on thin sections of biopsies of colon (Stone, et al., 2004; Lasch, et al., 2004; Li, et al., 2005), cervix (Wood, et al., 2004; Mordechai, et al., 2004), stomach (Ling, et al., 2002; Fujioka, et al., 2004), breast (Fabian, et al., 2002), skin (Mordechai, et al., 2004; Mendelsohn, et al., 2003; Gniadecka, et al., 2004; Tfayli, et al., 2005), barrett's epithelium (Boere, et al., 2003) and oral carcinoma (Murali Krishna, et al., 2004). Similarly, other kinds of diseases such as osteoporosis (Bi, et al., 2005) or aortic pathologies (Colley, et al., 2004) can be detected and investigated. These studies aim at developing such techniques as complementary analytical tools for histopathological examination of lesions but also as a new technique for in vivo diagnosis. Indeed, in cancer diagnosis, technical developments in the real-time optical recognition of dysplasia will provide the opportunity to more effectively target biopsies or ultimately to bypass the need of biopsies. This will lead to reductions in biopsy-associated risks and pathology costs.

In order to assess the potential of a new portable Raman system for in vivo diagnosis, we present here experiments on tissues corresponding to two different kinds of pathology: skin lesions that present the advantage of an easy accessibility, and aortic tissue (ex vivo analysis for these preliminary experiments)

2. EXPERIMENTAL ASPECT

2.1 Portable Raman system.

A description of the set up, a portable Raman system coupled to a bundle of optical fibres is presented in Figure 1. The axial spectrometer has been developed by Horiba Jobin Yvon (France) with the aim to be a portable, high throuput Raman system. The spectrometer has an axial geometry 60 cm long without any movable component. The dispersion of the signal is done by a GRISM, conjugation of a prism and a grating that is deposited on the output face of the prism. The spectrometer is equipped with a charge-coupled device (Andor Technology) as detector and Peltier-cooled at -65°C. With this new dispersive component, the spectral resolution reaches remarkably 2 cm⁻¹.

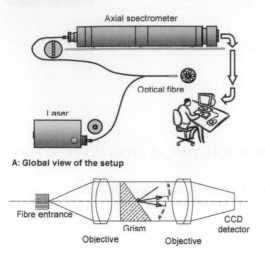

A: Global view of the setup

B: Details of the optical components of the axial spectrometer

Fig. 1. Global schematic view of the setup (A), and detailed view of the axial spectrometer (B).

Excitation and scattered (elastic and Raman) light are transported through a bifurcated fibre-optic bundle (SEDI Fibres Optiques, France). The 830 nm wavelength excitation, delivered by a diode laser (Renishaw, United Kingdom), has been chosen for i/ the significant decrease of tissue fluorescence compared to a more energetic excitation and ii/ providing a good penetration of the light in the tissue. This is particularly important for early diagnosis of skin cancers, in which malignancy takes birth in the basal cells layer located at the dermis / epidermis interface, roughly 100 – 150 μm below the skin surface.

At the distal end, 9 collection fibres of 200 μm-diameter core surround the delivery fibre of 400 μm-diameter core, whereas at the proximal end, the collection fibres are aligned along the entrance slit of the spectrograph. Their numerical aperture is 0.22. With this geometry, the area from which the scattered light is gathered from the tissue is maximized and full advantage is taken of the binning capabilities in the vertical direction of the CCD detector without compromising spectral resolution. To ensure a good transmission of the near infrared signal, low OH silica fibres, constituted of pure silica core and doped silica cladding, were chosen. The size of the bundle has been limited to 1.6 mm-diameter in order to be incorporable into an endoscope. The materials are medically sterilizable.

The output power at the central delivery fibre was 110 mW, which does not present any danger for in vivo application. Collection time for each spectrum was 30s. Furthermore, the set-up was EC-certified.

2.2 Spectral data pre-processing.

The spectra recorded on tissue, skin or aorta, present an intense signal below 1100 cm⁻¹ due to the silica signal (Fig. 2). A typical spectrum of biological tissue collected on a thin section with Labram microspectrometer (Horiba Jobin Yvon) is also presented. In order to avoid taking into account this contribution in treatment of tissue spectra, the spectral window was reduced from 1100 to 1800 cm⁻¹ (upper spectral limit with the axial dispersive system). On this reduced region, silica fibre contribution can be mathematically corrected by a polynomial baseline correction, available on the Labspec software (Horiba Jobin Yvon). All tissue spectra were corrected on the 1100 - 1800 cm⁻¹ region by the same baseline function. A more accurate correction should consider the detector response as a function of the frequency and the silica fibre signals collected on different types of tissue. This last signal, being generated by back reflected laser and scattered Rayleigh beam of the tissue, whose optical properties (optical index, reflectivity) are specific, is consequently dependent of the analysed tissue. For example, it should be checked if keratinisation of the tissue induces a reflectivity change.

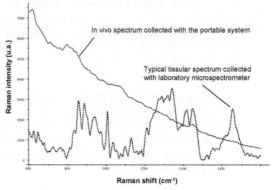

Fig. 2. Overall view of an in vivo spectrum and of a typical spectrum of epithelial tissue.

2.3 Multivariate analysis.

Hierarchical cluster analysis (HCA) was performed using the OPUS software (Bruker Optik GmbH, Germany) to classify the spectral data. A thorough description of this statistical analysis can be found in Tfayli, *et al.* (2005). The result is visualised in a tree-like diagram (dendrogram), presenting the regrouping of the spectra in clusters according to a heterogeneity scale.

2.4 Biological specimens.

Description of the skin lesions. Skin can present different types of lesions, benign such as nevi or malignant such as malignant melanomas or basal cell carcinomas (BBC). Today, skin cancer is the cancer with the highest incidence worldwide (Greinert, *et al.*, 2003). But the prognosis is related to early detection which is difficult in numerous cases, due to the difficulty to identify the various lesions that present a clinical aspect very similar even for expert dermatologists. For the study, 10 patients treated for BBC consented to participate to the study.

The comparison of mean spectra of normal skin and basocellular carcinomas is shown in Figure 3. For spectra of normal skin, the measurements were done in similar regions as those of the lesion sites, i.e. at the periphery of the lesions. The spectra are presented after baseline correction. Slight changes appear: a frequency shift in the C-H deformation mode (around 1450 cm⁻¹) when normal and pathological skins are compared, a weakly intense shoulder at 1685 cm⁻¹ in the protein amide I band of carcinoma spectra, differences in the 1200 – 1250 cm⁻¹ region relative to amide III band and phospholipid content are also observed.

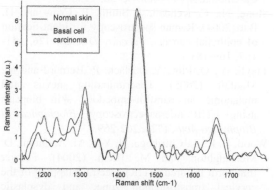

Fig.3. Comparison between mean spectrum of normal skin (connected line) and the basal cell carcinoma mean spectrum (dashed line).

HCA was performed on the set of skin spectra, collected directly on patients before surgical intervention. The result is presented in the dendrogram shown in Figure 4.

Such a result, even if does not present a one hundred percent separation is very promising, in spite of the poor quality of tissue Raman signal due to the high contribution of the fibre silica, the combination of spectral data and HCA enables a relatively good separation. Further works are going on to produce a more reliable optical fibre for Raman studies , and further experiments will concern a larger number of patients with respect of inter-lesions variability. Sex, age, location of the skin lesion on the body will also be taken into account.

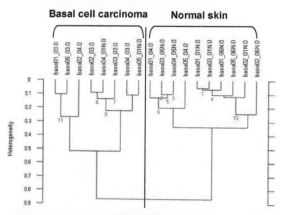

Fig.4. Dendrogram separating in two groups spectra of normal and cancerous skin.

Aortic tissues. Human aneurysm is very common case with a high rate of mortality. The actual problem for surgeons is to determinate, during surgical intervention, the necessity to replace the ascending part of aortas at the same time. Molecular criteria such as content and structure of elastin and collagen are involved in the process of aneurysm and are also thought to influence the risk of occurrence. In vivo characterisation of the molecular structure of the aorta could help the surgeon to assess the aneurysm risk during surgical intervention.

For this present preliminary study, Raman spectra were recorded ex vivo on a whole normal aorta (ascending part and arch). Spectra were collected at different points all around the aorta periphery and at different heights for the ascending aorta.

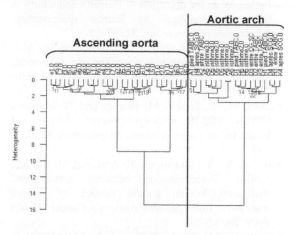

Fig. 5. Dendrogram showing separation of the Raman spectra, from the ascending aorta and the aortic arch, into two separate clusters.

The dendrogram presented in Figure 5 shows that it is possible, from ex vivo Raman measurements, to distinguish two anatomical parts of a normal aorta (ascending part and arch). A finer analysis of the dendrogram reveals that spectra of the ascending aorta form two sub-clusters that could correspond to different tissue composition and structure. Further experiments will of course include pathological aorta and collection of spectra directly on patients during surgical intervention.

3.   CONCLUSION AND PERSPECTIVES

The examples presented here show that portable Raman system could in the future potentially be used as diagnostic tool in medical care centres. Recent studies on *in vivo* cancer characterisation by Raman spectroscopy have just been published (Haka *et al.*, 2006). This research team uses a sophisticated and expensive system that is limited for in routine medical application. Our system presents the advantage to have a more simple optical configuration and a miniaturized measurement probe. This probe ill allow a more precise analysis of the tumor tissue and, in the future, an access to the inner organs via the working channel of endoscopes. Formerly, improvements in optical instrumentation are foreseen and in data treatment are expected by setting up appropriate filters at the tip of the bundle, by changing fibre geometry and by testing another excitation wavelength (better detector sensibility). Also, more advanced data analysis method such as Independent Component Analysis should permit to modelise silica fibre signal in order to be able to subtract it correctly from the collected signal and thus to improve signal quality.

4. REFERENCES

Bi, X., G. Li, S.B. Doty and N.P. Camacho (2005). A novel method for determination of collagen orientation in cartilage by Fourier transform infrared imaging spectroscopy (FT-IRIS). *OsteoArthritis and Cartilage*, **13(12)**, 1050-1058.

Boere, I. A., T. C. B. Schut, J. V. D. Boogert, R. W. F. D. Bruin and G. J. Puppels (2003). Use of fiber optic probes for detection of Barrett's epithelium in the rat oesophagus by Raman spectroscopy. *vibrational spectroscopy*, **32**, 47-55.

Colley, C.S., S.G. Kazarian, P.D. Weinberg and M.J. Lever (2004). Spectroscopic imaging of arteries and atherosclerotic plaques. *Biopolymers*, **74**, 328-335.

Fabian, H., P. Lasch, M. Boese, and W. Haensch (2002). Mid-IR microspectroscopic imaging of breast tumor tissue sections. *Biopolymers*, **67**, 354-357.

Fujioka, N., Y. Morimoto, T. Arai and M. Kikuchi (2004). Discrimination between normal and malignant human gastric tissues by Fourier transform infrared spectroscopy. *Cancer Detect Prev*, **28**, 32-36.

Gniadecka M., P. A. Philipsen, S. Sigurdsson, S. Wessel, O. F. Nielsen, D. H. Christensen, J. Hercogova, K. Rossen, H. K. Thomsen, R. Gniadecki, L. K. Hansen and H. C. Wulf (2004). Melanoma diagnosis by Raman spectroscopy and neural networks: structure alterations in proteins and lipids in intact cancer tissue. *J Invest Dermatol*, **122**, 443-449.

Greinert, R., B. Volkmer, A. Wende, S. Voss and E. W. Breitbart (2003). Prevention of skin cancer: Necessity, implementation and success. *Hautarzt*, **54**, 1152-1163.

Haka A.S., Volynskaya Z., Gardecki J.A., Nazemi J., Lyons J., Hicks D, Fitzmaurice M., Dasari R.R., Crowe J.P., Feld M.S. (2006) In vivo margin assessment during partial mastectomy breast surgery using Raman spectroscopy. *Cancer Res*, **66**, 3317-3322.

Lasch, P., W. Haensch, D. Naumann and M. Diem (2004). Imaging of colorectal adenocarcinoma using FT-IR microspectroscopy and cluster analysis. *Biochim Biophys Acta*, **1688**, 176-186.

Li, Q. B., Z. Xu, N. W. Zhang, L. Zhang, F. Wang, L. M. Yang, J. S. Wang, S. Zhou, Y. F. Zhang, X. S. Zhou, J. S. Shi and J. G. Wu (2005). In vivo and in situ detection of colorectal cancer using Fourier transform infrared spectroscopy. *World J Gastroenterol*, **11**, 327-330.

Ling, X., Y. Xu, S. Weng, W. Li, Z. Xu, R. Hammaker, W. Fateley, F. Wang, X. Zhou, R. Soloway, J. Ferraro and J. Wu (2002). Invsetigation of normal and malignant tissue samples from the human stomach using Fourier Transform Raman spectroscopy. *Applied Spectroscopy*, **53**.

Mendelsohn, R., H.C. Chen, M.E. Rerek and D.J. Moore (2003). Infrared microspectroscopic imaging maps the spatial distribution of exogneous molecules in the skin. *J Biomed Opt.*, **8**, 185-90.

Mordechai, S., R. K. Sahu, Z. Hammody, S. Mark, K. Kantarovich, H. Guterman, A. Podshyvalov, J. Goldstein and S. Argov (2004). Possible common biomarkers from FTIR microspectroscopy of cervical cancer and melanoma. *J Microsc*, **215**, 86-91.

Murali Krishna, C., G.D. Sockalingum, J. Kurien, L. Rao, L. Venteo, M. Pluot, M. Manfait and V.B. Kartha (2004). Micro-Raman Spectroscopy for Optical Pathology of Oral Squamous Cell Carcinoma. *Appl Spectrosc*, **58**, 1128-35.

Stone, N., C. Kendall, J. Smith, P. Crow and H. Barr(2004). Raman spectroscopy for identification of epithelial cancers. *Faraday Discuss*, **126**, 141-157; 169-183.

Tfayli, A., O. Piot, A. Durlach, P. Bernard and M. Manfait (2005). Discriminating nevus and melanoma on paraffin-embedded skin biopsies using FTIR microspectroscopy. *Biochimica et Biophysica Acta*, **1724**, 262-269.

Wood, B. R., L. Chiriboga, H. Yee, M. A. Quinn, D. McNaughton and M. Diem (2004). Fourier transform infrared (FTIR) spectral mapping of the cervical transformation zone, and dysplastic squamous epithelium. *Gynecol Oncol*, **93**, 59-68.

ANALYSIS OF DOUBLE-TRACER GLUCOSE KINETICS IN HUMANS DURING ORAL GLUCOSE TOLERANCE TEST

Karl Thomaseth* Amalia Gastaldelli**
Alessandra Pavan* Rachele Berria***
Leonard Glass*** Ralph DeFronzo***

*CNR Institute of Biomedical Engineering, Padova, Italy
**CNR Institute of Clinical Physiology, Pisa, Italy
*** Univ of Texas Health Science Center at San Antonio, USA

Abstract: A mathematical model based on minimal physiological assumptions for describing simultaneously multiple glucose measurements during modified oral glucose tolerance test is presented. Parameter identification was carried out using a population approach, which allowed precise characterisation of average glucose kinetic parameters in the studied cohort, as well as between–subject variability associated with glucose tolerance state and other covariates. The statistical and computational complexity added with the formulation of non-linear hierarchical population kinetic models is compensated by improved robustness, over the traditional two–stage approach, in selecting the most adequate model structure/order at the individual level and the most significant determinants of glucose kinetics at the population level. Copyright © 2006 IFAC

Keywords: Mathematical models, Medical applications, Parameter identification, Physiological models, Reduced-order models, Statistical analysis

1. INTRODUCTION

The oral glucose tolerance test (OGTT) is increasingly used as clinical test for studying glucose tolerance and insulin secretion in cohorts at risk of type 2 diabetes and for assessing the efficacy of new antidiabetic drugs. In its simplest form (oral load of 75 g glucose dissolved in water and a single measure of plasma glucose concentration after 2 hours) the OGTT is recommended by the World Health Organization for the diagnosis of diabetes in presence of elevated fasting plasma glucose. Given its moderate invasiveness for patients and usefulness in providing dynamic information on the kinetics of glucose and other endogenous substances, more complex OGTT-based protocols have been employed, e.g. with frequent blood sampling and administration of exogenous substances, combined with mathematical modelling of dynamic concentration profiles.

In this study we consider the double-tracer labeled OGTT, which consists of a primed-continuous infusion of tritiated glucose ($[3\text{-}^3\text{H}]$-glucose) (to quantify endogenous glucose turnover by achieving steady state concentrations of $[3\text{-}^3\text{H}]$-glucose) and carbon labeled glucose ($[1\text{-}^{14}\text{C}]$-glucose) added to the oral glucose load (to determine exogenous glucose absorption rates). The applicability of mathematical modelling to these kinds of experiments have been already demonstrated by others (Dalla Man et al., 2002; Dalla Man et al., 2004; Dalla Man et al., 2005). In particular, the so-called Bergman's minimal model of glucose disappearance (MINMOD) (Bergman et al., 1979), which had been developed for modelling frequently sampled IVGTT (FSIGT) data, has proven to adequately describe, after straightforward modifications, also glucose kinetics during OGTT. More specifically, by explicitly modelling the exogenous glucose appearance rate (R_a) of orally administered unlabeled and [1-^{14}C]-glucose, it has been shown that MINMOD is able to accurately match the R_a profile determined with another, independent, modelling approach and to provide a figure of insulin sensitivity of glucose disappearance equivalent to that measured with the more laborious glucose clamp technique. Disadvantages of the model proposed in (Dalla Man et al., 2005) include the relatively high number of model parameters to be estimated from experimental data collected in a single individual and the use of two different models (similar structure but with different parameter values) for unlabeled and tracer glucose kinetics.

Aims of this study were to re-assess the minimal modelling approach applied to double-tracer OGTT experiments within a unifying framework using: (i) a single model for describing simultaneously [3-^{3}H]-glucose, [1-^{14}C]-glucose and unlabeled glucose kinetics; (ii) a simplified model with reduced number of parameters, each having a unique value and physiological interpretation for different glucose measurements; (iii) a more robust population parameter estimation approach to better separate statistical variability of parameter estimates due to measurement and modelling errors from between-subject variability of kinetic parameters dependent from different metabolic states and other covariates, the characterisation of which is of major interest in population studies.

The next section briefly summarises the studied cohort and the experimental protocol, and provides a detailed description of the mathematical model used to fit experimental data and the statistical population approach used to estimate model parameters. Section 3 presents results of the population modelling analysis, which are commented in section 4 together with a critical discussion about the proposed modelling approach.

2. MATERIALS AND METHODS

2.1 Subjects and protocol

Twelve type 2 diabetic patients (7 males and 5 females; age = 53.6±2.5 years; body weight (BW) = 81.9±3.6 kg; body mass index (BMI) = 30.5±1.1 kg m^{-2}) and ten normal glucose-tolerant subjects (5 males and 5 females; age = 39.6±3.7 years; BW = 90.1±3.9 kg; BMI = 31.1±0.9 kg m^{-2}), matched for BMI and used as control subjects, underwent after overnight fast a double-tracer OGTT consisting of a primed-constant in-fusion of [3-^{3}H]-glucose (0.25 μCi min^{-1}) starting at time −120 min and an oral glucose load at time 0 of 75 g of glucose diluted in water containing 75 μCi [1-^{14}C]-glucose. Blood samples were collected every 15 minutes starting at time −30 min until 240 min for determination of plasma concentrations of unlabeled and labeled glucose and insulin. Concentration measurements are expressed as follows: glucose (mg dl^{-1}), [3-^{3}H]-glucose (dpm ml^{-1}), [1-^{14}C]-glucose (dpm ml^{-1}) and plasma insulin (μU ml^{-1}).

2.2 Mathematical Modelling

The model of glucose kinetics was formulated by assuming, for any of the three different glucose measurements, a one-compartment structure with fixed unknown glucose distribution volume (V_G). The generic mass balance equation is described by

$$\dot{X}(t) = -R_d(t) + R_p(t) + R_a(t) \quad (1)$$

where $X(t)$ represents compartmental mass, expressed in (mg) and (dpm) for unlabeled and tracer glucose, and with time derivative $\dot{X}(t)$ (mg min^{-1}) and (dpm min^{-1}), respectively; glucose disappearance rate (R_d) is defined as the product of instantaneous glucose clearance (CL) (dl min^{-1}) and the corresponding plasma glucose concentration; the endogenous glucose production rate (R_p) is nonzero only for unlabeled glucose; the exogenous glucose appearance rate (R_a) is constant and known for [3-^{3}H]-glucose and time-varying and unknown for unlabeled and [1-^{14}C]-glucose, yet with known total area under the curve (AUC) over an infinite horizon equal to the administered doses.

Modelling glucose disappearance rate (R_d). Given the above definition of R_d it is sufficient to define the mathematical structure for glucose clearance (CL). According to the minimal model of glucose disappearance (MINMOD) CL is described as the sum of a constant insulin-independent term, the glucose effectiveness at zero insulin (GEZI) (Abbate et al., 1993), and a time-varying term given as the product of insulin sensitivity index (S_I) (dl min^{-1} μU^{-1} ml) and insulin concentration in a remote compartment ($I_R(t)$)

$$CL(t) = GEZI + S_I I_R(t) \quad (2)$$

It is worth noting that the adopted parameterisation is different, but mathematically equivalent, to that conventionally used in the MINMOD literature, i.e. parameters expressing clearances (dl min^{-1}) are obtained by multiplying the conventional counterpart of fractional clearances (min^{-1}) by the glucose distribution volume (V_G);

moreover the more commonly used glucose effectiveness at basal insulin (S_G) is related to the other model parameters through the equation

$$S_G = GEZI + S_I I_b \qquad (3)$$

The dynamics of insulin concentration in a remote compartment is described by

$$\dot{I}_R(t) = -P_2(I_R(t) - I(t)) \qquad (4)$$

with initial condition equal to basal plasma insulin concentration (I_b); plasma insulin concentration profile ($I(t)$) reconstructed by linear interpolation of measurements; and remote insulin turnover rate (P_2). Thus $I_R(t)$ is simply a lagged profile of plasma insulin, and is related to the traditional MINMOD insulin action by: $X(t) = S_I(I_R(t) - I_b)$.

Modelling exogenous glucose appearance rate (R_a). Exogenous unlabeled and [1-^{14}C]-glucose, administered through the oral load, share the same absorption time profile. A mathematical function, $\overline{R_a}(t, \mathbf{p})$, parametrised by $\mathbf{p}$, is a suitable candidate for representing gastrointestinal glucose absorption if it is nonnegative and its total AUC is normalised to one, such that multiplication by administered dose yields effective absorption rate. For this purpose we adopted the following definition for $\overline{R_a}(t, \mathbf{p})$:

$$\int_0^T \overline{R_a}(t, \mathbf{p})\, dt = 1 - e^{-\left(\frac{T}{\alpha}\right)^\beta} \qquad (5)$$

which ensures, if the two parameters α and β are positive, that the incremental AUC of glucose absorption strictly increases with time and tends exponentially to 1 for $T \to \infty$.

Given the oral unlabeled glucose dose (D^G) and the specific activity of administered [1-^{14}C]-glucose (S_a^{14C}), the exogenous glucose appearance rate for unlabeled and [1-^{14}C]-glucose are:

$$R_a^G(t) = D^G \overline{R_a}(t, \mathbf{p}) \qquad (6)$$
$$R_a^{14C}(t) = S_a^{14C} D^G \overline{R_a}(t, \mathbf{p}) \qquad (7)$$

Modelling endogenous glucose production rate (R_p). In MINMOD endogenous glucose production is not modeled explicitly, but it is assumed that the control of net hepatic glucose balance (NHGB) parallels that of peripheral glucose utilisation. The MINMOD-derived insulin sensitivity index (S_I) for unlabeled glucose accounts thus also for the effects of insulin on NHGB. This leads to different values if S_I is estimated from tracer glucose kinetics, which depends on glucose disposal alone.

In view of our aim of defining a unique sensitivity index S_I we assumed endogenous glucose produc-

tion rate (R_p) being dependent on deviations of remote insulin from basal through an empirical Hill-type equation. Given the glucose effectiveness at basal insulin (S_G), Eq. (3), and basal glucose concentration (G_b), endogenous glucose production rate was modeled as

$$R_p(t) = S_G\, G_b \frac{I_{50}^{h}}{I_{50}^{h} + (I_R(t) - I_b)^h} \qquad (8)$$

where I_{50} characterises the remote insulin concentration for 50% inhibition of basal glucose production, and the exponent h is an empirical parameter.

Final model equations. The mathematical model equation used to fit double-tracer OGTT experiments can be summarised as follows

$$\dot{X}^G(t) = -CL(t)\frac{X^G(t)}{V_G} + R_p^G(t) + R_a^G(t) \qquad (9)$$

$$\dot{X}^{14C}(t) = -CL(t)\frac{X^{14C}(t)}{V_G} + R_a^{14C}(t) \qquad (10)$$

$$\dot{X}^{3H}(t) = -CL(t)\frac{X^{3H}(t)}{V_G} + u_{inf}^{3H} \qquad (11)$$

with initial conditions $X^G(0) = G_b V_G$, $X^{14C}(0) = 0$, $X^{3H}(0) = G_b^{3H} V_G$ where $CL(t)$ is derived from Eq. (2) with remote insulin determined through Eq. (4); $R_p^G(t)$ is expressed by Eq. (8); $R_a^G(t)$ and $R_a^{14C}(t)$ by Eq. (6) and (7), respectively; u_{inf}^{3H} represents the steady state constant infusion rate.

The final set of estimated model parameters consist of: $\{P_2,\ GEZI,\ S_I,\ V_G,\ \alpha,\ \beta,\ I_{50},\ h\}$, with the first four parameters pertaining to the original MINMOD and two new parameters each for describing glucose absorption and production. Additional assigned model parameters are: test dose D^G (75 g); individually measured S_a^{14C} and u_{inf}^{3H}; basal concentration values G_b, I_b and G_b^{3H} obtained for each individual as the average of measurements taken before the beginning of the test. Moreover, individual plasma insulin concentration profile ($I(t)$) is determined from insulin concentration measurements. Model equations were implemented using the modelling software PANSYM (Thomaseth, 2003).

2.3 Parameter estimation

Having defined the kinetic model for describing the concentration profile of unlabeled glucose, [3-^{3}H]-glucose and [1-^{14}C]-glucose, the i-th data set of the i-th subject can be formally represented through a non-linear regression model such as

$$\mathbf{y}_i = \mathbf{f}(\mathbf{t}_i, \boldsymbol{\theta_i}) + \mathbf{e}_i \qquad (12)$$

where $\mathbf{y}_i$ is the vector of all measurements collected in the i-th subject, $\mathbf{f}(\mathbf{t}_i, \boldsymbol{\theta}_i)$ represents the model predictions at the sampling times $\mathbf{t}_i$ for given vector of parameters $\boldsymbol{\theta}_i$, and $\mathbf{e}_i$ represents measurement (and modelling) noise, which was chosen among various alternatives as homoscedastic with a different variance estimated for each type of glucose measure.

To guarantee the fulfillment of positivity constraints on parameters and to reduce the risk of identification problems in presence of large inter-individual variability of kinetic parameters, logarithmic transformations were applied to model parameters before their estimation. Thus $\boldsymbol{\theta}$ represent in the following the vector of log-transformed parameters, i.e. $\{\log P_2, \log GEZI, \log S_I, \log V_G, \log \alpha, \log \beta, \log I_{50}, \log h\}$, which were the actually estimated parameters. Before their use in numerical simulation of model equations they were back-transformed through exponentiation. Results and statistical figures of precision (confidence intervals) will also be presented for the original, back-transformed, parameters.

For obtaining information on the average kinetic response and on between-subject variability, individual parameter estimates, $\hat{\boldsymbol{\theta}}_i$, could have been obtained for each subject by non-linear weighted least squares fitting with subsequent statistical analysis to determine those covariates that affect kinetic parameters (this is the so-called two-step procedure). A more robust and dependable approach is the population modelling technique based on simultaneous analysis of all data using a statistical model that explicitly accounts for intra- and inter-individual variations of parameters (Davidian and Giltinan, 1995). In particular the non-linear mixed effects (NLME) approach was employed, which is based on maximum likelihood estimation of model parameters and covariance matrices of random variables under the assumption of normal distributions (Pinheiro and Bates, 2000).

In this context, the k-th component of the individual parameter vector $\boldsymbol{\theta}_i$ is in general described by a linear model as follows

$$\theta_{ik} = \theta_{0k} + \mathbf{X}_{ik}\boldsymbol{\xi}_k + \delta_{ik} \qquad (13)$$

where θ_{0k} represents the average population value, $\mathbf{X}_{ik}$ is a row vector of explicative variables (continuous and factorial covariates) to predict inter-individual variability. Parameters θ_{0k} and $\boldsymbol{\xi}_k$ are called *fixed effects* because, by hypothesis, they don't change between subjects of the studied population; δ_{ik} are the so-called *random effects* that represent unpredictable between-subject variations. Yet, not all kinetic parameters were described using the complete structure of Eq. (13). To select the minimum number of estimated pa-

rameters able to quantify the statistically significant determinants of intra- and inter-individual variability, the inclusion of a covariate within $\mathbf{X}_{ik}$ or the actual need for a random effect δ_{ik} was assessed on the basis of physiological plausibility of results and statistical criteria for precision of parameter estimates and minimum model complexity (Davidian and Giltinan, 1995). For instance, the decision rule for including a covariate in the model was that the corresponding multiplicative regression parameter be estimated with a significance level of at least P=0.05 of being different from zero.

3. RESULTS

The ability of the model to fit experimental data was excellent on pooled data (not shown) and very good on average data for normal control and diabetic groups, separately. Figure 1 shows the average concentrations (mean±SE) and model predictions for cold glucose, [3-^{3}H]-glucose, and [1-^{14}C]-glucose. For direct comparison each matching glucose measure is plotted with same vertical range but possibly with different offset. With regard to model performance at an individual level, the percentage error in model prediction (residual/fitted) had a low bias, being on average -0.02% for unlabeled glucose, 2.1% for [3-^{3}H]-glucose, and 0.47% for [1-^{14}C]-glucose, and had an acceptable dispersion with standard deviations (a measure of mean coefficient of variation) of 6.2%, 16.4% and 7.8%, respectively.

Fixed effects parameter estimates, characterizing both subgroups at the population level as one ensemble, are reported in Table 1 together with figures of precision, i.e. coefficient of variation and lower (L) and upper (U) limits of 95% statistical confidence intervals. It can be observed that parameter estimates have physiologically plausible values, such as GEZI = 0.72 dl min^{-1} that corresponds to a fractional glucose clearance of 0.0067 min^{-1}; S_I = 0.098 dl min^{-1} μU^{-1} ml in normal subjects, corresponds to a value of 9.17 10^{-4} min^{-1} μU^{-1} ml. The insulin sensitivity index in diabetic patients resulted in low values (only 4.9% of S_I of normal subjects). In addition to the differences in S_I between normal and diabetic subjects the only covariate found to significantly affect glucose kinetics was BW influencing GEZI. The value of %GEZI/kg reported in Table 1 quantifies the % variation in glucose effectiveness at zero insulin for increases in 1 kg BW. The reported reference value of GEZI corresponds to an arbitrarily chosen nominal BW of 85 kg. An interesting result is the quite low value estimated of 16 μU ml^{-1} for insulin concentration for 50% inhibition of basal glucose production (I_{50}).

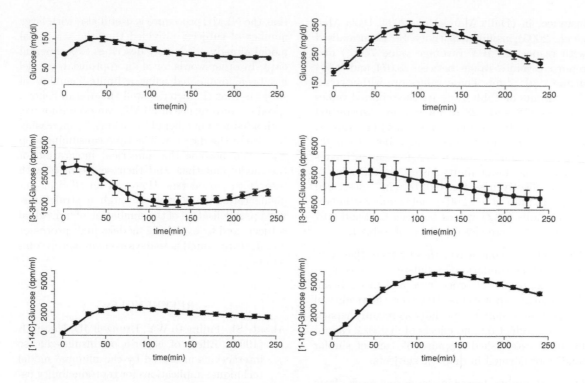

Fig. 1. Experimental data (mean±SE) and best average model predictions in normal controls (left panels) and diabetic subjects (right panels). Equivalent data are drawn with same scales but, whenever convenient, with different offsets.

Table 1. Fixed effects population parameter estimates and precision.

Parameter	Value	CV%	95%(L)	95%(U)
P_2	0.0163	28.9	0.0093	0.0287
GEZI	0.72	9.74	0.59	0.87
%GEZI/kg	2.09	0.70	0.71	3.5
$S_{Inormal}$	0.0981	14.8	0.073	0.13
$S_{Idiabetic}$	0.0048	18.2	0.0033	0.0068
V_G	107	18.1	75.1	152.5
α	123.1	9.3	102.5	147.8
β	1.451	3.1	1.36	1.55
I_{50}	16.11	24.7	9.92	26.2
h	1.425	22.7	0.91	2.22

4. DISCUSSION

This is the first report, to our knowledge, on simultaneous modelling of multiple sampled glucose data from double-tracer oral glucose tolerance test in healthy and diabetic subjects using a population modelling approach. A similar approach has been adopted for the analysis of non-steady state glucose kinetics during euglycemic hyperinsulinemic glucose clamp performed in cats (Hoenig *et al.*, in press). The proposed model is closely related to previous work by others, e.g. (Dalla Man *et al.*, 2004), the main difference being that glucose production is modeled here explicitly with a heuristic Hill-type equation dependent on remote insulin. This allows to define a unique time-varying glucose clearance for the three types of measured unlabeled and tracer glucose. In addition, the model provides parameter estimates for inhibition of glucose production by insulin, I_{50} and h, whose usefulness and reliability in providing information on glucose homeostasis still needs to be ascertained. Another difference with (Dalla Man *et al.*, 2004) consists in the representation of glucose absorption rate, i.e. a smooth function with two parameters versus a piecewise linear function with several parameters and a fixed constraint on total glucose absorption during the test. The proposed simplified model imposes a constraint only on the shape of the absorption profile, e.g. it cannot represent biphasic gastro-intestinal glucose absorption. Nevertheless, thanks to the modeled between-subject variability of absorption parameters, α and β, the model is able to fit well also individual glucose profiles. Modelling glucose absorption with a parametric function with few degrees of freedom has the additional advantage of allowing estimation of all model parameters, at least with a population approach, without the need of fixing some of the model parameters.

Parameter estimates obtained in healthy subjects are comparable with those reported in previous studies if normalisation is taken into account. For instance, in (Dalla Man *et al.*, 2004; Dalla Man *et al.*, 2005) insulin sensitivity, S_I, is normalised with respect to BW (average value 77 kg) and reported values range between 0.071 and 0.094 dl min$^{-1}\mu$U^{-1} ml. These values are within confidence limits of Table 1, as are the reported values between 112 and 123 dl for glucose distribution volume, V_G. In contrast, remote insulin turnover, P_2, whose previous values range between 0.011 and 0.043 min^{-1}, match the present estimates only at their lower limit. Also, only the value of glucose effectiveness S_G=0.0118 min^{-1} described in (Dalla Man *et al.*, 2005) yields under standard assumptions GEZI values between 0.42 and 0.67 dl min^{-1} that are close to those of Table 1.

Although not conclusive, these results thus support a cross-validation of different, yet comparable, experimental procedures and model-based data analysis approaches. However, the validity of the proposed model, especially as regards hepatic glucose production and effects of diabetes, cannot be fully established because of lack of similar studies performed in diabetic subjects.

One confounding factor in comparing results from different studies depends also on different model parameterisations. In particular, applying the log-transformation to parameters in the NLME procedure corresponds to the implicit assumption of lognormal distribution for the original model parameters. This choice has two advantages: (i) parameters are automatically constrained to be non-negative, and (ii) robustness with respect to outlying parameter values is improved, because the lognormal distribution can show heavier tails than the normal distribution, i.e. it can assign higher probabilities to large deviations from the mean for certain parameter values. Within a NLME population approach with log-normal parameter distribution, the presence of few outlying values can therefore be compensated mostly through a higher standard deviation of random effects rather than a bias on both standard deviation and mean, as usually seen under normality assumptions. Thus, even if one could compare population means of log-transformed with geometric means of un-transformed parameters, robustness with respect to outlier and efficiency of different identification procedures can strongly affect parameter estimates.

Practical experience shows that population modelling with NLME can help solving model identification problems in small groups of subjects, which would be otherwise unfeasible at individual basis. The reason is that individual estimates benefit from group estimates on occasionally little informative experiments. Improved estimates of fixed and random effects could have been, obviously, obtained with a larger cohort. Experience teaches that the NLME procedure is useful also with large number of subjects provided that the statistical model already adequately describes experimental data. In other words, once an appropriate model has been formulated using a limited number of subjects that characterise well the overall cohort, speed of convergence of NLME can even improve, with a reduced number of iterations, by increasing the size of the data set. The time-consuming step may then become the numerical integration of the model equations and their sensitivities with respect to parameters. However, an efficient implementation is possible through a straightforward parallelisation of the simulation of individual subjects and by exploiting modern multiprocessor architectures found nowadays even on laptop computers.

REFERENCES

Abbate SL, Fujimoto WY, Brunzell JD, Kahn SE (1993). Effect of heparin on insulin-glucose interactions measured by the minimal model technique: implications for reproducibility using this method. *Metabolism* **42**, 353–357.

Bergman RN, Ider YZ, Bowden CR, Cobelli C (1979). Quantitative estimation of insulin sensitivity. *Am J Physiol* **236**, E667–677.

Dalla Man C, Caumo A, Cobelli C (2002). The oral glucose minimal model: estimation of insulin sensitivity from a meal test. *IEEE Trans Biomed Eng* **49**, 419–429.

Dalla Man C, Caumo A, Basu R, Rizza R, Toffolo G, Cobelli C (2004). Minimal model estimation of glucose absorption and insulin sensitivity from oral test: validation with a tracer method. *Am J Physiol Endocrinol Metab* **287**, E637–643.

Dalla Man C, Caumo A, Basu R, Rizza R, Toffolo G, Cobelli C (2005). Measurement of selective effect of insulin on glucose disposal from labeled glucose oral test minimal model. *Am J Physiol Endocrinol Metab* **289**, E909-914.

Davidian M, Giltinan DM (1995). *Nonlinear Models for Repeated Measurement Data*. Chapman & Hall. London.

Hoenig M, Thomaseth K, Brandao J, Waldron M, Ferguson DC (in press). Assessment and mathematical modeling of glucose turnover and insulin sensitivity in lean and obese cats. *Domest Anim Endocrinol*.

Pinheiro JC, Bates DM (2000). *Mixed-Effects Models in S and S-plus*. Springer. New York.

Thomaseth K. Multidisciplinary modelling of biomedical systems. *Comput Methods Programs Biomed* **71**:189-201, 2003.

TOWARDS A RELIABLE POSTURE ESTIMATION FOR STANDING IN PARAPLEGIA

Gaël Pages [*,**] **Nacim Ramdani** [**]
Philippe Fraisse [**] **David Guiraud** [**]

* *MXM, 2720 Chemin Saint Bernard, 06224, Vallauris,*
France
** *DEMAR Project, INRIA LIRMM*
LIRMM, 161 rue Ada, 34392 Montpellier, France

Abstract: A new approach aiming posture estimation using only forces measurements exerted on handles and geometric constraints is outlined. The behavior of the system is modeled by an ordinary differential equation (ODE) which includes parameters whose value is uncertain. The insufficiency in precision while computation may affect safe decision making. Interval arithmetic is a method for performing computations on measurements that are only known within a fixed error range. The uncertainties are propagated throughout the calculation to obtain safe bounds interval domains. In order to investigate the feasibility of posture estimation by interval methods in this particular case, a simplified model of the human body was developed, in regards to a three degrees of freedom link-segment model. *Copyright © 2006 IFAC.*

Keywords: Robotics, Intervals, Integration, Differential equation, Uncertainty, Paraplegia, Rehabilitation, Posture estimation.

1. INTRODUCTION

Paraplegia results from a severe spinal cord injury which causes the interruption of the signal path from the central nervous system to lower limbs muscles, and thus implies the loss of sensation and the inability to stand and walk. Functional movement restoration is possible for paraplegics by the use of Functional Electrical Stimulation (FES). Unfortunately, movement generation induced by FES remains mostly open looped and is tuned empirically.

A preliminary phase before a complete closed loop solution is to let the patient act upon the system through a rich interface consisting in an instrumented walker. Although walker assisted-gait is not fully investigated, several research projects

use instrumented walkers for various purposes, including approaches that aim to infer navigational intent of the walker's user based on forces and torques measurements applied to a walker's handles (Alwan *et al.*, 2005; Wasson *et al.*, 2004). These walkers are mostly used as mobility aids and are studied to improve independent mobility. They are intended for persons having functional ability and activity difficulties, and are in no case suitable for paraplegic persons.

The long term objective of this study is to enable paraplegic patients to teleoperate the lower limbs by means of an instrumented walker through forces and torques measurements applied on the walker's handles.

The patient interacts with the system in three ways:

- He decides which movements he wants to achieve and informs the system.
- He performs voluntary movements in a cooperative way, knowing that he could disturb the system if a closed loop control is running.
- Passive actions like arm supports through the walker are used to control the balance and posture.

The primary focus of this paper deals with estimating a patient's upper body posture, only from the measurement of the efforts exerted on the walker's handles as well as ground reaction force.

The method proposed is based on the numerical integration of a kinematic and dynamic model of the human body, where forces measurements are considered as inputs to the model. In order to guarantee reliability in computation for safe posture estimation, and prevent cases like falling, the numerical methodology to be used must be fail-safe from numerical errors introduced by the integration schemes. It must also account for any uncertainties in either initial posture values or with the anthropometric parameters which act in the biomechanical model.

Standard methodologies for propagating uncertainties in mathematical models rely on random sampling techniques (Helton *et al.*, 2004), which leads to numerous simulation runs. Furthermore, conventional numerical integration schemes only yield approximate solutions but with uncontrolled global error.

The key feature in this paper brings out a strategy which uses a self-validated numerical integration method which yields valid results for any initial state or model parameter vector taken in prior uncertainty domains. This numerical integration method is capable of proving existence and uniqueness of a solution for the differential equation, as well as computing a tight domain that contains the actual solution in a guaranteed way. In this paper, *guarantee* means that we can *prove* statements via numerical computations obtained with a computer of limited memory and finite precision.

In order to validate the methodology, a simulation study was performed in a simple case where the kinematic system is considered as a three degrees of freedom planar manipulator.

2. APPROACH TO POSTURE ESTIMATION

The aim in estimating human upper body posture is to distinguish the user's motion states such as support phase or voluntary movement. Another significant reason, and not the least, to this study is to detect unfavorable motions like falling. It is necessary to prevent this type of situation before it occurs.

Part of the study consists in detecting motion by analyzing the external forces acting upon the body, that is ground force reaction, measured by flexible pressure insoles, and forces exerted on the walker's handles, measured by two 6 axis force/torque sensors. Motion is detected if the resultant external force vector is different from zero. These measurements are processed throughout the established dynamic model of the human body at sampling time.

2.1 The User Interface

In order to adapt the walker to the walk of a paraplegic subject, a new type of walker has been designed and conceived as shown in Figure 1. One of the innovations is its front-open structure, allowing any user a greater freedom of movement.

During a functional electric stimulation on a paraplegic subject, muscle fatigue appears very quickly, the walker is thus equipped with a seat, adjustable in height, allowing the patient to sit down as soon as needed. The rear wheels are motorized. The two front wheels are caster wheels for steering direction. The two 6-axis force/torque sensors, from *ATI Industrial Automation*, are fitted between the handles and the walker.

The experiment scenario is demonstrated in Figure 1. The image shows the user in an initial upright posture. Forces are recorded throughout the whole process in order to measure the movement and attitude of the user.

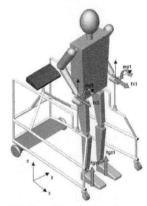

Fig. 1. The Walker/User Experiment Scenario.

2.2 The Biomechanical Model

A three dimensional model of the human body has been developed, in terms of kinetics. It is based on robotics considerations and therefore

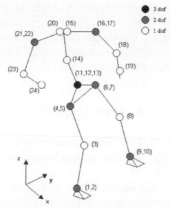

Fig. 2. Biomechanical Model Description.

take advantage of the big amount of research carried out in this field as regards both theoretical results and practical tools (Khalil and Dombre, 1999). Our simplified model is inspired from the basic skeleton structure. It contains 24 degrees of freedom (DOF) and can be seen as a tree-structured robot manipulator, which is composed of three end-effectors with the right foot as the starting point of the structure as shown in Figure 2.

A minimum set of DOF was defined to describe all the possible postures. The model is composed, for the upper limbs, of three DOF (ball joint) on the pelvis and two DOF for each shoulder. The movement of the wrist, the elbow, the shoulder girdle and the spinal cord are each represented by one DOF. On the lower limbs, ankle and thigh joints are represented by two DOF and the knee joints by one DOF.

The dynamic behavior can be expressed as a relationship between applied torques, $\mathbf{\Gamma}$, and motion trajectories $\mathbf{q}$, $\dot{\mathbf{q}}$, $\ddot{\mathbf{q}}$ of joints. It can be described by the following Lagrangian form:

$$\mathbf{\Gamma} = \mathbf{M}(\mathbf{q})\ddot{\mathbf{q}} + \mathbf{C}(\mathbf{q}, \dot{\mathbf{q}})\dot{\mathbf{q}} + \mathbf{G}(\mathbf{q}) + \mathbf{\Gamma}_c \quad (1)$$

Here $\mathbf{q}$, $\dot{\mathbf{q}}$, $\ddot{\mathbf{q}}$ denote respectively joint angle, angular velocity and angular acceleration vectors, which are function of time. They are expressed as column vectors.

The generalized inertia matrix, $\mathbf{M}(\mathbf{q})$ is represented by a 24×24 symmetric and positive-definite matrix. Centrifugal and Coriolis effects are defined by $\mathbf{C}(\mathbf{q}, \dot{\mathbf{q}})$ which is a 24×24 matrix. The gravitational contributions are described by $\mathbf{G}(\mathbf{q})$ which is a 24×1 vector. The term $\mathbf{\Gamma}_c = \mathbf{J}_c^{\mathrm{T}}(\mathbf{q})\mathbf{f}_c$, where $\mathbf{J}_c(\mathbf{q})$ is the Jacobian matrix, interprets torques induced by external forces applied at the end-effector, denoted by $\mathbf{f}_c$.

The contacts between the hands and the handles as well as the left foot with the ground creates

a closed kinematic linkage. These interactions are described by:

$$\mathbf{\Gamma}_c = \mathbf{\Gamma}_{c_1} + \mathbf{\Gamma}_{c_2} + \mathbf{\Gamma}_{c_3} \quad (2)$$

$\mathbf{\Gamma}_{c_1}$, $\mathbf{\Gamma}_{c_2}$ and $\mathbf{\Gamma}_{c_3} \in \mathbb{R}^{24}$ represent respectively the torque-induced vectors generated by the forces located at the foot, the left hand and the right hand.

By analogy with the expression of $\mathbf{\Gamma}_c$, we can define the following expression for each end-effector:

$$\mathbf{\Gamma}_{c_j} = \mathbf{J}_{c_j}^{\mathrm{T}}(\mathbf{q})\mathbf{f}_{c_j} \quad (3)$$

where $\mathbf{f}_{c_j} = \begin{bmatrix} {}^j f_x & {}^j f_y & {}^j f_z & {}^j m_x & {}^j m_y & {}^j m_z \end{bmatrix}^T$ is the measured force/torque vector.

Estimating upper body posture from force/torques measurements, at sampling times $\{ t_1, t_2, \ldots t_N \}$, involves evaluating the forward dynamics equation:

$$\ddot{\mathbf{q}}(t) = \mathbf{M}^{-1}(\mathbf{q}) \left\{ \mathbf{\Gamma} - \mathbf{\Gamma}_c - \mathbf{H}(\mathbf{q}, \dot{\mathbf{q}}) \right\} \quad (4)$$

where $\mathbf{H}(\mathbf{q}, \dot{\mathbf{q}}) = \mathbf{C}(\mathbf{q}, \dot{\mathbf{q}})\dot{\mathbf{q}} - \mathbf{G}(\mathbf{q})$.

A safe estimation of upper-body posture cannot be evaluated if we do not take in account the propagation of inaccuracies in the model due to badly known anthropometric parameters as well as initial conditions and force measurements.

This problem can be computed in a reliable way with interval-based techniques. In contrast with more classical numerical approaches for solving differential equations with initial values, uncertainty in modeling is quantified and propagated when using interval algorithms. Moreover, the results provided are obtained in a guaranteed way and in finite time, even when strong nonlinearities are involved in the problem. Safe enclosures for the trajectory are then computed, explicitly keeping the error term within safe interval bounds.

2.3 Validated Numerical Integration

Our system is a non linear differential equation defined by:

$$\begin{cases} \dot{\mathbf{x}}(t) = \mathbf{f}(\mathbf{x}(t)) \\ \mathbf{x}(0) \in \mathbf{x}_0 \end{cases} \quad (5)$$

The state space vector is defined by $\mathbf{x} = \begin{bmatrix} \mathbf{q} & \dot{\mathbf{q}} & \mathbf{p} \end{bmatrix}^T$, where $\mathbf{p}$ symbolizes the parameter vector.

The method relies on interval arithmetic to calculate, between two consecutive sampling times, approximation of the solution, taking in account the error term within appropriate interval bounds in a guaranteed way.

Interval analysis was initially developed to account for the quantification errors introduced by the floating point representation of real numbers with computers and was extended to validated numerics (Moore, 1966).

Consider a function $\mathbf{f} : \mathbb{R}^n \to \mathbb{R}^m$. The range of this function over an interval vector $[\mathbf{a}]$ is given by:

$$\mathbf{f}([\mathbf{a}]) = \{ \mathbf{f}(\mathbf{x}) \mid \mathbf{x} \in [\mathbf{a}] \} \qquad (6)$$

The interval function $[\mathbf{f}]$ from $\mathbb{IR}^n$ to $\mathbb{IR}^m$ is an inclusion function for $\mathbf{f}$ if:

$$\forall [\mathbf{a}] \in \mathbb{IR}^n, \ \mathbf{f}([\mathbf{a}]) \subseteq [\mathbf{f}]([\mathbf{a}]) \qquad (7)$$

An inclusion function of $\mathbf{f}$ can be obtained by replacing each occurrence of a real variable by the corresponding interval and each standard function by its interval counterpart. The resulting function is called the natural inclusion function. The performances of this inclusion function depend on the formal expression for $\mathbf{f}$.

The method used for solving relationship (5) consists in two phases. First it is necessary to validate the existence and the uniqueness of a solution and evaluate a prior enclosure, $[\tilde{\mathbf{x}}_j]$, of the true trajectory between each sampling time. This can be done by using the Picard-Lindelöf operator and the Banach fixed-point theorem (Moore, 1966). Function $\mathbf{f}$ needs to be Lipschitz over $[\tilde{\mathbf{x}}_j]$.

In practice, it is sufficient to find a box $[\tilde{\mathbf{x}}_j]$ which satisfies the following inclusion:

$$[\mathbf{x}_j] + [0, h]\, \mathbf{f}([\tilde{\mathbf{x}}_j]) \subseteq [\tilde{\mathbf{x}}_j] \qquad (8)$$

The usual procedure starts with $[\tilde{\mathbf{x}}_j] = [\mathbf{x}_j]$, then inflates $[\tilde{\mathbf{x}}_j]$ by a coefficient α, generally chosen such as $0.5 \leq \alpha \leq 1$, until it satisfies (8).

In a second part, a tighter enclosure of the trajectory is obtained through interval arithmetic over the chosen numerical approximation step as the Taylor expansion method of order k, denoted by:

$$[\mathbf{x}_{j+1}] = [\mathbf{x}_j] + \sum_{i=1}^{k-1} h^i\, \mathbf{f}^{[i]}([\mathbf{x}_j]) + h^k\, \mathbf{f}^{[k]}([\tilde{\mathbf{x}}_j]), \quad (9)$$

where $h = t_{j+1} - t_j$ denotes the integration step and the $\mathbf{f}^{[i]}$ are the Taylor coefficients of the solution $\mathbf{x}(t)$ which are recursively obtained by:

$$\mathbf{f}^{[1]} = \mathbf{x}^{(1)} = \mathbf{f}$$
$$\mathbf{f}^{[i]} = \frac{1}{i!}\, \mathbf{x}^{(i)} = \frac{1}{i}\, \frac{\partial \mathbf{f}^{[i-1]}}{\partial \mathbf{x}}\, \mathbf{f}, \ i \geq 2 \qquad (10)$$

Commonly, the approach in evaluating expression (9) is done through the extended mean value (E.M.V) algorithm based on mean value forms and matrices preconditioning (Rihm, 1994; Lohner, 1987; Eijgenraam, 1981).

3. APPLICATION

In order to conduct preliminary investigation into the feasibility of the methodology exposed in section 2, we chose to concentrate our study using computer simulation on a simplified model, before proceeding with experimental evaluations on human subjects and full models.

3.1 Numerical Benchmark Description

The human body was described as a four bar linkage with a three degrees of freedom dynamic structure in a 2 dimensional world frame $\{W\}$, which corresponds to the sagittal plane, as shown in Figure 3. All links are assumed to be rigid bodies.

The segments length are denoted with L_j, their center of mass (COM) with l_j, their mass and inertia are represented with m_j and I_j parameters. The COM locations are expressed as a distal distance from the joint with the same index. The anthropometric values used were taken from literature (Winter, 2004) and based on a subject weighting 70 kilograms and measuring 1.70 meters. The gravitational acceleration g was taken to be 9.81 m.s^{-2}.

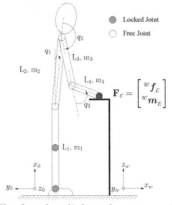

Fig. 3. The four bar linkage human model.

In order to investigate the interactions of contact forces on the joint variables position, a model of the contact between the end-effector of the robot and a horizontal surface is used. The coordinate of the contact point is at a fixed height, z_s. To simulate a normal contact force variation on the end-effector the contact surface is modeled as a spring, defined by equation (11). A constraint is then set between the position of the end-effector, P_z, and z_s, to keep contact.

$$f_c = K_z(z_s - P_z) \qquad (11)$$

K_z represents the spring stiffness (N/m).

3.2 Dynamics Modeling

The forward kinematic problem is a nonlinear system represented by the following differential equation:

$$\begin{cases} \ddot{\mathbf{q}}(t) = \mathbf{M}^{-1}(\mathbf{q}) \left\{ \mathbf{J}^{\mathrm{T}}(\mathbf{q}) \, \mathbf{F}_\Sigma - \mathbf{f}_v \, \dot{\mathbf{q}}(t) \right\} \\ \mathbf{q}(0) = \mathbf{q}_0 \\ \dot{\mathbf{q}}(0) = \dot{\mathbf{q}}_0 \end{cases} \qquad (12)$$

Where parameter $\mathbf{f}_v$ corresponds to viscous frictions matrix and $\mathbf{F}_\Sigma$ is the resultant force vector. In this case $\mathbf{F}_\Sigma = \begin{bmatrix} 0 & 0 & \sum f_z & 0 & 0 & 0 \end{bmatrix}^T$ and is available at sampling times $t_i \in \{ t_1, t_2, \ldots, t_N \}$.

To have complete knowledge on the forces acting upon the manipulator, ground reaction force contributed by gravity must be taken in account. This force is expressed by:

$$f_g = \mathbf{J}^{\mathrm{T}}(\mathbf{q}) \, \mathbf{G}(\mathbf{q}) \qquad (13)$$

Hence if condition (14) is verified, then the manipulator is in static equilibrium, otherwise motion is then detected. This is also a useful information for apprehending user intent.

$$\sum f_z = f_c - f_g = 0 \qquad (14)$$

The force data obtained by the previous relationship at each sampling time is then used for posture estimation with the interval analysis method.

Having defined the dynamics of the system, the difficulty now lies in integrating numerically relationship (12) while propagating the uncertainties in the model, onto estimated posture.

3.3 Posture Estimation Simulation

The algorithms for numerical integration by interval techniques, exposed in section 2, is implemented for the three degrees of freedom model previously described. Simulations are done with INTLAB [1] toolbox (Rump, 1990) for MATLAB

---

[1] Found at http://www.ti3.tu-harburg.de/rump/intlab/

used for interval evaluation and automatic differentiation. The idea is to point out the feasibility of the method in estimating posture in a guaranteed way with uncertain values in parameters.

In the approach, the dynamic model of the manipulator was simplified. The diagonal elements of the inertia matrix $\mathbf{M}(\mathbf{q})$ were considered as constant. The resultant force vector, shown in Figure 4, was obtained by simulating the dynamics of the robot. The collected data was sampled at 0.5 ms and was then used in the integration schemes. Several sets of uncertainties, built on percentage of the exact value, associated to each parameter, were used for simulation as denoted in Table 1. The numerical integration of the differential equation was evaluated by a second order Taylor expansion for different error bounding on each variable.

The results obtained with such a model are represented in Figures 5, 6 and 7. An analysis of these curves shows that the estimated trajectories for the joint variables q_1 and q_2 stay in a constant range throughout the whole process in regards to the different uncertainties states for each parameter. Notice that the bounds of the last articular joint's trajectory tends to diverge, for increasing sets of uncertainties, towards the end of the simulation. Further research needs to be carried out to determine the causes of this divergence and to progress in the study of posture estimation for a dynamic behavior closer to reality. Nevertheless, the objective of providing the feasibility of the method has been accomplished.

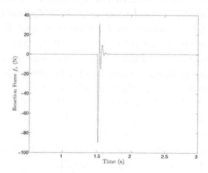

Fig. 4. Reaction Force.

Table 1. Percentage Error On Parameters.

Parameters	Uncertainties		
	Case 1	Case 2	Case 3
Joint Position $[q_i]$	1%	3%	10%
Joint Velocity $[\dot{q}_i]$	1%	3%	5%
Reaction Force $[f_z]$	1%	5%	5%
Masses $[m_i]$	1%	5%	5%
Lengths $[d_i]$	1%	10%	5%
Inertia $[I_i]$	1%	5%	5%
Viscous Frictions $[f_{v_i}]$	1%	10%	10%

4. CONCLUSION AND FUTURE WORK

A method for reliable posture estimation, based on measuring forces exerted on a walker's handles, has been presented. It constitutes a relatively new research direction in robotics field. The approach is based on interval analysis methods, which is a mean of representing uncertainty by replacing real floating point values with intervals. The interesting aspect of the method is that the numerical interval integration scheme used is self-validated and provides guaranteed results. This is a non negligible condition since in walker-assisted gait in paraplegia, unpropitious movements such as falling can occur. This situation must be anticipated.

To validate the proposed methodology, we have used a three degrees of freedom robot manipulator and simulated force measurements exerted by the end-effector. The computer simulated results suggest the feasibility of the methodology and much future research is required to discern all the complexities associated with the model.

Further study will deal with much more complex models to finally work our way to the biomechanical model, adequate for estimating posture of an actual person. The issue of real-time computation will also be addressed.

REFERENCES

Alwan, M., G. Wasson, P. Sheth, A. Ledoux and C. Huang (2005). Passive derivation of basic walker-assisted gait characteristics from measured forces and moments. *26th International IEEE Engineering in Medicine and Biology Conference (EMBC 05)* pp. 2691–2694.

Eijgenraam, P. (1981). *The Solution of initial value problems using interval arithmetic.* Amsterdamm : Mathematisch Centrum.

Helton, J.C., J.D. Johnson and W.L. Oberkampf (2004). An exploration of alternative approaches to the representation of uncertainty in model predictions. *Reliability Engineering and System Safety* **85**, 39–71.

Khalil, W. and E. Dombre (1999). *Modï¿½isation , Identification et Commande des Robots.* 2nd Edition, Hermes Sciences Publications. Paris.

Lohner, R. J. (1987). Enclosing the solutions of ordinary initial and boundary value problems. In: *Computer Arithmetic: Scientific Computation and Programming Languages* (Wiley, Ed.). Stuttgart. pp. 255–286.

Moore, R.E. (1966). *Interval Analysis.* Prentice-Hall. Englewood Cliffs.

Rihm, R. (1994). Interval methods for initial value problems in odes. In: *Validated computations: proceedings of the IMACS-GAMM International Workshop on Validated Computations* (Elsevier Studies in Computational Mathematics, Ed.). J. Herzberger. Amsterdam. pp. 173–208.

Rump, S. (1990). Intlab - interval laboratory. In: *Developments in reliable computing.* pp. 77–104.

Wasson, G., P. Sheth, M. Alwan, C. Huang and A. Ledoux (2004). A physics-based model for predicting user intent in shared-control pedestrian mobility aids. *IEEE/RSJ International Conference on Intelligent Robots and Systems (IROS 04).*

Winter, D.A. (2004). *Biomechanics and Motor Control of Human Movement.* 3rd Edition, John Wiley Sons, Inc. Ontario.

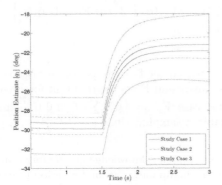

Fig. 5. Joint Position q_1 Estimate.

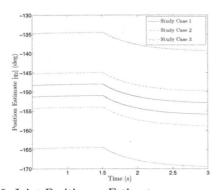

Fig. 6. Joint Position q_2 Estimate.

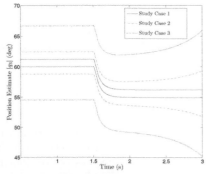

Fig. 7. Joint Position q_3 Estimate.

Copyright © IFAC Modelling and Control in Biomedical Systems
Reims, France, 2006

CLINICAL CARDIOVASCULAR IDENTIFICATION WITH LIMITED DATA AND FAST FORWARD SIMULATION

Christopher E. Hann*, **J. Geoffrey Chase***,
Geoffrey M. Shaw**, **Steen Andreassen*****,
Bram W. Smith***

* *Centre for Bioengineering, University of Canterbury,
Christchurch, New Zealand*
** *Christchurch Hospital Department of Intensive Care
Medicine,Christchurch, New Zealand*
*** *Centre for Model-based Medical Decision Support,
Aalborg University, Aalborg, Denmark*

Abstract: A minimal cardiac model has been developed that captures the major dynamics of the cardio-vascular system (CVS). This model is extended to simulate time varying disease state including reflex actions and an integral based identification method is presented that enables linear and convex parameter identification. Two common time varying disease states are identified to within 10% without false identification. Also the valve law in this model is reformulated in terms of Heaviside functions, and a unique closed form analytical solution is obtained for the ventricular interaction equation. This enables rapid forward simulations of the model. Clinically, the method ensures medical staff can rapidly obtain a patient specific model and can simulate a large number of therapy combinations to find the best treatment. *Copyright © 2006 IFAC*

Keywords: Biomedical Systems, Physiological Models, Integrals, Parameter Identification, Diagnosis

1. INTRODUCTION

Cardiovascular disease is difficult to diagnose and treat due to limited measurements available in an Intensive Care Unit (ICU). The particular disease state does not generally show up with any individual measurement but involves complex interactions between a wide range of data including the body's natural reflex response which seeks to restore circulatory equilibrium. Thus often diagnosis and the chosen treatment depends on the experience and intuition of clinical staff.

A minimal cardiac model which captures all the major dynamics and interactions observed in stan-dard clinical measurements and can be tailored to an individual patient, could therefore assist medical staff in diagnosis and the prediction of drug effects to optimize therapy. "Minimal" model refers to a model that minimizes the number of parameters while still capturing the essential macro dynamics of the CVS within the measurements available.

There is a variety of CVS models in the literature that range from very complex finite element models to more relatively simpler pressure volume approaches. Although there are models that describe the whole CVS, patient specific parameter optimization is either not considered or restricted to small subsets of the whole parameter set describing specific aspects of the CVS (e.g. (Mukkamala and Cohen, 2001)). The approach of this research is to develop a highly flexible minimal model that can adapt to wide ranges of patient dynamics seen in an ICU, including responses to potentially many different therapies. In the ICU environment, catheters are often already in place so a larger range of measurements are available. Furthermore, as this paper shows, using an integral based optimization enables virtually all of the parameter set to be identified.

This research builds on a previously developed minimal model which accurately simulates a variety of CVS dysfunctions, (Smith *et al.*, 2004). However, the model does not lend itself to a convex identification problem (Smith, 2004). Thus, potentially false solutions could be found. Furthermore, to implement common non-linear regression identification methods (Carson and Cobelli, 2001) requires many computationally expensive model simulations (Smith, 2004). Hence, computational intensity severely limits the number of optimization iterations available to find a solution in a clinically useful time period.

In this paper, an integral-based patient specific identification method is presented which is an extension of (Hann *et al.*, 2005; Hann *et al.*, 2004). All measurements assumed are available in critical care using Swan-Ganz catheters or ultra-sound.

Two common disease states, Pericardial Tamponade and Cardiogenic shock are simulated from onset. Each disease state is then identified in the presence of 10% uniformly distributed noise to prove the concept. The body's reflex actions to keep the pressure in the aorta stable are included.

Also a fast forward solver is critical as there remains the task of trialling many different therapies to find the best treatment. Two methods of significantly speeding up the current model are discussed.

2. METHODOLOGY

2.1 Cardiac Model

The full model consists of six elastic chambers as shown in Figure 1. Each of the ventricles is treated as a single elastic chamber. The differential equations for the single elastic chamber with inertia and upstream and downstream pressures P_1 and P_3, are defined (Smith *et al.*, 2004):

$$\dot{V} = Q_1 - Q_2 \tag{1}$$

$$\dot{Q}_1 = \frac{P_1 - P_2 - Q_1 R_1}{L_1} \tag{2}$$

$$\dot{Q}_2 = \frac{P_2 - P_3 - Q_2 R_2}{L_2} \tag{3}$$

where Q_1 and Q_2 are the flows in and out, L_1 and L_2 are inertances of the blood, R_1 and R_2 are resistances. The driving pressure in the chamber is defined:

$$P_2 = e(t)E_{es}(V - V_d)$$
$$+ (1 - e(t))P_0(e^{\lambda(V - V_0)} - 1) \tag{4}$$

$$e(t) = e^{-80(t - 0.375)^2} \tag{5}$$

where E_{es} is elastance, V_d is the unstressed chamber volume, $e(t)$ is a driving function that simulates ventricular contraction and P_0, λ, and V_0 define gradient, curvature and volume at zero pressure of the EDPVR curve in the cardiac cycle shown in Figure 2 (Smith *et al.*, 2004).

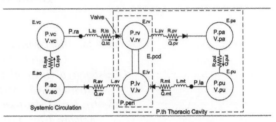

Fig. 1. The full six chamber cardio-vascular system model

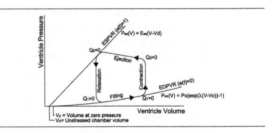

Fig. 2. Pressure-volume diagram of the single cardiac chamber model.

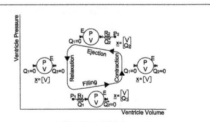

Fig. 3. Model state at each part of the cardiac cycle.

The original solution procedure (Smith *et al.*, 2004) for incorporating valve dynamics in the chambers is to solve the Equations (1) and (2) when $Q_1 > 0$, during the filling stage, and to solve Equations (1) and (3) when $Q_2 > 0$, during the ejection stage. This model has an open on pressure, close on flow valve law as shown in Figure 2 (Smith *et al.*, 2004; Smith, 2004). Figure 3 shows the states used for each portion of the cardiac cycle.

2.2 Reflex actions

The effect of heart disease and shock on the CVS can be significantly altered by the body's natural reflex response that attempts to maintain enough blood pressure and flow to sustain life. The effect of reflex actions can thus often mask the underlying problem and must be accounted for in the CVS model.

Reflex actions included are divided into four groups: vaso-constriction, venous constriction, increased heart rate (HR) and increased ventricular contractility (Burkhoff and Tyberg, 1993). Their activation is assumed to be proportional to the drop in the average pressure in the aorta (P_{ao}). The proportionality constants are estimated based on clinically observed CVS hemodynamic responses reported in the literature (Braunwald, 1997).

Specifically, vaso-constriction is simulated in the model based on increasing the systemic resistance R_{sys} by 35% for a drop in average P_{ao} from 100 mmHg to 80 mmHg. Similarly, venous constriction, HR and ventricular contractility are increased based on increasing the venous dead space $V_{d,vc}$, HR and the left and right ventricle free wall contractilities $E_{es,lvf}$ and $E_{es,rvf}$ by 67%, 80 to 120 beats per minute and 35% respectively for a drop in average P_{ao} to 80 mmHg. In the model simulations, reflex actions are applied every heart beat.

2.3 Integral parameter identification

The differential equations associated with the left and right ventricles can be reformulated in terms of integrals of the measured flows through the chambers, see (Hann et al., 2004). Similarly the differential equations of (Smith et al., 2004) describing volume changes in the aorta, pulmonary artery, vena cava and pulmonary vein can be reformulated in terms of integrals by choosing suitable sampling periods.

The end result is that given the pressure waveforms through the aorta and pulmonary artery, the flows into and out of the left and right ventricles and their maximum and minimum volumes, a system of linear equations can be defined:

$$A\underline{\beta} = b \qquad (6)$$
$$\underline{\beta} = [\underline{\alpha}, P_{ao0}, P_{pu0}, P_{pa0}, P_{vc0}] \qquad (7)$$

$$\underline{\alpha} = [L_{av}, L_{mt}, L_{tc}, L_{pv}, E_{es,lvf}, P_{0,lvf}, E_{es,rvf},$$
$$P_{0,rvf}, R_{av}, R_{mt}, R_{tc}, R_{pv}, E_{vc}, E_{pu}, E_{ao}, E_{pa},$$
$$R_{sys}, R_{pul}] \qquad (8)$$

where A is an $N \times 22$ matrix, $N >> 22$ is the number of chosen integration periods over which the parameters are constant, b is an $N \times 1$ vector, $\underline{\alpha}$

are the patient specific parameters and the initial conditions, P_{ao0}, P_{pu0}, P_{pa0} and P_{vc0} are treated as extra unknown variables. Equation (6) can then be solved by linear least squares to uniquely determine $\underline{\alpha}$.

2.4 Simulating Disease States

The disease states that are simulated are Pericardial Tamponade and Cardiogenic Shock. Pericardial tamponade is an excessive build up of fluid in the pericardium limiting ventricular expansion. It is simulated by reducing the pericardium deadspace volume $V_{0,pcd}$ by 20 ml every 10 heart beats for a total of 50 heart beats.

Cardiogenic shock occurs when the heart is unable to pump a sufficient amount of blood to provide oxygen to the tissues and myocardium (Braunwald, 1997). Lack of oxygen supply to the myocardium causes further depression of cardiac function by decreasing ventricular contractilities and increasing diastolic elastance. Hence, a patient beginning to suffer from left ventricular infarction due to a coronary artery becoming blocked is simulated from an initial healthy state. The left ventricle contractility is reduced in piecewise constant steps to 50% of normal and diastolic elastance is increased in piecewise constant steps to a factor of 2.5 due to ischemia.

2.5 Heaviside formulation and Ventricular Interaction

For the full model described in (Smith et al., 2004) there are two valves for each of the left and right ventricles giving rise to a number of combinations of open and closed positions of the valves to capture. This formulation can be coded with some effort, but is computationally heavy, constantly searching for sign changes in model states. Another significantly simpler formulation that does not require an event solver is to automatically account for the valve opening or closing using Heaviside functions.

For the left ventricle the upstream pressure P_1 is the pressure in the pulmonary vein (P_{pu}) and the downstream pressure P_2 is the pressure in the aorta (P_{ao}). The Heaviside formulation of Equations (1)-(3) is defined as follows:

$$\dot{V} = H(Q_1)Q_1 - H(Q_2)Q_2 \qquad (9)$$
$$\dot{Q}_1 = H\left(H(P_1 - P_2) + H(Q_1) - 0.5\right)$$
$$\frac{(P_1 - P_2 - R_1 Q_1)}{L_1} \qquad (10)$$
$$\dot{Q}_2 = H(H(P_2 - P_3) + H(Q_2) - 0.5)$$
$$\frac{(P_2 - P_3 - R_2 Q_2)}{L_2} \qquad (11)$$

where the Heaviside function $H(K(t))$ is defined:

$$H(K(t)) = 0, \quad K(t) < 0$$
$$= 1, \quad K(t) \geq 0 \qquad (12)$$

Note that a more compact form for the Heaviside function can be defined as follows:

$$H(K(t)) = \frac{1}{2} + \frac{1}{\pi}\left(\tan^{-1}(K(t)) + \tan^{-1}(\frac{1}{K(t)})\right) \qquad (13)$$

By using a triangle with base $K(t)$ and height 1 it is easily shown that Equation (13) and (12) are precisely equivalent. Simulations have shown that Equation (13) is a computationally more efficient form than Equation (12).

During filling, $Q_2 = 0$ and $P_2 < P_3$ so the right hand side of Equation (11) is zero and thus Q_2 remains at zero and Equations (9)-(10) are solved. The pressure P_2 will then increase but when P_2 becomes greater than P_1, the inlet valve does not shut off (that is $\dot{Q}_1 = 0$) until Q_1 becomes 0 or negative. This implementation of the close on flow portion of the valve law occurs because

$$H(H(P_1 - P_2) + H(Q_1) - 0.5) = 1,$$
$$P_2 > P_1, \; Q_1 > 0$$
$$H(H(P_1 - P_2) + H(Q_1) - 0.5) = 0,$$
$$P_2 > P_1, \; Q_1 \leq 0$$

Hence, this valve law captures the effect of inertia for the inlet valve by closing on flow.

The explanation for the contraction, ejection and relaxation periods is similar. This cycle is continued for as many heart beats as required. Thus, the two flow differential equations and the volume differential equation are solved simultaneously for all time without needing the event solver to switch models and sets of equations (Smith, 2004). All that is required are initial conditions at the start, with no implicit searches for sign changes as for any input $K(t)$ in Equation (13) the output is simply determined from the sum of two $\tan^{-1}$ evaluations. By avoiding switching models and equations the small errors that occur with an event solver will not build up over long simulations and contaminate the results and model stability.

However a computationally simpler set of differential equations with fewer Heavisides, for a single chamber can be defined as follows:

$$\dot{V} = H(Q_1)Q_1 - H(Q_2)Q_2 \qquad (14)$$
$$\dot{Q}_1 = \frac{P_1 - P_2 - Q_1 R_1}{L_1} \qquad (15)$$
$$\dot{Q}_2 = \frac{P_2 - P_3 - Q_2 R_2}{L_2} \qquad (16)$$

Equations (14)-(16) behave in a similar way to Equations (9)-(11) except that when $P_2 = P_3$ which signals the start of the ejection stage, Q_2 is not necessarily at 0 as it would be if Equations

(9)-(11) were solved. The analytical solution of Equation (16) is given by:

$$Q_2(t) = Q_2(t_1)e^{-(\frac{R_2}{L_2})(t-t_1)}$$
$$+ \frac{1}{L_2}\int_{t_1}^{t} e^{-(\frac{R_2}{L_2})(t-\tau)}(P_2(\tau) - P_3)d\tau \qquad (17)$$

where t_1 is the time where P_2 first equals P_3. However, since inductances are approximately a factor of 100 smaller than resistances of the valves (Smith, 2004) there is a very small time constant of the order of 0.01s so that the transient effect of a non-zero will die away quickly. A similar analytical construction can be done for Q_1 to show that Q_1 converges quickly onto the solution of Equations (9)-(11) during the filling stage. This process is applied to both the left and right ventricles to form a Heaviside formulation of the full model and continues for as many heart beats as required. Note that in practice, this simpler Heaviside formulation could be run for a number of heart beats until the solution settles to a steady state and then Equations (9)-(11) could be simulated for one more heart beat to correct for the error in this transient period at the beginning stages of filling and ejection.

Ventricular interaction is an important dynamic in obtaining accurate CVS dynamics (Smith *et al.*, 2004). The septum volume, V_{spt} is calculated from numerically solving the equation (Smith, 2004; Smith *et al.*, 2004):

$$e(t)E_{\text{es,spt}}(V_{\text{spt}} - V_{\text{d,spt}})$$
$$+ (1 - e(t))P_{0,\text{spt}}(e^{\lambda_{\text{spt}}(V_{\text{spt}}-V_{0,\text{spt}})} - 1)$$
$$= e(t)E_{\text{es,lvf}}(V_{\text{lv}} - V_{\text{spt}})$$
$$+ (1 - e(t))P_{0,\text{lvf}}(e^{\lambda_{\text{lvf}}(V_{\text{lv}}-V_{\text{spt}})} - 1)$$
$$- e(t)E_{\text{es,rvf}}(V_{\text{rv}} + V_{\text{spt}})$$
$$- (1 - e(t))P_{0,\text{rvf}}(e^{\lambda_{\text{rvf}}(V_{\text{rv}}+V_{\text{spt}})} - 1) \qquad (18)$$

at each time step in the numerical differential equation routine, where $E_{\text{es,spt}}, P_{0,\text{spt}}, \lambda_{\text{spt}}, V_{\text{d,spt}}, V_{0,\text{spt}}$ are fixed generic parameters (Smith, 2004; Smith *et al.*, 2004).

Due to the high non-linearities in Equation (18) this procedure is very computationally expensive. As Equation (18) stands there is no closed form analytical solution. However, at each time step of the DE solver the V_{spt} value does not change significantly (< 0.1 ml) from the previous value. Thus, given the previous V_{spt} value, denoted $V_{\text{spt,old}}$, the exponential terms $e^{\lambda_{\text{spt}}V_{\text{spt}}}, e^{\lambda_{\text{lvf}}V_{\text{spt}}}$ and $e^{-\lambda_{\text{rvf}}V_{\text{spt}}}$ can be approximated by the Equations:

$$e^{\lambda_{\text{spt}}V_{\text{spt}}} = a_{\text{spt}}V_{\text{spt}} + b_{\text{spt}} \qquad (19)$$
$$e^{-\lambda_{\text{lvf}}V_{\text{spt}}} = a_{\text{lvf}}V_{\text{spt}} + b_{\text{lvf}} \qquad (20)$$
$$e^{\lambda_{\text{rvf}}V_{\text{spt}}} = a_{\text{rvf}}V_{\text{spt}} + b_{\text{rvf}} \qquad (21)$$

where $a_{\rm spt}, b_{\rm spt}$ are each a function of $V_{\rm spt,old}$ and can be derived from finding the equation of the straight line joining the two points $(x_2, e^{\lambda_{\rm spt} x_2})$ to $(x_1, e^{\lambda_{\rm spt} x_1})$, where $x_1 = V_{\rm spt,old} - \Delta V_{\rm spt}$ and $x_2 = V_{\rm spt,old} + \Delta V_{\rm spt}$ and $\Delta V_{\rm spt} = 0.1$ml. The parameters $a_{\rm lvf}, b_{\rm lvf}, a_{\rm rvf}, b_{\rm rvf}$ can be found similarly.

Substituting Equations (19)-(21) into Equation (18), gives an equation which is linear in $V_{\rm spt}$ and thus a closed form analytical solution for $V_{\rm spt}$ can be obtained.

3. RESULTS

A healthy human is simulated first, producing the results shown in Table 1. These results are consistent with an average human (Guyton and Hall, 2001).

Table 1. Pressure and volume outputs for a healthy human.

Volume in left ventricle	111.7/45.7 ml
Volume in right ventricle	112.2/46.1 ml
Cardiac output	5.3 L/min
Max $P_{\rm lv}$	119.2 mmHg
Max $P_{\rm rv}$	26.2 mmHg
Pressure in aorta	116.6/79.1 mmHg
Pressure in pulmonary artery	25.7/7.8 mmHg

Pericardial tamponade is then simulated producing a significant rise in the pressure in the pulmonary vein to 7.9 mmHg, a reduction in cardiac output to 4.1 L/min and a reduction in mean arterial pressure to 88.0 mmHg. This result captures the physiological trends (Braunwald, 1997).

Similarly Cardiogenic Shock produces trends in agreement with known physiological response including decreased mean arterial pressure, decreased cardiac output and elevated pulmonary vein pressure. Trend magnitudes are also in good agreement with limited clinical data.

The output pressures through the aorta and pulmonary artery and the flows through the chambers for all disease states are then discretized by sampling every 0.005s and 10% random uniformly distributed noise is added using a random number generator in Matlab, analogous to measured data. A uniform distribution is a conservative choice where outliers are more likely to occur. Figure 4 shows the non-smooth pressure in the aorta for Pericardial Tamponade for one heart beat after random noise is added.

The integral method is then applied to identify each disease state as it progresses from an initial healthy state in the presence of 10% uniformly distributed noise. Note that one extra parameter, the pericardium dead-space volume $V_{0,\rm pcd}$, is included in the optimization for all disease states. This parameter is embedded non-linearly in the matrix

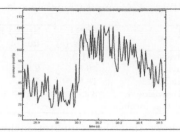

Fig. 4. The pressure through the aorta for one heart beat after 10% random uniformly distributed noise is added.

A of Equation (6), so it is optimized by a depth first search to minimize $||A(V_{0,\rm pcd})\underline{\beta} - b||_2$. Each evaluation of $||A(V_{0,\rm pcd})\underline{\beta} - b||_2$ involves solving Equation (6) by linear least squares.

Table 2 shows the identification results for Pericardial Tamponade. The particular disease state values of $V_{0,\rm pcd}$ are all identified within 3% and all other parameters are identified within a mean error of 10%. Table 3 shows the results for Cardiogenic Shock. The total mean over the two disease states and values identified was 3.2%, ranging from $0 - 10\%$. Note that when inertances are not included the mean and standard deviation values are significantly reduced. The reason for this last result is that inertances can change quite significantly (approximately $10 - 30\%$) without having a major effect on dynamics. As they represent the inertia of blood volumes, they are difficult to measure and not well defined (Smith, 2004). The total mean error in all parameters across the two disease states including inertances was 7.3% and without inertances was 4.1%.

Table 2. Pericardial tamponade (determining $V_{0,\rm pcd}$).

Change	True value (to the nearest ml)	Optimized value	Error (%)
First	180	176	2.22
Second	160	158	1.25
Third	140	138	1.43
Fourth	120	117	2.50
Fifth	100	100	0

Table 3. Cardiogenic Shock (determining $[E_{\rm es,lvf}, P_{0,\rm lvf}]$ ([mmHg ml^{-1}, mmHg])).

Change	True values	Optimized values	Error (%)
First	[2.59, 0.16]	[2.61, 0.15]	[0.89, 5.49]
Second	[2.30, 0.19]	[2.30, 0.18]	[0.34, 4.39]
Third	[2.02, 0.23]	[2.02, 0.21]	[0.43, 8.03]
Fourth	[1.73, 0.26]	[1.70, 0.24]	[1.48, 9.85]
Fifth	[1.44, 0.30]	[1.43, 0.27]	[0.47, 9.39]

The simpler Heaviside formulation + analytical formula for $V_{\rm spt}$ is now simulated for 19 heart beats then the first Heaviside formulation is simulated for 1 heart beat. The outputs and CPU time are compared with the original event solver method of (Smith *et al.*, 2004).

Table 4. Computational speeds.

Method	CPU time (s)	Speed increase factor
Event solver	101.9	
First Heaviside	36.8	2.8
Simpler Heaviside	18.8	5.4
Simpler Heaviside + analytical V_{spt} formula	3.1	32.9

Table 4 shows that the computationally simpler Heaviside formulation is approximately 5 times faster than the previous event solver method of (Smith *et al.*, 2004) and 2 times faster than the initial Heaviside formulation. Combining both methods gives a 33 times speed increase over the previous method, and a 6× improvement on the simpler Heaviside formulation alone.

To test the accuracy of the new method four disease states: mitral and aortic stenosis, pulmonary embolism and septic shock are simulated (Smith, 2004). The mean errors in all simulations are no greater than 0.2% showing the method is very accurate and that the improved computational approach does not impact model validity or accuracy.

4. DISCUSSION AND CONCLUSIONS

The minimal cardiac model (Smith *et al.*, 2004) is extended to simulate two common heart diseases: Pericardial tamponade and Cardiogenic Shock from onset including the autonomic nervous system. The model accurately captures the physiological trends. An integral based parameter identification method is presented which identified each disease as it developed with errors ranging from 0-10% in the presence of significant simulated measurement noise. These results show that the model can be rapidly identified using measurements common in the ICU. Furthermore, a major advantage of the integral method is that it allows significant flexibility in adding further complexity to the model, such as atrial dynamics without significantly affecting computational time.

Future work will also look at the case of very limited data when only discrete measurements are available, for example the maximum pressure in the aorta rather than the continuous waveform. However the integral method can still be used, as a previously simulated aorta waveform could be scaled to have a peak the same as the measured peak. The integral method could then be applied to get a very fast approximate matching to the data. Then after an iteration between forward simulations and the integral method the model could be matched to the data. Thus a fast forward solver of the model is important to maintain real-time clinical application in the case of very limited discrete data.

Also a fast and accurate forward simulation is critical in the process of simulating a large number of therapy combinations to find the best treatment. The Heaviside formulation, and analytical formula for V_{spt} presented, significantly increase the forward simulation speed so that many more simulations can be readily performed, making clinical application of the model more realistic.

Overall, the speed and accuracy of the integral based identification method and the efficient forward simulation method, demonstrates the potential of using this model in a clinical setting, to assist medical staff in diagnosis and therapy in clinically useful time (3-5 minutes) on a standard desktop computer.

REFERENCES

Braunwald, E. (1997). *Heart Disease, A text book of cardiovascular medicine, 5th edition*. W.B. Saunders Company, Philadelphia.

Burkhoff, D. and J. V. Tyberg (1993). Why does pulmonary venous pressure rise after onset of lv dysfunction: a theoretical analysis. *Am J Physiol* **265**, H1819–H1828.

Carson, E. and C Cobelli (2001). *Modelling Methodology for Physiology and Medicine*. Academic Press.

Guyton, A.C. and J.E. Hall (2001). *Textbook of Medical Physiology*. Philadelphia: W.B. Saunders Company.

Hann, C.E., J.G. Chase, G.M. Shaw and B.W. Smith (2004). Identification of patient specific parameters for a minimal cardiac model. *Proc 26 th International Conf of IEEE Engineering in Med and Biology Society (EMBS 2004), San Francisco, CA, Sept 1-5* pp. 813–816.

Hann, C.E., J.G. Chase, J. Lin, T. Lotz, C.V. Doran and G.M. Shaw (2005). Integral-based parameter identification for long-term dynamic verification of a glucose-insulin system model. *Computer Methods and Programs in Biomedicine* **77**(3), 259–270.

Mukkamala, R. and R. J. Cohen (2001). A forward model-based validation of cardiovascular system identification. *Am J Physiol Heart Circ Physiol* **281**, H2714–H2730.

Smith, B.W. (2004). Minimal Haemodynamic Modelling of the Heart and Circulation for Clinical Application. PhD thesis. University of Canterbury.

Smith, B.W., J.G. Chase, R. I. Nokes, G.M. Shaw and G. Wake (2004). Minimal haemodynamic system model including ventricular interaction and valve dynamics. *Med. Eng. Phys* **26**(2), 131–139.

MODELLING OF HAEMODIALYSIS IN LIMITING SERUM FREE LIGHT CHAINS IN PATIENTS WITH RENAL FAILURE

N.D. Evans* J. Hattersley* C. Hutchison**
Y. Hu* K.R. Godfrey* A.R. Bradwell***
G.P. Mead** M.J. Chappell*

School of Engineering, University of Warwick, Coventry, CV4 7AL, UK
** *The Binding Site, Birmingham, B14 4ZB UK*
*** *Department of Immunology, Medical School, University of Birmingham, Birmingham, B15 2TT UK*

Abstract: A mathematical model for the *in vivo* kinetics of free light chains is developed. The model consists of two compartments, one containing the plasma and the other the interstitial fluid. It is used to examine the effects of dialysis on myeloma, a form of cancer that results in high free light chain concentrations. The structural identifiability of the model is analysed using the Taylor series approach, and it is confirmed that the model is structurally globally identifiable provided data are collected both during dialysis and after it. The model is then used to fit clinical data from a myeloma patient suffering chronic renal failure. The data show that dialysis causes a reduction in free light chain concentrations, and this is reflected in the model responses. *Copyright © 2006 IFAC*

Keywords: Compartmental models; free light chains; haemodialysis; myeloma; parameter estimation; structural identifiability

1. INTRODUCTION

Immunoglobulin, or antibody, comprises two peptide chains, referred to as heavy and light chains, which are produced separately. There are two types of light chains, kappa (κ) and lambda (λ), which are created by specific plasma cells and incorporated into immunoglobulin molecules during B lymphocyte development (Bradwell *et al.*, 2005). Light chains are produced in excess of heavy chains leading to unbound light chains being secreted into the blood stream along with intact antibodies. These unbound chains are referred to as free light chains (FLCs). In healthy individuals the FLCs are removed through the reticuloendothelial system and natural kidney function.

Myeloma is a cancer of plasma cells that results in a continuous over-production of a monoclonal light chain resulting in dangerous levels of FLCs. It has been found that high levels of FLC can cause severe damage to renal function (Bradwell *et al.*, 2005), resulting in complete renal failure if untreated. When this occurs the patient is unable to remove toxins and fluid from the body effectively. In addition to chemotherapy that is used to treat patients with myeloma, several trials have considered plasma exchange as a method of reducing FLC levels quickly, but have not been able to demonstrate a clinical benefit. It is proposed that haemodialysis may be an alternative solution. Compartmental modelling (Jacquez, 1996) is used in this paper to assess the effects of dialysis on a myeloma (κ producing cells) patient with complete renal failure. Previous compartmental models for dialysis have concentrated on the removal of metabolic waste products, such as urea and creatinine, which have significant differences in molecular properties compared to FLCs.

Dialysis uses a semi-permeable membrane, a dialyzer, to remove unwanted toxins from the blood. Blood is passed across the membrane with a dialysate flowing in a converse direction resulting in diffusion and convection gradients via which FLCs can be removed from the patient. Whilst there are several methods for applying dialysis treatment the current paper is concerned only with conventional dialysis regimes with the patient being dialysed periodically, in sessions typically lasting four hours. Dialysis is included in the model as an additional periodic elimination pathway to replace clearance via normal renal function.

To assess the appropriateness of parameter estimates from fits to clinical data a structural identifiability analysis was performed. This analysis tests whether the output structure imposed on the model by the experiment used to collect the data uniquely determines all of the unknown parameters. Alternatively one may regard this as the problem of determining whether the model output contains enough information to determine all of the unknown parameters uniquely (Jacquez, 1996), and relates to the structure of the model and output.

For linear models there are many techniques for structural identifiability analysis (see, for example, (Walter, 1987) and the papers therein). These techniques reduce the problem to one of determining the set of solutions to a system of nonlinear algebraic equations. In this paper only the Taylor series approach of Pohjanpalo (1978) will be applied. This approach exploits the uniqueness of the coefficients of the Taylor series expansion of the output to consider the corresponding uniqueness of the model parameters.

2. MODEL FOR FLC KINETICS

A two compartment model is proposed for the kinetics of free light chains (FLCs), with the first compartment representing FLCs in plasma and the second FLCs in the interstitial fluid. Assuming first order flows between compartments and eliminations the model is as shown schematically in Figure 1.

The rate constant k_{re} corresponds to clearance of free light chains from either compartment via the reticuloendothelial system, whilst k_{1e} corresponds to other clearance from Compartment 1.

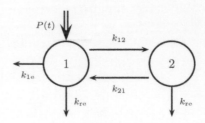

Fig. 1. Schematic of two compartment model for the *in vivo* kinetics of κ free light chains.

A model, with identical structure to that shown in Figure 1, can be used to model λ-FLCs. The only difference between the two models would be the values used for the respective rate constants and production rates. Coupling of the two models occurs through the production of the two forms of light chains, since both are produced within plasma cells, but this is beyond the scope of the current study. Since the data to be used to estimate the unknown model parameters are from a κ-myeloma patient and comprise serum κ-FLC concentration measurements only the κ-FLCs are modelled in this study.

If q_i denotes that quantity of κ-FLCs in Compartment i, then the system of differential equations for the model is given by:

$$\begin{aligned}
\dot{q}_1 &= -\left(k_{1e} + k_{re} + k_{12}\right)q_1 + k_{21}q_2 + P \\
\dot{q}_2 &= k_{12}q_1 - \left(k_{re} + k_{21}\right)q_2 \\
q_1(0) &= q_{10} \\
q_2(0) &= q_{20}
\end{aligned} \tag{1}$$

where $P(t)$ denotes the rate of production of κ FLCs into the plasma. Bradwell *et al.* (2005) quote a normal rate of total production of both light chains as around 500 mg per day. With a ratio of κ producing cells to cells that produce λ light chains of approximately 1.8, one would expect a normal production rate of κ FLCs of 321 mg per day (0.22 mg/min). Since the model will be considered over a relatively short time period corresponding to a single dialysis session (approximately 4 hours), the rate of production is assumed to be constant $P(t) = p_0$.

Treating capillary exchange in terms of complete mixing within the capillary bed and within the tissue pool (Jacquez, 1996), it is assumed that the ratio of the rate constants k_{12} and k_{21} is the same as the ratio of the volumes of the compartments, that is,

$$k_{12}/k_{21} = V_2/V_1.$$

For a patient with complete renal failure the only elimination of FLCs from the first compartment is via the reticuloendothelial system, so that $k_{1e} = 0$. During a dialysis session FLCs are cleared artificially so that the rate *constant* k_{1e} is replaced by the rate *coefficient* given by

$$K_{1e}(t) = \begin{cases} 0 & t \notin [\tau_s, \tau_f] \\ k_d & t \in [\tau_s, \tau_f] \end{cases}$$

where τ_s denotes the start of a dialysis session and τ_f the end.

The model has a single steady state corresponding to the amounts necessary in each compartment so that the total elimination from the system (namely $(k_{1e} + k_{re})q_1^* + k_{re}q_2^*$) balances the total production (namely p_0). The steady state values for the compartments (q_1^* and q_2^*) for a patient with complete renal failure are given by

$$q_1^* = \frac{p_0(k_{12}V_1 + k_{re}V_2)}{k_{re}(k_{re}V_2 + k_{12}(V_1 + V_2))}$$

$$q_2^* = \frac{p_0 k_{12} V_2}{k_{re}(k_{re}V_2 + k_{12}(V_1 + V_2))}.$$

For a patient in renal failure ($k_{1e} = 0$) the clearance from plasma of κ-FLCs drops from a half-life of approximately 2 hours to one of approximately 3 days (Bradwell *et al.*, 2005). Regarding the first compartment separately, with elimination only via the reticuloendothelial system, this gives an estimate of $k_{re} = \ln 2/3 = 0.23$ (day^{-1}). With normal renal function, so that the total elimination from Compartment 1 is $(k_{re} + k_{1e})q_1$, an estimate of $k_{1e} = 12 \ln 2 - 0.23 = 8.09$ (day^{-1}) is obtained.

To further reduce the number of parameters to be estimated from the clinical data standard estimates for the volume of plasma (2.5 L) and interstitial fluid (12 L) are used for the volumes of the compartments, V_1 and V_2 (Chappell *et al.*, 1991).

3. STRUCTURAL IDENTIFIABILITY

Before attempting to estimate the remaining, unknown, parameters in the model from real data, it must first be established that they are uniquely determined by the output structure corresponding to the experiment. Data were collected during and after a dialysis session and consist of serum FLC concentration measurements. In terms of the model, this corresponds to the following output function:

$$y(t, \boldsymbol{p}) = q_1(t, \boldsymbol{p})/V_1$$

where $\boldsymbol{p} \in \Omega$ is a vector comprising the unknown model parameters and is included to highlight the dependence of the measurements on these unknowns. The set Ω represents the set of admissible parameter vectors.

For generic $\boldsymbol{p} \in \Omega$, the parameter p_i is said to be *locally identifiable* if there exists a neighbourhood of vectors around $\boldsymbol{p}$, $\mathcal{N}(\boldsymbol{p})$, such that, if $\overline{\boldsymbol{p}} \in \mathcal{N}(\boldsymbol{p}) \subseteq \Omega$ and

$$y(t, \boldsymbol{p}) = y(t, \overline{\boldsymbol{p}}) \quad \text{for all } t \geq 0,$$

then $\overline{p}_i = p_i$. In particular, if $\mathcal{N}(\boldsymbol{p}) = \Omega$ can be used then p_i is said to be *globally identifiable*. If

the parameter p_i is not locally identifiable, i.e., there is no suitable neighbourhood $\mathcal{N}(\boldsymbol{p})$, then it is said to be *unidentifiable*.

If p_i is unidentifiable, then every neighbourhood containing $\boldsymbol{p}$ also contains a $\overline{\boldsymbol{p}}$, with $\overline{p}_i \neq p_i$, that gives rise to identical input-output behaviour. The experiment that this input-output relation corresponds to cannot be used to distinguish between p_i and $\overline{p}_i$.

Generally one is interested in the identifiability of the whole unknown parameter vector, or equivalently, of the model structure:

Definition 1. (SGI). A model is said to be *structurally globally identifiable* if, for generic $\boldsymbol{p} \in \Omega$, all of the parameters p_i (in $\boldsymbol{p}$) are globally identifiable.

Definition 2. (SLI). A model is said to be *structurally locally identifiable* if, for generic $\boldsymbol{p} \in \Omega$, all of the parameters p_i (in $\boldsymbol{p}$) are locally identifiable and at least one is not globally identifiable.

Definition 3. (SUI). A model is said to be *structurally unidentifiable* if, for generic $\boldsymbol{p} \in \Omega$, any one of the parameters p_i (in $\boldsymbol{p}$) is unidentifiable.

Following the approach used by Pohjanpalo (1978) the output is expanded as a Taylor series about $t = 0$ to give:

$$y(t, \boldsymbol{p}) = y(0, \boldsymbol{p}) + \cdots + y^{(k)}(0, \boldsymbol{p})\frac{t^k}{k!} + \cdots$$

where

$$y^{(k)}(0, \boldsymbol{p}) = \left.\frac{\mathrm{d}^k y}{\mathrm{d} t^k}\right|_{t=0} \quad (k = 1, 2, \dots).$$

The coefficients $y^{(k)}(0, \boldsymbol{p})$ are, in principle measureable, and hence unique for a given output. Thus one may analyse the uniqueness of the parameters with respect to the output by considering these coefficients.

Since data were collected during and after a dialysis session the identifiability of the model is considered with respect to two separate experiments: In the first, corresponding to the dialysis session (for $t \in [0, \tau_f]$, i.e., with dialysis starting at $t = \tau_s = 0$), $k_d \neq 0$ is an unknown so that

$$\boldsymbol{p} = \begin{pmatrix} k_{12} & p_0 & k_d & q_{10} & q_{20} \end{pmatrix}^{\mathrm{T}},$$

while in the second, corresponding to post dialysis (for $t \geq \tau_f$), $k_d = 0$ and

$$\boldsymbol{p}^* = \begin{pmatrix} k_{12} & p_0 & q_{1f} & q_{2f} \end{pmatrix}^{\mathrm{T}}$$

where $q_1(\tau_f) = q_{1f}$ and $q_2(\tau_f) = q_{2f}$. By considering the uniqueness of the coefficients of the Taylor series expansions of $y(t, \boldsymbol{p})$ (about $t = 0$) and $y(t + \tau_f, \boldsymbol{p}^*)$ (about $t = 0$) in a symbolic computer

Table 1. Parameter estimates together with calculated steady states (q_1^* and q_2^*). UC refers to unconstrained (p_0), PC to partially constrained and FC to fully constrained fits.

Parameter	Units	UC	PC	FC
k_{12}	min^{-1}	0.1135	0.0697	0.0687
p_0	mg/min	114.5	2.2996	0.3500
k_d	min^{-1}	0.0147	0.0071	0.0069
q_{10}	mg	24441	24279	24279
q_{20}	mg	105903	104700	104731
q_1^*/V_1	mg/L	49172	991.3	150.9
q_2^*/V_2	mg/L	48852	980.8	149.3

package such as MATHEMATICA (Wolfram, 2004) it is found that from the combined experiments all of the following parameters are globally identifiable:

$$k_{12}, \quad p_0, \quad k_d, \quad q_{10}, \quad q_{20}, \quad (q_{1f}, \quad q_{2f}).$$

Hence the model is SGI provided that the data are collected both during and after dialysis.

4. PARAMETER ESTIMATION

Parameter estimation was performed in the computer package BERKELEY MADONNA[1] using clinical data collected from a κ-myeloma patient undergoing dialysis treatment of chronic renal failure. This package obtains parameter estimates via minimisation of the root mean squared error (RMS error) and permits bounds to be placed on the parameters.

Data were collected for the serum κ-FLC concentration at various times during a dialysis session, both during dialysis (first 215 minutes) and for a period of 45 minutes post-dialysis. At 120 minutes the dialysis membrane was changed, with the change taking approximately 15 minutes. The new membrane was used for the remaining 95 minutes.

With no constraints on the unknown parameter values the estimates presented in column UC in Table 1 were obtained. Note that an estimate for the production rate (p_0) of 114.5 mg/min (165 g/day) was obtained. This value is more than 500 times the expected normal rate (321 mg/day). Since the patient has undergone high-dose chemotherapy to treat the underlying κ-FLC producing tumour it would be expected that an estimate closer to the normal rate be achieved.

To assess the impact of assuming that production has been reduced by the prior chemotherapy the value of p_0 was constrained to be less that 10 times normal (i.e., less than 2.3 mg/min). The parameter estimates obtained are presented in

column PC of Table 1. In further estimation, p_0 was constrained to be less than 500 mg/day (0.35 mg/min); the resulting estimates are presented in column FC of Table 1.

The estimates for the clearance during dialysis (k_d) for the fits in Table 1 are (FC) 1.2, (PC) 1.3 and (UC) 2.6 times the calculated normal clearance rate constant (0.0056 min^{-1}). All of these values indicate faster clearance through dialysis than through normal renal function. This might be expected since dialysis is applied only periodically and for relatively short time intervals.

Provided the production rate remains constant the steady states for the model can be calculated using the estimates in Table 1. These steady states correspond to the long term behaviour of the system in the absence of dialysis or renal clearance. The unconstrained estimates give a steady state plasma concentration (see Table 1, Column UC) in excess of the patient's current levels (approximately 10 g/L). In addition, the model simulation (see Figure 2) indicates that plasma FLC concentration is increasing post-dialysis. These factors might indicate that chemotherapy has failed to kill sufficient of the tumour to cause a reduction in the production of FLCs, or that the tumour is continuing to grow. Both of the other cases (PC and FC) give steady states below the current levels and would indicate a decline in plasma FLC concentration with time, even in the absence of dialysis. Such a situation would occur if the chemotherapy was successful and FLC production was being reduced to normal levels.

The model fits are shown in Figure 2 where it is seen that all three fits (UC, PC and FC) give good visual correspondence with the data. The three fits are comparable in features with the principal differences being in the recovery of plasma FLC levels when dialysis is not applied. The corresponding model predictions for the unobserved (interstitial) compartment are presented in Figure 3. Again, these predictions are comparable with only a difference in the final phase of the simulation; both of the constrained cases have decreasing levels of FLC in compartment 2, while the unconstrained case has an increasing level consistent with the predicted steady state. These predictions and the fits in Figure 2 suggest a lack of sensitivity of the quality of the fit to the value of the production rate. Such sensitivity might be increased by further data covering the post-dialysis period, since the production rate will not be obscurred by the dialysis clearance.

5. DISCUSSION

The fits presented in the previous section share a common feature that in each case better cor-

---

[1] See www.berkeleymadonna.com for details

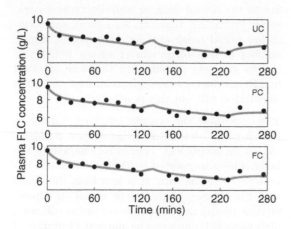

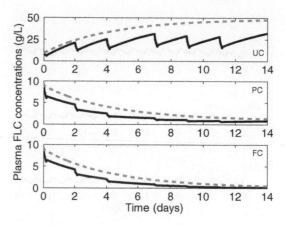

Fig. 2. Fits of model (solid line) to clinical data (circles) for the unconstrained (UC), partially constrained (PC, $p_0 \leq 2.3$ mg/min) and fully constrained (FC, $p_0 \leq 0.35$ mg/min) cases.

Fig. 4. Model prediction of effect of a weekly schedule of 3 dialysis sessions of 4 hours duration (solid line) with untreated case (dashed line).

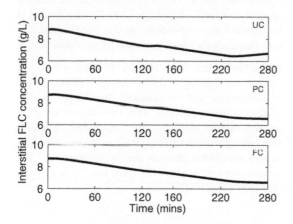

Fig. 3. Model predictions for concentration of FLCs in the interstitial fluid.

respondence with the data was observed before the dialysis membrane was changed. Following the change the data exhibit a more marked decrease than the model fits. The reason for the change was to ascertain any accumulation of FLCs on the membrane and consequent reduction in clearance. At present, the model does not account for any loss in clearance rate due to changes in or at the membrane.

For this pilot study the removal of excess fluid from the patient is neglected, thereby keeping compartment volumes constant. However, the excess fluid might be considered located in a third compartment, in which κ-FLCs are also present, that exchanges more slowly with Compartment 2. This would act as an additional reservoir of FLCs that would slowly equilibrate with the other compartments after dialysis. The result would be to see more marked increases in FLC quantities than predicted here.

In the case of a stable dialysis treatment schedule it might be possible to provide better estimates for the production rate and the initial conditions for the compartments. This would be done by including the dependency of the starting conditions for a single session on the end conditions of the previous one (in a stable situation the same as the end conditions of the current session) and the net production rate. However, for myeloma patients the purpose of initial dialysis sessions is to reduce the plasma FLC concentrations quickly in order to prevent further or permanent renal damage. Simultaneously, chemotherapy is used treat the tumour and hence reduce the production rate for FLCs in plasma.

One of the purposes of a validated mathematical model for the clearance of FLCs through dialysis would be for informing treatment regimes. A standard dialysis regime consists of three sessions of 4 hours per week. The predicted effect of such a schedule on the myeloma patient considered here is given in Figure 4. In each case the untreated situation is shown for comparison.

Figure 4 shows the benefits of dialysis in removing excess levels of FLCs in patients with complete renal failure. Following successful treatment with high-dose chemotherapy, resulting in a reduced production rate, the FLC concentration would be expected to drop over time (as seen in the FC and PC cases). Dialysis ensures a faster decrease to less damaging FLC concentrations. However, if chemotherapy is less effective (such as the UC case) it is seen that the plasma FLC concentration would continue to increase with time. In this case dialysis helps to significantly reduce levels from the steady state ones (from around 50 g/L to around 30 g/L).

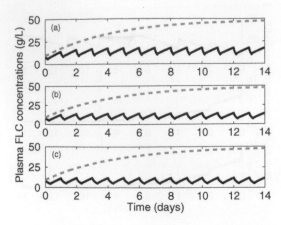

Fig. 5. Model prediction of effect of a daily schedule of dialysis of (a) 4 hours, (b) 6 hours and (c) 8 hours duration (solid line) with untreated case (dashed line).

Various schedules for dialysis treatment were considered to assess their impact on reducing FLC levels in myeloma patients with limited response to chemotherapy (using the UC case of the model). In Figure 5 model predictions for the UC case are presented where dialysis is applied daily for a duration of (a) 4 hours, (b) 6 hours and (c) 8 hours.

It can be seen from Figure 5 that for a production rate (p_0) so high, a daily dialysis schedule of 8 hours duration is needed (within the model) to maintain the current FLC levels (Figure 5(c)). Therefore to reduce FLC levels significantly, without reducing the production rate through additional chemotherapy, a much longer period of dialysis would be required.

6. CONCLUSIONS

A simple two-compartment linear model has been proposed for the production and kinetics of FLCs *in vivo* to assess the impact of haemodialysis on plasma FLC concentrations. The model was applied to a patient with κ-myeloma and complete renal failure. Serum FLC measurements were taken during the course of normal dialysis treatment.

With access to clinical data giving serum FLC concentrations both during and after dialysis the model is structurally globally identifiable. This means that the unknown parameters to be estimated from the data are uniquely determined by the corresponding model of the experiment. It should be emphasised that identifiability is a theoretical prerequisite to parameter estimation and does not address the quality of the estimates given noisy data. Thus a structurally globally identifiable model is not guaranteed to give good

fits to the actual data or well-determined parameter estimates. However, structural unidentifiability would mean that an uncountably infinite number of sets of parameter values would give rise to identical outputs and therefore identical fits. Hence the structural identifiability analysis is essential to rule out this possibility.

The data show the positive effect of dialysis on reducing FLC levels to further reduce problems caused by excess FLC concentrations within the body. This is supported by the model once it has been fitted to the data. It is seen from the model that the efficacy of treatment seems to depend on the production rate. In a number of cases dialysis could improve the natural clearance of FLCs resulting in a much more rapid return to approximately normal levels. If the production rate remains high, for example if chemotherapy has proven unsuccessful, then the model suggests that dialysis could be used to artificially reduce FLC concentrations. However, the duration of dialysis needed and frequency with which it would need to be applied are dependent on the production rate and the dialysis clearance rate (rate constant k_d).

In further work, the impact of changes to the membrane during dialysis and of different types of membrane will be assessed. Similarly, the loss of fluid during dialysis and the impact on FLC concentrations will also be considered. Through the collection of further data a more complete model validation process can be undertaken. The model presented here will form the basis of more complex ones.

REFERENCES

Bradwell, A.R., G.P. Mead and H.D. Carr-Smith (2005). *Serum Free Light Chain Analysis.* 3rd Ed. The Binding Site Ltd. Birmingham.

Chappell, M. J., G. D. Thomas, K. R. Godfrey and A. R. Bradwell (1991). Optimal tumor targeting by antibodies: Development of a mathematical model. *Journal of Pharmacokinetics and Biopharmaceutics* **19**, 227–260.

Jacquez, J. A. (1996). *Compartmental Analysis in Biology and Medicine.* 3rd Ed. BioMedware. Ann Arbor.

Pohjanpalo, H. (1978). System identifiability based on the power series expansion of the solution. *Mathematical Biosciences* **41**, 21–33.

Walter, E., (Ed.) (1987). *Identifiability of Parametric Models.* Pergamon Press. Oxford.

Wolfram, S. (2004). *The Mathematica Book.* 5th Ed. Wolfram Media Incorporated. Mathematica Version 5.1.

Copyright © IFAC Modelling and Control in Biomedical Systems
Reims, France, 2006

EXTRACTION OF REPRODUCIBLE
EPILEPTIC PATTERNS ON SCALP EEG

Matthieu Caparos*, **Valerie Louis***
Fabrice Wendling** **Jean–Pierre Vignal*****
Didier Wolf*

* *CRAN, UMR INPL UHP CNRS 7039, Nancy, France*
** *LTSI, UMR INSERM 642, Rennes, France*
*** *CHU, Service de Neurologie, Nancy, France*

Abstract: The objective of this work is to characterize evolution of the similarities in the dynamic of epileptic seizures, using non invasive EEG. A comprehensive method is presented and applied to temporal lobe epileptic seizures. It is based on the degree of correlation between scalp electrodes at seizure onset, determined by a nonlinear regression analysis. Results show that reproducible patterns may be extracted from different seizure of the same patient and confirm the existence of different subtypes of temporal lobe epilepsy. *Copyright © 2006 IFAC*

Keywords: EEG, epilepsy, seizure, similarity, edit distance

1. INTRODUCTION

Epilepsy is characterized by the sudden abnormal synchronization between a large group of neurons (Witte *et al.*, 2003). Temporal lobe epilepsy (TLE), the most common form of partial epilepsy in adults, is refractory to medical treatment in 20% to 30% of the cases. Surgery, which consists in removing the epileptogenic zone (EZ), is then the last resort for about half of patients suffering from it (Iasemidis, 2003). Localization of epileptic seizure onset is thus a really important point before considering a surgical operation (Engel Jr, 1998; Ebersole and Pacia, 1996). Actually, the base of the surgery is that EZ and the epileptic network is stable for all seizures of a patient. Many techniques are used to produce a reliable diagnosis, from clinical signs to imaging (MRI) (Asano *et al.*, 2004; Knake *et al.*, 2004; Lee *et al.*, 2000). Among these techniques, electrophysiological methods are the most adapted to better understand the organization and propagation of the brain electrical activity of a seizure (Wendling *et al.*, 2001b). Electrophysiological methods are di-

vided into two groups: scalp ElectroEncephaloGraphy (EEG) and invasive techniques StereoElectroEncephaloGraphy (SEEG), ElectroCortiGraphy (ECoG).

Signal processing methods have been successfully used on SEEG to complete visual inspection of seizure, in several studies (Wendling *et al.*, 2001b; van der Heyden *et al.*, 1999; Wu and Gotman, 1998). It was showed that seizure evolution was closely linked to EZ organization and allowed to objectively characterize the seizure. The implantation of electrodes directly in cerebral structures let the electrophysiological signal be recorded directly at his source and then its evolution inside temporal lobe is relatively easy to described.

Few similar researches have been proceed on scalp EEG. This may be explained by at least two factors. First, scalp EEG is a global reflection of cerebral activity, so during seizure, EEG signal correspond to a projection of the brain activity on scalp electrodes. Second, surface EEG signal is often artefacted, especially during seizures while uncontrolled muscular and eyes movements may occur. The main difficulty for the signal processing is then the extraction of a non-stationary event from a non-stationary noise. In this context, classical pattern extraction (mean detectors, spike detection method, ...) that have been applied to scalp EEG, prove to be non sufficiently robust. Another approach could then be the use of the decorrelation property between epileptic event and noise. As scalp EEG data is multidimensional, relationship between EEG channel could reinforce epileptic event hypothesis.

Measure of relationships between scalp electrodes is a technique often used in neurophysiological applications to point out the way cerebral structures work together. Concerning partial TLE, several methods of relationship measure have been successfully applied to SEEG signal (Lehnertz, 1999; Mormann *et al.*, 2003; Wendling *et al.*, 2001*b*; Chavez *et al.*, 2003) in order to better understand interdependencies between anatomical structures during TLE seizures. The depth synchronization may be expressed by correlations on scalp electrodes, even if the transfer function of electrophysiological activity from depth to surface is only partially defined in literature. This assumption is reinforced by (Franaszczuk and Bergey, 1998), who shows that the cause of the rhythmic activity, observed in ECoG, is an increase of functional couplings between a certain amount of brain regions.

The aim of this study is to characterize the evolution of TLE using scalp EEGs, in order to enhance preoperative diagnosis. In literature, several parametric and non-parametric methods are described to estimate these synchronizations at seizure onset: Directed Transfer Function in ECoG by Franaszczuk et al. (Franaszczuk and Bergey, 1998), the non-linear regression method introduced by Pijn (1990) and applied to SEEG by (Wendling *et al.*, 2001*b*), phase synchronization developed in (Chavez *et al.*, 2003),.... In this study, non-linear non-parametrical methods are preferred because they take into account nonlinearity in observed electrophysiological system (Ansari-asl *et al.*, 2005). In (Wu and Gotman, 1998), authors developed algorithms to group seizure of similar morphology using scalp EEG. They based their method on computation of the edit distance, to give a quantitative information on seizure similarity. After adequate signal coding of non-linear regression signal, the method described in (Wendling *et al.*, 1996) is employed to compute the similarity.

It the second section of the paper the procedure used for data base collection is summarized. Signal processing methods used to point out non-linear correlation between electrodes is explained. Signal encoding that leads to the extraction of similarities between two seizures is shown in following subsection. In third section results intra and inter patient is shown. Finally, these results are discussed and the conclusion on this work is presented.

2. MATERIAL AND METHODS

2.1 Patients

Seizures of forty three patients presenting TLE are studied. Two seizure for each patients were recorded in order to be able to point out intrapatient reproducible patterns. They are aged 16-45 years old and all underwent long term preoperative EEG recording at the neurology unit of Nancy's CHU (France). A comprehensive evaluation including detailed history and neurological examination, neuropsychological testing, magnetic resonance testing (MRI) study and interictal and ictal SPECT has been performed for all of them. The diagnosis of a partial TLE has been confirmed and they all underwent successful surgical resection of the EZ.

2.2 Data selection and signal acquisition

EEG signal was recorded on a Micromed system, according to 10/20 system using a 24 channels referential EEG montage. Data are sampled at 512Hz and recorded to hard disk. For further signal processings, eight couples of electrodes of the longitudinal montage are selected with the help of the neurologist. In order not to loose any usefully epilectical information that may be contained in EEG signal no pre-processings are applied, except a digital filtering in the $[0.5 - 30]Hz$ frequency band. As frequency of interest are under 30Hz, data are digitally filtered by a [0.5 30]Hz band-pass FIR filter and downsampled to 256Hz, to improve the signal processing time. Data files are then divided into two groups:

- 27 patients (55 seizures) were used to develop our methodology and optimize parameters
- 16 patients (32 seizures) were used to verify for the method validation

All data files of first group are formatted to last 500s around the beginning of a seizure (350s before / 150s after). Seizure onsets are indicated by the expert and all data files are positioned from this indication. Data files of the second group last 450s, seizure onset time is known, but can arise at any time. No other selection criteria were applied to choose data files, what signify that even seizures hard to analyze for neurologists are included.

The different steps of the signal processing methodology that leads to the extraction of reproducible patterns between TLE seizures will be detailed in the following. The methodology may be divided into three main steps: a) First, the non-linear correlations between some EEG channels are computed to characterize the synchronisation of cerebral regions at the seizure onset. b) Then, the evolution of the correlation is encoded. c) Finally, the similarities between encoded seizures are extracted by a dynamic programming algorithm.

Characterization of correlations Before a seizure, structures of the brain organize themselves in synchronized neural network (Wendling *et al.*, 2001*b*; van der Heyden *et al.*, 1999). The seizure activity can then be seen as a flow of energy from one part of the brain to another (Franaszczuk and Bergey, 1998). To measure the relationship that is established in such cases, two main types of techniques have been used:

- Techniques based on parametric methods (for example AR-modelization of the system),
- Techniques based on non parametric methods in the correlation space.

Both kind of methods are joining themselves in the aim, which is identifying interdependency of groups of neurons that are working together, through the exchange of energy flow. AR-modeling techniques present the main disadvantage to first search a model that suits the signal, implicating all problems such as the choice of model order, error in the parameters identification, definition of a time of quasi-stationary duration, etc... . All these not-well-defined parameters tend to make validation of the method more difficult. In this paper non parametric method are then preferred.

In (Wendling *et al.*, 2001*b*), the non-linear correlation method introduced in 1989 by (Lopes da Silva *et al.*, 1989), was successfully used to identify coupling between cerebral region on SEEG. The basic principle of this method is the identification of a non-linear dependency between two signals X and Y.

The non-linear correlation coefficient h^2_{XY} is obtained by considering the amplitude of signal $Y(t+\tau)$ as a perturbed function of the amplitude of the signal X(t). The variance of this perturbed function is assumed to be the conditional variance of $Y(t+\tau)$ given X(t) normalized by the variance of $Y(t+\tau)$. This quantity is subtracted from 1 to obtain the quantity so called h^2_{XY}:

$$h^2_{XY} = 1 - \frac{var[Y(t+\tau)/X]}{var[Y(t+\tau)]} \qquad (1)$$

where

$$var[Y(t+\tau)/X] = argmin(E[Y(t+\tau)-g(X(t))]^2)$$

g is the approximation of the mapping function from x to y.

The computation of $h^2_{Y|X}$, is reiterated for different values of a time shift τ between x and y. The use of this time shift gives the information of "delay" between both signals.

$$h^{2*}_{XY} = \max_{\tau_{min} < \tau < \tau_{max}} [h^2_{Y|X}(\tau)], \qquad (2)$$

The values of h^{2*}_{XY} are comprised between 0 (Y is independent of X) and 1 (Y is linearly or non-linearly dependent of X). In case of linear relationship between X and Y, h^{2*}_{XY} reduce to common linear correlation coefficient r^2_{XY}. Generally, h^{2*}_{XY} is not symmetric and $\triangle h^2 = h^{2*}_{XY} - h^{2*}_{XY} \neq 0$. As described in (Arnhold *et al.*, 1999), causality relations between X and Y can be deduced from $\triangle h^2$ and τ giving and indication on coupling direction.

In theory, the energy flow between two parts of the brain, generated during epileptic seizure is then well characterized by its level (correlation) and direction (coupling direction). That would be right if the stationarity hypothesis was verified on $X(t)$ and $Y(t)$. In practice h^2_{XY} is computed on a 5s sliding window, as $X(t)$ and $Y(t)$ are considered quasi stationary, with an overlap of 0.5s. $h^2_{XY}(t,\tau)$ was calculated for all values of delay τ included in an interval $[-40\ 40]ms$ around current time t, and only the maximum value for $h^2_{XY}(t,\tau)$ was kept (see fig. 1).

Signal coding The goal of the method is the identification of reproducible epileptic patterns in h^2_{XY} signal. Before, these patterns may be highlighted by a similarity extraction method, described in next subsection, the first step is the encoding of data.

An important synchronization (respectively desynchronization) between temporal lobe structures is traduced on scalp EEG by a significatively high (respectively low) correlation coefficient h^{2*}_{XY}. The level of correlation is considered significatively important if the signal oversteps a predefined threshold Γ_{XY_H}. Its choice should answer to two major points:

- allowing the detection of high correlation coefficients corresponding to seizures
- encode as less artifacts as possible

The definition of an absolute threshold for all channels does not suit because the level of correlation is highly dependent on channel pairs. Moreover, artefacts sometimes generate higher correlations than those observed at the seizure onset. To adapt to each channel, Γ_{XY_H} is chosen through

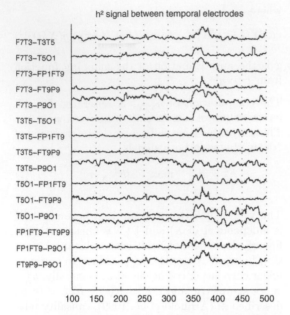

h² signal between temporal electrodes

Fig. 1. Evolution of h^2 coefficient before and during seizure. Appearance of first epileptic given at 350s by a neurologist, on the figure one can see a sort of "spike" and then a sudden decrease in correlation. This is one of epileptic patterns observed.

analyse of its statistical distribution. The threshold Γ_{XY_H} is then defined as follows:

$$\Gamma_{XY_H} = h^2_{XY}(\gamma) \qquad (3)$$

where γ is given by

$$\frac{\sum_{i=1}^{\gamma} N_i}{N_p} = \alpha\% \qquad (4)$$

With Np the total number of samples of X or Y and N_i the points number in each class i of the histogram of h^2_{XY}. Definition of the low level threshold Γ_{XY_L} is similar, the difference is in the choice of α. Once Γ_{XY_H} and Γ_{XY_L} are set, encoded signal $S_{e_{XY}}(n)$ is defined as follows:

$$\begin{cases} S_{e_{XY}}(n) = a \; if \; h^2_{XY}(n) > \Gamma_{XY_H}, \\ S_{e_{XY}}(n) = x \; or \; y \\ \qquad if \; \Gamma_{XY_H} > h^2_{XY}(n) > \Gamma_{XY_L}, \\ S_{e_{XY}}(n) = c \; if \; \Gamma_{XY_L} > h^2_{XY}(n). \end{cases} \qquad (5)$$

a, x, y and c are characters of the coding alphabet in which h^2_{XY} is transcript. In the description of an epileptic process, only high and low correlations are important. The extraction of similarities should then only occur on high and low coding levels. A different coding (x or y) is then needed in both seizures, in order not to extract similarities due to their preponderance in the h^2_{XY} coding matrices intermediate level.

Extraction of similarities The goal of the similarity extraction between two seizures is to find

epileptic patterns in coding matrices. As shown by (Wendling *et al.*, 1996), a particularly well adapted algorithm is the Wagner and Fisher (Wagner and Fisher, 1974) extension to multichannel case. This algorithm allows the determination of the "distance between two strings of symbols as measured by the minimum cost sequence of *edit operations* needed to change one string into the other".

In the multichannel case, presented here, the operations are done on matrices, coded as sequence of vectors, instead of strings. Three *edit operations* are defined: insertion, deletion and substitution. All these operations have a certain cost chosen as follows:

- deletion and insertion: 1
- substitution: 2 if characters to substitute are different, 0 if they are the same

The edit distance is found through the computation of a cost matrix by a dynamic programming algorithm which iteratively estimate the lowest trace operation cost. A second algorithm, is then charged to extract the trace of minimal cost from the computed cost matrix. The characters that are found similar (substitution with cost 0) are outlined as shown in figure 2. A freedom degree may be let on extracted patterns as shown. For example, on fig. 2, pattern (4-5) lasts 2 samples in second matrix, but 5 samples in the first matrix.

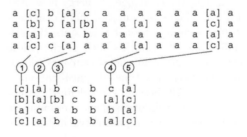

Fig. 2. Example of similarity extraction by the use of Wagner and Fisher algorithm on simulated matrices. One can notice, that both matrices don't need to be the same length, and that some time distortion is allowed in subsequences recovering.

In figure 2 application of the Wagner and Fisher algorithm is presented on simulated matrices. Only the costless result is shown, but some other possible sequence may be obtained with a change in the costs of the basic *edit operations*.

3. RESULTS

For all the results presented here, value used for α in equation 4 is chosen with the *a priori* information that temporal lobe seizure lasts for about 50s on the 500s of the file duration. To compute high threshold, α is set to 90% in order to keep only 10% of the highest correlations. As low correlations are rare threshold α is set to 5%.

In figure 3, result of Wagner and Fisher algorithm on two real seizures of a same patient is presented. Similarities can be extracted on eleven out of twenty-eight channels. Similarities are also extracted before the seizure but are caused by artefacts. What make artefacts and seizure different after similarity research is the length of the longest subsequence. Another important point, is that onset of the seizure indicated by neurologist does not exactly correspond to the same instant in both patterns extracted from each seizure.

To avoid subjective decision, concerning pattern recognition, one can use an objective index based previous remark. It is defined by the ratio of similarities observed in a seizure by those observed everywhere else defined as:

$$Sim_{index} = \frac{\sum\limits_{channels}\sum\limits_{window} similarities}{\sum\limits_{channels}\sum\limits_{global} similarities} \qquad (6)$$

Results obtained computing Sim_{index} are summarized in table 1. As only early seconds of the seizure are interesting for its characterization, a [-10,+20] seconds window is positioned from seizure onset (the seizure onset is indicated by a neurologist: vertical line on figure 3). 82.5% of the 87 seizures have an index Sim_{index} greater than 1, what signify that more similarities are observed during the seizure. 64% of the seizure have an index greater than 2. When more longer windows are used to compute the index, results are worse. In fact global mean of the index is respectively 2.97, 2.37 and 1.24 for windows length of [-10 +20]s, [-30 +30]s and [-150 +150]s.

Table 1. Percentage of seizure that have a similarity index over than value of the first column. Higher is the similarity index, better is the pattern recognition during seizure.

Value of Index	[-10 +20]s window	[-30 +30]s window	[-150 +150]s window
1	82.5%	82.5%	87.2%
1.5	73.2%	72.1%	8.14%
2	64.0%	60.5%	0%
mean	45.3%	48.8%	51.16%

4. DISCUSSION

An important point to notice, is that correlation, previously applied to SEEG signal (Wendling *et al.*, 2001*a*; Chavez *et al.*, 2003) can be used on scalp EEG with good results. That was unsure because scalp EEG signal is the recording of a

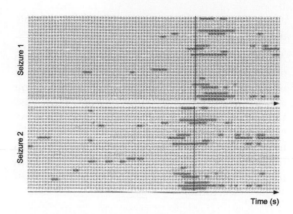

Fig. 3. Result of the similarities extraction on encoded matrices (each line of a seizure represent a encoded h_{XY}^2) by Wagner and Fisher algorithm on two seizures of the same patient. Black regions are those which were found the most similar in both seizures. Onset of the seizure indicated by neurologist is indicated by a vertical line.

global information whereas SEEG is the recording of a focal activity.

The similarity method described here to characterize seizure onset proves to be efficient as more than 83% of the seizures presented a high level of similarities. Only 17% of seizures (15 out of 87) presented a really poor similarity index (less than one). Comparing these seizures with clinical files of the patients, one can notice that for the most part of them, they are either multifocal or bilateral.

In (Caparos *et al.*, 2005), authors showed that most important information on seizure were contained in its early seconds. Results obtained with a [-10,+20] second window seem to confirm it as longest windows give worst results. For example with a [-30,+30] s window only 60% of the seizures have a similarity index greater than 2. This percentage quickly fall to less than 50% with the augmentation of the window size. With [-150,+150]s window results obtained have no sense as practically all the file is used to compute index. This information let then the pattern discrimination be easier for short windows.

Results obtained for the measure of the edit distance computed intr-patients gives more difficult to analyse results, as mean of the edit distance is 0.95 (s.d. 0.03). Patient with a low edit distance (under mean-std) are not obviously patients that present a high Sim_{index}. Actually, data with many artefacts have generally a low edit distance, that don't reflect what happens during the seizure. Result obtained for Wagner and Fisher algorithm reflect the similarity of the whole data file. To overcome this problem a more local edit distance should maybe be used. Smith and Waterman algorithm (Smith and Waterman, 1981), for example may be able to localize more local similarity zones.

As reproducible patterns can be extracted at the onset of seizures, the extraction of similarities may reinforce the medical diagnosis. This assumption is the base of the surgery that only works because the EZ and the neuronal network involved in several seizures are stable for a given patient. The next step of similarities study on scalp EEG is to realize a seizure classification based on the coupling of intra cerebral structure measured between surface electrodes.

REFERENCES

Ansari-asl, K., L. Senhadji, F. Wendling and J.J. Bellanger (2005). Quantitative comparison of signal analysis methods for characterization of brain functionnal connectivity. In: *The 3rd European Medical and Biological Engineering Conference. EMBEC'05.*

Arnhold, J., P. Grassberger, K. Lenherz and C.E. Elger (1999). A robust method for detecting interdependences : application to intracranially recorded eeg. *Physica D* **134**, 419–430.

Asano, E., O. Muzik, A. Shah, C. Juhasz, D.C. Chugani, K. Kagawa, K. Benedeka, S. Sood, J. Gotman and H.T. Chugani (2004). Ictal localization of temporal lobe seizures with scalp/sphenoidal recordings. *Clin. Neurophysiol.* **115**, 2718–2727.

Caparos, M., V. Louis-Dorr, F. Wendling, J.P. Vignal and D. Wolf (2005). Automatic laterlization of tle based on non-linear correlation on scalp eeg: Study on 43 patients. In: *The 3rd European Medical and Biological Engineering Conference. EMBEC'05.*

Chavez, M., M. Le Van Quyen, V. Navarro, M. Baulac and J. Martinerie (2003). Spatio-temporal dynamics prior to neocortical seizurres : Amplitude versus phase couplings. *IEEE Trans. Biomed. Eng.* **50**(1), 571–583.

Ebersole, J.S. and S.V. Pacia (1996). Localization of temporal lobe foci by ictal eeg patterns. *Epilepsia* **37**, 386–399.

Engel Jr, J. (1998). Research on the human brain in an epilepsy surgery setting. *Epilepsy Research* **32**, 1–11.

Franaszczuk, P.J. and G.K. Bergey (1998). Application ot the directed transfer function method to mesial and lateral onset temporal lobe seizures. *Brain Topography* **11**(1), 13–21.

Iasemidis, L.D. (2003). Epileptic seizure prediction and control. *IEEE Trans. Biomed. Eng.* **50**(5), 549–558.

Knake, S., A. Haag, G. Pilgramm, J. Reis, K.M. Klein, H. Hoeffken, P. Barstein, W.H Oertel, H.M. Hamer and F. Rosenrow (2004). Ictal functional tcd for the lateralization of the seizure onset zone - a report of two cases. *Epilepsy Research* **62**, 89–93.

Lee, S.K., K.K. Kim, K.S. Hong, J.Y. Kim and Chung C.K. (2000). The lateralizing and surgical prognostic value of a single 2-hour eeg in mesial tle. *Seizure* **9**, 336–339.

Lehnertz, K. (1999). Non-linear time series analysis of intracranial eeg recordings in patients with epilepsy - an overview. *International Journal of Psychophysiology.*

Lopes da Silva, F.H., J.P. Pijn and P. Boeijing (1989). Interdependence of eeg signals: Linear vs. nonlinear associations and the significance of time delays and phase shifts. *Brain Topography* **2**, 9–18.

Mormann, F., T. Kreuz, R. G. Andrzejak, P. David, K. Lehnertz and C. E. Elger (2003). Epileptic seizures are preceded by a decrease in synchronization. *Epilepsy Research* **53**(3), 173–185.

Smith, T.F and M.S. Waterman (1981). Identification of common molecular subsequences. *J.Mol. Bio.* **147**, 195–197.

van der Heyden, M.J., D.N. Velis, B.P.T. Hoekstra, J.P.M. Pijn, W. van Emde Boas, C.W.M. van Veelen, P.C. van Rijen, F.H. Lopes da Silva and J. DeGoede (1999). Non linear analysis of intracranial human eeg in temporal lobe epilepsy. *Clin. Neurophysiol.* **110**, 1726–1740.

Wagner, R.A. and M.J. Fisher (1974). The string to string correction problem. *J. Assoc. Comput. Mach.* **21**, 168–173.

Wendling, F., F. Bartolomei, JJ. Bellanger and P. Chauvel (2001*a*). Identification de réseaux épileptogènes par modélisation et analyse non linéaire des signaux seeg. *Neurophysiol. Clin.* **31**, 139–151.

Wendling, F., F. Bartolomei, JJ. Bellanger and P. Chauvel (2001*b*). Interpretation of interdependencies in epileptic signals using a macroscopic physiological model of the eeg. *Clin. Neurophysiol.* **112**, 1201–1218.

Wendling, F., J.J. Bellanger and J.L. Coatrieux (1996). Extraction of spatio-temporal signatures from depth eeg seizure signals based on objective matching in warped vectorial observations. *IEEE Trans. Biomed. Eng.* **43**, 990–1000.

Witte, H., L.D. Iasemidis and B. Litt (2003). Special issue on epileptic seizure prediction. *IEEE Trans. Biomed. Eng.* **50**(5), 537–538.

Wu, L. and J. Gotman (1998). Segmentation and classification of eeg during epileptic seizures. *Electroenceph. Clin. Neurophysiol.* **106**(4), 344–356.

MULTIPLE STRATEGIES FOR PARAMETER ESTIMATION VIA A HYBRID METHOD: A COMPARATIVE STUDY

H. Alonso [*,1,2] **H. Magalhães** [*,1,2] **T. Mendonça** [*,2]
P. Rocha [**,2]

[*] *Departamento de Matemática Aplicada - FCUP*
Rua do Campo Alegre, 687, 4169-007 Porto, Portugal
E-mail: {hugo.alonso,hfmagalh,tmendo}@fc.up.pt
[**] *Departamento de Matemática - UA*
Campo de Santiago, 3810-193 Aveiro, Portugal
E-mail: procha@mat.ua.pt

Abstract: In this paper, two different strategies are considered for application of a previously proposed hybrid method designed to parameter estimation. This method combines the feedforward neural networks ability to produce initial parameter estimates close to the true values with the fast convergence of the Levenberg-Marquardt method using such estimates. The first strategy is of general applicability, while the second one is intended for models having a structure defined by various blocks in series. The neuromuscular blockade model parameter estimation problem is taken as the case study for comparing the performances of the two strategies. Copyright © 2006 IFAC

Keywords: Levenberg-Marquardt Method, Feedforward Neural Networks, Parameter Estimation, Pharmacokinetic-Pharmacodynamic Model, Atracurium

1. INTRODUCTION

In practical applications, classical parameter estimation techniques often diverge or do not converge to the true values. This is mainly due to their iterative nature, high sensitivity to the choice of parameters used in their tuning and to the initial guesses for the parameters to be estimated. In methods like the Levenberg-Marquardt (LM) (Levenberg, 1944; Marquardt, 1963), a guaranteed and fast convergence to the true values of the parameters can however be accomplished if

their initial guesses are sufficiently close. These guesses are usually taken from a finite set of known realizations for the parameters, so that some measure of distance between observed and computed model outputs is minimized. Even if such set is designed, knowing the parameter statistical distribution, one can never be sure of its "richness" to guarantee the convergence to the true values when curve fitting is carried out by application of the LM method. In order to overcome this problem and to improve the speed of convergence, it has been proposed in Alonso *et al.* (2005*a*) that initial guesses should be given by a feedforward neural network (FNN) able to produce estimates closer to true values than the ones in the set. This combination represents a Hybrid Method (HM) between a non-iterative - FNN - and an iterative - LM. It was shown to have better performance

[1] The author would like to thank the Fundação para a Ciência e a Tecnologia (FCT) for the financial support (PhD grant) during the course of this project.
[2] The author has been partially supported by the Unidade de Investigação Matemática e Aplicações, UA, through the Programa Operacional "Ciência e Tecnologia e Inovação" of the FCT, co-financed by the EU fund FEDER.

than a separate traditional application of LM and FNN, methods having comparable performances. In this paper, two different strategies for applying the HM are compared. Neuromuscular blockade model parameter estimation is used as a case study. In the sequel, notation and relevant concepts that will be used throughout the paper are introduced.

All observed data are supposed to be free from noise. Assume that the model structure and the input u as a real function of time are known. Thus, the model output y can be described as

$$y(\Theta, t) = f_\Theta(t), \qquad (1)$$

i.e., by means of a parametric real function of time, where $\Theta \in \mathbb{R}^{p \times 1}$ is the vector of the p model parameters having a not necessarily known statistical distribution. Furthermore, suppose that f_Θ is at least twice continuously differentiable with respect to the parameters. For some realization θ of Θ, let

$$\mathbf{y}(\theta) = (y(\theta, t_1), \ldots, y(\theta, t_n))^T \qquad (2)$$

denote the corresponding n observations vector of the model output at time instants $t_1, \ldots, t_n$ such that $0 \leq t_1 < \ldots < t_n$. As is the general case, consider that $n \geq p \geq 1$. The sensitivity of the observations to the parameters is given by

$$\mathbf{S}(\theta) = \left(\mathbf{S}(\theta)_{ij} \right)_{i=1,\ldots,n,\, j=1,\ldots,p}, \qquad (3)$$

where, for $i = 1, \ldots, n$, $j = 1, \ldots, p$,

$$\mathbf{S}(\theta)_{ij} = \partial y_i(\theta) / \partial \theta_j. \qquad (4)$$

Assume for now that the probability density function p_Θ of Θ is known. Then, the observation covariance matrix is defined as

$$\mathbf{\Sigma} = E_\Theta \left[\left(\mathbf{y}(\Theta) - \boldsymbol{\mu}_\mathbf{y} \right) \left(\mathbf{y}(\Theta) - \boldsymbol{\mu}_\mathbf{y} \right)^T \right], \qquad (5)$$

where $E_\Theta[\cdot] = \int_{D_\Theta} \cdot \; p_\Theta(\theta) \, d\theta$ represents the mathematical expectation over the parameter space D_Θ and $\boldsymbol{\mu}_\mathbf{y} = E_\Theta[\mathbf{y}(\Theta)]$ represents the mean observation vector. Additionally, the vector of the p first principal components of $\mathbf{y}(\theta)$ is

$$\mathbf{z}(\theta) = \mathbf{V}^T \left(\mathbf{y}(\theta) - \boldsymbol{\mu}_\mathbf{y} \right), \qquad (6)$$

where $\mathbf{V} \in \mathbb{R}^{n \times p}$ is a matrix whose orthonormal columns are eigenvectors corresponding to the p largest eigenvalues of $\mathbf{\Sigma}$. If p_Θ is not known, assume that a sample $\{\theta_s\}_{s=1}^N$ of size N, exhaustively covering D_Θ, is available. Then, $\boldsymbol{\mu}_\mathbf{y}$ and $\mathbf{\Sigma}$ are replaced by $\bar{\mathbf{y}}$ and $\hat{\mathbf{\Sigma}}$, the sample mean vector and covariance matrix. It follows that $\mathbf{z}$ in (6) gives place to a $\hat{\mathbf{z}}$, as $\mathbf{V}$ is also replaced by a $\hat{\mathbf{V}}$ obtained from $\hat{\mathbf{\Sigma}}$.

The problem of parameter estimation is that of determining an estimate $\hat{\theta}$ of θ from $\mathbf{y}(\theta)$ or $\mathbf{z}(\theta)$ ($\hat{\mathbf{z}}(\theta)$, if $\mathbf{z}(\theta)$ is not available).

2. METHODS

This section presents a brief overview of the Levenberg-Marquardt Method and Feedforward Neural Networks, and a description of the two proposed strategies for applying the Hybrid Method.

2.1 The Levenberg-Marquardt Method

The problem of parameter estimation can be viewed as an optimization one described by

$$\min_{\hat{\theta}} \left\{ E_\mathbf{y}(\hat{\theta}) = e_\mathbf{y}^T(\hat{\theta}) e_\mathbf{y}(\hat{\theta}) \right\}, \qquad (7)$$

where $\hat{\theta}$ is an estimate of θ and

$$e_\mathbf{y}(\hat{\theta}) = (e_1, \ldots, e_n)_\mathbf{y}^T(\hat{\theta}) = \mathbf{y}(\theta) - \mathbf{y}(\hat{\theta}). \qquad (8)$$

The minimization of $E_\mathbf{y}$ in $\hat{\theta}$ can be reduced to a linear problem in $\Delta\hat{\theta}^k = \hat{\theta} - \hat{\theta}^k$ for the current k-th estimate $\hat{\theta}^k$. Firstly, expanding $e_\mathbf{y}$ in a Taylor series about $\hat{\theta}^k$ and ignoring nonlinear terms as

$$e_\mathbf{y}(\hat{\theta}^k + \Delta\hat{\theta}^k) \cong e_\mathbf{y}(\hat{\theta}^k) + J(\hat{\theta}^k)\Delta\hat{\theta}^k, \qquad (9)$$

where

$$J(\hat{\theta}^k) = \left(\partial e_{i,\mathbf{y}}(\hat{\theta}^k) / \partial \hat{\theta}_j \right)_{i=1,\ldots,n,\, j=1,\ldots,p} \qquad (10)$$

is the Jacobian matrix of $e_\mathbf{y}$ evaluated at $\hat{\theta}^k$. Then, replacing (9) in the definition (7) of $E_\mathbf{y}$ to obtain a quadratic approximation around $\hat{\theta}^k$,

$$\tilde{E}_\mathbf{y}(\Delta\hat{\theta}^k) = e_\mathbf{y}^T(\hat{\theta}^k) e_\mathbf{y}(\hat{\theta}^k) + 2 e_\mathbf{y}^T(\hat{\theta}^k) J(\hat{\theta}^k)\Delta\hat{\theta}^k +$$
$$\Delta\hat{\theta}^{k^T} J^T(\hat{\theta}^k) J(\hat{\theta}^k)\Delta\hat{\theta}^k, \qquad (11)$$

the linear problem arises from finding a minimizer $\Delta\hat{\theta}^k$ for $\tilde{E}_\mathbf{y}$, which amounts to the solution of

$$J^T(\hat{\theta}^k) J(\hat{\theta}^k)\Delta\hat{\theta}^k = -J^T(\hat{\theta}^k) e_\mathbf{y}(\hat{\theta}^k), \qquad (12)$$

derived from $\nabla\tilde{E}_\mathbf{y}(\Delta\hat{\theta}^k) = 0$. This establishes the basis for the Gauss method, resumed in the following algorithm:

(1) Compute $J(\hat{\theta}^k)$.
(2) Compute $\Delta\hat{\theta}^k$ from equations (12).
(3) Set $\hat{\theta}^{k+1} = \hat{\theta}^k + \Delta\hat{\theta}^k$, $k = k+1$.
(4) Repeat from 1 until a stopping criterion is met.

The Gauss method is descendent, in the sense that there exists a step $\Delta\hat{\theta}^k$ for which

$$E_\mathbf{y}(\hat{\theta}^k + \Delta\hat{\theta}^k) = E_\mathbf{y}(\hat{\theta}^k) + \Delta\hat{\theta}^{k^T} \nabla E_\mathbf{y}(\hat{\theta}^k) +$$
$$\mathcal{O}(\Delta\hat{\theta}^{k^T} \Delta\hat{\theta}^k) < E_\mathbf{y}(\hat{\theta}^k), \qquad (13)$$

as $\Delta\hat{\theta}^{k^T} \nabla E_\mathbf{y}(\hat{\theta}^k) < 0$ for all $\Delta\hat{\theta}^k$. Nevertheless, this method exhibits a poor performance and is potentially divergent whenever $J^T(\hat{\boldsymbol{\theta}}^k)J(\hat{\boldsymbol{\theta}}^k)$ is ill-conditioned, *i.e.*, when the ratio between the maximum and minimum eigenvalues of this matrix is too large. Levenberg (1944) and Marquardt (1963) solved this problem by introducing an additional term in equations (12) to have

$$\left(J^T(\hat{\boldsymbol{\theta}}^k)J(\hat{\boldsymbol{\theta}}^k) + \lambda_k I\right)\Delta\hat{\boldsymbol{\theta}}^k = -J^T(\hat{\boldsymbol{\theta}}^k)e_{\mathbf{y}}(\hat{\boldsymbol{\theta}}^k).$$
(14)

The choice of the value for λ can be controlled in each iteration by the gain ratio

$$\gamma = \frac{E_{\mathbf{y}}(\hat{\boldsymbol{\theta}}^k) - E_{\mathbf{y}}(\hat{\boldsymbol{\theta}}^k + \Delta\hat{\boldsymbol{\theta}}^k)}{\tilde{E}_{\mathbf{y}}(0) - \tilde{E}_{\mathbf{y}}(\Delta\hat{\boldsymbol{\theta}}^k)},$$
(15)

where $\tilde{E}_{\mathbf{y}}(0) = E_{\mathbf{y}}(\hat{\boldsymbol{\theta}}^k)$ and $\tilde{E}_{\mathbf{y}}(0) - \tilde{E}_{\mathbf{y}}(\Delta\hat{\boldsymbol{\theta}}^k) > 0$. Thus, a large value of γ indicates that $\tilde{E}_{\mathbf{y}}(\Delta\hat{\boldsymbol{\theta}}^k)$ is a good approximation to $E_{\mathbf{y}}(\hat{\boldsymbol{\theta}}^k + \Delta\hat{\boldsymbol{\theta}}^k)$, and λ can be decreased so that the next Levenberg-Marquardt step is closer to the Gauss step; if γ is small then $\tilde{E}_{\mathbf{y}}(\Delta\hat{\boldsymbol{\theta}}^k)$ is a poor approximation to $E_{\mathbf{y}}(\hat{\boldsymbol{\theta}}^k + \Delta\hat{\boldsymbol{\theta}}^k)$, and λ should be increased with the aim of getting a step closer to the steepest descent direction (determined by $-\nabla\tilde{E}_{\mathbf{y}}(0) = -\nabla E_{\mathbf{y}}(\hat{\boldsymbol{\theta}}^k)$) and of reduced length. The stopping criterion for the described optimization methods can be the satisfaction of at least one of the conditions:

- $\left\|\nabla\tilde{E}_{\mathbf{y}}(0)\right\| \le \epsilon_1$;

- $\left\|\hat{\boldsymbol{\theta}}^k - \hat{\boldsymbol{\theta}}^{k-1}\right\| \le \epsilon_2\left(\left\|\hat{\boldsymbol{\theta}}^{k-1}\right\| + \epsilon_2\right)$;

- $k \ge k_{max}$;

where $\epsilon_1, \epsilon_2 \in \mathbb{R}^+$ and $k_{max} \in \mathbb{Z}^+$ are chosen by the user. For further details see Gill *et al.* (1981).

2.2 *Feedforward Neural Networks*

The purpose here is to describe the use of FNNs for estimation of realizations $\boldsymbol{\theta}$ of the parameter vector either from $\mathbf{y}(\boldsymbol{\theta})$ or $\mathbf{z}(\boldsymbol{\theta})$ ($\hat{\mathbf{z}}(\boldsymbol{\theta})$, if $\mathbf{z}(\boldsymbol{\theta})$ is not available). Hence, a brief overview of the relevant concepts is given. For further details on FNNs refer to Haykin (1999).

The neuron, the FNN elementary unit, is capable of receiving, processing and transmitting data. The common representation of the neuron function is

$$\varphi_{\mathbf{w}}(\mathbf{x}) = \sigma\left(\mathbf{w}^T\tilde{\mathbf{x}}\right),$$
(16)

where $\mathbf{x} = (x_1, \ldots, x_n)^T \in \mathbb{R}^n$ is the vector of neuron inputs and $\mathbf{w} = (w_0, w_1, \ldots, w_n)^T \in \mathbb{R}^{n+1}$ is the vector of neuron parameters weighting $\tilde{\mathbf{x}} = (1, \mathbf{x}^T)^T$ to produce the neuron output $\varphi_{\mathbf{w}}(\mathbf{x})$ through the activation function σ. The standard logistic sigmoidal function is a usual choice for σ, a C^∞ function, hence so is $\varphi_{\mathbf{w}}$. A (multilayer) FNN has an architecture defined by

a directed acyclic graph: the neurons are disjointly split into ordered layers, the connections among neurons lead only from lower layers to upper ones, and each neuron in one layer is connected to all neurons in the next one. The input, hidden or intermediate, and output neurons belong to the first, intermediate, and last layers, respectively. The function of the input neurons is the identity, so for p output neurons the FNN function is

$$\boldsymbol{\phi}_{\mathbf{w}}(\mathbf{x}) = (\phi_1, \ldots, \phi_p)_{\mathbf{w}}(\mathbf{x}),$$
(17)

where, for $l = 1, \ldots, p$,

$$\phi_{l\mathbf{w}}(\mathbf{x}) = \sigma_l\left(w_{l0} + \sum_k w_{lk}\sigma_k\left(\ldots\left(\sum_i w_{ji}\tilde{x}_i\right)\ldots\right)\right),$$
(18)

being w_{ji} the weight of the connection from the i-th to the j-th neurons, σ_k the activation function of the k-th neuron, etc. Assume that the standard logistic sigmoidal function is the activation function of all hidden neurons and that σ_l is the identity, $\forall l$. Therefore, $\boldsymbol{\phi}_{\mathbf{w}}$ is a C^∞ function.

Let Ψ denote the set of all C^m functions from $\mathbb{R}^n$ to $\mathbb{R}^p$ and Φ the subset of Ψ of all one hidden layer FNNs functions. The universal approximation property of this class of networks is presented in the following theorem.

Theorem 1. (Hornik *et al.*, 1990) Given $\psi \in \Psi$, a compact $X \subset \mathbb{R}^n$ and $\epsilon > 0$, there exists $\boldsymbol{\phi}_{\mathbf{w}} \in \Phi$ such that, for $l = 1, \ldots, p$,

$$\max_{\alpha \le m}\sup_{\mathbf{x} \in X}|D^\alpha(\psi_l - \phi_{l\mathbf{w}})(\mathbf{x})| < \epsilon,$$

where $D^\alpha = \frac{\partial^\alpha}{\partial x_1^{\alpha_1}\ldots x_n^{\alpha_n}}$ for $\alpha = \alpha_1 + \ldots + \alpha_n$.

Once the FNN architecture is set, the weights are determined to minimize a performance function relative to a set $T = \{(\mathbf{x}_s, \psi(\mathbf{x}_s))\}_{s=1}^N$ as

$$E_T(\mathbf{w}) = \frac{1}{N}\sum_{s=1}^N\left\|\psi(\mathbf{x}_s) - \boldsymbol{\phi}_{\mathbf{w}}(\mathbf{x}_s)\right\|^2.$$
(19)

This is known as training the network. Several optimization methods, such as the Levenberg-Marquardt (Hagan and Menhaj, 1994), are used in practice to obtain (off-line) a near-optimal $\mathbf{w}$ for E_T. It is important to stress that the success and the duration of the training is intimately related to the complexity of the network architecture, in particular with the number of inputs. That is why dimensionality reduction by principal components analysis is often considered. Finally, note that an already trained network implements a ready-to-use function.

The problem of parameter estimation using FNNs is formalized as follows. Consider the functions

$$\psi_1 : \boldsymbol{\theta} \mapsto \mathbf{y}(\boldsymbol{\theta}),$$
(20)

$$\psi_2 : \boldsymbol{\theta} \mapsto \mathbf{z}(\boldsymbol{\theta}),$$
(21)

where $\mathbf{y}(\boldsymbol{\theta})$ and $\mathbf{z}(\boldsymbol{\theta})$ are defined as in (2) and (6), respectively. When do there exist FNNs implementing left inverse functions $\phi_{1,\mathbf{w}_1}$ and $\phi_{2,\mathbf{w}_2}$

of ψ_1 and ψ_2, respectively? Furthermore, does the existence of $\phi_{1,\mathbf{w_1}}$ is equivalent to the existence of $\phi_{2,\mathbf{w_2}}$? The following theorems give the answers to these questions.

Theorem 2. (Alonso *et al.*, 2005*b*) There exists a FNN implementing a left inverse function $\phi_{1,\mathbf{w_1}}$ of ψ_1 if and only if $\mathbf{S}$ has full column rank.

Theorem 3. (Alonso *et al.*, 2005*b*) There exists a FNN implementing a left inverse function $\phi_{2,\mathbf{w_2}}$ of ψ_2 if and only if $\mathbf{V^T S}$ is invertible.

Theorem 4. (Alonso *et al.*, 2005*b*) If there exists a FNN implementing a left inverse function $\phi_{2,\mathbf{w_2}}$ of ψ_2 then there exists another one implementing a left inverse function $\phi_{1,\mathbf{w_1}}$ of ψ_1. The converse is false.

2.3 *Hybrid Method*

The implementation of the HM can be divided into two phases: the first one consists in training a FNN to approximate well the map between the space of model input-output observations and the space of model parameters; the second one, carried out after a predetermined time-interval where data collection occurs, consists in applying the trained network to obtain a parameter estimate that will be further refined by application of the LM method. The following algorithm fully describes the HM:

(1) *First phase*:
  - Using Theorem 3 verify if there exists a FNN capable of estimating $\boldsymbol{\theta}$ from $\mathbf{z}(\boldsymbol{\theta})$. If so, continue, else, stop.
  - Given $T = \{(\mathbf{z}(\boldsymbol{\theta}_s), \boldsymbol{\theta}_s)\}_{s=1}^{N}$, with $\{\boldsymbol{\theta}_s\}_{s=1}^{N}$ exhaustively covering $D_{\boldsymbol{\Theta}}$, choose to take it as one of: the set for selecting and training the best architecture, using cross-validation to estimate the generalization error of each of the candidate architectures; the randomly split set into two disjoint sets, T_1 and T_2, the first one for training the best architecture chosen from a set of candidate architectures whose generalization error is estimated on the second one.
  - Find a FNN using T and let $\phi_{\mathbf{w}}$ denote its function. Goto the second phase.
(2) *Second phase*:
  - Observed $\mathbf{y}(\boldsymbol{\theta})$, find $\mathbf{z}(\boldsymbol{\theta})$ from (6).
  - Take $\mathbf{y}(\boldsymbol{\theta})$ and the initial parameter estimate $\hat{\theta}^{\,i} = \phi_{\mathbf{w}}(\mathbf{z}(\boldsymbol{\theta}))$ as inputs for the LM method.
  - Take for final estimate $\hat{\theta}^{\,f}$ the solution $\hat{\theta}$ determined by the LM method to the minimization problem (7).

Remark: an analogous description of the method can be obtained for $T = \{(\mathbf{y}(\boldsymbol{\theta}_s), \boldsymbol{\theta}_s)\}_{s=1}^{N}$. By Theorem 4, this description has to be considered if the condition of Theorem 3 fails.

It is expected that the LM method converges to the true value and in fewer iterations when taking as first estimate the one produced by the FNN. Note that the estimate produced by the FNN is in principle closer to the true value than one minimizing, in a set of parameter realizations, some measure of distance between the model outputs computed from such a set and the observed output $\mathbf{y}(\boldsymbol{\theta})$ (or correspondent $\mathbf{z}(\boldsymbol{\theta})$).

This original implementation strategy of the HM will be referred from now on as HM1. A second implementation strategy, HM2, is specifically considered here for the case where the model structure is defined by various blocks in series as in Fig. 1. It is based on classical approaches to the problem of estimating the parameters of generally overparameterized models of this kind. The key idea behind HM2 is to estimate all parameters from $u(t)$ to $y(t)$ and then, in a stepwise fashion, recover each of the intermediate signals while further parameter refinement is made. An algorithmic description of HM2 is given for a model structure like the one in Fig. 1 with $m \geq 2$:

(1) Apply HM1 to $\prod_{b=1}^{m} H_{b,\Theta_b}(s)$ to estimate $\left(\boldsymbol{\theta}_1^T, \ldots, \boldsymbol{\theta}_m^T \right)^T$.
(2) For $c = m$ to 2 do:
  - Recover $v_{c-1}(t)$ from $v_c(t)$ and $H_{c,\hat{\boldsymbol{\theta}}_c}(s)$.
  - Apply HM1 to $\prod_{b=1}^{c-1} H_{b,\Theta_b}(s)$ to refine $\left(\hat{\boldsymbol{\theta}}_1^T, \ldots, \hat{\boldsymbol{\theta}}_{c-1}^T \right)^T$.

This second strategy of the HM application should be implemented if one verifies that the resulting estimation of the parameters is improved and pays for the increase of the computational burden.

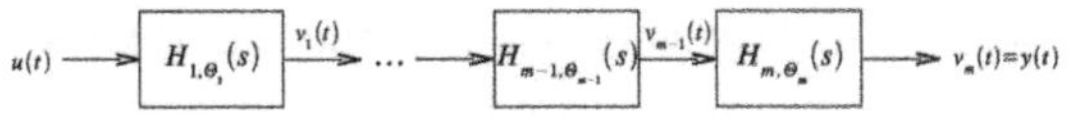

Fig. 1. Block diagram of a model whose structure is defined by various blocks in series.

3. CASE STUDY

3.1 *Neuromuscular blockade model*

The dynamic response of the neuromuscular blockade to intra-venously administered *atracurium* may be modelled as shown in Fig. 2 (Mendonça and Lago, 1998). The drug infusion rate $u(t)$ $[\mu g\, kg^{-1}\, min^{-1}]$ is related with the effect concentration $c_e(t)$ $[\mu g\, ml^{-1}]$ by means of a linear dynamic pharmacokinetic-pharmacodynamic model, and the latter with the relaxation level $r(t)$ $[\%]$ by

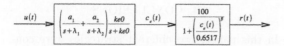

Fig. 2. Block diagram of the neuromuscular block-ade model.

a non-linear static Hill equation. Hence, the relaxation level can be expressed as the parametric real function of time

$$r(\mathbf{\Theta}, t) = \frac{100}{1 + \left[\frac{\mathcal{L}^{-1}\left[\left[\frac{a_1}{s+\lambda_1} + \frac{a_2}{s+\lambda_2}\right]\frac{ke0}{s+ke0}U(s)\right](t)}{0.6517}\right]^\beta},$$
(22)

being $\mathbf{\Theta} = (a_1, \lambda_1, a_2, \lambda_2, ke0, \beta)^T (a_i\,[kg\,ml^{-1}], \lambda_i, ke0\,[min^{-1}], \beta)$ the vector of patient dependent parameters, and $U(s) = \mathcal{L}\,[u(t)]\,(s)$. Note that the $c_e(t)$ normalization factor, known as C_{50}, has been fixed in its mean value $0.6517\,[\mu g\,ml^{-1}]$, since it has been shown in Alonso *et al.* (2005*b*) that this parameter cannot be estimated from a *bolus* response ($u(t) = B\delta(t - t_B)$) here considered.

3.2 Results

A random sample with $N = 9000$ realizations of $\mathbf{\Theta}$ was generated according to the multidimensional log-normal distribution characterized in (Lago *et al.*, 1998). The relaxation level to a *bolus* of 500 $\mu g\,kg^{-1}$ administered at $t = 0$ min was calculated. Data collection for parameter estimation was confined to the first 10 min as this is the instant after which control action taking into account the estimates for the parameters is initiated. Since the relaxation level was calculated every 20 sec, let

$$\mathbf{r}(\boldsymbol{\theta}) = (r(\boldsymbol{\theta}, t_1), \dots, r(\boldsymbol{\theta}, t_{31}))^T \qquad (23)$$

denote the resulting vector of 31 observations at time instants $t_i = (i-1)/3$ min, $i = 1, \dots, n = 31$. The resulting set $\{(\mathbf{r}(\boldsymbol{\theta}_s), \boldsymbol{\theta}_s)\}_{s=1}^{9000}$ was randomly split into two disjoint sets: $T\,(\#T = 5000)$ for FNN selection and training, and $T^{'}\,(\#T^{'} = 4000)$ for HM1 and HM2 testing.

Table 1 includes some statistics relative to

$$AREE(\boldsymbol{\theta}_i) = 100 \times \left|1 - \hat{\boldsymbol{\theta}}_i/\boldsymbol{\theta}_i\right|\,[\%], i = 1, \dots, 6,$$
(24)

the individual parameter absolute relative estimation error on the test set, when estimation is carried out by application of FNN, HM1 and HM2 (the results concerning the FNN should be seen as the starting point for the estimation process carried out by the HM). In what concerns error central tendency, one reads from the table that the estimates for all parameters are much better when produced by the comparable HM strategies than by the FNN, in the sense that they are less biased, if biased at all. Note that the worst HM case is that of a_1 estimation by HM1, where Med is only about 0.1%. With respect to the error dispersion,

it can be seen that IQR for HM1 is greater than that for HM2, specially in the cases of a_1 and a_2, the two most important parameters to the description of the relaxation level as one will show. Finally, worst estimation cases are worse in the HM application, with the exception of parameter β. This is due to the sensitivity of the LM method to the initial estimates in few isolated cases, as seen by the difference between IQR and Max.

In order to evaluate the overall impact of estimating all parameters, one has first investigated the contribution of each of these to the shape of the relaxation curve. To that end, it was first computed a time-varying parameter weight for each of the 6, raging from 0 (no contributing parameter) to 1 (only contributing parameter), and given by

$$w_i(t) = \frac{SAD(\boldsymbol{\theta}_i, t)}{\sum_{j=1}^6 SAD(\boldsymbol{\theta}_j, t)}, i = 1, \dots, 6, \qquad (25)$$

being the sum of absolute deviations

$$SAD(\boldsymbol{\theta}_i, t) =$$
$$\eta_{\mathbf{\Theta}}\left[\sum_{\tilde{t}=0:1/3:t} \left|r(\mathbf{\Theta}, \tilde{t}) - r(\mathbf{\Theta}(\theta_i = \bar{\theta}_i), \tilde{t})\right|\right],$$
(26)

where $\eta_{\mathbf{\Theta}}$ denotes the median with respect to the vector of parameters. Fig. 3 illustrates $w_i(t)$, $i = 1, \dots, 6$, for $t = 0, 5, \dots, 120$ min, and it can be seen that the relaxation level is dominated in the beginning by a_1 and by a_2 beyond 35 min. The global estimation error was then defined as

$$GEE(\boldsymbol{\theta}, t) = 100 \times \sum_{i=1}^6 w_i(t)\left|1 - \hat{\boldsymbol{\theta}}_i/\boldsymbol{\theta}_i\right|\,[\%].$$
(27)

Note that the LM method carries out a curve fitting producing small residuals that do not necessarily reflect a good parameter estimation, so GEE is important in identifying bad estimation cases. Fig. 4 shows that: HM produce an overall unbiased estimation; the GEE IQR for HM2 is, as expected, clearly lower than that for HM1, which is in turn, and not as expected, greater than that for FNN.

Table 1. Absolute relative error on the test set (Pr - Parameter; Mt - Method; Min - Minimum; Med - Median; IQR - Inter-quartile range; Max - Maximum).

Pr	Mt	AREE [%]			
		Min $\mathcal{O}(\bullet)$	Med	IQR	Max $\mathcal{O}(\bullet)$
	FNN	E-3	6.9	8.8	E+2
a_1	HM1	E-6	9.3E-2	1.2E+1	E+3
	HM2	E-7	2.6E-2	2.4	E+2
	FNN	E-4	2.1	2.9	E+2
λ_1	HM1	E-8	4.0E-4	2.1E-2	E+2
	HM2	E-9	2.1E-4	9.2E-3	E+3
	FNN	E-3	3.4	4.9	E+1
a_2	HM1	E-8	3.1E-2	3.9	E+4
	HM2	E-9	8.8E-3	7.8E-1	E+2
	FNN	E-3	4.1	5.4	E+1
λ_2	HM1	E-6	1.5E-2	8.3E-1	E+3
	HM2	E-7	5.1E-3	2.0E-1	E+3
	FNN	E-3	4.7	5.8	E+1
$ke0$	HM1	E-6	5.9E-2	8.1	E+3
	HM2	E-7	1.7E-2	1.6	E+3
	FNN	E-4	5.1E-1	6.9E-1	E+1
β	HM1				
	HM2	E-12	8.3E-7	4.3E-5	E+0

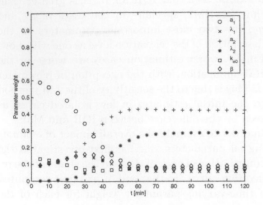

Fig. 3. Contribution of each parameter to the time course description of r.

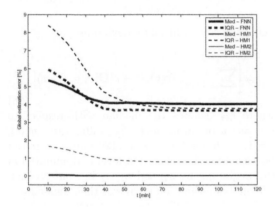

Fig. 4. Overall impact to r description through time of estimating all parameters in the test set.

Finally, in order to illustrate the great predictive ability of the HM method, and the clear improvement over the FNN in this context, Fig. 5 depicts the absolute relative deviation

$$ARD(\boldsymbol{\theta}, t) = 100 \times \left| 1 - r(\hat{\boldsymbol{\theta}}, t)/r(\boldsymbol{\theta}, t) \right| \ [\%]. \quad (28)$$

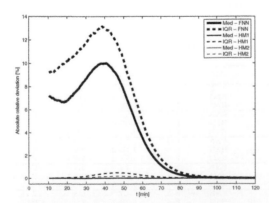

Fig. 5. Prediction ability on the test set.

4. CONCLUSIONS

In this paper, two different strategies were considered for application of a previously proposed hybrid method designed to parameter estimation. The first strategy is of general applicability, while the second one is intended for models having a structure defined by various blocks in series, as is the case of the neuromuscular blockade model used as a case study for comparing the performances of the two hybrid strategies. One could conclude that both are comparable in terms of the estimates biases, but not of the variances, in which case the second strategy is better at the expense of a higher computational burden. Nevertheless, both strategies exhibit a high prediction ability. Future work will consider the presence of noise at the model output, and a similar analysis to the one carried out here will be developed.

5. REFERENCES

Alonso, H., H. Magalhães, T. Mendonça and P. Rocha (2005a). A hybrid method for parameter estimation. In: *Proc. of the IEEE Int. Symp. on Intelligent Signal Processing - WISP 2005*. Faro, Portugal. pp. 304–309.

Alonso, H., T. Mendonça and P. Rocha (2005b). Contributions to parameter estimation using neural networks. Cadernos de Matemática - Série de Investigação. UA. http://pam.pisharp.org/handle/2052/86.

Gill, P., W. Murray and M. Wright (1981). *Practical Optimization*. Academic Press.

Hagan, M. T. and M. Menhaj (1994). Training feedforward networks with the Marquardt algorithm. *IEEE Trans. Neural Netw.* **5(6)**, 989–993.

Haykin, S. (1999). *Neural Networks, A Comprehensive Foundation*. 2nd ed.. Prentice-Hall. New Jersey.

Hornik, K., M. Stinchcombe and H. White (1990). Universal approximation of an unknown mapping and its derivatives using multilayer feedforward networks. *Neural Netw.* **3**, 551–560.

Lago, P., T. Mendonça and L. Gonçalves (1998). On-line autocalibration of a PID controller of neuromuscular blockade. In: *Proc. of the 1998 IEEE Int. Conf. on Control Applications*. Trieste, Italy. pp. 363–367.

Levenberg, K. (1944). A method for the solution of certain nonlinear problems in least squares. *Q. Appl. Math.* **2**, 164–168.

Marquardt, D. (1963). An algorithm for least-squares estimation of nonlinear parameters. *SIAM J. Appl. Math.* **11**, 431–441.

Mendonça, T. and P. Lago (1998). PID control strategies for the automatic control of neuromuscular blockade. *Control Eng. Pract.* **6(10)**, 1225–1231.

MULTI-LEAD T WAVE END DETECTION BASED ON STATISTICAL HYPOTHESIS TESTING

Alfredo Illanes Manriquez * **Qinghua Zhang** *
Claire Medigue ** **Yves Papelier** ***
Michel Sorine **

* *INRIA-IRISA, Rennes, France*
** *INRIA Rocquencourt, Le Chesnay, France*
*** *Hôpital Antoine-Béclère, Clamart, France*

Abstract: Automatic detection of electrocardiograms (ECG) waves provides important information for cardiac disease diagnosis. A new T wave end location algorithm based on multi-lead ECG processing is proposed in this paper. A statistical hypothesis testing algorithm is applied to two auxiliary signals computed by filtering and differentiating ECG signals. The performance of the algorithm has been evaluated using the PhysioNet QT database. The standard deviation of the errors between automatic annotations and manual ones are within tolerance accepted by cardiologist. *Copyright © 2006 IFAC*

Keywords: Signal processing, Biomedical systems, Detection algorithms, Electrocardiogram (ECG), T wave end location

1. INTRODUCTION

The electrocardiogram (ECG) makes possible the exploitation of information about cardiac electric activities. Each cardiac cycle in the ECG is characterized by successive waveforms, known as P wave, QRS complex and T wave as illustrated in Figure 1. These waveforms represent the depolarization and repolarization activities in heart's cells of atrium and ventricle.

The automatic detection of ECG waves is important to cardiac disease diagnosis. Time intervals defined between onset and offset of different waves are significant because they reflect physiological processes of the heart and autonomous nervous system (ANS). One of the most important intervals is the QT interval, which reflects the ventricular depolarization modelling repolarization duration. It is calculated on the ECG signal as the time

distance from the onset of the QRS complex to the end of the T wave. QT interval prolongation may be associated with high risk of ventricular arrhythmias and sudden death (Schuartz and Wolf, 1978; Moss *et al.*, 1985), consequently a method to measure QT interval is desired. Determination of QT interval requires T wave end detection, which is a difficult task due to the low SNR, its low frequency components, the baseline drift and the unclearly defined waveform shape.

Several approaches have been proposed in the literature for the T wave end detection. A method based in filters and thresholds has been described in (Laguna *et al.*, 1990; Laguna *et al.*, 1994) and evaluated in (Jané *et al.*, 1997). This method is based on linear derivative filters to get an indicator of signal variation. After R peak detection and windowing to roughly locate T wave, the algorithm find T wave end from the derivative of

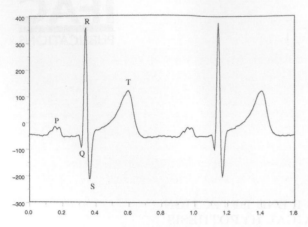

Figure 1. ECG signal and P-Q-R-S-T waves

ECG signal. When the derived signal exceeds an experimentally chosen threshold, it regards this moment as the T wave end.

Another T wave end detection method has been described in (Martinez *et al.*, 2004) based on wavelets. Wavelets are used to estimates derivatives at different scales. These estimated derivatives are then used for detection of T wave end in a similar way to the previous method.

A third method has been described in (Last *et al.*, 2004). This method is based on pattern matching. The basic idea for waveform detection is to first build a template for each ECG event and then to locate the corresponding form in the processed signal by looking for signal segments highly correlated with the template.

Another method has been described in (Zhang *et al.*, 2005). This method consists of the computation of an indicator related to the area covered by the T wave curve. Based essentially on the concavity of the T wave form, it is proved that the maximum of the computed indicator inside each cardiac cycle coincides with the T wave end.

Although these methods allow an efficient measurement of T wave end, like most known ECG detection methods, they are based on only one ECG lead processing, although several leads are recorded simultaneously. Consequently, for reliable detection of T wave end, such single lead algorithms need the assistance of a human operator to choose the ECG lead to be processed before detection.

A new algorithm is proposed in this paper for T wave end detection in ECG signals. This algorithm is based on simultaneously multiple lead processing and on a statistical test to detect mean changes in two auxiliary signals computed from the derivative and second derivative of the ECG signal. In the case of orthogonal ECG leads, the two auxiliary signals are equivalents to the squared modules of the spatial velocity and spatial

acceleration of the vectorcardiogram. Nevertheless, leads orthogonality is not necessary for the proposed algorithm.

Although statistical tests, in particular the CUSUM test, have been applied to one lead ECG signals (Carrault *et al.*, 1990) and spatial velocity of vectorcardiogram has been used in template matching methods to detect QRS complex (Rubel and Ayad, 1986), the algorithm described in the present study is novel since it uses a combination of both. As an advantage, the problem of choosing the lead to be processed is clearly avoided. Moreover, robustness against baseline drift is ensured by the differential nature of the used auxiliary signals; these auxiliary signals have values near zero in the isoelectric line section.

The performance of our algorithm has been evaluated using the PhysioNet QT database. Results indicate that the standard deviation of errors is within tolerances accepted by cardiologists.

The paper is organized as follows. The proposed algorithm is described in section 2 and the results of evaluations with the QT Database are shown in section 3, finally some concluding remarks are shown in section 4.

2. METHODS

The procedure to locate T wave offset is composed of 4 steps: preprocessing of ECG signals based on two linear filters, computation of auxiliary signals from ECG derivatives and second derivatives, then windowing to roughly locate T wave, and finally detection of mean changes by CUSUM test.

2.1 Preprocessing

In a first step, in order to obtain information about the slope of the T wave, and to reduce the effect of noise, a differentiation filter to each ECG lead and then a smoothing filter to the resulting signals are applied (Laguna *et al.*, 1990).

$$G_1(z) = 1 - z^{-6} \qquad (1)$$

$$G_2(z) = \frac{1 - z^{-8}}{1 - z^{-1}} \qquad (2)$$

We will denote $ECG(k)$ as the raw ECG signal and $ECGF(k)$ as the resulting signal after the two filters. $ECG(k)$ will be used to calculate the first auxiliary signal (that in orthogonal lead case represents the spatial velocity of the VCG) and $ECGF(k)$ will be used to calculate the second auxiliary signal (that in orthogonal lead case represents the spatial acceleration of the VCG).

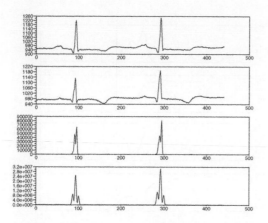

Figure 2. Two leads of an ECG record of the QT database and the auxiliary signals AS_1 and AS_2.

2.2 Auxiliary signals definition

The auxiliary signals are computed by using the following equations:

$$AS_1(k) = \sum_{i=1}^{L} (ECG_i'(k))^2 \qquad (3)$$

$$AS_2(k) = \sum_{i=1}^{L} (ECGF_i'(k))^2 \qquad (4)$$

L is the number of ECG leads that are used typically ($L = 2$ or 3). $ECG_i'(k)$ and $ECGF_i'(k)$ are respectively the derivatives at sample time k of ECG_i and $ECGF_i$ estimated with the parabola which best fits the five points of the signals $ECG_i(k)$ and $ECGF_i(k)$ around time location k (Rubel and Ayad, 1986), following the formulae

$$ECG_i'(k) \approx \tfrac{1}{10}\big(2(ECG_i(k+2)-ECG_i(k-2)) \qquad (5)$$
$$+ECG_i(k+1)-ECG_i(k-1)\big)$$

$$ECGF_i'(k) \approx \tfrac{1}{10}\big(2(ECGF_i(k+2)-ECGF_i(k-2)) \qquad (6)$$
$$+ECGF_i(k+1)-ECGF_i(k-1)\big)$$

We can note that in the orthogonal lead case, $\sqrt{AS_1}$ and $\sqrt{AS_2}$ are the spatial velocity and spatial acceleration of the VCG respectively.
Figure 2 shows the auxiliary signals waveform for a record of the QT Database over about 2 cardiac cycles.

2.3 Windowing

In order to limit the research of T wave end, an interval of time in each cardiac cycle including the end of T wave is defined. To this end, once the signal is filtered, and after the computation of the auxiliary signals, we first detect the R peak and use it as a reference. This event is the easiest to detect in a cardiac cycle, see for example (Nygards and Sornmo, 1983; Pan and Tompkins, 1985; Laguna et al., 1990).

After R peak detection, the RR interval average ($\overline{RR}$) is calculated from actual RR interval (RR_a) (Laguna et al., 1990).

$$\overline{RR}=\begin{cases} 0.8\overline{RR}+0.2RR_a & \text{if } 0.5\overline{RR}<RR_a<1.5\overline{RR} \\ \overline{RR} & \text{otherwise} \end{cases} \qquad (7)$$

From the current R wave peak position (R_p), a search window that depends on $\overline{RR}$ (in milliseconds) is defined and whose limits are:

$$winstart = R_p + a \qquad (8)$$
$$winend = R_p + b \cdot \overline{RR} \qquad (9)$$

The values of a and b are experimentally selected so that they minimize the variance of the errors between the automatic and manual annotations over the whole QT database. A minimum searching algorithm has been used to find a local minimum around chosen initial values. The obtained result is a=166[ms] and b=0.555.
This window will be used to the compute of CUSUM test in order to search T wave end in the auxiliary signals.

2.4 CUSUM test

The auxiliary signals AS_1 and AS_2 are assumed to follow the model:

$$AS_d(k) = \mu^d(k) + \varepsilon^d(k) \qquad (10)$$

with $\mu^d(k)$ being the mean of AS_d at time k and $\varepsilon^d(k)$ a zero mean noise to each auxiliary signal ($d = 1, 2$).

These auxiliary signals can be considered as signals with changes in their mean, thus, a decision rule can be computed to test between the two following hypothesis about mean (Basseville and Benveniste, 1986).

$$H_0 : \mu^d(k) = \mu_0^d \text{ for } k = 1, \ldots, n$$
$$H_1 : \mu^d(k) = \begin{cases} \mu_0^d \text{ for } k = 1, \ldots, r-1 \\ \mu_1^d \text{ for } k = r, \ldots, n \end{cases}$$

where μ_0^d and μ_1^d are the means before and after change respectively of auxiliary signal AS_d and $r \leq n$ is the supposed mean change time.

As long as the decision is taken in favour of H_0, the test continues. The test is stopped after the first sample of observations for which the decision is taken in favour of H_1. The acceptance of the hypothesis H_1 means that a mean change is detected.

If we consider that the observations are independent of each other, the likelihood ratio between these two hypotheses has the following form:

$$R = p_0(AS_d(1)) \cdots p_0(AS_d(r-1)) \cdot$$
$$\cdot \frac{p_1(AS_d(r)) \cdots p_1(AS_d(n))}{p_0(AS_d(1)) \cdots p_0(AS_d(n))} \quad (11)$$

or,

$$R = \prod_{k=r}^{n} \frac{p_1(AS_d(k))}{p_0(AS_d(k))} \quad (12)$$

denoting by p_0 and p_1 respectively the probability density function of $\mu_0^d + \varepsilon^d(k)$ and $\mu_1^d + \varepsilon^d(k)$.

If we suppose that $\varepsilon^d(k)$ is a Gaussian noise with variance σ_d^2 for each auxiliary signal, we have,

$$p_i(AS_d(k)) = \frac{1}{\sigma_d \sqrt{2\pi}} \exp\left(-\frac{(AS_d(k) - \mu_i^d)^2}{2\sigma_d^2}\right) \quad (13)$$

$i = 0, 1$.

Therefore, the log-kelihood ratio is as follows:

$$\Lambda_n^d(r) = \frac{\mu_1^d - \mu_0^d}{\sigma_d^2} \sum_{k=r}^{n} \left(AS_d(k) - \frac{\mu_0^d + \mu_1^d}{2}\right) \quad (14)$$

$$= \frac{\nu_d}{\sigma_d^2} \sum_{k=i}^{j} (AS_d(k) - \mu_0^d - \frac{\nu_d}{2}) \quad (15)$$

where $\nu_d = \mu_1^d - \mu_0^d$ is the jump magnitude.

The unknown time occurrence r is replaced by its maximum likelihood estimate under H_1, and the detector is thus:

$$g_d(n) = \max_{1 \le r \le n} \Lambda_n^d(r) \quad (16)$$

$$\text{if } g_d(n) \begin{cases} \le \lambda & \text{accept } H_0 \\ > \lambda & \text{accept } H_1 \end{cases} \quad (17)$$

This detector is called the Page-Hinkley test or the cumulative sum (CUSUM) test. When the value of $g_d(n)$ exceeds a conveniently chosen threshold (λ) we accept the hypothesis H_1, otherwise we accept H_0. The detector of equation 16 can be rewritten in a recursive manner as (M. Basseville, 1993):

$$g_d(0) = 0$$
$$g_d(n) = \left[g_d(n-1) + log\frac{p_1(AS_1(n))}{p_0(AS_1(n))}\right]_+ \quad (18)$$

with

$$[x]_+ = \begin{cases} x & si \ x > 0 \\ 0 & si \ x \le 0 \end{cases} \quad (19)$$

Figure 3 shows the waveforms of AS_1 and AS_2 versus the detector $g_d(n)$ for each auxiliary signal.

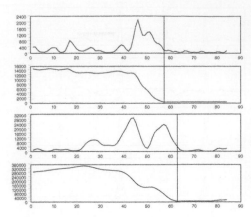

Figure 3. Auxiliary signals and their respective detector $g_d(n)$.

For the value of μ_0^d we compute the mean of AS_d in time interval from $winend - 0.1\overline{RR}$ until $winend$ and μ_1^d is computed as the mean of AS_d in the time interval between $winstart + 36$ and $winend$. The threshold (λ) for both auxiliary signals is set equal to $1.4 \max \sqrt{AS_2}$ at each cycle for each ECG record. The values 0.1, 36[ms] and 1.4 are experimentally chosen after optimization of the algorithm.

We consider the detection time in AS_1 and AS_2 as the last zero crossing point in $g_1(n)$ and $g_2(n)$ respectively. We will call these points as T_1 and T_2 respectively.

In principle, only AS_1 should be used for T wave end detection. Because of the presence of low frequency components in the T wave end, the instant T_1 is frequently earlier than T ends marked by manual expert. Since the detection in AS_2 is often after that manual expert, we estimate that T wave end is between the stopping time in AS_1 and the stopping time in AS_2 or more clearly (see Figure 4),

$$T_{end} = 0.6T_1 + 0.4T_2 \quad (20)$$

where 0.6 and 0.4 are values experimentally chosen after optimization of the algorithmin in a similar way than equations 8 and 9.

3. RESULTS

For validation purposes, we have used the QT database presented in (Laguna et al., 1997) available on the PhysioNet website. This database has been built by researchers specifically for the evaluation of algorithms which detect waveform boundaries in the ECG signal. The database consists of 105 fifteen minutes excerpts of two channels ECG Holter recording sampled at 250 Hz. The recording were chosen to include a broad variety of ECG morphologies and were extracted from other

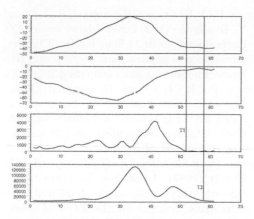

Figure 4. In the top we show T wave in two leads of an ECG record in the QT Database. Below we show AS_1 and AS_2 and the time detection T_1 and T_2.

existing electrocardiographic signal database. For each record, between 30 and 100 representative beats were manually annotated by cardiologists. The markers include mainly P wave, QRS complex and T wave peaks, onsets and offsets. Only the T wave ends annotations are used in this paper.

In order to evaluate the performance of our algorithm we compare the time detection of our method with cardiologist's manual measurement. We can deduce a statistical conclusion about detector based on the great number (3542 annotations) of T wave ends marked by cardiologists.

To quantify the performance of the algorithm, in each signal the mean and standard deviation (STD) of the difference between automatic detection and cardiologist's markers are used.

In (Party, 1985) tolerance for standard deviation of errors between detection algorithms and manual annotations for the onset and offset of ECG waves are presented. These tolerances are accepted bye cardiologists. The tolerance for T wave offset is 30.6[ms].

There are several ways to calculate the mean and standard deviation of errors in one recording and in the whole QT Database. In (Martinez *et al.*, 2004) on one hand, a detection algorithm is applied to each of the two leads of an ECG record in the QT Database. For each T wave end, the result obtained with a posteriori best lead is chosen. In (Jané *et al.*, 1997) the best lead performance in each ECG record is chosen to calculate the standard deviation. With our algorithm it is impossible to apply any of this two methods to calculate the performance in one ECG record because it works over the two (or three) leads, consequently we can not choose the a posteriori best error performance. In this sense,

our algorithm is penalized compared to the other ones.

For the whole QT Database it is not clear how to calculate the overall mean and standard deviation. It seems that in (Martinez *et al.*, 2004) and in (Jané *et al.*, 1997) these values are simply taken as the mean of the mean values and the mean of standard deviation of each record. These values (called mean1 and STD1 in Table 1 and 2) will be used to compare the results of the algorithm of this work with the other algorithms found in literature.

Let us compare the performance of our algorithm which three T wave end detection algorithms that have been validated with the whole QT database: WT (Martinez *et al.*, 2004), LPD (Jané *et al.*, 1997) and TU (Vila *et al.*, 2000). Table 1 shows the mean and standard deviation of this 3 algorithms and the mean and standard deviation of the algorithm presented in this paper. The abbreviation of the names of the algorithms follow those of (Martinez *et al.*, 2004). The time unit is millisecond. The numerical values for the WT, LPD, TU come from the publication (Martinez *et al.*, 2004).

Table 1. Evaluations of the algorithms with the 3542 annotations of the QT Database.

Method	mean1	STD1
this paper	0.57	22.81
WT	-1.6	18.1
LPD	13.5	27.0
TU	0.8	30.3
Tolerance		30.6

We show in this section two other ways to calculate mean and standard deviation of the whole QT Database.

- The mean and standard deviation are computed as the weighted mean of the mean values and the weighted mean of standard deviation respectively at each record. The weights are calculated from the number of beats in each record (mean2 and STD2 in Table 2).
- The mean and standard deviation are computed from a vector that collects every error between algorithm and manual experts over all the records. Then we compute a single mean and single standard deviation over this vector (mean3 and STD3 in Table 2).

Table 2 shows the three kinds of mean values and the three kinds of standard deviation values in each sub-database and in the whole QT Database.

4. DISCUSSION AND CONCLUSIONS

In this paper a new T wave end detection algorithm has been presented and validated with the

Table 2. Evaluation of our algorithm with each Database of the QT Database, where MIT is MIT-BIH Arrhythmia; MST is MIT-BIH ST Change; MSV is MIT-BIH Supraventricular Arrhythmia; N is BIH Hospital Normal Subjects; EST is European ST-T; SD is BIH Hospital Sudden Death Patients; LT is MIT-BIH Long Term ECG; and Total is the whole QT Database.

Database	mean1	mean2 mean3	STD1	STD2	STD3
MIT	-25.52	-30.64	28.4	30.6	58.15
MST	-10.93	-9.55	17.69	17.41	34.39
MSV	10.54	9.65	16.5	18.09	22.17
N	9.92	9.92	11.44	11.44	12.74
EST	4.15	3.59	17.74	17.73	48.7
SD	-2.04	-1.88	34.1	34.1	78.89
LT	44.52	62.72	37.98	45.21	100.54
Total	0.57	-0.94	22.81	23.83	58.49

PhysioNet QT database. The algorithm is based on multi-lead ECG processing and hypothesis test application in two auxiliary signals calculated from ECG first and second derivatives.

The algorithm has the followings advantages: (a) it is not necessary to choose the best lead before T wave end detection; (b) it is robust to the baseline derive because of the nature of the auxiliary signals.

Table 2 shows that the algorithm provides better results with the MST, MSV, N, and EST databases while in MIT, SD and LT database the standard deviation are not within the tolerances accepted by cardiologists. MIT, SD and LT database include signals with poor SNR and with large different morphologies.

We can conclude that the algorithm presented in this work produces results with errors within the accepted tolerance recommended by experts.

REFERENCES

Basseville, M. and A. Benveniste (1986). *Detection of Abrupt Changes in Signals and Dynamical Systems*. Springer-Verlag.

Carrault, G., L. Senhadji, J.J. Bellanger and J.P. Le Pichon (1990). ECG segmentation by means of change detection theory. *Annual International Conference of the IEEE Engineering in Medicine and Biology Society* **12**, 817–818.

Jané, R., A. Blasi, J. Garcia and P. Laguna (1997). Evaluation of an automatic threshold based detector of waveform limits in holter ECG with the QT database. *Computers in Cardiology, IEEE Computer Society* **24**, 295–298.

Laguna, P., N.V. Thakor, P. Caminal, R. Jané and Y. Hyung-Ro (1990). New algorithm for QT interval analysis in 24 hour holter ECG: Performance and applications. *Medical and Biological Engineering and Computing* **29**, 67–73.

Laguna, P., R. Jané and P. Caminal (1994). Automatic detection of wave boundaries in multilead ECG signals: Validation with the CSE database. *Computers and Biomedical Research* **27**, 45–60.

Laguna, P., R.G. Mark, A. Goldberg and G.B. Moody (1997). A database for evaluation of algorithms for measurement of QT and other waveforms intervals in the ECG. *Computers in Cardiology, IEEE Computer Society* **24**, 673–676.

Last, T., C.D. Nugent and F.J. Owens (2004). Multi-components based cross correlation beat detection in electrocardiogram analysis. *Biomedical Engineering OnLine*.

M. Basseville, I.V. Nikiforov (1993). *Detection of abrupt changes - Theory and Application*. Prentice-Hall, Inc.

Martinez, J.P., R. Almeida, S. Olmos, A.P. Rocha and P. Laguna (2004). A wavelet-based ECG delineator: Evaluation on standard database. *IEEE Trans. on Biomedical Engineering* **51**, 570–581.

Moss, J., P.J. Scuartz, R. Crampton, E. Locati and E. Carleen (1985). The long QT syndrome: a prospective international study. *Circulation* **71**, 17–21.

Nygards, M.E. and L. Sornmo (1983). Delineation of the QRS complex using the envelope of the ECG. *Medical and Biological Engineering and Computing* **21**, 538–547.

Pan, J. and W.J. Tompkins (1985). A real time QRS detection algorithm. *IEEE Transaction on Biomedical Engineering* **32**, 230–236.

Party, CSE Working (1985). Recomendations for measurements standards in quantitative electrocardiography. *Eur. Heart J.* **6**, 815–825.

Rubel, P. and B. Ayad (1986). The true boundary recognition power of multidimensional detection functions. an optimal comparison. *Elsevier Sciences Publishers* pp. 97–103.

Schuartz, P.J. and S. Wolf (1978). QT interval prolongation as predictor of sudden death in patients with myocardial infarction. *Circulation* **57**, 1074–1079.

Vila, J., Y. Gang, J. Presedo, M. Fernandez Delgado, S. Barro and M. Malik (2000). A new approach for TU complex caracterization. *IEEE Trans. on Biomedical Engineering* **24**, 764–772.

Zhang, Q., A. Illanes Manriquez, C. Medigue, Y. Papelier and M. Sorine (2005). Robust and efficient location of T-wave ends in electrocardiogram. *Computers in Cardiology, IEEE Computer Society*.

STRUCTURAL IDENTIFIABILITY OF
PARALLEL PHARMACOKINETIC EXPERIMENTS AS CONSTRAINED SYSTEMS

S.Y. Amy Cheung[1], James W.T. Yates[2], Leon Aarons[1]

[1]*School of Pharmacy and Pharmaceutical Sciences, University of Manchester, Oxford Road, U.K.*
[2]*Discovery DMPK, AstraZeneca, Alderley Park, Macclesfield, U.K.*

Abstract: Pharmacokinetic analysis in humans using compartmental models is restricted with respect to the estimation of parameter values. This is because the experimenter usually is only able to apply inputs and observations in a very small number of compartments in the system. This has implications for the structural identifiability of such systems and consequently limits the complexity and mechanistic relevance of the models that may be applied to such experiments. A number of strategies are presented whereby models are rendered globally identifiable by considering a series of experiments in parallel. Examples are taken from the pharmacokinetic literature and analysed using this parallel experiment methodology. *Copyright © 2006 IFAC*

Keywords: Algebraic approaches, Constrained parameters, Controllability, First-order systems, Identifiability, Parameter identification, Parameterization, Pharmacokinetic data, State-space models.

1. INTRODUCTION

Pharmacokinetics is the study of the absorption, distribution, metabolism and elimination of a therapeutic agent in the body. There are a number of 'classical' compartmental models for such purposes (Wagner 1993), however any introduction of greater complexity or physiological relevance can result in problems for parameter estimation. This is because in humans it is usually only practical to apply inputs to and observe the compartment representing the blood.

Structural identifiability (Bellman and Åström 1970; Anderson 1983) is the property of a model that there is sufficient information in the experimental input-output design to uniquely identify the unconstrained model parameters. Testing a pharmacokinetic model for structural identifiability is an important aspect of experimental design (Saccomani and Cobelli 1993). It is an a priori test because the system structure determines it and as such can be performed prior to experimentation. Modeller and experimenter should always follow this order of model analysis because strictly speaking without this unique 'behaviour to parameter value' correspondence any characterisation

of the system by parameter values might be invalid. This is, of course, dependent upon the application in hand and structural identifiability analysis can indirectly indicate which parameter values may be uniquely identified and the nature of any indeterminacy.

A non-unique correspondence between observed dynamics and model parameter values presents problems for the experimenter. Not least of these is that the experiment would have been designed to investigate the kinetics of the real system, but interpretation of the data by the model might give more than one explanation of the behaviour via estimated parameter values.

This restriction limits the scope and application of more mechanistic pharmacokinetic models. Here a mathematical analysis is presented of methods that may render models globally identifiable. These methods are to be found implicitly in the pharmacokinetic literature (Moghadaminia *et al* 2003; Nelson and Schaldemose 1959), however the authors believe this is the first time that such experimental arrangements have been analysed formally.

Parallel experiments as formal model structures are discussed as well as the implications for structural identifiability. Three case studies are presented that demonstrate the concepts discussed.

2. STRUCTURAL IDENTIFIABILITY ANALYSIS

Consider a parameter vector p that parameterises the linear compartmental system

$$\dot{x}(t) = A(p)x(t) + B(p)u(t)$$
$$x(0) = x_0(p) \qquad\qquad (1)$$
$$y(t) = C(p)x(t)$$

where in the case of pharmacokinetic modelling, x_i is the quantity of drug in compartment i, and y is the drug concentration in the observed compartments. The function $u(t)$ corresponds to some input to the system (for example an intravenous bolus dose). The entries of the matrices A, B and C are dependent upon the parameter vector p.

Let U be the set of continuous inputs/doses (to which $u(t)$ in (1) belongs) and Y be the set of the associated continuous responses (to which $y(t)$ belongs). Then define the *behaviour* of the compartmental system Σ_p to be

$$\Sigma_p : U \rightarrow Y , \qquad\qquad (2)$$

a map from time continuous inputs to time continuous outputs subject to the system specification (1). This is the input-output behaviour of the system viewed as a 'black box'. For a given experimental design there is a corresponding fixed input function, $u(t)$ for $0 < t \leq T$. This will result in a particular observed output

$$y_p(t) = \Sigma_p(u(t)) . \qquad\qquad (3)$$

The subscript p designates that the behaviour of the system is implicitly dependent upon the parameter vector p.

The observed output defines an equivalence relation[1] on the parameter space with classes of indistinguishable parameter vectors $[p]$. Thus:

$$p \sim p' \Leftrightarrow y_p \equiv y_{p'} . \qquad\qquad (4)$$

Thus we have that (Evans *et al* 2002):

1. $p \in P$ is globally identifiable if and only if $[p] = \{p\}$, that is to say a single parameter set is associated with the observed behaviour.
2. $p \in P$ is locally identifiable if $[p]$ is countably infinite[2].
3. $p \in P$ is unidentifiable otherwise.

Thus, as a structural property, the model σ is globally (locally) structurally identifiable if all $p \in P$ are globally (locally) identifiable. Otherwise the model is said to be unidentifiable.

2.1 Similarity Transformation Method

The similarity transformation method (Walter 1982) provides a method for exhaustively searching for all models that give the same input-output behaviour. The method of similarity transformation is based upon finding an isometry (Vajda and Rabitz 1989) between systems of the form (1).

In the case of linear systems, given two systems (A, B, C) and $(\widetilde{A}, \widetilde{B}, \widetilde{C})$ then if the following conditions (1-3) are satisfied then the systems have equivalent input-output behaviour.

1. The two systems are structurally observable (Cobelli and Romanin-Jacur 1976).
2. The two systems are structurally controllable.
3. There exists a non-singular matrix T such that the systems are similar (see below).

For two systems (A, B, C) and $(\widetilde{A}, \widetilde{B}, \widetilde{C})$ to be similar, there must exist a non-singular matrix T such that (Sontag 1990):

$$AT = T\widetilde{A}$$
$$B = T\widetilde{B} \qquad\qquad (5)$$
$$CT = \widetilde{C}$$

Only parameter in the controllable and observable component of a component model can possibly be identifiable (Cobelli and Romanin-Jacur 1976). Therefore controllability and observability are verified in order to avoid trivial cases of non-identifiability. For linear systems of low complexity, as will be considered in this paper, these criteria are easily checked using a set of 'geometric' criteria (Godfrey and Chapman 1990) that are reproduced in a simplified form for the models considered below:

1. A compartmental model is structurally controllable if and only if there is a path to every compartment from an input.

---

[1] Partitions the set of all possible parameter values into classes that give the same observed behaviour.

[2] Possibly infinite number but no 'close' neighbouring parameter sets give the same observed behaviour. For more information see (Evans *et al* 2002).

2. A compartmental model is structurally observable if and only if there is a path from each compartment to at least one observed compartment.

By path is meant a route along the arrows of flux in the compartmental diagram.

This method (5) can therefore be used to find different parameter values that give the same output. In the sequel, a tilde denotes an alternative parameter value.

3. CONSTRAINED STRUCTURES

It is sometimes possible to carry out the 'same' experiment several times on a system in which it can be assumed *a priori* that some, but not all, of its rate constants change between experiments. The models representing each experimental observation thus share some common rate constant values. A parallel experiment structure is constructed as follows: the basic pharmacokinetic model is reproduced a number of times corresponding to the number of experiments to be performed. The new model structure is reparameterised with a constrained parameterisation representing prior knowledge of the changes in parameter values between experiments. This forms a much more constrained structure than the individual model.

In order to perform structural identifiability analysis, it is necessary to formulate the concept of a parallel experiment in the form of a linear system. Consider a single pharmacokinetic model of the form (1) represented by the triple $(A(p), B(p), C(p))$ (in pharmacokinetic experiments it is reasonable to assume that the initial condition is the zero state). Let superscripts represent the experiment number. Then the parallel experiment structure representing n experiments and parameterised by P' may be represented by the triple $(A'(p'), B'(p'), C'(p'))$ where

$$A'(p') = \begin{bmatrix} A(E^1(p')) & 0 & 0 \\ 0 & \ldots & 0 \\ 0 & 0 & A(E^n(p')) \end{bmatrix} \quad (6)$$

$$B'(p') = \begin{bmatrix} B(E^1(p')) & 0 & 0 \\ 0 & \ldots & 0 \\ 0 & 0 & B(E^n(p')) \end{bmatrix} \quad (7)$$

$$C'(p') = \begin{bmatrix} C(E^1(p')) & 0 & 0 \\ 0 & \ldots & 0 \\ 0 & 0 & C(E^n(p')) \end{bmatrix} \quad (8)$$

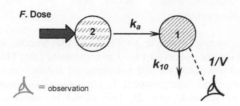

Fig. 1. One-compartment model with first order absorption. This model represents the one compartment distribution of a compound after absorption from the gut.

Here

$$E^i : P' \to P \qquad i = 1...n \qquad (9)$$

is a map between the constrained parallel experiment parameters and the individual model parameters. Notice that

$$dimension\,(P') < n \cdot dimension(P)\,, \qquad (10)$$

which is as a result of the constraints.

Thus the systems $(A(p), B(p), C(p))$ are unconnected but the functions E^i represent the *a priori* assumptions of common and changing parameter values. Notice that if $(A(p), B(p), C(p))$ is controllable and observable then $(A'(p'), B'(p'), C'(p'))$ is controllable and observable. This is because of the block structures defined in (6)–(8) result in the individual unconnected structures being controllable and observable.

The parallel experiment structure $(A'(p'), B'(p'), C'(p'))$ is now of the form (1) and may be analysed using the similarity criteria (5).

4. THREE CASE STUDIES

Three different models are now examined with respect to parallel experiments in order to demonstrate the mathematical ideas discussed above. It is shown how individually unidentifiable or locally identifiable models may be rendered globally structurally identifiable by considering them in the context of some parallel experiment.

Structural observability, controllability and identifiability analysis were performed using MATHEMATICA (Wolfram Research Inc., Illinois, U.S.A.). Solutions of the simultaneous equations in (5) could not be found automatically, a large amount of operator 'supervision' was required to guide the software to the solution set.

4.1 One-compartment model with first order absorption

As a simple example to illustrate the process of analysis, the model in Fig. 1 is considered first. This model represents the one compartment distribution of a compound (compartment 1) after absorption from the gut (compartment 2). This model is commonly referred to as a 'one-compartment model with first order absorption'. It can be seen that from the rules presented above that the model is both controllable and observable, thus the similarity transformation method may be applied. The resulting structural identifiability status of this model is well known, however the analysis is presented here so that the connection between a model and potential parallel experiment structures may be appreciated. The system in Fig 1 may be written in the form (1) thus

$$A = \begin{bmatrix} -k_{10} & k_a \\ 0 & -k_a \end{bmatrix}, \tag{11}$$

$$B = \begin{bmatrix} 0 \\ F \end{bmatrix}, \tag{12}$$

$$C = \begin{bmatrix} 1/V & 0 \end{bmatrix}. \tag{13}$$

The resulting simultaneous equations (5) may be solved to show that the model is unidentifiable. There are, for a given $p = (F, V, k_a, k_{10})$ an infinite number of possible matrices T of the form

$$T = \frac{F}{\widetilde{F}} \begin{bmatrix} \dfrac{k_a}{k_{10}} & 0 \\ \dfrac{k_{10} - k_a}{k_{10}} & 1 \end{bmatrix}. \tag{14}$$

It can be seen that a new parameter vector may be generated from p by varying $\widetilde{F}$. The model becomes locally identifiable by considering the parameterisation

$$p_{new} = (V/F, k_a, k_{10}). \tag{15}$$

This can be seen to be locally identifiable because (5) implies that

$$t_{11} = V/\widetilde{V} \tag{16}$$

and so that

$$\frac{k_a}{k_{10}} = \frac{t_{11}}{t_{22}} = \frac{V}{F}\frac{\widetilde{F}}{\widetilde{V}}. \tag{17}$$

This means that the two solutions are $\left(\dfrac{V}{F}, k_a, k_{10}\right)$

and $\left(\dfrac{Vk_{10}}{Fk_a}, k_{10}, k_a\right)$.

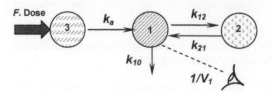

Fig. 2. 'Classical' two compartment Pharmacokinetic model with a third compartment representing the absorption of an orally administered dose.

Consider the case now that the same drug is dosed orally using two different formulations. It can therefore be assumed that the body pharmacokinetics parameters V and k_{10} are constant between the two experiments, but that the bioavailability F and absorption rate k_a will vary. The parallel experiment structure can be written in the form (8)-(10):

$$A(p') = \begin{bmatrix} -k_{10} & k_a^1 & 0 & 0 \\ 0 & -k_a^1 & 0 & 0 \\ 0 & 0 & -k_{10} & k_a^2 \\ 0 & 0 & 0 & -k_a^2 \end{bmatrix} \tag{18}$$

$$B(p') = \begin{bmatrix} 0 & 0 \\ F^1 & 0 \\ 0 & 0 \\ 0 & F^2 \end{bmatrix} \tag{19}$$

$$C(p') = \begin{bmatrix} 1/V & 0 & 0 & 0 \\ 0 & 0 & 1/V & 0 \end{bmatrix} \tag{20}$$

where

$$p' = \left(V, k_{10}, k_a^1, k_a^2, F^1, F^2\right). \tag{21}$$

and

$$\begin{aligned} E^1\left(V, k_{10}, k_a^1, k_a^2, F^1, F^2\right) &= \left(F^1, V, k_a^1, k_{10}\right) \\ E^2\left(V, k_{10}, k_a^1, k_a^2, F^1, F^2\right) &= \left(F^2, V, k_a^2, k_{10}\right) \end{aligned} \tag{22}$$

An analysis of this structure yields that T in (5) must be

$$T = \frac{F^1}{\widetilde{F}^1} \begin{bmatrix} 1 & 0 & 0 & 0 \\ 0 & 1 & 0 & 0 \\ 0 & 0 & 1 & 0 \\ 0 & 0 & 0 & 1 \end{bmatrix}. \tag{23}$$

This means that the parameterisation p' is unidentifiable. However the uniquely identifiable parameter combinations are:

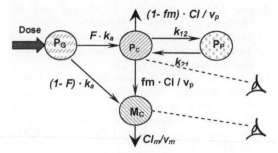

Fig. 3. Compartmental diagram of the parent-metabolite model used to model the pharmacokinetics of dextromethorphan and dextrophan.

$$p'_{new} = \left(V/F^1, V/F^2, k_a^1, k_a^2, k_{10}\right). \quad (24)$$

Thus the parallel experiment has eliminated the local identifiable indeterminacy between the absorption rate constant and the rate of elimination.

4.2 Classical Two Compartment Model with Oral Dosing

Another common structural identifiability issue is with two compartment models following absorption of an oral dose (Fig 2). Such models have a tri-exponential impulse (bolus dose) response. A structural identifiability analysis (Godfrey *et al* 1980) demonstrates that there are 3 solution sets of parameters and thus the model is locally identifiable. This is by again considering V/F as a parameter.

Consider the case where the same compound is dosed orally on two separate occasions where the formulation is different (Nelson and Schaldemose 1959). This might be as a result of different crystal states, vehicle or tablet form. In this case it can be assumed that post absorption the pharmacokinetics, represented by V_1, k_{12}, k_{21} and k_{10} will be the same in both experiments: the same compound is dosed.

However the absorption kinetics, as represented by k_a and F, will vary. An analysis of this proposed parallel experiment shows that the disposition parameters k_{12}, k_{21} and k_{10} are globally identifiable, as are the two absorption rates k_a^1 and k_a^2. The two combination parameters V_1/F^1 and V_1/F^2 are also shown to be globally identifiable.

4.3 Parent-Metabolite Model with Oral Dose

An important example of parallel experimental design is the inhibition of metabolism by co-administering a suitable enzyme inhibitor (Moghadamnia *et al* 2003). The dextrorotatory morphinan codeine synthetic analogue, dextromethorphan (DEX) is an anti-tussive

Table 1. Parameters used in the parent-metabolite model shown in fig. 3.

Parameter	Meaning
V_p	Volume of parent drug central compartment
V_m	Volume of metabolite central compartment
CL	Total clearance of parent drug
CL_m	Total clearance of metabolite
k_{12}	Transfer rate constant
k_{21}	Transfer rate constant
k_a	Oral dose absorption rate constant
f_m	Fraction metabolised
F	Bioavailability of parent

therapeutic agent. DEX metabolise to a major active metabolite dextrorphan (DOR).

Blood concentration levels for DEX and DOR were recorded separately after an oral dose of DEX. The proposed model structure for a single experiment is detailed in Fig. 3. The first pass effect is incorporated into the model by connecting the parent and metabolite central compartments, P_C and M_C, to the oral dose compartment P_G. The parameterisation of this model is

$$p = \left(V_p, V_m, CL_m, k_{12}, k_{21}, k_a, f_m, CL, F\right) \quad (25)$$

See table 1 for an explanation of these parameters.

Structural identifiability analysis of this model shows it to be unidentifiable with respect to the proposed inputs and outputs. The identifiable parameter combinations are:

$$p_{new} = \begin{pmatrix} \dfrac{V_p}{F}, \dfrac{V_m}{1-F}, \dfrac{CL}{V_p}, \dfrac{CL_m}{V_m}, \dfrac{Ff_m}{1-F} \\ k_{12}, k_{21}, k_a \end{pmatrix}. \quad (26)$$

As it will be shown, this situation may be remedied by creating a parallel experiment design. The orally administrated regimen was divided into two parts, DEX was dosed with either 50 mg of quinidine sulphate or placebo. Quinidine is an inhibitor of DEX conversion to DOR (Moghadamnia *et al* 2003). Thus the parallel experiment using the same model structure was:

1. DEX (30mg), quinidine placebo anteceded at 1 hour.
2. DEX (30mg), quinidine sulphate 50mg anteceded at 1 hour.

The constraints that are placed on the parallel experiment model parameterisation are that the parameters will remain constant for the two experiments except for those influenced by the rate of metabolism. These are the bioavailability F, the clearance of the parent-drug CL and the fraction metabolised f_m. There is some evidence that quinidine can affect active transport of drugs across the gut wall, however for the analysis here it is assumed that the absorption rate is constant. Thus the parallel structure model has the parameterisation

$$p' = \begin{pmatrix} V_p, V_m, CL_m, k_{12}, k_{21}, k_a, \\ f_m^1, f_m^2, CL^1, CL^2, F^1, F^2 \end{pmatrix} \quad (27)$$

This parallel structure with parameterisation (27) is then globally structurally identifiable.

5.CONCLUSIONS

Parallel experiments to enhance the structural identifiability of pharmacokinetic models have been implicitly discussed previously (Nelson and Schaldemose 1959; Moghadamnia *et al* 2003). However, there appears to have never been a formal formulation and analysis of this experimental design problem. A preliminary formulation has been presented here that places the concept of a parallel experiment in the context of a single constrained model structure.

Three case studies have been examined in order to illustrate the constrained model concept. The parallel experimental design has been shown to be beneficial with regards to structural identifiability. It is apparent as well that multiple experiments will be beneficial from a system identification point of view.

There are other potential examples of parallel experiments. In (Yuasa *et al* 1995) it is discussed how anaesthesia can influence the rate of absorption and elimination of certain pharmaceuticals. This has a physiological justification due to the lowered blood pressure that anaesthesia induces. In (Brown *et al* 2004) it is noted that the pharmacokinetics of a drug, especially metabolism and elimination, alters dependent on whether the individual is at rest or exercising. Again this is mainly influenced by blood pressure and flow rate.

Incorporation of prior knowledge into parallel experiment model structures with constrained parameterisation allows sufficient information to be present in the input-output behaviour to give unique parameter estimates. It is apparent from the results presented here that parallel experiment strategies can be very powerful in providing globally structurally identifiable pharmacokinetic models.

REFERENCES

Anderson. D.H. (1983) Compartmental Modelling and Tracer Kinetics. *Springer-Verlag, Berlin.*

Bellman R. and K.J. Astrom. (1970) On structural identifiability. *Mathematical Biosciences.* **7** 329-339

Brown, M., A. Bjorksten, I. Medved and M. McKenna. (2004) Pharmacokinetics of intravenous N-acetylcysteine in men at rest and during exercise. *European Journal of Clinical Pharmacology.* **60**: 717-723

Cobelli, C., and Romanin-Jacur, G. (1976) Controllability, observability and structural identifiability of multi input and multi output biological compartmental systems. *IEEE Transactions on Biomedical Engineering.* **BME-23** (2) 93-100

Evans, N.D. M.J. Chappell, M.J. Chapman and K.R. Godfrey. (2002) Identifiability of uncontrolled rational systems. *Automatica.* **38** 1799-1805.

Godfrey, K.R., R. P. Jones,and R.F. Brown. (1980) Identfiable pharmacokinetic models: The role of extra inputs and measurements. *Journal of Pharmacokinetics and Biopharmaceutics.* **8**:633-648.

Godfrey, K.R. (1986) The identifiability of parameters of models used in biomedicine. *Mathematical Modelling.* **7** 1195-1214

Godfrey, K.R., and Chapman, M.J. (1990). Identifiability and indistinguishability of linear compartmental models. *Mathematics and Computers in Simulation.* **32** 273-295.

Moghadamnia, A.A., A. Rostami-Hodjegan, R. Abdul-Manap, C. E. Wright, A. H. Morice and G. T. Tucker. (2003). Physiologically based modelling of inhibition of metabolism and assessment of the relative potency of drug and metabolite: dextromethorphan vs. dextrorphan using quinidine inhibition. *British Journal of Clinical Pharmacology.* **56**: 57-67.

Nelson, E. and I. Schaldemose. (1959). Urinary excretion kinetics for evaluation of drug absorption I. *Journal of the American Pharmaceutical Association.* **48**: 489-495.

Saccomani M.P. and C. Cobelli. (1993) A minimal input output configurationfor a priori identifiability for a compartmental model of leucine metabolism. *IEEE Transactions on Biomedical Engineering.* **40** 797-803

Sontag, E. (1990). Mathematical control theory: Deterministic finite dimensional systems. *Springer-Verlag, New York.*

Vajda S. and H. Rabitz, (1989). State isomorphism approach to global identifiability of nonlinear systems, *IEEE Transactions on Automatic control.* **AC-34**: 220-223

Wagner, J.G. (1993). Pharmacokinetics for the pharmaceutical scientist. *Technomic Publishing Company Inc., Pennsylvania U.S.A.*

Walter, E. (1982) Identifiability of State Space Models. *Springer-Verlag, New York.*

Yuasa, H., K. Matsuda, and J. Watanabe. (1995) Influence of anesthetic regimens on the intestinal absorption of 5-Fluorouracil in rats. *Biological and Pharmaceutical Bulletin.* **18**: 747-752.

SEPARATION OF ARTERIAL PRESSURE INTO SOLITARY WAVES AND WINDKESSEL FLOW

Taous-Meriem Laleg * **Emmanuelle Crépeau** **
Michel Sorine *

* INRIA Rocquencourt, 78153 Le Chesnay cedex, France
*** Laboratoire de mathématiques appliquées, UVSQ,
France*

Abstract: A simplified model of arterial blood pressure intended for use in model-based signal processing applications is presented. The main idea is to decompose the pressure into two components: a travelling wave describes the fast propagation phenomena predominating during the systolic phase and a windkessel flow represents the slow phenomena during the diastolic phase. Instead of decomposing the blood pressure pulse into a linear superposition of forward and backward harmonic waves, as in the linear wave theory, a nonlinear superposition of travelling waves matched to a reduced physical model of the pressure, is proposed. Very satisfactory experimental results are obtained by using forward waves, the N-soliton solutions of a Korteweg-de Vries equation in conjunction with a two-element windkessel model. The parameter identifiability in the practically important 3-soliton case is also studied. The proposed approach is briefly compared with the linear one and its possible clinical relevance is discussed. *Copyright © 2006 IFAC*

Keywords: pressure, wave, linear theory, nonlinear theory, identifiability

1. INTRODUCTION

In order to understand and assess the behaviour of the circulatory system both in normal and pathological conditions, many studies have been devoted to modelling the arterial tree. There are two types of models for arterial blood pressure (ABP) in large arteries. Lumped, or $0D$, models (nD stands for n space variables), like the popular windkessel models, are based on an analogy with simple RLC electrical circuits, the pressure being represented by a voltage and the blood flow-rate by a current (Frank and Zhaorong, 1989). In order to enlarge its frequency domain, the basic two-element windkessel model, a resistance in parallel with a capacitor, has been extended to three and four elements by adding in series a resistance, alone or with an inductance in parallel (Stergiopulos *et al.*, 1999). Windkessel models

successfully explain the diastolic phase but, with their low order, they can not explain propagation phenomena like the transit delay of the pressure pulse. The $3D$ distributed models are based on computational fluid dynamic principles and can explain observed phenomena (McDonald, 1974). Too complex for some applications, they can be reduced to $2D$ or $1D$ models (Canic *et al.*, 2005). Then $0D$ models can be deduced from $1D$ models (Monti *et al.*, 2002) and (Milisic and Quarteroni, 2004) to be used as boundary conditions for $1D$ models (Olufsen, 1999) and (Fernandez *et al.*, 2005) or in signal analysis as is done here.

During the propagation of the Pressure Pulse (PP) along the arterial tree, phenomena like "Peaking" and "Steepening" are observed. This has been explained by the linear superposition of direct and reflected waves, the reflected waves being created when the forward waves, from the heart to the periphery, encounter discontinuities in the arterial properties like a bifurcation or a stenosis. This model has been well known for decades and many studies have been carried out in order to separate the PP into its forward and backward components, as in the pioneering work of Westerhof (Westerhof et al., 1972), followed by many others (Li, 1986), (Parker and Jones, 1990), (Berger et al., 1993), (Stergiopulos et al., 1993), (Pythoud et al., 1995) and (Pythoud et al., 1996).

The main idea in this article is to decompose the pressure into a travelling wave representing the fast propagation phenomena during the systolic phase and a windkessel term representing slow phenomena during the diastolic phase. A decomposition of this kind has been studied in (Wang et al., 2002) but the novelty here consists in choosing a forward solitary wave which already captures essential properties of the PP, like the "Peaking" and the "Steepening" phenomena. Solitons resulting from a balance between shock wave creation and wave dispersion are proposed. They possess an analytical expression which leads to a reduced ABP model that is easy to identify, an important advantage of the approach. So, instead of the usual decomposition of the ABP as a linear superposition of forward and backward harmonic waves, the suggestion is to use a nonlinear superposition of forward solitary waves completed by a windkessel flow. The use of solitons for analyzing the ABP has been proposed in (Crépeau and Sorine, 2005), where based on results of (Yomosa, 1987) a quasi-$1D$ Navier-Stokes equation is chosen and reduced to a Korteweg-de Vries equation (KdVE) with solitons as particular solutions. In (Crépeau and Sorine, 2005), it is shown that 2 or 3 interacting solitons are sufficient for a good description of the systolic phase.

The next section, after recalling the linear theory, presents a soliton + windkessel correction-term decomposition needed in the diastolic phase. In section 3, the identifiability of the 3-soliton's parameters and of a two-element windkessel model is studied. In section 4 experimental results are presented, followed by a discussion in section 5.

2. REDUCED ARTERIAL BLOOD PRESSURE MODEL

The blood pressure $P(z,t)$ and flow $Q(z,t)$, with z the position on the arterial tree and t the time, are described in (Westerhof et al., 1972) as the following linear superposition of forward and backward waves (with subscripts f and b respectively):

$$P(z,t) = P_f(z - c_0 t) + P_b(z + c_0 t), \quad (1)$$

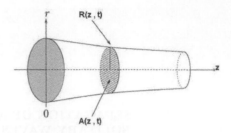

Fig. 1. Blood flow vessel

$$Q(z,t) = Q_f(z - c_0 t) + Q_b(z + c_0 t), \quad (2)$$

$c_0 = \sqrt{\frac{E h_0}{2\rho R_0}}$ is the Moens-Korteweg sound waves velocity in an elastic vessel filled with blood of density ρ. E is the wall elasticity coefficient. R_0 and h_0 are respectively the equilibrium radius and the thickness of the vessel. The impedance $Z(z,\omega)$ at position z and frequency ω is given by the ratio of the time Fourier transforms of the pressure and flow at this position:

$$Z(z,\omega) = \frac{\hat{P}(z,\omega)}{\hat{Q}(z,\omega)} = \frac{\hat{P}_f(z,\omega) + \hat{P}_b(z,\omega)}{\hat{Q}_f(z,\omega) + \hat{Q}_b(z,\omega)}. \quad (3)$$

The global reflection coefficient Γ is given by (Berger et al., 1993) and (Westerhof et al., 1972):

$$\Gamma(z,\omega) = \frac{Z(z,\omega) - Z_c}{Z(z,\omega) + Z_c}. \quad (4)$$

where Z_c denotes the characteristic impedance that can be estimated by several methods (in the case of a reflectionless tube $Z_c = Z$)(Li, 1982), (Li, 1986), (Quick et al., 2001) and (Westerhof et al., 1972). Knowing Z and Z_c it is possible to estimate Γ and the forward and backward components of the pressure are given by (Westerhof et al., 1972) and (Westerhof et al., 2005):

$$\hat{P}_f = \frac{\hat{P}}{1 + \Gamma}, \qquad \hat{Q}_f = \frac{\hat{Q}}{1 - \Gamma}, \quad (5)$$

$$\hat{P}_b = \Gamma \hat{P}_f, \qquad \hat{Q}_b = -\Gamma \hat{Q}_f. \quad (6)$$

This method has the advantage of requiring pressure and flow measurements at only one location but it assumes a linear model of the flow, the impedance. Many studies have followed, aiming to take the nonlinearities into account when separating the PP into forward and backward components. In (Parker and Jones, 1990) and (Stergiopulos et al., 1993), quasi-nonlinear methods for $1D$ flow models are used (method of characteristics and split coefficient matrix for the Euler equation) under the linearizing assumption that intersecting forward and backward waves are additive. In (Berger *et al.*, 1993) the linear superposition of multiple forward and reflected waves is considered. In (Pythoud *et al.*, 1995) and (Pythoud *et al.*, 1996), a nonlinear separation is proposed using Riemann invariants which takes into account nonlinearities in the area-pressure relationship and in the convective term.

Surprisingly, if the radial acceleration is also taken into account in a quasi $1D$ Navier-Stokes equation, the model becomes simpler as observed in (Crépeau and Sorine, 2005): using a singular perturbation technique, it leads to a KdVE, a simpler situation because this equation is integrable, admitting soliton solutions. As proposed in (Crépeau and Sorine, 2005), solitons are then a natural choice of base functions to analyze the ABP, the reference model being the KdVE:

$$\frac{\partial P_s}{\partial z} + (d_0 + d_1 P_s)\frac{\partial P_s}{\partial t} + d_2 \frac{\partial^3 P_s}{\partial t^3} = 0, \quad (7)$$

where $P_s(z,t)$ is the ABP and

$$d_0 = \frac{1}{c_0}, \; d_1 = -\frac{2\alpha+1}{2\rho c_0^3}, \; d_2 = -\frac{\rho_\omega h_0 R_0}{2\rho c_0^3}$$

with α a momentum-flux correction coefficient and ρ_ω the wall density. Remark in (7) the pressure dependent velocity $d_0 + d_1 P_s$ and the dispersion term $\frac{\partial^3 P_s}{\partial t^3}$ that are at the origin of solitons.

With the new variables $\xi = t - d_0 z$, $\tau = d_2 z$ and $y = \frac{d_1}{6d_2}P_s$, (7) becomes a normalized KdVE:

$$\frac{\partial y}{\partial \tau} + 6y\frac{\partial y}{\partial \xi} + \frac{\partial^3 y}{\partial \xi^3} = 0, \quad y(\xi,0) = y_0(\xi). \quad (8)$$

The general analytical expression of an N-soliton solution of (8) can be found in (Whitham, 1999):

$$y(\xi,\tau) = 2\frac{\partial^2 (\ln\det(\mathbf{M}))}{\partial \xi^2}, \quad (9)$$

$\mathbf{M}$ is a $N \times N$ matrix with coefficients given by:

$$M_{mk} = \delta_{mk} + \frac{2a_m}{a_m + a_k}f_m, \quad m, \; k = 1...N \quad (10)$$

where δ_{mk} is the Kronecker symbol and

$$f_m(\xi,\tau) = \exp[-a_m(\xi - s_m - a_m^2\tau)]$$

$(a_m, s_m) \in \mathbb{R}^+ \times \mathbb{R}$.

One can notice from real data that the ABP can be approximated by 2 or 3-solitons. In the following, 3-solitons are considered. The parameters d_0, d_1 and d_2 characterize the KdVE and depend on the characteristics of the vascular compartment while the parameters a_1, a_2 and a_3 characterize the solitons. As is noticed in (Crépeau and Sorine, 2005) solitons lead to a good estimation of the systolic phase but need some correction in the

diastolic phase. So this work proposes to describe slow phenomena with a two-element windkessel model. Then, the ABP can be written in the following form:

$$P(z,t) - \bigoplus_{j=1}^{n}(P_{sj}(z,t)) + P_{wk}(t), \quad (11)$$

where $\bigoplus_{j=1}^{n} P_{sj}(z,t)$ is a wave term given by a nonlinear superposition of solitary waves $P_{sj}(z,t)$. For example a 2-soliton can be written as a nonlinear superposition of two solitary waves. $P_{wk}(t)$ is the output of a two-element windkessel model given by the following differential equation (Stergiopulos *et al.*, 1999) and (Wang *et al.*, 2002):

$$\frac{dP_{wk}}{dt}(t) + \frac{P_{wk}(t)}{RC} = \frac{P_\infty}{RC} + \frac{Q(t)}{C}, \quad (12)$$

where R denotes the peripheral resistance, $C = \frac{dV_{wk}}{dP_{wk}}$ the compliance of the arteries and $Q(t)$ the inflow. The inflow can be taken proportional to P_s (Wang *et al.*, 2002). So it is written $Q = \frac{P_s}{R_s}$.

3. IDENTIFIABILITY OF THE MODEL'S PARAMETERS

3.1 Identifiability of a 3-soliton's parameters

In this section identifiability of the 3-soliton's parameters is studied. For this purpose, the normalized KdVE (8) is considered. Then, a 3-soliton solution of (8) is given by (9). For studying identifiability, the definition given in (Walter and Pronzato, 1994) is used. So, two solutions of (8) in the form of a 3-soliton are assumed such that:

$$M_{mk}^j = \delta_{mk} + \frac{2a_m^j}{a_m^j + a_k^j}f_m^j, \quad (13)$$

where $j = 1, 2$, $m = 1, 2, 3$ and $k = 1, 2, 3$.

The determinant of $\mathbf{M}^j$, $j = 1, 2$ is given by:

$$\det(\mathbf{M}^j) = 1 + f_1^j + f_2^j + f_3^j + \left(\frac{a_1^j - a_2^j}{a_1^j + a_2^j}\right)^2 f_1^j f_2^j +$$

$$\left(\frac{a_1^j - a_3^j}{a_1^j + a_3^j}\right)^2 f_1^j f_3^j + \left(\frac{a_2^j - a_3^j}{a_2^j + a_3^j}\right)^2 f_2^j f_3^j +$$

$$\left(1 + \frac{16a_1^j a_2^j a_3^j}{(a_1^j + a_2^j)(a_1^j + a_3^j)(a_2^j + a_3^j)} - \frac{4a_1^j a_2^j}{(a_1^j + a_2^j)^2} - \frac{4a_1^j a_3^j}{(a_1^j + a_3^j)^2} - \frac{4a_2^j a_3^j}{(a_2^j + a_3^j)^2}\right)f_1^j f_2^j f_3^j.$$

For $\tau = 0$, f_i^j can be rewritten as follows:

$$f_i^j(\xi,0) = \exp(-a_i^j\xi)\exp(a_i^j s_i^j), \quad (14)$$

where $j = 1, 2$ and $i = 1, 2, 3$.

The a_i^j are positive and can be ordered: $a_1^j > a_2^j > a_3^j$. Then when $\xi \to +\infty$, the asymptotic behaviour is:

$$\det(\mathbf{M}^j) = k^j \exp(-(a_1^j + a_2^j + a_3^j)\xi), j = 1, 2.\ (15)$$

Now, the question is: does $y^1(\xi, 0) = y^2(\xi, 0)$ imply unicity of the 3-soliton (i.e $\mathbf{M}^1 = \mathbf{M}^2$)? When $y^1(\xi, \tau) = y^2(\xi, \tau)$:

$$\frac{\partial^2(\ln \det(\mathbf{M}^1))}{\partial \xi^2} = \frac{\partial^2(\ln \det(\mathbf{M}^2))}{\partial \xi^2}.\quad (16)$$

Remark that equation (9) with the boundary condition (15) is a Poisson equation. Therefore, from the Dirichlet theorem, its solution is unique. So,

$$\det(\mathbf{M}^1) = \det(\mathbf{M}^2).\quad (17)$$

Now, does the unicity of the determinant of such a matrix (13) imply the unicity of the matrix and therefore the unicity of the 3-soliton? From the asymptotic behaviour (15):

$$\text{if}\quad \det(\mathbf{M}^1) = \det(\mathbf{M}^2),$$
$$\text{then}\quad a_1^1 + a_2^1 + a_3^1 = a_1^2 + a_2^2 + a_3^2.$$

By isolating the different exponential terms in the determinant expression, different cases have to be studied. For example, $a_1^2 + a_2^2$ is equal to either $a_1^1 + a_2^1$ or $a_2^1 + a_3^1$ or $a_1^1 + a_3^1$. So the solutions a_j^2 consist of a permutation of the a_j^1. A similar result is found for the s_j^2. So, there exists a finite number of matrices $\mathbf{M}$ such that: $\det(\mathbf{M}^2) = \det(\mathbf{M}^1)$. But, it is important to notice that the greatest of the a_j^2 coincides with the greatest of a_j^1 and so on. Therefore, if $a_1^2 > a_2^2 > a_3^2$ then the following unique solution is found:

$$a_i^2 = a_i^1, \quad s_i^2 = s_i^1, \quad i = 1, 2, 3.\quad (18)$$

In other terms, if $\det(\mathbf{M}^1) = \det(\mathbf{M}^2)$ then the 3-solitons defined by $\mathbf{M}^1$ and $\mathbf{M}^2$ are the same.

3.2 Identifiability of the two-element windkessel model

Assuming that $P_s(t)$ is known, the parameters to identify are R, C, P_∞ and R_s in equation (12). Let $P_{wk}^j(t)$, $j = 1, 2$ be such that:

$$P_{wk}^1(t) = P_{wk}^2(t),\quad (19)$$

The equality of the corresponding parameters, R^j, C^j, P_∞^j and R_s^j, $j = 1, 2$ has to be shown. Applying the Laplace transform to equation (12) gives:

$$\left(s + \frac{1}{RC}\right)P_{wk}(s) - P_0 = \frac{1}{s}\frac{P_\infty}{RC} + \frac{P_s(s)}{R_s C},\quad (20)$$

then, for $j = 1, 2$, P_{wk}^j is given by:

$$P_{wk}^j(s) = \frac{sR^jC^jP_0^j + P_\infty^j}{s(1 + sR^jC^j)} + \frac{\frac{R^j}{R_s^j}P_s(s)}{1 + sR^jC^j}.\quad (21)$$

From equations (19) and (21) it can be deduced:
- For the pole 0: $P_\infty^1 = P_\infty^2$.
- For the zero at infinity :

$$P_0^1 + \frac{1}{R_s^1 C^1}\lim_{s \to \infty} P_s(s) = P_0^2 + \frac{1}{R_s^2 C^2}\lim_{s \to \infty} P_s(s).$$

As

$$P_s(0) = \lim_{s \to \infty} sP_s(s) < +\infty,$$

it follows:

$$P_0^1 = P_0^2 \quad \text{and} \quad R_s^1 C^1 = R_s^2 C^2.$$

- For the finite pole: $R^1 C^1 = R^2 C^2$.

It can be noticed that the parameters R, C and R_s are not identifiable. However $T = RC$, $T_s = R_s C$ and P_∞ are identifiable, so that it is better to write equation (12) as follows:

$$\frac{dP_{wk}}{dt}(t) + \frac{P_{wk}(t)}{T} = \frac{P_\infty}{T} + \frac{P_s(t)}{T_s}.\quad (22)$$

The parameters to identify are now T, P_∞ and T_s.

4. EXPERIMENTAL RESULTS

Some first comparisons of measured and computed ABP signals are presented. ABP has been measured at the finger with a FINAPRES. The parameters of the two parts of our model, the 3-soliton and the windkessel flow, were estimated from real data. Figures 2 and 3 illustrate the satisfactory experimental results obtained. First, the model was superposed to a single beat. Then the procedure was extended to a sequence of beats. In figure 4 the estimation error when using a 3-soliton alone is represented and is well approximated by a two-element windkessel model.

5. DISCUSSION

The different phenomena observed when the PP propagates along the arterial tree were explained in the linear theory by the existence of backward waves. For example, the "Peaking" was associated with the increase of the backward wave velocity, this wave going back earlier. The increase in the velocity results from the changes in the vessels' characteristics (the increase in stiffness and the decrease in section). However, the nonlinear superposition of forward solitons can also explain this phenomenon. Therefore, the "Peaking" can be explained by the increase in the soliton velocity which leads to the increase in its amplitude (this is one of the interesting characteristics of the solitons). The "Steepening" also can be explained by the conservation laws: the increase in the amplitude leads to a decrease in the width.

There is always some arbitrariness in choosing a function basis to represent the solution of an evolution equation, unless this basis has some special properties as in the case of eigenfunctions for a linear system. The decomposition of the PP wave into a superposition of harmonic forward and backward waves corresponds to a small amplitude, high frequency approximation of the linearized flow equations which, in this case can be reduced into a linear second order wave equation. It is also a convenient representation of functions due to Fourier analysis and calculus. This linear decomposition of waves necessitates in general between 6 and 12 components. As described before, the proposed approach, due to the choice of forward waves matched to the pressure waveform (in fact particular solutions of a reduced model of the flow) can neglect the backward waves and needs only a small number of components: 2 or 3 solitons are sufficient. An important advantage of this approach is that it leads to a reduced PP model with a small number of identifiable parameters, as was proved in the previous section.

The linear theory leads to a good local model of the PP (Westerhof *et al.*, 1972) but it can not help to solve the problem of the distal-to-proximal transfer function estimation. Remark that this interesting problem is still open (Remmen *et al.*, 2002). It gives a good description of the PP at the measurement point of the arterial tree but it doesn't allow the description of the PP in a different location because it does not take into account propagation phenomena. The nonlinear superposition of solitons constitutes a global model in time and space and it is a good candidate to tackle this problem of transfer-function estimation. This may lead to the estimation of proximal pressure (at aortic or ventricle levels) from distal one (at finger level for example) using only non-invasive measurements. This problem is the subject of current research.

Another important point concerns clinical applications. In the case of the linear decomposition, pressure and flow measurements at a same point are needed. But, it is difficult to have joint measurements of flow-rate and aortic pressure. The latter can be obtained with invasive techniques and the former from image processing. In the proposed approach, only non-invasive pressure measurements are needed to identify the model. This is potentially an important advantage. Also,

with this approach, some parameters are identified which have to be interpreted. The arterial tree is represented by the characteristics d_i, $i = 0, 1, 2$ of an equivalent unique vessel and of a windkessel model; the PP by the parameters a_j, $j = 1, 2, 3$ of a soliton. All these parameters seem to give new insight on the blood flow.

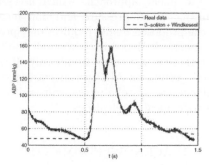

Fig. 2. Pressure at the finger: real and estimated data

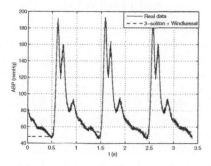

Fig. 3. Pressure at the finger: real and estimated data

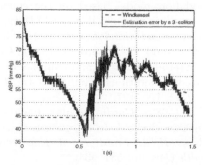

Fig. 4. The estimation error by a 3-soliton alone is well approximated by a two-element windkessel model

6. CONCLUSION

In this paper, a reduced blood pressure model is proposed. The theoretical considerations suggest that ABP can be seen as the sum of two terms: an N-soliton (with N= 2 or 3 in the present experiments) and a two-element windekessel model. The former takes into account fast wave phenomena and the latter slow phenomena. The agreement between estimated and real pressure is satisfactory. The introduction of forward solitons explains the "Peaking" and the "Steepening" phenomena. Unlike the linear approach, which necessitates simultaneous blood pressure and flow measurements, the proposed model requires only pressure measurements. It depends on a small number of parameters that are easy to identify. It seems that these results on ABP waveform analysis, in particular in the systolic phase, can lead to some interesting clinical applications.

7. ACKNOWLEDGMENTS

The authors would like to thank Y.Papelier and Hospital Beclere for providing us pressure data.

REFERENCES

Berger, D.S., J.K.J. Li, W.K. Laskey and A. Noordergraaf (1993). Repeated reflection of waves in the systemic arterial system. *The American Physiological Society* pp. 269–281.

Canic, S., D. Lamponi, A. Mikelic and J. Tambaca (2005). Self-consistent effective equations modeling blood flow in medium-to-large compliant arteries. *SIAM Multiscale Modeling and Simulation* **3**(3), 559–596.

Crépeau, E. and M. Sorine (2005). Identifiability of a reduced model of pulsatile flow in an arterial compartment. *IEEE CDC and ECC*.

Fernandez, M., V.Milisic and A. Quarteroni (2005). Analysis of a geometrical multiscale blood flow model based on the coupling of ode's and hyperbolic pde's. *SIAM Multiscale Modeling and Simulation* **4**(1), 215–236.

Frank, C.P. and L. Zhaorong (1989). Estimating arterial resistance and compliance during transient conditions in humans. *Am. J. Physiol* (257), 190–197.

Li, J.K.J. (1982). Cardiovascular diagnostic parameters derived from pressure and flow pulses. *IEEE Frontiers of Engineering in Health Care* pp. 531–534.

Li, J.K.J. (1986). Time domain resolution of forward and reflected waves in the aorta. *IEEE Transactions on Biomedical Engineering* **33**(8), 783–785.

McDonald, D.A. (1974). *Blood flow in arteries.* 2nd ed.. Edward Arnold.

Milisic, V. and A. Quarteroni (2004). Analysis of lumped parameter models for blood flow simulations and their relation with 1d models. *M2AN* **IV**, 613–632.

Monti, A., C. Medigue and M. Sorine (2002). Short-term modelling of the controlled cardivascular system. In: *ESAIM:Proceedings.* Vol. 12.

Olufsen, M. (1999). structured tree outflow condition of blood flow in larger systemic arteries. *The American Physiological Society.*

Parker, K.H. and J.H. Jones (1990). Forward and backward running waves in arteries: analysis using the method of characteristics. *ASME J. Biomech. Eng* (112), 322–326.

Pythoud, F., N. Stergiopulos and J.J. Meister (1995). Forward and backward waves in the arterial system: nonlinear separation using riemann invariants. *Technology and Health Care* **3**, 201–207.

Pythoud, F., N. Stergiopulos and J.J. Meister (1996). Separation of arterial pressure waves into their forward and backward running components. *Journal of Biomechanical Engineering* **118**, 295–301.

Quick, C.M., D.S. Berger and A. Noordergraaf (2001). Constructive and destructive addition of forward and reflected arterial pulse waves. *AJP-Heart and Circulatory Pysiology* (280), 1519–1527.

Remmen, J.J., W.R. Aengevaeren and F.W. Verheugt *et al* (2002). Finapres arterial pulse wave analysis with modelflow is not a reliable non-invasive method for assessment of cardiac output.. *Clinical Science* (103), 143–149.

Stergiopulos, N., B.E. Westerhof and N. Westerhof (1999). Total arterial inertance as the fourth element of the windkessel model. *The American Physiological Society* pp. 81–88.

Stergiopulos, N., N. Tardy and Y. Meister (1993). Nonlinear separation of forward and backward running waves in elastic conduits. *J.Biomechanics* (26), 201–209.

Walter, E. and L. Pronzato (1994). *Identification de modèles paramétriques à partir de données expérimentales.* Edition Masson.

Wang, J.J., A.B. O'Brien, N.G. Shrive, K.H. Parker and J.V. Tyberg (2002). Time-domain representation of ventricular-arterial coupling as a windkessel and wave system. *AM J Physiol Heart Circ Physiol.*

Westerhof, N., N. Stergiopulos and M.I.M. Noble (2005). *Snapshots of Hemodynamics, An Aid for Clinical Research and Graduate Education.* Springer Science.

Westerhof, N., P. Sipkema, G.C. VanDenBos and G. Elzinga (1972). Forward and backward waves in the arterial system. *Cardiovascular Research* **6**, 648–656.

Whitham, G.B. (1999). *Linear and nonlinear Waves.* J.Wiley & sons.

Yomosa, S. (1987). Solitary waves in large vessels. *Journal of the Physical Society of Japan* **50**(2), 506–520.

MULTI VARIABLE EVENT DETECTION IN INTENSIVE CARE UNITS

Sylvie Charbonnier

Laboratoire d'Automatique de Grenoble (UMR 5528 CNRS, INPG, UJF)
BP 46, 38402 St Martin d'Hères France
email : Sylvie.Charbonnier@inpg.fr

Abstract : This paper presents a methodology to automatically detect specific medical events occurring on patients from ICU high frequency physiological variables. The physiological variables are transformed into a succession of temporal episodes (trend) and residual by an adaptive trend extraction method. Event models using temporal episodes from several variables are proposed. Results obtained on 70 hours of recordings from 23 adult patients hospitalised in ICU assess the capacity of the method to recognize events. *Copyright © 2006 IFAC*

Keywords: Biomedical engineering, trends analysis, qualitative signal representation, Pattern matching

1. INTRODUCTION

In Intensive Care Units (ICU), where the medical staff has to take care of several critically ill patients, the personnel is often overwhelmed by the large amount of data collected on patients. The interpretation of this important flow of data has to be done many times a day, each time the physician visits a patient. Though the therapeutic decisions made by the physician may have serious consequences in this context of critical care, no system has been developed to assist the physician in his fastidious task of data analysis. Yet, a system able to recognize specific events occurring on a patient would lighten the physician's cognitive load. Data collected on patients are numerous because of the important number of physiological parameters monitored, but also because of the high sampling rate used to collect them. Data can be provided every second and form huge time series that must be analyzed to determine what happened to the patient since the last visit. Any system providing an automatic analysis of these data should take into account this temporal behavior.

Several propositions have been made in the literature to automatically recognize specific events on medical systems. The methods differ in the way data are processed. One solution is to perform a numeric to symbolic transformation of each signal and use the symbolic information to recognize the events. Chambrin et al (2004) estimate qualitative trends by calculating the parameters of the linear function that best fit the data on fixed sliding time windows of different lengths. The qualitative trend, increasing, decreasing or steady, is given by the value of the slope at each sample time. They add a fourth category, unsteady, when the variance of the signal is superior to a given threshold. Comparison between symbolic trends extracted from a single signal, SpO_2, using a small time window and a larger one, enables the discrimination between two specific events occurring on patients hospitalised in ICU: SpO_2 probe disconnection, true desaturation. Hunter and McIntosh (1999) used the off line bottom up segmentation algorithm developed by Keogh (1997) to extract temporal intervals from ICU physiological time series. The intervals were used to recognize artefacts associated with an O_2 probe displacement on new born infants hospitalised in neonates. Another solution is to model events through predefined trend templates. A trend template is a pre defined time-varying pattern in multiple variables associated with an event. Automatic recognition is achieved by determining on line if the monitored signals match the trend templates. Regression trend templates were used by Haimowitz, Phillip and Kohane (1995) to monitor children growth and fuzzy trend templates were used by Lowe, Harrison and Jones (1999) to conduct on line diagnosis during anaesthesia.

The aim of this paper is to present a methodology to automatically recognize specific events that may occur on a patient, through a multi variable analysis of the physiological variables usually monitored in ICU. The method consists in transforming each physiological variable into a succession of temporal episodes (called the signal trend) and into a residual signal. Temporal models using episodes and residuals are proposed to describe some specific medical events. An event is recognized when the episodes extracted from several physiological signals match the event model. A confidence indicator is provided with each event detected.

The trend is defined as a succession of contiguous and non overlapping temporal episodes describing the temporal variations of the signal. A methodology to extract the signal trend has been proposed previously (Charbonnier, 2005), which is tuned by three fixed tuning parameters. In this paper, an adaptive version of the trend extraction method is presented, that takes into account the variations affecting the physiological variables.

Ten physiological variables, monitored every second, are processed in this study: oxygen saturation rate (SpO_2), systolic, diastolic and mean blood pressures (SBP, DBP, MBP), heart rate (HR), maximal pressure in the airways (Pmax), respiratory rate (RR), expired volume (VE), maximal flow in the airways (Dmax) and minute ventilation (MV). They are used to recognize three specific events: artefacts due to a flush on an arterial catheter, change associated with a tracheal suction, patient's state change.

The outline of the paper is the following. The non adaptive version of the trend extraction methodology is briefly reminded in section 2. The adaptive version is presented in section 3. Multi variable models proposed to recognize specific events are described in section 4 and results obtained on 70 hours of recordings are presented in section 5.

2. ON LINE TREND EXTRACTION AND RESIDUAL CALCULATION

2.1. Trend extraction

The methodology developed to extract on-line the trend from an univariate time series is briefly described in this section. The trend is a succession of contiguous temporal episodes. An episode is defined by equation (1):

$$Episode = \{primitive, k_0, y_0, k_f, y_f\} \qquad (1)$$

with: k_0 the time when the episode begins, y_0 the signal value at time k_0, k_f the time when the episode ends, y_f the signal value at time k_f. Three primitives are used to describe the signal trend: *Steady, Increasing, Decreasing*. An episode corresponds to a time interval during which the property corresponding to the primitive holds. The methodology consists of four successive steps, completed on-line at each sampling time.

First step : Segmentation of the data A segmentation algorithm approximates the data by successive segments expressed by equation (2):

$$y(k)=p_i(k-k_{ai})+y_{ai} \qquad (2)$$

with k_{ai} the time when the segment begins, p_i its slope and y_{ai} the ordinate at time k_{ai}. The segments may be discontinuous. The segmentation algorithm uses the cumulative sum (CUSUM) to determine on line the moment when the linear approximation is no longer acceptable and the new linear function (2) that now best fits the data has to be calculated. The CUSUM consists in the cumulative sum of the difference between the signal $y_m(k)$ and the linear model extrapolation $y(k)$, computed at each sampling time. At time $k_{ai,1}$, the time when the CUSUM value crosses a first threshold (th_1, first tuning parameter), the corresponding signal is stored. At time $k_{ai,2}$, when the CUSUM crosses a second threshold (th_2, second tuning parameter), the algorithm calculates the data linear least squares approximation between $k_{ai,1}$ and $k_{ai,2}$. The CUSUM is then reset to zero.

The signal decomposition into line segments is mainly tuned by parameter th_2, which fixes the filtering effect. Any transient variation which change integral is lesser than th_2 is filtered. As instance, a step transient of amplitude A and duration D is filtered if the product AxD is less than th_2.

Second step : Classification At each sampling time, the shape formed by the current segment and the previous one is classified into one of 7 temporal shapes: Steady, Increasing, Decreasing, Positive or Negative Step, Increasing/Decreasing or Decreasing/Increasing Transient. This classification allows modelling signal discontinuities.
The classification is tuned by th_c, (third tuning parameter). th_c determines the amplitude above which a variation on a physiological variable is considered significant. Any variation which amplitude is less than th_c is filtered.

Third step : Episode generation The obtained shape is transformed into semi-quantitative episodes, as in equation (1) using 3 primitives: {Steady, Increasing, Decreasing}.

Fourth step: Aggregation The current episode, ending at the current time, is then aggregated, if possible, with the previous one to form the longest possible episode.

2.2. Residual Calculation

The difference between the linear approximation calculated by the segmentation algorithm, *y(k)*, and the measured signal, $y_m(k)$, can be calculated. This variable is called the residual *Res(k)* (equation(3)). It corresponds to the part of the signal that is filtered by the segmentation algorithm.

$$Res(k) = y_m(k) - y(k) \qquad (3)$$

The trend expresses the time evolution of the signal mean whereas the residual expresses the signal variations.

3. ADAPTIVE VERSION OF THE TREND EXTRACTION METHOD

In the non adaptive version, the three tuning parameters $\{th_1, th_2, th_c\}$ are fixed. Their values depend of the physiological parameter considered but are the same for every patient. The under lying assumption is that the noise corrupting the signal differs from one parameter to another, but is the same for every patient. However, in practice, this assumption may be wrong. The variance of the physiological variables may be different from one patient to the other, or may even change in time for the same patient. Indeed, the physiological signal variance may depend on the patient's physiological state (patient awake or asleep, for example) or on the care context (controlled or assisted ventilation). An adaptive version of the trend extraction method has been developed to take into account these changes on the signal variance. Tuning parameters $\{th_1, th_2, th_c\}$ are adapted on line from the estimated standard deviation of the signal (square root of the variance), under the assumption that two states are possible: one corresponding to small variations on the signal and the other corresponding to large variations. The current state can be detected from the signal standard deviation.

3.1. Estimation of the standard deviation of the signal

The standard deviation of the signal is estimated through the residual, defined in equation (3). It is a non stationary signal, of zero mean and time varying variance.

The standard deviation of the residual is estimated at each sampling time, k, on a sliding time window with equation (4).

$$m(k) = \frac{1}{N} \sum_{i=k-N}^{k} Res(i) \qquad (4)$$

$$\sigma_{res}(k) = \sqrt{\frac{1}{N-1} \sum_{i=k-N}^{k} (Res(i) - m(k))^2}$$

with *N*, the size of the sliding window, chosen equal to 60 sampling periods. This value is short enough for the stationnarity assumption to hold and long enough to result in an unbiased estimation of standard deviation.

The median of the standard deviation of the residual is calculated on a training period composed of the x latest sampling periods:

$$M_x(k) = \underset{k-x \le i \le k}{median}(\sigma_{res}(i)) . \qquad (5)$$

The use of the median instead of the mean enables to filter the increase of standard deviation due to artefacts corrupting the signal, which are common in physiological variables. x was chosen equal to 300 sampling periods. It is a compromise between the past period to take into account and the sentivity of Mx to artefacts : the shorter x, the more up to date Mx. The longer x, the less sensitive Mx to artefacts.

3.2. Tuning parameters adaptation function

Each time a new linear approximation is calculated by the segmentation algorithm (at time $k_{ai,2}$ defined in section 2), new values are assigned to the tuning parameters $\{th_1, th_2, th_c\}$ depending on the value of $Mx(k_{ai,2})$. Two sets of thresholds can be applied to the algorithm : $\{th_1, th_2, th_c\}_{high}$ when the standard deviation of the signal is high and $\{th_1, th_2, th_c\}_{low}$ when the standard deviation of the signal is low. $\{th_1, th_2, th_c\}_{high}$ correspond to the tuning values proposed in (Charbonnier, 2005). $\{th_1, th_2, th_c\}_{low}$ correspond to $\{th_1, th_2, th_c\}_{high}$ with each value divide by 2. The adaptation function is a hysteresis loop, with two commutations thresholds Com1, Com2. When the current selected set is the low one and the signal standard deviation crosses Com2, the set switches to the high set. The signal standard deviation must drop below Com1 for the current selected set to switch back to the low one. Dividing th_2 by 2 enables to segment transients which change integral is twice smaller (change integral equal to A.D, for a step change of amplitude A and duration D). Dividing th_c by 2 enables to detect changes which amplitude is twice smaller. The use of an hysteresis cycle enables to avoid frequent commutations between the two tuning sets when Mx is close to the commutation threshold.

3.3. Commutation thresholds

In this study, 10 physiological variables are used. Commutation thresholds of the hysteresis cycle (Com1, Com2) are function of the standard deviation of the signal and depend thus on the considered physiological variable. In order to avoid the multiplication of tuning parameters, they are normalised for each variable, using the distribution function of the standard deviation of each signal. Com1 is arbitrarily set to 15% of the 95th percentile of the signal standard deviation distribution and Com2 is set to 25%. The signal standard deviation distribution function was previously estimated for each of the 10 considered variables. To do so, the standard deviation of each variable was estimated at each sampling time on a sliding window of 60 sampling periods (using equation (4) with *Res* replaced by y_m) on 20 recordings from 20 different patients. It provided about 140 000 values of the estimated standard deviation for each physiological variable. A quarter of these values were then randomly selected and used to estimate the distribution functions.

The set $\{th_1, th_2, th_c\}$ is initialized to $\{th_1, th_2, th_c\}_{low}$ and kept as long as the value of Mx does not cross Com2. Once the set $\{th_1, th_2, th_c\}$ has commuted to $\{th_1, th_2, th_c\}_{high}$, it is maintained as long as the value of Mx does not go under Com1.

An illustration of the adaptive extraction trend method is presented in figure 1. SBP signal and the trend extracted is shown in the upper part of the figure, the residual and the value of Mx calculated each time a new segment is calculated is shown in the middle part, and the set of tuning parameters used by the adaptive method is shown in the lower part.

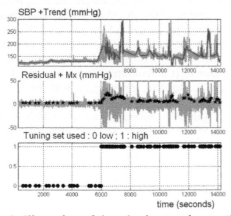

Fig. 1: Illustration of the adaptive trend extraction method

During the first part of the recording, the patient is asleep. He wakes up during the recording. A significant change in the variance of the signal, and then in the standard deviation of the residual can be observed. The tuning parameters are automatically switched from the low set values to the high set values. A small amplitude change in SBP is detected in the first part whereas changes of the same amplitude are ignored in the second part.

4. SPECIFIC EVENT MODELS

As presented in introduction, ten physiological variables, monitored every second, are processed in this study. They are used to recognize three specific events: artefact generated by a flush on an arterial catheter (named flush), changes associated with a tracheal suction (named tracheal suction), a patient's state change.

Each variable is now expressed by its trend, composed of successive temporal episodes, and the residual. In the following subsection, definitions of terms used in the event models are given.

4.1. Definitions

Episode amplitude and duration: An episode is defined on the time interval $\left[k_0..k_f\right]$ by equation (1). Its amplitude *Amp* and duration *Dur* are defined as :

$$Amp = \left| y_f - y_0 \right| \; ; \; Dur = k_f - k_0 . \tag{6}$$

Unsteady episode: Information provided by the residual is transformed into symbolic information in the following way : if the standard deviation of the residual, calculated by equation (4) is superior to the 95th percentile of the standard deviation distribution function, the residual is unsteady. Successive unsteady periods lasting more than 60 sampling periods form an unsteady episode.

Decreasing Spike: a decreasing spike is a monovariable temporal shape formed of three successive episodes : $\{steady\}\{decreasing\}\{increasing\}$ or $\{decreasing\}\{increasing\}\{steady\}$

Concomitant episodes: Two episodes defined on $\left[k_{0_1}..k_{f_1}\right]$ and $\left[k_{0_2}..k_{f_2}\right]$ are concomitant(Δ) if $k_{o_2} - \Delta \leq k_{f_1} \leq k_{f_2} + \Delta$ or $k_{o_1} - \Delta \leq k_{f_2} \leq k_{f_1} + \Delta$, with Δ in sampling periods.

4.2. Flush on the arterial catheter

An artefact generated by a flush on an arterial catheter is modelled by the following multivariate temporal shape:

[SBP{*increasing*, Amp>80mmHg}] concomitant(10) with [MBP{*increasing*, Amp>80mmHg}] or concomitant(10) with [DBP{*increasing*, Amp>80mmHg}]

It means that a flush is detected if at least two large increasing episodes are detected concomitantly on the blood pressure signals. The number of variables implicated in the detection provides a confidence index (2 or 3).

4.3. Patient's state change

A patient's state change is modelled by :

[Var1{*steady*, Dur>300s}{*increasing/decreasing*}]
concomitant(30) with
[Var2 {*steady*, Dur>300s}{*increasing/decreasing*}]

It means that a state change is detected if an increasing or decreasing episode preceded by a steady episode lasting at least 300 sampling periods is detected concomitantly on at least two variables. The number of variables implicated in the detection provides a confidence index (2 to 10).

4.4. Tracheal suction

A tracheal suction is modelled by:

[Pmax{*decreasing*, yf<threshold$_{Pmax}$} or
VE{*decreasing*, yf<threshold$_{VE}$} or
VM{*decreasing*, yf< threshold$_{VM}$ }]
concomitant(10) with
[Pmax, VE, VM, FR, Dmax {*decreasing spike*}]
or concomitant(10) with
[Pmax, VE, VM, FR, Dmax {*unsteady*}].

It means that a tracheal suction is detected if at least a drop of Pmax or VM or VE below a threshold is detected concomitantly with an unsteady episode on Pmax, VE, VM, FR or Dmax or concomitantly with a decreasing spike on Pmax, VE, VM, FR or Dmax. At least two variables must be implicated in the detection.

A confidence index is proposed by associating a cost dependent of the temporal shape to each variable implicated in the detection and by summing up the costs. Thus, a drop below a threshold counts for 2 or 3 depending on the value of the threshold, an unsteady episode counts for 1 and a decreasing spike counts for 1. The cost of each variable corresponds to the maximal cost detected for the variable. As instance, if a drop below a threshold is detected concomitantly with an unsteady episode on the same variable, the cost of the variable is the cost of the drop. The confidence index is the sum of the costs of each temporal shape on all the variables implicated in the detection. It varies between 3 and 11.

5. RESULTS ON REAL DATA

The adaptive trend extraction procedure and the event models have been applied on real data recorded every second on adult patients hospitalized in the Intensive Care Unit of Lyon-Sud Hospital. The data base is composed of 25 recordings, lasting either 2 hours or 4 hours, from 23 different patients. The data were collected during specific clinical contexts: mechanical ventilation, weaning from mechanical ventilation and ending of sedative drug administration. Data acquisition was achieved in real time, without interference from the usual daily care. During the data acquisition phase, an observer stayed at the patient's bed side and annotated all the clinical events that occurred during the recording (modification of drug therapy, of ventilator settings, nurse care …). 10 recordings were achieved when the patient was awake, either assisted by a ventilator (assisted ventilation mode) or breathed spontaneously. 15 recordings were achieved when the patient was sedated and his breathing was controlled by the ventilator (controlled ventilation mode).

The event detection method was applied off line on the whole data base. Each time an event was detected from the data (when episodes matched one of the models), time stamps of the event (beginning, end) and its confidence index were stored.

An expert made a posterior analysis of the events detected by visual inspection of the signals, taking into account the annotations made by the observer during data collection. For each recording, the 10 physiological variables were displayed with the bed side observer annotations. A zoom could be done on any part of the recording. Periods of time when an event had been recognized were spotted using different colours but the trend and residual extracted were not displayed. Each event was classified by the expert as correct (1), incorrect (2) or undetermined (2). A global inspection of the recording was then achieved to detect if some event had been missed by the automatic detection (missed event).

5.1. Flush on the arterial catheter

27 flushes on the arterial catheter were detected by the automatic system. The expert classified 26 of these events into correct and one into undetermined. 4 of the 27 flushes were detected with a confidence index equal to 2 (minimal value), the other 23 with a confidence index equal to 3 (maximal value). 3 flushes were missed by the system.

5.2. Tracheal suction

47 tracheal suctions were detected by the automatic system. The expert classified 43 of them into correct, 3 into incorrect and 1 into undetermined. Arterial suctions classified as incorrect were detected with a confidence index equal to 3 (minimal value), the undetermined with a confidence index equal to 4. 2 tracheal suctions were missed by the system.

5.3. Patient's state change

109 patient's state changes were detected by the system. The expert classified 86 of them as correct, 9 as incorrect and 14 as undetermined. No obvious state changes were missed by the system. 7 of the incorrect state changes were detected with a confidence equal to 2 (minimal value), and 2 with a confidence index equal to 3.

An illustration of the patients' state change detection is presented in figure 2 which shows 50 min of recording. Physiological variables are displayed in grey, trends in black. Two state changes were detected, spotted by thick black lines.

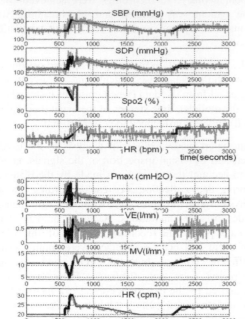

Figure 2 : SBP, SDP, Spo2, HR, Pmax, VE, MV, HR signals (grey), the corresponding trends (black lines) and the two patient's state changes (thick black lines)

6. CONCLUSION

This paper presents a methodology to automatically recognize specific events that may occur on a patient hospitalized in ICU, through a multi variable analysis of the physiological variables usually monitored in ICU. The method uses an adaptive version of the trend extraction methodology previously presented in (Charbonnier, 2005). The results obtained on 70 hours of recordings show that the event detection method works correctly. The percentage of incorrect detection is 0% for flushes (3.7% if the undetermined events are considered as incorrect), 6.4% for tracheal suctions (8% if the undetermined events are considered as incorrect) and 8% for patient's state changes (21% if the undetermined events are considered as incorrect). Percentage of missed detections is 11% for flushes, 4.6% for arterial suctions, and 0% for patient's state changes.

The performance of the method depends mainly on the accuracy of the temporal models proposed and on the ability of the adaptive trend extraction method to extract reliable information from the signals. The interesting results obtained serve thus as a validation for the adaptive trend extraction method.

A confidence index has been proposed that takes into account the number of physiological variables implicated in the event detection. In the future, these indices could be improved by using fuzzy logic. Each monovariable temporal shape that forms the inputs of the temporal models could be described with a fuzzy membership function and the global confidence index could be obtained by aggregating the fuzzy indicators. The simplification in data representation obtained by the trend extraction method could make it possible to use data mining methods to automatically build the temporal models from the data base. It will be study in the future.

In this paper, ICU physiological variables have served as an example for the event detection method. However, the method could be applied to perform diagnosis on other processes where the signature of events can be described with temporal shapes.

ACKNOWLEDGMENT

Special thanks are extended to Drs. P.Y. Carry and J.P. Perdrix from the ICU of CHU Lyon Sud, for their help in this study.

REFERENCES

Chambrin M.C., Charbonnier S., Sashar S., Becq, G., Badji L.(2004) Automatic caracterization of events on spo2 signal : a comparison of two methods 26th Annual International Conference of the IEEE Engineering in Medicine and Biology Society, September 1 – 4, San Francisco

Charbonnier S. (2005) On Line Extraction of Temporal Episodes from ICU High-Frequency Data: a visual support for signal interpretation Computer Methods and Programs in Biomedicine, 78, 115-132.

Haimowitz I., Phillip P.L., Kohane I., (1996) Managing temporal worlds for medical trend diagnosis, Artificial intelligence in medicine 8 299-321.

Hunter J., McIntosh N., (1999) Knowledge based event detection in complex time series data, AIMDM'99, Lecture Notes in Artificial Intelligence 1620 271-280,

Keogh E., (1997). A Fast and Robust Method for Pattern Matching in Time Series Databases, Proceedings of 9th International Conference on Tools with Artificial Intelligence TAI '97,

Lowe A., Harrison M., Jones R. (1999).Diagnostic monitoring in anaesthesia using fuzzy trend templates for matching temporal patterns. *Artificial Intelligence in Medicine* 16, 183-199.

KNOWLEDGE EXTRACTION ABOUT SLEEP/WAKE STAGES USING DATA DRIVEN METHODS

Lukáš Zoubek[1,2], Sylvie Charbonnier[2], Suzanne Lesecq[2], Alain Buguet[3], Florian Chapotot[4,5]

[1] *VSB-Technical University of Ostrava, Department of Measurement and Control, 17.listopadu 15/2172, Ostrava-Poruba, 708 33, Czech Republic*
[2] *Laboratoire d'Automatique de Grenoble, Ecole Nationale Supérieure d'Ingénieurs Electriciens de Grenoble, rue de la Piscine, BP 46, 38402 Saint Martin d'Hères Cedex, France*
[3] *Neurobiologie des états de vigilance, EA 3734,Université Claude-Bernard Lyon 1, Lyon, France*
[4] *Centre de Recherches du Service de Santé des Armées, 24 Avenue des Maquis du Grésivaudan, BP 87, 38702 La Tronche Cedex, France*
[5] *PhiTools - www.phitools.com, 1 rue du Général de Castelnau, Strasbourg, France*

Abstract: This paper describes the process of sleep/wake stage classification. It mainly focuses on the problem of selection of relevant features extracted from the polysomnographic recordings. Iterative features selection methods were applied on a large database composed of several night recordings from different healthy adults. The results showed that the use of relative power of EEG in five frequency bands enables to correctly classify 71% of the whole data base. The addition of features extracted from EOG enables to reach 75% of agreement with the expert classification, but no significant improvement was obtained when adding features extracted from EMG. *Copyright © 2006 IFAC*

Keywords: decision making, diagnosis, medical applications, pattern recognition, signal processing

1.INTRODUCTION

Polysomnography consists in the analysis of electroencephalogram (EEG), electromyogram (EMG) and electroocular (EOG) signals to recognize the different sleep/wake stages: wake, NREM sleep stages 1 to 4 and Paradoxical Sleep. Recognition of sleep stages from physiological signals recorded during a night sleep enables to build a hypnogram, a temporal succession of sleep/wake stages. Hypnogram is a tool used to diagnose sleep disorders, which are rather common (about 5% of

people suffer from a sleep disorder). Hypnogram is an overall representation of the sleep architecture. Until now, the analysis of a night sleep has been made visually by the physician, who scores every 20s of the recording (named epoch) into one of 6 sleep/wake stages (wake, NREM I, NREM II, NREM III, NREM IV, Paradoxical Sleep). This manual classification is a tedious and time-consuming task. Thanks to the development of computer technology, automated systems to built hypnograms have emerged, either using classical algorithms or artificial intelligence methods, such as neural networks

(Robert, *et al.*, 1998; Oropesa, *et al.*, 1999). Features used for classification are extracted from each epoch. They are obtained using signal processing techniques operating in the time domain or in the frequency domain. Studies are still in progress to improve the performance of these automatic sleep/wake classifiers. The aim of this paper is to show how data mining methods can be used to extract knowledge about sleep stages classification. Knowledge extraction is performed from a large database composed of 47 night sleep recordings from 41 healthy subjects. Feature selection methods are applied so as to determine which physiological signals are the most relevant, and to decide which techniques are the most suitable to process them, in order to perform accurate sleep/wake stage classification. EEG signal is processed in the frequency domain using Fourier Transform and Wavelet Transform. EEG, EOG and EMG signals are processed in the time domain using functions of the first moments of the signals, i.e. the standard deviation, the skewness and the kurtosis.

The outline of the paper is the following. The whole database and the features extracted are presented in the second section. Features selection methods and classifiers are described in section 3. Results obtained are presented and discussed in section 4.

2. MATERIALS

2.1 Presentation of the database

In this study, a large database of polysomnographic recordings has been used. The full database contains 47 whole night recordings from 41 healthy subjects (19 – 47 years old, 39 males and 2 females). Recordings have been made continuously during the whole night (8 hours). Four EEG channels (C3-A2, P3-A2, C4-A1, and P4-A1), one diagonal electrooculogram (EOG) and one chin electromyogram (EMG) have been registered and digitized with the sampling frequency f_s = 128 Hz. The EEG signals were measured on the scalp according to the International 10-20 EEG System of Electrodes Placement.

All the 47 polysomnographic recordings were separately and visually classified by two experts. Visual classification was performed on each epoch of the whole night sleep, according to the classical sleep stage classification manual (Rechtschaffen and Kales, 1968). Each epoch was classified into one of 5 different stages (wake, NREM I, NREM II, NREM III&IV, and Paradoxical Sleep) defined for sleep stage classification. Only the epochs classified in the same stage by both experts have been considered in this project. They represent 84% of the whole recordings and form the data base. The first line of Table 1 presents the number of epochs classified in

each sleep stage for the database. The total number of epochs is 63,254.

As it can be seen in Table 1, during a night sleep, the number of epochs classified in a stage is not the same for every stage. Stage NREM II lasts a long time, whereas stage NREM I is rather short. In this study, the database has been reduced to a smaller one where each class is composed of about the same number of epochs, so as to avoid errors in the classification results that could be induced by this difference in classes representation. The numbers of epochs classified in each sleep stage for the reduced database are presented in the second line of Table 1.

Table 1 Description of the database used in this study. Number of epochs in the sleep stages

	wake	NREM I	NREM II	NREM III&IV	REM
Full database	*5 232*	*1 989*	*32 966*	*7 701*	*15 366*
Test database	*1 914*	*1 879*	*2 206*	*1 902*	*2 099*

The database used in this study consists then of 10,000 randomly selected epochs, each classified into one of the five sleep stages by both experts. This set S of 10,000 classified epochs is then split in ten subsets $S = \{S_1, S_2,..., S_{10}\}$, each subset S_k containing 1,000 epochs, equally distributed in the five classes.

2.2 Features extracted from the physiological signals

Each epoch stored in the database consists of a 20 seconds recording of six signals (four EEG, one EOG and one EMG). During these 20 seconds, the physiological signals are assumed to be stationary. Since the signals were sampled at 128 Hz, each one of the 6 recorded time series contains 2,560 samples. Features are extracted on each epoch using the 6 signals. Features are information describing different characteristics of the signal. They are extracted using different signal processing techniques. The PRANA software was used to visualize the polysomnographic recordings and to extract the features.

EEG features
- Five features express the relative power of the EEG signal in given frequency bands. They are calculated using Fourier transformation. Total spectral power (P_{tot}) is computed in frequency band [0.5 ; 32.5] Hz.
  - $P_{rel}(EEG, \delta_{FT})$ with δ_{FT} = [0.5 ; 4.5] Hz;
  - $P_{rel}(EEG, \theta_{FT})$ with θ_{FT} = [4.5 ; 8.5] Hz;
  - $P_{rel}(EEG, \alpha_{FT})$ with α_{FT} = [8.5 ; 11.5] Hz;
  - $P_{rel}(EEG, \sigma_{FT})$ with σ_{FT} = [11.5 ; 15.5] Hz;
  - $P_{rel}(EEG, \beta_{FT})$ with β_{FT} = [15.5 ; 32.5] Hz.

- Five features characterize the wavelet coefficients generated by discrete wavelet transformation. In this study, a 4-level wavelet packet decomposition of the EEG signal has been used to construct a set of wavelet coefficients. The signal decomposition has been performed using the Daubechies3 wavelet. Only the coefficients containing frequency information about the five frequency bands:

- $\delta_{WT} = [0 \; ; 4]$ Hz;
- $\theta_{WT} = [4 \; ; 8]$ Hz;
- $\alpha_{WT} = [8 \; ; 12]$ Hz;
- $\sigma_{WT} = [12 \; ; 16]$ Hz;
- $\beta_{WT} = [16 \; ; 32]$ Hz

have been considered. The information contained in the selected arrays of wavelet coefficients is characterized by the quadratic mean value (root mean square value, RMS) of the coefficients:

$$RMS_{FB} = \sqrt{\frac{1}{m-1} \sum_{i=1}^{m} c_{FB}(i)^2} \qquad (1)$$

where m is the number of wavelet coefficients $c_{FB}(i)$ in each frequency band FB and $FB \in \{\delta_{WT}, \theta_{WT}, \alpha_{WT}, \sigma_{WT}, \beta_W\}$. The features are then expressed as relative values of RMS_{FB} computed over these five frequency bands and are labeled as $\{RMS_{rel} \, \delta, RMS_{rel} \, \theta, RMS_{rel} \, \alpha, RMS_{rel} \, \sigma, RMS_{rel} \, \beta\}$.

- Three features describe the signal in the time domain, i.e. the standard deviation, the skewness and kurtosis numbers.
The standard deviation, std_{EEG}, is defined as:

$$std_{EEG} = \left[\frac{1}{n-1} \cdot \sum_{i=1}^{n} \left(y(i) - \bar{y} \right)^2 \right]^{\frac{1}{2}} \qquad (2)$$

where n is the number of samples $y(i)$ of the measured signal y in the epoch and $\bar{y}$ represents the mean value (3) of the signal y.

$$\bar{y} = \frac{1}{n} \sum_{i=1}^{n} y(i) \qquad (3)$$

The skewness, $skew_{EEG}$, is defined as:

$$skew_{EEG} = \frac{M_3}{M_2 \sqrt{M_2}} \qquad (4)$$

with

$$M_k = \frac{1}{n} \sum_{i=1}^{n} \left(y(i) - \bar{y} \right)^k \qquad (5)$$

The kurtosis, $kurt_{EEG}$, is defined as:

$$kurt_{EEG} = \frac{M_4}{M_2 \, M_2} \qquad (6)$$

EMG and EOG features
EMG and EOG signals have only been processed in the time domain. Both signals are characterized by their standard deviation $\{std_{EMG}, std_{EOG}\}$, their skewness $\{skew_{EMG}, skew_{EOG}\}$ and their kurtosis $\{kurt_{EMG}, kurt_{EOG}\}$ as defined in equations (2) to (6).

2.3 Features transformations

In order to reduce the influence of extreme values that are often observed on physiological variables, each feature of the database was first transformed using nonlinear transformations (transformations towards normal distribution) (Becq, *et al.*, 2002). They were then normalised using z-score normalisation.
Each epoch is represented by a set of 19 features, which are summarized in Table 2.

Table 2 Set of features used in the study to characterize an epoch

$P_{rel} \, \delta$	$RMS_{rel} \, \delta$			
$P_{rel} \, \theta$	$RMS_{rel} \, \theta$	std_{EEG}	std_{EMG}	std_{EOG}
$P_{rel} \, \alpha$	$RMS_{rel} \, \alpha$	$skew_{EEG}$	$skew_{EMG}$	$skew_{EOG}$
$P_{rel} \, \sigma$	$RMS_{rel} \, \sigma$	$kurt_{EEG}$	$kurt_{EMG}$	$kurt_{EOG}$
$P_{rel} \, \beta$	$RMS_{rel} \, \beta$			
EEG signal	EEG signal	EEG signal	EMG signal	EOG signal

3. FEATURE SELECTION METHODS

In this section, the methods used to select the most relevant features are presented.
Let $f_1, f_2, ..., f_n$ be a set of n features to select. Let F be a subset of these n features and $\bar{F}$ be the subset of features that are not in F:

$$F \cup \bar{F} = \left\{ f_1, f_2, ..., f_n \right\}$$
$$F \cap \bar{F} = \varnothing$$

Let J be a criterion to be maximised and $J(F)$, the criterion J that is calculated with the features contained in the subset F. The sequential selection is an iterative technique which selects at each step i the subset F_i of features that maximises J (Eq. 8).

3.1. Sequential Forward Selection (SFS)

The method consists in increasing at each step i the number of features contained in F_{i-1} by one. Let F_{i-1} be the subset of features selected at step i-1, that maximises J. F_{i-1} contains i-1 features, which were previously selected. $\bar{F}_{i-1}$ contains the n-i+1 features still to be selected. At step i, a new feature f_i is selected out of $\bar{F}_{i-1}$ as $J(F_{i-1} \oplus f_i) = \max(J(F_{i-1} \oplus f_k)$ with $f_k \in \bar{F}_{i-1}$.
The first subset is initialised to the empty set $F_0 = \{\varnothing\}$.

3.2. Sequential Backward Selection (SBS)

It consists in decreasing at each step i the number of features contained in F_{i-1} by one. Let F_{i-1} be the subset of features selected at step i-1, that maximises J. F_{i-1} contains n-i+1 features, which were previously selected. $\bar{F}_{i-1}$ contains the i-1 features that have been rejected. At step i, a new feature fi is rejected out of F_{i-1} as $J(F_{i-1} - f_i) = \max(J(F_{i-1} - f_k))$ with $f_k \in F_{i-1}$. The first subset is initialised to the subset containing all the features. $F_0 = \{f_1, f_2, ..., f_n\}$.

3.3 Criterion

In this study, the criterion J to be maximised is a function of the percentage of epochs correctly classified by a classifier C.

As presented in section 2, the data base S has been split into 10 subsets, $S = \{S_1, S_2,..., S_{10}\}$. Each subset S_k contains 1,000 epochs, where each of the five classes to recognise are equally represented. A classifier C is trained on one subset S_k and validated on the 9 other subsets $S_{\bar{k}}$, $S_{\bar{k}} \in \bar{S}_k$, with $\bar{S}_k = S - S_k$. An accuracy function is calculated on each of the 9 subsets $S_{\bar{k}}$ as:

$$Acc(k, \bar{k}) = \frac{card\left[\left\{epoch(i) \in S_{\bar{k}} / C(epoch(i)) - E(epoch(i)) = 0\right\}\right]}{card\left[S_{\bar{k}}\right]} \quad (7)$$

where $epoch(i)$ is an epoch belonging to $S_{\bar{k}}$, $C(epoch(i))$ is the class assigned to epoch(i) by the classifier C, trained on the subset k. $E(epoch(i))$ is the class assigned by the experts to $epoch(i)$.

A circular permutation is performed on the 10 subsets S_k. The classifier is trained 10 times using the different data sets S_k. Thus, 90 values of $Acc(k, \bar{k})$ are obtained. The criterion J used to select the features is:

$$J = \frac{1}{10} \cdot \sum_{k=1}^{10}\left(\frac{1}{9} \cdot \sum_{\substack{j=1 \\ j \neq k}}^{10} Acc\ (k, j)\right) \quad (8)$$

$J(Fi)$ is the value of criterion J defined by (7) and (8) using the features contained in the feature subset F_i.

In equation (8), the term in brackets corresponds to the mean accuracy obtained on the 9 validation sets, when the classifier C is trained on one training set. J corresponds to the mean accuracy obtained on the validation sets, when the classifier C is trained 10 times with 10 different training sets. Calculating J this way ensures that the accuracy obtained is insensitive to the used training set. The standard deviation of the accuracy Acc obtained using classifier C can be computed by:

$$std\ _{Acc} = \left[\frac{1}{89}\sum_{k=1}^{10}\left(\sum_{\substack{j=1 \\ j \neq k}}^{10} (Acc\ (k, j) - J\ )^2\right)\right]^{\frac{1}{2}} \quad (9)$$

Actually, std_{Acc} is an indicator of the dispersion of the results. It can be used to determine if the results obtained using different classifiers or different features are statistically different.

3.4 Classifiers

To ensure that the results obtained are independent of the classifier used, the features selection methods have been processed with three different classifiers, each of them calculating the frontiers of each class in different ways (Dubuisson, 2001):
- two Bayes rule-based classifiers :
  - a parametric one, the quadratic classifier, where the probability density function of each class is assumed to be a multidimensional Gaussian model, the mean and covariance matrix being estimated for each class from the training set.
  - a non parametric one (no prior assumptions are made on the probability density functions), the k-nearest neighbours classifier, where the probability density function is estimated with the volume occupied by a fixed number of neighbours. We used 10 nearest neighbours.

- a multi layer perceptron (MLP), where the frontiers of each class are directly calculated from the training set. The architecture of the neural network is the same as in (Becq, et al., 2002).

4. RESULTS

The results obtained by the data mining methods are presented in this section. Only one EEG channel (C3-A2) has been used to obtain the results that are presented below. Tests have been performed using each of the four EEG channels. The results show that no EEG channel outperforms the others. The mean accuracies obtained using criterion J (Eq. 8) were not statically different, whatever the channel used.

4.1 Comparison of Fourier and Wavelet transform

In this first part, the Wavelet decomposition ability to process the EEG signal is analysed. To do so, only the features describing the frequency bands of EEG signals, using the Fourier transform or the Wavelet transform have been used to train the classifiers. The classification accuracy (8), and its standard deviation (9), obtained using only the features $\{P_{rel}\ \delta, P_{rel}\ \theta, P_{rel}\ \alpha, P_{rel}\ \sigma, P_{rel}\ \beta\}$ extracted from the Fourier transform or using only the features obtained thanks to the Wavelet transform $\{RMS_{rel}\ \delta, RMS_{rel}\ \theta, RMS_{rel}\ \alpha, RMS_{rel}\ \sigma, RMS_{rel}\ \beta\}$ are presented in Table 3.

Table 3 Classification accuracies for the initial tests – mean values and standard deviations

%	Classification accuracy	
	Fourier transform	Wavelet transform
Quadratic	69.91 ± 1.73	67.58 ± 1.34
Neural network	71.56 ± 1.46	68.85 ± 1.23
k-NN	67.83 ± 1.57	63.49 ± 1.44

The results are quite similar because the Wavelet transform performs a decomposition of the signal over different frequency bands. Nonetheless, Table 3 shows that the accuracy is higher (t-test; p = 0.01) when the relative power in the frequency bands are calculated from the Fourier transform, whatever the classifier used. The best result (71.56 ± 1.46%) is obtained by the neural network classifier.

4.2 Selection of the most relevant features

The Sequential Forward Selection (SFS) and the Sequential Backward Selection (SBS) methods have been both applied to the set of features presented in Table 2. The features corresponding to EEG signal processed by Wavelet transform (RMS_{rel} EEG) were removed from the set. The subset of features representing the relative power of EEG in the frequency bands obtained thanks to the Fourier transform was considered as a single feature (P_{rel} EEG).

The results obtained using the SFS method with the neural network classifier are shown in Fig. 1. The points show the classification accuracy (8), obtained at each step of the process, the bars express the standard deviation (9). The axis of abscissas shows the features selected at each step. The most relevant feature is the set expressing EEG relative power in frequency bands, which is able to correctly classify 71% of the epochs. The accuracy is significantly increased (t-test; p=0.01) when the kurtosis of EOG, the standard deviation of EEG and the standard deviation of EOG are added (increase from 71.56 ± 1.46% to 75.57 ± 1.80%). Adding the other features, i.e. the features extracted from EMG or the skewness numbers does not improve the classification accuracy. The optimal set of features is then $\{(P_{rel} \delta, P_{rel} \theta, P_{rel} \alpha, P_{rel} \sigma, P_{rel} \beta), kurt_{EOG}, std_{EEG}$ and $std_{EOG}\}$. The same selection of optimal features has been obtained when J is calculated using the quadratic classifier or the k nearest neighbours classifier. Adding $kurt_{EOG}$, std_{EEG} and std_{EOG} increases the global classification accuracy approximately of about 5 percents for each classifier.

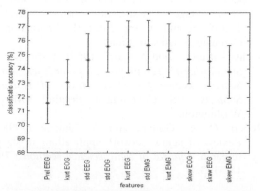

Fig. 1. Sequential forward selection performed by the neural network classifier.

When applying the SBS method, the features from the EMG, the skewness numbers of all the three signals and the kurtosis of the EEG have been detected as non relevant features (there is no decrease in the classification accuracy when these features are removed).

Table 4 presents the confusion matrix obtained when only P_{rel} EEG features are used and Table 5 presents the confusion matrix obtained when the optimal set of features is used. The columns represent the stages predicted by the classifier and the rows represent the stages determined by the physician.

Table 4 Confusion matrix – performance of neural network classifier using EEG relative power in frequency bands (P_{rel} EEG)

%	wake	NREM I	NREM II	NREM III, IV	PS
wake	**81.05**	10.16	2.30	1.77	4.72
NREM I	10.86	**45.42**	6.19	1.02	36.51
NREM II	1.66	4.56	**79.35**	11.14	3.29
NREM III, IV	0.56	0.42	9.23	**88.43**	1.36
PS	5.81	27.65	2.95	0.77	**62.82**

Table 5 Confusion matrix – performance of neural network classifier using optimal set of features

%	wake	NREM I	NREM II	NREM III, IV	PS
wake	**84.41**	7.90	2.16	1.28	4.25
NREM I	9.58	**55.22**	7.20	1.65	26.35
NREM II	1.63	4.21	**82.77**	8.96	2.43
NREM III, IV	1.18	0.27	8.69	**89.74**	0.12
PS	6.64	24.09	3.38	0.71	**65.18**

Wake, NREM II and NREM III&IV are correctly classified using EEG relative power spectra, whereas NREM I and PS are more difficult to distinguish. Adding the kurtosis of EOG, the standard deviation of EEG and the standard deviation of EOG improves significantly NREM I accuracy and slightly wake, NREM II and PS accuracies. Classification of epochs into the stage NREM III&IV is not improved by the new features.

The analysis of the confusion matrix at each step of the selection, using SFS, shows that the stage NREM I accuracy is especially improved by $kurt_{EOG}$. This feature helps to distinguish stages NREM I and Paradoxical Sleep, which are hardly distinguishable by the EEG signal analyzed in the frequency domain. The parameter std_{EEG} improves the wake and PS stage accuracies.

5. DISCUSSION

The use of data mining methods enables to extract knowledge from the available database. The methods have been implemented so as to ensure that the results obtained were insensitive to the classification method used or to the chosen training set.

Data have been selected so that each class was equally represented in the database. The classification accuracy J is then a fair compromise between each class. The selection of features does not favor one class to another one. The large amount of data used in this study, coming from a large number of healthy adults, ensures that the results are not specific to one subject and that they could be extrapolated to new subjects. These methods are data driven. No prior knowledge is introduced in the decision process. Results can then be confronted to a neurophysiologist's point of view.

Results have shown that the EEG relative power spectrum is the most discriminant feature to classify sleep stages, which is common knowledge among neurophysiologists. It seems that the Fourier transform is sufficient to extract relevant spectral information from EEG. Processing the signal with the Wavelet transform does not improve the classification results.

The skewness number of any of the three physiological signals is irrelevant to discern the sleep stages. The reason for this could come from the shape of the physiological signals. The skewness characterizes the degree of asymmetry of a distribution around its mean value. Most often, the measured physiological signals are symmetric during whole night. The occasional signal asymmetries are not significant and not specific of any sleep stage, which explains why skewness was rejected by both selection features methods. On the contrary, the kurtosis number of the signals seems to be relevant. The kurtosis is a measure of whether the distribution is peaked or flat relative to the normal distribution. The kurtosis of the signal measures the presence of irregular values, such as transitory sharp variations in the signal. These sharp variations of the EOG signals occur during stage NREM I. The standard deviation extracts different information from the signals. It measures the level of variations of the signal around its mean value. Std_{EEG} measures the level of electrical brain activity, which is larger during wake. Std_{EOG} measures the level of eyes movements.

The feature selection methods show that the EMG signal is not relevant to classify sleep stages. Features using EMG signal were selected neither by SFS nor by SBS. Moreover, no class accuracy was improved by adding EMG features. This result surprised the neurophysiologist that classifies sleep stages who thought he used EMG to discriminate between NREM1 and PS. One explanation could be that the EMG signal is artefacted which causes the automatic classification to make errors. Improvement in the classification could be obtained by preprocessing the EMG so as to automatically detect artefacts.

6. CONCLUSION

In this paper, data mining methods have been applied on a large database in order to select the most relevant features for sleep stage classification. Methods were processed so as to be insensitive to the implemented classifiers, and to the training set used. The results show that appropriate selection of the features improves the classification of sleep stages. The relative power spectrum of EEG, computed over different frequency bands, enables to correctly classify about 71% of the sleep stages. Adding the standard deviation of EOG, the standard deviation of EEG and the kurtosis of EOG improves the classification accuracy by about 4%. Information extracted from the EMG signal appears to be irrelevant for sleep stage classification, but this may due to the artefacts affecting this signal.

Future work could be oriented on the extraction of new features from the polysomnographical signals to improve discrimination between stages NREM I and Paradoxical Sleep. Indeed, the classification accuracy of these two stages is lower compared to the other sleep stages. EMG could also be introduced in the decision system, separately from the other signals.

7. ACKNOWLEDGEMENT

Special thanks are expressed to the PhiTools (Strasbourg, France) for lending the PRANA software and the sleep recording database.

REFERENCES

Becq, G., S. Charbonnier, F. Chapotot, A. Buguet, L. Bourdon and P. Baconnier (2002). Comparison between five classifiers for automatic scoring of human sleep recordings. In: *Proceedings of the 1ˢᵗ international conference on fuzzy systems and knowledge discovery* (Lipo Wang, Saman Halgamunge and Xin Yao), Singapore

Dubuisson, B. (2001). *Diagnostic, intelligence artificielle et reconnaissance de formes*. Hermès science Europe, Paris.

Oropesa, E., H. L. Cycon and M. Jobert (1999). Sleep Stage Classification using Wavelet Transform and Neural Network. International Computer Science Institute.

Rechtschaffen, A. and A. Kales (1969). *A Manual of Standardized Terminology, Techniques and Scoring System for Sleep Stages of Human Subjects*. US Government Printing Office, Washington.

Robert, C., C. Guilpin and A. Limoge (1998). Review of neural network applications in sleep research. *Journal of Neuroscience Methods*, **79**, 187-193.

ISOMETRIC MUSCLE CONTRACTION INDUCED BY REPETITIVE PERIPHERAL MAGNETIC STIMULATION [1]

Bernhard Angerer * **Michael Bernhardt** ** **Martin Buss** **
Dierk Schröder * **Albrecht Struppler** ***

* *Institute for Electrical Drive Systems, Technische Universität München, Germany, www.eat.ei.tum.de*
** *Institute of Automatic Control Engineering, Technische Universität München, Germany, www.lsr.ei.tum.de*
*** *Sensorimotor Research Group, Klinikum rechts der Isar, München, Germany, www.netstim.de*

Abstract: Repetitive peripheral magnetic stimulation (*RPMS*) is an innovative approach in treatment of central paresis, e.g. after stroke, by inducing muscle contractions and relaxations. The therapeutic effect can be increased by a closed loop control to induce coordinated movements in the forearm and the fingers. An appropriate model of muscle contractions induced by *RPMS* provides the basis for the controler design. In the presented paper a model based on a Hammerstein–structure for the contraction of the biceps brachii will be established. This model also builds the basis for a nonlinear system identification which is used to individualize the model to a single subject. *Copyright © 2006 IFAC*

Keywords: Magnetic stimulation, muscle contraction model, parameter identification

1. INTRODUCTION

A central paresis of the arm and/or hand, e.g. after stroke, reduces the quality of life dramatically. Nevertheless, studies on large clinical cohorts, using standard therapeutic methods, showed that approximately 45 % of patients with completed stroke have persistent hemiparesis [Gresham and Stanson 1998]. This data indicates the importance of innovativ approaches in rehabilitation of central paresis.

Cortical reorganization probably forms the basis of relearning lost motor functions. Morphological and functional investigations due to central paresis revealed that the sensorimotor cortex retains a great capability to adapt to altered afferent input [Ziemann *et al.* 1998]. The adaptation to changes in input or output can occur quickly, first only as a functional modulation

[Classen *et al.* 1998], later as a lasting reorganization [Nicolelis *et al.* 1998]. Therefore the integrity of both the executive motor structures and the afferent sensory loop for motor recovery is important.

In order to activate a beneficial reorganization process, the lost (reduced) proprioceptive input should be compensated. Currently physiotherapy aims to achieve such a compensation through externally applied movements. When the lost movements are induced by muscle stimulation, the proprioceptive input is much higher and corresponds closer to the lost voluntary action patterns which increases the therapeutic effectiveness [Struppler *et al.* 2003]. In this context the functional electrical stimulation (fES) is a well–known method for muscle stimulation. However, the fES not only activates somatosensory nerve fibers, also cutaneous receptors are activated which causes pain. Therefore the usability of fES for rehabilitation purposes is limited [Conforto *et al.* 2002, e.g.].

[1] supported by "Deutsche Forschungsgemeinschaft"

As a new, deeper penetrating, focused and painless stimulation method repetitive peripheral magnetic stimulation (*RPMS*) is used. As depicted in fig. 1 the proprioceptive inflow to the CNS is elicited by magnetic field impulses in two ways: a direct part by the depolarization of the terminal sensory nerve branches and an indirect part by the depolarization of the terminal motor nerve branches and a physiological activation of the muscle-length receptors.

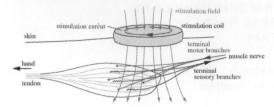

Fig. 1. Schematic of the *RPMS* application

The repetitive applied field impulses are sinusoidal half-waves with a fixed duration of $100\,\mu$s and a variable amplitude called stimulation intensity. The maximum stimulation intensity of 100 % corresponds to a magnetic flux density of approx. $2.0\,$T. The field impulses are generated by a self-built stimulation device [Schmid *et al.* 1993].

The therapeutic concept of *RPMS* is the activation of a reorganization processes by inducing a proprioceptive input to the CNS physiologically corresponding to the lost input during active movements [Struppler *et al.* 1996, e.g.]. In clinical experimental studies [see Struppler *et al.* 2004] on spasticity, cognitive functions, cerebral activation, stiffness around the elbow joint and goal-directed motor performances it could be shown, that the sensorimotor dysfunctions due to brain lesions can be remarkably improved by *RPMS*.

In this paper a model for the isometric muscle contraction of the biceps brachii based on experimental data will be presented. Since this is a qualitative model which does not encounter individual parameters like muscle fatigue, a nonlinear system identification presented in [Angerer *et al.* 2004] will be used to adapt the model to a single subject. This is illustrated by the identification results for two different subjects and a parallel stimulation of the biceps and the triceps brachii.

2. ISOMETRIC CONTRACTION MODEL

The muscle contraction behavior has already been investigated with functional electrical stimulation (fES) (overview in [Veltink *et al.* 1992]). Since compared to *RPMS* there are fundamental differences in pulse shape and pulse propagation also the muscle response induced by fES might differ from that induced by *RPMS*. The modelling approach introduced in the following sections will describe the nonlinear control path and its structure qualitative on one hand, and on

the other hand the necessary adaptation of the main parameters to a individual patient will be taken into account.

In the following the force generated by a muscle stimulated with magnetic pulses under isometric conditions (no movement in the elbow joint, see fig. 2) will be modelled. According to the approaches used with fES the dynamic behavior (activation dynamics) as well as static behavior (recruitment characteristics) will be analyzed. In order to investigate on the contraction dynamics an experimental setup as depicted in fig. 2 is used. A stimulation coil is placed above the innervation area of the biceps brachii muscle, and the force resulting from stimulation is measured with a force sensor attached to the subject's wrist. In order to compare *RPMS* with fES, all experiments concerning the activation dynamics have been accomplished with electrical stimulation as well.

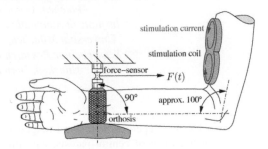

Fig. 2. Experimental setup

2.1 Activation dynamics

As a first parameter the latency T_l between the peripheral stimulus and the mechanical muscle response is considered. In [Popovic and Jaukovic 2000] the typical latencies of electrical stimulation are $T_l = 20 - 50$ ms. In order to determine the latency for *RPMS* the force response to a single magnetic pulse as shown in fig. 3 is considered. The raw force signal F_{raw} shows an artefact due to the strong magnetic pulse. The maximum of this artefact is taken to determine the particular time of stimulation. The time derivative $\dot{F}$ is obtained by numerical differentiation of the filtered signal F (moving average filter without phase shift). The latency in fig. 3 is $T_l = 1.75$ ms. In order to determine the average latency $\overline{T}_l$, 3698 data sets of 8 healthy subjects (aged from 20 to 32 yrs) with different stimulation intensities and pulse widths have been evaluated. The result is summarized in tab. 1. A dependency of T_l on the stimulation intensity or the stimulation pulse width could not be shown.

Table 1. Latency T_l and its mean value over all subjects, and standard deviation $\overline{s}_{T_l}$

	electr. stim.	magnetic stim.
T_l in ms	20.83 - 28.24	2.52 - 3.85
mean value $\overline{T}_l$ in ms	24.4	3.45
s_{T_l} in ms	3.05	0.93

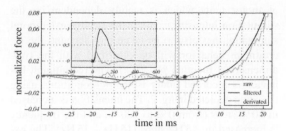

Fig. 3. Typical force responce due to a single magnetic stimuli (small window: entire force response)

Secondly the dynamics of the muscle twitch caused by a single peripheral stimulus (see fig. 3) is analyzed. In fES related work [Veltink *et al.* 1992, e.g.] the dynamics are mostly modelled as a second order transfer function with two identical real poles at $-1/T_a$. Hence the transfer function is

$$G'_a = K\frac{1}{(1+sT_a)^2} \quad . \tag{1}$$

For a more appropriate modelling in [Havel 2002] a third order transfer function with three identical real poles has been proposed. Since there is no oscillation in the muscle twitch (fig. 3), the poles have to be real. In the following a transfer function of nth order and its time-domain equation will be considered:

$$K\frac{1}{(1+sT_a)^n} \quad \bullet\!\!-\!\!\circ \quad \frac{K}{T_a^n(n-1)!}t^{n-1}e^{\frac{-t}{T_a}} \tag{2}$$

By calculating the gain K so that the peak value of the time domain eq. (2) is 1, and with the time discretisation $t = kT_s$ follows the modelled force response

$$y_a(T_a)[k] = \frac{(kT_s)^{n-1}e^{-(kT_s)/T_a}}{((n-1)T_a)(n-1)e^{-(n-1)}} \quad . \tag{3}$$

Thus, $y_a[k]$ can be compared with the normalized force response $F[k]/\hat{F}$, whereas $\hat{F}$ is the respective peak value. In order to evaluate the approximation of eq. (3), the quadratic error

$$E(T_a) = \sum_{k=0}^{N}\left(\frac{F[k]}{\hat{F}} - y_a(T_a)[k]\right)^2 \tag{4}$$

is defined, whereas N is the length of the truncated force response. The optimal time constant $T_{a,\text{opt}}$ is computed by minimizing the quadratic error $E(T_a)$ with a recursive search algorithm. 3143 data sets have been evaluated. First it could be shown that neither with fES nor with *RPMS* the pulse width of the applied stimuli has any significant effect on T_a, which is not explicitly explained in this paper. Fig. 4 shows the minimized quadratic errors E_{min} dependent on the normalized peak value $\hat{F}/\hat{F}_{\text{max}}$, whereas $\hat{F}_{\text{max}}$ is the peak value of the force response generated with a maximum stimulation intensity.

From fig. 4 it can be seen that a transfer function with identical real poles models the muscle twitch generated by *RPMS* better than the muscle twitch generated by fES. In both cases the 4th order transfer function doesn't yield significant improvement compared to

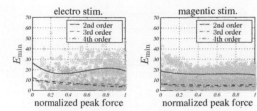

Fig. 4. Minimized quadratic errors E_{min} dependent on the normalized peak value $\hat{F}/\hat{F}_{\text{max}}$

the 3rd order model. The average time constants are $\overline{T}_{a,\text{opt}} = 36,62$ ms for fES and $\overline{T}_{a,\text{opt}} = 38,35$ ms for *RPMS*. Setting $n = 3$ in eq. (3) and transforming it into Laplace domain and considering the latency T_l the transfer function

$$G_a(s) = G'_a(s)e^{-sT_l} = \frac{T_{a,\text{opt}}}{2e^{-2}}\frac{1}{(1+sT_{a,\text{opt}})^3}e^{-sT_l} \tag{5}$$

is obtained, to describe the activation dynamics of single muscle twitch. In order to analyze the dispersion of the parameter T_a between the individual subjects, data with 12 additional subjects has been recorded. 2984 data sets of in total 20 subjects (aged from 20 to 35 yrs) have been evaluated. The average time constant $\overline{T}_a$ and its standard deviation $s_{T_{a,\text{opt}}}$ have been calculated. The results are summarized in tab. 2.

Table 2. Average time constant $\overline{T}_a$ with standard deviation $s_{T_{a,\text{opt}}}$

	electr. stim.	magnetic stim.
$\overline{T}_a$ in ms	22.58 - 53.22	26.71 - 49.81
$s_{T_{a,\text{opt}}}$ in ms	1.04 - 5.21	0.99 - 5.88

From this table it can be seen, that T_a varies a lot between the individual subjects, but the standard deviations of the particular subjects are small. Also there is a strong dependency of T_a to the peak value of the generated force. These results have to be taken into consideration, when the parameters of the model and the controller are adapted to the individual patient. The average time constant is $T_{a,\text{opt}} = 38.4$ ms.

As the third step the derived model for single muscle twitches is enhanced for repetitive stimulation. By increasing the stimulation frequency the individual force responses begin to merge which results in a partial or complete tetanus. This effect is called temporal summation. The pulse rate f_{rep} is for discrete realization expressed as the number of samples between two stimuli and is calculated as $k_{\text{rep}} = f_s/f_{\text{rep}}$ whereas f_s is the sample rate of the discrete implementation. Based on eq. (3) the temporal summation can be written as

$$y_{a,\text{rep}}[k] = \sum_{i=0}^{\infty}y_a[k - ik_{\text{rep}}] \quad . \tag{6}$$

Fig. 5 illustrates the principle of temporal summation. It can be seen that in steady state, the superposition has a periodic and a constant part. After applying some algebra it can be shown that the constant part $\hat{y}_{a,\text{rep}}$ can be calculated as

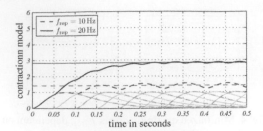

Fig. 5. Principle of temporal summation

$$\hat{y}_{a,\mathrm{rep}} = \frac{1}{k_{\mathrm{rep}}} \sum_{k=0}^{f_s/1\mathrm{Hz}} y_a[k] \ , \qquad (7)$$

whereas it is assumed that a muscle twitch is decayed after 1 s or $k = f_s/1\mathrm{Hz}$ samples. Fig. 6 shows the force response of isometric muscle contractions with different stimulation intensities. It can be seen, that

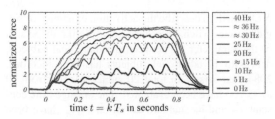

Fig. 6. Measured force response induced by *RPMS* dependent on the repetition rate f_{rep}

the constant values in steady state differ from those in fig. 5 despite normalization with respect to the maximum peak value $\hat{F}_{max}$ measured at the muscle twitch of a single stimulus. This is due to the so called nonlinear pulse rate dependent temporal summation. To simplify the model structure this nonlinearity will be taken into account by modelling the nonlinear recruitment behavior in the subsequent section. For further analysis this nonlinearity will be compensated by normalizing the recorded muscle forces with respect to their respective constant values $\hat{y}_{a,\mathrm{rep}}$. Fig. 7 shows that the average muscle contraction can be modelled very well with a reference function that has the average time constant $\overline{T}_{a,\mathrm{opt}} = 38.44\,\mathrm{ms}$.

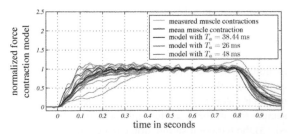

Fig. 7. Isometric muscle contraction induced by *RPMS* with $f_{\mathrm{rep}} = 20\,\mathrm{Hz}$

2.2 Recruitment behavior

As mentioned in the introduction of section 2 the recruitment behavior describes the spatial summation

of motor units which is mainly dependent on the stimulation intensity u. Since the nonlinear temporal summation has also to be taken into account, the recruitment behavior will be described with the two-dimensional function $p(u, f_{\mathrm{rep}})$. The recruitment behavior is recorded under isometric conditions using the setup depicted in fig. 2. The intensity u is increased in 20 % steps (from 0 % to 100 %) and the frequency is increased in 2.5 Hz steps (15 Hz – 35 Hz). The experiment has been made with seven healthy subjects so that in total 882 data sets have been evaluated. This data indicates, that a frequency of 20 Hz is the best tradeoff between force generation and coil heating. As can be seen in fig. 8, the relative recruitment p is obtained by normalizing the measured steady state forces F_{ss} with respect to the forces $F_{ss,\mathrm{max}}$ measured at maximum stimulation intensity at a stimulation frequency of $f_{\mathrm{rep}} = 20\,\mathrm{Hz}$.

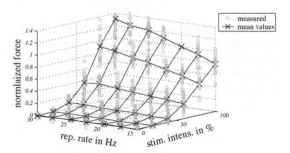

Fig. 8. Measured recruitment behaviour

Assuming that p_u and p_f are independent, the relative recruitment field can be calculated as

$$p(u, f_{\mathrm{rep}}) = p_u(u)p_f(f_{\mathrm{rep}}) \qquad (8)$$

where p_u describes the recruitment dependent on the stimulation intensity and p_f describes the component dependent on the repetition rate.

In order to analytically describe the nonlinearity the formula (proposed in [Riener 1997])

$$p_u(u) = \beta_1((u - u_{thr}) \arctan(\alpha_{thr}(u - u_{thr})) - (u - u_{sat}) \arctan(\alpha_{sat}(u - u_s at)) + \beta_2) \qquad (9)$$

is used.

Similar to p_u the dependency of the recruitment behavior on the stimulation frequency has been determined with the same normalization. The formula

$$p_f(f_{\mathrm{rep}}) = \delta_1(f_{\mathrm{rep}} - (f_{\mathrm{rep}} - f_{sat}) \cdot \\ \cdot (1/\pi \arctan(\gamma_{sat}(f_{\mathrm{rep}} - f_{sat})) + 0.5)) + \delta_2 \qquad (10)$$

approximates the average nonlinear recruitment $p_{\mathrm{rec},f}$.

The manually adapted parameters of eq. (9) and eq.(10) are summarized in tab. 3 and the normalized recruitment field is shown in fig. 9.

In order to obtain the absolute stationary value of the generated muscle force, $p(u, f_{\mathrm{rep}})$ has to be multiplied with the force $F_{ss,max}$ recorded at maximum intensity

Table 3. Parameters of eq. (9) und eq. (10) to approximate the average relative recruitment of *RPMS*

	u_{thr}	u_{sat} f_{sat}	α_{thr}	α_{sat} γ_{sat}	β_1 δ_1	β_2 δ_2
p_u	48%	98%	5	4	0.738	0.539
p_f	—	25 Hz	—	0.05	0.0597	-0.321

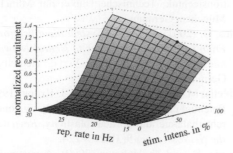

Fig. 9. Modeled recruitment behaviour

u and at a stimulation frequency of $f_{\text{rep}} = 20$ Hz (marked reference point in fig. 9):

$$F_{ss}(u, f_{\text{rep}}) = F_{ss,\max}\, p(u, f_{\text{rep}}) \qquad (11)$$

2.3 Complete isometric contraction model

In order to obtain a complete model of the muscle contraction with *RPMS* the components of section 2.1 and 2.2 are integrated in a common model. Since the recruitment represents the number of recruited motor units, and the activation dynamics model the time response of the twitch of the respective motor units it seems appropriate to choose the order of the models as depicted in fig. 10. This Hammerstein-structure is also assumed for fES related models.

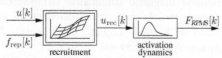

Fig. 10. Model of the induced muscle contraction in hammerstein-structure

When eq. (6) and eq. (11) are combined in order to calculate the generated force F_{RPMS} one has to consider, that the model of the activation dynamics as well as the recruitment model contain the stationary value of the linear temporal summation $\hat{y}_{a,\text{rep}}$. Since the activation dynamics are modelled as a LTI-system, the dependency of $\hat{y}_{a,\text{rep}}$ on the stimulation frequency f_{rep} can be described as

$$\hat{y}_{a,\text{rep}}(f_{\text{rep}}) = \hat{y}_{a,\text{rep},20\text{Hz}}\, \frac{f_{\text{rep}}}{20\text{Hz}}\ , \qquad (12)$$

where $\hat{y}_{a,\text{rep},20\text{Hz}}$ is the reference value at a stimulation frequency of 20 Hz. Thus the signal $u_{rec}(u, f_{\text{rep}})[k]$ can be calculated as

$$u_{rec}(u, f_{\text{rep}})[k] = \frac{F_{ss,\max}}{\hat{y}_{a,\text{rep},20\text{Hz}}}\, \frac{p_{rec}(u[k], f_{\text{rep}}[k])}{f_{\text{rep}[k]}/20\text{Hz}}\ . \qquad (13)$$

3. SYSTEM IDENTIFICATION

The used approach for the nonlinear systemidentification is based on a normalized radial basis function network (NRBF, [Broomhead and Lowe 1988]) and a truncated convolution sum. To reduce the number of unknown parameters orthonormal basis functions (OBF) [Nelles 2001] are used. The theory and the capabilities of this approach in conjunction with *RPMS* are described in [Angerer *et al.* 2004].

To describe the system identification the OBF $\mathbf{R} \in \mathbb{R}^{m_r \times m}$ are defined by

$$r_{ji} = \frac{1}{\sqrt{m/2}}\, \sin\left(j\,\pi\,\left(1 - \exp\left(-i^{-0.5}/\varsigma\right)\right)\right) \quad (14)$$

$$\forall\, j = 1 \ldots m_r \qquad \text{and} \qquad \forall\, i = 1 \ldots m$$

with the length m of the truncated convolution sum, the number m_R of OBF and a form factor $\zeta \in \mathbb{R}$. These functions are orthonormalized by a Cholesky decomposition according to $\tilde{\mathbf{R}} = (\mathbf{C}^T)^{-1} \mathbf{R}$ with $\mathbf{C}^T \mathbf{C} = \mathbf{R}\mathbf{R}^T$ and $\tilde{\mathbf{R}} \in \mathbb{R}^{m_r \times m}$.

The NRBF is defined by its activation functions:

$$\mathcal{A}_l = \frac{\mathcal{E}_l}{\sum_{j=1}^{p} \mathcal{E}_j} \text{ with } \mathcal{E}_l = \exp\left(-\frac{(u - \chi_l)^2}{2\,\sigma^2}\right) \quad (15)$$

where $\chi_l \in \mathbb{R}$ are the centers and $\sigma \in \mathbb{R}^+$ is a smoothing parameter.

If these definitions are included in a truncated convolution sum, the estimated system can be written as

$$\hat{y}[k] = \left[\mathcal{A}_1^T[k]\, \tilde{\mathbf{R}}^T \ldots \mathcal{A}_q^T[k]\, \tilde{\mathbf{R}}^T\right] \cdot \hat{\Theta}[k] \qquad (16)$$

This approach requires no model or system feedback, respectively. The output signal of the model is only used to calculate the cost function

$$E = \frac{1}{2N} \sum_{k=1}^{N} (y[k] - \hat{y}[k])^2 \qquad (17)$$

which is minimized by a recursive least squares [Nelles 2001, e.g.] algorithm in order to obtain the optimal parameter set $\hat{\Theta}$.

The identification approach is used to determine the unknown parameters $\hat{\Theta}$ to describe the isometric muscle contraction for a single subject. Therefore the setup depicted in fig. 2 is used with a second stimulation coil, placed above the innervation area of the triceps brachii. The biceps and the triceps are stimulated over 30 seconds with a randomized stimulation intensity and a repetition rate of 20 Hz. The identification approach is configured with 96 parameters and the model described above is used to determine the initial parameters $\hat{\Theta}[0]$. In fig. 11 and 12 the identification results are depicted as recruitment behavior and activation dynamics of the biceps and the triceps. As can be seen in these figures the determined contraction model matches the presented model whereas the possible range of the different charachteristics has to be taken into account.

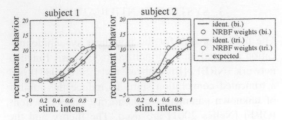

Fig. 11. Identification results: recruitment behavior

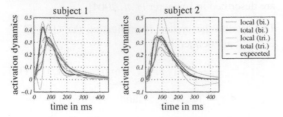

Fig. 12. Identification results: activation dynamics

4. CONCLUSIONS AND FUTURE WORK

The presented experiments and the identification process indicates that the developed model is very usefull as description for nonlinear control path in order to induce forearm (and finger) movements by *RPMS*. However, the different model parameters (recruitment behavior and activation dynamics) have to be adapted for a single subject. To avoid time-consuming experiments as described in section 2, the proposed identification process can be used to determine the model parameters for a single subject. The presented model and the system identification have to be expanded for non-isometric conditions in further studies.

REFERENCES

Angerer, B. T., D. Schröder and A. Struppler (2004). Nonlinear system identification of muscle contractions induced by repetitive peripheral magnetic stimulation. In: *NOLCOS 2004 — Stuttgart Symposium on Nonlinear Control Systems, Preprints Volume 2.* IFAC. VDI/VDE. pp. 696–674.

Broomhead, D. S. and D. Lowe (1988). Multivariable functional interpolation and adaptive networks. *Complex Systems* **2**(3), 321–355.

Classen, J., J. Liepert, S. P. Wise, M. Hallett and L. G. Cohen (1998). Rapid plasticity of human cortical movement representation induced by practice. *Journal of Neurophysiology* **79**(2), 1117–1123.

Conforto, A. B., A. Kaelin-Lang and L. G. Cohen (2002). Increase in hand muscle strength of stroke patients after somatosensory stimulation. *Annals of Neurology* **51**(1), 122–125.

Gresham, G. E. and W. B. Stanson (1998). Stroke therapy: Rehabilitation of the stroke survivor. In: *Stroke — Pathophysiology, Diagnosis and Management* (H. J. M. Barnett, J. P. Mohr,

B. Stein and F. M. Yatsu, Eds.). 3rd ed.. Chap. V, pp. 1389–1401. Churchill Livingstone. New York, New York (USA).

Havel, P. M. (2002). Geregelte Induktion von Reich- und Greifbewegungen am Menschen mittels repetitiver peripherer Magnetstimulation. Dissertation. Fakultät für Elektro- und Informationstechnik, Technische Universität München. München, Germany.

Nelles, O. (2001). *Nonlinear System Identification — From Classical Approaches to Neural Networks and Fuzzy Models.* Springer–Verlag. Heidelberg, Germany.

Nicolelis, M. A. L., D. Katz and D. J. Krupa (1998). Potential circuit mechanisms underlying concurrent thalamic and cortical plasticity. *Reviews in the Neurosciences* **9**(3), 213–224.

Popovic, D. and N. Jaukovic (2000). A customized model for control of movement with neuroprostheses. In: *6th Internet World Congress for Biomedical Sciences.* INABIS. http://www.uclm.es/inabis2000/symposia/pdf/s063.pdf (Jun. 2. 2005).

Riener, R. (1997). Neuropysiologische und biomechanische Modellierung zur Entwicklung geregelter Neuroprothesen. Dissertation. Fakultät für Elektro- und Informationstechnik, Technische Universität München. München, Germany.

Schmid, M., T. Weyh and B.-U. Meyer (1993). Entwicklung, Optimierung und Erprobung neuer Geräte für die magnetomotorische Stimulation von Nervenfasern. *Biomedizinische Technik* **38**(12), 317–324.

Struppler, A., B. T. Angerer, C. Gündisch and P. M. Havel (2004). Modulatory effect of repetitive peripheral magnetic stimulation (RPMS) on the skeletal muscle tone (stabilization of the elbow joint) on healthy subjects. *Experimental Brain Research* **157**(1), 59–66.

Struppler, A., C. Jakob, P. Müller-Barna, M. Schmid, H.-W. Lorenzen, M. Prosiegel and M. Paulig (1996). Eine neue Methode zur Frührehabilitation zentralbedingter Lähmungen von Arm und Hand mittels Magnetstimulation. *Zeitschrift für EEG und EMG* **27**, 151–157.

Struppler, A., P. M. Havel and P. Müller-Barna (2003). Facilitation of skilled finger movements by repetitive peripheral magnetic stimulation (RPMS) — A new approach in central paresis. *NeuroRehabilitation* **18**(1), 69–82.

Veltink, P. H., H. J. Chizeck, P. E. Crago and A. El-Bialy (1992). Nonlinear joint angle control for artificially stimulated muscle. *IEEE Transactions on Biomedical Engineering* **39**(4), 368–380.

Ziemann, U., B. Corwell and L. G. Cohen (1998). Modulation of plasticity in human motor cortex after forearm ischemic nerve block. *Journal of Neuroscience* **18**(3), 1115–1123.

ELSEVIER
IFAC
PUBLICATIONS

NEEDLE INSERTIONS MODELLING :
IDENTIFIABILITY AND LIMITATIONS

L. Barbé, B. Bayle, M. de Mathelin* A. Gangi**

* LSIIT, UMR CNRS 7005
Bld Sébastien Brant, F-67400, Illkirch, France
barbe,bernard,demath@eavr.u-strasbg.fr
** *Radiology Dept. B*
University Hospitals of Strasbourg
67091 Strasbourg, France

Abstract: Soft tissues modeling is a very present preoccupation in different scientific fields, from computer simulation to biomechanics or medical robotics. In this article, we consider the interaction of a needle with living tissues, which is a particularly complex modeling problem since it is characterized by inhomogeneity and nonlinearity properties. We propose a robust method to online estimate the interaction between living tissues and a surgical needle. The ability to obtain physically consistent models during *in vivo* insertions is discussed. *Copyright* © *2006 IFAC*

Keywords: soft tissue modeling, online robust estimation, *in vivo* needle insertion.

1. INTRODUCTION

Interventional radiology is a developing medical field in which specialists use medical imaging techniques (CT-scan, C-arms, Ultrasound) to insert surgical needles, in order to reach internal organs. It allows to achieve minimally invasive local treatments, from simple biopsies to cancer treatments, as stated in (Rhim *et al.*, 2001). Unfortunately, this procedure has two main drawbacks. Firstly, it is difficult to precisely place the needle tip in the target organ, whereas this has an important influence on the success of the treatment. Secondly, during a CT-scan guided operation, the radiologist is exposed to harmful X-rays radiations.

For a few years, the modelling of the interaction forces during needle insertions has become a challenging task. Pioneer works recently appeared, principally in the medical robotics context ((DiMaio and Salcudean, 2004; Okamura *et al.*, 2004)). Indeed, they have been motivated by the development of systems to robotically assist needle insertion training, guidance or teleoperation ((Stoianovici *et al.*, 1997; Maurin *et al.*, 2004)).

To characterize the interaction between a needle and soft living tissues, let us first describe a puncture into a single layer sample. We assume that the needle tip is initially motionless and in contact with the surface of the tissue. The needle insertion is a 3 phases procedure illustrated by figure 1:

- Phase 1: The needle pushes the tissue surface which becomes deformed.

[1] This work has been supported by the Alsace Regional Council and the French National Center for Scientific Research (CNRS). The authors would like to thank the IRCAD/EITS staff for their help in arranging ideal surgical facilities, with a special thanks to Antonello and Stefano for their assistance during surgical acts.

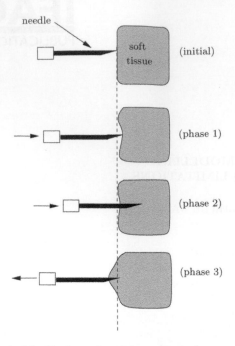

Fig. 1. Needle insertion into a single layer soft tissue

- Phase 2: When the force applied by the needle on the tissue reaches a given energetic threshold (see (Hervely *et al.*, 2005)), the needle penetrates into the tissue by cutting its surface. While the needle is inserted, the friction forces attract the skin along the needle shaft.
- Phase 3: The needle is extracted from the tissue. Again, the tissue is attracted in the needle motion direction. Consequently, the position of the needle when it is extracted does not correspond to the initial position.

The first phase corresponds to a viscoelastic interaction as described in (Fung, 1993). In accordance with (Okamura *et al.*, 2004) the interaction forces during the second phase are due to the effects of cutting, friction, and to the relaxation of the skin after the puncture. In the third case, the interaction between the needle and the tissue is only due to friction. It is particularly difficult to study the mechanics of the insertion in living tissues because:

- the different tissues in interaction with the needle are inhomogeneous;
- these tissues exhibit nonlinear properties;
- their contributions to the interaction are superimposed.

For all these reasons, needle insertions modelling is a challenging task.

(Okamura *et al.*, 2004) study the forces involved in the needle penetration and withdrawal. The insertion is controlled by a robotic translator and the associated forces and displacements measure-

ments are obtained for bovine livers. The characteristic properties of needle insertion forces are identified and a methodology is given to separate the contributions of stiffness, friction and cutting forces in order to derive a complete force model. Though suitable for the characterization of efforts and haptic simulation, the previous methodologies involve different specific *ex vivo* tests to adjust parameters to patient variability. The rheological characterization of tissues, proposed in (Kobayashi *et al.*, 2004) has the same limitations.

In the following, we will assume for obvious reasons that the insertion of the needle in a patient should be strictly limited to the necessary medical task. From this point of view, the identification of a needle insertion model from data collected during the medical act itself is required. (DiMaio and Salcudean, 2004) estimate an elastostatic linear model derived from the needle tip force and position measurements and from the deformation of the pierced material. The deformations are given by markers placed on the surface of the material. It is difficult to use this procedure in the clinical conditions, specially in the case of internal organs. In the context of the interaction of robot with a soft environment, (Diolaiti *et al.*, 2005) focus on the online estimation of viscoelastic linear and nonlinear models. The proposed methodology is of interest though results are given for small motions of a translator system in contact with thin layers of stiff (polycarbonate) and soft (silicone gel) samples. Since it is applied to artificial materials and viscoelastic stimuli, *i.e.* without cutting, it does not directly adapt to the problem of needle insertion. Nevertheless, this approach undoubtly shares similar motivations with our study.

In this article, we analyze the modeling and identification of needle insertion interactions during *in vivo* experiments. The limitations of the modeling and identification procedure are discussed. In section 2, the estimation techniques and the experimental setup are presented. Section 3 presents modeling issues and the results of online estimations obtained during *in vivo* experiments. Finally, the conclusion summarizes the main contributions of this work.

2. METHODS

2.1 Experimental Setup

As already stated, the aim of this paper is to model the needle insertion from measurable informations in operating conditions. We consider that the tissues in which the needle is inserted are not equipped with particular fiducials that may allow to capture the organs motions, as in (DiMaio and Salcudean, 2004). We suppose that the only informations at disposal are the position or the velocity of the needle tip and the interaction forces measured by a force sensor. These can be obtained if the needle is instrumented or hold by a robotic assistant.

To estimate needle insertion models we use a PHANToM haptic device from Sensable Technologies as an instrumented passive needle holder. The PHANToM end effector is equipped with an ATI Nano17 6 axis force sensor. A needle holder is mounted on the force sensor, so that needles of different sizes can be attached (see figure 2). The PHANToM encoders are used to measure the motions of the needle, with a precision of 30 μm. During a manual insertion, the velocity

Fig. 2. Instrumented needle

of the needle tip is generally very low. Since it is derived from position encoders, it is corrupted by an important quantization noise. To reduce its effect we estimate the velocity with a standard Kalman filter. Measurements are acquired at a frequency rate of 1 kHz, under real-time constraints imposed by the software implemented on Linux RTAI operating system.

2.2 Online Estimation Method

We use a recursive estimation method in order to identify a model of the tissue. This method is based on *a priori* models, that will further be discussed. Recursive parametric estimation algorithms are based on a discrete time linear parameterization of the system output (see (Goodwin and Sin, 1984)):

$$y_{k+1} = \varphi_k^T \theta_k^* + w_{k+1} \qquad (1)$$

where θ_k^* is the vector of unknown parameters to be estimated, φ_k is the regression vector build from the measured signals and y_{k+1} is the measured output signal, at time $k+1$. The output measure noise is represented by the signal w_{k+1}.

From the estimation $\hat{\theta}_k$ of θ_k^* at time k, we can estimate the output signal at time $k+1$ as:

$$\hat{y}_{k+1} = \varphi_k^T \hat{\theta}_k. \qquad (2)$$

We define the *a priori* prediction error as the error between the measured output and the estimated output:

$$e_{k+1} = w_{k+1} + \varphi_k^T (\theta_k^* - \hat{\theta}_k).$$

Finally, we define the *a posteriori* prediction error:

$$\hat{e}_{k+1} = y_{k+1} - \varphi_k^T \hat{\theta}_{k+1}.$$

We use Recursive Least Squares (RLS) algorithm which is probably the most used technique for online estimation. The RLS algorithm writes:

$$\hat{\theta}_k = \hat{\theta}_{k-1} + \frac{F_{k-1}\varphi_{k-1}e_k}{\frac{1}{\alpha_{k-1}} + \varphi_{k-1}^T F_{k-1}\varphi_{k-1}}$$

$$F_k = F_{k-1} - \frac{F_{k-1}\varphi_{k-1}\varphi_{k-1}^T F_{k-1}}{\frac{1}{\alpha_{k-1}} + \varphi_{k-1}^T F_{k-1}\varphi_{k-1}}$$

where α_k is a weighting function ($\alpha_k = 1$ corresponds to the classical RLS algorithm). Note that the gain factor F_k is recursively adapted.

Additionally to the standard algorithm we use a dead-zone function ((Ioannou and Sun, 1996)) so that the estimation may remain robust when the absolute value of the error signal is under a given threshold, denoted as N_0. Its value is chosen so that $N_0 > \nu_0$, with ν_0 the magnitude of the noise w_k. The resulting algorithm is obtained by premultiplying F_k by $\delta(e_k)$, with:

$$\delta(e_k) = \begin{cases} 1, & \text{if } |e_k| \geq 2N_0 \\ \frac{|e_k|}{N_0} - 1, & \text{if } N_0 \leq |e_k| < 2N_0 \\ 0, & \text{if } |e_k| < N_0 \end{cases}$$

The parameters adaptation freezing allows a sensible robustness improvement.

The variations of the gain factor F_k has some influence on the estimation of varying parameters. Indeed, a persisting excitation of the regression vector, *i.e.* a sufficient level of input measurements, is required for the convergence of the parameters estimation. Nevertheless, in the case of the RLS method, the convergence of the algorithm causes the decrease of F_k towards zero. In this case, the estimated parameters no longer vary. For that reason, the method cannot directly apply to estimate varying parameters. The RLS algorithm with covariance resetting (RLS-CR) solves this problem by resetting the covariance matrix at time k_r with:

$$\{k_r\} = \{k | \lambda_{min}(F_k) \leq \alpha_0^{-1} \leq \lambda_{min}(F_{k-1})\}$$

To reduce the computing complexity of k_r, an equivalent condition on the trace of the covariance matrix can be used:

$$\{k_r\} = \{k | x_k = tr(F_k^{-1}) \geq \alpha_0\}.$$

Indeed, it is shown that x_k can be computed recursively by $x_k = x_{k-1} + \alpha_{k-1}\varphi_{k-1}^T \varphi_{k-1}$. The resetting is achieved by setting $F_{k_r} = F_0$, what implies $x_{k_r} = x_0$.

3. *IN VIVO* EXPERIMENTAL RESULTS

We lead two different tests.

Firstly, we identified the viscoelastic behavior of the tissues occurring in the first phase of the insertion. Since no piercing was necessary, we performed the test on the abdomen of an adult living human. The final part of the needle holder was removed and the force sensor mounted on the end effector directly applied on the abdomen. The corresponding results are given in section 3.1.

The second part of the experiments were performed in operating *in vivo* conditions. Needle insertions in the liver of anesthetized pigs were adopted as benchmarks for two reasons:

- the abdominal tissues of a young pig are rather similar to human ones;
- the properties of the tissues are much more realistic in vivo because of blood irrigation and breathing which considerably influence the mechanical properties of the tissues.

The insertion was done through a small incision on the epidermis (a new one each time), as usually done in interventional radiology. The insertion was then performed through the dermis, the fat and the muscle to finally access the liver. The corresponding results are given in section 3.2.

3.1 Viscoelastic Experiments

Modelling To model the interaction during the viscoelastic phase of the needle insertion, we considered two classical viscoelastic models. The linear Kelvin-Voigt(KV) model is certainly the most common model used in the literature. In our case it writes:

$$f = \begin{cases} -(Kp + Bv), & \text{if } p > 0 \\ 0, & \text{if } p \leq 0 \end{cases} \quad (3)$$

where f is the force exerted on the tissue, p and v represent the position and the velocity of the needle tip, K is the stiffness coefficient and B the damping coefficient. The position p=0 corresponds to the initial contact point. In fact, the representation of living tissues by this linear model is generally not adequate. Indeed, except for very small motions the interaction model varies in an nonlinear way regardless to the tissue motion. The Hunt-Crossley (HC) model intrinsically takes into account the penetration depth between two bodies. It states that the interaction model varies in a nonlinear way regardless to the tissue motion, as presented in (Hunt and Crossley, 1975):

$$f = \begin{cases} -(\mu p^n + \lambda p^n v), & \text{if } p > 0 \\ 0, & \text{if } p \leq 0 \end{cases} \quad (4)$$

where μ, λ and n are constant parameters that depend on the material properties.

Experimental results From the previous remarks, and from comparative tests between the KV and HC models, we used the HC model for the estimation in the viscoelastic case. Characteristic results are presented on figures 3.

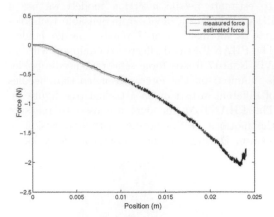

Fig. 3. Force reconstruction with the HC model during the viscoelastic phase

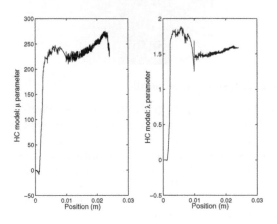

Fig. 4. Estimated parameters of the HC model during the viscoelastic phase

Figure 3 illustrates the quality of the force reconstruction. The absolute mean value of the reconstruction error is 0.0194 N with a standard deviation of 0.0125 N. Force is given as a function of the needle tip position. This allows to emphasize the nonlinearity of the model. The HC model allows to obtain quasi constant parameters during the viscoelastic interaction as illustrated on 4. We observe the convergence of the algorithm to: $\mu = 240$ and $\lambda = 1.5$. In that study we assumed that the n coefficient is constant. This is generally assumed in the biomechanics literature. According to (Johnson, 1989), $n \approx 1.5$ in the case of spheres contacting in static conditions. (Diolaiti *et al.*, 2005) established that $n \approx 1.3$ describes accurately the viscoelastic behavior of soft materials and proposed a solution for the simultaneous online estimation of μ, λ and n.

Remarks According to (Fung, 1993) most living tissues have a viscoelastic behavior, as long as small displacements are considered. In practice, we could observe that the viscoelastic phase during a needle insertion corresponds to relatively large motions. This increases the nonlinear behavior of the tissue. We could also observe an even more disturbing artifact. When the needle is inserted in very viscous organs, they trend to slip in the abdominal cavity. This of course is very difficult to model. In practice, it is avoided by the physician, which often tries to minimize the viscoelastic phase of the insertion by piercing the organs with an abrupt motion of the needle. The effect of speed on the way the needle perforates an organ are studied in (Hervely *et al.*, 2005).

3.2 Needle Insertion Experiments

Modelling In order to understand the interactions during a needle insertion we consider the simple case of an insertion into a one layer soft tissue. As underlined previously, the behavior of the tissue during the first phase of the insertion can be approximated by a viscoelastic model. So, if we denote as p_s the position of the entry point on the surface of the tissue, the motion of the tissue can be described by : $p = p_s$. During this first phase the tissue surface becomes shapeless until the penetration of the needle tip. After the puncture the needle tip position is different from the position of the entry point on the surface of the tissue (see figure 5).

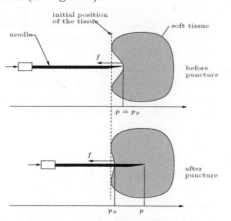

Fig. 5. Descriptive model of the needle insertion

The motion of the tissue is due to the force applied by the needle. With a linear representation of the viscoelastic component of the effort, according to (3), the force writes:

$$f = -K_{ins}p_s - B_{ins}(v_s - v) + f_f$$

with v_s the tissue velocity and f_f the dry friction force on the needle. So the interaction effort depends on the tissue extension, on the relative velocity of the tissue with respect to the needle and on a nonlinear friction term. With a nonlinear representation of the viscoelastic term, according to (4), the extrapolation of the former equation would lead to :

$$f = -\mu_{ins}v_s^n - \lambda_{ins}p_s^n(v_s - v) + f_f.$$

The online identification of one of these models is very difficult in particular because the position of the tissue is not available. Moreover the needle punctures several inhomogeneous layers, which have all different behaviors.

(Yen *et al.*, 1996) proposed a model of tissue for needle insertion based on a KV model with piecewise constant parameters. It is also very difficult to online estimate a such model since the organs transitions are not easily detectable. Consequently, we decided to use a model in the form of the KV model, but for which the parameters K and B are varying in time, with the position and the velocity of the needle tip, *i.e.* such that $K = K(p, v, t)$ and $B = B(p, v, t)$. In the following we will denote this model as the KV generalized model (KVG). This model is no longer physically consistent since it does not take into account the tissues deformations. However it allows to reconstruct the force with a simple parameters description. To apply the RLS algorithm to the estimation of forces we will have : $\varphi_k = (p_k \ v_k)^T$, $\hat{\theta}_k = (\hat{K}_k \ \hat{B}_k)^T$, $y_k = f_k$ and $\hat{y}_k = \hat{f}_k$ as parameters of equations (1) and (2).

Experimental results The results obtained for the reconstruction of the force based on the estimation of the KVG model are represented on figure 6. The estimation results shown on figure 6 are characterized by a very accurate reconstruction: the absolute error mean value is 0.0486 N for a force amplitude ranging from -5.69 N to 2.45 N. This emphasizes the fact that most of the

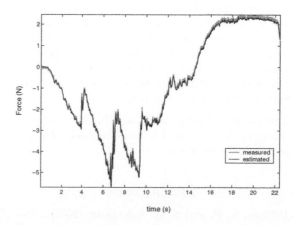

Fig. 6. Force reconstruction with the KVG model during needle insertion

sensed forces that a physician feels while inserting a needle are due to the skin, the fat and the muscles. The main interest of this model is limited to the parameters analysis. The evolution of the estimated parameters of the KVG model during the needle insertion are represented on figure 7. The profile of both parameters of the KVG model

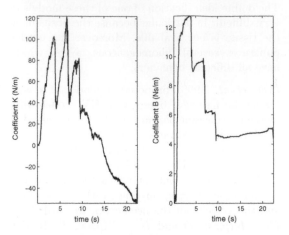

Fig. 7. Estimated parameters of the KVG model during a typical needle insertion

are not continuous, because of the rupture of the different tissues surfaces. Nevertheless, we notice that the parameters are bounded and fluctuate slowly excepted during transitions phases. This may open opportunities in the control of a robotized needle insertion systems.

4. CONCLUSION

In this paper we presented a method to online characterize needle insertions. This method is based on a robust recursive least squares algorithm with covariance resetting. First experiments allowed to evaluate the viscoelastic behavior of the skin and to prove the effectiveness of the estimation technique. The *in vivo* insertion of a needle was then described and the complex behavior of the tissues emphasized. To allow the online characterization of the needle insertion we proposed a varying parameters model. With this model, we achieved the estimation of the interactions with very good tracking properties.

The estimated parameters will further be introduced in the control of a force feedback teleoperated robotic assistant.

REFERENCES

DiMaio, S. P. and S. E. Salcudean (2004). Needle insertion modeling and simulation. *IEEE Transactions on Robotics and Automation* **5**(19), 864–875.

Diolaiti, N., C. Melchiorri and S. Stramigioli (2005). Contact impedance estimation for robotic systems. *IEEE Transactions on Robotics* **21**(5), 925–935.

Fung, Y. C. (1993). *Biomechanics : Mechanical Properties of Living Tissues*.

Goodwin, G. and K. S. Sin (1984). *Adaptive Filtering Prediction and Control*. Information and System Sciences. Prentice-Hall.

Hervely, M., P. Dupont and J. Triedman (2005). Trajectory optimization for dynamic needle insertion. In: *IEEE International Conference on Robotics and Automation*. Barcelona, Spain. pp. 1658–1663.

Hunt, K. and F. Crossley (1975). Coefficient of restitution interpreted as damping in vibroimpact. *ASME Journal of Applied Mechanics* pp. 440–445.

Ioannou, P. and J. Sun (1996). *Robust adaptive control*. Prentice-Hall.

Johnson, K.L. (1989). Contact mechanics. Cambridge University Press. Cambridge, U.K.

Kobayashi, Y., J. Okamoto and M.G. Fujie (2004). Physical properties of the liver for needle insertion control. In: *IEEE/RSJ International Conference on Intelligent Robots and Systems*. Sendai, Japan. pp. 2960–2966.

Maurin, B., J. Gangloff, B. Bayle, M. de Mathelin, O. Piccin, P. Zanne, C. Doignon, L. Soler and A. Gangi (2004). A parallel robotic system with force sensors for percutaneous procedures under CT-guidance. In: *Medical Image Computing and Computer Assisted Intervention*. Saint-Malo, France. pp. 176–183.

Okamura, A., C. Simone and M. O'Leary (2004). Force modeling for needle insertion into soft tissue. *IEEE Transactions on Biomedical Engineering* **51**(10), 1707–1716.

Rhim, H., S. N. Goldberg, G. D. Dodd, L. Solbiati, H. K. Lim, M. Tonolini and O. K. Cho (2001). Essential techniques for successful radio-frequency thermal ablation of malignant hepatic tumors. *RadioGraphics* **21**, S17–S35.

Stoianovici, D., J. A. Cadeddu, R. D. Demaree, H. A. Basile, R. H. Taylor, L. L. Whitcomb and L. R. Kavoussi (1997). A novel mechanical transmission applied to percutaneous renal access. *ASME Dynamic Systems and Control Division* **DSC-Vol. 61**, 401–406.

Yen, P.-L., R.D. Hibberd and B.L. Davies (1996). A telemanipulator system as an assistant and training tool for penetrating soft tissue. *Mechatronics* **6**(4), 423–436.

SINGLE BLACK-BOX MODELS FOR TWO-POINT NON-INVASIVE TEMPERATURE PREDICTION

C. A. Teixeira* M. Graça Ruano* A. E. Ruano*
W. C. A. Pereira** C. Negreira***

* Centre for Intelligent Systems, Universidade do Algarve,
Portugal
** Biomedical Engineering Program, Universidade Federal do Rio
de Janeiro, Brazil
*** Laboratory of Ultrasound Acoustics, Universidad de la
Republica, Uruguay

Abstract: In this paper the performance of a genetically selected radial basis functions neural network is evaluated for non-invasive two-point temperature estimation in a homogeneous medium, irradiated by therapeutic ultrasound at physiotherapeutic levels. In this work a single neural network was assigned to estimate the temperature profile at the two considered points, and more consistent results were obtained than when considering one model for each point. This result was possible by increasing the model complexity. The best model predicts the temperature from two unseen data sequences during approximately 2 hours, with a maximum absolute error less than 0.5 ^oC, as desired for a therapeutic temperature estimator. Copyright © 2006 IFAC

Keywords: Temperature profiles, Temperature control, Neural Networks-models, Radial base function networks, Multiobjective optimisations

1. INTRODUCTION

One of the major limitations of thermal therapies is the lack of accurate knowledge of the temperature in the region under treatment. Accurate temperature predictors (absolute error less than 0.5 ^oC(Arthur *et al.*, 2003)) would enable a correct therapy guidance by means of an efficient instrumentation control. In the past many publications describing ways of estimating temperature non-invasively and instrumentation control schemas were published. Possible reported methods were: electrical impedance tomography (Paulsen *et al.*, 1996), microwave radiometry (Meaney and Paulsen, 1996), magnetic resonance imaging (Hynynen *et al.*, 1996), and backscattered ultrasound (Ueno *et al.*, 1990; Seip and Ebbini, 1995; Simon *et al.*, 1998; Arthur *et al.*, 2003). The use of backscattered ultrasound has some advantages: ultrasound is a non-ionising and

low-cost modality with relatively simple signal processing requirements. Moreover, it can reach deep regions inside the body, have a good spatial and temporal localisation and the possibility of using a unique technology for generating heat and for non-invasive temperature estimation (Simon *et al.*, 1998; Arthur *et al.*, 2003). Different approaches for temperature estimation using backscattered ultrasound were reported: analysis of the frequency dependent attenuation (Ueno *et al.*, 1990), analysis of the changes on backscattered energy (Arthur *et al.*, 2003) and analysis of the change on speed of sound and medium expansion (Seip and Ebbini, 1995; Simon *et al.*, 1998). In Simon *et al.* (1998) a linear relationship between the temperature change and the echo shifts in the time domain was reported, and a maximum error of 0.44 ^oC, an average error of -0.02 ^oC and a mean squared error of 0.03 $(^{o}C)^{2}$ were obtained at the focus of a hight intensity focused ultrasound (HIFU) transducer, for a temperature change of 4.22 ^{o}C, in a estimation horizon of 90 seconds. In Seip and Ebbini (1995) it was assumed that the temperature change are linearly related with the frequency variations of the echoes components in the spectral domain. In both methods using the echoes time-shift temperature dependence or the frequency variation temperature dependence, the a-priori determination of medium-dependent constants was necessary.

The present work evaluates the potential of a single non-linear neural network (NN) (black-box) model to non-invasively estimate the temperature profile at two discrete points in a glycerine reservoir, submitted to therapeutic ultrasound at physiotherapeutic levels. The NNs used were Radial Basis Functions Neural Networks (RBFNN). This paper reports the continuation of the work developed by our group in the field of invasive (Teixeira et al., 2004), and non-invasive (Teixeira et al., 2005; Teixeira et al., 2006) temperature estimation using RBFNN. In Teixeira et al. (2006) the potential of the proposed black-box models was evaluated for a single point estimation, and the work exposed in Teixeira et al. (2005) showed that it is possible to predict the temperature profile at two different points, using two different models.

2. MATERIALS AND METHODS

The complete experimental setup is shown in Figure 1, where a circular-shape therapeutic ultrasound (TUS) transducer (Ibramed Sonopulse Generation 2000, São Paulo, Brazil) working in continuous mode at 1 MHz, with a nominal effective radiation area of 3.5 cm^{2}, irradiated a 1400-ml glycerine reservoir. To prevent standing waves formation, the walls of the reservoir were lined with a rough surface material. Three lead spheres (3mm radius), acting like scatterers, were placed in the glycerine medium in order to obtain acoustic information from the points under study. The scatterers were placed in a plan parallel to the TUS transducer face. They were 1-cm spaced and the central one was 24-mm or 48-mm distant from the TUS transducer face centre. The spheres were sustained in the liquid medium by nylon wires connected to a metal support. A cromel-alumel (type K) thermocouple was closely sited to the central sphere. The μV present at the thermocouple terminals were amplified and converted to a mV scale (where $1mV = 1^{o}C$) using a thermocouple module with integrated cold junction compensation (Fluke 80 TK, USA). Then the output of the thermocouple module was read by a digital multimeter (HP 34401A, USA) connected to a PC via a GPIB bus. The RF-lines

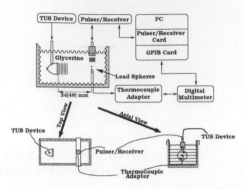

Fig. 1. Experimental arrangement, showing the lateral, top, and axial view of the glycerine reservoir

Table 1. Temperature ranges obtained at the two considered points, for the three applied intensities

Distance (mm)	Intensity W/cm^{2}	Temperature (^{o}C)		
		Initial	Max.	Final
	1.0	29.6	35.7	29.7
24	1.5	29.9	37.8	30.7
	2.0	24.6	34.7	29.8
	1.0	28.3	33.1	29.2
48	1.5	24.5	34.8	28.3
	2.0	28.2	38.2	31.2

used for non-invasive temperature estimation were collected with a 5-MHz non focused imaging ultrasound (IUS) transducer (Sonic, USA), driven by a PC controlled pulser/receiver (Corelec, France). As shown in Figure 1, the IUS beam reaches the scatterers in a plan perpendicular to the TUS beam. At each 10 seconds, during a 2-hour experiment time, an RF-line (2048 points, sampled at 40 MHz) was saved with its correspondent temperature value. For each distance (24 or 48 mm), three data sets were collected, corresponding to TUS intensities of 1, 1.5 and 2 W/cm^{2}. The temperature ranges obtained for each distance and then for each intensity are presented in Table 1. For each set a total of 720 temperature points and RF-lines were obtained for future features extraction. The medium was only heated in the first 60 minutes. Then, the TUS beam was interrupted and the glycerine allowed cooling till room temperature.

The construction of RBFNN temperature estimators required temperature-dependent features extraction from the measured RF-lines. In this paper the same features extracted in Teixeira et al. (2005) and Teixeira et al. (2006) were used. Since temperature measurements were only performed in the central scatterer, features extraction was only performed in the echo originated by this scatterer in conjunction with the thermocouple, in order to discard information from the other scatterers where the temperature is unknown. A boxcar window was used to isolate the echo originated by the central sphere. Afterwards, a Fast

Fourier Transform was applied, and six spectral features extracted. These features were: the amplitude of the fundamental component originated by the TUS beam, located at approximately 1 MHz; the amplitude of the first and second harmonics of the fundamental component originated by the TUS beam, located at approximately 2 MHz and 3 MHz, respectively; and amplitude, bandwidth (-6 dB), and central frequency of the component originated by the IUS beam, located at approximately 5.5 MHz. The unique extracted temporal feature was the time-position of the echo originated by the central sphere. Afterwards, the features extracted and the past temperature values were filtered using a causal low-pass Butterworth digital filter (order=1 ; cut-off frequency = 1/20 of the Nyquist frequency), and normalised to values between 0 and 1. This filter parameters were selected having in mind the noise reduction, maintaining the signals fundamental behaviour. The normalisation was necessary to eliminate scales differences between the features. Both processes were necessary to enable a correct RBFNN training and structure selection. At this point we have the following information for non-invasive temperature modelling: normalised and filtered amplitude of the fundamental component originated by the TUS beam (AF_{TUS}); normalised and filtered amplitude of the 1st and 2nd harmonics of the fundamental component originated by the TUS beam ($AH1_{TUS}$ and $AH2_{TUS}$); normalised and filtered amplitude, bandwidth, and central frequency of the component originated by the IUS device (A_{IUS}, BW_{IUS} and F_{IUS}); normalised and filtered temporal position (TP); normalised and filtered temperature (T). In the applied framework the data set which is used for NN parameters optimisation is called the training set, and the data used in the NN evaluation during the structure selection procedure is called the test set. After training and structure selection procedures, the best fitted NNs should be evaluated using unseen data sequences, called validation data sets. In this work the training set was obtained by randomly selecting data from the six measured sets (1/3 from each set). In this way, the NNs were trained for having good performance in the two spatial points and for the three applied intensities. The complete data sequences collected at 1.5 W/cm^2 were selected as the two test sets. The best-fitted RBFNN validation was performed using the complete data sequences collected at 2 W/cm^2 (one for each distance), which is the more non-linear data and where one of the measured temperature range includes the normal human body temperature, making the validation process more realistic.

A RBFNN is composed by three layers with three different rules. The first layer is composed by a set of inputs, which connects the network to its environment. The second layer, the unique hidden layer in the NN, applies a non-linear transformation on the input data, and is formed by a set of processing elements, called neurons. The outputs of the hidden layer are linearly combined at the last layer, to produce the overall output of the RBFNN (Haykin, 1999). The input/output relation for a RBFNN is:

$$f(x_j) = b + \sum_{i=1}^{n} \alpha_i \varphi \left(||x_j - c_i|| \right), \qquad (1)$$

where n is the number of neurons or processing elements in the hidden layer, b is the bias term, $|| \cdot ||$ is a norm, normally and in the case of this work, an Euclidean norm was employed, and $\{\varphi(\cdot)\}_{i=1}^{n}$ is a set of radial basis functions centred at $\{c_i \in R^d\}_{i=1}^{n}$, being d the number of inputs. These basis functions are evaluated at points $x_j \in R^d$ and are weighted by $\{\alpha_i\}_{i=1}^{n}$ at the last layer. Normally the basis functions are Gaussian:

$$\varphi_i = e^{\frac{1}{2\sigma_i^2} ||x_j - c_i||^2}, \qquad (2)$$

where σ_i is the spread of the ith function.

Manual selection of the best-fitted NN is a hard task given the enormous number of possible structures. In this work, the Multi-Objective Genetic Algorithm (MOGA)(Fonseca and Fleming, 1993) was applied to solve this problem. The MOGA is an evolutionary computing approach, based on the natural selection notion, which performs a population-based search by employing operators such as selection, crossover, and mutation. This algorithm is designed to minimise (or maximise) a number of problem-dependent objectives, which in the majority of the problems are conflicting. In order to obtain feasible individuals, the objectives must be defined as goals to met with an associated priority. The priority value is defined according to the relative importance of the related goal for the final individual application. At the end of a MOGA run a set of best-fitted individuals is obtained, which are the ones that fulfil or almost fulfil more of the a-priory defined goals.

In this work, the MOGA was allowed to optimise the RBFNNs structure, where the structure variables were the number of neurons in the hidden layer (n) and the inputs. The possible input candidates were the lags of AF_{TUS}, $AH1_{TUS}$, $AH2_{TUS}$, A_{IUS}, BW_{IUS}, F_{IUS}, TP, and T. This paper intends to estimate the temperature at two discrete spatial points using a single RBFNN model, in this way an extra input was assigned. This input is always present (i.e. it is not selected by the MOGA) and contains the spatial information necessary for the attainment of well-fitted RBFNN, being 0 if the data used was collected at 24-mm or 1 if the data was collected at 48-mm. In Fig. 2 a schematic representation of the black-

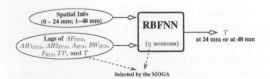

Fig. 2. Schematic diagram of the black-box model applied, showing the structure variables chosen by the MOGA

box model used is presented. The MOGA spans 100 generations (iterations) of 100 RBFNN (individuals) each. The crossover and mutation probabilities were defined as 0.7 and 0.5, respectively. To maintain population diversity, 10 % of the old population was replaced, at each iteration by a set of randomly generated RBFNN, called random immigrants. These MOGA parameters were selected after several tests considering other parameters arrangements. The MOGA search space was bounded by defining the possible number of neurons, the possible number of inputs, and the maximum lag (MLAG) considered for the inputs variables. The number of neurons was defined as a number in the interval [10,25], the number of inputs was defined as an integer in the interval [2,20]. These values were selected after the analysis of other runs, where the best-fitted individuals had the number of inputs and the number of neurons in the defined intervals. The choice of the value for MLAG was based on the time constants of the measured temperature signals. The dominant time constants give us an idea about how much past information is necessary to estimate the actual temperature. After an exponential fitting of the form:

$$\hat{T}_{exp} = C_1 e^{-a_1 t} + C_2 e^{-a_2 t}, \qquad (3)$$

using a non-linear least squares strategy, the values of a_1 and a_2 were found and the time constants (in this case two time constants were considered) for one particular temperature signal evaluated ($\tau_1 = 1/a_1$ and $\tau_2 = 1/a_2$). After the computation of the dominant time constants for the six temperature signals, an idea of the appropriate value for MLAG was achieved. All the temperature signals presented a dominant time constant inferior to 227 seconds, except one temperature signal that presents an exacerbated dominant time constant due to bad fitting, thus not being considered in these calculations. If the sampling time is 10 seconds, then the number of lags present in 227 seconds is 22. The MLAG was defined as 25 in order give a little more freedom to the MOGA.

The NNs non-linear parameters (radial basis functions centres and spreads) were found using the Levenberg Marquardt (LM) algorithm, which is recognised as the best method for non-linear least-squares problems (Ruano and Fleming, 1992),

which is the case of RBFNN training. In the other hand, the linear parameters (bias and weights) were computed using the linear least squares method. The initial values of the centres and spreads were found using the Optimal Adaptive K-means clustering algorithm (Chinrungrueng and Séquin, 1995) and the "early stopping" criterion was used to stop the training. This method accesses the NNs performance in the test data sequences (in this work the data collected at 1.5 W/cm^2) and stops the training when this performance deteriorates, preventing model overtraining (i.e. NNs which models the noise and are only specialised in the training data), being the recommended stop criterion for real-world applications (Principe *et al.*, 2000). In each MOGA generation, after NNs training, the performance of each individual was accessed having in mind the extraction of objectives to minimise, and consequently to rank the individuals. In the ranking operation the NNs are sorted to improve the selection and reproduction of the best fitted. In this work the performance was evaluated according to the following measures:

- Root Mean Square Error in the TRaining set ($RMSE_{TR}$);
- Root Mean Square Error in the TEst set collected at 24 mm distance ($RMSE24_{TE}$);
- Root Mean Square Error in the TEst set collected at 48 mm distance ($RMSE48_{TE}$). This error and the previous one are obtained by estimating the temperature 1 step ahead (10 seconds) using the past measured temperature values;
- Maximum root mean square error in all the prediction steps using the test sequence collected at 24 mm ($MPE24$).
- Maximum Root Mean Square Error in all the Prediction Steps using the test sequence collected at 48 mm ($MPE48$). This error and the previous one are obtained by estimating the temperature 60 steps (10 minutes) in the future using the past estimated temperature values, and taking the maximum RMSE obtained in all the predictions steps;
- Model-validity tests;
- Linear Weights Norm (LWN);
- Model Complexity (MC).

The model-validity tests are explained in Billings and Voon (1986), and used in Teixeira *et al.* (2004), Teixeira *et al.* (2006), and Teixeira *et al.* (2005). These model-validity tests involve the computation of first and high-order correlation between model inputs, outputs and residuals. In this paper, as in the previous work, we use only the conditions involving the first-order correlations (the error autocorrelation (R_{ee}) and the correlation between the inputs and the error (R_{ue})), because the results obtained using the high-order correlations were not better.

The MC was computed as the total number of parameters for a particular NN structure:

$$MC = NC \times NI + NS + NW, \quad (4)$$

where NC is the number of centres, NI is the number of inputs, NS is the number of spreads, and NW is the number of linear weights.

An efficient RBFNN structure selection requires the minimisation of the previously referred model measures. The MOGA was assigned to attain, if possible, both goals defined for the model measures. The $RMSE_{TR}$ was defined as a goal with value 0.004 (normalised value) and priority 1. In order to improve the attainment of models with a high generalisation capacity, i.e. good performance in data sets different from the ones used for training and test, the $RMSE24_{TE}$, $RMSE48_{TE}$, $MPE24$ and $MPE48$ were defined as goals with priority 2 and value 0.002 (normalised value) . The maximum of the two considered correlations tests was defined as a goal of value 0.0516 (confidence interval) and priority 1. Neural networks with a high LWN are normally models specialised in the training data, which in other data sets tend to have an exacerbated error, thus LWN was defined as a goal with value 2.0 and priority 1. This goal value was defined having in mind the maximum number of neurons defined and the data normalisation. It is possible to realise that a large model with a large computation capacity probably estimates better than a smaller model with smaller computation capacity. But in a real application the resources are limited and very large models are uncomputable, so the search of best-fitted and also smaller models is essential. In this way, MC was defined as a goal with value 400 and priority 1. This goal value was defined having in mind the search space defined.

3. RESULTS & DISCUSSION

At the end of the training and structure selection phases (MOGA in conjunction with the LM), a set of 75 preferable individuals was obtained, and the "election" of the best individual was based on the performance attained in the validation data sequences. In this paper 2 validation data sequences were used: one collected at 24 mm distance from the TUS transducer, and other collected at 48 mm distance from the TUS transducer, both measured at 2 W/cm². The measured temperature for both distances, as well as, the predicted temperature attained by the best model are presented in Fig. 3. The maximum absolute, average and mean squared errors for this individual are presented in Table 2. Analysing this table it can be said that the best individual presents a

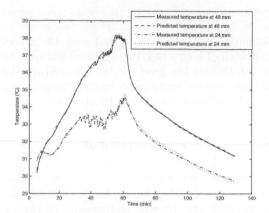

Fig. 3. Performance of the best model for the data collected at 2 W/cm²

Table 2. Errors committed by the best individual in the 2 validation sequences

Distance (mm)	24	48
MAE (^{o}C)	24.3E-1	3.4E-1
AE (^{o}C)	-9.1E-3	-3.0E-4
MSE (^{o}C)²	1.3E-2	4.8E-3

MAE - Maximum Absolute Error
AE - Average Error
MSE - Mean Squared Error

maximum absolute error less than 0.5 ^{o}C, which is the value pointed as the borderline between an appropriate and an undesired temperature estimator. In general the values obtained are better than the ones referred in Simon *et al.* (1998) where: a quantitative performance evaluation was only performed at the focus of the therapeutic transducer, the temperature ranges were smaller and the prediction horizon was only 90 seconds. Present results are substantially better than the ones presented in Teixeira *et al.* (2005), where two models were trained one for each point using the same data. This means that the single RBFNN assigned for multi-point temperature estimation was capable to integrate the "knowledge", which was distributed between two models in Teixeira *et al.* (2005). In addition, the information was integrated in such a way that better results were obtained.

The best model fulfils 6 out of 9 goals defined at the beginning of the MOGA execution. The ones that were not fulfilled are the model complexity (MC), and the two correlation tests. The obtained MC is 463 which is a value more or less closer to the a-priori defined goal (which is 400). The values obtained for the correlation tests were: $R_{ee} = 0.0746$ and $R_{ue} = 0.0707$ this is closer to the defined goals which were 0.0516.

Despite the good performance, this best model has 22 neurons which is approximately the double of the one obtained in Teixeira *et al.* (2005) where 11 and 12 neurons were attained for the best models. In the same way, the number of inputs also increased from 12 and 13 (previous publication) to 18 in the present work. These two structure parameters are directly related with the model complexity (MC) which changes from 166 and 169 to 463. Despite the good results, in the future, the increase in complexity must be investigated when more than two points are to be predicted.

4. CONCLUSION

The work hereby presented deals with the training and structure selection of single RBFNN for multi-point non-invasive temperature estimation in a homogeneous medium. The results obtained are better than the ones presented in the literature (Simon et al., 1998) and better than the ones attained in Teixeira et al. (2005), where two models were trained for temperature prediction at the two points considered. The maximum absolute error obtained for the points considered is less than 0.5 ^oC. These results are encouraging and open the possibility of real-time monitoring of specific points in a medium using a single model.

The next step is to test the feasibility of these black-box models for more than 2 points and estimate the temperature in multi-layered (inhomogeneous) medium.

ACKNOWLEDGEMENTS

The authors acknowledge the financial support of: Fundação para a Ciência e a Tecnologia (grant SFRH/BD/14061/2003), Portugal; Conselho Nacional de Desenvolvimento Científico e Tecnológico (project CNPq/CYTED 490.013/03-1), Brazil. The authors also acknowledge the help of Eng. Hector Gomez and MSc. Guillermo Cortela in the experimental setup.

REFERENCES

Arthur, R.M., W.L. Straube, J.D. Starman and E.G. Moros (2003). Noninvasive temperature estimation based on the energy of backscattered ultrasound. *Medical Physics* **30**, 1021–1029.

Billings, S. and W. Voon (1986). Correlation based model validity tests for non-linear models. *Int J Control* **44**, 235–244.

Chinrungrueng, Chedsada and Carlo H. Séquin (1995). Optimal adaptive k-means algorithm with dynamic adjustment of learning rate. *IEEE Transactions on Neural Networks* **6**(1), 157–169.

Fonseca, C.M. and P.J. Fleming (1993). Genetic algorithms for multi-objective optimization: Formulation, discution and generalization. In:

Proc. 5th Int Conf Genetic Algorithms. Vol. -. pp. 416–423.

Haykin, S. (1999). *Neural Networks: A comprehensive foundation*. Prentice Hall. New Jersey.

Hynynen, K., A. Chung, T. Fjield, M. Buchanan, D. Daum, V. Colucci, P. Lopath and F. Jolesz (1996). Feasibility of using ultrasound phased arrays for mri monitored noninvasive surgery. *IEEE Trans Ultrason Ferroelec Frequency Control* **43**, 1043–1052.

Meaney, P.M. and K.D. Paulsen (1996). Microwave imaging for tissue assessment: initial evaluation in multitarget tissue-equivalent phantoms. *Int J Hyperthermia* **43**, 878–890.

Paulsen, K.D., M.J. Moskowitz, T.P. Ryan, S.E. Mitchell and P.J. Hoopes (1996). Initial in vivo experience with eit as a thermal estimator during hyperthermia. *Int J Hyperthermia* **12**, 573–591.

Principe, J.C., N.R. Euliano and W.C. Lefebvre (2000). *Neural and adaptive systems: Fundamentals throught simulations*. Jonh Wiley & Sons. New York.

Ruano, A. E. and P. J. Fleming (1992). A connectionist approach to pid autotuning. In: *IEE Proceedings*. Vol. 138. pp. 279–285.

Seip, R. and E.S. Ebbini (1995). Noninvasive estimation of tissue temperature response to heating fields using diagnostic ultrasound. *IEEE Trans on Biomed Eng* **42**, 828–839.

Simon, C., P. VanBaren and E.S. Ebbini (1998). Two-dimensional temperature estimation using diagnostic ultrasound. *IEEE Trans Ultrason Ferroelec Frequency Control* **45**, 1088–1099.

Teixeira, C.A., A. E. Ruano, C. Negreira, M. Graça Ruano and W.C.A. Pereira (2005). Neural network model for non-invasive two-point temperature monitoring in a homogeneous medium irradiated by therapeutic ultrasound. In: *IFMBE Proceedings*. Vol. 11.

Teixeira, C.A., A.E. Ruano, C. Negreira, M. Graça Ruano and W.C.A. Pereira (2006). Non-invasive temperature prediction of *in-vitro* therapeutic ultrasound signals using neural networks. *Medical and Biological Engineering and Computing*. Accepted.

Teixeira, C.A., G. Cortela, H. Gomez, M.G. Ruano, A.E. Ruano, C. Negreira and W.C.A. Pereira (2004). Temperature models of a homogeneous medium under therapeutic ultrasound. *IFMBE News* **69**, 52–56.

Ueno, S., M. Hashimoto, H. Fukukita and T. Yano (1990). Ultrasound thermometry in hyperthermia. In: *Proc IEEE Ultrason Sympos*. Vol. 3. pp. 1645–1652.

Copyright © IFAC Modelling and Control in Biomedical Systems
Reims, France, 2006

3D HEART MOTION ESTIMATION USING ENDOSCOPIC MONOCULAR VISION SYSTEM

Mickaël Sauvée   Philippe Poignet
Jean Triboulet   Etienne Dombre   Ezio Malis
Roland Demaria

Sinters, 5 rue Paul Mesple, 31000 Toulouse, France
LIRMM, 161 rue Ada, 34292 Montpellier, France
INRIA, 2004 route des Lucioles, 06902 Sophia
Antipolis, France
Service de chirurgie Cardiovasculaire, CHU Arnaud de
Villeneuve, 371 av. G. Giraud, 34295 Montpellier, France

Abstract: In robotic assisted beating heart surgery, motion of the heart surface might be virtually stabilized to let the surgeon work as in on-pump cardiac surgery. Virtual stabilization means to compensate physically the relative motion between instrument tool tip and point of interest on the heart surface, and to o er surgeon a stable visual display of the scene. In this way, motion of the heart must be estimated. This article focus on motion estimation of heart surface. Classical computer vision method has been applied to reconstruct 3D pose of interest point. Experimental results obtained on *in vivo* images show the estimated motion of heart surface points. Copyright © 2006 IFAC

Keywords: Medical applications - Motion estimation - Vision - Robot control - Spectral analysis

1. INTRODUCTION

One of the most widely spread intervention in cardiac surgery is coronary artery bypass grafting (CABG). Currently most of them are performed using heart lung machine and arrested heart, which allows the surgeon to achieve complex and ne suture on motionless heart surface. However cardiopulmonary bypass (CPB) have deleterious e ects. For instance, systemic in ammatory response have been observed (Picone *et al.* (1999)). To avoid the CPB problems, solutions for operate on the beating heart should be proposed. Among proposed solutions, passive mechanical stabilizer have been used on the heart surface to cancel the motion (e.g. Octopus™ by Medtronic, Jansen *et al.* (1997)). The idea is to apply a mechanical

constraint on the heart surface to stabilize the working area. To ensure contact between heart surface and mechanical device, vacuum suction or suture technique have been developed. However remaining motion inside the stabilized area still exists. Lemma *et al.* (2005) have observed excursion up to 2.4 mm on the stabilize area. So surgeon have to manually cancel the movement of the target coronary. Another way to perform beating heart surgery is to compensate the organ motion with a robotized assistive device.

Initially proposed to overcome minimally invasive surgery (MIS) di culties, the introduction of telerobotic systems (e.g. Da Vinci™ system by Intuitive Surgical, Guthart and Salisbury (2000)) in operating room o ers the possibility to provide systems for motion compensation. Thus the surgeon can concentrate on his task. In robotic assisted beating heart surgery, the surgeon desired movement might be superimposed to the trajectory generate by the motion compensation algorithm. Hence the surgeon could work on a virtually stabilized heart as in on-pump surgery. In this scheme, the key issues are listed bellow:

(1) **Heart motion estimation**
    Movement must be extracted from visual feedback from endoscopic view of highly deformable and non structured surface, so development of specified algorithm must be done
(2) **Control system design**
    Robot manipulator must compensate for high bandwidth motion (up to 5Hz), with high precision (suture task perform on 2 millimeter diameter vessels). Moreover, stability must be guarantied for motion in both free space and in interaction with environment.
(3) **Visual stabilization**
    A stable view of suturing area must be display to the surgeon screen.

Related work have been proposed in the literature. First solution was proposed by Nakamura *et al.* (2001). They used a high speed camera which tracked artificial markers placed on the heart. Visual feedback control was used to control a light mini-robot. *In vivo* experiments performed on porcine model show good 2D trajectory tracking, but errors of about 1 mm had been observed. More recently, motion estimation based on natural landmark have been presented by Ortmaier *et al.* (2005). In this paper, measurements are based on natural landmark tracking, with a prediction algorithm based on ECG signals and respiratory pressure signal to improve robustness of landmark detection. Nevertheless, experimental evaluation is restricted to tracking of landmarks inside a mechanically stabilized area and presented results were expressed in image coordinate. In Ginhoux *et al.* (2005), active markers are placed on the heart and pointing laser system observed by a 500 Hz video sensor allows to compute the distance between the instrument tool tip and the reference surface, used in an adaptive model predictive controller. *In vivo* evaluation on porcine model exhibits motion cancellation with error about 1.5 mm. However the given estimation reflect a global motion of the heart surface if we consider the large dimension of their active marker system. Recently Cavusoglu *et al.* (2005) proposed to combine biological signals (ECG signal, arterial and ventricular blood pressures) and heart motion measurement in a model based predictive algorithm to add feedforward path to robot motion control. To analyze heart motion, measurements are obtained by Sonomicrometric system (manufactured by Sonometric). This technique is based on ultrasound signals, transmitted by small piezoelectric crystals fixed to the heart surface. To perform this experiment, the pericardial sac has to be filled with a saline solution. This constrain does not rely on feasibility procedure during CABG.

In this paper, we focus on heart motion estimation. Estimation of displacement and acceleration of heart surface is a key issue in robotic assisted surgery for control design. Moreover estimated motion will be used in biomechanical model. This model will improve the robustness of robot control architecture; it will also allow to model displacement of area locate behind the area of estimated motion. We proposed to use available information, i.e. endoscopic image, to perform heart motion estimation. Reconstruction of motion of observed scene from images need extra information such as metric. In first evaluation, we introduced artificial passive markers with known dimension.

In the remainder of this paper, we first present the method applied on endoscopic images to estimate motion of interest points. Experimental evaluation of this method is detailed in a second section. We conclude in the last section and discussion about on going work is exposed.

2. METHODS

The chosen approach for extracting visual information and estimating motion of the interest region could be described as follows :

(1) Image acquisition using calibrated endoscopic vision system,
(2) Tracking of a given and geometrical pattern, small enough to be assumed planar,
(3) Pose estimation of the template using metric of the object.

2.1 Endoscopic vision model

A pinhole model is applied to describe image formation in classical vision system, based on thin lens hypothesis. Although endoscope is a long rigid tube composed of a succession of lenses that provide light from extremity of the tube to camera lens, pinhole model is assumed in literature to model endoscopic image (Caban and Seales (2004), Marti *et al.* (2004)). Nevertheless pinhole model is a linear approximation of the real camera projection. Therefore with endoscopic system which induces high radial distortion, it is necessary to improve accuracy of the model by adding nonlinear compensation (Zhang and Payandeh (2002)).

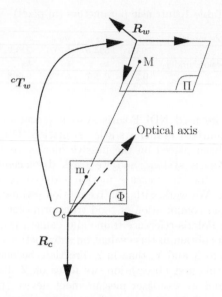

Fig. 1. Projection model : frame description

The pinhole model is split into two parts. First part (see Figure 1) maps the coordinates of point M defined in world frame R_w (attach to the plane Π) to coordinates of point m on plane Φ at a distance Z=1 from camera projection center O_c (center of camera frame R_c) (equation (1)). The coordinates $(x_n, y_n)^t$ of point m are the normalized coordinates, obtained form perspective projection without considering camera intrinsic parameters. The next step takes into account the intrinsic parameters of the vision system by applying frame transform from camera frame to image frame (equation (2)).

$$ s \begin{pmatrix} x_n \\ y_n \\ 1 \end{pmatrix} = \boldsymbol{P}{}^{\boldsymbol{c}}\boldsymbol{T_w} \begin{pmatrix} {}^wX \\ {}^wY \\ {}^wZ \\ 1 \end{pmatrix} \qquad (1) $$

$$ \begin{pmatrix} u \\ v \\ 1 \end{pmatrix} = \boldsymbol{K} \begin{pmatrix} x_n \\ y_n \\ 1 \end{pmatrix} \qquad (2) $$

The pinhole model is composed of :

- s is scale factor induced by perspective projection,
- $\boldsymbol{K}$ is the (3*3) intrinsic parameter matrix, compose of optical center coordinates (u_0, v_0) and focal length in X and Y direction (f_{c1}, f_{c2}),
- $\boldsymbol{P}$ is a (3*4) projection matrix,
- ${}^{\boldsymbol{c}}\boldsymbol{T_w}$ is the rigid transform matrix defining world frame (attach to object plan) w.r.t. camera frame.

Distortion model adds extra displacements on the normalized coordinates of point m. The model is composed of two components. First one takes into account radial distortion (equation (3)) , and second one approximates tangential distortion (equation (4)):

$$ \begin{pmatrix} x_d \\ y_d \end{pmatrix} = (1 + k_1 r^2 + k_2 r^4) \begin{pmatrix} x_n \\ y_n \end{pmatrix} + dx \qquad (3) $$

$$ dx = \begin{pmatrix} 2k_3\ x_n y_n + k_4(r^2 + 2x_n^2) \\ k_3(r^2 + 2y_n^2) + 2k_4 x_n y_n \end{pmatrix} \qquad (4) $$

The intrinsic parameters and coefficients of distortion model have been computed using Matlab Calibration Toolbox [1] (based on algorithm proposed by Zhang (1998)). Since model is an approximation of reality, workspace calibration must include volume created by heart motion interest point.

2.2 Pattern tracking algorithm

For each image acquired, we need to track the pattern resulting from the perspective projection of the object on image plane. We choose a pattern based algorithm able to track the whole image of the square object. We used Efficient Second order Method (ESM) proposed by Benhimane and Malis (2004). The application of the ESM algorithm to visual tracking allows an efficient homography estimation with high inter-frame displacements. In this algorithm, an iteratively estimate procedure find the optimal homography which minimizes the Sum of Square Differences between the reference pattern (defined off line) and the current pattern (which has been reprojected in the reference frame using the current homography). Because initial prediction of the homography is not available, we start with initial estimation equal to the identity matrix. Both the image derivatives of the template and the image derivatives of the current pattern are used to obtain an efficient second-order update. It is an efficient algorithm since only first derivatives are used and the Hessians are not explicitly computed.

Once we have compute the homography matrix $\boldsymbol{G(k)}$, at time k, between the reference and the current pattern, we extract image coordinates of the four corners points of the square pattern $(u_i(k), v_i(k))^t$ using image coordinates in the reference pattern $(u_i(0), v_i(0))^t$ through equation (5). The coordinates of the four corners in the reference pattern are manually selected during off line procedure and automatically refined by detecting nearest corner location at subpixel level.

$$ \lambda \begin{pmatrix} u_i(k) \\ v_i(k) \\ 1 \end{pmatrix} = \boldsymbol{G(k)} \begin{pmatrix} u_i(0) \\ v_i(0) \\ 1 \end{pmatrix} \quad \forall i = 1 \ldots 4 \quad (5) $$

[1] available on : http://www.vision.caltech.edu/bouguetj/calib_doc/ (last updated : 2005)

At the end of this step, we have only compute information in image space. We now have to integer metric information about the pattern to estimate 3D pose.

2.3 Pose estimation

The method used here was inspired from Zhang (1998) with known intrinsic parameters and implemented with OpenCV Library [2]. Assuming world frame attach to object plane, the 4 points respect $^wZ = 0$, so we can rewrite equation (1) in equation (6) without loss of generality.

$$\begin{pmatrix} x_n \\ y_n \\ 1 \end{pmatrix} = s^{-1} [r_1 r_2 t] \begin{pmatrix} {}^wX \\ {}^wY \\ 1 \end{pmatrix} = H(k) \begin{pmatrix} {}^wX \\ {}^wY \\ 1 \end{pmatrix} \tag{6}$$

where r_1 and r_2 are the first two columns of the rotation matrix and t is the translation vector from the rigid transformation $^cT_w(k)$ at time k.

Image plane coordinates related to world coordinates are used to compute perspective projection matrix estimation $\hat{H}(k)$ between $(x_n, y_n, 1)^t$ to $(^wX, ^wY, 1)^t$ (see Appendix A of Zhang (1998)). Scale factor s is retrieved computing the mean of norms of the first two columns of matrix $\hat{H}(k)$ ($\hat{s} = 0.5 * (||h_1|| + ||h_2||)^{-1}$). Then from equation (6), we have:

$$\hat{r_1} = \hat{s}h_1, \quad \hat{r_2} = \hat{s}h_2, \quad \hat{t} = \hat{s}h_3 \tag{7}$$

The third vector of rotation matrix is obtained using orthogonality property of this matrix :

$$\hat{r_3} = \hat{r_1} \times \hat{r_2} \tag{8}$$

3. RESULTS

3.1 Precision evaluation

Before applying this approach to estimate heart motion, we have evaluated accuracy of the method using calibrated measurement system. Different error sources can be listed: camera model approximation, pattern tracking accuracy, 3D reconstruction algorithm.

The endoscopic vision system is composed of a rigid endoscope (Hopkin's II from Karl Storz Inc), mounted on 35 mm focal lens optic and CMOS camera Dalsa 1m75. 300 W xenon light source is connected to the rigid endoscope. Frame rate is adjusted at 125 Hz, and 512*512 pixel image size is selected.

---

[2] available on : http://www.intel.com/technology/computing/opencv/index.htm (last updated : 2005)

Table 1. Intrinsic parameters (in pixel)

Pinhole model	f_{c1}	f_{c2}	u_0	v_0
	593.6	594.5	279.6	223.7
Distortion model	k_1	k_2	k_3	k_4
	-0.241	0.207	0.005	0.008

First we used NDI Polaris system (accuracy = 0.35 mm) to evaluate static estimation. Object have been placed on the passive marker tool of the Polaris system, and we track displacement of this tool to measure motion induced to the object. We work with relative motion estimation to avoid computation of rigid transformation between Polaris reference frame and camera frame. Results obtain in this evaluation show better precision in X and Y, than in Z direction. Secondly, from this first observation, we focus on Z direction and we use laser measurement device (precision = 0.05 mm) to evaluate the precision of our approach in dynamic. Object was manually displaced constrained to a plane parallel to image plane. Maximum error of 0.8 mm is observed w.r.t. laser measures (standard deviation : 0.34 mm). So we consider that our complete system (endoscopic calibrated camera + pattern tracking + pose estimation) give us estimation of motion with precision of 1 mm.

3.2 In vivo experimentation

The proposed approach have been applied on porcine model of 25 kg. The animal have been anaesthetised before intervention. Pig was under respiratory machine which constrain respiratory cycle to 20 cycles per minute. A thoracotomy have been performed to facilitate heart access. We assume that chest opening modify heart motion, but we think that in endoscopic situation, heart motion must be more constraint and observed displacement amplitude might be less important in real endoscopic context. Images have been acquired using endoscopic vision system presented in section 3.1. Endoscopic vision system is calibrated for a workspace of 20*15*15 mm, centered at a distance of 55 mm from the endoscope tip. Intrinsic parameters are shown in Table 1.

Artificial passive markers have been placed on the heart surface as shown in Figure 2. Each planar marker are square of 5 mm side, drawn on white paper. To avoid lack of information for tracking algorithm, variable grey value have been used inside the pattern. Sequences of 1900 images have acquired with a sampling time of 8 ms.

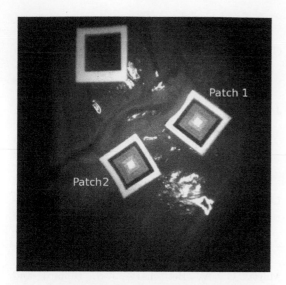

Fig. 2. Endocsopic image of the heart with patchs

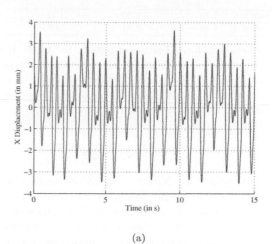

(a)

Table 2. Spectral analysis

Frequency (in Hz)	0.34	0.67	1.19	2.38	3.57	4.76
Density in X direction	8.7%	0%	21.8%	60%	2.8%	6.7%
Density in Y direction	3.9%	1.9%	45.6%	33%	3.9%	11.7%
Density in Z direction	70.9%	11.5%	5.9%	8.7%	1.2%	1.8%

3.3 Motion analysis

Estimation of heart motion are presented in figure 3. Motion is estimated over the entire acquired sequence, that is 15 s.

A spectral analysis have been performed to evaluate frequency component of the estimated signal (see table 2). The first two components ($f_1 = 0.34$ Hz, and $f_2 = 0.68$ Hz) must be associated with respiratory activity. f_1 is equal to frequency impose by the respiratory machine (20 cycles per minute). The second one must be treated as harmonic component of the respiratory activity ($f_2 = 2f_1$). Heart activity provides 4 other frequencies. $f_3 = 1.19$ Hz might represent the heart beat cycle (around 70 beats per minute), and the three others are harmonics of f_3. The spectral analysis shows that estimated motion are dominated by cardiac and respiratory activities. From power spectral density analysis, we can see that motion in X and Y direction (parallel to image plane) are mostly governed by cardiac activity, whereas amplitude of the motion in Z direction is greatly induced by respiratory activity. By applying low pass filter of 1Hz cutoff frequency, we could extract respiratory component from estimated motion in Z direction (see bold plot on Figure 3-c). Thus maximum amplitude observed in Z direction around 11 mm is composed of respiratory displacement of 6 mm.

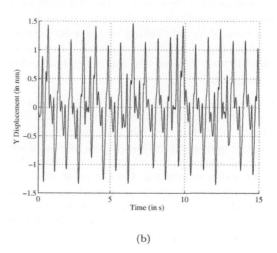

(b)

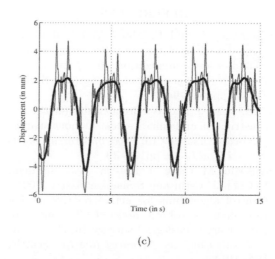

(c)

Fig. 3. Motion estimation of patch 1 : (a) X direction, (b) Y direction, (c) Z direction

Table 3. Maximum acceleration of the
estimated motion

	$\ddot{x}$ (in $m.s^{-2}$)	$\ddot{y}$ (in $m.s^{-2}$)	$\ddot{z}$ (in $m.s^{-2}$)
patch 1	1.73	1.09	3.33
patch 2	1.38	0.94	3.67

Acceleration have been computed (see table 3). Heart motion exhibit maximum acceleration larger than $3\ m.s^{-2}$. Moreover, estimation obtain from other square objects placed at other location on the heart exhibits acceleration around $4\ m.s^{-2}$.

4. CONCLUSIONS

In this paper, we have presented the estimation of heart motion using available vision system in operating room. Proposed method exhibits result with precision better than 1 mm. *In vivo* experimentation have been performed on porcine model. Estimated heart motion is clearly governed by cardiac and heart cycle activities. Depending on location on heart surface, acceleration up to $4\ m.s^{-2}$ have been observed. Taking into account acceleration obtained, robotic system must be able to follow $10\ m.s^{-2}$ to ensure motion compensation in large security.

On going work is about improvement of the proposed approach. We currently work on in two different way. On one hand we develop a real-time (sample time less than 10 ms) version of the proposed approach to perform motion estimation during video acquisition. On the other hand, we work on the development of biomechanical model to describe local surface displacement based on estimation of few points around the working area (defining some limit conditions).

REFERENCES

Benhimane, S. and E. Malis (2004). Real-time image-based tracking of planes using efficient second-order minimization. In: *Proc. of Int. Conf. on Intelligent Robot and Systems*. Sendai, Japan. pp. 943–948.

Caban, Jesus J. and W. Brent Seales (2004). Reconstruction and enhancement in monocular laparoscopic imagery. In: *Proc. of Medicine Meets Virtual Reality 12*. pp. 37–39.

Cavusoglu, M. Cenk, J. Rotella, W.S. Newman, S. Choi, J. Ustin and S.Shankar Sastry (2005). Control algorithms for active relative motion cancelling for robotic assisted off-pump coronary artery bypass graft surgery. In: *Proc. of the 12th Int. Conf. on Advanced Robotics*. Seattle, WA, USA.

Ginhoux, R., J. Gangloff, M. de Mathelin, L. Soler, M. M. Arena Sanchez and J. Marescaux (2005). Active filtering of physiological motion in robotized surgery using predictive control. *IEEE Trans on Robotics* **21**(1), 67–79.

Guthart, G. S. and J. K. Salisbury (2000). The intuitive telesurgery system: overview and application. In: *Proc. of Int. Conf. Of Robotics and Automation*. pp. 618–621.

Jansen, E. W.L., P. F. Gründeman, C. Borst, F. Eefting, J. Diephuis, A. Nierich, J. R. Lahpor and J. J. Bredée (1997). Less invasive off-pump cabg using a suction device for immobilization: the octopus method. *Eur. Jour. of Cardio-Thoracic Surgery* **12**, 406–412.

Lemma, M., A. Mangini, A. Reaelli and F. Acocella (2005). Do cardiac stabilizers really stabilize? experimental quantitative analysis of mechanical stabilization. *Interactive Cardiovascular and Thoracic Surgery* **4**, 222–226.

Marti, G., V. Bettschart, J.-S. Billiard and C. Baur (2004). Hybrid method for both calibration and registration of an endoscope with an active optical marker. In: *Proc. of Computer Assisted Radiology and Surgery*. pp. 159–164.

Nakamura, Y., K. Kishi and H. Kawakami (2001). Heartbeat synchronization for robotic cardiac surgery. In: *Proc. of Int. Conf. on Robotics and Automation*. Seoul, Korea. pp. 2014–2019.

Ortmaier, T., M. Groger, D. H. Boehm, V. Falk and G. Hirzinger (2005). Motion estimation in beating heart surgery. *IEEE Trans. on Biomedical Engineering* **52**(10), 1729–1740.

Picone, A. L., C. J. Lutz, C. Finck, D. Carney, L. A. Gatto, A. Paskanik, B. Searles, K. Snyder and G. Nieman (1999). Multiple sequential insults cause post-pump syndrome. *Annals of Thoracic Surgery* **67**, 978–985.

Zhang, X. and S. Payandeh (2002). Application of visual tracking for robotic-assisted laparoscopic surgery. *Journal of Robotics Systems* **19**(7), 315–328.

Zhang, Z. (1998). A flexible new technique for camera calibration. Technical Report MSR-TR-98-71. Microsoft Research.

INVESTIGATION ON BIOMEDICAL MEASUREMENT ACCURACY IN ELECTRODE-SKIN TESTS

W Wang, L Wang, B Tunstall, M Brien[1] and D-W Gu[1]

Biomedical Engineering Group. School of Engineering and Technology, De Montfort University, Leicester LE1 9BH, UK
1 Control & Instrumentation Group, Department of Engineering, University of Leicester, Leicester LE1 7RH, UK

Abstract. The paper investigates three sources of potential error in measurements that may be taken as part of a clinical protocol using Electrical Impedance Tomography (EIT). The findings of an investigation show that the error of two types of electrode used (Stainless Steel and ECG) could produce 13.5-44.5%, 1.5-34.8% and 9.9-83.7% errors in repeatability, contact drift and electrode mismatching studies, respectively. Such widely varying errors challenge EIT imaging both when measurements are taken at different clinical visits and even at the same visit. The paper discusses the consequence of such measurement inaccuracies and proposes a "best practice" showing how to reduce these errors. *Copyright © 2006 IFAC*

Keywords: Biomedical, Contact resistance, Electrodes, Repeatability, Variance

1. INTRODUCTION

The three most commonly recognized electrode related errors when investigating the repeatability of electrical impedance tomography (EIT) images in clinical applications are: Electrode positioning; Electrode-skin artefacts; and variations in electrode-skin contact impedance during either a single clinical measurement or between different clinical measurements.

The first two factors have been comprehensively investigated in the preceding decades. To reduce electrode positioning errors a flexible, screen printed harnesses has been developed for thoracic applications (McAdams et al 1994) whilst 32-electrode based electrode system (Kerner et al 2002) has been used for breast cancer applications. Whilst the electrode-skin artefact has been addressed by a number of groups (Gonzalez-Correa et al 2005, Asfaw and Adler 2005, Jossinet et al 1994, Wang et al 1995a). The final error source is typically addressed by using the four-electrode impedance measurement while keeping the output impedance of the current source as high as possible. However no systematic studies have been made into the potential effect of such errors on a clinical protocol.

Measurement variation caused by electrode-skin contact impedance can be termed as electrode contact impedance (ECI) errors. The ECI errors or variation could, in practice, produce larger variations than the internal impedance changes measured on the electrodes. Although the required accuracy of the EIT system depends upon the application, it is generally considered that 10% of the minimum change is required. This gives the minimum acceptable accuracy for lung ventilation measures as 1% whilst cardiac related changes demand 0.1% accuracy (Brown et al 1994, Wang et al 1994, Wang et al 1995b). For other clinical applications, such as detecting a deeply embedded breast cancer the required accuracy could be better than 0.01%. Furthermore, the ECI affected Repeatability Errors (RPE) can be one of the most dominant factors in present "contact-electrode" based EIT techniques. The most commonly appearing ECI errors to affect the repeatability are:

Inter-testing Variation Error (IVE): Random variations caused by ECI generated between different measurements on a given subject. This results in poor repeatability of measurements taken from the same patient at different clinical visits such as those required for cancer detection (Wang et al 1998) and lung ventilation studies (Smit ct al 2003);

Time-dependant Variation Error (TVE): Random errors produced by ECI on an individual set of electrode measurements during a given, longer, measurement period, such as during long term monitoring. This can also affect mismatching between electrode pairs;

Inter-electrode Mismatching Error (IME): Random

variations between each electrode in any measurement, this RPE can cause electrode-skin contact variation to produce ECI in differential mode that may mimic the measured, differential, bioimpedance signal;

Additional errors: these could be introduced by variations of pressure on the electrodes such as may result from varying constrictive force applied to a body during measurements, or the force applied when resting a planar array of electrodes on an area of the body; and the contact agent used;

Therefore a series of experiments that emulate the procedures that may be used during a clinical application of EIT have been undertaken at De Montfort University. In addition to investigating the named error sources, IVE and TVE with their associated IME, a further experiment was performed to clarify the effect caused by varying the pressure used to ensure electrode-skin contact. In this preliminary study it was decided to use the two most commonly used electrodes among EIT groups: stainless steel and the silver/silver chloride (Ag/AgCl) based ECG electrode, which have been used in clinical applications.

2. EXPERIMENTAL METHODOLOGY

Experiments were undertaken using a subset of the De Montfort Mk3A Electrical Impedance Mammography (EIM) system functionality. The De Montfort Mk3a EIM system is a 256 channel, DSP based system utilizing a 65MSPS analogue-to-digital converter with 12-bit resolution coupled to a 6-bit Programmable Gain Amplifier.

A single 32 channel ring electrode was selected for this series with the electrodes arranged in the interlaced configuration (16 current driver and 16 voltage receive electrodes); However due to the limited space available on the volunteers forearm, data from only 9 electrodes are analyzed using electrodes 4 and 6 as the current drive pair, with the largest measurements being on electrode pair 3&5 (termed V2) and pair 5&7 (termed V3), and the 2nd largest signal being present on electrode pair 1&3 (termed V1) and electrodes 7&9 (termed V4).

The frequency selected for this study, was 200 kHz;

At each measurement 40 data sets were collected, and averaged, in a period of 30-40 seconds. This was undertaken in order to reduce movement, ventilation and cardiac related artefacts that may have been present during each test;

The DSP system was setup for a long integration period, the overall measurement accuracy presented on this paper is better than 0.01%

Both a ring of 5mm diameter electrodes and ECG electrodes were pressed against the volunteers forearm (Fig 1). Where the electrode ring (Fig 2) was used it was placed to minimise any differences

between the two electrode arrangements, although inter-electrode spacing, 12mm for electrode ring and 25mm for ECG electrodes, could not be matched.

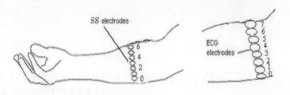

Fig 1. The placement of the stainless steel (SS) electrode ring and ECG electrodes, on the healthy male volunteers forearm

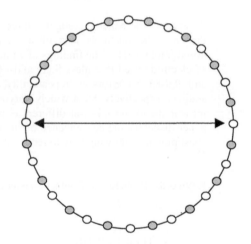

Fig 2. Arrangement of 32-electrode ring used for the experiments, shading indicates electrodes used to drive current into the object under test. The pair used to inject current during this study was electrodes 4 & 6 with the surrounding electrodes 1, 3, 5, 7 and 9 being used for voltage detection

2.1. Inter-testing Variation Error (IVE)

This experiment was repeated using three different electrode types:

    Stainless steel without conductive gel (Dry)
    Stainless steel with conductive gel (Gel)
    ECG electrodes (ECG)

The electrodes were removed from the subject between each experiment thus simulating the taking of readings from the same patient at different clinical visits, data being collected from the same positions using identical electrodes. The volunteers' skin was carefully prepared using conventional techniques between each experiment. The experiments were undertaken at intervals of 22.5 minutes (± 7.5 minutes) with ten collections for the Stainless Steel electrodes, seven collections were used for the ECG electrodes due to skin irritation at the contact point. Each collection of data comprised of taking 40 readings and averaging them to remove effects such as cardiac related changes and artefacts related to patient movement that might otherwise have affected the variations detected.

2.2. Time-dependant Variation Error (TVE)

The methodology used was the similar to that undertaken in 2.1, using the same variations in electrode environment and type. However the electrodes were placed on the volunteers forearm and remained in contact with the skin throughout each test for a period of 50 minutes. Ten data collections were undertaken during this period. As in the previous case each collection of data comprised of taking 40 readings and calculating the average. Further measures were made of the effect of differential drift causing mismatching errors, IME, between the electrode pairs.

2.3. Contact force variations

The methodology for each test was the same as in 2.1; however the tests used only the stainless steel electrodes under the two environments: Dry and Gel. Furthermore the loading used to ensure contact between the electrodes and the skin was varied, the loadings used, in simulation of a clinical procedure, were:

> Light (hand) pressure
> 25kPa overpressure
> 50kPa overpressure

In addition to the analysis of the variations at each electrode pairing an analysis of effect of varying the contact pressure on the IME was undertaken.

2.4. Analysis

The data resulting from the experiments were analysed for the mean and standard deviation of the findings with the measurement error in the findings being defined as:

$$Error = \frac{SD}{Mean}$$

(1)

Further, where determining the effect of mismatching between measurements on the electrode pairs this was defined as being:

$$Mismatch = \frac{|Vn_1 - Vn_2|}{Vn_2}$$

(2)

Vn1 and Vn2 indicate the measurements to either side of the current injection pair. For example, pairing 4-6/3-5 indicates the measurement at electrode pair 3 & 5 when current is driven at electrode pair 4 & 6 i.e. measurement V2. Whilst "Mismatch (V2 V3)" utilises reading V2, detection electrode pair 3 & 5, as Vn1 and V3, detection electrodes 5 and 7, as Vn2.

3. RESULTS AND DISCUSSION

The data given in the following tables are voltage readings, all have been normalized to 1, corresponding to 0.5 volts with the De Montfort MK3A EIM system.

3.1. Inter-testing Variation Error (IVE)

As can be seen, in the tables below, from the tests on the three electrode types (Stainless steel without gel, Stainless steel with gel, and ECG) the maximum errors in the adjacent electrode pair (Table 1a) are 18%, 22% and 21% respectively and in the 2nd electrode pair (Table 1b) are 44%, 38% and 43% respectively. Thus it is obvious that the RPE increases with the poorer signal-to-noise ratio (SNR) resulting from the reduced signal size produced at the 2nd electrode pair.

Further the use of conducting gel with the steel electrodes does not show a significant reduction in variation as expected. This could be a result of the conduction being improved for each contact generally, whilst enlarging the variations between each measurement amongst the electrode pairs. We postulate that such variations are caused by difficulty controlling the amount of gel on each electrode, this if from observations of random amounts of residual gel between the electrodes.

Table 1a. Findings from experiments investigating errors in the repeatability of measurements from independent tests using Dry, Gel and ECG electrodes

| | Receive Pair | | | | | |
| | Electrodes 3 & 5 [V2] | | | Electrodes 5 & 7 [V3] | | |
	Dry	Gel	ECG	Dry	Gel	ECG
Mean	0.4714	0.7392	0.4053	0.4640	0.7174	0.4582
SD	0.0693	0.1565	0.0858	0.0838	0.1591	0.0617
Error	0.1470	0.2117	0.2116	0.1806	0.2217	0.1347

Table 1b. Findings from experiments investigating IVE from independent tests using Dry, Gel and ECG electrodes (alternative pairs)

| | Receive Pair | | | | | |
| | Electrodes 1 & 3 [V1] | | | Electrodes 7 & 9 [V4] | | |
	Dry	Gel	ECG	Dry	Gel	ECG
Mean	0.3335	0.44156	0.3676	0.2564	0.4001	0.3921
SD	0.1155	0.1452	0.0608	0.1140	0.1504	0.1675
Error	0.3463	0.3289	0.1653	0.4446	0.3758	0.4271

Table 1c. Mismatching between electrode pairs during IVE experiments using the three electrode types: Dry, Gel and ECG

| | Mismatch on the largest measurement (V2 V3) | | | Mismatch on the 2nd largest measurement (V1 V4) | | |
	Dry	Gel	ECG	Dry	Gel	ECG
Mean	0.0985	0.1972	0.2280	0.3887	0.3855	0.4891
SD	0.0447	0.2380	0.1645	0.3218	0.4429	0.6080
Error	0.4537	1.2068	0.7215	0.8278	1.1487	1.2431

The ECG electrode result for measurement V4 is inconsistent with the other findings for this electrode type. We postulate two potential causes for this finding. The first is that the contact with the skin was poorly managed. Such management problems could be due to the location on the volunteer or movement in the arm between measurements. An alternative explanation is that there was a localized skin artefact at the measurement point. The effect is not shown in the steel electrode findings due to slightly different spacing between the steel and ECG electrodes.

In terms of mismatching, using the Stainless Steel electrode without gel gives much better results than other two methods. This would suggest that great care should be taken if conductive gel is used due to the poorer IME repeatability. Thus we can conclude that dry steel electrodes are preferable when repeatedly taking measurements from the same patient.

3.2. Time-dependant Variation Error (TVE)

As can be seen, in the tables below, from the long-duration tests on the three electrode types (Stainless steel without gel, Stainless steel with gel, and ECG), the maximum errors in the adjacent electrode pair (Table 2a) are 7%, 18% and 11% respectively and in the 2nd electrode pair (Table 2b) are 23%, 35% and 12% respectively. Thus the findings appear to indicate that the use of ECG electrodes offers the most consistent electrode interface over a period of time. Further analysis between the two steel electrode types, using gel does not improve the repeatability but has doubled the RPE from an average of 14% (7% & 23%) to 24% (18% & 35%).

For non-ECG electrodes, where no gel is used, the mismatching Error can be 67%, this compares with 124% when gel is used. This is once again contrary to our expectations that the Gel would provide a better result. This could be, as previously suggested, due to the varying amount of gel on each electrode. This further supports ECG electrodes as offering the most constant interface over a period of time.

However where ECG electrodes are used for long duration studies has been found to result in a mean mismatch of between 13% and 32% depending upon the pairs considered. This compares with 26% and 24% for dry electrodes and between 22% and 31% where gel is used with steel electrodes. Such a finding is disconcerting as it indicates that the use of ECG electrodes offers no better resistance to IME than the other electrode types.

Thus it can be stated, with reservations, that ECG electrodes are the best suited of the three types to monitoring experiments. However despite offering little variation in the results from individual pairs the potential for large IME would appear to challenge the use of such electrodes for EIT experiments of an extended period.

3.3. Contact force variations

The following data does not include individual test results; only the calculated mean, SD and error are given.

Table 2a. Findings from TVE experiments using the three electrode types, Dry, Gel and ECG

| | Receive Pair | | | | | |
| | Electrodes 3 & 5 [V2] | | | Electrodes 5 & 7 [V3] | | |
	Dry	Gel	ECG	Dry	Gel	ECG
Mean	0.5420	0.7049	0.3843	0.4320	0.7220	0.4466
SD	0.0331	0.1045	0.0374	0.0323	0.1326	0.0477
Error	0.0612	0.1483	0.0973	0.0749	0.1837	0.1069

Table 2b. Findings from TVE experiments using the three electrode types, Dry, Gel and ECG (alternative pairs)

| | Receive Pair | | | | | |
| | Electrodes 1 & 3 [V1] | | | Electrodes 7 & 9 [V4] | | |
	Dry	Gel	ECG	Dry	Gel	ECG
Mean	0.3560	0.4926	0.3515	0.3308	0.5372	0.5189
SD	0.0693	0.1713	0.0051	0.0776	0.1483	0.0607
Error	0.1948	0.3478	0.0145	0.2346	0.2761	0.1170

Table 2c. Mismatching between electrode pairs during TVE experiments using the three electrode types, Dry, Gel and ECG

| | Mismatch on the largest measurement (V2 V3) | | | Mismatch on the 2nd largest measurement (V1 V4) | | |
	Dry	Gel	ECG	Dry	Gel	ECG
Mean	0.2568	0.2195	0.1326	0.2394	0.3102	0.3158
SD	0.0564	0.2723	0.1274	0.1597	0.2965	0.1035
Error	0.2196	1.2409	0.9607	0.6673	0.9559	0.3278

Table 3a. Findings from experiment investigating errors due to variations in applied pressure using Dry and Gel electrodes

| | Receive Pair (Stainless Steel) | | | | Mismatching (V2 V3) | |
| | Electrodes 3 & 5 [V2] | | Electrodes 5 & 7 [V3] | | | |
	Dry	Gel	Dry	Gel	Dry	Gel
Light						
Mean	0.5420	0.7049	0.4320	0.7220	0.2568	0.2195
SD	0.0331	0.1045	0.0323	0.1326	0.0564	0.2723
Error	0.0611	0.1482	0.0748	0.1837	0.2196	1.2409
25kPa						
Mean	0.4934	0.7101	0.4210	0.7576	0.1737	0.1995
SD	0.0295	0.0699	0.0234	0.1411	0.0734	0.2237
Error	0.0598	0.0984	0.0556	0.1862	0.4229	1.1210
50kPa						
Mean	0.4607	0.8212	0.4106	0.8493	0.1383	0.5486
SD	0.0237	0.1303	0.0219	0.2306	0.0481	1.0600
Error	0.0514	0.1587	0.0533	0.2715	0.3480	1.9322

Table 3b. Findings from experiment investigating errors due to variations in applied pressure using Dry and Gel electrodes (alternative pairs)

| | Receive Pair (Stainless Steel) | | | | Mismatch (V1 V4) | |
| | Electrodes 1 & 3 [V1] | | Electrodes 7 & 9 [V4] | | | |
	Dry	Gel	Dry	Gel	Dry	Gel
Light						
Mean	0.3560	0.5225	0.3308	0.5252	0.2425	0.2720
SD	0.0693	0.1185	0.0776	0.1592	0.1391	0.2404
Error	0.1948	0.2268	0.2346	0.3031	0.5737	0.8838
25kPa						
Mean	0.4112	0.5743	0.2336	0.7059	0.8370	0.4029
SD	0.0329	0.1032	0.0484	0.2688	0.4371	0.2064
Error	0.0801	0.1796	0.2071	0.3807	0.5223	0.5124
50kPa						
Mean	0.3769	0.6901	0.2837	0.7491	0.4754	0.2023
SD	0.0311	0.0674	0.0754	0.1717	0.5391	0.2018
Error	0.0825	0.0977	0.2659	0.2293	1.1340	0.9977

Table 3c. Mean error values from contact force experiment at different electrode pairings

| Pair | Stainless Steel without Gel | | | | | |
| | Overpressure | | | Change | | |
	None	25kPa	50kPa	25kPa	50kPa	Average
V2	0.5420	0.4934	0.4607	9.0%	15.0%	7.9%
V3	0.4320	0.4210	0.4106	2.5%	5.0%	
V1	0.3560	0.4112	0.3769	15.5%	5.9%	16.3%
V4	0.3308	0.2336	0.2837	29.4%	14.2%	

| Pair | Stainless Steel with Gel | | | | | |
| | Overpressure | | | Change | | |
	None	25kPa	50kPa	25kPa	50kPa	Average
V2	0.7049	0.7101	0.8212	0.7%	16.5%	9.9%
V3	0.7220	0.7576	0.8493	4.9%	17.6%	
V1	0.5225	0.5743	0.6901	9.9%	32.1%	29.8%
V4	0.5252	0.7059	0.7491	34.4%	42.6%	

Using the largest signal pair it can be seen, from the mean and the SD that the use of gel not only increases the apparent impedance at the interface but increases the variation across the experiments. The former can be considered as due to the gel forming an additional resistive layer at the electrode-skin interface. The latter we postulate is due to an inconsistency between the interfaces, thereby increasing the range between the best and worst electrode pairs

For dry electrodes increasing the contact load is shown to reduce the error for individual electrode pairs. However the mismatching between pairs can be seen to increase from 22% to 35% as the overpressure rises to 50kPa. This contrasts with the use of conductive gel where for individual pairs there is no effect, the mismatching between pairs increases potentially due to exacerbation of the differences between gel coverage of the electrodes under investigation.

Variation in overpressure has a considerable effect on the signal detected. From table 3c we can see that for the V2 and V3, pressure effects average 7.9% with a maximum of 15% for a 50kPa change of electrode pair V2. Whilst for V1 and V4 these changes averaged 16.3% with a 29.4% maximum for V4 under 25kPa pressure. Considering the gel covered electrodes, the results are 9.9% and 17.6% (V3 under 50kPa) and 29.8% and 42.6% (V4 under 50kPa) for the largest and second largest signal pairs

respectively. The pressure effect for the 1st and 2nd largest pairs of electrodes is from 7.9% to 9.9% and 16.3% to 29.8% respectively, which means the effect of pressure changes could introduce an average error of up to 29.8%, with an individual electrode having an IME of 42.6%. We postulate that such pressure sensitivity may be attributed to the contact area varying dependant upon the force applied. This finding has a critical importance as such an effect would severely compromise any ability of an EIT system to detect change within the underlying tissues. Where the pressure is controlled data indicates an average error of 20%, i.e. a four-fold improvement against when there is no pressure control.

These findings have shown that the electrode-skin interface is particularly susceptible to RPE introduced by poor, or no, control on the pressure experienced. Such findings offer the greatest challenge to systems whereby the electrode interface is placed upon the subject although it would, to a lesser degree, affect other constrictive-based interfaces due to their improved overpressure control.

4. CONCLUSIONS

The paper has introduced terminology for a number of problems associated with the electrode-skin interface and has attempted to quantify the effect of those sources under conditions that may be encountered during a clinical evaluation of EIT. The tests have shown that EIT may be considered as being poorly suited to the clinical environment and as such these error sources may lead to issues related to clinical acceptance of this technology as a diagnostic tool.

The difficulties are typified by the effect of contact force variation as shown in Table 3c where differences between the signals of up to 42.6% have been detected due to this change. Associated errors including electrode mismatch as given in Table 3b have been indicated as being in excess of 100%. These would, in the authors' opinion, preclude an EIT system from reliably detecting all but the grossest changes in underlying pathology. Such pressure sensitivity of the interface shows that great care must be taken when applying the electrodes to the skin. For example a methodology whereby an array of electrodes are placed on the skin need stringent protocols applied to the force used to the overall array and the pressure experienced at each individual electrode as it touches the skin.

Further the choice of electrode type used is of importance. An example of this is shown in the DME experiment where the use of stainless steel electrodes leads to large mismatching errors. Thus indicating that long-term monitoring applications (Table 2a-c) are better suited to the use of ECG electrodes only. However the reverse is true when taking into account the repetition of measurements (Table 1a-c). Here the use of stainless steel electrodes are indicated, however conductive gel has been shown to severely affect the repeatability and therefore must also be considered when using such electrodes. Thus the conclusion that can be drawn from the findings of this preliminary study is that the choice of electrodes may be critical to the application under investigation.

Although this study has indicated that all of the investigated electrode designs present problems to the clinical utility of EIT a "best practice" can be derived that should include:

Ensuring the same amount of conductive gel is used on all electrodes wherever possible

Ensuring that the overpressure experienced at each electrode is the same

Reducing the period for which electrodes are in contact with the skin

Preparing the skin contacted using best possible techniques

Following such practices will however leave a residual RPE of approximately 18% in the result; this will continue to challenge users of conventional electrodes. Work is continuing at De Montfort to further investigate the properties and problems of the electrode-skin interface utilising other methods across a range of frequencies. This work offers the hope of finding novel electrode-skin interfacing techniques and procedures that should further reduce RPE at this critical boundary.

REFERENCES

Asfaw Y, and Adler A 2005 Automatic detection of detached and erroneous electrodes in electrical impedance tomography. *Physio. Meas,* **26** S175–S183

Brown B H, Barber D C , Wang W, Lu L, Leathard A D, Smallwood R H, Hampshire A R, Mackay R and Hatzigalanis 1994 Multi-frequency imaging and modelling of respiratory related electrical impedance changes. *Physiol Meas,* **15(2A)** A1-A12

Gonzalez-Correa C A, Brown B H, Smallwood R H, Walker D C and Bardhan K D 2005 Electrical bioimpedance readings increase with higher pressure applied to the measuring probe. *Physiol. Meas,* **26** S39–S47

Jossinet J, Tourtel C and Jarry R 1994 Active current electrodes for in vivo electrical impedance tomography. *Physiol Meas* **15** A83-A90

Kerner T. E., Paulsen K. D., Hartov A., Soho S. K., Poplack S. P. (2002): Electrical Impedance Spectroscopy of the Breast: Clinical Imaging Results in 26 Subjects. *IEEE Trans. Med. Imaging,* **21(6)**: 638-645

McAdams E T, McLaughlin J A and J McC Anderson, 1994 Multi-electrode systems for electrical impedance tomography. *Physiol Meas,* **15** A101-AI06

Smit H J, Handoko M L, Noordegraaf A V, Faes T J C, Postmus P E, de Vries P and Boonstra A (2003): Electrical impedance tomography to measure pulmonary perfusion: is the reproducibility high enough for clinical practice? *Physiol. Meas,* **24** 491–9

Wang W, Brown B H and Leathard A D 1994 Noise equalisation within EIT images *Physiol Meas* **15(2A)** 211-16

Wang W, Brown B H and Barber D C 1995a System errors, noise and artefacts in Sheffield MK3 electrical impedance tomographic spectroscope (EITS) system In: *Proceedings of the IX ICEBI* (E Gersing and H Schaffer (Ed))

Wang W, Barber D C and Brown B H 1995b Recovery of cardiac related changes in Sheffield EIT images by advanced signal processing techniques, In: *Proceedings of the IX ICEBI* (E Gersing and H Schaffer (Ed))

Wang W, Tunstall B, Chauhan D and McCormick M 1998 The design of De Montfort Mk2 electrical impedance mammography system, In: *Proceedings of the 20th IEEE, EMBS* (H K Chang and Y T Zhang (Ed))

IDENTIFICATION OF REGULATORY PATHWAYS OF THE CELL CYCLE IN FISSION YEAST

F. Amato[*], M. Bansal[†], C. Cosentino[*,§],
W. Curatola[*], D. di Bernardo[†]

[*]School of Computer and Biomedical Engineering,
Università degli Studi Magna Graecia di Catanzaro,
viale Europa, loc. Germaneto, 88100 Catanzaro (Italy)
[†]Telethon Institute of Genetics and Medicine,
via P. Castellino 111, 80131, Napoli, (Italy)

Abstract: A novel identification method is presented, aimed at the reconstruction of genetic network structures. The iterative identification algorithm is based on least square linear regression, tailored to the case of scale free networks. The devised technique is assessed by comparing identification results with a well established *in silico* model of fission yeast cell cycle. Finally it is exploited for identifying the genetic network of fission yeast from experimental data available in the literature. *Copyright © 2006 IFAC*

Keywords: system identification, identification algorithm, regression algorithm, biotechnology.

1. INTRODUCTION

The goal of our research is to devise algorithms able to identify the interaction network between genes from gene expression data. The devised approach has been applied to the gene network regulating the fission yeast cell cycle. The cell cycle is divided into a number of distinct phases. Normal, non-proliferating cells exist in the phase known as G0. In G1 phase, the cell increases in size and begins to produce the molecules required for DNA replication. The process of DNA replication occurs in S-phase. Following a second preparatory phase, called G2, the cell initiates the process of mitosis, or M phase, eventually forming two daughter cells. An important point in the cell cycle occurs at the restriction point, where the cell commits itself to completing the cell cycle. In addition to the restriction point, there are other points along the cell cycle, called checkpoints, in which cells check on the integrity of the DNA and other key structural components to ensure proper progression of the cell cycle. At the molecular level,

the cell cycle is a complex process that is controlled by a vast network of biochemical pathways within cells. These pathways become deregulated in cancer cells, resulting in abnormal cell proliferation and accumulation. As a result, cancer cells undergo cell division in an uncontrolled way. Virtually all cancer cells have major defects in apoptosis and cell cycle pathways. Experiments show clusters of genes that exhibit similar expression profiles.

This observation can be exploited in order to obtain reduced order models, in spite of the large number of genes involved in the cell cycle of even the simplest organisms.

Identifying and predicting expression profiles and interrelations between genes can yield positive outcomes not only on the knowledge of the process itself, but also on the way biologists deal with it: Abnormal expression of a certain gene is typically a marker for a disease (if the gene is involved in cell cycle, the disease is typically a cancer) and an accurate *in silico* model can provide valuable information on how to bring back the system to a normal operative condition (Bower and Bolouri, 2001), (Kitano, 2001).

[§] This author is responsible for correspondence:
carlo.cosentino@unicz.it.

The first step to devise and refine an identification technique consists of applying it to simple monocellular organisms, e.g. yeasts, for which there is a huge availability of experimental data and also extensive prior knowledge about transcriptional regulatory networks.

Given two genes, they will be said adjacent if one influences the expression of the other, thus our goal is to draw a map of adjacent genes. The data to utilize for this purpose are derived from microarray experiments, which allow to analyze in parallel the expression level of thousands of genes, and also to pick several samples in a cycle period. We will exploit the data presented by Rustici *et al.* (2004).

Previous approaches to the identification of genetic networks through continuous-time dynamical models have been presented by Di Bernardo *et al.*(2005, 2004) and Gardner *et al.* (2003), where the key point is to demonstrate suitability of linear models to describing the dynamics of the cell cycle, by assuming small perturbations.

The present work introduces a refinement of the identification technique devised by Amato *et al.* (2005), where promising results were obtained by using an algorithm tailored for the identification of sparse matrices, such as the ones derived when modelling scale-free networks (i.e. networks exhibiting loose connectivity). The method presented here is first validated on the well known *in silico* model of fission yeast by Novak and Tyson (Novak and Tyson, 1997), (Novak *et al.*, 2001), (Steuer, 2004). Finally, the technique is applied to the data presented by Rustici *et al.* (2004): A model is identified exploiting one set of experimental measurements, and it is subsequently validated on a second set of data.

The paper is structured as follows: Section 2 introduces the notations and describes the network reconstruction algorithm. A virtual identification experiment is then performed in Section 3, by using the Novak-Tyson model to generate virtual "experimental" data points and evaluate the identification results. Finally the data by Rustici et al. (2004) are examined in Section 4 and conclusions are drawn in Section 5.

2. NETWORK RECONSTRUCTION ALGORITHM

Let us consider a discrete-time system, composed by a system of n difference equations, in the corrensponding n state variables
$$x(k+1) = Ax(k),$$
where
$$x(k) = \begin{pmatrix} x_1(k) \\ \vdots \\ x_n(k) \end{pmatrix}, \quad A \in R^{n \times n}.$$

Assume that m data points (number of experiments) are available, then
$$\Xi := (x(m) \cdots x(1)) = A\Omega,$$
where
$$\Omega := (x(m-1) \cdots x(0)).$$

Our aim is to reconstruct the matrix A from the values $x(k)$, for $i=0,...,m$; note that a non zero coefficient in the A matrix corresponds to a link between two states (which represent the genes of our network). At first hand, if $m>n$, it is a classical linear regression problem, that can be put in the form
$$\widetilde{x}_i^T := (x_i(m) \cdots x_i(1)) = a_{i,*} \cdot \Omega, \quad i=1,...,n$$
where $\widetilde{x}_i^T$ is the vector of experimental observations of state x_i and $a_{i,*}$ represents the i-th row of A. The coefficients of the linear regression can be computed as
$$a_{i,*} = \widetilde{x}_i^T \Omega^\dagger, \quad i=1,...,n \qquad (1)$$
where $\Omega^\dagger$ is the right pseudo-inverse of Ω, that is $\Omega^\dagger = \Omega^T (\Omega\Omega^T)^{-1}$.

By applying (1) to each row of A one can obtain an estimate of the connection matrix. Due to the nature of the system, the network is scale-free, that means each gene has only few adjacent nodes; from a mathematical point of view, this corresponds to a sparse matrix (i.e. a matrix with a large percentage of null entries). The proposed algorithm exploits such information by nullifying some of the identified coefficients. To clarify this concept, let us consider the evolution of the i-th state, and assume that the j-th element of vector $a_{i,*}$ is zero, then the i-th equation reads
$$x_i(k+1) = a_1 x_1(k) + \cdots + a_{j-1} x_{j-1}(k) + 0$$
$$+ a_{j+1} x_{j+1}(k) \cdots + a_n x_n(k) = a_{i,*} x(k), \quad i=1,...,j,...,n.$$
Therefore, the i-th state/gene does not depend on the dynamics of the j-th one; at the same time, it is possible to state that the j-th state/gene does not influence the i-th one. If these two statements are true, there exists no direct link between the j-th and the i-th state.

In view of such observations, it is possible to state that
   a) On the i-th row of A, a non zero coefficient corresponds to an incoming link to the i-th gene
   b) On the j-th column of A, a non zero coefficient corresponds to an outgoing link from the j-th gene
   c) A positive (negative) coefficient means that the interaction between the two genes expresses in the form of activation (inhibition).

The numerical value of the coefficient represents the intensity of the influence of one gene on the other. Such value is not actually relevant, because the purpose of the model is not to deduce a detailed description (which, besides, is not likely to be simply linear), but just to derive the structure of the network, where a connection is represented by any value different from zero. Nevertheless, in the proposed method the value of the coefficient plays a key role in the determination of the sparsity pattern of the matrix A, as will be described later.

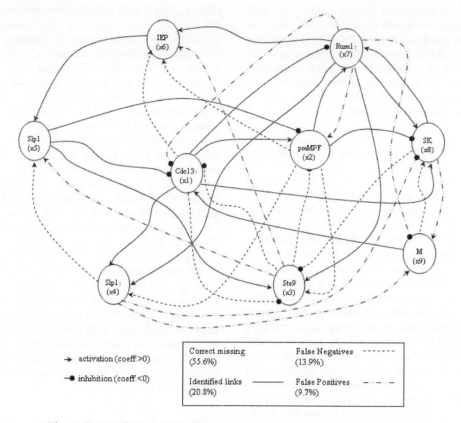

Fig. 1. Connection network of the genes involved in Novak-Tyson model

In order to compare the intensity of the links, that is the coefficients, each row of A, identified by means of (1), is normalized by Euclidian length

$$\hat{a}_{i,*} = \frac{a_{i,*}}{\|a_{i,*}\|}, \qquad i = 1, \ldots, n,$$

where $\hat{a}_{i,*}$ represents the i-th row of the normalized matrix, $\hat{A}$.

Let us consider two thresholds

$$\bar{\eta} = \min\left(\left|\hat{a}_{i,*}\right|\right) + median\left(\left|\hat{a}_{i,*}\right|\right),$$

$$\bar{\kappa} = \min\left(\left|\hat{a}_{*,j}\right|\right) + median\left(\left|\hat{a}_{*,j}\right|\right),$$

where *median* returns the median value of the vector. The algorithm sets a coefficient to zero when

$$if \left|\hat{a}_{i,j}\right| \in [0, \bar{\eta}) \cap [0, \bar{\kappa}) \ then \ a_{i,j} = 0. \qquad (2)$$

The rule expressed in (2) is a mathematical translation of conditions a) and b). The coefficient is set to zero only if it is among the lowest of both its row and column. In this way there is a double check on the identified coefficients: If $\hat{a}_{i,j}$ satisfies (2), then the pathway $x_j \rightarrow x_i$ is one of the weakest among those influencing the dynamics of x_i and also among those generated from x_j, therefore it is a good candidate for elimination from the network structure. Once a set of candidates have been determined for elimination, the next step consists of a re-identification of matrix A, this time forcing the coefficients chosen for elimination to be null.

To this aim, a new linear regressor is defined for each row of coefficients $a_{i,*}$,

$$\hat{\Omega}^{(i)} := \left(\omega_{1,*}^T \ \cdots \ \omega_{q-1,*}^T \ 0 \ \omega_{q+1,*}^T \ \cdots \ \omega_{m,*}^T\right)^T,$$

where $\omega_{j,*}$ is the j-th row of Ω, and thus

$$\tilde{x}_i^T := a_{i,*} \cdot \hat{\Omega}^{(i)}, \qquad i = 1, \ldots, n.$$

By setting to zero the q-th column of Ω, the algorithm implicitly requires a solution of the regression problem with $a_{i,q} = 0$. Therefore, it is sufficient to nullify the columns of the regressor corresponding to the null coefficients, and then compute the solution to

$$a_{i,*} = \tilde{x}_i^T \cdot \hat{\Omega}^{(i)\dagger}. \qquad (3)$$

In summary, the algorithm is articulated in the following steps:

1) identification of the A matrix, by solving a classical linear regression problem;
2) normalization of the rows;
3) comparison of each coefficient with the elements of its row and column;
4) elimination of the negligible coefficients;
5) new identification with fixed structure;
6) results evaluation, and possible reduction of the thresholds.

Results evaluation in step 6) is performed by computing the estimation error obtained with the current identification structure

$$e = \left\|\tilde{x}_i^T - \hat{a}_{i,*}\hat{\Omega}^{(i)}\right\|,$$

where $\hat{a}_{i,*}$ is drawn by (3).

Steps 2)-6) can be iterated several times, varying the thresholds $\bar{\eta}$ and $\bar{\kappa}$, until the error e remains small (i.e. below a prescribed value); when the error becomes large it means that the algorithm has eliminated a coefficient/link that exerts a significant influence on the dynamics of x_i; in this case the algorithm first try to lower the thresholds, then, if the error remains large, the iteration stops and the network structure found at the previous step is chosen as the best approximation.

3. VALIDATION THROUGH IN SILICO MODEL

Along the lines of (Amato *et al.*, 2005), a first validation of the proposed technique has been performed by applying the algorithm to the reconstruction of a large number of randomly generated systems (having stable, sparse A matrices). In order to assess such method, it has been tested on a large number of randomly generated quadratic systems of order ten. The proposed identification approach, on one hand, aims at providing information on the links between the states/genes, but, on the other hand, is also required to exhibit a good rejection rate of false positives, i.e. to not create interconnections between the states of the identified model that do not correspond, in the biological counterpart, to direct functional relationships between genes. A possible drawback of state-space model identification techniques is represented by the large number of coefficients to identify. To deal with this issue, the technique presented here exploits the knowledge coming from the biological domain: it assumes that the genetic network has a scale-free structure, that is each gene influences (is influenced) just (by) a few other genes and only the products between two state variables at the time are considered. These assumptions reflect in a high sparsity of the system matrices, which is a key point for building a computationally efficient identification algorithm. The results have been analyzed on a statistical base, focusing especially on the occurrences of false positives and false negatives; they exhibit very low error percentage and the related diagrams are not reported here because they are very similar to those presented in (Amato *et al.*, 2005).

A first improvement, with respect to the algorithm presented in the previous paper, is that the number of coefficients eliminated on a row, at each step, is not fixed, but adaptive in order to yield good estimation error (step 6 of the procedure). Therefore, it may happen to have some rows with many non zero coefficients and others with only few ones, which reflects the real nature of the system, that is some genes have many adjacents, and others exert influence on (are affected by) only few ones.

Although the statistical evaluation provides comforting results, a better assessment of the identification technique can be performed by applying it to a well established case study, for which not only experimental data are already available, but also a sufficiently assessed map of the connections between genes. The most similar thing to this ideal validation tool is an *in silico* model of the fission yeast cell cycle, developed by Novak and Tyson (Novak and Tyson, 1997), (Novak *et al.*, 2001),

(Steuer, 2004). Such model allows performing virtual experiments, thus providing data points for the identification procedure, and, on the other hand, has a well known mathematical structure, in the form of a system of nonlinear differential and algebraic equations, which can be easily translated into a map of the connections between states/genes of the model. The experimental model has been implemented and simulated in Matlab/Simulink™ and only forty data points have been picked within a single period of the cell cycle, in order to take into account that with *in vitro* experiments it is not possible to have many data points, mainly due to the high cost of microarrays. Therefore a suitable identification technique must give effective results with few data points.

The identified genetic network is depicted in Fig. 1. The percentage of correct identifications is over 76%; such result includes not only the links existing in the experimental model, but also those that are missing and are correctly identified as zero coefficients in the reconstructed model. The results show that the algorithm is robust in the face of false negatives, and, more important, of false positives: It is, indeed, important to reconstruct the larger possible number of links existing in the original system, but it is even more important not to introduce bogus links.

4. IDENTIFICATION FROM IN VITRO EXPERIMENTS

The final part of the work is devoted to the identification of a model of the genetic network of fission yeast cell cycle, exploiting existing experimental data by Rustici *et al.* (2004)[1]. Note that the model one can deduce from these data is not equivalent to the N-T one: The latter is composed of differential and algebraic equations involving heterogeneous data, e.g. concentrations of proteins, genes, enzymes, cellular mass. Therefore it is not possible to derive such model just on the basis of genetic expression profiles microarray data. Furthermore, it is worth to point out that the original model is nonlinear, time-varying, and subject to jumps on the state variables, so it is not possible to faithfully reproduce its dynamics by means of a linear model.

The final aim of this section is rather an identification of a part of the network structure that involves various genes whose expression is also used in the model by Novak-Tyson, namely *cdc13*, *cdc2*, *ste9*, *slp1*, *rum1*, *cig1*, *cig2*, *puc1*, *cdc25*, *wee1*. This simplification has been also adopted because of the large number of genes in yeast (ca. 6000), that renders impossible the definition and inclusion in the model of all the genes related to all the variables used in the N-T model. Experimental data considered for identification comprise two cell cycles, with a sampling period of 15 minutes, for a total of 10 data points, and have been obtained from *Elutriation1* microarray experiment (see (Rustici *et al.*, 2004) for

---

[1] The data are available at the URL
http://www.sanger.ac.uk/PostGenomics/S_pombe/projects/cellcycle/

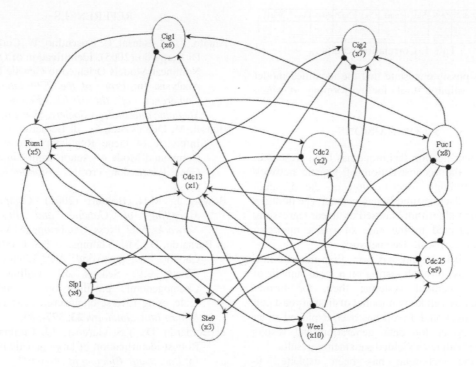

Fig. 2. Genetic connection network identified for the fission yeast

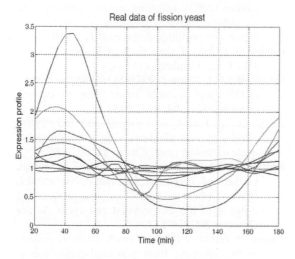

Fig. 3. Experimental data for the identification (after smoothing)

further details). Smoothing technique described in (Bansal *et al.*, 2006) has been applied, in order to filter the measurement noise and increase by interpolation the observation points up to 25 (Fig. 3). The application of the identification algorithm to this set of data yields the gene connection network reported in Fig. 2. Differently from the case of N-T model, here the original network is not available to assess the quality of the identification; nonetheless, it is possible to draw some considerations, which find also confirmation in the N-T model and in experimental practise:

- ◆ *cdc13* is the gene with the biggest number of connections, indeed it is well known that it plays a key role in all the phases of the cycle;
- ◆ *ste9*, *rum1*, *slp1* interact with each other and with *cdc13* in the G1/S phase and in the final phase;

- ◆ *cig1*, *cig2*, *puc1* participate to the inhibition of the complex *ste9* & *rum1* in the G1/S phase, and they also interact with *cdc13*;
- ◆ *wee1*, *cdc25* prevalently interact with *cdc13*, *cdc2* in the G2/M phase.

Another assessment of the quality of the identified model is derived by comparing another set of data with the prediction provided by such model: A second set of experimental data, *Elutriation2*, serves as a validation set for the identified system.

The expression profiles are derived *in silico*, by setting initial states to the values provided by experimental data, and then simulating the model free evolution response, reported in Fig. 4.

The dynamics of the identified system are stable and the vector of correlations between the simulated profiles and the experimental data show a low estimation error, reported in Tab. 1.

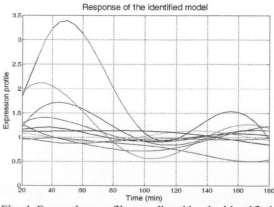

Fig. 4. Expression profiles predicted by the identified model

	Cdc13	Cdc2	Ste9	Slp1	Rum1	Cig1	Cig2	Puc1	Cdc25	Wee1
Corr (X,Y)	0.93	0.34	0.94	0.93	0.94	0.91	0.89	0.74	0.93	0.74

Tab. 1. Correlation results

Thus, it is possible to state that the identified model is also a suitable tool for performing *in silico* experiments.

5. CONCLUSIONS

A novel identification technique has been presented, tailored to the reconstruction of genetic network structures through identification of the dynamic matrix of a discrete-time linear system. The iterative identification algorithm is based on linear regression, which is adapted to the case of sparse matrices, representative of scale-free networks.

The proposed technique has been first assessed in a statistical way, through testing on a large number of randomly generated systems; then, for further validation, the well known model of fission yeast cell cycle by Novak and Tyson has been exploited as an *in silico* model for data generation and results evaluation; both tests yielded satisfactory results.

Finally, the technique has been exploited to identifying the genetic network of fission yeast, starting from experimental data available in literature.

Future works foresee the determination of a more detailed model of the fission yeast cell cycle, including transcription factors, for which the adjacent genes are known, so that it will be possible to evaluate the quality of the reconstructed network; moreover, an effort will be done for the identification of larger networks, possibly including the whole set of genes of fission (or budding) yeast. In particular, the latter objective clearly requires the use of statistical techniques, for analyzing the expression profiles of a large number of genes, combined with techniques for model order reduction, i.e. genes clustering.

REFERENCES

Amato, F., M. Bansal, C. Cosentino, W. Curatola, D. Di Bernardo (2005). Identification of Quadratic Nonlinear Models Oriented to Genetic Network Analysis. In: *Proc. of the 27th International Conference of the IEEE Engineering in Medicine and Biology Society*, Shangai, China.

Bansal, M, Della Gatta, G., di Bernardo, D. (2006). Inference of Gene Regulatory Networks and Compound Mode of Action from Time Course Gene Expression Profiles. *Bioinformatics*, in press

Bower, J., M.H. Bolouri (2001). *Computational Modelling of Genetic and Biochemical Networks*, MIT Press, Cambridge (MA).

di Bernardo, D., M.J. Thompson, T.S. Gardner, S.E. Chobot, E.L. Eastwood, A.P. Wojtovich, S.J. Elliott, S.E. Schaus, J.J. Collins (2005). Chemogenomic profiling on a genomewide scale using reverse-engineered gene networks. *Nature Biotechnology*, **23**, 377-383.

di Bernardo, D., T.S. Gardner, J.J. Collins (2004). Robust identification of large genetic networks. In: *Pac. Symp. Biocomput.*, 486-497.

Gardner, T.S., D. Di Bernardo, D. Lorenz, J.J. Collins (2003). Inferring genetic networks and identifying compound mode of action via expression profiling. *Science*, **301**, 102-105.

Kitano, H. (2001). *Foundations of Systems Biology*, MIT Press, Cambridge (MA).

Novak, B., J. J. Tyson (1997). Modeling the control of DNA replication in fission yeast. *Proc. Natl. Acad Sci. USA*, **94**, 9147-9152.

Novak B., Z. Pataki, A. Ciliberto and J. J. Tyson (2001). Mathematical model pf the cell division cycle of fission yeast. *Chaos*, **11**, 277-286.

Rustici, G., J. Mata, K. Kivinen, P. Liò, C. J. Penkett, G. Burns, J. Hayles, A. Brazma, P. Nurse and J. Bähler (2004). Periodic gene expression program of the fission yeast cell cycle. *Nature Genetics*, **94**, 809-817.

Steuer, R. (2004). Effects of stochasticity in models of the cell cycle: from quantized cycle times to noise-induced oscillations. *J. of Theoretical Biology*, **228**, 293-30.

REDUCED MODEL FOR FORCED EXPIRATION
AND ANALYSIS OF ITS SENSITIVITY

Janusz Mroczka and Adam G. Polak

*Chair of Electronic and Photonic Metrology, Wroclaw University of Technology
ul. B. Prusa 53/55, 50-317 Wroclaw, Poland*

Abstract: Pathological changes in the lung modify the shape of the flow-volume curve registered during forced expiration. Computational models allowing simulation of the test results are too complex for the estimation of their parameters. In this study a complex model was reduced by introduction of the functions scaling airway properties. Influence of the individual parameters of the reduced model on the flow-volume curve was evaluated by means of the sensitivity analysis. The conclusion is that the parameters of the scaling functions and elastic properties of lung tissue affect the measured data most significantly and that the descending part of the curve should be used to assess them. *Copyright © 2006 IFAC*

Keywords: Biomedical systems, Modelling, Model reduction, Sensitivity analysis, Inverse problem.

1. INTRODUCTION

Forced expiration is the most common test of the lung function. It has been shown that the registered maximal expiratory flow-volume (MEFV) curve is effort-independent and simultaneously sensitive to respiratory disorders (Hyatt, *et al.*, 1958). The observed connection between the respiratory state and the shape of the MEFV curve encourage to elaborate a method for the quantitative evaluation of lung parameters using the flow-volume data. Solving this so-called inverse problem requires application of a mathematical model that couples the respiratory mechanical properties with the MEFV curve. Three useful approaches to model and simulate the forced expiration, incorporating morphological data and main physiological phenomena, can be found in the literature (Lambert, *et al.*, 1982; Elad, *et al.*, 1988; Polak, and Lutchen, 2003). They are, however, too complex for the estimation of the respiratory system parameters. The early study by Lambert (1984) exposed these difficulties and finally failed in solving the problem. Recently, Lambert and co-workers were

successful predicting individual flow-volume curves with the use of their model (Lambert, *et al.*, 2004; Lambert, and Beck, 2004). It has been, however, proved that the set of parameters determining maximal expiratory flow is much bigger than the maximal airway areas adjusted in those studies.

The aim of this study was to transform the chosen complex computational model for the forced expiration into a model characterized by a reduced number of free parameters and then to analyse its sensitivity. These activities are the first step towards solving, if possible, the inverse problem in the forced expiration. Such an inverse model would have been very useful clinically (e.g. in case of asthmatic or COPD patients) giving the possibility to retrieve airway and/or lung tissue properties from the MEFV curve.

The paper is organised as follows. At the beginning (section 2) the complex model chosen for further analysis is briefly described. Then a method of its reduction, engaging sigmoid functions that rescale airway mechanical properties distributed along the bronchial tree, is proposed. Introduction of the scaling functions results in the reduced number of the free model parameters. Next, the sensitivity of the reduced model is analysed. Section 3 presents results of the model reduction and sensitivity analysis, and conclusions exposing the most influential model parameters as well as other insights following the study are drawn in section 4.

2. METHODS

2.1 Complex computational model

A complex model with a symmetrically bifurcating airway structure has been chosen since it describes airway morphology correctly, allows independent adjustment of their mechanical properties and simultaneously is computationally efficient (comparing to other approaches). This model has been discussed extensively elsewhere (Lambert et al., 1982; Polak, 1998) and will be quoted briefly here. Its bronchial tree structure, following the geometry proposed by Weibel (1963), consists of 24 symmetrical generations, each consisting of identical airways arranged in parallel, with the trachea categorised as generation 0 (Fig. 1).

The mechanical properties of the airways can be specified independently for each generation. First of all, they include parameters describing the dependence of the airway lumen area A on transmural pressure P_{tm}, i.e.the tube law; Lambert et al., 1982):

$$A(P_{tm}) = \begin{cases} A_m \alpha_0 (1 - P_{tm}/P_1)^{-n_1}, & P_{tm} \le 0, \\ A_m \left[1 - (1 - \alpha_0)(1 - P_{tm}/P_2)^{-n_2} \right], & P_{tm} > 0, \end{cases} \quad (1)$$

where A_m is the maximal lumen area, α_0 is the normalized area (i.e. A/A_m) at zero transmural pressure, and n_1 and n_2 are shape-changing scalars. P_1 and P_2 are pressure asymptotes given by:

$$\begin{aligned} P_1 &= n_1 \alpha_0 / \alpha_0', \\ P_2 &= n_2 (\alpha_0 - 1) / \alpha_0', \end{aligned} \quad (2)$$

where α_0' denotes the slope of the A-P_{tm} curve (i.e. dA/dP_{tm}) at $P_{tm} = 0$. Additionally, intrapleural bronchi lengths alter with the lung volume (V_L):

$$l(V_L) = l_{1.5} \left(\frac{V_t + V_L}{V_t + 1.5} \right)^{\frac{1}{3}}, \quad (3)$$

where $l_{1.5}$ is the length of an airway at lung volume of 1.5 dm³, and V_t is lung tissue volume. Weibel has proposed exponential equations to represent the airway diameter and length dependences on the generation number (Weibel, 1963).

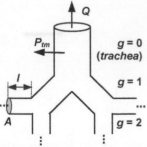

Fig. 1. Schematic representation of the first 3 generations of the bronchial tree: Q is expiratory flow, g is the generation number, A is the airway lumen area, l is the airway length, and P_{tm} is transmural pressure.

Another model feature is the use of a nonlinear characteristics for the lung recoil (Bogaard, et al., 1995; see Fig. 2):

$$P_{st}(V_L) = \begin{cases} \dfrac{V_L - V_0}{C_E}, & V_L \le V_{tr}, \\ \dfrac{V_m - V_{tr}}{C_{st}} \ln\left(\dfrac{V_m - V_{tr}}{V_m - V_L} \right) + \dfrac{V_{tr} - V_0}{C_{st}}, & V_L > V_{tr}, \end{cases}$$

$$(4)$$

where P_{st} is static lung recoil pressure, V_L is lung volume, V_m and V_0 are maximal and minimal lung volumes, V_{tr} is transition volume, and C_{st} is lung compliance at zero recoil pressure.

During simulations, pressure drops along compliant airways are calculated by numerical integration of the formula for the pressure gradient (including both wave-speed flow limitation and viscous pressure losses) at every lung volume analysed (Lambert et al., 1982). Since the bronchial tree is fully symmetrical, the calculated pressure drop is simultaneously the pressure loss along a generation that the given airway belongs to. Integration is interrupted at each junction between airway generations for the evaluation of convective acceleration of gas according to the Bernoulli law. The calculated total pressure drop across the bronchial tree is then summarized with the pressure loss in the upper airways which depends on the scaling coefficients R_u and r (Polak, 1988), and equated to the driving pressure produced by the lung elastic recoil and expiratory muscle. The driving pressure (P_d) is the function of expiration time and lung volume (Polak, 1988):

$$P_d(t, V_L) = P_m (1 - e^{-t/\tau}) \left(\frac{V_L - RV}{VC} \right), \quad (5)$$

where P_m is maximal expiratory pressure, t stands for time of expiration, τ is a time constant of expiratory muscle, RV denotes residual volume, and VC is vital capacity.

A total amount of 159 parameters is used in the complex model: 144 describe properties of 24 airway generations, 11 parameters for the lung recoil characteristics and other features of the respiratory system (including VC), and 4 physical or semi-physical constants. Using known forced vital capacity (FVC) instead of VC, 154 of the parameters should be regarded as the free ones.

The Lambert model for the forced expiration has been proven to be a valuable tool in the analysis of the respiratory system for the last two decades. Its computational abilities have been enhanced (Polak, 1998) by applying a method of succeeding approximations when finding maximal airflows in the quasi-static conditions at the consecutive lung volumes in the whole range of vital capacity.

2.2 Reduction of the complex model

Proposed by Weibel equations expressing the relationship between airway dimensions and the generation number follow the fact that the mechanical properties of neighbouring airways are not independent. In the complex model, airway elastic properties, described by Eqs 1-2, include five parameters specified for each generation. This huge number of parameters can be reduced by the use of scaling functions that would capture changes in distribution of the airway mechanical properties along the bronchial tree (Habib, et al, 1994; Polak, and Mroczka, 1998). Such changes may result from possible pathology or intersubject variability. Let us denote the baseline values of the airway parameters generally as θ^* and the rescaled ones as θ, then the following rescaling, depending on the generation number (g), can be proposed:

$$A_m(g) = \frac{2}{1+\exp(p_{a1}g + p_{a2})} A_m^*(g), \quad (6)$$

$$\alpha_0(g) = \frac{1+\exp(0.33g - 2.4)}{1+\exp(p_{z1}g + p_{z2})} \alpha_0^*(g), \quad (7)$$

$$\alpha_0'(g) = \frac{2}{1+\exp(p_{c1}g + p_{c2})} \alpha_m'^*(g), \quad (8)$$

$$n_1(g) = (p_{n11}g + p_{n12}) \cdot n_1^*(g), \quad (9)$$

$$n_2(g) = (p_{n21}g + p_{n22}) n_2^*(g), \quad (10)$$

where p_{a1}, p_{a2}, p_{z1}, p_{z2}, p_{c1}, p_{c2}, p_{n11}, p_{n12}, p_{n21}, p_{n22} are the scaling parameters. Two features, A_m and α_0', are rescaled by sigmoid functions with two degrees of freedom and values between 0 and 2 (Eqs 6 and 8). Since α_0 cannot exceed 1 (it is a relative parameter), the form of the numerator in Eq. (7) has been chosen to satisfy this relationship for all generations.

Table 1: Parameter values of the reduced model for the normal and diseased lung. *H* was presumed as equal to 176 cm, and VC as equal to 5.5 dm^3 (normal lungs) and 4 dm^3 (diseased lungs)

Symbol	Parameter value	
	Normal lung	Diseased lung
$A_m(0)$ (mm^2)	237	237
$\alpha_0(0)$	0.882	0.882
$\alpha'_0(0)$ (kPa^{-1})	0.11	0.11
$n_1(0)$	0.5	0.5
$n_2(0)$	10	10
p_{a1}	0.0	0.0
p_{a2}	0.0	0.0
p_{z1}	0.33	0.36
p_{z2}	-2.4	-2.4
p_{c1}	0.0	0.04
p_{c2}	0.0	1.1
p_{n11}	0.0	0.0
p_{n12}	1.0	1.0
p_{n21}	0.0	0.0
p_{n22}	1.0	1.0
RV (dm^3)	1.5	4.0
ΔV_0 (dm^3)	0.0	0.0
ΔV_{tr} (dm^3)	2.5	1.0
ΔV_m (dm^3)	5.8	4.1
V_t (dm^3)	0.9	0.9
C_{st} (dm^{3}kPa^{-1})	3.5	6.0
P_m (kPa)	24	24
τ (s)	0.2	0.2
R_u	0.11	0.11
r	1.68	1.68

To include, however, their intersubject variability, the airway lengths at lung volume of 1.5 dm^3 ($l_{1.5}$) are related to the known patient's height (*H*) (Habib, et al, 1994; Polak, and Mroczka, 1998), assuming that the baseline data derive from a man of 176 cm:

$$l_{1.5}(g) = \frac{H}{176} l_{1.5}^*(g). \quad (11)$$

The effect of variation in residual volume (RV), seen as a parallel shift of the recoil pressure – lung volume relationship, on the MEFV curve is small (Lambert, 1984), and it has been investigated in this study by introducing the following reparameterisation into the model: $V_0 = RV + \Delta V_0$, $V_{tr} = RV + \Delta V_{tr}$ and $V_m = RV + \Delta V_m$, where ΔV_0, ΔV_{tr}, and ΔV_m are new "shift" parameters applied instead of V_0, V_{tr}, and V_m used originally. All the parameters of the reduced model are listed in Table 1.

2.3 Sensitivity analysis

The sensitivity analysis enables to figure out if the model is suitable for estimation of any of its parameters, which of them, what accuracy may be excepted and which part of data should be used to this end. The primary point of the analysis consists in the determination of the output sensitivity ($\mathbf{X}$) to the parameters:

$$\mathbf{X} = \frac{\partial \mathbf{y}}{\partial \boldsymbol{\theta}}, \qquad (12)$$

where $\mathbf{y}$ denotes a vector of output data (expiratory flow in our case) and $\boldsymbol{\theta}$ is a vector of the model parameters. Since the parameters may differ in the magnitude by several orders, so may the sensitivity vectors (i.e. the columns in matrix $\mathbf{X}$). It is better to use the normalized sensitivity $\mathbf{X}_N$,

$$\mathbf{X}_N = \mathbf{X} \cdot \text{diag}\big(\text{diag}\big(\mathbf{X}^T \mathbf{X}\big)\big)^{-1/2}, \qquad (13)$$

to observe the connection of the individual parameters with specific fractions of the output data (Thomaseth, and Cobelli, 1999; operator *diag* transforms a matrix into a vector including the matrix diagonal elements or a vector into a diagonal matrix).

Another advantage following the sensitivity analysis is the possibility to evaluate correlations between the sensitivity vectors. High correlation indicates that the parameters influence the measured model output in a very similar way and their values cannot be estimated precisely from noisy data.

The sensitivity of the reduced model derived in section 2.2 was analysed with the intention to assess the model abilities in solving the inverse problem and to plan further investigations. The sensitivity vectors could not be derived analytically, so they were computed numerically.

2.4 Values of the parameters

The complex model was simulated using the published baseline data (Lambert, 1984; Polak, 1998). Being aware of the dependence of the nonlinear model analysis on the considered point in the parameter space, the investigations were performed in two cases: for the normal lung with baseline values of the parameters and for the diseased lung characterized by hyperinflation, loss of lung elastic recoil and airway obstruction, the symptoms found in asthmatic and emphysematic patients (Gelb, and Zamel, 2000; Baldi, *et al.*, 2001). The relevant lung static recoil characteristics are shown in Fig. 2.

Taking into account the quantitative effects of airway constriction (Gelb, and Zamel, 2000; Morlion, and Polak, 2005), the obstruction was simulated by adequate alternation of the scaling parameters p_{z1}, p_{z2}, p_{c1}, and p_{c2}. This modification reduced α_0 twice in generation 23 (leaving it unchanged in the generation 1), and α'_0 was decreased from two-fold in the generation 1 up to four-fold in the generation 23. The resulting MEFV curves are presented in Fig. 3.

3. RESULTS

In the reduced model, the values of the intrapleural airway properties (i.e. generations 1 to 23) are calculated with the use of the functions rescaling the baseline values, so the model possesses 25 free parameters: 5 of the trachea (generation 0), 10 of the rescaling functions, 2 of upper airway resistance, 4 of the lung recoil characteristics, and 4 others.

For the parameter values of the normal lung (Table 1), the complex and reduced model outputs overlap (Fig. 3, solid line), since the scaling functions equal unity for all generations. The outputs of the models would overlap also in case of the diseased lung, if the airway parameters of the complex model were the same as baseline values multiplied by the rescaling functions with parameter values given in Table 1 (the diseased lung column).

The impact of the individual parameters on the flow-volume data is shown in Figs 4 and 5. Parameters describing the extrapleural airways and expiratory muscle determine only the ascending part of the MEFV curve (see Fig. 3), both for the normal and diseased lung (Fig. 4). On the contrary, parameters of the intrapleural airways and lung recoil of the normal as well as diseased lung affect expiratory flow in the whole range of VC (Fig. 5).

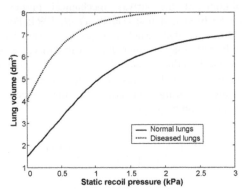

Fig. 2. Static recoil pressure – lung volume curves of the normal and diseased lung used in the study.

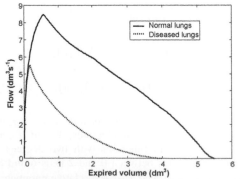

Fig. 3. Maximum expiration flow-volume curves of the normal and diseased lung.

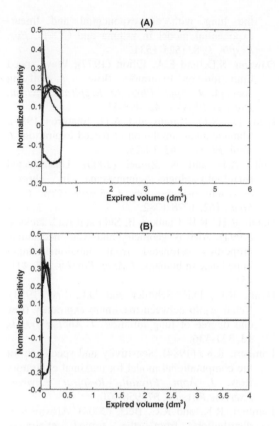

Fig. 4. Normalized sensitivities to parameters ($\mathbf{X}_N$) characterizing extrapleural airways and expiratory muscle of normal (A) and diseased lungs (B). The vertical dashed line indicates the volume related to peak expiratory flow (PEF).

Some of the sensitivity vectors of the reduced model appeared strongly correlated (absolute values of the relevant correlation coefficients were greater than 0.99), and the number of the correlated pairs was bigger in case of the diseased lungs.

4. DISCUSSION AND CONCLUSIONS

Application of the functions scaling airway properties according to their generation number goes back as far as the first Weibel's models of the bronchial tree geometry (Weibel, 1963). Since then such an approach has been practised many times demonstrating that the properties of the neighbouring generations are related to each other. In the present work, the proposed functions rescale airway baseline properties rather than follow strictly the former approaches. Their form implies that the reduced model will efficiently mimic a serial distribution of pathological changes in the bronchial tree. Sigmoid shape of the functions rescaling A_m and α'_0, used also by others (Habib, *et al.*, 1994), enables capturing nonlinear decrease or increase of these parameters along the generations. Additionally, more complicated form of the function scaling α_0 allows imitating its non-monotonic variations.

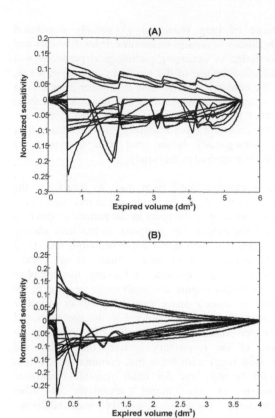

Fig. 5. Normalized sensitivities to parameters ($\mathbf{X}_N$) characterizing intrapleural airways and lung recoil of normal (A) and diseased lungs (B).

Recent experimental results show that airway obstruction during metacholine challenge may have just such serial character (Lambert, and Beck, 2004). Nevertheless, the case of selective constriction of individual airway generations, investigated by Lambert and Beck (2004), cannot be well described by this model.

The sensitivity analysis (Fig. 4) has revealed that the descending part of the MEFV curve is insensitive to the parameters describing the extrathoracic airways and expiratory muscle. As shown by others, this portion of flow-volume data is set by the flow limiting mechanism and the resulting expiratory flow does not depend on the properties of the airways situated downstream to the site of flow limitation (Dawson, and Elliott, 1977). Simultaneously, this part of the curve is effort-independent (Hyatt, *et al.*, 1958) and the parameters describing muscle action cannot influence its shape. The conclusion is that the data following peak expiratory flow (PEF) should be used to estimate the parameters of the intrapleural airways and the lung recoil characteristics. This is in line with the practice of earlier trials (Lambert, 1984; Lambert, and Beck, 2004).

The proposed form of the reduced model implies that all processes modifying the MEFV curve shape will be seen as variations in the free parameters during identification of the model, and then interpreted as a change of lung recoil or as serially distributed alternations of airway mechanics. Prior diagnosis and knowledge of occurring pathological processes will predestine the use of the model in some diseases or, on the contrary, will devalue it in other disorders. In the latter case, however, it is still possible to propose another parameterisation of the reduced model, e.g. by the choice of other rescaling functions that will fit the pathogenesis better, and then to repeat the procedure applied in this study.

Linear methods have been used to investigate the nonlinear model, so the results are correct only in the neighbourhood of the point in the parameter space, at which the model was analysed. It has been shown, however, that such linear approximations may yield quite accurate description (Yuan, et al., 1998), justifying this approach. Achieving the complete results would require the analysis to be done in the whole parameter space consisting of an infinitive number of points. To generalise the outcomes, we have performed investigations at two representative states of the respiratory system (the normal and diseased lung) with hope that common conclusions would be also true for other possible conditions. Analysis of the model sensitivity at other characteristic points unquestionably needs additional studies. On the other hand, the very precise quantitative outcomes seem to be unnecessary at this stage of investigations.

Summarizing, this study has shown that the model for the forced expiration can be reduced to 25 free parameters describing intrapleural airway mechanics and the lung static recoil. Only these parameters influence the descending part of the MEFV curve and it should be chosen for the model identification. High correlations between some of the sensitivity vectors indicate that the reduced model cannot be properly identified and this reveals the need for further investigations. One of possible approaches is the selection of the most influential and less-correlated parameters for the estimation (Polak, 2001). This should be the next step towards elaboration of the inverse model for the forced expiration.

REFERENCES

Baldi, S., M. Miniati, C.R. Bellina, L. Battolla, G. Catapano, E. Begliomini, D. Giustini and C. Giuntini (2001). Relationship between extent of pulmonary emphysema by high-resolution computed tomography and lung elastic recoil in patients with chronic obstructive pulmonary disease. *Am. J. Respir. Crit. Care Med.*, **164**, 585-589.

Bogaard, J.M., S.E. Overbeek, A.F.M. Verbraak, C.Vons, H.T.M. Folgering, Th.W. van der Mark, C.M. Roos, P.J. Sterk, and the Dutch CNSLD study group (1995). Pressure-volume analysis of the lung with an exponential and linear-exponential model in asthma and COPD. *Eur. Respir. J.*, **8**, 1525-1531.

Dawson, S.D. and E.A. Elliott (1977). Wave-speed limitation on expiratory flow - a unifying concept. *J. Appl. Physiol.: Respirat. Environ. Exercise Physiol.*, **43**, 498-515.

Elad, D., R.D. Kamm and A.H. Shapiro (1988). Mathematical simulation of forced expiration. *J. Appl. Physiol.*, **65**, 14-25.

Gelb, A.F. and N. Zamel (2000). Unsuspected pseudophysiologic emphysema in chronic persistent asthma. *Am. J. Respir. Crit. Care Med.*, **162**, 1778-1782.

Habib, R.H., R.B. Chalker, B. Suki and A.C. Jackson (1994). Airway geometry and wall mechanical properties estimated from subglottal input impedance in humans. *J. Appl. Physiol.*, **77**, 441-451.

Hyatt, R.E., D.P. Schilder and D.L. Fry (1958). Relationship between maximum expiratory flow and degree of lung inflation. *J. Appl. Physiol.*, **13**, 331-336.

Lambert, R.K. (1984). Sensitivity and specificity of the computational model for maximal expiratory flow. *J. Appl. Physiol.: Respirat. Environ. Exercise Physiol.*, **57**, 958-970.

Lambert, R.K. and K.C. Beck (2004). Airway area distribution from the forced expiration maneuver. *J. Appl. Physiol.*, **97**, 570-578.

Lambert, R.K., R.G. Castile and R.S. Tepper (2004). Model of forced expiratory flows and airway geometry in infants. *J. Appl. Physiol.*, **96**, 688-692.

Lambert, R.K., T.A. Wilson, R.E. Hyatt and J.R. Rodarte (1982). A computational model for expiratory flow. *J. Appl. Physiol.: Respirat. Environ. Exercise Physiol.*, **52**, 44-56.

Morlion, B. and A.G. Polak (2005). Simulation of lung function evolution after heart-lung transplantation using a numerical model. *IEEE Trans. Biomed. Eng.*, **52**, 1180-1187.

Polak, A.G. (1998). A forward model for maximum expiration. *Comput. Biol. Med.*, **28**, 613-625.

Polak, A.G. (2001). Indirect measurements: combining parameter selection with ridge regression. *Meas. Sci. Technol.*, **12**, 278-287.

Polak, A.G. and K.R. Lutchen (2003). Computational model for forced expiration from asymmetric normal lungs. *Ann. Biomed. Eng.*, **31**, 891-907.

Polak, A.G. and J. Mroczka (1998). A metrological model for maximum expiration. *Measurement*, **23**, 265-270.

Thomaseth, K. and C. Cobelli (1999). Generalized sensitivity functions in physiological system identification. *Ann. Biomed. Eng.*, **27**, 607-616.

Yuan, H., B. Suki and K.R. Lutchen (1998). Sensitivity analysis for evaluating nonlinear models of lung mechanics. *Ann. Biomed. Eng.*, **26**, 230-241.

Weibel, E.R. (1963). *Morphometry of the Human Lung*. Springer, Berlin.

A MODEL OF FREE FATTY ACID KINETICS DURING INTRAVENOUS GLUCOSE TOLERANCE TEST

Alessandra Pavan* Karl Thomaseth*
Giovanni Pacini* Attila Brehm Michael Roden****

* CNR Institute of Biomedical Engineering, Padua, Italy
** Dept. Internal Med. III, Medical Univ. Vienna, Austria

Abstract: The dynamics of non-esterified free fatty acids (FFA) during modified intravenous glucose tolerance test (IVGTT) is studied. The first step is to formulate a physiological model suitable to describe FFA kinetics. A single compartment model is utilized, with FFA production controlled by insulin in a remote compartment and indirectly by intracellular glucose. Then, from the analysis of the experimental data, the kinetic parameters of the model are estimated using a population modelling approach and their dependence upon individual characteristics is investigated. The proposed model is a promising tool for investigating the relationship between glucose and lipid metabolism and their control by insulin. *Copyright © 2006 IFAC*

Keywords: Mathematical models, Medical applications, Parameter identification, Physiological models, Statistical analysis

1. INTRODUCTION

Glucose and Free Fatty Acid (FFA) kinetics are both regulated by variations of insulin levels. There is an interaction between the metabolism of these two substances, but the mechanism is still unknown. Furthermore FFA seem to have an important role in the development of insulin resistance and in the impairment in glucose utilization, that are disfunctions typical of obesity and noninsulin-dependent diabetes mellitus. The formulation and validation of a FFA physiological model is therefore of particular interest, for a deep understanding of complicated mechanisms involved in diabetes.

Aims of this study are the development of a physiological model suitable to describe FFA kinetics, the estimation of model parameters, using a population approach, and the analysis of their dependence from individual characteristics.

In section 2 the physiological background is described, in section 3 the model explanation is given together with the description of data, protocol, statistical methods and mathematical equations. In sections 4 and 5 results are presented and conclusions are drawn.

2. PHYSIOLOGICAL BACKGROUND

Lipid metabolism is tightly coupled with that of carbohydrates, both having insulin as common hormonal control signal that regulates after ingestion of meals the storage in depot cells of fuel substances such as glucose and FFA. In fasting conditions the main energy supply for basal cell metabolism is provided by the oxidation of FFA. These are released by adipocytes into the systemic circulation through the action of the intracellular enzyme hormone sensitive lipase (HSL) responsible for hydrolysis of triglycerides (TG)

(Laffel, 1999). More rapidly available, but far less extensive, energy stores are represented by the glucose polymer glycogen. Following ingestion of mixed meals, after gastrointestinal absorption, fat droplets are cleared from the circulation by the intravascular enzyme lipoprotein lipase (LPL), which breaks down TG allowing FFA to be taken up by adipocytes. At the same time, pancreatic stimulation of insulin secretion by glucose increases plasma insulin levels that promote glucose disposal and slow down FFA release by inhibiting HSL. Moreover, transport of glucose into adipocytes is essential for FFA reesterification to TG because glucose is the substrate for glycerol, which binds three FFA molecules to form TG, while glycerol released intracellularly with hydrolysis of TG is not utilized for *de novo* re-esterification of FFA to TG (Lewis *et al.*, 2002).

3. METHODS

3.1 Modelling assumptions

According to the knowledge that FFA undergo a rapid turnover within the vascular pool and that their production is inhibited by insulin through intracellular signalling pathways, FFA dynamics could be described by first order (single compartment) kinetics with FFA production controlled by insulin in a remote compartment, as done in Bergman's minimal model (MM) of glucose disappearance (Bergman *et al.*, 1979). The proposed mechanism of insulin action on FFA kinetics is based on the knowledge that suppression of lipolysis by insulin is strong but circulating FFA may not be completely suppressed (Lewis *et al.*, 2002; Riemens *et al.*, 2000; Meijssen *et al.*, 2001). In fact insulin inhibits HSL but not lipoprotein lipase LPL, which are responsible for intracellular and intravascular lipolysis, respectively. In a previous study (Thomaseth and Pavan, 2005), a FFA kinetic model was proposed to analyze OGTT data, which takes into account only insulin's antilipolytic action. Considering IVGTT data, it was necessary modifying the earlier model to describe faster and higher FFA response. In addition to this main mechanism of insulin action, also a secondary control on FFA production by glucose is therefore considered to describe differences in FFA dynamics observed during standard insulin modified IVGTT (IM-IVGTT) and modified with glucose clamp (GC-IM-IVGTT). In particular, except for a few cases where FFA concentrations rose above basal at the end of the IM-IVGTT (most likely due to induced hypoglycemia and counterregulatory response) the observed differences in FFA dynamics between IM-IVGTT and GC-IM-IVGTT consist in a delayed or blunted return to basal values at

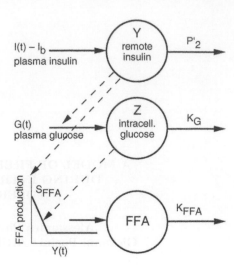

Fig. 1. Proposed model of FFA kinetics with FFA production directly controlled by remote insulin and indirectly by intracellular glucose.

the end of the GC-IM-IVGTT. To explain this delay it was assumed that increased availability of intracellular glucose due to increased insulin levels, may promote local re-esterification of FFA reducing the release of FFA from the cell and thus modifying apparently the FFA production rate.

3.2 Mathematical model

The compartmental representation of the proposed FFA kinetic model is shown in Figure 1. It is assumed that plasma insulin must first enter a remote compartment before inhibiting FFA production and stimulating glucose uptake. The compartmental state variable $Y(t)$ is a delayed profile of supra-basal insulin, $I(t) - I_b$, characterized by the fractional clearance P'_2 (min^{-1}), which is equivalent to P_2 in the MM because it describes the same process, although it is not necessarily identical. For approximating with a simple equation experimentally determined dose-response curves (Coppack *et al.*, 1994), FFA production is considered linearly dependent on deviations from the basal value of remote insulin with saturable inhibition. More specifically, relative to basal FFA production at basal insulin, insulin-dependent FFA production decreases with slope S_{FFA} $(ml\,\mu U^{-1})$ for suprabasal increases in remote insulin up to a value beyond which FFA production becomes constant. The maximum inhibitory capacity of insulin on circulating FFA is expressed as a unitless fraction, ρ_{FFA}, of basal production. So $1 - \rho_{FFA}$ is the fraction of FFA production that does not depend on insulin action. The production function, normalized with respect to basal production, is expressed as

$$P_{FFA}(t) = 1 - \rho_{FFA} + \rho_{FFA}\, P_{FFA}^{HSL}(Y)\,, \quad (1)$$

where $P_{FFA}^{HSL}(Y)$ depends on insulin action through inhibition of HSL:

$$P_{FFA}^{HSL}(Y) = max\{1 - S_{FFA}Y(t), 0\} \,. \quad (2)$$

The secondary control mechanism of FFA production is represented by the action of a quantity proportional to intracellular glucose: $Z(t)$ $(mg\,dl^{-1}\,\mu U\,ml^{-1})$, on $P_{FFA}^{HSL}(Y)$, see Figure 1. Note that $Z(t)$ has the dimension of the product of insulin and glucose concentrations (as can be derived from model differential equations reported in Eqs. (4)-(6)). More specifically, suprabasal insulin in the remote compartment, $Y(t)$ $(\mu U\,ml^{-1})$, increases glucose uptake, which is an essential substrate for re-esterification of FFA. This produces a delayed effect on FFA production because high intracellular glucose can have an effect only when insulin is returning to low levels. Turnover of $Z(t)$ has been assumed first order and characterized by parameter K_G (min^{-1}). The inhibitory effect of glucose on FFA release was described by a Michaelis-Menten type equation leading to:

$$P_{FFA}(t) = 1 - \rho_{FFA} + \rho_{FFA}P_{FFA}^{HSL}(Y)\frac{Z_{50}}{Z(t) + Z_{50}}. \quad (3)$$

The differential equations of the kinetic model are:

$$\frac{dFFA(t)}{dt} = -K_{FFA}(FFA(t) - FFA_b P_{FFA}(t)) \quad (4)$$

$$\frac{dY(t)}{dt} = -P_2'(Y(t) - (I(t) - I_b)) \quad (5)$$

$$\frac{dZ(t)}{dt} = -K_G(Z(t) - Y(t)G(t)) \quad (6)$$

with initial conditions $FFA(0) = FFA_b$, $Y(0) = 0$, $Z(0) = 0$ and FFA production given by Eq. (3), that can be expressed as $P_{FFA}(t) =$

$$1 - \rho_{FFA}\left(\frac{Z(t) + Z_{50}\ min\{S_{FFA}Y(t), 1\}}{Z(t) + Z_{50}}\right).$$

The time course of insulin and glucose, $I(t)$ and $G(t)$ in Eqs. (5)-(6), where obtained by linear interpolation of measured concentrations during the IVGTT experiments.

Summarizing, the parameters describing FFA kinetics are below.

$S_{FFA}(ml\ \mu U^{-1})$ the slope of the linear part of the relation that describes the decrease of plasma FFA, expressing the sensitivity of lipolysis inhibition due to suprabasal remote insulin variations;

ρ_{FFA} (unitless) the maximum inhibitory capacity of insulin on circulating FFA: it is related to the fraction of FFA produced intravascularly that escapes cellular uptake;

$K_{FFA}(min^{-1})$ the fractional FFA turnover rate: it is related to basal FFA production rate, expressed

in $(\mu mol\,l^{-1}\,min^{-1})$ and calculated as $FFA_b \times K_{FFA}$;

$Z_{50}(mg\ dl^{-1}\ \mu U\ ml^{-1})$ is related to the level of intracellular glucose necessary to reduce by 50% insulin-dependent FFA production, compared to basal conditions;

$P_2'(min^{-1})$ the fractional clearance of $Y(t)$;

$K_G(min^{-1})$ the fractional turnover rate of $Z(t)$.

3.3 Subjects and protocol

Thirteen nondiabetic volunteers (7 male and 6 female, age: 26 ± 1 years, body mass index: 22.1 ± 0.7 kg/m^2) were studied in random order during insulin modified intravenous glucose tolerance test (IM-IVGTT): 0.3 g/kg glucose at time 0 and 0.03 U/kg insulin at 20 min. During identical conditions, the same subjects, underwent a test with variable glucose infusion preventing a decrease of plasma glucose concentration below euglycaemia (GC-IM-IVGTT). Insulin, glucose, FFA plasma concentrations were measured at frequent intervals, from 15 min before the beginning of the test and during the three following hours. Also plasma concentrations of five counterinsulin hormones (epinephrine, norepinephrine, cortisol, glucagon, growth hormone) were measured. Protocol and experiment are described in detail in (Brehm *et al.*, in press).

3.4 Statistical methods

Concentration data of FFA, insulin and glucose were simultaneously analyzed by a non-linear mixed-effects modelling approach (Pinheiro and Bates, 2000). By means of this technique, population average (fixed effects) as well as between- and within-subject variability (random effects) of model parameters can be estimated. Let $\boldsymbol{\vartheta}$ be the model parameter vector. For each subject this vector will assume different values $\boldsymbol{\vartheta}_i$, where i is an index distinguishing different subjects. Instead of separately estimating each subject's parameter vector, mixed-effects models rearrange the estimation problem in terms of population average $\boldsymbol{\eta}$ (fixed effects) and individual variations around these values $\mathbf{b}_i$ (random effects), so $\boldsymbol{\vartheta}_i = \boldsymbol{\eta} + \mathbf{b}_i$. Under the assumption that random effects are independent and identically distributed, the estimation problem is solved by the evaluation of the fixed effects and of the variance of the random effects. This approach has several benefits: most of all the reduced number of parameters when the number of subject is large and the simultaneous utilization of all information that becomes very useful with sparse data but with many subjects.

In particular, fixed and random effects were simultaneously estimated for the following model parameters: FFA_b, S_{FFA}, ρ_{FFA}, K_{FFA}, P_2', K_G and Z_{50} (the actually estimated parameters were their logarithms). Basal FFA, FFA_b, was estimated to avoid systematic errors due to large fluctuations of FFA measurements at the beginning of the tests and to compensate slight differences at the end. In 4 subjects with overshoot of FFA concentrations at the end of the IM-IVGTT, FFA data were used only up to 70 minutes.

The analysis was conducted in the statistical environment R, using the package NLME (Pinheiro and Bates, 2000) combined with the modelling tool PANSYM (Thomaseth, 2003).

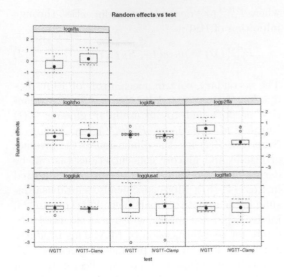

Fig. 3. Random effects versus test. The random effects of model parameters are plotted versus the different kind of experiment. Only for parameter lnP_2' (logp2ffa) there is an evident difference between the two kind of test.

4. RESULTS

The model was able to fit well individual FFA data (not shown) as well as the average profile (Fig. 2). Mean and standard deviation of the percentage

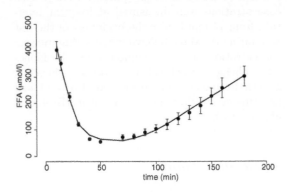

Fig. 2. FFA data (mean±SE) and average fit.

fitting error over individual data are 17.6% ± 13.0%.

Estimates of population's fixed effects (obtained by backtransformation of non-linearly transformed parameters) with 95% statistical confidence limits are reported in Table 1.

In order to detect which individual characteristics would be introduced as covariate in the model, plots of the random effects of all parameters versus the individual characteristics (see Fig. 3) are investigated (Pinheiro and Bates, 2000). If a continuos variable has to be considered as a covariate to be introduced in the model, then this is achieved through a linear relationship of the kind: $\eta = \beta_0 + \beta \cdot x$, where η was the former fixed effect, x is the continuous covariate, and β_0 and β are coefficients to be estimated. So now, η varies, in a deterministic way, inside the population and the new fixed effects are β_0 and

β. Otherwise, if the covariate to be introduced is a discrete variable, then the relationship is: $\eta = \beta_1 + \sum_{i=2}^{n} \beta_i \, I(x = x_i)$, where x_i, with $i = 1, 2, ..., n$ are the n values that the covariate x takes within the examined population, and $I(A)$ is the indicator function, assuming value 1 in the points of the set A and 0 outside A. So x_1 is taken as reference values and β_i, with $i \neq 1$ accounts for the difference of parameter η in the group x_i, with respect to the group x_1. Note that correlation between parameters and individual characteristics is investigated over the population as a whole. As can be seen in Fig. 3, there is clear evidence of the effect of the kind of test on the parameter $ln\ P_2'$ (logp2ffa). When a model has to be modified, it is better to introduce only one covariate at a time, and thus the most promising relationship is investigated. In this case, two different values (one for test IM-IVGTT and the other for test GC-IM-IVGTT) for the fixed effect of $ln\ P_2'$ are assumed. The significance level for the difference of these two estimated values was high (p-value = 0.0242). So a significant difference was found with regard to the remote insulin turnover rate, P_2', between IM-IVGTT and GC-IM-IVGTT. The lower value estimated with the glucose clamp suggests that the inhibitory effect of insulin on HSL may last longer in absence of counterinsulin hormone response due to hypoglycemia induced by conventional IM-IVGTT (Brehm et al., in press).

Using the same kind of visual inspection with testing of modifications of the model by new parameter estimation, no significant correlation was found with other covariates (i.e. BW, BMI, gender) of individual parameter variations from population average values. Between-subject variability of parameter estimates (random effects) resulted significant for all parameters except for K_G, Z_{50}, and S_{FFA}.

Table 1. Population fixed effects parameter estimates and approximate 95% lower and upper confidence limits

Parameter	Value	95% CI
FFA_b	620.2	[528.5, 727.7]
K_{FFA}	0.100	[0.087, 0.116]
$P'_{2IM-IVGTT}$	0.087	[0.060, 0.13]
$P'_{2GC-IM-IVGTT}$	0.034	[0.020, 0.058]
ρ_{FFA}	0.915	[0.891, 0.934]
S_{FFA}	0.106	[0.096, 0.117]
K_G	0.0135	[0.011, 0.017]
Z_{50}	1444	[1159, 1798]

Using NLME methods, the expected values for group i at time t_{ij} is $y_{ij} = f(\boldsymbol{\vartheta}_i, t_{ij}) + \epsilon_{ij}$, where ϵ_{ij} are the within-group errors and $\boldsymbol{\vartheta}_i$ are the individual model parameter, that are function of the fixed effects $\boldsymbol{\eta}$, eventually some covariates $\mathbf{x}_{ij}$ (that can remain constant over time t_{ij} or may not), and the random effects $\mathbf{b}_i$. In the basic model formulation, the assumption of identically distributed (with mean zero and constant variance) within-group errors is made: $\epsilon_{ij} \sim \mathcal{N}(0, \sigma^2)$, which is adequate for many different types of grouped data observed in practice. However there is the possibility to adapt the model to account for heteroschedastic and/or correlated within-group errors. In the present work, after using a basic model (with constant variance) for within-group errors and examining the standardized residual plot versus fitted values, heteroschedastic variance was introduced (because residuals tended to increase with increasing fitted values): so $\epsilon_{ij} \sim \mathcal{N}(0, \sigma^2|y_{ij}|^{2\gamma})$, where σ and γ have to be estimated. Note that, imposing this distribution, the within-group errors are no longer independent from the random effects, because their variance depends on the fixed effects and the random effects through the expected values y_{ij}. Estimated values of σ and γ resulted 1.88 and 0.58 respectively. Inspection of qq-plot and residuals plot (not reported here), did not reveal any severe departure from model assumptions.

With regard to the normal distribution assumed for the between-group errors (random effects) it is clear that population fitting can not ignore outlying data, but they have often little influence on the estimation of fixed effects (the fit corresponding to this data is accomplished through individual random effect). So, in general, outlying data increase between-group variance, rather than influencing fixed effects estimation.

Simultaneous estimation of all model parameters in a single individual is not feasible, at least for most subjects, due to the large number of parameters. Generally in cases of practical identifiability, to obtain individual estimates, some model parameters are held fixed. With population methods this problem is reduced because individual estimates benefit from group estimates. Using a Bayesian approach, prior distributions on parameters must be provided, tacking advantage of extra-experimental information. Then model parameters are characterized by their posterior distributions, condensing experimental and extra-experimental information. With NLME the choice of the value for fixed parameters can be avoided all together. However there are two kinds of problems that arise in the parameter estimation. One is related to the possible existence of multiple solutions, all leading to the same good fit. Generally some of these solutions are not plausible, especially if model parameters have a physiological meaning. The other problem is generated by the fact that sometimes experimental data are not very informative with regard to some parameters. So these parameters are not well characterized, and large variations of one parameter is compensated by variations of another one. In these cases there is a strong correlation between parameters. In the present work, to investigate the first problem, some tests with different initial conditions were made (results not reported here) and the algorithm gave the same results or did not converge at all. For the second problem, the correlations between parameters were checked. The absolute value of the correlation of the fixed effect stayed between 0.006 and 0.36, for all pairs of parameters, with the exception of the correlation between $lnP'_{2IM-IVGTT}$ and lnK_G which was -0.63 and that between $lnP'_{2IM-IVGTT}$ and $lnP'_{2GC-IM-IVGTT}$ which was -0.65, but this latter is not surprising because these two coefficients are relative to the same parameter lnP'_2. So the correlation is not so strong to believe that trade off between parameters exists.

5. DISCUSSION

In the present study data collected in thirteen non diabetic subjects during IM-IVGTT and GC-IM-IVGTT have been analyzed. A FFA physiological model has been formulated, that accounts for the strong antilipolytic action of insulin and the indirect effect of intracellular glucose. FFA dynamics is described by a single compartment model, with FFA production controlled by insulin in a remote compartment, in analogy with the minimal model of glucose disappearance (Bergman et al., 1979). FFA production depends linearly on supra-basal remote insulin, but with saturable inhibition. So only a fraction ρ_{FFA} of the production is insulin-dependent. The model gives satisfactory fits of the experimental data, also in the IM-IVGTT test, without taking into account counterregulatory hormones levels.

Among model parameters, ρ_{FFA}, S_{FFA}, Z_{50} are the most interesting for their physical meaning. These parameters in fact relate FFA metabolism to glucose and insulin dynamics and represent a promising tool for investigating short-term regulation of glucose and lipid metabolism.

Correlation between model parameters, estimated via population methods, and individual characteristics have been investigated. No such correlation was found, but subjects were all non diabetic. Since FFA play an important role in the development of insulin resistance and in the impairment in glucose utilization (McGarry, 2002), future development will be the analysis and comparison of other groups of subjects (diabetic or obese).

In this preliminary analysis individual insulin sensitivity of glucose disappearance, as derived from the minimal modelling approach, was not considered, but will be included into the model in the future. This choice was determined by the opportunity of considering a low number of model parameter. The introduction of that parameter will change the measurement unit of the variable $Z(t)$ $(mg\ dl^{-1}\ \mu U\ ml^{-1})$, such that it will become a glucose concentration and thus $Z(t)$ will be considered intracellular glucose (instead of a quantity proportional to it). The parameter Z_{50} would then represent the glucose level needed to reduce by 50% insulin-dependent FFA production. Moreover, instead of using the remote insulin $Y(t)$ that controls FFA production, the insulin action of the glucose minimal model will be evaluated, which has a dynamics determined by parameter P_2 that may be different from the present P_2'.

6. ACKNOWLEDGMENTS

We gratefully acknowledge O. Lenter for technical assistance and the staff of the Endocrine Laboratory, Department of Internal Medicine III, University of Vienna. This study was supported in part by grants to MR from the Austrian Science Foundation (FWF, P15656), the European Foundation for the study of Diabetes (ESFD, Novo Nordisk Type 2 diabetes grant), the Herzfelder Family Trust, and financial support to ISIB-CNR by Regione Veneto (BIOTEC project).

REFERENCES

Bergman, R.N., Y.Z. Ider, C.R. Bowden and C. Cobelli (1979). Quantitative estimation of insulin sensitivity. *Am J Physiol*, **236**, E667–677.

Brehm, A., K. Thomaseth, E. Bernroider, P. Nowotny, W. Waldhäusl, G. Pacini and M. Roden (2006). The role of endocrine counterregulation for estimating insulin sensitivity from intravenous glucose tolerance tests. *J Clin Endocrinol Metab*, in press.

Coppack, S.W., M.D. Jensen and J.M. Miles (1994). In vivo regulation of lipolysis in humans. *J Lipid Res*, **35**, 177-193.

Laffel, L. (1999). Ketone bodies: a review of physiology, pathophysiology and application of monitoring to diabetes. *Diab Metab Res Rev*, **15**, 412-426.

Lewis, G.F., A. Carpentier, K. Adeli and A. Giacca (2002). Disordered fat storage and mobilization in the pathogenesis of insulin resistance and type 2 diabetes. *Endocrine Reviews*, **23**, 201-229.

McGarry, J.D. (2002). Dysregulation of fatty acid metabolism in the etiology of type 2 diabetes. *Diabetes*, **51**, 7-18.

Meijssen, S., M.C.Cabezas, C.G.M. Ballieux, R.J. Derksen, S. Bilecen and D.W. Erkelens (2001). Insulin mediated inhibition of hormone sensitive lipase activity in vivo in relation to endogenous catecholamines in healthy subjects. *J Clin Endocrinol Metab*, **86**, 4193-4194.

Pinheiro, J.C. and D.M. Bates (2000). *Mixed-Effects Models in S and S-plus*. Springer, New York.

Riemens, S.C., W.J. Sluiter and R.P.F. Dullaart (2000). Enhanced escape of non-esterified fatty acids from tissue uptake: its role in impaired insulin-induced lowering of total rate of appearance in obesity and type II diabetes mellitus. *Diabetologia*, **43**, 416-426.

Thomaseth K. (2003). Multidisciplinary modelling of biomedical systems. *Comput Methods Programs Biomed*, **71**, 189-201.

Thomaseth, K. and A. Pavan (2005). Model-based analysis of glucose and free fatty acid kinetics during glucose tolerance tests. In *Mathematical Modeling in Nutrition and Toxicology* (J.L. Hargrove and C.D. Berdanier, Eds.). pp. 21-40. Mathematical Biology Press, Athens, GA.

MODELING THE EFFECTS OF THE ELECTRODES POSITION ON THE SURFACE EMG CHARACTERISTICS

Jérémy Terrien[1], Sandy Rihana[1], Jean Gondry[2], Catherine Marque[1]

1 UMR 6600, Université de Technologie de Compiègne, France
2 Centre de Gynécologie et d'Obstétrique d'Amiens, France

Abstract — The uterine electromyogram (EMG) or electrohysterogram (EHG) could be used to detect a potential risk of preterm delivery in woman by analyzing its frequency content. In this study, we explore the effects of electrodes position, in terms of inactive tissues depth below the recording site and distance of electrodes to the potentials source, on the spectral characteristics of recorded signals. To explore these effects on skeletal muscle EMG and EHG, we used two numerical models but also real EHG. We have been able to notice specific effects in each situation but also cumulative effects. On real EHG, we could see that the main effect concerns the attenuation of high frequencies. Thus, the standardization of the electrode position during recording is a factor of importance. Copyright © 2006 IFAC

Keywords—Electromyogram, Electrohysterogram, Signal modeling, Uterine contraction, Pregnancy monitoring, Time-Frequency Representation, Spectral characteristic

1. INTRODUCTION

The uterine electromyogram (EMG), the so called electrohysterogram (EHG), could be used for the monitoring of contractions. This signal has very low frequencies mainly parted in two frequency components called FWL (Fast Wave Low) and FWH (Fast Wave High) (Devedeux, et al., 1993). FWL is located in low frequencies (< 0.2 Hz) and could be related to the propagation of the electrical activity of the uterus. FWH is located in higher frequencies (> 0.2 Hz and < 3 Hz) and could be related to the excitability of the uterus. Thus, the correct recording of these frequency components could provide useful information on the contractility of women, especially for women with preterm delivery risk. However, the physiological properties of the conducting volume between the electrodes and the muscle, in EMG recording, could vary between patients, but also with the electrode position on the same subject. Particularly in external EHG recording, the anatomical properties of the pregnant abdomen could modify the spectral characteristics of the EHG signal

in relation to the electrode position. For example, there are more visceral tissues between the skin and the uterus in periphery of the uterus rather than on the middle of the median axis of woman's abdomen.

Thus, in this study, we explore the effects of the electrode position but also of the thickness of non contractile tissues on the spectral characteristics of the EMG (skeletal muscle), on a first step, and the EHG (uterine muscle), on a second step.

2. MATERIALS AND METHODS

2.1 Skeletal muscle model description

The model is composed of three parts: the source plan, the conducting volume and the output plan.
Source plan: Several motor units (MU) are distributed uniformly in the muscle volume. In each MU, several muscular fibers are also distributed uniformly. All fibers located close to a given depth are grouped to form a source plan that contains the action potential (AP) of each active fiber. The AP is

obtained by the Rozenfalk equation (Rosenfalck, 1969).

The conducting volume: It is a two-dimensional spatial filter. We used the transfer function defined by Farina et Merletti (2001). This transfer function takes into account fat and skin thicknesses but also the muscle depth (the source plan depth in our model). We used a skin thickness of 1 mm and a fat thickness of 3 mm.

The output plan: It represents the potential distribution on the skin obtained by the summation of all source plans filtered by their conducting volume. The output plan is then filtered by a filter which represents the electrodes (Farina and Merletti, 2001). The transfer function of electrodes depends only on the electrode shape and dimension. We used disk electrodes with a 10 mm diameter similar to the ones used for EHG recording.

2.2 Uterine muscle model description

The only uterine models in the literature focuses only on the intra uterine pressure (Andersen and Barclay, 1995; Young, 1997). The uterus, a smooth muscle, does not contain long muscle fiber. So, we considered the uterine muscle activity at a given time, as the sum of individualized active cells. No work has already defined a realistic equation related to the electrical activity of the uterus. Thus, we used, instead of a physiological description of this electrical activity, a signal description of an electrical cell activity burst. It could be described as a position modulation of individual AP within the electrical burst (Devedeux, 1995). There is more frequent AP in the middle of the burst than at the beginning or the end of it. We choose to consider each AP of uterine cells as a Dirac impulsion. The position modulation is modelized by the inverse of a Blackman window. Thus, the signal generated by a cell k is:

$$h_k(t) = \sum_{i=1}^{NbAP} \delta(t - t_0^{(k)}(i)) \quad (1)$$

where NbAP is the total number of AP of the cell k during the contraction, δ the Dirac impulsion and t_0 the signal which create the position modulation of the considered cell. This approach of the electrical modeling of the uterine electrical activity gives only a modulated high frequency (FWH). To represent the low frequency component (FWL), we added to $h_k(t)$ a sinusoid modulated in amplitude, where the maximum energy is at the beginning and at the end of the contraction. The electrical signal generated during a contraction could be described as the filtered integral of the signal of several individual cells and then expressed as:

$$S(t) = \left[\sum_{k=1}^{NbCell} h_k(t - t_k) \right] * b(t) \quad (2)$$

where NbCell is the total number of active cell, t_k is a random variable specific to each cell, b(t) the impulse response of the low pass filter which models the conducting volume.

In this first approach, we have chosen not to model the propagation of the electrical activity on the uterus. Thus, we distributed randomly the electrical signal of each cell on a local area of a source plan and filtered these potentials firstly by the conducting volume (inactive tissues, fat and skin over the uterus) then by the electrodes filter used in the EMG model.

2.3 Modelization of the effects of the electrode position and of inactive tissue depth

In each model, we used a reference position which is located in the middle, of the skeletal muscle source plan, and of the potential distribution area for uterine cells. In this position, and for two distant positions (5 and 8 cm away), we recorded differentially the electrical signals. The distance between the two electrodes was 1.2 cm (distance used for real EHG recording). These values (electrode distances 5 and 8 cm) have been chosen because they correspond to real values used while recording EHG signals to study the effect of placental influence on EHG characteristics (Terrien, 2005).

To model the effect of the inactive tissue filtering, we chose to use for this inactive tissue the same electrical properties than for the active muscle. We compared the effect of 0, 0.5 and 1 cm inactive tissues depth (ITD).

In each situation, we computed the three differential signals for the same source plans. For the EHG model we also studied the cumulative effects of the two parameters (electrode position and inactive tissue depth) in order to simulate in a more realistic way the situation met in pregnant women.

2.4 Real EHG monitoring

We recorded simultaneously two external EHG on women hospitalized for high risk of preterm delivery. All patients presented posterior placenta. This rejection criterion was used in order to avoid any effect of the placenta on the spectral characteristics of contractions (Terrien, et al., 2003). On each patient, one EHG was recorded with an electrode pair in the middle of the median axis near the umbilicus, and another one located 5 cm left of the middle electrodes. The bipolar EHG were band pass filtered and digitalized at 16 Hz, using a specific device suited for EHG recording (Voisine, et al., 2002). The different contractions were segmented manually by a peer review of each signal. The EHG could be corrupted by the maternal ECG when recorded externally. Thus, we filtered each contraction by a method based on wavelet packets previously developed by Leman et al. (2000).

All patients gave their informed consent before any recording. Recordings were done for a period of about 3 hours.

2.5 EMG/EHG analyses

We calculated the time-frequency representation (TFR) of EMG signals by using the periodogram. The TFR of simulated CT were obtained by using autoregressive (AR) modeling, and for real signals, the continuous wavelet transform (CWT). The different methods of TFR calculation have proved to be the best ones for the different kind of signals (Devedeux, 1995; Leman, et al., 1999).

The analysis of TFR is often complex. Thus we used, for a first global analysis, their relative energy spectrum (RES), defined as:

$$SER(f) = \frac{\int_{t=0}^{T\max} TFR(f,t)\,dt}{\int_{f=0}^{F\max}\int_{t=0}^{T\max} TFR(f,t)\,dt\,df} \quad (3)$$

The different RES were divided into several energy bands with respect to the maximal frequency of each signal. Especially for simulated signal, we have observed an important fall of the signal energy whatever the frequency band related to any change (ITD, distance). So, the use of the RES analysis permitted us to evidence the changes in the frequency content distribution, whatever the signal energy, and to compare the different situations.

Then, the RES of the simulated EMG or EHG were compared by analysis of variance and t-test with a significant difference of p = 0.05. RES of real EHG signals where compared by Kruskall-Wallis and Mann-Whitney W tests, with a significant difference of p = 0.05.

3. RESULTS

3.1 Striated muscle EMG

The influence of ITD is presented figure 1. This effect mainly concerns the high frequencies (> 40 Hz). These frequency bands are attenuated while increasing the ITD. The most significant differences are observed between 0 cm and 1 cm ITD.

The effects of the electrode position on the EMG SER are presented figure 2. These effects are more important than those obtained by increasing the ITD. Moreover, the significant bands are not concerned with the same frequencies. The attenuated bands are mainly located in the medium frequencies (9–40 Hz). The differences between the reference SER content and the ones obtained at other electrode positions increase with the distance.

3.2 Simulated EHG

We could notice, on TFR of simulated EHG, a frequency modulation of the higher frequency component. The obtained frequencies are similar to those obtained in contractions for women in labor.

Like in the EMG analysis, the effects of the ITD are smaller than those obtained by changing the electrodes position. However, the attenuations noticed in each condition are smaller.

By increasing the ITD, only the frequency bands 0.5-0.75 Hz and 2.5-2.75 Hz are modified. The significantly different bands obtained when changing the electrode position seem to cover the whole frequencies, except for the bands located between 4 and 5.5 Hz. We could notice an increase in the number of significant bands while increasing the distance between the electrode pairs. The main effects on the signal spectral characteristics were observed with a simultaneous increase in the two

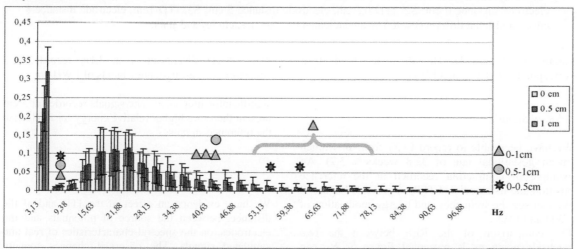

Fig. 1. Comparison of the mean SER of EMG for different inactive tissue depth and electrode position of 0 cm. Significant differences at 5% are indicated by stars, circles and triangles.

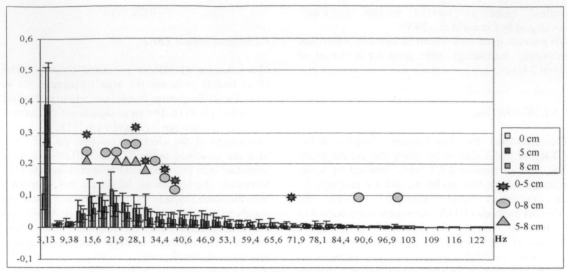

Fig. 2. Comparison of the mean SER of EMG for different electrode distances from the source of potentials and ITD of 0 cm. Significant differences at 5% are indicated by stars, circle and triangle.

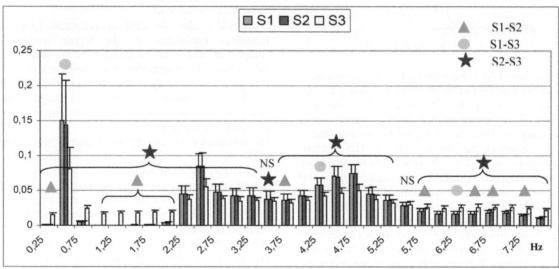

Fig. 3. Comparison of the mean SER of EHG for different electrode positions and ITD (S1: ITD 0 cm, electrode distance 0 cm; S2: ITD 0.5 cm, electrode distance 5 cm; S3: ITD 1cm, electrode distance 8 cm). Significant differences of 5 % are indicated by triangles, circles and stars.

parameters (Figure 3). The attenuated bands then corresponded to FWL and FWH.

3.3 Real Signal

We have been able to record EHG from 14 women (mean gestational age of 32.8 weeks ± 5.7). An example of contraction recorded at the reference position and its associated TFR, is presented figure 4. We can see the frequency and energy modulation of FWH and FWL.

The comparison of the RES between the two electrode positions is presented figure 5. We can clearly notice that the energy maximum of FWH

(0.4-0.45 Hz) disappears on the EHG recorded at 5 cm. Moreover, all frequency bands of FWH are

significantly attenuated. The signals recorded at 5 cm present therefore higher relative energy for FWL than the reference signals.

4. DISCUSSION

We have evidence an effect of the ITD and of the distance, between the source of potentials and the electrodes, on the spectral characteristics of real and simulated signals. The observed changes concern mainly the high frequencies, but several low frequencies were also attenuated. This could be

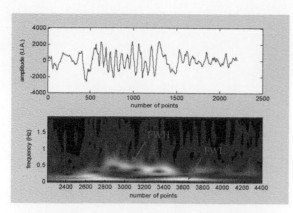

Fig. 4. Example of uterine contraction recorded in woman during labor and its TFR calculated by continuous wavelet transform

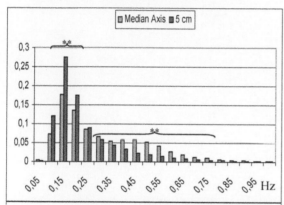

Fig. 5. Example of TFR of simultaneously recorded uterine signals recorded in woman with two different electrode positions

explained first, by the fact that the conducting volume, here influenced by the inactive tissues, corresponds to a low pass filter. The frequencies modified by the variation of the two parameters seemed to be different. However, the simultaneous variation of the two parameters presented a major effect on EHG characteristics, and covered the whole bandwidth of the signals. However, we can discuss the choice made to give to the inactive tissues the same electrical properties than the active muscle ones. This hypothesis may have a major influence in the attenuation effect related to inactive tissue depth.

Indeed, the ITD have been chosen arbitrary. Only muscle, skin and fat tissue electrical properties were given by the literature (Farina and Merletti, 2001). It could be interesting for example to measure the ITD in pregnant women by MRI and to determine its electrical properties by impedancemetry.

EHG model has been obtained by changing mainly the potential source of the EMG model. However, this model takes into account neither the propagation of the electrical activity nor the depth of the different fibers in the uterine muscle. This could explain the smaller attenuations observed with this model than those obtained with the skeletal muscle due, to less interference between individual electrical activities.

The main effects obtained for real EHG seems to concern high frequencies. We can therefore think that this effect is due to the distance of the electrodes from the source of action potentials. However, more recording must be done in order to confirm this hypothesis. This attenuation of FWH, which is related to the excitability of the uterus, could influence the diagnosis of preterm delivery risk. In fact, a very excitable uterus could be seen as a uterus exerting a normal contractility, when analyzing the contraction recorded in other positions than the reference one, median axis of woman.

5. CONCLUSION AND PERSPECTIVES

Based on simulated EMG or EHG, we have been able to show an effect of electrode position. This effect is not the same for each frequency band. This non homogenous attenuation has been identified on simulated signals but also on real signals. However, it seems important to confirm our result by increasing the different studied populations.

In recording of bioelectrical signal, it seems to be very important to take into account the electrode position. Therefore, a standardization of the recordings could permit to avoid the effect of electrode position. For example, the EHG could be used to detect a preterm delivery risk in woman by analyzing its frequency contents (Leman, et al., 1999). We could think that this diagnosis may give different results when based on signals obtained with different recording electrode positions. The median axis of women seems to be the best position for EHG frequency content monitoring.

6. ACKNOWLEDGEMENT

The authors whish to thank the Gynecological and Obstetrical Center of Amiens, France, and Imad Hajj Dib, University of Compiègne, France, for their contribution to this work. This research was supported by grant from the Biomedical Pôle "Perinatalité/Enfance" of the Picardy Region, France.

REFERENCES

Andersen, H. F. and M. L. Barclay (1995). A computer model of uterine contractions based on discrete contractile elements. *Obstet Gynecol*, **86**(1), 108-11.

Devedeux, D. (1995). Evaluation quantitative de certaines caractéristiques de distribution temps/fréquence : Application à l'EMG utérin. UMR6600. Compiègne, Université de Technologie de Compiegne.

Devedeux, D., C. Marque, S. Mansour, G. Germain and J. Duchêne (1993). Uterine electromyography: a critical review. *Am J Obstet Gynecol*, **169**(6), 1636-53.

Farina, D. and R. Merletti (2001). A novel approach for precise simulation of the EMG signal detected by surface electrodes. *IEEE Trans Biomed Eng*, **48**(6), 637-46.

Leman, H. and C. Marque (2000). Rejection of the maternal electrocardiogram in the electrohysterogram signal. *IEEE Trans Biomed Eng*, **47**(8), 1010-7.

Leman, H., C. Marque and J. Gondry. (1999). Use of the electrohysterogram signal for characterization of contractions during pregnancy. *IEEE Trans Biomed Eng*, **46**(10), 1222-9.

Rosenfalck, P. (1969). Intra and extracellular potential fields of active nerve and muscle fibers. A physio-mathematical analysis of different models. *Acta Physiol Scand Suppl*, **321**, 1-168.

Terrien, J. (2005). Etude des répercutions de la position du placenta sur les caractéristiques des contractions utérines. Département de Biomécanique et génie biomédical. Compiègne, Université de technologie de Compiègne.

Terrien, J., C. Marque and G. Germain (2003). Study of the local influence of the placenta on the characteristics of monkey uterine electrical activity. *25th Annual International Conference of the IEEE*, Cancun Mexico.

Voisine, M. L., C. Marque, H. Leman and J. Gondry (2002). Analysis of uterine electromyogram for the monitoring of preterm birth. Instrumentation developpement and data analysis. *4th BSI International Workshop*.

Young, R. C. (1997). A computer model of uterine contractions based on action potential propagation and intercellular calcium waves. *Obstet Gynecol*, **89**(4), 604-8.

MULTIPARAMETRIC HUMAN LIVER FIBROSIS IDENTIFICATION FROM ULTRASOUND SIGNALS

Mahmoud Meziri[a], Wagner C. A. Pereira[b], Christiano B Machado[c], Bouzid Boudjema[d], and Pascal Laugier[e]

[a]*Laboratoire LSC, Université Badji Mokhtar, BP 12, Annaba, Algérie*
[b,c]*Biomedical Eng. Program -COPPE, Federal University of Rio de Janeiro, Rio de Janeiro,RJ, 21945-970, Brazil*
[d]*Laboratoire de surfaces et d'interfaces, Université de Skikda, Algérie*
[e]*Laboratoire d'Imagerie Paramétrique CNRS/Paris, 15, Rue de l'Ecole de Médecine, France*
mmahmouddz@yahoo.fr   wagner@peb.ufrj.br

Abstract: Classical acoustic parameters (wavespeed, attenuation and backscattering coefficients and mean scatterer spacing) have been used in the characterisation of biological tissue pathologies. Liver fibrosis is a common disease, classified according to the Metavir Scale (from F0: normal, to F4: cirrhosis). The present work evaluates fibrosis discrimination by combining the mentioned parameters and applying a discriminant analysis on ultrasonic backscattering signals from 20 in vitro human liver samples. The highest correct classification percentages (85-90%) happened for parameters combination in groups of there. The limits and potentiality of the study are also discussed. A greater number of samples and non-linear classification methods are presently being pursued. *Copyright © 2006 IFAC*

Keywords: Signal Analysis, Parametrization, Discriminant Analysis

1. INTRODUCTION

The application of acoustical parameters to aid on the diagnosis of liver pathologies (e.g. steatosis, cirrhosis and cancer) has been an important research topic for the last four decades (Bamber et al., 1981; Romijn, et al., 1989; Kirk. Shung, et al., 1993; Zagzebski, et al., 1993; Lu, et al., 1999). In the last years some work has been done trying to explore the potential of these parameters to follow the evolution of liver fibrosis. These works have demonstrated that none of the parameters alone is capable to discriminate the different fibrosis stages (Abdel, et al., 2002; Meziri, et al., 2005; Machado, et al., 2004).

The objective of the present work is to explore the liver fibrosis differentiation by an acoustical multiparametric approach applied to *in vitro* liver samples. Four standard acoustical parameters (wavespeed, attenuation and backscattering coefficients and mean scatterer spacing) are combined in groups (two by two, etc) and discriminant analysis indicates the best parameter combination.

2. MATERIALS AND METHODS

Twenty degassed fresh human liver specimens were positioned on a polished steel plate (6 x 4 mm^2) beneath a thin plastic membrane, and then placed in a saline-water-filled reservoir kept at 25°C to 37°C by immersing it in a temperature controlled water bath (Figure 1).

For ultrasound (US) backscattered echoes acquisition, a 20-MHz transducer was placed above the perfect plane reflection at its focal distance (Panametrics M316, 0.125" diameter, 0.75" focal length, 6-dB bandwidth from 6 to 30 MHz, 460 μm-

6dB spatial resolution). It was adjusted perpendicularly to the steel plate so as to maximize the amplitude of the received echo. Then a first scan is made in a plane parallel to the surface of the steel plate. At each site, the RF signal was received and amplified (MODEL 5052 PRX Sofranel, France), digitized at 100 MHz with an oscilloscope (LeCroy 9350 AL, 500 MHz), then transmitted to a computer for subsequent processing. To improve the signal-to-noise ratio, a signal time-averaging was performed for each transducer position. Figure 2 gives an example of a typical RF ultrasound echo collected from a liver specimen.

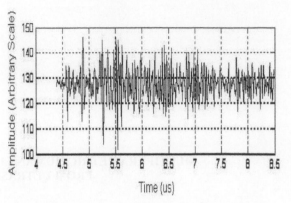

Fig. 2. An example of a RF signal collected from an *in vitro* healthy human liver tissue.

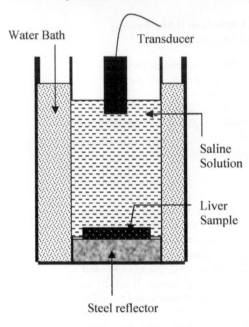

Fig. 1. RF signals acquisition set up from in vitro human liver tissues.

The liver sample is then inserted in between the transducer and the plane reflector, and the scan is repeated. After US scanning, histological sections were prepared for each measured region of the liver. The samples were fixed (4% formalin), paraffin-embedded, cut in 5 μm thick sections and stained for staging of fibrosis and grading of activity. The sections for light microscopy were stained according to the Goldner trichrome, hematoxylin and eosin, picro Sirius, Gordon and Sweets and Perls staining techniques. They were then reviewed without knowledge of the ultrasound findings to class tissue according to a French scoring system, the METAVIR (Poynard, et al., 1997), with scores 0 for normal, 1 to 3 for fibrosis and score 4 for cirrhosis. The histopathological study revealed that the 20 specimens were divided in four groups with five elements in each one (F0, F1, F3 and F4). There were no specimens for the F2 group.

The estimations of the wave speed (V), attenuation coefficient (A), integrated backscatter coefficient (C) and the mean scatterer spacing (M) were made by standard methods already described in detail in other publications of our group (Abdel, et al., 2002; Meziri, et al., 2005; Machado, et al., 2004). However, it is good to recall the main equations of those parameters.

2.1. Wave speed.

The wave speed (V) was estimated by using the substitution method according to the equation (Van Der Steen, *et al.*, 1991)

$$c_{foie} = c_{s\phi} \cdot \left(\frac{t_p - t_s}{t_{p/f} - t_s} \right) \qquad (1)$$

where:

$t_{p/f}$ and t_p are the time-of-flight for the transducer-steel plate distance with $t_{p/f}$ and without t_p the liver sample respectively and t_s the time-of-flight for the distance transducer - water/tissue interface. $c_{s\phi}$ represents the speed of sound in the saline solution.

2. 2 Attenuation coefficient

Assuming negligible transmission loss at the interface between saline and biological tissue, the attenuation coefficient as a function of frequency expressed in (dB.MHz⁻¹.cm⁻¹) can be obtained from equation (2) (Van Der Steen, et al., 1991)

$$\alpha(f) = \frac{1}{2.l_{foie}} 10 \log_{10} \left[\frac{|S_p(f)|}{S_{p/f}(f)} \right] \qquad (2)$$

where :

f : frequency
l_{foie} : thickness of the sample
$|S_p(f)|$: power spectrum without specimen
$|S_{p\setminus f}(f)|$: power spectrum with specimen

2. 3. The integrated backscatter coefficient

The quantity used to evaluate backscattering from biological tissue is the backscatter coefficient. It has been shown that this parameter may be sensitive to subtle micro-architectural and pathologic changes in tissue. Numerous works have been done to measure the backscatter coefficient from liver tissue, for example (Bamber, et al., 1991; Lu, et al., 1999; Wear, et al., 1995).

The estimation of backscatter coefficient expressed in decibels was evaluated using the following equation: (Roberjot, et al., 1996):

$$\eta(f,z) = 10\log_{10}\left\{ \frac{\langle|s(f,z)|^2\rangle}{\langle|s_{ref}(f,F)|^2\rangle} C_A(f,z) \frac{1}{d} \frac{R_p^2 k^2 a^2}{8\pi\left[1+\left(\frac{ka^2}{4F}\right)^2\right]} \right\}$$

(3)

where:

f : the frequency.
z: the depth.
$\eta(f,z)$: backscatter coefficient in the liver.
$\langle|s(f,z)|^2\rangle$: spatial average spectrum of the backscattered signal from the specimen placed at the focal region.
$\langle|s_{ref}(f,F)|^2\rangle$: average spectrum of the backscattered signal from plane reflector placed at the focal region.
$C_A(f,z)$: attenuation correction term, its expression can be found in (Roberjot, 1996):
R_p : Reflection coefficient from the plane reflector.
d: thickness of the processing window at depth z.
k :wave vector.
a : Transducer radius.
F : Transducer focal distance.
The compensation for the attenuation requires the knowledge of the attenuation coefficient

2. 4. The mean scatter spacing

The basic equation to estimate MSS is (Varghese and Donohue, 1993; 1994; Pereira, et al., 2002):

$$MSS = c/2f \qquad \textbf{(4)}$$

where c is the propagation speed of ultrasound (US) in the medium, and f is the frequency related to the maximum peak in the spectrum that corresponds to the periodicity of the scatters. The aim of a spectral analysis method is to identify this frequency, and use it to estimate MSS from equation 4.

2.5. Discriminant Analysis

Linear discriminant analysis (LDA) was carried out to test the potentiality of combining the four parameters: wave speed (V), attenuation coefficient (A), integrated backscatter coefficient (C) and the mean scatterer spacing (M) to separate the different

fibrotic stages. It was found a set of prediction equations that were used to classify individual samples into groups. More details on the LDA can be found in Marques de Sá (2003).

3. RESULTS

The results of the classification of specimens in the different groups (F0, F1, F3 and F4) are represented in the Tables 1 to 4, according to parameter combination (three by three). Figures 3, 4, 5 and 6 illustrate the respective plots. Figure 7 illustrate the combination of all four parameters. The results considering parameters pairs are not presented here once they do not contribute for the discussion.

Table 1: Discriminant Analysis for the parameter group (VCA)

Metavir Groups	Correct ↓	classification			
		F0	F1	F3	F4
F0	80 %	4	0	0	1
F1	100 %	0	5	0	0
F3	100 %	0	0	5	0
F4	80 %	1	0	0	4
Total	90 %	5	5	5	5

Lines: correct classification
Columns: obtained classification

Table 2: Discriminant Analysis for the parameter group (CAM)

Metavir Groups	Correct ↓	classification			
		F0	F1	F3	F4
F0	80 %	4	1	0	0
F1	100 %	0	5	0	0
F3	100 %	0	0	5	0
F4	60 %	2	0	0	3
Total	85 %	6	6	5	3

Lines: correct classification
Columns: obtained classification

Table 3: Discriminant Analysis for the parameter group (VCM)

Metavir Groups	Correct ↓	classification			
		F0	F1	F3	F4
F0	60 %	3	0	0	2
F1	80 %	0	4	1	0
F3	100 %	0	0	5	0
F4	100 %	0	0	0	5
Total	85 %	3	4	6	7

Lines: correct classification
Columns: obtained classification

Table 4: Discriminant Analysis for the parameter group (VAM)

Metavir Groups	Correct ↓	classification			
		F0	F1	F3	F4
F0	60 %	3	1	1	0
F1	40 %	1	2	1	1
F3	60 %	0	0	3	2
F4	60 %	0	0	2	3
Total	55 %	4	3	7	6

Lines: correct classification
Columns: obtained classification

In Figures 3, 4, 5, 6 and 7 it is illustrated the 2D graphics of the Discriminant Analysis presented in the tables.

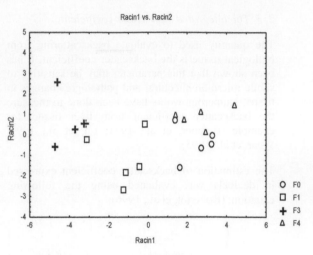

Fig. 5. Plot diagram of Discriminant function scores (Racin1 x Racin2) for the parameters VCM (○ = F0; □ = F1; + = F3; Δ = F4).

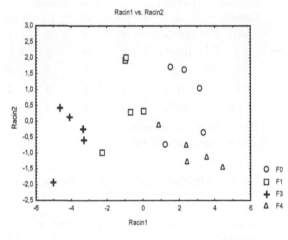

Fig. 3. Plot diagram of Discriminant function scores (Racin1 x Racin2) for the parameters VCA (○ = F0; □ = F1; + = F3; Δ = F4).

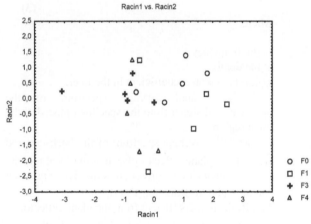

Fig. 6. Plot diagram of Discriminant function scores (Racin1 x Racin2) for the parameters VAM (○ = F0; □ = F1; + = F3; Δ = F4).

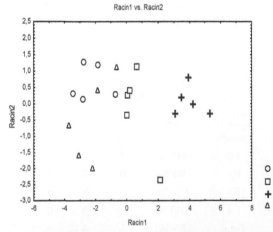

Fig. 4. Plot diagram of Discriminant function scores (Racin1 x Racin2) for the parameters CAM (○ = F0; □ = F1; + = F3; Δ = F4).

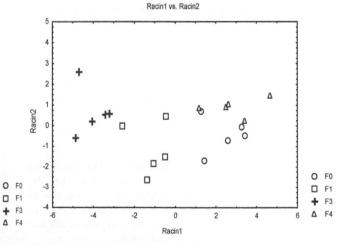

Fig. 7. Plot diagram of Discriminant function scores (Racin1 x Racin2) for the parameters VCAM (○ = F0; □ = F1; + = F3; Δ = F4).

Table.5. Discriminant analysis for parameters combinations in groups of three

Groups	VCA	CAM	VCM	VAM
F0 %	80	80	60	60
F1 %	100	100	80	40
F3 %	100	100	100	60
F4 %	80	60	100	60
Total %	90	85	85	55

4. DISCUSSION AND CONCLUSION

This work presented a multiparametric study to try to identify the different fibrosis degree from human in vitro liver samples, which is an original approach.

The combinations VCA, CAM and VCM have resulted in an important classification percentage (between 85 and 90%). Nevertheless, the performance of the parameter combination VAM has dropped to 55%. This is perhaps due to the fact that the MSS is dependent of the wave speed and so they somehow carry a certain degree of similar information. This possibility is reinforced by the fact that the classification of the group composed by all four parameters resulted in the same percentage (90%) which is illustrated in the Figure 7.

The parameter combination VCA (wave speed, integrated backscatter coefficient and attenuation coefficient) reached a high discrimination capacity (90%), specially if it is observed that it could correctly separate the samples belonging to neighbouring classes (F1 and F3), which are expected to have more subtle structural differences.

The main conclusion from Table 5 is that VCA is the most appropriate combination to discriminate between fibrosis stages. This conclusion should, however, be considered with some reservation. In some cases one of these combinations may be equal or higher in discriminating the score (i.e. VCM is more appropriate than VCA for differencing F4, etc)

An important overall conclusion from this study is that the results display some trends which may be useful in the diagnosis of different stages of fibrosis.

Nevertheless these initial results, though promising, should be regarded with precaution due to the limited number of samples. Presently efforts are being made to work with a more statistically significant sample group. Other classification methods like neural network are also being considered.

REFERENCES

Abdelwahab, A., Meziri, M., Pereira, W.C.A., Bridal, L., Laugier, P., and. Grimaud, J.A (2002). In vitro ultrasonic tissue Characterization for evaluation of hepatic diseases. In Proc. IEEE Ultras. Symp, p.1306-1309, Munich, 8-12 October.

Bamber, J.C. and Hill, C.R. (1981). Acoustic properties of normal and cancerous human liver-Dependence on pathological condition. Ultrasound. in Med. &. Biol, 7: p. 121-133.

Lu, Z.F., Zagzebski, J. A., and Lee, F.T. (1999). Ultrasound Backscatter and Attenuation in Human Liver with Diffuse Disease. Ultrasound in Med. & Biol, 25(7): p. 1047-1054.

Machado, C.B., Meziri, M., Pereira, W. C. A., and Laugier, P. (2004). Characterization of in vitro normal human liver tissue periodicity using backscattered ultrasound signals, in Proceedings of the International Federation for Medical and Biological Engineering, p. 1567 - 1570.

Marques de Sá, J.P. (2003). Applied statistics using SPSS, STATISTICA and MATLAB. Springer ed.

Meziri, M., Pereira W.C.A., Abdelwaheb, A., Degott, C., and Laugier, P. (2005). In vitro chronic hepatic disease characterization with a multiparametric ultrasonic approch. Ultrasonics. 43(5): p. 305-313.

Pereira, W.C.A., Abdelwahab, A., Bridal, S. L., and Laugier, P. (2002) Singular spectrum analysis applied to 20MHz backscattered ultrasound signals from periodic and quasi-periodic phantoms, in Acoustical Imaging. p. 239-246.

Poynard, T., Bedossa, P., Opolon, P., and Lancet, C. (1997). Natural history of liver fibrosis progression in patients with chronic hepatitis. 349: p. 825-832.

Roberjot, V., Bridal, S. L., Laugier, P., and Berger, G. (1996). Absolute Backscatter Coefficient over a Wide Range of Frequencies in a Tissue Mimicking Phantom Containing two Populations of Scatters. IEEE Trans. UFFC, 43(5): p. 970-978.

Romijn, R.L., Thijssen, J.M., and Van-Beuningen, G.W.J. (1989). Estimation of scatter size from backscattered ultrasound: a simulation study. IEEE.Transactions on Ultrasonics, Ferroelectrics and Frequency Control., 36(6): p. 593-606.

Van Der Steen. A.F.M, Cuipers, H. M., Thijssen, J. M., and Wilde, P.C.M.D. (1991). Influence of histochimical preparation on acoustic parameters of liver tissue a 5-MHz study. Ultrasound in Med. & Biol, 17(9): p. 879-891.

Varghese, T., and Donohue K.D. (1993). Characterization of tissue microstructure scatterer distribution with spectral correlation. Ultrasonic Imaging, 15: p. 238-254.

Varghese, T.,and Donohue, K.D. (1994). Mean-scatter spacing estimates with spectral correlation. J. Acoust. Soc. Am, 96(16): p. 3504-3515.

Wear, K.A., Garra, B. A., and Hall, T.J. (1995). Measurements of ultrasonic backscatter coefficients in human liver and kidney in vivo. J. Acoust. Soc. Am, p. 1852-1857.

Zagzebski, J.A., Lu, Z.F., and Lao, L.X. (1993). Quantitative ultrasound imaging: in vivo results in normal liver. Ultrasonic Imaging, 15: p. 335-351.

HUMAN SKIN THERMAL PROPERTIES IDENTIFICATION BY PERIODIC METHOD IN THE FREQUENCY DOMAIN

C. Lormel[(*)], L. Autrique[(*,**)], L. Perez[(**)], M. Gillet[(*)]

(*) DGA-EHF, BP 59, 66121 Font-Romeu Odeillo, France, tel: +33 468 307 688,
fax: +33 468 307 680, email : lormel.ghf@wanadoo.fr
(**) IUP-GSI, Université de Perpignan, 52 avenue Alduy, 66000 Perpignan, France

Abstract: Temperature evolution in human skin samples exposed to a laser irradiation is investigated in this communication. A 2 dimensional axis symmetric multi-layered model is presented and transient temperature is numerically estimated according to a finite elements method. A sensitivity analysis using reduced sensitivity functions has been performed in order to find out the most influent model input parameters and a specific experimental bench was set up in order to identify some of the crucial parameters: the volumetric heat capacities of each of the skin layers. This characterization device, developed also for *in vivo* measurements, is presented and results are commented. *Copyright © 2006 IFAC*

Keywords: Biomedical systems, Mathematical model, Sensitivity analysis, Thermal diffusivity, Identification, Inverse problem.

1. INTRODUCTION

In a military framework, it is crucial to ensure the protection of soldiers on the battlefield. Considering the development in the past decades of laser based devices and weapons, scientific investigation about risk of eye and skin laser burn injury becomes necessary.

The ocular domain has already been widely investigated, and is now well known thanks to medical and ophthalmologic researches. Oppositely, few studies regarding laser-skin interactions have been conducted so far, mostly because pre-existing technologies did not lead to significant damages. Nevertheless, due to the improvements and recent developments in laser technology, the prediction of skin damages is required in order to optimize human protection.

The main objective of this work is the determination of skin damage criterion and disabling limits for human submitted to an intense irradiative flux aggression. In that purpose, a mathematical model describing thermal transfer and optical phenomenon through skin is developed. After a brief presentation of skin physics and laser-skin interactions, this model is detailed in this communication in an axis symmetric 2-dimensional configuration. The determination of key thermal parameters is performed, based upon a sensitivity analysis using reduced sensitivity functions. Results provided by numerical designs of experiments applied to a one-dimensional model presented in a preceding communication (Lormel *et al.*, 2004, 2005) are then validated.

An experimental device for volumetric heat capacities identification based on periodic methods is presented. Moreover, in order to obtain *in vivo* measurements, several modifications have been proposed and tests have been carried out. Experimental results corresponding to tested samples close to human skin (pig skin) are presented and compared to the available data in the literature.

2. HUMAN SKIN AND ITS INTERACTIONS WITH LASERS

Skin is a three-layered material (for further information, refer to (Alberts *et al.,* 2002) :

- Epidermis, which thickness ranges from 0.05 mm for the eyelid to 1.5 mm for hands and feet.

- Dermis, located under the epidermis. Its average thickness is 2 mm, and ranges from 0.5 mm (eyelid) to 5 mm (bottom of the back).

- Hypodermis is the deepest of skins layers. It is made of fat cells and water of tissue.

Laser wave propagation through these three layers is influenced by absorption and diffusion phenomenon which depend on laser's wavelength and skin elements reacting selectively with the wave in function of its wavelength: the chromophores. Chromophores are not similar in epidermis, dermis and hypodermis and these heterogeneities have to be taken into account. However, the following behaviours can basically be considered:

- In the ultraviolet domain (UV), two highly concentrated chromophores (haemoglobin and melanin) influence the radiations absorption dramatically, reducing penetration depth to 10 μm for wavelengths under 300 nm.

- Water in the tissue absorbs the infrared (IR) radiations and limits their absorption to 10 μm for wavelengths over *2.5 μm.*

- UV and IR rays diffusion is limited to a few cells, and therefore can be neglected.

- Skin's behaviours in the near UV and visible domains are quite different. Absorption by skin elements is weaker and decreases from the UV to near IR. Diffusion is the main limitation factor of penetration depth for radiation in the tissue.

3. MATHEMATICAL MODEL

The human skin is assumed to have a homogeneous three layered structure. The optical, physical and thermal properties are different in each of the three layers (epidermis, dermis and hypodermis).

In order to describe skin structure as realistically as possible, a two dimensional axis symmetric model is proposed. Considering a finite element approach, Femlab® bio-heat transfer module allows to simulate the temperature evolution based on the bio heat transfer equation first described in (Pennes, 1948).

$$\rho_i C_i \frac{\partial T}{\partial t} + \nabla(-k_i \nabla T) = \Phi_b + Q \qquad (1)$$

Where $(i = e)$ corresponds to the epidermis layer, $(i = d)$ the dermis, $(i = h)$ the hypodermis. The temperature is denoted by T. Time variable is t, $\rho_i C_i$ is the volumetric heat of layer i, k_i is the thermal conductivity and heat losses due to blood

circulation are described by $\Phi_b = \rho_b C_b \omega_b (T_b - T)$ where the blood temperature is T_b. In the heat source term Q, the optical properties which depend on the wavelength (λ) are taken into account through the expression:

$$Q(\lambda, r, z, t) = \beta_i(\lambda) I_0(t) e^{-2r^2/R^2} \exp(\beta_i(\lambda) z)$$

z is the axial coordinate and r is the radial coordinate. The extinction coefficient $\beta_i(\lambda)$ is connected to the absorption and the diffusion of each layer. R is the laser beam radius. This is the radius at which the beam irradiance (intensity) has fallen to $1/e^2$ (13.5%) of its peak, or axial value.

The laser beam is assumed to be applied on a disk (10 mm radius). Simulations have been performed for a 1s laser radiation exposure (that corresponds to the time necessary for the soldier to get away from the radiation) and for a laser power of $I_0 = 130 \, kW.m^{-2}$. On the following figure, an example of simulated temperature distribution in the whole skin domain studied is shown at $t = 1s$.

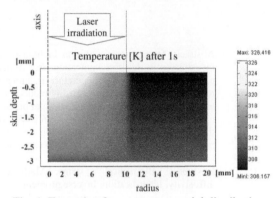

Fig. 1. Example of temperature spatial distribution

Few changes are observed in the non irradiated domain. These results explain the weak interest on laser aggression for skin during the last decade. Indeed, in a recent past the laser beam radius was too small to generate an important potentially disabling spatial damage.

4. SENSITIVITY ANALYSIS

The set of input parameters, specifically the thermo-optical parameters, has to be carefully considered so as to determine effect of the uncertainties on the simulation results. In this purpose, a sensitivity analysis has been performed. Sensitivity functions are defined as the absolute variation of a simulation output η induced by an absolute variation of the input parameters considered $\gamma = [\gamma_1, \gamma_2, ..., \gamma_n]$. In order to compare these coefficients with each other, the reduced sensitivity functions of η versus parameter γ are defined by the following relation (2):

$$X^{*}_{\gamma_i} = \gamma_i \frac{\partial \eta(\gamma)}{\partial \gamma_i} \qquad (2)$$

In this study, the outputs we are interested in are the temperatures in some key space positions:
- the skin surface
- the Epidermis/Dermis interface (E/D)
- the Dermis /Hypodermis interface (D/H)

The sensitivity study has been performed for the unknown parameters but also for the known parameters (which are *a priori* known with given uncertainties).
- thermo physical parameters known with a given accuracy : k_i, C_i, ρ_i, and $\omega_b \rho_b c_b$
- thermo physical and experimental parameters which are not well-known : convective exchange coefficient h, layers thickness x_i, blood temperature T_b, extinction coefficient β
- experimental conditions : heating flux due to the laser radiation I_0, external temperature T_{ext}, duration of the laser pulse

Simulations have been performed considering parameters values given in (Lormel *et al.*, 2004, 2005).
Here are the results on the skin surface. All the reduced sensitivity functions are plotted on graphics with the same scale, [-18 K; 26 K] that leads to an easier comparison of the calculated functions versus the time.

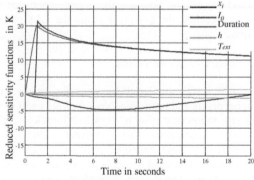

Fig. 2. Reduced sensitivity functions on the skin surface (external parameters)

On the previous figure, only the parameters that depend on the external conditions are depicted. The laser power and pulse duration are correlated, that means that the simulations are sensitive to a power density. Uncertainties on the skin thickness are more influent at 8 seconds. This result agrees with the fact that the temperature is observed on the surface and influence of depth is not immediate. As expected, the external temperature T_{ext} and the convective exchange coefficient h are correlated, but their effects are neglected. On figure 3, the influence of the other parameters on the skin surface is shown.

The most important parameters are the extinction coefficient β, the epidermis volumetric heat $\rho_e C_e$ and the dermis volumetric heat $\rho_d C_d$. Sensitivity to the other parameters (thermal conductivity of the three skin layers k_i, blood temperature T_b, blood perfusion $\omega_b \rho_b c_b$) is least.

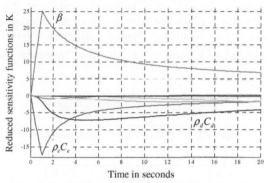

Fig. 3. Reduced sensitivity functions on the skin surface (thermophysical parameters)

By considering the other interfaces (E/D, D/H), the same influent parameters can be listed. However their uncertainties generate fewer errors on the simulated temperature except for the hypodermis volumetric heat $\rho_h C_h$ that becomes more important at the D/H interface.

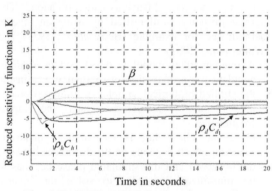

Fig. 4. Reduced sensitivity functions on the Dermis/Hypodermis interface

The influent thermal parameters shown in this sensitivity analysis have been identified with a specific experimental device based on a periodic method. This method is presented in the next paragraph.

5. THERMAL PROPERTIES IDENTIFICATION

In this chapter a technique for the parametric identification of skin thermal properties is presented. The periodic heating method employed is devoted to identification of material thermal diffusivity $a = \dfrac{k}{\rho C}$ in $m^2 . s^{-1}$, see (Gervaise *et al.*, 1997) for millimetric scale and (Dilhaire *et al.*, 2004) for micrometric applications.

5.1 Principle

The experimental bench is based on the thermal response of a sample submitted to a periodic heating excitation located on a millimeter-scale spot. The distance on which the heat has propagated during a period is called thermal diffusion length $\delta = \sqrt{a/(\pi f)}$ where f is the frequency of modulation.

Table 1. Diffusion length estimation

frequency [Hz]	diffusivity $\left[\mathrm{m}^2.\mathrm{s}^{-1}\right]$	diffusion length [mm]
$f = 1$	$a = 4\,10^{-8}$	$\delta \approx 0.1$
$f = 0.01$	$a = 10^{-7}$	$\delta \approx 1.8$

In the studied configuration, the thermally excited volume does not exceed some mm³. A biological sample is exposed to a periodic heating. The periodic temperature observed on the surface depends on the distance to the exciting source. Modulus and phase lag of the measured signal are characteristic of the material thermal properties. Analysis of phase lag leads to thermal diffusivity identification. The thermal property is identified by using an inverse method; see for example (Beck *et al.*, 1977) and (Walter *et al.*, 2001):

1. A mathematical model is developed in order to simulate the propagation of thermal waves inside the studied biological sample. A simulated phase-lag is then calculated versus the inputs frequencies.
2. Once the phase lag is measured, a quadratic criterion which depends on the difference between the observed and the simulated phase lags has to be minimized in order to solve the inverse problem.
3. The Levenberg Marcquard numerical algorithm allows to minimize the quadratic criterion

The algorithms have been developed using Matlab® software.

5.2 Experimental setup

The heating source is a coupled fiber-diode laser system emitting at 1950 nm. This wavelength is attenuated in the superficial layer of the skin. Lens L1 allows adjustment of the gaussian-shaped heating spot size (about 20 mm in diameter). A computer controls the modulation frequency and the power. A part of the heating beam is picked up with a beamsplitter and sent to a photodiode which signal is used as a phase reference. An HgCdTe infrared sensor monitors the sample front face temperature. Lenses L2 and L3 adjust the measurement zone size

and a water-cooled diaphragm placed between them intercepts disturbing hot sources radiation.

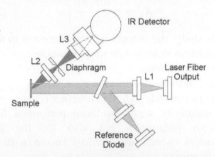

Fig. 5. Experimental principle

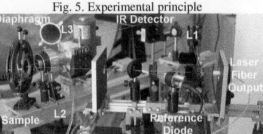

Fig. 6. Experimental device

In a general manner, the periodic methods present some advantages when the signal/noise ratio on observable output is low. This is linked to the processing of the signal coming from the sensor that allows to extract its amplitude and phase, even when noise level is high. The implemented technique is the lock-in detection that is achieved by a device. A lock-in amplifier (LIA) measures the phase lag between the temperature sensor and the reference photodiode output. For each frequency, when steady state is reached the computer reads the LIA phase output.

5.3 Heat transfer modelling

Thermal waves produced by periodic heating in homogeneous and heterogeneous solids are examined from the theoretical point of view in (Gurevich *et al.*, 2003). Application to thermal diffusivity measurement using harmonic and one-dimensional propagation of thermal waves is proposed in (Muscio *et al.*, 2004). Since time dependent solutions are numerically difficult to estimate, complex temperature is considered and leads to the determination of both phase lag and modulus in stationary state. These methods have been used in order to investigate thermal transfer in the material. Considering the equations system as linear and that the steady state is reached, the system state at each point of the sample can be written as a sum of a steady component and a periodic component which period is the same as excitation (3). Thus:

$$T(z,t) = T_{steady}(z) + T_{periodic}(z,t) \qquad (3)$$

with $T_{periodic}(z;t)$ a periodic function and where

$T_{periodic}$ can be written as (4):

$$T_{periodic}(z,t) = M(z)e^{j\omega t}e^{j\varphi} \qquad (4)$$

where M is the modulus (in K), φ the phase lag (in rad) and ω the pulsation (in s^{-1}) of the heating input $\Phi(z,t) = \Phi(z)e^{j\omega t}$. Thus, $T_{periodic}(z,t)$ can be written as a complex temperature and leads to the determination of both phase and modulus in stationary state ; see (Autrique *et al.*, 2003).

Let us consider the material L thickness versus z axis. The thermal excitation produced by a periodic heat flux is centred on its front face. The convective heat losses are taken into account on the front face and on the rear face ($z = L$) of the sample. Conduction and radiation extinction are also taken into account in the three-layered material. These conditions are resumed on figure 6.

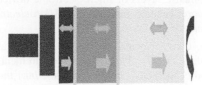

Fig. 6. Considered heat transfer modes

Then the evolution of $\tilde{T}(z) = M(z)e^{j\varphi}$ can be described by the following system S_{comp} :

$$\begin{cases} \forall x \in \,]0,L[\\ j2\pi f \tilde{T}(z) - \dfrac{k_i}{\rho_i C_i}\Delta\tilde{T}(z) = \dfrac{\rho_b \omega_b c_b}{\rho_i C_i}\left[T_b - \tilde{T}(z)\right] \\ \qquad\qquad\qquad\qquad + \dfrac{\beta_i}{\rho_i C_i}\Phi_0 \exp\left(-\beta_i z\right) \\ -k_e \dfrac{\partial \tilde{T}(0)}{\partial z} = -h\tilde{T}(0) \\ \tilde{T}(L) = 0 \\ \begin{cases} k_e \dfrac{\partial \tilde{T}^{(e)}(z)}{\partial z} = k_d \dfrac{\partial \tilde{T}^{(d)}(z)}{\partial z} \quad z \in \Gamma_{e \leftrightarrow d} \\ \tilde{T}^{(e)}(z) = \tilde{T}^{(d)}(z) \end{cases} \\ \begin{cases} k_d \dfrac{\partial \tilde{T}^{(d)}(z)}{\partial z} = k_h \dfrac{\partial \tilde{T}^{(h)}(z)}{\partial z} \quad z \in \Gamma_{d \leftrightarrow h} \\ \tilde{T}^{(d)}(z) = \tilde{T}^{(h)}(z) \end{cases} \end{cases}$$

In the studied specific geometry, the previous one dimensional model is valid since each layer is isotropic. Moreover, for the experimental device configuration, the excited zone is ten time larger than the measured zone and boundary effects can be neglected.

5.4 Sensitivity analysis

Sensitivity analysis of the thermal system using the reduced sensitivity functions presented in paragraph 4 has been performed. In an experimental framework, the sensitivity functions analysis allows to discuss the possibility of accurate physical parameters identification by:

- estimating model input parameters uncertainties on the simulated phase lag
- ensuring that measured outputs allow to identify the concerned parameter (in this case volumetric heat). This means that $\dfrac{\partial \varphi}{\partial \rho_i C_i}$ is not close to zero.

- Making sure that the uncertainties of the known parameters p_i do not dramatically the simulated results. This mean that $\dfrac{\partial \rho}{\partial p_i}$ is minimal.

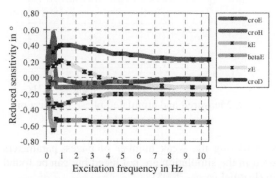

Fig. 7. Sensitivity function in frequency domain

The results show that it is necessary to work with frequencies over 0.7 Hz since phase lag is sensitive to all input parameters uncertainties at low frequencies. Over 0.7 Hz, the extinction coefficient of epidermis and skin thickness have to be known with a great accuracy in order to be able to identify volumetric heat capacity. To avoid the necessity of knowing precisely the extinction coefficient of epidermis, the laser wavelength has been chosen in a range where all the radiation is absorbed on skin surface, therefore, skin optical semi-transparency can be neglected.

5.5 Results on pig sample

The experimental setup has been tested on an inert material (a semi transparent disk of PTFE poly-tetrafluoroethylene Teflon ®) and the results are in good agreement with the values found in literature for this sample. Therefore, the system has to be validated on a sample more similar to human skin and pig skin samples have been studied (figure 8).

Fig. 8. Sample photography

In order to make this experimental setup compliant with *in-vivo* measurements, temperature elevation on the sample never exceeds 7°C. On the following picture (9), the phase lags measured (black circles), and the phase lags calculated with the identified values of the volumetric heats (red curve) are plotted. Identified values are for the epidermis:

$$\rho_e C_e : 2{,}1\ 10^6\ \text{J.m}^{-3}.K^{-1}$$

and for the dermis:

$$\rho_d C_d : 3{,}2\ 10^6\ \text{J.m}^{-3}.K^{-1}.$$

These values are in agreement with those found in literature for a desiccated sample (Davies, 1959)

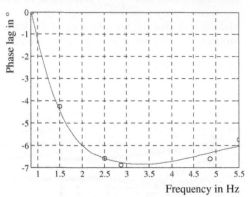

Fig. 9. Measured and simulated phase lag for a pig skin sample

Considering the weak number of pages, parameters used in the simulation are not listed but can be found in (Lormel *et al.*, 2005).

6. CONCLUDING REMARKS

In this communication, the field of laser aggression effects on human skin is investigated. Firstly, a mathematical model in an axis symmetric configuration has been considered and simulation results are presented. It has been shown according to a sensitivity analysis that in order to validate this predictive tool, it is crucial to carefully estimate several of the model parameters: an optical property (extinction coefficient in human skin) and thermal properties of several skin layers (epidermis and dermis).
For thermal properties, determination is based on periodic methods. Sensitivity analysis has been performed in order to determine optimal configurations (frequency range is defined). An important constraint is to avoid damages on human skin during measurements. Observations on phase lag between periodic heating laser (at a given wavelength) and resulting oscillating temperature (on skin surface) lead to the determination of volumetric heat capacity. According to the excitation frequency, various skin depths are affected. Parametric identification results achieved with pig skin samples are in agreement with those found in literature and further experimental investigations on human skin *in vivo* will be investigated. Thus, superficial and subcutaneous (respectively for epidermis and dermis) volumetric heats could be identified with non-intrusive observations.

REFERENCES

Alberts B., A. Johnson, J. Lewis, M. Raff, K. Roberts, P. Walter (2002), Molecular biology of the cell, *ed. Garland Science fourth*, p. 1259-1264.

Autrique, L., J.J. Serra, (2003), On the implementation of a finite element method for parameter identification, *LUXFEM, Int. Conf. on Finite Elements Applications, in CD-ROM*, Luxembourg.

Beck, J.V., K.J. Arnold, (1977), Parameter estimation in engineering and science, *New-York, Editions Wiley*.

Dilhaire, S., S. Grauby, W. Claey and J.C. Batsale, (2004), Thermal parameters identification of micrometric layers of microelectronic devices by thermoreflectance microscopy, *Microelectronics Journal*, **35**, 811-816.

Gervaise, C., C. Nouals, J.J. Serra, C. Calderan, B. Claudet, (1997), Diffusivity measurements by periodic methods, *in Proc., 24th Int. thermal conductivity conf., October 1997*, Pittsburgh, USA, 229-240.

Gurevich, Y.G., G.N. Logvinov, G.G. de la Cruz and G.E. Lopez, (2003), Physics of thermal waves in homogeneous and inhomogeneous (two-layer) samples, *Int. J. of thermal Sc.*, **42**, 63-69.

Lormel, C., L. Autrique and B. Claudet, (2004) Mathematical modelling of skin behavior during a laser radiation exposure, *2nd European Survivability Workshop March 2004, in CD-ROM*, Noordwijk, Pays Bas.

Lormel, C., L. Autrique, J.J. Serra and B. Claudet, Parametric identification for a biological system : model and experimentations, *World Congress IFAC July 2005*, Prague, République Tchèque.

Lormel, C., Analyse d'un système mathématique modélisant les interactions laser-peau pour la prediction de la brûlure. *PhD thesis, Univ. of Perpignan, December 2005*, France, pp.178.

Muscio, A., P.G. Bison, S. Marinetti and E. Grinzato, (2004), Thermal diffusivity measurement in slabs using harmonic and one-dimensional propgation of thermal waves, *Int. J. thermal Sc.*, **43**, 453-463.

Pennes, H.H, (1948), Analysis of tissue and arterial blood temperatures in the resting human forearm. *J.Appl. Physiol.* **18**, 93-122.

Walter, E. and L. Pronzato, (1997), Identification of parametric models from experimental datas, *Springer-Verlag*, Berlin, Germany, pp. 413.

Davies, J., (1959), The effects of intense thermal radiation on animal skin, a comparison of calculated and observed burns, Report T-24 US Army HQREC Natick, pp. 139.

MODELLING AND ANALYSIS OF HRV UNDER PHYSICAL AND MENTAL WORKLOADS

J. Zhang[*] , **A. Nassef**[*] , **M. Mahfouf**[*] , **D.A. Linkens**[*] ,
E. El-Samahy[*] , **G.R.J. Hockey**[+] , **P. Nickel**[+] , and **A.C. Roberts**[+]

[*] *Department of Automatic Control and Systems Engineering*
[+] *Department of Psychology*
The University of Sheffield
The United Kingdom
Tel: +44 (0) 114 222 5607
Email: m.mahfouf@sheffield.ac.uk

Abstract: In the first part of this paper we propose to revisit the closed-loop physiological model relating to human volunteers who are subjected to physical workload (stress), first proposed by Luczak and his research team in 1970s. The original model is further investigated and its parameters optimised via Genetic Algorithms using real data. The second part of this paper relates to the possible extensions of the model to model the effect of mental workload (psychological stress) on the cardiovascular system, namely heart rate variability. The autoregressive modelling based spectral analysis method is described and its application to spectral analysis of heart rate variability is evaluated. The assessment of heart rate spectra aimed at providing a meaningful measure of mental workload is also discussed. *Copyright © 2006 IFAC*

Keywords: Physiological model, power spectral analysis, workload, heart rate variability, auto-regressive model, optimisation.

1. INTRODUCTION

Heart rate (HR) is defined as the rate of occurrence of the cardiac beats, usually expressed in beats per minute. Several research studies into heart rate are related to the influence of physical stress and mental stress on the HR Variability (HRV). These studies concluded that the power spectrum of the HR signal involves three peaks occurring at 0.05, 0.1, and 0.25 Hz which belong to Temperature, Blood Pressure (BP) and respiration frequencies respectively.

The autonomous control of heart rate and blood pressure involves several feed-forward and feedback mechanisms. In addition, it is also known that respiration affects HR and BP through neural and mechanical mechanisms.

Luczak and Raschke (1975) developed a model of the structure and the behaviour of human heart rate control. This model was built by combining the transfer functions of physiological elements that take part in the control process. The previous authors considered that the main factors that influence the attitude of momentary heart rate are: respiration, blood pressure, metabolic effects and parameters of work physiology, such as the physical stress and psychological stress. The original version of this model was later extended to include muscular workload conditions above endurance limits-anaerobic work; additionally, the mechanisms of rhythm generation and control frequency and amplitude of respiration and blood pressure were developed (Luczak, *et al.*, 1980).

While the study of the effect of physical workload can seem to be relatively easier to investigate and model on one hand, modelling mental workload, on the other hand, is not so straightforward. The difficulty in quantifying mental stress is one reason, and the difficulty to identify a single index that is directly linked to such a workload is another. In the second part of this study, cardiovascular fluctuations can be investigated by monitoring and calculating the mean values and variances of the beat-to-beat BP and HR. The frequency domain analysis technique has been used to divide the variability of BP and HR into different frequency components and to quantify the variance or power at each discrete frequency (Kay and Marple, 1981). In this paper, the autoregressive modelling algorithm is employed to investigate the HR Variability (HRV) and its relationship to the mental workload (MWL) strength. The algorithmic procedure used for performing the power spectral analysis and the possible psycho-physiological interpretations of the simulation results are also presented.

This paper is organised as follows: Section 2 will review the equations associated with the original Luczak model and how it was modified according to some of our physiological considerations, while Section 3 shows how the model parameters have been optimised via Genetic Algorithms (GA) (Goldberg, 1989) to fit real data from healthy human volunteers. Section 4 outlines the experimental set-up for mental workload data collection from healthy subjects and Section 5 describes the idea behind the proposed spectral analysis algorithm. Section 6 discusses the simulation results hence obtained and Section 7 finishes with conclusions relating to this overall study.

2. MODEL ANALYSIS AND GA-BASED PARAMETER OPTIMISATION

One of those models that describe the relationship between the various physiological variables is the model suggested by Luczak and Raschke (1975). This model demonstrates the influence of the physical and mental stresses on the HR, BP, Total Peripheral Resistance (TPR), and respiration. Our proposed model includes improvements compared to the original Luczak model with respect to the following:

1- It solves the problem of the response onset (Transient part);
2- It considers the influence of the workload on both the amplitude and frequency of respiration;
3- In our model the sympathetic activity is considered to be proportional to the workload as long as the workload does not exceed a certain endurance limit.

2.1 The Main Model Equations

Space prohibits discussing all the physical equations involved in the model of Fig. 1 but suffice to outline the equations relating to HR only:
In the original model the HR equation was expressed as follows:

$$HR = HR_0\left(1 - \frac{F_{veff}}{a + b.F_{veff}}\right)\left(1 + F_{seffo} + K_{PF}.W_s\right)$$
$$\cdot\left(\frac{w_n^2}{s^2 + 2\eta w_n s + w_n^2}\right) \quad (1)$$

Where,

HR = Momentary heart rate in beats/min.
HR_o = Heart rate at rest (without vagus activity) = 120 beats/min.
F_{veff} = Efferent vagus activity.
F_{seffo} = Efferent sympathetic activity at rest = 0.64.
W_s = Reference variable of sympathico-tonic activity under workload.
K_{PF} =Constant
W_n = 1 rad/s.
η = 0.65.

In the model proposed in this paper, Equation (1) was modified to include the transient part proposed by Miyawaki (1966) such that:

$$HR = HR_0\left(1 - \frac{F_{veff}}{a + b.F_{veff}}\right)\left(1 + F_{seffo} + K_{PF}.W_s\right)G(s)$$
$$G(s) = \frac{w_n^2(1 + \tau s)}{s^2 + 2\eta w_n s + w_n^2} \quad (2)$$

Where $G(s)$ expresses the dynamic behaviour of HR and $(1 + \tau s)$ is a term that appears only when the F_{veff} increases; this is referred to as the on-transient term (Miyawaki, 1966); it allows the system to start with a transient effect and then reach a steady-state value for the heart rate.

2.2 Model Parameters Optimisation Via Genetic Algorithms (GA)

To optimise the parameters included in system Equations (2) and others relating to BP and respiration, a GA-based optimisation route was adopted. This algorithm appears to be an attractive tool as it does not require any knowledge of the function gradient and it tends to avoid being stuck in local minima most of the time. However, it requires the definition of a fitness function to guide it to the 'optimal' solution, which in our case is defined as follows:

$$Fitness = \frac{1}{n}\sum_{k=1}^{n}(HR_{error})^2 + (BP_{error})^2 + (TPR_{error})^2 \quad (3)$$

where the errors relate to differences between model predictions and actual measurements for HR, BP, TPR, and n is the number of data samples.

Fig. 1 shows the result of the optimisation process with a close fit between measured and predicted variables.

3. EXPERIMENTAL SETUP AND DATA COLLECTION FOR MENTAL WORKLOAD

In this experiment, a healthy subject was selected from a participant pool based on the training level (> 10 hours) and mission control expertise (i.e., process control engineering) on the simulated process control environment: Automation-enhanced Cabin Air Management System (AUTO-CAMS) (Hockey et al., 2005).

The experiment were carried out in an air-conditioned laboratory room (3.75×4.25m) without windows, illuminated with 2 pairs of high-frequency fluorescent lamps and furnished with movable walls for separation. The process control software AUTOCAMS was run on a PC and displayed on a 19'' TFT monitor on the subject's desk at about 50cm visual distance. A PC keyboard and a mouse were used for hardware control. Subjective ratings and system performance were recorded on the process control computer, whereas psycho-physiological data were recorded on another PC. The BioSemi® system was used to sample the psycho-physiological data at the rate of 2048 Hz.

The task requires the subject to manage a system that controls the atmospheric environment (i.e., air quality, temperature, pressure, humidity, etc.) of a closed human-machine system. The subject interacts with a dynamic visual display that provides data on system variables and functions via a range of control tools. The primary task of the operator is to maintain the system variables in their normal ranges using manual control when automatic control components failed to do so. In order to vary the level of task load imposed on an operator, different automation failures were programmed for the process control operation. Individual conditions (#1, #2, ..., #8) correspond to different number of system variables (1, 3, 4, 5) to be under manual control. For an experimental session, the cyclic loading method resulted in a loading phase (condition #1-2-3-4) and an unloading phase (condition #5-6-7-8). Each condition lasted 15 minutes and there was a 20-second break between one condition and the next. The collected information was stored in the BioSemi® generated data-files for future analysis.

4. SPECTRAL ANALYSIS USING AUTO-REGRESSIVE MODELS (ARM)

4.1 Spectral Analysis via the Auto-Regressive Modelling (ARM) Algorithm

It has been shown that the AR modelling method is ideally suited to the signal data where rhythms are present for short periods of time only (Linkens, 1979). In this section, the mathematical details about the AR spectral analysis method will be presented.

Linear prediction filters can be used to model the second-order statistical characteristics of a signal $y(k)$. The filter output can be used to model the signal when the input is a white-noise sequence $\{\varepsilon(k)\}$. Mathematically, in the form of a difference equation this is given by the following:

$$y(k) = -\sum_{i=1}^{p} a_i y(k-i) + \varepsilon(k) \tag{4}$$

where $a_i (i = 1,2,\cdots,p)$ are the coefficients in the AR model, and p is the model order. By using z^{-1} as a unit backward shift operator, (4) can be rewritten as follows:

$$Y(z) = -a_1 z^{-1} Y(z) - \cdots - a_p z^{-p} Y(z) + \Xi(z)$$
$$= -Y(z) \sum_{i=1}^{p} a_i z^{-i} + \Xi(z) \tag{5}$$

This may produce a filter with the following transfer function:

$$H(z) = \frac{Y(z)}{\Xi(z)} = \frac{1}{A(z^{-1})} \tag{6}$$

where $A(z^{-1})$ is a coefficient polynomial in z^{-1} given as follows:

$$A(z^{-1}) = 1 + \sum_{i=1}^{p} a_i z^{-i} \tag{7}$$

The spectral components are determined by representing the roots of polynomial (7) in the z-plane. The rhythms are indicated by a pair of conjugate roots close to the unit circle. The damping ratio of the roots is given as follows:

$$\varsigma = \frac{\ln(|z_p| / \omega T_s)}{\sqrt{1 + (\ln(|z_p| / \omega T_s))^2}} \tag{8}$$

where T_s is the data sampling interval and ω the angular frequency of the conjugate roots.

The relative spectral amplitude is calculated as follows:

$$A = \gamma \cdot \frac{1}{2\varsigma} \cdot \frac{1}{1 + \sum_{i=1}^{p} \hat{a}_i} \tag{9}$$

where γ is the root mean square value of the residuals and the ARM filter parameters are estimated via the least-squares estimation algorithm adopted in (Linkens, 1979).

4.2 Model Structure Determination

In the ARM method, the HR signal data are used to identify an AR model from which the power spectrum is analytically derived. In this process, those HR signal components, which do not well fit the model, are treated as noise and are partially or totally removed. Since the ARM spectral analysis algorithm fits the signal data to an all-pole model, *a priori* choice of the model order p is important for successful applications. It is worth noting that the model order must be carefully chosen to optimize the frequency resolution and accuracy in spectral estimation. Excessively higher-order ARM may give spurious spectral peaks and hence should be avoided, while too low order may yield scarcely informative spectra. Nevertheless, when the power spectral analysis is focused on broadband powers, the ARM method suitably calculates the spectrum only if an appropriately high model order is used. The optimal model order may need to be empirically corrected on the basis of the user's experience, which may sometimes amount to a trial-and-error operation.

5. ANALYSIS AND DISCUSSION

5.1 Analysis of the Results

Three HR rhythms were identified as individual peaks in the frequency spectrum of Fig. 2(b). These peaks reflect (1) oscillations with a frequency of 0.3292 Hz, defined as high-frequency (HF) respiratory activity; (2) oscillations with a frequency of 0.0942 Hz, physiologically due to BP and normally referred to as the 0.1 Hz component; and (3) oscillations with a frequency of 0.0201 Hz, defined as very low-frequency (LF) component.

The FFT spectrum and the 14th-order ARM spectrum of the 15 min. HR time-series under condition 3 (i.e., four process variables are under manual control and the human operator experiences the second highest level of WML) are shown in Fig. 3(a) and (b), respectively. It is obvious that the ARM spectral analysis technique can well identify the three sharp spectral peaks corresponding to three main rhythms in the HR time-series, while they are all un-recognized in the spectra which were obtained via FFT analysis.

The individual HR spectra of 7 data segments under condition 3 are shown in Fig. 4. Results show that the trend of the seven individual spectra displays considerable changes due to the intrinsic non-stationary nature of the HR time-series even in the same condition of task load. Furthermore, the simulation results also show that the trend of the individual HR spectra has marked variations under nine different conditions of task load, including 4 loading conditions (C#1-4), 4 unloading conditions (C#5-8) plus one rest baseline condition (C#0) used for comparison.

These findings have indicated that the change of level of mental workload can be reflected in the HR frequency spectrum. This may be better quantified by using the time-varying spectral analysis techniques, such as the sequential spectral approach or the Wigner-Ville technique, which are capable of tracking the time-varying features of HR on the level of task-load conditions. The simulation results have indicated that the amplitude and frequency of the three main rhythms are not constant but vary under nine task-load conditions, as shown in Fig. 5. Under simulation, the significant spectral peaks as well as the broadband powers (see Fig. 6) are both considered. This may offer a broader description of the effect of Mental Workload (MWL) on HR variability.

5.2. Discussion

Fig. 6(a) shows that there was a continuous decrease in mean HR from one condition to the next, indicating a deactivation process in the experimental session. From Figs. 5 and 6, it can be clearly observed that the ARM spectral analysis yielded apparent effects of the level of conditions on the HRV frequency spectral characteristics. An increase in the LF frequency band power shown in Fig. 6(b) in C#1-3, #4-5, and #6-8 may be a consequence and hence marker of the increased mental workload. However, the decreased LF power in other conditions does not necessarily mean a reduction of the mental workload since other psycho-physiological factors, in particular fatigue and habituation due to long-time experiment (2-3 hours in our case), must also be taken into account.

It is usually assumed that sympathetic and vagal cardiac influences are normally altered in antagonist (inverse) relationship. Thus, one can use the LF (around 0.1 Hz) powers and HF (0.3 Hz) powers as the sensitive markers of sympathetic and vagal cardiac drive, respectively and use their ratio as a measure of sympatho-vagal balance. However, in this work it was found that under certain workload conditions (e.g., conditions 2-5 and conditions 7-8, refer to Fig. 6(b) and (c)) the two spectral components undergo concordant changes of similar or different magnitude. This discrepancy is likely to be due to the fact that HR fluctuations are linked to a wide variety of stimuli, such as thermoregulation, periodic breathing, hemodynamic instability, and physical or mental stress (Kitney, 1975).

The simulation results have shown that the LF (0.03-0.15 Hz) and HF (0.18-0.4 Hz) band powers are satisfactory but incomplete measures of the changes in mental workload imposed on the operator. Nevertheless, the HR spectra in the HF or LF bands are not invariably sensitive and reliable markers of mental load, which may also depend on other physiological variables and mechanisms, including the EEG activity. However, conducting more experiments, where the volunteers can be selected to undergo a wider variety of task-load conditions, may enhance the reliability of these HR spectral indices in reflecting MWL change.

6. CONCLUSIONS

One facet of this research paper proposed a closed-loop physiological model which succeeded to predict the behaviour of certain physiological variables under the effect of a physical workload. The model solves the problem of response onset by including the on-transient term to the HR transfer function to mimic the measured signals.

The other aim of this paper was to use the spectral analysis approach to improve the MWL assessment by coupling the information obtained from the recorded HRV signal with the spectral characteristics derived from the ARM algorithm. It is essential to analyse the HRV signal, especially in the frequency domain, when its spectral indices somehow correlate to the MWL of the operator. In this paper, we described the ARM algorithm for estimating PSD of the HRV signal. The ARM spectral analysis method was validated by using the experimental data obtained from a healthy subject. The advantages of the proposed ARM method include:

- It is statistically consistent even for short data segments. Under certain conditions, the ARM spectral response is a maximum entropy spectrum (Linkens, 1979);

- It may perform on-line monitoring of the sympatho-vagal balance through directly updating the spectral parameters of physiological interest;

- The frequency resolution of the ARM algorithm does not depend on the quantity of the data, while in FFT analysis the major parameter is the number of cycles of data available since it determines the attainable frequency resolution;

- It may offer the possibility of obtaining usable markers to characterize the change of MWL of the operator in both laboratory and real-life situations and thus represent a useful tool for the investigation of the MWL and in turn operator's functional states in complex human-machine systems.

Preliminary simulation results have also shown that individual spectral components of the HRV signal may be related to different mechanisms under different conditions of task load. In particular, although the change in task load appears to be reflected by HR powers of its 0.1 Hz component, the sensitivity of these powers as indices of MWL in different task-load conditions are not always optimal.

ACKNOWLEDGEMENTS

The authors wish to thank the UK-EPSRC for their financial support of parts of this project under Grant GR/S66985/01.

REFERENCES

Goldberg D.E. (1989) Genetic Algorithms in Search, Optimization, and Machine Learning: Addison-Wesley.

Hockey G.R.J., P. Nickel, A. Roberts, M. Mahfouf, and D.A. Linkens (2005), Implementing adaptive automation using on-line detection of high risk operator function state, in *Proc. of the 9th Intl. Symp. of the ISSA Research Section*, 1-3 March 2006, Nice, France.

Kay, S.M. and Marple S.L. (1981), Spectrum analysis: a modern perspective. *Proc IEEE*. Vol. **69**, pp. 1380-1418.

Kitney RI. (1975), An analysis of the nonlinear behavior of the human thermal vasomotor control system. *J Theor Biol*. Vol. **52**, pp. 231-248.

Linkens, D.A. (1979), Maximum entropy analysis of short time-series biomedical rhythms, *J. Interdiscipl. Cycle Res.*, Vol. **10** (2), pp. 145-163.

Luczak, H., F. Raschke (1975). A Model of the Structure and Behaviour of Human Heart Rate Control. *Biological Cybernetics*.**18**, 1-13.

Luczak, H., U. Philipp, and W. Rohmert (1980). Decomposition of heart-rate variability under the ergonomic aspects of stressor analysis. In: *The Study of Heart Rate Variability* (R.I. Kitney, and O. Rompelman.(Ed)). 123-142. Oxford University Press, New York.

Miyawaki, K., Takashi Takahashi, and Hikaru Takemura (1966). Analysis and Simulation of the Periodic Heart Rate Fluctuation. *Technical Report*.**16**, 315-325.

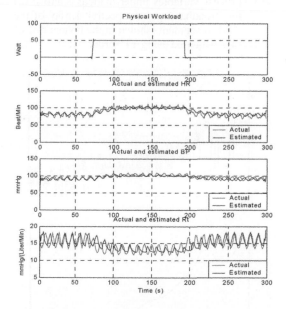

Fig. 1: The actual and estimated physiological variables in response to a 50-watt step input reflecting the physical workload.

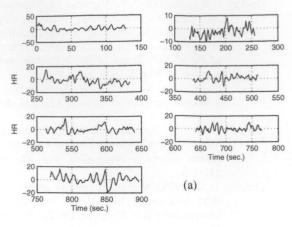

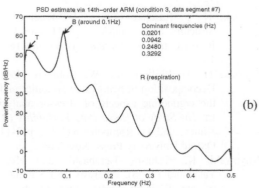

Fig. 2: (a) 7 consecutive HRV data sequences (each lasting 128 sec.) under condition 3 (i.e., 4 process variables under manual control); (b) the broadband power spectral density of the 7th data segment (shown in the bottom row of (a)) evaluated using 14th-order ARM.

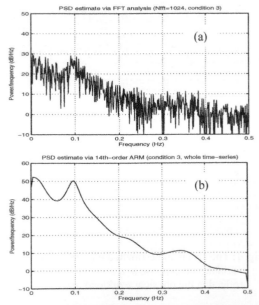

Fig. 3: Comparison of the spectra of the 15-minute HRV time-series, shown in Fig. 2(a) segment by segment, using (a) FFT analysis; and (b) 14th-order ARM analysis.

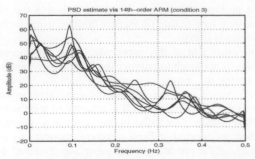

Fig. 4: The PSDs estimated over 7 consecutive HR data segments of 128 seconds throughout a two-hour experiment under condition 3.

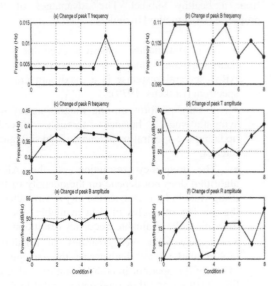

Fig. 5: The changes in the frequency and amplitude of significant HRV spectral peaks under nine conditions of task load (i.e., C#0-8, here C#0 denotes load-free baseline with eyes of the operator closed for 5 minutes).

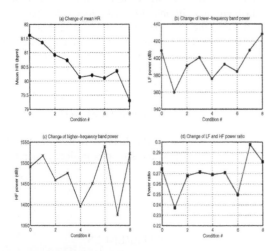

Fig. 6: The changes in the broadband HRV spectral indices in nine conditions of task load, where the LF and HF powers are computed within 0.03-0.15 Hz and 0.18-0.40 Hz, respectively, based on the individual HRV spectra.

Copyright © IFAC Modelling and Control in Biomedical Systems
Reims, France, 2006

SYSTEM IDENTIFICATION OF PHOTOSENSITISER
UPTAKE KINETICS IN PHOTODYNAMIC THERAPY

T. Bastogne * L. Tirand ** M. Barberi-Heyob ** A. Richard *

*Université Henri Poincaré, Nancy 1,
Centre de Recherche en Automatique de Nancy (CRAN),
CNRS-INPL-UHP UMR 7039,
BP 239, F-54506 Vandœuvre-lès-Nancy Cedex, France*
*** Centre Alexis Vautrin, Centre de Lutte contre le Cancer
Brabois, Av. de Bourgogne, 54511 Vandœuvre-lès-Nancy Cedex*

Abstract: This study presents the contributions of system identification techniques to the experimental modelling of photosensitiser uptake kinetics in photodynamic therapy. The experimental framework is limited to one cancer cell line (HT29-A4), one photosensitiser (Chlorin e6), one photosensitiser dose ($5\mu g \cdot ml^{-1}$), four albumin rates in a monolayer culture and eight measurements between $1h$ and $24h$. Issues associated with this experimental modelling study are the deficiency of measurement points, low signal-to-noise ratios and 'poor' excitation signals (step signals). This paper deals with model structure selection, parameter estimation and parameter uncertainty description by probabilistic confidence regions. Moreover, an explicit relationship between the static gain of the estimated model and the albumin rate of the culture medium has been established. *Copyright © 2006 IFAC*

Keywords: system identification, pharmacokinetics, drug delivery, photodynamic therapy

1. INTRODUCTION

Photodynamic therapy (PDT) (Moser, 1998) is an emerging therapy for displastic tissues such as cancers. This therapy involves selective uptake and retention of a photosensitive drug (photosensitiser, PS) in a tumour, followed by irradiation with light at an appropriate wavelength. The activated photosensitiser is thought to produce singlet oxygen at high doses and thereby to initiate apoptotic and necrotic death of tumour. In current clinical practice, photodynamic therapy is carried out with prescribed drug doses and light doses as well as fixed drug-light intervals and illumination fluence rates. These doses are determined from a physical model, see *e.g.* (Patterson *et al.*, 1990; Hetzel *et al.*, 2005), defined in equation (1).

$$[R] = k_s \cdot b \cdot \epsilon \cdot I_\lambda \cdot T \cdot [^1P] \cdot \Phi \cdot f \qquad (1)$$

where: $[R]$ is a threshold concentration of oxidising events radicals that needs to occur in a sensitive location within a cancer cell to elicit the cascade toward cell death, I_λ is the irradiance on the tissue surface, T is the exposure time of treatment light and $[^1P]$ is the concentration of intracellular photosensitive drug (photosensitiser P). k_s is the backscatter factor due to reflected light from underlying tissue, b is a conversion factor, ϵ is the extinction coefficient of photosensitive drug, Φ is the quantum yield for conversion of activated drug to oxidising radicals, which usually depends on the oxygen concentration dissolved in the cells and f is the fraction of generated oxidising radicals, which attack sensitive cellular sites, while the fraction $(1 - f)$ of the radicals attack lesser sites and have minor effect. Despite its current use in clinical applications, several polemical points can be addressed against this model:

- Equation (1) shows a simple reciprocity of photosensitiser concentration and light. Nevertheless, several experiments have shown contradictory results (Moesta *et al.*, 1995; Yuan *et al.*, 1997). Moreover Potter *et al.* have shown that a reduction in photosensitiser concentration during treatment, *e.g.* PS photodegradation, is an important consideration (Potter, 1986) .
- The term (Φ) is function of oxygenation but is usually a unknown factor during PDT (Tromberg *et al.*, 1990; Nichols and Foster, 1994; Hetzel *et al.*, 2005; Dysart *et al.*, 2005).
- Sites of photodamage mainly depend on the location of the PS in the cell. Sites of action for singlet oxygen in PDT include mitochondria, endoplasmic reticulum, Golgi apparatus, lysosomes, DNA and lipid membranes (Henderson and Dougherty, 1992; Epe *et al.*, 1993). Some of them are critical sites. Unfortunately, equation (1) does not take into account the intracellular location of PS.
- In fact, all quantities are generally time dependent, *i.e.* their concentrations (or in the case of light, its fluence rate) can change during irradiation. In other words, PDT is a dynamic process but equation (1) is just a static model (Georgakoudi *et al.*, 1997; Georgakoudi and Foster, 1998; Dysart *et al.*, 2005).

This previous list is not exhaustive but presents some of the main modelling requirements and challenges for increasing scientific knowledge of PDT. System identification (Ljung, 1987; Söderström and Stoica, 1989; Walter and Pronzato, 1997) is the field of mathematical modelling of dynamic systems from experimental data. No identification study has ever been applied to the PDT problem. It is therefore interesting to assess the contributions of system identification to the experimental modelling of PDT.

The problem addressed in this paper deals with system identification of *in vitro* photosensitiser uptake kinetics, *i.e.* the first phase of PDT. Problems encountered are generic problems in biology, *i.e* few measurement points ($n_e \cdot n_t < 20$), low signal-to-noise ratios due to a great measurement variability and 'poor' stimulus signals (step signals in general). In this experimental framework, objectives are : (1) selecting a model structure ($\mathcal{M}(\mathbf{p})$), (2) estimating its parameters ($\mathbf{p}$), (3) determining the parameter uncertainties and if necessary explaining how the serum concentration in the culture medium ($[Se]$) can influence model parameters, *i.e.* determining the relationship $f(\cdot)$ such that $\hat{\mathbf{p}} = f([Se])$.

This paper is organised as follows. A macroscopic model of PDT is firstly presented in section 2 to introduce the system identification problem of PS uptake kinetics under a restricting experimental framework. The remaining sections are put into a chronological order of system identification steps. Section 3 deals

with model structure selection, section 4 presents the estimation step, section 5 describes the parameter uncertainty, section 6 concerns the validation of the noise hypothesis and section 7 discusses on the explicit influence of the serum concentration.

2. MATHEMATICAL MODEL OF PDT

2.1 Macroscopic model

Table 1. Main notations

Symb.	Description	
$[x]$	concentration of x	M
Q_x	quantity of x	mol
D_x	dose of x	$M \cdot s$
t	time	s
P	photosensitiser molecule	
P_a	administrated PS	
P_i	intracellular PS	
P_x	extracellular PS	
P_{PP}	photoproduct of PS	
z_P	photosensitiser intraC. colocation	A.U.$\cdot$ cell^{-1}
M	Medium	
Se	serum (proteins) in the medium	%
CCL	cancer cell line	
A_{th}	critical intracellular damage threshold	
L	light	
I_λ	fluence rate of light with wavelength λ	$W \cdot m^{-2}$
S	cancer cell survival rate	%
$\mathbf{p}$	parameter vector of a model	
$\mathcal{M}(\cdot)$	model structure	
s	differentiation operator	
n_t	number of measurement points	
n_e	number of repeated experiments	
SNR	signal-to-noise ratio	dB

A macroscopic model of PDT is described by a block diagram in figure 1. Main variables, except the standard notations of chemical elements, are given in table 1. This macroscopic model is composed of three macro-blocks associated with the three main phases of PDT, *i.e.* the PS uptake, the irradiation and the cytotoxicity phases. The photosensitiser, light generator, cell culture medium and cancer cell line are described by signal generators (grey blocks). The main input variables, I_λ, Q_{Pa} and $[O_2]$ are represented by bold arrows. $[S_e]$ and CCL are usually supposed to be constant during the therapy. λ is regarded as a parameter of the light source. The PS uptake and cytotoxicity phases are described by black-box models since their dynamic behaviour is not well understood currently. e_P, $e_{[O_2]}$, e_S are error variables describing the combined effects of modelling errors, measurement noises and disturbances.

2.2 PS uptake kinetics

A sketch of the PS uptake phenomenon under *in vitro* condition is shown in figure 2. During this phase, a mass balance equation applied to the PS molecules is:

$$Q_{Pa}(t) = Q_{Pi}(t) + Q_{Px}(t) \qquad (2)$$

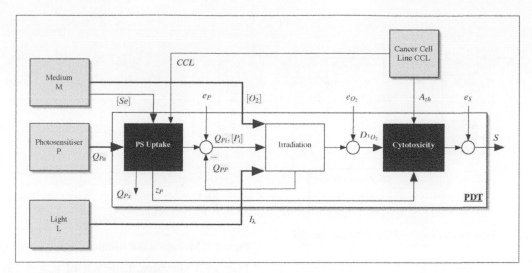

Figure 1. Block diagram of the PDT

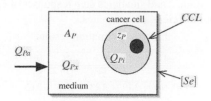

Figure 2. PS uptake phenonenon

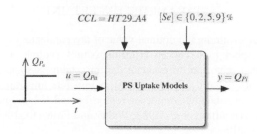

Figure 3. Experimental protocol

The uptake kinetics between the input variable $Q_{Pa}(t)$ and the output variable $Q_{Pi}(t)$ is described as follows:

$$Q_{Pi}(t) = \mathcal{M}(t, \mathbf{p}, Q_{Pa}) + e(t) \qquad (3)$$

where the model structure $\mathcal{M}(\cdot)$ and its parameters $\mathbf{p}$ are unknown. $e(t)$ corresponds to the output error, *i.e.* the error between the measured output ($Q_{Pi}(t)$) and the model output ($\hat{Q}_{Pi}(t) = \mathcal{M}(t, \mathbf{p}, Q_{Pa})$). $e(t)$ is assumed to be a random variable with a normal distribution defined by $\pi_e(e(t)) \propto \mathcal{N}(0, \sigma_e^2)$. The sequence $\mathbf{e} = \begin{pmatrix} e(t_1) & \cdots & e(t_{n_t}) \end{pmatrix}$ is supposed to be independent and identically distributed.

2.3 Experimental data

Materials and methods concerning PS uptake experiments are described in (Barberi-Heyob *et al.*, 2004). The experimental protocol is summarised in figure 3. A step signal was applied to Q_{Pa} (step magnitude $5\mu g \cdot ml^{-1}$). CCL is a human colon cancer cell line (HT29A4) and the PS molecule (P) is chlorin

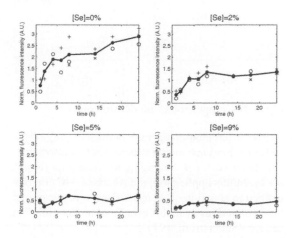

Figure 4. Four estimation data sets

e6 (Ce6). Four experiments were carried out for four different doses of albumin ($[Se] \in \{0, 2, 5, 9\%BSA\}$) where BSA denotes bovine serum albumin. The four responses of Q_{Pi}, measured with spectrofluorimeter, are shown in figure 4. Measurement times are defined in the vector $\mathbf{t} = \begin{pmatrix} 1 & 2 & 4 & 6 & 8 & 14 & 18 & 24h \end{pmatrix}$. Each experiment was repeated two or three times and the full line plot corresponds the mean response. Note that the variation between two samples measured at the same time can reach about 66%, i.e. a signal-to-noise ratio estimated to $RSB \approx 3,5dB$.

3. SELECTION OF A KINETIC MODEL STRUCTURE

The first question deals with the determination of a parsimonious model structure ($\mathcal{M}(\mathbf{p})$) among a set $\mathbb{M}$ of candidate model structures. Three *a priori* distinguishable model structures (Walter and Pronzato, 1997) are examined, $\mathbb{M} = \{\mathcal{M}_1, \mathcal{M}_2, \mathcal{M}_3\}$ with:

$\mathcal{M}_1$: $(1 + T_1 \cdot s)Q_{Pi}(t) = k_1 \cdot Q_{Pa}(t)$;
$\mathcal{M}_2$: $(1 + T_{21} \cdot s)(1 + T_{22} \cdot s)Q_{Pi}(t) = k_2 \cdot Q_{Pa}(t)$;
$\mathcal{M}_3$: $(1 + T_{31} \cdot s)(1 + T_{32} \cdot s)Q_{Pi}(t) = k_3 \cdot (1 + T_{33} \cdot s)Q_{Pa}(t)$.

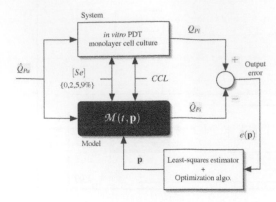

Figure 5. Output error method for a parallel model

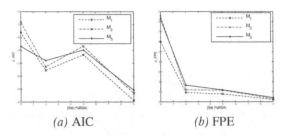

(a) AIC   *(b)* FPE

Figure 6. Comparison of model structures

s is the differentiation operator defined by: $s \cdot Q_P(t) \overset{\text{def}}{=} \partial Q_P / \partial t$. For each model structure $\mathcal{M}_i$ is associated a parameter vector $\mathbf{p}_i$ belonging to some prior feasible set $\mathbb{P}_i$. In this application, the Akaike's AIC criterion, defined in equation (4) is used. For a synoptic presentation of various available criteria of model structures, see *e.g.* (Söderström, 1977).

$$\widehat{\mathcal{M}}(\hat{\mathbf{p}}) = \arg \min_{\mathcal{M}_i \in \mathbb{M}} \min_{\mathbf{p}_i \in \mathbb{P}_i} J_{AIC}(\mathcal{M}_i(\mathbf{p}_i), t), \quad (4)$$

with $J_{AIC} = 1/n_t(-\ln(\pi_{\mathbf{Q}_{Pi}}(\mathbf{Q}_{Pi}^k|\mathbf{p}_i)) + \dim(\mathbf{p}_i))$, $\mathbf{Q}_{Pi} = (Q_{Pi}(t_1) \cdots Q_{Pi}(t_{n_t}))$ and $\mathbf{Q}_{Pi}^k$ is the kth realisation of the output measurement vector $\mathbf{Q}_{Pi}$. By taking into account the probabilistic distribution of output errors (see paragraph 2.2), minimising J_{AIC} comes to minimise:

$$\tilde{J}_{AIC} = n_t \cdot \ln(\sigma_e^2) + 2 \dim(\mathbf{p}_i), \quad (5)$$

where the variance σ_e^2 is a function of $\mathcal{M}_i(\mathbf{p}_i)$. For each model structure, $\hat{\mathbf{p}}_i$ is obtained by a non linear least squares estimator, as shown in figure 5. Results of the model structure selection are gathered in figure 6. The most parsimonious model structure corresponds to $\mathcal{M}_1$ since it minimises J_{AIC} for three different values of $[Se]$. As illustrated in figure 6(b), this choice is confirmed by the final prediction error (FPE) criterion.

4. PARAMETER ESTIMATION

The parameter estimation relies on the output error method for a parallel model as shown in figure 5 in which the optimisation step is based on a Levenberg

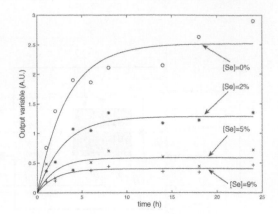

Figure 7. Measured and simulated responses of Q_{Pi}

Marquardt algorithm. Estimates of $\mathbf{p}_1 = (k_1 \ T_1)$ are given in table 2. Figure 7 compares the measured (mean values) and simulated step responses of Q_{Pi} for the four different albumin rates.

Table 2. Estimation results

$[Se]$	0%	2%	5%	9%
k_1	501	257	117	81
$T_1 \ (h)$	3.19	2.93	2.02	2.03

5. PARAMETER UNCERTAINTY

Determining the optimal value of the parameters with respect to a chosen criterion is not enough. It is also important to evaluate the uncertainty associated with those estimates. Herein, parameters uncertainty is described by confidence regions, noted $\mathcal{R}^\alpha$, defined in (Hamilton *et al.*, 1982; Walter and Pronzato, 1997) as follows:

$$\mathcal{R}^\alpha = \left\{ \mathbf{p} \in \mathbb{R}^{n_p} | \frac{e^T(\mathbf{p})\Pi(\mathbf{p})e(\mathbf{p})}{n_p \hat{\sigma}^2} \leq F_\alpha(n_p, n_e - 1) \right\} \quad (6)$$

$\mathcal{R}^\alpha$ defines a $100(1 - \alpha)\%$ confidence region for the parameters. $F_\alpha(n_1, n_2)$ denotes a Fisher-Snedecor distribution with n_1 and n_2 degrees of freedom. $e(\mathbf{p}) = \mathbf{Q}_{Pi} - \hat{\mathbf{Q}}_{Pi}(\mathbf{p})$ is the output error vector $\in \mathbb{R}^{n_t}$. The orthogonal projection matrix $\Pi(\mathbf{p})$ is given by:

$$\Pi(\mathbf{p}) = S_{\hat{\mathbf{Q}}_{Pi}}(S_{\hat{\mathbf{Q}}_{Pi}}^T \cdot S_{\hat{\mathbf{Q}}_{Pi}})^{-1} S_{\hat{\mathbf{Q}}_{Pi}}^T, \quad (7)$$

where $S_{\hat{\mathbf{Q}}_{Pi}} = \partial \hat{\mathbf{Q}}_{Pi}(\mathbf{p}) / \partial \mathbf{p}^T$ is the sensitivity function (gradient) of the output model in respect with the parameter vector. The estimated noise variance is given by:

$$\hat{\sigma}^2 = \frac{1}{n_e n_t - 1} \sum_{i=1}^{n_t} \sum_{k=1}^{n_e} (Q_{Pi}(t_{i,k}) - \bar{Q}_{Pi,i})^2$$

$$\bar{Q}_{Pi,i} = \frac{1}{n_e} \sum_{k=1}^{n_e} Q_{Pi}(t_{i,k}). \quad (8)$$

n_e refers to the number of repeated experiments. Figure 8 shows the four 95% confidence regions associated with the four values of the albumin rate. This result reveals a large uncertainty about the estimates, mainly for $\hat{T}_1$. The number of time instants cannot be significantly increased in practice. Nevertheless, adapting materials and measurement systems in order to increase the number of samples at each time instant is possible. This solution could significantly reduce the area of confidence regions.

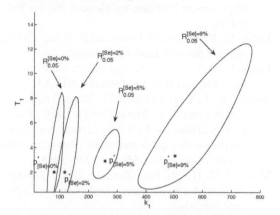

Figure 8. 95% confidence regions for $\hat{k}_1$ and $\hat{T}_1$

6. NOISE HYPOTHESIS VALIDATION

The determination of the confidence regions relies on the assumption that $\{e(t_i, \mathbf{p})\}$ is a sequence of normal random variables, independent and identically distributed, i.e. $e(t_i, \mathbf{p}) \propto \mathcal{N}(0, \sigma_e^2)$. Histograms of output residuals are depicted in figure 9. Their empirical distribution is clearly dependent on the serum rates ($[Se]$). Unfortunately, the number of realisations is too small (≤ 20) to accurately check the Gaussian distribution of the residuals. However, the assumption about the nullity of the mean is perceptibly valid. Moreover, almost all histograms are symmetric. There is thereby no convincing reason to reject the initial hypothesis. In other terms, no conclusion can be drawn about the validity of the noise assumption. In fact, in this experimental setup, the gaussian and i.i.d. assumption, usual stochastic paradigm in system identification, is not suited to the description of the parameter uncertainty. In perspective, it would be interesting to assess recent alternative approaches like the interval analysis (Jaulin et al., 2001) or the Leave-out Sign-dominant Correlation Regions proposed by Campi and Weyer in (Campi and Weyer, 2006).

7. ANALYSIS OF THE SERUM DEPENDANCE

Figure 10(a) shows that $\hat{k}_1$ is a decreasing function of $[Se]$. The dotted graph refers to the four estimates of k_1 and the continuous curve is a regression model, defined in equation (9).

$$\hat{k}_1 \approx \frac{922}{[Se] + 1.83}. \tag{9}$$

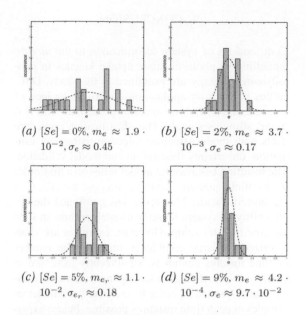

(a) $[Se] = 0\%$, $m_e \approx 1.9 \cdot 10^{-2}$, $\sigma_e \approx 0.45$ (b) $[Se] = 2\%$, $m_e \approx 3.7 \cdot 10^{-3}$, $\sigma_e \approx 0.17$

(c) $[Se] = 5\%$, $m_{e_r} \approx 1.1 \cdot 10^{-2}$, $\sigma_{e_r} \approx 0.18$ (d) $[Se] = 9\%$, $m_e \approx 4.2 \cdot 10^{-4}$, $\sigma_e \approx 9.7 \cdot 10^{-2}$

Figure 9. Histograms of output residuals for $\mathcal{M}_1$

This model expresses an inversely proportional relationship between the static gain $\hat{k}_1$ and the serum rate $[Se]$. A new in vitro model (monolayer culture) of the PS uptake kinetic, defined in equation 10, can thereby be put forward.

$$T_1 \dot{Q}_{Pi}(t) + Q_{Pi}(t) = \frac{\alpha}{[Se] + \beta} \cdot Q_{Pa}(t) + e(t), \tag{10}$$

where the parameters T_1, α and β are functions of the cancer cell line. The output error $e(t)$ is supposed to be an independent stochastic process normally distributed $\mathcal{N}(0, \sigma^2)$. No significant relationship has been pointed out between $\hat{T}_1$ and $[Se]$.

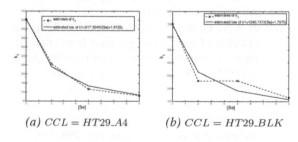

(a) $CCL = HT29\_A4$ (b) $CCL = HT29\_BLK$

Figure 10. Relationship between k_1 and $[Se]$ for two different CCL

8. MODEL VALIDATION

The previous model has not been cross validated yet but a similar model, i.e. a first-order model, has been identified for another cancer cell line ($HT29\_BLK$). Ffigure 10(b) corobore the inversely proportional relationship between k_1 and $[Se]$ for the $HT29\_BLK$ line.

9. CONCLUSION

Contributions of system identification to the *in vitro* modelling of photosensitiser uptake kinetics in photodynamic therapy are examined in this study. Difficulties of such an application are triple: (i) lack of measurement, (ii) low signal-to-noise ratio and (iii) 'poor' stimulus signals. The identification procedure deals with model structure selection, parameter estimation, uncertainty description and model validation. The resulting behavioural model relies on a first-order differential equation taking into account the effects of the protein factor. This result has confirmed the applicability of system identification algorithms in such an experimental setup. However, estimates are characterized by large confidence regions. The number of time instants cannot be significantly increased in practice. Nevertheless, adapting materials and measurement systems in order to increase the number of samples at each time instant is possible. Future experiments will be carried out to check the validity of the proposed behavioural model for other photosensitisers and cancer cell lines.

REFERENCES

Barberi-Heyob, M., P.-O. Védrine, J.-L. Merlin, R. Millon, J. Abecassis, M.-F. Poupon and F. Guillemin (2004). Wild-type p53 gene transfer into mutated p53 HT29 cells improves sensitivity to photodynamic therapy via induction of apoptosis. *Int. J. Oncol.* (24), 951–958.

Campi, M. C. and E. Weyer (2006). Identification with finitely many data points: The lscr approach. In: *Proc. of the 14th IFAC Symposium on System Identification (SYSID).*

Dysart, J. S., G. Singh and M. Patterson (2005). Calculation of singlet oxygen dose from photosensitizer fluorescence and photobleaching during mTHPC photodynamic therapy of MLL cells. *Photochem. Photobiol.* (81), 196–205.

Epe, B., M. Pflaum and S. Boiteux (1993). DNA damage induced by photosensitizers in cellular and cell-free systems. *Mutat. Res.* **299**, 135–145.

Georgakoudi, I. and T. H. Foster (1998). Singlet oxygen- versus nonsinglet oxygen-mediated mechanisms of sensitizer photobleaching and their effects on photodynamic dosimetry. *Photochem. photobiol.* **67**(6), 612–625.

Georgakoudi, I., M. G. Nichols and T. H. Foster (1997). The mechanism of photofrin© photobleaching and its consequences for photodynamic dosimetry. *Photochem. Photobiol.* **65**(1), 135–144.

Hamilton, D. C., D. G. Watts and D. M. Bates (1982). Accounting for intrinsic nonlinearities in nonlinear regression parameter inference regions. *The Annals of Stat.* **10**, 386–393.

Henderson, B. W. and T. J. Dougherty (1992). How does photodynamic therapy work?. *Photochem. Photobiol.* **55**, 145–157.

Hetzel, F. W., S. M. Brahmavar, Q. Chen, S. L. Jacques, M. S. Patterson, B. C. Wilson and T. C. Zhu (2005). Photodynamic therapy dosimetry. AAPM report No.88. American Association of Physicists in Medicine by Medical Physics Publishing.

Jaulin, L., M. Kieffer, O. Didrit and E. Walter (2001). *Applied Interval Analysis*. Springer.

Ljung, L. (1987). *System identification : theory for the user*. Prentice Hall. Englewood Cliffs, NJ.

Moesta, K. T., W. R. Greco, S. O. Nurse-Finlay, J. C. Parsons and T. S. Mang (1995). Lack of reciprocity in drug and light dose dependence of photodynamic therapy of pancreatic adenocarcinoma in vitro. *Cancer Res.* **55**(14), 3078–3084.

Moser, J. G. (1998). *Photodynamic Tumor Therapy: 2nd and 3rd Generation*. Gordon & Breach Science Publishers.

Nichols, M. G. and T. H. Foster (1994). Oxygen diffusion and reaction kinetics in photodynamic therapy of multicell tumor spheroids. *Phys. Med. Biol.*

Patterson, M.S., B.C. Wilson and R. Graff (1990). In vivo tests of the concept of photodynamic threshold dose in normal rat liver photosensitized by aluminum chlorosulphonated phthalocyanine. *Photochem. Photobiol.* **51**, 343–349.

Potter, W. R. (1986). The theory of photodynamic therapy dosimetry: consequences of photodestruction of sensitizer. *Lasers Med.* **712**, 124–129.

Söderström, T. (1977). On model structure testing in system identification. *Int. J. Control* **26**, 1–18.

Söderström, T. and P. Stoica (1989). *System identification*. University Press, Cambridge, Prentice Hall.

Tromberg, B. J., A. Orenstein, S. Kimel, S. J. Barker, J. Hyatt, J. S. Nelson and M. W. Berns (1990). *In vivo* oxygen tension measurements for the evaluation of the efficiency of photodynamic therapy. *Photochem. Photobiol.* **52**, 375–385.

Walter, E. and L. Pronzato (1997). *Identification of Parametric Models from experimental data*. Springer, Masson.

Yuan, J., P. A. Mahama-Relue, R. L. Fournier and J. A. Hampton (1997). Predictions of mathematical models of tissue oxygenation and generation of singlet oxygen during photodynamic therapy. *Radiat. Res.* **148**, 386–394.

ELSEVIER

IFAC

PUBLICATIONS

ON THE MODELING OF PARAFFIN THROUGH RAMAN SPECTROSCOPY

Valeriu Vrabie * **Régis Huez** * **Cyril Gobinet** *
Olivier Piot ** **Ali Tfayli** ** **Michel Manfait** **

* *CReSTIC, University of Reims Champagne-Ardenne*
(URCA), Moulin de la Housse, 51687 Reims, France
** *MéDIAN, CNRS UMR 6142, URCA, 51 rue Cognacq*
Jay, 51096 Reims, France

Abstract: Raman spectroscopy is employed to record spectra which highlight vibrational information of biological structures. These spectra provide useful information about molecular composition of a tissue. However, the tissues are usually embedded into paraffin for a preservation purpose. The Independent Component Analysis (ICA) technique can be used to numerically dewax Raman spectra and to extract the specific information of the tissue. We show in this paper that the paraffin must be modeled by a three-source model in order to succeed. This linear model, confirmed also by analyzing paraffin blocks exclusively, should be preferred instead of commonly used one-source model. *Copyright © 2006 IFAC*

Keywords: Raman Spectroscopy, Independent Component Analysis, Paraffin Embedded Tissues, Three-Source Linear Model of Paraffin

1. INTRODUCTION

Raman spectroscopy is employed to record the vibrational state of molecules by measuring at one wavelength the intensity of light scattered by a tissue. Varying the wavelength, for one measurement point, this technique provides a signal called Raman spectrum. As the chemical species of the analyzed tissue are mixed with different proportions in each measurement point, the recorded Raman spectra give useful information about molecular composition of biological structures.

The development of portable Raman spectrometer opens up new horizons for non-invasive diagnosis. However, diagnoses and investigations are first led on paraffin wax embedded tissues before being applied *in vivo*. This is motivated by a preservation purpose because the tissues are usually stored in tissue banks for further studies. These additional studies allow the identification, the classification

and the survey of different diseases (see for example (Jackson *et al.*, 1999)). Furthermore, the spectroscopy requires thin slices of tissues to transmit light. As paraffin offers excellent cutting and preserving properties on tissues, it is commonly used for the wax embedding process.

Paraffin embedded tissues are usually dewaxed and rehydrated before any analysis (Lowry *et al.*, 1997; Endl *et al.*, 2001; Ó Faoláin *et al.*, 2005). This is a common practice for the examination of tumoral tissues, including breast cancer (Haka *et al.*, 2002) and skin cancer (Gniadecka *et al.*, 1997). However, three main drawbacks are linked with the dewaxing step (Ó Faoláin *et al.*, 2005). First, this process is time and reagents consuming. Second, tissues structures can be altered by the high pressure and temperature conditions required by some dewaxing techniques as Heat-Mediated Antigen Retrieval (HMAR). Third, most popular dewaxing methods are not so efficient. A residual layer of paraffin remains after the dewaxing step in some parts of tissues. The analysis of dewaxed and rehydrated tissues will be thus biased. Hence, the Raman spectra must be recorded directly on embedded tissues.

The use of Raman spectroscopy directly on paraffin embedded tissues was very restricted until now due to energetic Raman peaks of paraffin that mask important vibrational bands of tissues in recorded spectra. Recently, the Fourier Transform Infrared (FTIR) Spectroscopy was used successfully to discriminate between nevi and melanomas on non dewaxed skin sections (Tfayli et al., 2005). However, the discrimination was based on narrow bands where the paraffin has no contribution.

A method to numerically dewax the Raman spectra by using the Independent Component Analysis (ICA) was recently proposed (Gobinet et al., 2005). This method allows extracting a discriminant source specific to benign or malignant tumors. This source can be employed as a molecular descriptor of the type of pathology. Furthermore, this work shows that the ICA must be used instead of the commonly encountered Principal Component Analysis (PCA). However, this method suggests that the paraffin spectrum must be decomposed into more than one source in order to identify the discriminant source specific to tissues.

We propose in this paper to model the paraffin by a three-source linear model. The ICA is applied on different Raman spectra. These spectra were recorded on paraffin blocks exclusively or on benign/malignant tumor tissues embedded into paraffin. The obtained results confirm this model. For any numerical method applied on Raman spectra recorded on paraffin wax embedded tissues, this three-source linear model should be preferred to the commonly used one-source model.

2. RAMAN SPECTRA

Since several years, Raman spectroscopy has been proved to be an efficient tool for investigations in biomedical applications (Gniadecka et al., 1997; Choo-Smith et al., 2002; Haka et al., 2002). It is a non-destructive optical technique which records the vibrational state of molecules. In each measurement point, this technique provides a signal called Raman spectrum. The chemical species being mixed in different proportions, the different recorded Raman spectra give useful information about molecular composition of a tissue.

2.1 Acquisition

In a measurement point indexed in the XY-plane by the (x, y) coordinates, the Raman spectroscopy outlines the intensity $I_{x,y}(\overline{\nu})$ of light scattered at

the wavenumber $\overline{\nu}$ (which depends on the wavelength of the light). Supposing $N_{\overline{\nu}}$ wavenumbers available during an acquisition, the measured intensities define the signal called Raman spectrum:

$$\mathbf{I}_{x,y} = [\dots, I_{x,y}(\overline{\nu}), \dots]^T \in \mathbb{R}^{N_{\overline{\nu}}} \qquad (1)$$

where $.^T$ denotes the transpose.

For different measurement points, let say $1 \leq x \leq N_x$ and $1 \leq y \leq N_y$, the Raman spectroscopy gives a cube dataset made up by the different recorded Raman spectra. In order to use existing matrix algebra algorithms, the cube dataset can be reorganized into a matrix format:

$$\mathbf{I} = [\dots, \mathbf{I}_k, \dots]^T \in \mathbb{R}^{N_x N_y \times N_{\overline{\nu}}} \qquad (2)$$

where k is an index which depends on x and y according to the reorganization operation used. In this notation, which will be used in the following, the kth recorded Raman spectrum represents the kth line of the matrix dataset $\mathbf{I}$.

2.2 Model

Commonly, the chemical species are Raman active and each possesses its unique Raman spectrum also called spectrum of a pure species. The recorded Raman spectra result from a weighted sum of spectra of pure species present in an acquisition (Manoharan et al., 1992; van de Poll et al., 2002).

The recorded dataset $\mathbf{I}$ in Eq. (2) can be written as a sum $\mathbf{Z}$ of pure species spectra $\mathbf{S}_j = [\dots, S_j(\overline{\nu}), \dots]^T \in \mathbb{R}^{N_{\overline{\nu}}}$ weighted by the concentration profile $\mathbf{A}_j = [\dots, A_{kj}, \dots]^T \in \mathbb{R}^{N_x N_y}$ corrupted by a noise $\mathbf{N}$:

$$\mathbf{I} = \mathbf{Z} + \mathbf{N} = \sum_{j=1}^{M} \mathbf{A}_j \mathbf{S}_j^T + \mathbf{N} \qquad (3)$$

where $S_j(\overline{\nu})$ is the intensity of the jth pure species at the wavenumber $\overline{\nu}$, A_{kj} is the concentration of the jth pure species in the kth measurement point and M represents the number of pure species present in the analyzed tissue. The concentration profile $\mathbf{A}_j$ allows to visualize the distribution of the jth pure species into the tissue.

$\mathbf{N}$ denotes the recorded noise such as the response of the spectrometer (for example the dark current), the parasitic fluorescence usually present when analyzing a biological tissue, etc.

2.3 Properties

Raman spectroscopy is very sensitive to paraffin. Classically, as the paraffin defines a pure species, it is modeled by a unique source made up by thin energetic peaks. However, as will be proved in this paper, the paraffin must be modeled by a three-source linear model. This property can be verified by a simple visual inspection of different recorded Raman spectra: depending on the measurement point, the amplitudes of the Raman peaks of the paraffin have different proportions. Thus, the influence $\mathbf{Z}_{para}$ of the paraffin (shown in Fig. 1(a) for one measurement point of a biological tissue) will be modeled by three sources $\mathbf{S}_1, \mathbf{S}_2, \mathbf{S}_3$:

$$\mathbf{Z}_{para} = \mathbf{A}_1 \mathbf{S}_1^T + \mathbf{A}_2 \mathbf{S}_2^T + \mathbf{A}_3 \mathbf{S}_3^T \qquad (4)$$

The Raman spectroscopy provides an additional source $\mathbf{S}_4$ when it is used to investigate biological tissues (Gobinet et al., 2005). Contrary to paraffin, this source includes the contribution of different molecules (of tissue) and is employed as molecular descriptor of the type of pathology. This source allows a classification of tissues into benign respectively malignant tumors. The influence $\mathbf{Z}_{tiss}$ of the analyzed tissue, as shown in Fig. 1(c) for one measurement point, can be modeled as:

$$\mathbf{Z}_{tiss} = \mathbf{A}_4 \mathbf{S}_4^T \qquad (5)$$

Furthermore, paraffin wax embedded tissues are generally fixed on a slide whose chemical composition depends on the considered experiment. Usually, the slide is chosen to be Raman inactive or active in a thin spectral band. The CaF_2 slide was used for the acquisitions on biological tissues presented in sections 4.2 and 4.3. Its influence, characterized by an unique thin energetic peak as shown in Fig. 1(b), can be modeled as (Gobinet et al., 2005):

$$\mathbf{Z}_{slide} = \mathbf{A}_5 \mathbf{S}_5^T \qquad (6)$$

When the Raman spectroscopy is used to analyze either paraffin blocks exclusively or biological tissues, other sources defined by pure species spectra may exist. The influence of these sources, denoted in the following as $\mathbf{Z}_{oth}$, is removed in the pre-withening step of the ICA as shown in section 3.2 by projection of the dataset into a signal subspace spanning the interesting sources only.

2.4 Preprocessing

Before applying numerical processing, the recorded spectra must be preprocessed to eliminate the noise $\mathbf{N}$. The noise consists into a background or baseline signal coming from the parasitic fluorescence of the tissue and the response of the spectrometer. This baseline varies slowly and has not a linear behavior from a spectrum to another, hence it can be modeled by a polynomial function for each spectrum. The polynomial coefficients have been estimated here by an algorithm based on the minimization of an asymmetric truncated quadratic cost function (Mazet et al., 2005). We obtain the noise free dataset $\mathbf{Z} = \mathbf{I} - \mathbf{N}$, called also preprocessed dataset, by subtracting the correspondent estimated baseline from each spectrum.

The peaks of paraffin and slide are ideally aligned from one spectrum to another. However, due to the spectrometer artifacts, these peaks are not perfectly aligned and further processing without alignment will provide badly estimators of sources. The alignment procedure proposed in (Gobinet et al., 2005) was used here. It consists in upsampling spectra in spectral bands where a peak is localized, in computing the shift between a reference spectra peak (the first recorded spectrum) and the other spectra peaks, in shifting back the peaks in order to align their maxima, and finally in downsampling spectra.

Furthermore, the recorded spectra are centered in order to apply the ICA and each one normalized to unit variance to ensure that even weak recording are well represented within the input dataset.

3. NUMERICAL PROCESSING

The goal is to prove the validity of the linear model of the paraffin proposed in Eq. (4). In order to succeed, a numerical processing based on the statistical properties of the pure species spectra must be used. The ICA is used to identify the interesting pure species spectra $\mathbf{S}_j$ and associated concentration profiles $\mathbf{A}_j$, with $j = 1 \ldots 3$ for the analysis of paraffin blocks exclusively or $j = 1 \ldots 5$ for biological tissues.

3.1 Statistical properties of pure species spectra

Into one measurement point of a biological tissue, Fig. 1 shows the influence $\mathbf{Z}_{para}$ of the paraffin, $\mathbf{Z}_{slide}$ of the CaF_2 slide and $\mathbf{Z}_{tiss}$ of the tissue. The contributions of paraffin and CaF_2 slide are composed of few thin and energetic peaks which can be modeled as sparse. Consequently, the sources $\mathbf{S}_1, \mathbf{S}_2, \mathbf{S}_3$ of the paraffin and the source $\mathbf{S}_5$ of the CaF_2 slide are also sparse. The tissue is composed of several chemical compounds which activate almost the entire spectral range. Thus, the source $\mathbf{S}_4$ of the tissue is not sparse and not composed of thin energetic peaks. However, sparsity and non-overlapping of the different peaks lead to statistical independence between the sources $\mathbf{S}_j$ (Gobinet et al., 2005).

The other sources that might be present in an acquisition are supposed decorrelated from the interesting ones that are defined in section 2.3.

3.2 Independent Component Analysis (ICA)

The ICA is a blind decomposition of a multi-channel dataset composed of an unknown linear mixture of unknown sources, based on the only

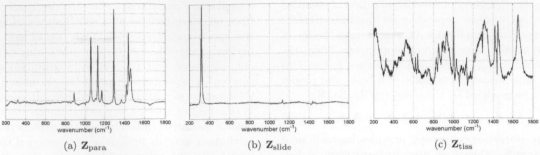

(a) $\mathbf{Z}_{\text{para}}$ (b) $\mathbf{Z}_{\text{slide}}$ (c) $\mathbf{Z}_{\text{tiss}}$

Fig. 1. Contributions of paraffin, slide and tissue into one measurement point of a biological tissue

assumption that these sources are mutually statistically independent. It is used in Blind Source Separation (BSS) to recover independent sources (modeled as vectors) from a set of recordings containing linear combinations of these sources (Cardoso and Souloumiac, 1993; Comon, 1994).

As mentioned above, the sources of paraffin, slide and tissue can be characterized as statistical independent and the model of the recorded spectra (see Eq. (3)) is a linear one. All conditions are thus fulfilled to apply the ICA on Raman spectra in order to identify the interesting sources.

ICA is resolved by a two-step algorithm: prewhitening and high-order steps. In the prewhitening step, estimators $\mathbf{W}_j \in \mathbb{R}^{N_{\overline{\nu}}}$ of the interesting sources can be obtained from the preprocessed dataset $\mathbf{Z}$:

$$\mathbf{Z} = \sum_{j=1}^{M} \mathbf{B}_j \mathbf{W}_j^T \qquad (7)$$

Note that this step is also assimilated to commonly used Principal Component Analysis (PCA). However, the prewhitening is based uniquely on second order statistics and the estimated spectra $\mathbf{W}_j$ are only decorrelated. Practically speaking, each $\mathbf{W}_j$ will be a linear combination of pure species spectra $\mathbf{S}_j$. Nevertheless, as the other sources that might be present in an acquisition are decorrelated from the interesting ones, the PCA allows identifying the linear combinations which will give the interesting spectra in the second step. This can be assimilated as a subspace separation of the preprocessed dataset:

$$\mathbf{Z} = \mathbf{Z}_{\text{int}} + \mathbf{Z}_{\text{oth}} = \sum_{j=1}^{J} \mathbf{B}_j \mathbf{W}_j^T + \sum_{j=J+1}^{M} \mathbf{B}_j \mathbf{W}_j^T \quad (8)$$

with $J = 3$ and $\mathbf{Z}_{\text{int}} = \mathbf{Z}_{\text{para}}$ for analysis of paraffin blocks exclusively and $J = 5$ and $\mathbf{Z}_{\text{int}} = \mathbf{Z}_{\text{para}} + \mathbf{Z}_{\text{tiss}} + \mathbf{Z}_{\text{slide}}$ for biological tissues.

The second step consists in finding a rotation matrix $\mathbf{R} \in \mathbb{R}^{J \times J}$ which, applied on previously estimated sources $\mathbf{W} = [\dots, \mathbf{W}_j, \dots]^T \in \mathbb{R}^{J \times N_{\overline{\nu}}}$

$$\mathbf{R}^T \mathbf{W} = \widehat{\mathbf{S}} = \left[\dots, \widehat{\mathbf{S}}_j, \dots \right]^T \in \mathbb{R}^{J \times N_{\overline{\nu}}}, \quad (9)$$

provides independent sources $\widehat{\mathbf{S}}_j \in \mathbb{R}^{N_{\overline{\nu}}}$ which are better estimators of interesting pure species spectra $\mathbf{S}_j$. Estimators of the associated concen-

tration profiles $\widehat{\mathbf{A}}_j$ are obtained by applying the pseudoinverse of $\widehat{\mathbf{S}}$ to the matrix $\mathbf{Z}_{\text{int}}$.

The independence of sources means that the cross-cumulants of any order vanish. Generally, the third order cumulants are discarded because they are generally close to zero and only fourth order statistics are used. This defines different algorithms to find the rotation matrix $\mathbf{R}$: Joint Approximate Diagonalization of Eigenmatrices (JADE) (Cardoso and Souloumiac, 1993), Maximal Diagonality (MD) (Comon, 1994), etc. The JADE algorithm was used here, but very similar results are obtained using the MD algorithm.

4. APPLICATIONS

The Raman spectra were recorded by a Labram spectrometer (Dilor-Jobin Yvon, Lille, France) in a point by point mode with a 10 μm step. The light source was a titanium-sapphire laser exciting at 785 nm. Each spectrum was recorded at $N_{\overline{\nu}} = 994$ wavenumbers covering a spectral region from 650 to 1820 cm^{-1} for the first application and at $N_{\overline{\nu}} = 1308$ wavenumbers from 200 to 1800 cm^{-1} for the other two applications. For a comparison purpose, the estimated sources are normalized into the range $700 - 1700$ cm^{-1} and also plotted into the same range.

4.1 Paraffin block exclusively

Firstly, a dataset recorded exclusively on a paraffin block was processed. The spectra were acquired on 5×4 measurement points, defining a dataset $\mathbf{I} \in \mathbb{R}^{20 \times 994}$. Applied on the preprocessed dataset $\mathbf{Z}$, obtained as described in section 2.4, the ICA method gives three independent sources presented in Fig. 2.

It can be shown that a linear mixing of these three sources defines completely the paraffin in each measurement point. This means that this model follows the linear formulation given in Eq. (4).

The processing was repeated on other four datasets recorded also on paraffin blocks exclusively. For all datasets, the paraffin is defined by three sources made up by the same peaks as shown in Fig. 2.

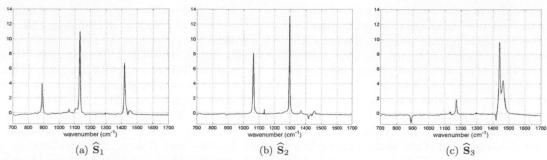

(a) $\widehat{\mathbf{S}}_1$ (b) $\widehat{\mathbf{S}}_2$ (c) $\widehat{\mathbf{S}}_3$

Fig. 2. The sources of the paraffin obtained while processing a paraffin block exclusively

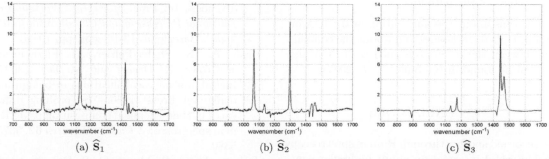

(a) $\widehat{\mathbf{S}}_1$ (b) $\widehat{\mathbf{S}}_2$ (c) $\widehat{\mathbf{S}}_3$

Fig. 3. The sources of the paraffin obtained while processing a benign tumor paraffin embedded tissue

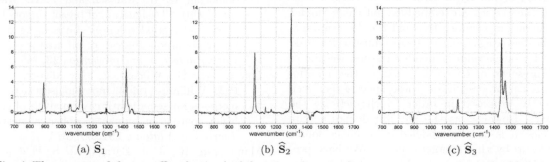

(a) $\widehat{\mathbf{S}}_1$ (b) $\widehat{\mathbf{S}}_2$ (c) $\widehat{\mathbf{S}}_3$

Fig. 4. The sources of the paraffin obtained while processing a malignant tumor paraffin embedded tissue

4.2 Benign tumor paraffin embedded tissues

A recording on a benign tumor paraffin embedded tissue gives the dataset $\mathbf{I} \in \mathbb{R}^{210 \times 1308}$. Applied on the preprocessed dataset $\mathbf{Z}$, the ICA provides five independent sources. The first three are related to the paraffin, the fourth to the tissue and the last to the CaF_2 slide.

Fig. 3 shows that the estimated three sources of the paraffin are made up by the same peaks as shown previously in Fig. 2.

This result is confirmed by processing other two datasets of different dimension recorded on benign tumor paraffin embedded tissues.

4.3 Malignant tumor paraffin embedded tissues

Finally, a malignant tumor paraffin embedded tissue defining the dataset $\mathbf{I} \in \mathbb{R}^{100 \times 1308}$ was processed. As previously, the ICA gives five independent sources, where the first three shown in Fig. 4 are related to the paraffin.

These three sources of the paraffin are made up by the same peaks as shown previously. Identical results were obtained while processing other two datasets of different dimension recorded on malignant tumor paraffin embedded tissues.

4.4 Discussion

The results depend on the quality of the preprocessing. For example, it can be noted that sometimes a peak is not completely described by one source, as the first peak of $\widehat{\mathbf{S}}_2$ which is still present in the source $\widehat{\mathbf{S}}_1$ for the third application. This is linked with some unfocused measurement points that lead to a variability of the width of the peaks. Also, the influence of the third source into the others two is linked with the noisiness of these sources: the better result is obtained for the paraffin block.

Note that each spectrum $\widehat{\mathbf{S}}_j$ estimated by the ICA was normalized, that is, it has the power equal to 1. Also, the associated concentration profile $\widehat{\mathbf{A}}_j$ is usually normalized. This quantity allows to visualize the distribution of the jth pure species into the tissue. The norm of $\widehat{\mathbf{A}}_j$ gives the relative presence of the jth pure species into the tissue.

For the different analyses, the three sources of the paraffin were not obtained in the same order and had not the same relative presence. However, the uniform distributions obtained for these sources confirm their presence in each measurement point and suggest a linear model such as Eq. (4).
Note that ICA was also tested with more than three or five sources for paraffin block exclusively and embedded tissues respectively, but without further decomposition of the sources of paraffin.

These results prove the proposed three-source linear model of the paraffin.

More details about the application of the ICA on paraffin embedded tissues and about the comparison between the results obtained with PCA and ICA can be found in (Gobinet et al., 2005).

5. CONCLUSIONS

The recorded spectra through Raman spectroscopy provide useful information about molecular composition of biological structures of tissues. Usually, the tissues are embedded into paraffin for preservation purpose. To avoid the disadvantages of the dewaxing step, the spectra must be recorded directly on paraffin embedded tissues. Despite of the presence of energetic peaks of the paraffin, numerical processing on these spectra has been recently proposed in order to characterize the tissues. However, as the paraffin defines a pure species, it is usually modeled by a unique source made up by thin energetic peaks. We have proposed here a three-source linear model in order to model the paraffin. The Independent Component Analysis applied on paraffin blocks exclusively or on benign/malignant tumor tissues embedded into paraffin confirms this model. This model should be preferred to the commonly used one-source model for all numerical processing of paraffin embedded tissue.

REFERENCES

Cardoso, J.-F. and A. Souloumiac (1993). Blind beamforming for non-Gaussian signals. *IEE Proc.-F* **140**, 362–370.

Choo-Smith, L.-P., H. Edwards, H. Endtz, J. Kros, F. Heule, H. Barr, J. Robinson, H. Bruining and G. Puppels (2002). Medical applications of Raman spectroscopy: From proof of principle to clinical implementation. *Biopolymers: Biospectroscopy* **67**, 1–9.

Comon, P. (1994). Independent component analysis, a new concept?. *Signal Processing* **36**, 287–314.

Endl, E., I. Kausch, M. Baack, R. Knippers, J. Gerdes and T. Scholzen (2001). The expression of Ki-67, MCM3, and p27 defines distinct subsets of proliferating, resting, and differentiated cells. *Journal of Pathology* **195**, 457–462.

Gniadecka, M., H. Wulf, N. Mortensen, O. Nielsen and D. Christensen (1997). Diagnosis of basal cell carcinoma by Raman spectra. *Journal of Raman Spectroscopy* **28**, 125–129.

Gobinet, C., V. Vrabie, A. Tfayli, O. Piot and R. Huez (2005). Independent component analysis and Raman microspectroscopy on paraffinised non dewaxed cutaneous biopsies: A promising methodology for melanoma early diagnosis. In: *Proc. of 1st Int. Workshop on Biosignal Processing and Classification (BPC 2005)*. Barcelona, 13-14 sept. pp. 19–26.

Haka, A., K. Shafer-Peltier, M. Fitzmaurice, J. Crowe, R. Dasari and M. Feld (2002). Identifying microcalcifications in benign and malignant breast lesions by probing differences in their chemical composition using Raman spectroscopy. *Cancer Research* **62**, 5375–5380.

Jackson, M., J. R. Mansfield, B. Dolenko, R. L. Somorjai, H. H. Mantsch and P. H. Watson (1999). Classification of breast tumors by grade and steroid receptor status using pattern recognition analysis of infrared spectra. *Cancer detection and prevention* **23**, 245–253.

Lowry, A., D. Wilcox, E. A. Masson and P. E. Williams (1997). Immunohistochemical methods for semiquantitative analysis of collagen content in human peripherical nerve. *Journal of Anatomy* **191**, 367–374.

Manoharan, R., J. J. Baraga, M. S. Feld and R. P. Rava (1992). Quantitative histochemical analysis of human artery using Raman spectroscopy. *Journal of Photochemistry and Photobiology B–Biology* **16**, 211–233.

Mazet, V., C. Carteret, D. Brie, J. Idier and B. Humbert (2005). Background removal from spectra by designing and minimising a non-quadratic cost function. *Journal of Cardiovascular Risk* **76**, 121–133.

Ó Faoláin, E., M. Hunter, J. Byrne, P. Kelehan, H. Lambkin, H. Byrne and F. Lyng (2005). Raman spectroscopic evaluation of efficacy of current paraffin wax section dewaxing agents. *Journal of Histochemistry and Cytochemistry* **53**, 121–129.

Tfayli, A., O. Piot, A. Durlach, P. Bernard and M. Manfait (2005). Discriminating nevus and melanoma on paraffin-embedded skin biopsies using FTIR microspectroscopy. *Biochimica et Biophysica Acta (BBA) - General Subjects* **1724**, 262–269.

van de Poll, S. W. E., T. J. Romer, G. J. Puppels and A. van der Laarse (2002). Raman spectroscopy of atherosclerosis. *Journal of Cardiovascular Risk* **9**, 255–261.

INSULIN SENSITIVITY INDEX ALSO ACCOUNTING FOR INSULIN ACTION DYNAMICS: IMPORTANCE IN DIABETES

Gianluigi Pillonetto * **Andrea Caumo** **
Claudio Cobelli ***

* *Department of Information Engineering*
University of Padova, Italy
** *San Raffaele Scientific Institute*
Milan, Italy
*** *Corresponding author*
Department of Information Engineering
University of Padova, Italy
email: cobelli@dei.unipd.it

Abstract: The standard measures of insulin sensitivity, S_I, obtained e.g. by clamp or minimal model (MM) techniques, do not account for how fast/slow insulin action reaches its plateau value. Recently, we have proposed a new dynamic insulin sensitivity index, S_I^D, that incorporates this information. We have shown that in normal subjects S_I^D offers, in comparison with S_I, a more comprehensive picture of insulin action on glucose metabolism. Here, we illustrate how S_I^D is even more appropriate when studying type 2 diabetic patients whose insulin action is not only impaired in magnitude but also slow. In particular, by identifying MM from an intravenous glucose tolerance test (IVGTT) experiment in 10 diabetic subjects via a Bayesian strategy, we show that S_I^D is not only more informative but also more precise than S_I. We conclude that S_I^D is the insulin sensitivity index of choice when studying subjects with impaired insulin action like impaired glucose tolerant or diabetics. Copyright ©2006 IFAC

Keywords: biomedical systems; insulin resistance; diabetes; parameter estimation; Bayesian estimation; Markov chain Monte Carlo

1. INTRODUCTION

Since its inception in the late seventies (Bergman *et al.*, 1979), the minimal model (MM) of glucose kinetics has been employed in nearly 600 papers. Part of such popularity is due to the possibility of measuring an index of insulin sensitivity (S_I), from an intravenous glucose tolerance test (IVGTT). During IVGTT, model equations are:

$$\begin{cases} \dot{G}(t) = -(S_G + X(t))G(t) + G_b S_G & G(0) = G_0 \\ \dot{X}(t) = -p_2(X(t) - S_I(I(t) - I_b)) & X(0) = 0 \end{cases} \quad (1)$$

where $G(t)$ ($mgdl^{-1}$) and $I(t)$ ($\mu U ml^{-1}$) are glucose and insulin concentrations in plasma respectively, G_b and I_b are their baseline values, G_0 accounts for the intravenous glucose dose injected at time 0, while glucose effectiveness S_G describes the glucose *per se* control (i.e. its ability to enhance its own rate of disappearance and to inhibit its endogenous production). Furthermore $X(t)$ denotes remote insulin, i.e. insulin action, whose dynamics are regulated by S_I and by parameter p_2.

S_I provided by MM is by definition a measure of insulin sensitivity at steady state. In order to grasp this point we can resort to the "thought experiment" originally discussed in (Bergman *et al.*, 1981). Let's perform an euglycemic hyperinsulinemic clamp on the model with insulin and glucose intravenously infused, respectively at a constant and variable rate, with the aim of clamping plasma glucose concentration at its basal value. When $I(t)$ and $X(t)$ have reached their plateau values, denoted with I_{ss} and X_{ss} respectively, one has from eq.(1)

$$S_I = \frac{X_{ss}}{I_{ss} - I_b} \qquad (2)$$

Thus, S_I provides quantitative information on insulin sensitivity when insulin action is at steady state, i.e. $\dot{X}(t) = 0$ in eq.(1). However, the dynamics of insulin action are also a critical factor for the efficacy of insulin control on glucose metabolism. These kinetic defects in insulin action have been studied in recent years by resorting to the euglycaemic hyperinsulinaemic clamp (Nolan *et al.*, 1997).

Motivated by the fact that the widely used insulin sensitivity index, albeit of paramount importance, only measures one ingredient of insulin action on glucose metabolism we have recently proposed (Pillonetto *et al.*, 2006) a new insulin sensitivity index that, at variance with the classic one, also accounts for the dynamics of insulin action. The new index, denoted as S_I^D, is a function of both two model parameters that characterize $X(t)$, i.e., the classic insulin sensitivity index, S_I, and p_2, which governs the dynamics of insulin action. The strength of S_I^D is that, while S_I measures the maximal metabolic response capacity of a given individual, the new index is able to account for both the speed and the capacity of response. Thanks to this peculiarity we have shown that in normal subjects S_I^D offers, in comparison with S_I, a more comprehensive picture of insulin action on glucose metabolism.

The aim of this contribution is to investigate the relative performance of S_I^D over S_I in type 2 diabetic patients. Of note, in these individuals insulin action is known to be slower than in normals, see e.g. (Avogaro *et al.*, 1996; Nolan *et al.*, 1997). Thus, S_I^D may turn out to be even more appropriate than S_I to classify their insulin sensitivity index. Furthermore, in diabetic patients estimation is often difficult because it is associated to a large uncertainty, see e.g. (Saad *et al.*, 1997; Pillonetto *et al.*, 2002). Thus, it appears important to assess how the new index also performs to this regard. The outline of the paper is as follows. In Section 2 we briefly review S_I^D theory and definition. In Section 3 the IVGTT data are described while in Section 4 MM identification is briefly reviewed.

Results are illustrated in Section 5 where S_I^D vs S_I performance is compared. Conclusions are finally reported in Section 6.

2. DYNAMIC INSULIN SENSITIVITY

2.1 Insulin Action Dynamics

Let's reformulate eq.(1) in order to obtain a closed form of MM glucose prediction $G(t)$, as function of model parameters and insulin profile. This goal can be accomplished by considering that the equation related to $\dot{X}(t)$ in eq.(1) can be integrated independently from that regarding $\dot{G}(t)$. Let's denote as $Z(t)$ the integral function of remote insulin $X(t)$:

$$
\begin{aligned}
Z(t) &= \int_0^t X(\sigma)d\sigma \\
&= \int_0^t \left[\int_0^\sigma S_I p_2 e^{-p_2(\sigma-\tau)}(I(\tau) - I_b)d\tau \right] d\sigma \quad (3) \\
&= S_I \int_0^t (1 - e^{-p_2(t-\tau)})(I(\tau) - I_b)d\tau
\end{aligned}
$$

By exploiting a result on linear differential equations (Braun, 1993), one has that glucose $G(t)$ can be written as

$$
\begin{aligned}
G(t) &= G_0 e^{-S_G t - Z(t)} \\
&\quad + S_G G_b \int_0^t e^{-S_G(t-\tau) - Z(t) + Z(\tau)} d\tau
\end{aligned} \quad (4)
$$

The second term of eq.(4) shows how plasma glucose concentration $G(t)$ is controlled by two signals, i.e. $S_G t$ and $Z(t)$. In particular the term $G_0 e^{-S_G t - Z(t)}$ is a single decaying exponential with a coefficient proportional to their sum. The first signal, i.e. $S_G t$, is linearly dependent on glucose effectiveness S_G. The second signal, i.e. $Z(t)$, is the ability of insulin to enhance glucose effectiveness and depends in a more complex way on both S_I and p_2. In fact it is evident from eq.(3) that $Z(t)$ is the output of a shift-invariant linear system having $I(t) - I_b$ as input and $h(t) = S_I(1 - e^{-p_2 t})$ as unit impulse response. This impulse response thus describes the dynamics by which insulin concentration (deviation from basal) elaborates the signal $Z(t)$ which, as shown in eq.(4), ultimately controls glucose concentration. We will refer to $h(t)$ as Integrated Insulin Action Impulse Response which is denoted as IAIR (Pillonetto *et al.*, 2003; Pillonetto *et al.*, 2006).

2.2 The new index

In light of the above considerations, the idea developed in (Pillonetto *et al.*, 2006) was to define a new index proportional to the integral of IAIR during a certain experimental time interval $[0, T]$. This new index has been called Dynamic Insulin Sensitivity (S_I^D) and is defined in mathematical terms as

$$
S_I^D = \frac{\int_0^T S_I(1 - e^{-p_2 t})dt}{T}
$$

$$
= S_I[1 - \frac{1 - e^{-p_2 T}}{p_2 T}] \qquad (5)
$$

S_I^D depends on both S_I and p_2 and also on an additional parameter, T that has to be fixed and whose choice is discussed at the end of this Section.

In order to point out the relationship between S_I^D and S_I it is useful to introduce the concept of efficiency η:

$$
\eta(p_2, T) = \frac{S_I^D}{S_I} = [1 - \frac{1 - e^{-p_2 T}}{p_2 T}] \qquad (6)
$$

When T is fixed, efficiency η takes on its values in $[0, 1]$ and is monotonically increasing with respect to p_2. Thus, we can think of η as the metabolic capability to adequately exploit a given insulin sensitivity by rapidly increasing insulin action concentration $X(t)$ in response to an increase of plasma insulin concentration. For instance, the closer η to 1, the higher the efficiency of the metabolic system in converting S_I into an effective control of insulin on glucose. On the other hand, a very low p_2 makes η close to zero, i.e. insulin action is virtually negligible during the experiment. This clearly shows that a high S_I value does not necessarily imply an effective control of insulin on glucose, since it can be associated with a low efficiency.

As concerns the choice of T, it is important to point out that it does not represent the length of that real experiment, e.g. an IVGTT or a glucose clamp, that is performed to determine S_I and p_2. Rather, T represents the duration of a "thought experiment" where IAIR can be directly observed and where efficiency η can be defined. In particular, the "optimal" value of T has to make η vary in the largest possible range of values so as to magnify differences between p_2 values of the subjects under study. To this aim, after considering a large population of normal, impaired glucose tolerant and diabetic individuals, a robust choice consists of setting T to 60 min (Pillonetto et al., 2006).

3. DATA BASE

Experimental data regard the same 10 type 2 diabetic subjects reported in (Avogaro et al., 1996; Pillonetto et al., 2002). Briefly, an insulin modified IVGTT (glucose dose of $300(mg kg^{-1})$

plus $0.05(U kg^{-1})$ of insulin given as a square wave between 20 and 25 min) was performed. Plasma glucose and insulin concentrations were frequently measured for 4h.

4. MM IDENTIFICATION

As concerns MM identification, the unknown model parameter vector $\theta = [S_I, S_G, p_2, G_0]$ is a priori uniquely identifiable given $G(t)$ and $I(t)$. In practice, $I(t)$ in eq.(1) is assumed to be known at any t by linearly interpolating its measured plasma concentration samples, while $G(t)$ is known in sampled and noisy form on a grid $\{t_1, t_2, ..., t_N\}$. In particular, the measurement error is assumed to be additive, zero-mean Gaussian with uncorrelated components and a 2% coefficient of variation (CV).

The MM parameters have been estimated by a Bayesian approach, see e.g. (Gelman et al., 1995) for an extensive survey on Bayesian estimation. As concerns the a priori information on θ incorporated in the estimator, since we know that all MM parameters are nonnegative, we adopt a prior $f_\theta(\theta)$ whose support extends only in the positive axis and assume that all the components of θ are independent. As regards S_G and G_0, we state that a priori each value is drawn from a uniform distribution in $[0, a]$ with $a \mapsto \infty$. For what concerns the prior for S_I, we take advantage from the information on diabetic subjects reported in literature, see e.g. (Owens et al., 1996). Following the same reasoning introduced in (Pillonetto et al., 2002), a threshold is defined over which S_I values are less and less probable. In particular, it is assumed for S_I an a priori probability density function where values less than $2 \times 10^{-4}(min^{-1}\mu U^{-1}ml)$ are equally probable, while values greater than $2 \times 10^{-4}(min^{-1}\mu U^{-1}ml)$ are less and less probable according to a decreasing exponential law (with exponent equal to $10^{-4}(min^{-1}\mu U^{-1}ml)$). Finally, for what p_2 is concerned, we define a non informative prior that consists of a uniform distribution in the interval $[0, 5]$, as in (Pillonetto et al., 2003). It is worth anticipating that the prior is virtually not influencing the results of the paper as discussed in the next Section.

As regards numerical determination of Bayesian estimation, computation of point estimates and confidence intervals is analytically intractable in our case, due to the complex relationship between θ and glucose measurements. In order to face this difficulty a Markov chain Monte Carlo (MCMC) strategy can be used (Gilks et al., 1996). In MCMC, first a Markov process is built which converges (in distribution) to the posterior of the parameters of interest. Then, after recovering the posterior in sampled form, a Monte Carlo integration step is performed to numerically compute the integrals of interest. This approach is especially advantageous in our case since it allows to reconstruct (in sampled form) the entire joint a posteriori probability density function of all MM parameters, from which S_I and S_I^D marginal posteriors become available, and this will permit to clearly compare the performance of the new index with respect to the classical one. The reader can find more details on our MCMC computational scheme for MM identification in (Pillonetto et al., 2003).

5. RESULTS

Table 1 shows the minimum variance estimates of S_I, p_2, S_I^D, S_G and G_0, with the 95% confidence interval in parenthesis. We start by considering results obtained in two paradigmatic cases. To this aim, in Figure 1 we report the marginal posteriors (obtained in sampled form by MCMC) of parameters S_I, p_2 and S_I^D for subject #2 (top) and #3 (bottom panel). Results concerning S_I (first column of Figure 1) show that in subject #2 this parameter is well estimated since the posterior is well concentrated around its mean. In fact, from Table 1 one can see that S_I point estimate takes on value 1.5 (1.4-1.6). On the other hand, in subject #3 S_I suffers of poor numerical identifiability with its estimate taking value 1.7 (0.4-4.1). In particular, its marginal posterior exhibits a long tail (mathematically explained by Proposition 2 in (Pillonetto et al., 2003)). Moreover, the fact that S_I point estimate in subject #3 is very close to the mean of the prior (whose value is around 1.67) suggests that IVGTT data provide little information to estimate S_I. It is thus difficult to establish in this case if S_I of #2 is greater than the one of #3. On the other hand, if one considers the posterior of S_I^D in the same two subjects (third column of Figure 1), both appear well concentrated around their means. This dramatically facilitates the comparison between the two individuals under study. In fact, the new index clearly reveals that insulin is in all likelihood more effective in #2 than in #3, since S_I^D takes on respectively values 1.17 (1.1-1.23) and 0.06 (0.028-0.1). In particular, the fact that S_I^D point estimate in #3 is much lower than in #2 can be explained by considering p_2 (second column of Figure 1): the 95% confidence interval in subject #3 includes many S_I values associated to very low values of p_2 and thus also of efficiency η.

The superiority of S_I^D also emerges when we consider the entire population of diabetic subjects. In particular, in Figure 2 we display with horizontal bars S_I^D and S_I estimates in all the subjects together with their 95% confidence intervals. These results show that in every subject S_I^D does not suffer by numerical identifiably problems, differently

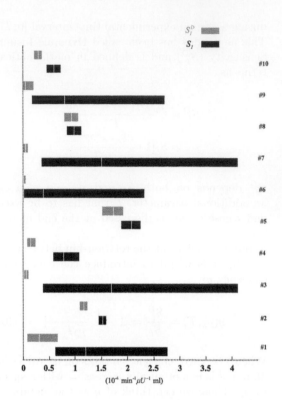

Fig. 2. Bayes S_I^D and S_I estimates in diabetic subjects. Point estimates are shown with the 95% confidence intervals (horizontal bars)

from what happens to S_I in subjects 1,3,6,7 and 9 where MM results are very difficult to interpret. Finally, to assess sensitivity of all the obtained results with respect to prior information adopted on MM parameters, we have repeated estimation in all the subjects under study by setting to higher values the thresholds over which S_I and p_2 values are less and less probable (results not shown). As discussed in (Pillonetto et al., 2002), as concerns S_I and p_2 it is clear that the prior model plays a crucial role in determining the vanishing of the tails of their marginal posteriors. However, the new index turns out to be poorly sensitive to the prior information. In other words, IVGTT data turn out to be very informative for estimating S_I^D, also in those conditions where S_I and p_2 suffer of poor numerical identifiability. To understand this point, one has to consider that the possible large uncertainty associated to S_I and p_2 values is due to the fact that there exist numerical non-identifiability regions in the parameter space where the likelihood is little sensitive to variations of these two parameters. In particular, many different couples of S_I and p_2 values may lead to virtually the same IAIR, see (Pillonetto et al., 2003). As a consequence, estimated S_I and p_2 values may be very uncertain, even if S_I^D estimate is not.

Table 1. Minimum variance parameter estimates in diabetic subjects with their 95% confidence intervals (interval between quantiles 0.025 and 0.975)

Subjects	$S_I(10^{-4}min^{-1}\mu U^{-1}ml)$	$p_2(10^{-2}min^{-1})$	$S_I^D(10^{-4}min^{-1}\mu U^{-1}ml)$	$S_G(10^{-2}min^{-1})$	$G_0(mgdl^{-1})$
1	1.2 (0.61-2.7)	1.3 (0.13-3.3)	0.3 (0.09-0.65)	1.59 (1.07-1.98)	299.7 (284.1-313.3)
2	1.5 (1.4-1.6)	7 (5.7-84)	1.17 (1.1-1.23)	2.1 (1.8-2.38)	382 (369.9-394.7)
3	1.7 (0.4-4.1)	0.18 (0.04-0.68)	0.06 (0.028-0.1)	1.06 (0.78-1.35)	434.6 (421.9-448.4)
4	0.77 (0.58-1.1)	0.8 (0.33-1.3)	0.15 (0.09-0.23)	1.02 (0.76-1.25)	318 (307.4-329.2)
5	2.1 (1.8-2.2)	9.8 (7.8-12)	1.7 (1.52-1.91)	0.89 (0.48-1.32)	411 (395.6-428.4)
6	0.39 (0.032-2.3)	0.7 (0.014-7)	0.02 (0.006-0.058)	1.35 (1-1.62)	563 (543.3-581.3)
7	1.51 (0.36-4.1)	0.19 (0.033-0.8)	0.05 (0.03-0.087)	1.48 (1.32-1.62)	314 (304.8-323.5)
8	0.98 (0.84-1.11)	35 (20-68)	0.93 (0.8-1.06)	0.92 (0.66-1.19)	325.4 (315.3-336.2)
9	0.8 (0.18-2.7)	0.6 (0.034-2.4)	0.06 (0.018-0.2)	1.61 (1-1.85)	350.9 (335.4-363.2)
10	0.6 (0.46-0.72)	2.5 (2.1-3)	0.29 (0.22-0.36)	0.84 (0.52-1.18)	263 (252.5-275.2)

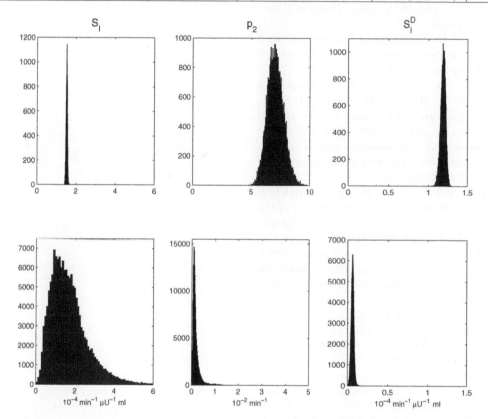

Fig. 1. Diabetic subjects #2 (upper) and #3 (lower panel). Posterior (recovered in sampled form by MCMC) of S_I (first column), p_2 (second column) and S_I^D (third column)

6. CONCLUSIONS

MM of glucose kinetics provides important clinical information for investigating glucose metabolism in humans and is widely used to estimate insulin sensitivity. The present paper is a follow up of (Pillonetto *et al.*, 2006) where we have shown some limitations of the classical index S_I and proposed a new index, S_I^D, which provides a better picture of insulin ability to control glucose, in particular in normal subjects.

Results reported in this paper reveal that the new dynamic index is even more important in subjects with slow insulin action since ignoring the role of p_2 may lead to contradictory results. In addition, our results show that the new index S_I^D also has an additional advantage over S_I. In fact, while S_I

is often at risk of poor numerical identifiability, S_I^D estimation is much more robust.

In light of this analysis, S_I^D appears particularly suitable to be employed in population studies where diabetic/glucose intolerant subjects are likely to be present as well as in search studies for diabetes-relevant genes in the human genome, see e.g. (Haffner *et al.*, 1999; Raffael *et al.*, 1996).

REFERENCES

Avogaro, A., P. Vicini, A. Valerio, A. Caumo and C. Cobelli (1996). The hot but not the cold minimal model allows precise assessment of insulin sensitivity in niddm subjects. *Am. J. Physiol. 270 (Endocrinol. Metab.)* **33**, E532–E540.

Bergman, R.N., C.R. Bowden and C. Cobelli (1981). *The minimal model approach to quantification of factors controlling glucose disposal in man.* Wiley, New York.

Bergman, R.N., Y.Z. Ider, C.R. Bowden and C. Cobelli (1979). Quantitative estimation of insulin sensitivity. *Am. J. Physiol. 236 (Endocrinol. Metab. Gastrointest. Physiol.)* **5**, E667–E677.

Braun, M. (1993). *Differential Equations and Their Applications.* Springer Verlag.

Gelman, A., J.B. Carlin, H.S. Stern and D.B. Rubin (1995). *Bayesian Data Analysis.* Chapman and Hall.

Gilks, W.R., S. Richardson and D.J. Spiegelhalter (1996). *Markov Chain Monte Carlo in Practice.* Chapman and Hall.

Haffner, S.M., R. DAgostino Jr, L. Mykkanen, R. Tracy, B. Howard, M. Rewers, J. Selby, P.J. Savage and M.F. Saad (1999). Insulin sensitivity in subjects with type 2 diabetes. relationship to cardiovascular risk factors: the insulin resistance atherosclerosis study. *Diabetes Care* **22**, 562–568.

Nolan, J.J., B. Ludvik, J. Baloga, D. Reichart and J.M. Olefsky (1997). Mechanisms of the kinetic defect in insulin action in obesity and niddm. *Diab. Med.* **46**, 994–1000.

Owens, D.R., S.D. Luzio and P.A. Coates (1996). Insulin secretion and sensitivity in newly diagnosed niddm caucasians in the uk. *Diab. Med.* **13**, S19–S24.

Pillonetto, G., A.Caumo, G. Sparacino and C. Cobelli (2006). A new dynamic index of insulin sensitivity. *IEEE Trans. on Biomedical Engineering* **53**, 369–379.

Pillonetto, G., G. Sparacino and C. Cobelli (2003). Numerical non-identifiability regions of the minimal model of glucose kinetics: superiority of bayesian estimation. *Mathematical Biosciences* **184(1)**, 53–67.

Pillonetto, G., P. Magni, R. Bellazzi, G. Sparacino and C. Cobelli (2002). Minimal model si=0 problem in niddm subjects: nonzero bayesian estimates with credible confidence intervals. *Am. J. Physiol. 282 (Endocrinol. Metab.)* **3**, E564–E573.

Raffael, J.R., D.C. Robbins, J.M. Norris, E. Boerwinkle, R.A. Defronzo, S.C. Elbein, W. Fujimoto, C.L. Hanis, S.E. Kahn, M.A. Permutt, K.C. Chiu, J. Cruz, D.A. Ehrmann, R.P. Robertson, J.I. Rotter and J. Buse (1996). The gennid study: a resource for mapping the genes that cause niddm. *Diabetes care* **19**, 864–872.

Saad, M.F., G.M. Steil, M. Riad-Gabriel, A. Khan, A. Sharma, R. Boyadjian, S.D. Jinagouda and R.N. Bergman (1997). Method of insulin administration has no effect on insulin sensitivity estimates from the insulin-modified minimal model protocol. *J. Clin. Invest.* **46(12)**, 2044–2048.

POSTURAL TIME-SERIES ANALYSIS OF ELDERLY AND CONTROL SUBJECTS USING ENTROPY

Hassan AMOUD[1], Madhur AGRAWAL[2], Uday BANDARU[3], David HEWSON[1], Michel DOUSSOT[1] and Jacques DUCHÊNE[1]

[1]*Institut Charles DELAUNAY, FRE CNRS 2848, Université de technologie de Troyes, 10010 Troyes, France*
[2]*Indian Institute of Technology, Kanpur, Assam, India*
[3]*Indian Institute of Technology, Guwahati, Assam, India*

Abstract: The present paper applies two methods commonly used to calculate entropy to postural time-series data of elderly and control subjects. Approximate entropy provided a biased estimate of regularity for small window lengths. In contrast, sample entropy was able to identify postural differences between elderly and control subjects. Elderly subjects showed less regularity in terms of anteroposterior displacement than did control subjects. However, the observed values of entropy were very small, as were the significant differences observed. Additional work is required to address concerns related to the time series length and the method used to calculate entropy. *Copyright © 2006 IFAC*

Keywords: entropy, nonlinear analysis

1. INTRODUCTION

Falls in the elderly are a major problem for healthcare services in the 21st century, for both medical and social reasons. In addition, the associated financial costs are considerable. For instance, in France alone, the number of deaths attributed annually to falls is estimated at more than 9000, with a resultant cost in excess of two billion euros (CFES, 2001). There have been many risk factors identified for falls, with no consensus reached, largely due to differences in methodology, study populations, and fall definition. However, those factors most commonly cited include an underlying muscular weakness, a previous fall, and balance and gait problems (Rubenstein and Josephson, 2002). Other risk factors for fall, such as visual impairment, may also manifest themselves in a balance problem.

An effective method of evaluating individuals with balance problems and thus an increased risk of falling is to use a force plate to measure postural sway (Prieto, et al., 1993). This technique measures centre of pressure (COP) displacement over time, which can be used as a measure of postural stability. Centre of pressure displacement can be measured in both anteroposterior (AP) and mediolateral (ML) directions. The representation of COP displacement in AP and ML directions is known as a stabilogram.

The parameters that are typically extracted from stabilograms bear no relation to the mechanisms underlying postural control (Riley, et al., 1997). These measures, which include temporal (mean, RMS), spatiotemporal (surface of the ellipse) and spectral (median frequency, deciles) parameters, provide purely statistical information. In contrast, non-linear analyses, which provide information related to signal complexity might be able to shed light on the organisation of the postural control processes, thus enabling balance disorders to be followed longitudinally (Goldberger, et al., 2002).

In the short time in which non-linear methods have been applied to COP data; several different parameters have been measured. For instance, the pioneering Stabilogram Diffusion Analysis (SDA) of Collins and De Luca, Rescaled Range Analysis (R/S) and Detrended Fluctuation Analysis (DFA) (Delignières, et al., 2003). Other variables analysed have included the Lyapunov Exponent (Harbourne and Stergiou, 2003, Yamada, 1995), and Recurrence Quantification Analysis (Riley, et al., 1999, Schmit, et al., 2005).

One of the major problems with the non-linear methods outlined above is the volume of data required for parameter calculation. Large data sets are not possible for stabilogram analysis of at-risk elderly subjects. In such individuals, it is difficult to remain standing for long periods of time. An interesting method to use for the shorter time series that are necessarily obtained from such subjects could be the rate of generation of new information, termed approximate entropy (ApEn) developed by Pincus (Pincus, 1991). A related measure of system complexity, termed sample entropy (SampEn) was introduced by Richman and Moorman (Richman and Moorman, 2000).

The aim of this study was to compare approximate and sample entropy for elderly and control populations in order to determine whether these parameters are able to identify the differences in postural control mechanisms known to exist between these two groups.

2. METHODS

2.1 Subjects.

Ten healthy control subjects (three males and seven females) of mean age 33.3 ± 7.4 y and ten healthy elderly subjects (four males and six females) of mean age 80.5 ± 4.7 y participated in the study. All subjects gave their informed consent, and no subjects reported any musculoskeletal or neurological conditions that precluded their participation in the study.

2.2 Data Acquisition and Data Processing.

Centre of pressure data were obtained from a Bertec 4060-08 force plate (Bertec Corporation, Columbus, OH, USA). The initial COP signals were calculated with respect to the centre of the force-plate before normalisation by subtraction of the mean value.

Data were recorded using ProTags™ (Jean-Yves Hogrel, Institut de Myologie, Paris, France), which was developed in Labview (National Instruments Corporation, Austin TX, USA). Data were sampled at 100 Hz, using an 8th-order low-pass Butterworth filter with a cut-off frequency of 10Hz. All subsequent calculations were performed using Matlab (Mathworks Inc, Natick, MA, USA).

2.3 Experimental Protocol.

Subjects were tested barefoot or wearing socks. Testing began with subjects standing upright with their arms by their sides in front of the force-plate while looking at a 10-cm cross fixed on the wall two metres in front of them. Upon verbal instruction, subjects stepped onto the force plate. Subjects were not required to use a pre-ordained foot position. Data recording lasted 15 s, during which time subjects maintained an upright posture. A second verbal command was given for subjects to step down from the force-plate.

2.4 Approximate Entropy.

In order to calculate approximate entropy (ApEn), two parameters, m and r need to be specified: m is the length of the data sequence to be compared, expressed in data points, and r is the tolerance for accepting a match. The tolerance is usually set as $r * SD$, where SD is the standard deviation of the data set.

For a time series of N points, $\{u(j) : 1 \leq j \leq N\}$, the (N-m+1) vectors $\mathbf{x}_m(i)$, $1 \leq i \leq N - m + 1$, are created:

$$\mathbf{x}_m(i) = \{u(i+k) : 0 \leq k \leq m-1\} \quad (1)$$

$\mathbf{x}_m(i)$ is the vector of m data points from $u(i)$ to $u(i+m-1)$. The distance d between vectors $\mathbf{x}_m(i)$ and $\mathbf{x}_m(j)$ is defined as the maximum difference in their respective scalar components:

$$d[\mathbf{x}_m(i), \mathbf{x}_m(j)] = \max\{|u(i+k) - u(j+k)| : 0 \leq k \leq m-1\} \quad (2)$$

Let B_i be the number of vectors $\mathbf{x}_m(j)$ within r of $\mathbf{x}_m(i)$ and let A_i be the number of vectors $\mathbf{x}_{m+1}(j)$ within r of $\mathbf{x}_{m+1}(i)$. Define the function $C_i^m(r) = B_i / (N - m + 1)$. The vector $\mathbf{x}_m(i)$ is called the template, and an instance where a vector $\mathbf{x}_m(j)$ is within r of it is called a template match. The $C_i^m(r)$ values measure within a tolerance r the regularity, or frequency of patterns similar to a given pattern of window length m. In other words, $C_i^m(r)$ is the probability that any vector $\mathbf{x}_m(j)$ is within r of $\mathbf{x}_m(i)$.

Eckmann and Ruelle (Eckmann and Ruelle, 1985) defined the function $\Phi^m(r)$:

$$\Phi^m(r) = (N - m + 1)^{-1} \sum_{i=1}^{N-m+1} \ln(C_i^m(r)) \quad (3)$$

They defined an approximation of the Kolmogorov entropy of this process as:

$$\lim_{r \to 0} \lim_{m \to \infty} \lim_{N \to \infty} \left[\Phi^m(r) - \Phi^{m+1}(r) \right] \quad (4)$$

However, this approximation is not suited to the analysis of the finite and noisy time series derived from experiments. Pincus (Pincus, 1991) defined an approximate entropy $ApEn(m, r)$. For finite data sets, $ApEn(m, r)$ is estimated by the statistic:

$$ApEn(m, r, N) = \left[\Phi^m(r) - \Phi^{m+1}(r) \right] \quad (5)$$

Which can be expressed as:

$$ApEn(m,r,N) =$$

$$(N - m + 1)^{-1} \sum_{i=1}^{N-m+1} \ln(C_i^m(r)) \qquad (6)$$

$$- (N - m)^{-1} \sum_{i=1}^{N-m} \ln(C_i^{m+1}(r))$$

When N is large, $ApEn(m,r,N)$ is approximately equal to:

$$ApEn(m,r,N) = (N - m)^{-1} \sum_{i=1}^{N-m} \ln(B_i / A_i) \qquad (7)$$

2.5 Sample Entropy.

A modification of the ApEn algorithm, known as sample entropy (SampEn), was proposed by Richman and colleagues (Richman, et al., 2004). The difference between SampEn and ApEn is that SampEn does not include self-matches, with the calculation of SampEn, explained as follows (Richman and Moorman, 2000):

Define $B_i^m(r)$ as $(N - m - 1)^{-1}$ times the number of vectors $\mathbf{x}_m(j)$ within r of $\mathbf{x}_m(i)$, where j ranges from 1 to (N-m), and $j \neq i$ to exclude self-matches. Then, define:

$$B^m(r) = (N - m)^{-1} \sum_{i=1}^{N-m} B_i^m(r) \qquad (8)$$

Similarly, define $A_i^m(r)$ as $(N - m - 1)^{-1}$ times the number of vectors $\mathbf{x}_{m+1}(j)$ within r of $\mathbf{x}_{m+1}(i)$, where j ranges from 1 to (N-m), and $j \neq i$, and $A^m(r) = (N - m)^{-1} \sum_{i=1}^{N-m} A_i^m(r)$.

Sample entropy $SampEn(m,r)$ can then be defined as:

$$SampEn(m,r) = \lim_{N \to \infty} \left[-\ln\left(A^m(r)/B^m(r)\right) \right] \qquad (9)$$

$SampEn(m,r)$ is estimated by the statistic $SampEn(m,r,N)$:

$$SampEn(m,r,N) = -\ln\left(A^m(r)/B^m(r)\right) \qquad (10)$$

2.6 Data Analysis.

Centre of pressure data were calculated from the instant that the second foot contacted the force plate (FC2). The time at which FC2 was considered to occur was calculated as time at which the maximum value of the second derivative of the ML displacement signal occurred. This instant in time corresponded to the moment when the second foot

touched the force plate, thus creating the largest acceleration of ML when the COP moved rapidly towards the second foot. This time was used for both AP and ML displacements. All entropy values were calculated for the 10-s period starting 1 s after FC2, in order to give both AP and ML displacement time to return to near central values.

Statistical analyses were performed with the Statistical Package for Social Sciences (SPSS Inc., Chicago, IL, USA). Data were checked for outliers using the Mahalanobis distance and for non-normality using measures of skewness and kurtosis (Tabachnick and Fidell, 2001). Analysis of variance (ANOVA) was used to test for the effect of group (control or elderly) on entropy values; subject group was the independent variable, while the different entropy values were the dependent variables. Repeated measures ANOVA was used to test for an effect of tolerance on entropy values. Data were expressed as means ± SD or means and 95% confidence intervals, with alpha levels for statistical significance set at $p < 0.05$.

3. RESULTS

Tolerance values from 0.01 to 1 (increments of 0.09, thereafter 0.1) were tested for both ApEn and SampEn for a fixed window length of 2 points. As no differences were observed between control and elderly subjects, only those data for elderly subjects are presented. Approximate entropy decreased significantly as tolerance increased until r=0.2 for both AP and ML displacements (Fig. 1. & Fig. 2.).

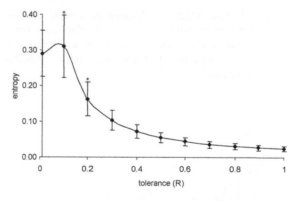

Fig. 1. The effect of tolerance on approximate entropy for elderly subjects for AP displacement for a fixed window length (m=2). Data are means ± SD. *Significant difference from previous tolerance.

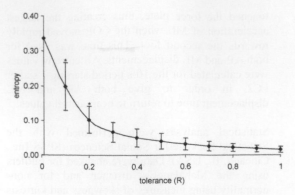

Fig. 2. The effect of tolerance on approximate entropy for elderly subjects for ML displacement for a fixed window length (m=2). Data are means ± SD. *Significant difference from previous tolerance.

Sample entropy decreased significantly as tolerance increased until r=0.2 for both AP and ML displacements (Fig. 3. & Fig. 4.).

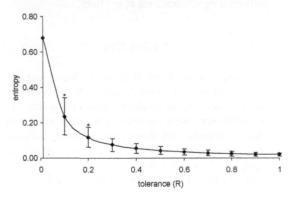

Fig. 3. The effect of tolerance on sample entropy for elderly subjects for AP displacement for a fixed window length (m=2). Data are means ± SD. *Significant difference from previous tolerance.

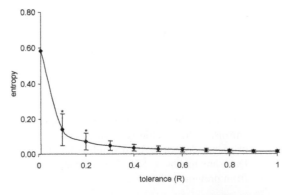

Fig. 4. The effect of tolerance on sample entropy for elderly subjects for ML displacement for a fixed window length (m=2). Data are means ± SD. *Significant difference from previous tolerance.

When tolerance values were fixed at 0.2, in keeping with the results of the statistical tests outlined above, significantly higher values of ApEn were observed for elderly subjects in comparison with control subjects, for window lengths of 1 and 2

points for both AP and ML displacement (Fig. 5. & Fig. 6.).

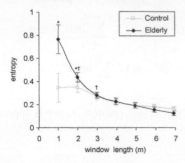

Fig. 5. Approximate entropy for control and elderly subjects for AP displacement for a fixed tolerance (r=0.2) with varying window length (m varies from 1 to 7 points). Data are means and 95% confidence intervals. *Significant difference from control group; †significant difference from previous window length.

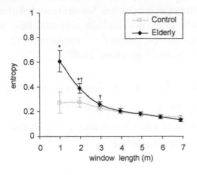

Fig. 6. Approximate entropy for control and elderly subjects for ML displacement for a fixed tolerance (r=0.2) with varying window length (m varies from 1 to 7 points). Data are means and 95% confidence intervals. *Significant difference from control group; †significant difference from previous window length.

Significantly higher values of SampEn were observed for elderly subjects in comparison with control subjects for AP displacement for all window lengths, except for m=7 (Fig. 7.).

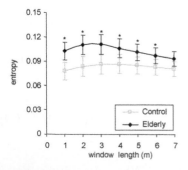

Fig. 7. Sample entropy for control and elderly subjects for AP displacement for a fixed tolerance (r=0.2) with varying window length (m varies from 1 to 7 points). Data are means and 95% confidence intervals. *Significant difference from control group.

In contrast, no significant differences were observed between control and elderly subjects for SampEn values for ML displacement (Fig. 8.).

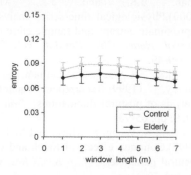

Fig. 8. Sample entropy for control and elderly subjects for ML displacement for a fixed tolerance (r=0.2) with varying window length (m varies from 1 to 7 points). Data are means and 95% confidence intervals.

The 95% confidence intervals of entropy values for control and elderly subjects for a window length of 2 points can be found in Table 1 and Table 2 (AP and ML displacement, respectively).

Table 1 Ninety-five percent confidence intervals of ApEn and SampEn for control and elderly subjects for AP displacement

| Group | Entropy | |
	Approximate	Sample
Control	0.31 - 0.39	0.07 - 0.09
Elderly	0.39 - 0.48	0.10 - 0.12

Table 2 Ninety-five percent confidence intervals of ApEn and SampEn for control and elderly subjects for ML displacement

| Group | Entropy | |
	Approximate	Sample
Control	0.23 - 0.31	0.08 - 0.10
Elderly	0.35 - 0.43	0.07 - 0.09

4. DISCUSSION

In respect to the effect of the parameters chosen (m, and r) on entropy, similar results were observed for both methods used. The entropy values obtained for both ApEn and SampEn decreased significantly as tolerance decreased, until r=0.2. From this point on, no significant decreases were observed. After obtaining this result, r=0.2 was used for all subsequent analyses. When the window length (m) was considered, the two methods differed, with values for ApEn decreasing until a window length of three. From this point on, no differences were observed. In contrast, window length had no significant effect on SampEn. This finding is in keeping with that obtained for cardiovascular data (Richman and Moorman, 2000). Values for

SampEn were noted to remain relatively consistent, unlike those of ApEn.

In respect to the interpretation of the SampEn results for the postural data of the present study, elderly subjects had significantly higher entropy values for anteroposterior displacement than did the control subjects. The increased entropy values observed for the elderly subjects were indicative of a less deterministic time series, in other words a less well-controlled posture. Although such a finding was expected, it should be noted that the entropy values were of the order of 0.1 or less. Such values correspond to a time series that is almost completely determinist in nature. Although significant differences were observed, these were so small as to be negligible. In contrast, other studies have identified a larger chaotic component in postural time series (Yamada, 1995). Further investigation is needed to address this difference, which might be related to the length of time series. For instance, the present study used a short 10-s time series, whereas Yamada collected data for 200 s.

Future work will include the use of additional methods to calculate entropy. For instance, Costa and colleagues have developed the concept of multiscale entropy (MSE) (Costa, et al., 2005). This method, which is based on the observation that physiological systems tend to be a combination of random and deterministic elements, combines observations of underlying long-range correlations on multiple spatial and temporal scales. However, a potential problem with the application of MSE is the requirement for large data sets. Another method used to calculate entropy is recurrence quantification analysis (RQA). This technique has already been used for postural data for adult subjects. An advantage of RQA is that it does not require data to be stationary, nor does it require large data sets (Riley, et al., 1999). This method has recently been used to compare ballet dancers with track athletes, and was able to identify different patterns of postural sway (Schmit, et al., 2005).

In conclusion, SampEn was better able to identify postural differences between elderly and control subjects. Elderly subjects showed less regularity in anteroposterior displacement than did control subjects. However, entropy values were very low, and the differences observed were so small as to be inconsequential. Additional work is required on different methods of calculating entropy, as well as the effect of the length of the time series studied.

5. REFERENCES

Comité Français d'Education pour la Santé (2001): 'Les clés du " bien vieillir " : prévention des chutes chez les seniors': Caisse Nationale de l'Assurance Maladie des Travailleurs Salariés, pp. 20.

Costa, M., A.L. Goldberger, and C.K. Peng, (2005).Multiscale entropy analysis of biological signals, *Phys Rev E Stat Nonlin Soft Matter Phys*, **vol.** 71, pp. 021906.

Delignières, D., T. Deschamps, A. Legros, and N. Caillou, (2003).A methodological note on nonlinear time series analysis: is the open- and closed-loop model of Collins and De Luca (1993) a statistical artifact?, *Journal of Motor Behavior*, **vol.** 35, pp. 86-97.

Eckmann, J.-P. and D. Ruelle, (1985).Ergodic theory of chaos and strange attractors, *Rev. Mod. Phys*, **vol.** 57, pp. 617–656

Goldberger, A.L., L.A. Amaral, J.M. Hausdorff, P. Ivanov, C.K. Peng, and H.E. Stanley, (2002).Fractal dynamics in physiology: alterations with disease and aging, *Proceedings of the National Academy of Sciences of the United States of America*, **vol.** 99 Suppl 1, pp. 2466-72.

Harbourne, R.T. and N. Stergiou, (2003).Nonlinear analysis of the development of sitting postural control, *Dev Psychobiol*, **vol.** 42, pp. 368-77.

Pincus, S.M., (1991).Approximate entropy as a measure of system complexity, *Proc Natl Acad Sci U S A*, **vol.** 88, pp. 2297-301.

Prieto, T.E., J.B. Myklebust, and B.M. Myklebust, (1993).Characterization and modeling of postural steadiness in the elderly: a review, *Rehabilitation Engineering, IEEE Transactions on [see also IEEE Trans. on Neural Systems and Rehabilitation]*, **vol.** 1, pp. 26-34.

Richman, J.S., D.E. Lake, and J.R. Moorman, (2004).Sample entropy, *Methods Enzymol*, **vol.** 384, pp. 172-84.

Richman, J.S. and J.R. Moorman, (2000).Physiological time-series analysis using approximate entropy and sample entropy, *Am J Physiol Heart Circ Physiol*, **vol.** 278, pp. H2039-49.

Riley, M.A., R. Balasubramaniam, and M.T. Turvey, (1999).Recurrence quantification analysis of postural fluctuations, *Gait Posture*, **vol.** 9, pp. 65-78.

Riley, M.A., S. Wong, S. Mitra, and M.T. Turvey, (1997).Common effects of touch and vision on postural parameters, *Exp Brain Res*, **vol.** 117, pp. 165-70.

Rubenstein, L.Z. and K.R. Josephson, (2002).The epidemiology of falls and syncope, *Clin Geriatr Med*, **vol.** 18, pp. 141-58.

Schmit, J.M., D.I. Regis, and M.A. Riley, (2005).Dynamic patterns of postural sway in ballet dancers and track athletes, *Exp Brain Res*, **vol.** 163, pp. 370-8.

Tabachnick, B.G. and L.S. Fidell, *Using multivariate statistics*, 4th ed. Needham Heights, MA, USA: Allyn and Bacon, 2001.

Yamada, N., (1995).Chaotic swaying of the upright posture, *Human Movement Science*, **vol.** 14, pp. 711-726.

A COMPARISON BETWEEN TWO FRACTIONAL MULTIMODELS STRUCTURES FOR RAT MUSCLES MODELLING

Laurent Sommacal[(1)], Pierre Melchior[(1)], Arnaud Dossat[(2)], Julien petit[(2)], Jean-Marie Cabelguen[(3)], Alain Oustaloup[(1)] and Auke Jan Ijspeert[(4)]

[(1)]*LAPS - UMR 5131 CNRS, Université Bordeaux 1 - ENSEIRB, 351 cours de la Libération F33405 TALENCE cedex, France. Email: surname.name@laps.u-bordeaux1.fr*
[(2)]*Laboratoire de Neurophysiologie - UMR 5543, Université Victor Ségalen Bordeaux2. Bat 2A, 146 rue Léo Saignat - 33076 BORDEAUX Cedex. julien.petit@fac-sci-sport.u-bordeaux2.fr*
[(3)]*INSERM E 0358, Institut Magendie, 1 rue Camille St Saëns, F33077 BORDEAUX cedex, France. Email: Jean-marie.cabelguen@bordeaux.inserm.fr*
[(4)]*EPFL, Swiss Federal Institute of Technology, School of Computer and Communication Sciences IC-ISIM-LSL INN 241, CH-1015, LAUSANNE, Switzerland. Email: auke.ijspeert@epfl.ch*

Abstract: *Peroneus digiti quarti* and *peroneus brevis* muscles responses of the rat are studied for 10 Hz pulses stimulations. A comparison between two multimodels structures is presented. These multimodels include fractional sub-models. The multimodels allow distinguishing contraction and relaxation phases for identification. Fractional orders used in the sub-models lead to minimize the size of transfer functions. The present study develops the multimodels structure earlier established, by including variation functions of extra parameters for IIA and IIB fibres and to explain muscle response for Motor Units (MU) stimulations at 10 Hz. The multimodels explains rat striated muscle responses, and so, allow its inclusion in a future muscle computer model. Copyright © 2006 IFAC

Keywords: Modelling, identification, multi systems, fractal systems, biomedical, muscle.

1. INTRODUCTION

The importance of the striated muscles contraction in animal organism physiology is considerable. Indeed, these muscles are involved during partial or global organism moves (locomotion). The knowledge of the effective contribution of muscular contractions to locomotor activity, makes possible to associate cinematic changes to physiological (tiredness) or pathological origin modifications of the muscle fibre properties (myopathies). The striated muscle structure is widely described in biology. Three fibre types make up this muscle (Shepherd, 1994): Fast (IIB), Medium (IIA) and Slow (I) fibres. These fibre types present different characteristics, like contraction, relaxation delays and feeding types. This study deals with IIA and IIB muscle fibres modeling. These experiments allow stimulating each MU separately. MUs are classified as FR, FF, and S types, which are

respectively connected to IIA, IIB, and I fibre types. Muscles, which are studied for modelling, are stimulated through nine FF MUs and seven FR MUs. Some recent studies (Cross, 1997; Ravier, 2005) have revealed fractional structure of the muscle. Thus contraction and relaxation phases are identified separately through two sub-models, whose fractional orders allow reducing notably the size of the transfer functions. The most important problem when modeling muscle comes from its irreproducible nature. Applying 10 Hz pulses stimulations, amplitude and dynamic behavior variations appear.

Extra parameters addition allows modifying slightly initial sub-models parameters. Thus modifications allow reporting amplitude and dynamic behaviour modification along experiment duration.

The experimental protocol is detailed in section 2. Section 3 presents fractional differentiation. In

Section 4, multimodels and sub-models structure are detailed. Then, Section 5 proposes rat fibre multimodels, through a comparison between both multimodels described in this paper.

2. METHODS

Experiments were carried out on a rat. The animal was anesthetized with an initial intraperitoneal dose of pentobarbital sodium (45 mg/kg), supplemented, as necessary by additional intravenous doses to maintain full anesthesia. The nerve to the peroneus digiti quarti was freed, and the distal tendon of the muscle was attached to a force transducer (Kulite BG300) fixed on the shaft of a servo-controlled puller (LDS 201). All other muscles of the himb limb were denervated. The region containing the muscle was formed into a pool filled with paraffin oil. A laminectomy was performed between L4 and S2 to expose the lumbosacral cord, and the skin flaps were elevated to form a pool that was filled with paraffin oil. The dorsal and ventral roots were cut near their entry into the spinal cord. Ventral roots were slit under oil into filaments and were raised onto a silver electrode that was used as the anode. A similar electrode, placed on the body mass near the root entry, served as cathode. Impulses in motor axons were detected by electrodes placed on the muscle nerve, which was elevated into oil. Potentials were amplified by Grass AC amplifiers and displayed on a Gould digital oscilloscope. A ventral root filament was shown to contain a single motor axon innervating the peroneus digiti quarti muscle when its stimulation evoked a unique potential in the muscle nerve. The muscle length-twitch force curve was determined during stimulation of the muscle nerve. The muscle length was then set to the optimal length for the muscle twitch force. Isometric contraction forces developed by single MUs were measured for three stimulation frequencies (10, 20, 40 Hz). The MU type of each MU was determined according to the protocol described in (Petit, et al., 1990). Briefly, the type of the MU is determined using the amplitude of the force oscillations and the mean level of the force developed by the MU during stimulation at 20 Hz and stimulation at 40 Hz. The force signal and the muscle length signal were digitized at 2 kHz and stored using a CED 1401 interface coupled to a PC computer running the Spike2 software.

3. FRACTIONAL DIFFERENTIATION AND DAVIDSON-COLE MODEL

3.1. Fractional differentiation

The fractional derivative of the function $f(t)$ at ν order is defined as (Grünwald, 1867),

$$D^\nu f(t) \approx \frac{1}{h^\nu} \sum_{k=0}^{\infty} (-1)^k a_k(\nu) f(t-kh), \quad (1)$$

with $t = Kh, K \in \mathbb{N}^+$ and h is the sampling period.

Assuming that $f(t) = 0 \ \forall t < 0$, the D^ν Laplace transform is (Miller, et al., 1993; Liouville, 1832; Samko, et al., 1987):

$$\mathcal{L}(D^\nu f(t)) = s^\nu \cdot \mathcal{L}(f(t)), \quad (2)$$

where ν can be real or imaginary number order. Linear model described with the fractional differential equation,

$$\sum_{l=1}^{L} a_l \frac{d^{n_l}}{dt^{n_l}} \hat{y}(t) = \sum_{q=1}^{Q} b_q \frac{d^{m_q}}{dt^{m_q}} u(t), \quad (3)$$

where

$$n_1, ..., n_L, m_1, .., m_Q \in \mathbb{R}^{L+Q}, \quad (4)$$

can be modeled as the following fractional transfer function, providing that the system is relaxed at t=0,

$$\hat{y}(s) = \frac{b_1 s^{m_1} + b_2 s^{m_2} + ... + b_q s^{m_Q}}{a_1 s^{n_1} + a_2 s^{n_2} + ... + a_L s^{n_L}} u(s). \quad (5)$$

The output model can then be simulated:

$$\hat{y}(Kh) = \frac{1}{\sum_{l=1}^{L} \frac{a_l}{h^{n_l}} \binom{n_l}{0}} \left(\begin{array}{c} \sum_{k=0}^{K} \sum_{q=1}^{Q} (-1)^k \frac{b_q}{h^{n_l}} \binom{n_q}{k} u((K-k)h) \\ -\sum_{k=1}^{K} \sum_{l=1}^{L} (-1)^k \frac{a_l}{h^{n_l}} \binom{n_l}{k} \hat{y}((K-k)h) \end{array} \right). \quad (6)$$

To model muscle responses, Cole-Cole model or Davidson-Cole model can be used. When orders are integers, both models led to the rational transfer function. The previous study (Sommacal, et al., 2006) demonstrates the advantage of using Davidson-Cole sub-models. Indeed, the output error is minimal and the size model is reduced to 6 parameters for both phases, corresponding to the minimal size model.

3.2. Davidson-Cole transfer function

A Davidson-Cole transfer function is defined as,

$$G(s) = \frac{G_i}{(s+\lambda)^\nu}, \quad (7)$$

where $G_i \in \mathbb{R}^{*+}$, $\lambda \in \mathbb{R}^+$ and $\nu \in [0,2[$.

Considering $H(s) = \dfrac{1}{s^\nu}$,

$$G(s) = G_i \cdot H(s+\lambda) \quad (8)$$

With the translation operator,

$$H(s+\lambda) = \mathcal{L}\left[exp(-\lambda \cdot t) \cdot \mathcal{L}^{-1}(H(s)) \right]. \quad (9)$$

So, $G(s)$ can be written as,

$$G(s) = G_i \cdot \lambda^\nu \cdot \mathcal{L}\left[exp(-\lambda \cdot t) \cdot \mathcal{L}^{-1}(H(s)) \right]. \quad (10)$$

Since, for $\mathrm{Re}[\nu] > 0$,

$$\mathcal{L}[H(s)] = \mathcal{L}\left[\frac{1}{s^\nu} \right] = \frac{t^{\nu-1}}{\Gamma(\nu)} \cdot u(t), \quad (11)$$

where $u(t)$ is the Heaviside function.

Thus, the transfer function becomes

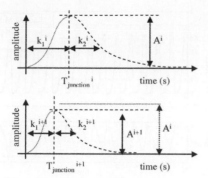

Fig. 1. Time dilatation/contraction.

$$G(s) = G_i \cdot \lambda^\nu \cdot \mathscr{L}\left(exp(-\lambda \cdot t) \cdot \frac{t^{\nu-1}}{\Gamma(\nu)} \cdot u(t) \right), \quad (12)$$

and so, the inverse Laplace transform,

$$s(t) = \frac{G_i \cdot \lambda}{\Gamma(\nu)} (t \cdot \lambda)^{\nu-1} \cdot exp(-\lambda \cdot t) \cdot u(t). \quad (13)$$

For any input $U(t)$, output $Y(t)$ becomes,

$$Y(t) = s(t) \otimes U(t) \quad (14)$$

3.3. Time dilatation/contraction influences

At 10 Hz pulses stimulation, responses under steady conditions are close to those of the transient state. Nevertheless, the difference appears whatever stimulated MU: under steady conditions, amplitude responses, contraction phase and relaxation phase are shorter than in transient state. Also it appears necessary to include parameters variation along experiment duration to improve the muscle model, and to take into account this observed biological phenomenon. The time dilatation/contraction influences not only dynamics of both response phases through k_1 and k_2 parameters, but also A^i, which represents maximum amplitude reached at $T_{junction}$ (figure 1).
$f(t)$ corresponds to a Davidson-Cole model, in time domain

$$f(t) \rightarrow F(s) = \frac{G_i}{(s+\lambda)^\nu}. \quad (15)$$

The k factor for time dilatation/contraction influences its Laplace transform as following,

$$f(k \cdot t) \rightarrow \frac{1}{k} \cdot F\left(\frac{s}{k}\right). \quad (16)$$

Finally, the Laplace transform of $f(k \cdot t)$ is,

$$\frac{1}{k} \cdot F\left(\frac{s}{k}\right) = \frac{1}{k} \frac{G_i}{\left(\frac{s}{k}+\lambda\right)^\nu} = \frac{G_i \cdot k^{\nu-1}}{(s+\lambda \cdot k)^\nu}. \quad (17)$$

Thus pole is then multiplied by the time dilatation factor. Besides, the gain is multiplied by this factor to the power of the order ν.

3.4. Output error model

Generally system identification of fractional model

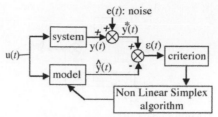

Fig. 2. Output error model.

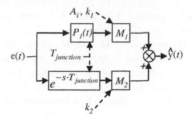

Fig. 3. Multimodels "A".

(linear or non linear) can be carried by minimizing the quadratic output error criterion J,

$$J = \sum_{k=1}^{N} (\varepsilon(kh))^2, \quad (18)$$

where

$$\varepsilon(kh) = y^*(kh) - \hat{y}(kh) \quad (19)$$

is the output error.

A non linear optimization algorithm can then be used for example, Newton, Marquard, Simplex... The nonlinear Simplex (Subrahmanyam, 1989; Woods, 1985) is chosen to be included in the output error model (figure 2).

4. MULTIMODELS

The multimodels (Malti, 1989) necessity is highlighted by asymmetric mechanisms during muscle activation. The first one is an active phenomenon (contraction) and the second one, a passive phenomenon (relaxation). Thus multimodels structures are chosen to process separately contraction and relaxation phases (Sommacal, et al., 2006)

4.1. Multimodels "A"

$$P(t) \begin{cases} 0, \forall t > T_{junction} \\ 1, \forall t \le T_{junction} \end{cases} \quad (20)$$

This multimodel (figure 3) is made up of two branches, each one corresponding to a sub-model. The top-branch is dedicated to contraction model and the bottom-branch is dedicated to the relaxation model. $P(t)$ is a weight-function, which is set to 1 during $T_{junction}$ when a pulse is detected (20). The delay function is added on the bottom-branch to shift the M_2 response, corresponding to the relaxation phase. The weight-function allows using M_1 and M_2 addition, even through both are active separately.

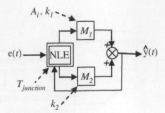

Fig. 4. Multimodels "B".

A_i is an extra gain applied on the response amplitude for each pulse. k_1 and k_2 correspond to dilatations/contraction in the time domain, respectively applied on M_1 and M_2 sub-models. These parameters influence independently the behaviour of each phase for each pulse response. These extra parameters can be fixed to 1 (time invariant) or determined by an evolution function (time varying).

4.2. Multimodels "B"

This multimodel (figure 4) is made up of two branches. The top-branch includes the M_1 sub-model corresponding to the contraction phase. The bottom-branch corresponds to the relaxation phase, through the M_2 sub-model. The Non Linear Element (NLE) is a switch, which orientates M_1 (as a pulse is applied) or M_2 (after $T_{junction}$ delay following the pulse application) output to the multimodels output.
The M_1 sub-model is used for duration of $T_{junction}$ following the pulse detection. After $T_{junction}$, the M_2 sub-model is used. Since a pulse is anew detected, M_1 sub-model is used with an offset corresponding to amplitude that is reached when this new pulse is detected. Unlike for multimodels "A", "B" uses only a part or totality of the relaxation and not inevitably the totality. Thus this multimodels structure is more flexible as the past is less taken into account.
A_i is an extra gain applied on the response to a pulse. k_1 and k_2 correspond to dilatations/contraction in the time domain, respectively applied on M_1 and M_2 sub-models. These parameters influence independently the behaviour (dynamics and amplitude) of each phase for each pulse response. These extra parameters can be fixed to 1 (time invariant) or determined by an evolution function (time varying).

4.3. Linear sub-models

Thus next stage of modelling consists in estimating M1 and M2 parameters. $T_{junction}$ is fixed as the twitch time of the muscle response to the first pulse. The two linear sub-models, M1 and M2, can be Cole-Cole model or Davidson-Cole model. When orders are integers, both models led to the rational transfer function. The previous study (Sommacal, *et al.*, 2006) demonstrates the advantage of using Davidson-Cole sub-models. Indeed, the output error is minimal and the size model is reduced to 6 parameters, corresponding to the minimal size model.
The Davidson-Cole model is defined as

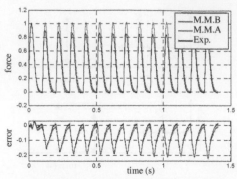

Fig. 5. Comparison between experimental responses for 10 Hz pulses pattern and multimodels "A" and "B" responses, with A_i fixed to 1; error for each multimodels are presented below.

$$F_{Davidson-Cole}(s) = \frac{G_i}{(s+\lambda)^\nu}, \qquad (21)$$

where A,ν,λ are respectively real gain, positive real order and positive real pole to estimate. Identification can be based on models (22) using sum or/and product of (21), where gain, orders and poles are let free.

$$M_{DC}(s) = \sum_{l=1}^{N} \prod_{j=1}^{M} \frac{G_{lj}}{(s+\lambda_{lj})^{\nu_{lj}}}. \qquad (22)$$

By including k factor for time contraction/dilatation, (22) becomes,

$$M_{DC}(s,k) = \sum_{l=1}^{N} \prod_{j=1}^{M} \frac{G_{lj} \cdot k^{\nu_{kj}-1}}{(s+k \cdot \lambda_{lj})^{\nu_{lj}}}. \qquad (23)$$

5. "A" AND "B" MULTIMODELS COMPARISON FOR A 10 HZ PULSES PATTERN AND PARAMETERS EVOLUTION

10 Hz pulses stimulations are applied on each muscle MUs. A particular MU response (representative of IIB fibres) is studied to understand mechanisms to be modelled and to improve the previous multimodels. As seen below, without extra parameters, multimodels response moves apart to muscle response. Extra parameters introduction induces a large modelling improvement.

5.1. Comparison between "A" and "B" multimodels with extra parameters fixed to one.

In the initial stage, the first pulse response is modelled through M_1 and M_2 parameters. Then, the 10 Hz pulses stimulation is applied on this multimodels. Figure 5 shows the multimodels "A" and "B" responses and the error with experimental response.

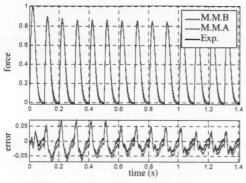

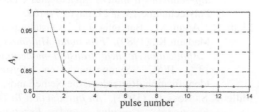

Fig. 6. Comparison between experimental responses at a 10 Hz pulses pattern and multimodels "A" and "B" responses, with A_i variation; errors are presented below

Fig. 7. A_i evolution function minimizing output error, included in "A" and "B" multimodels

Both multimodels responses become different of the experimental one from the second pulse. The error and the experimental response show an exponential shape. An improvement must be provided to report muscle mechanisms.

5.2. Comparison between "A" and "B" multimodels with extra parameters determined by evolution functions

To improve multimodels and reduce the output error, extra parameters are added. Figure 6 shows how the parameter A_i is useful. Another improvement is the insertion of the k_1 and k_2 parameters.

These extra parameters are completed by the possibility for $T_{junction}$ to vary. Extra parameters are applied, through exponential functions, whose coefficients are optimized to minimise output error.

5.2.1 Comparison between "A" and "B" multimodels with A_i determined by evolution function

By taking into account previous conclusion of paragraph 5.1, the A_i extra parameter is added. A_i values varying in time, its evolution is modelled through exponential function, whose coefficients are optimized to improve muscle modelling. Actually, maximum output error is divided by four compared to previous multimodels response.

Table 1. optimized values for extra parameters evolution functions

Extra parameter	Δ	τ
k_1	0.0208	0.0109
k_2	0.0322	0.0578
A_i	0.1250	0.1252
T_j	0.0025	0.009

Table 2. Mean values for sub-models M1 and M2 parameters and for extra parameter functions

	Δ_{IIA}	τ_{IIA} (s)	Δ_{IIB}	τ_{IIB} (s)
k_1	0.2498	0.045515	0.0361	0.046309
k_2	-0.2863	0.039196	-0.0158	0.080485
A_i	0.0110	0.060738	0.1158	0.047843
T_j	0.0350	0.042548	0.1120	0.038764

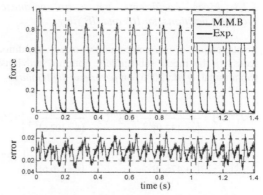

Fig. 8. Comparison between experimental responses for 10 Hz pulses pattern and multimodels "B" responses, with k_1, k_2, A_i, T_j evolution function; error is presented below

Figure 7 present evolution of the extra parameter, A_i, optimized to minimise the output error. The evolution function is reduced to

$$A_i = A_i o - \Delta A_i \cdot \left(1 - e^{-\frac{t}{\tau}} \right), \qquad (24)$$

where $A_i o$ is the amplitude response to the first pulse, ΔA_i is the difference between initial response amplitude and response in the transient state. τ is the time constant. Optimization leads to $\Delta A_i = 0.19$ and $\tau = 0.0715\,s$.

Due to a better modelling with the "B" structure, the following part deals with this multimodels. "A" structure allows another multimodels approach, whose disadvantage is to propagate the totality of relaxation phase, thus it may propagate modelling error. "B" multimodels provides a greater flexibility and better results at this stage of the muscle modelling.

5.2.2 Comparison between "B" multimodels with all extra parameters determined by evolution function

The final optimization stage consists to optimize every extra-parameter. Every extra parameter (V) is evaluated through exponential functions (25).

$$V = V_o - \Delta V \cdot \left(1 - e^{\frac{-t}{\tau}} \right), \qquad (25)$$

Values minimizing output error are given in the table (1). Figure 8 presents multimodels response for the 10 Hz stimulation. Compared to the previous improvement (A_i introduction), the output error is reduced by two. Every extra parameter introduction allow improving multimodels, that leads to minimizing output error, but overall, introduce possibility to sub-models to move around initial state toward state available under steady conditions.

5.2.3 Mean coefficients for extra parameters evolution functions, for IIA and IIB fibres

Identification of responses under steady conditions leads to the mean sub-models obtained previously (Sommacal, *et al.*, 2006) on *peroneus digiti quarti*:

$$\left\{ M_1^{IIA}(s) = \frac{A_3}{(s+432.9)^{3.5}} ; M_2^{IIA}(s) = \frac{A_4}{(s+107.6)^{2.4}} \right\} \quad (26)$$

$$\left\{ M_1^{IIB}(s) = \frac{A_1}{(s+476.9)^{3.5}} ; M_2^{IIB}(s) = \frac{A_2}{(s+176.6)^{3.1}} \right\} \quad (27)$$

Sub-models defined previously are still available for *peroneus brevis* muscle, as responses are close to those used for identification. Extra parameters functions are optimized for every MU stimulation (10 Hz pulses pattern). Optimum coefficients for each fibre type lead to mean values, which allows taking into account the transient state-steady condition transition (table 2).

6. CONCLUSION

This paper completes the previous study results, multimodels structure and Davidson-Cole sub-models, by taking into account the observed transient-state of muscle responses. Two multimodels structures are compared in this paper: the first one, used until this paper, takes into account the whole of every relaxation phase; the second one introduces a non linear element allowing switching between contraction and relaxation sub-models. Each sub-model, in both multimodels structures, depends on 6 parameters and fractional orders. Amplitudes and dynamic behaviors variations, that appear when 10 Hz pulse stimulation is applied, can be dealt by introducing extra parameters. Exponential functions describe parameters variations along time. Thus mean functions coefficients are proposed to solve transient state variations for IIA and IIB fibre types.

The next stage of this modelling consists to test multimodels structure validity with increasing frequencies solicitations as well as for random frequencies. Another improvement consists to take into account muscle length.

REFERENCES

Cross S. S., (1997), "*Fractals in pathology*", Journal of Pathology, John Wiley & sons, Inc., New York, Vol. 182, 1-8.

Grünwald A. K., (1867), "*Ueber begrenzte Derivationen und deren Anwendung*", Z Angew. Math. Phys.,12, pages 441-480.

Liouville.J., (1832), "*Mémoire sur le calcul des différentielles à indices quelconques*", Ecole Polytechnique,13, n°21, pages 71-162.

Malti R., Aoun M., Battaglia J.-L., Oustaloup A., Madami K., (1989), "*Fractional Multimodels - Application to heat transfert modelling*", 13th IFAC Symposium on System Identification, Rotterdam, the Netherlands.

Miller K.S., Ross, B., (1993), "*An Introduction To The Fractional Calculus and Fractional Differential Equation*", John Wiley & Sons, Inc., New York.

Petit J., Filippi G.M., Gioux M., Hunt C.C., and Laporte Y. (1990) "*effects of tetanic contractions of the motor units of similar type on the initial stiffness to ramp stretch of the cat peroneus longus muscle*", J Neurophysiol 64:1724-1732.

Ravier P., Buttelli O., Couratier P., (2005), "*An EMG fractal indicator having different sensitivities to changes in force and muscle fatigue during voluntary static muscle contractions*", Electromyogr Kinesiol, 15(2): 210-221.

Samko, A. G., Kilbas, A. A., Marichev, O. I., (1987), "*Fractional Integrals and Derivatives*", Gordon and Breach Science, Minsk.

Shepherd, G. M.., (1994), "*Neurobiology*", Oxford, New york.

Sommacal L., Melchior P., Mohamed Aoun, Cabelguen J.-M., Oustaloup A. et Ijspeert A., (2006a) "Modeling of a rat muscle using fractional multimodels", second International Symposium on Communications, Control and Signal Processing, Marrakech, Morocco, March 13-15, 2006

Subrahmanyam M. B., (1989), "*An Extension of the Simplex Method to Constrained Nonlinear Optimization*", Int. Journal of Optimization Theory and Applications, Vol. 62, no. 2, pages 311-319.

Woods D. J.,May (1985), "*An interactive Approach for solving Multi-Objective Optimization Problems*", Technical Report 85-5, Rice University, Houston.

CHARACTERISTIC PHASE PLANE PATTERN OF HUMAN POSTURAL SWAY

S. Gurses*, B.E. Platin**, S.T. Tumer**, N. Akkas*

**Engineering Sciences Department, **Mechanical Engineering Department,
Middle East Technical University, Ankara/Turkey*

Abstract: Reasons for the everlasting complex oscillatory behavior of human postural sway have been explored by constructing the phase-plane representation of the Center of Pressure data recorded experimentally. For this purpose, 275-seconds time records are received from a healthy subject while standing still in an upright posture. A Sensorial threshold has been proposed as being one of the nonlinear sources governing postural dynamics. Ethyl alcohol has also been introduced to the subject for provocation of the nonlinear behavior associated with the sensorial dynamics. *Copyright © 2006 IFAC*

Keywords: Postural Sway, Nonlinear Dynamics, Sensorial Threshold, Phase Plane, Motor Control, Chaotic Behavior

1. INTRODUCTION

The human upright posture exhibits an everlasting oscillatory behavior of complex nature, called as the postural sway. Maintaining balance during quiet stance is a complex task accomplished by various mechanisms depending on different senses relying on the passive properties of the musculo-skeletal machinery controlled by applying different strategies. Mechanisms responsible for these oscillations are recruited by the information coming from a variety of sensory events, which include proprioceptive, vestibular, visual, and cutaneous receptors. These sensory modalities were experimentally shown to have different frequency bands (Ishida, *et al.*, 1997; Mergner, 2002). The characteristic frequencies of the human postural sway have recently been reported (Gurses, *et al.*, 2001).

Attempts to reveal the dynamics behind the complex nature of the oscillatory behavior of human postural sway are numerous. Johansson, *et al.* (1988) made use of the parametric identification of a transfer function representing a PID-stabilized inverted pendulum model through a set of experimental results. The application of various stochastic models (Collins and De Luca, 1994; Chow and Collins, 1995; Newell, *et al.*, 1997; Chiari, *et al.*, 2000) either to show the existence of long-range correlations causing fractal properties of the natural human standing (Duarte and Zatsiorsky, 2000) or to diagnose the chaotic attractor of the human postural sway during a quiet bipedal stance by calculating the largest Lyapunov exponent of the system (Yamada Norimasa, 1995) is available in the literature.

It has always been a difficult task to describe the posture and to differentiate it from the movement, per se (Massion, 1998). An ecological approach treats the postural adjustments stabilizing every kind of motor behavior acting as an interface between the organism and its environment. The approach presents an analytical perspective whose functional topological characteristics are the dynamics of the system (Riccio, 1993; Slobounov, 1997; Yamada, 1995).

The present research aims to explore the reasons behind everlasting oscillations of human upright posture. A non-linear mathematical model is developed and tuned, in the frequency domain, using the experimental data collected. The existence and the physical characteristics of chaotic attractors related to the postural oscillations are investigated. The diagnostic tools, used to reveal the non-linear properties of the postural dynamics, are based upon the calculation of the largest Lyapunov exponent at the Poincaré sections of the phase-plane diagrams constructed from the time series recorded experimentally. Here we report some preliminary results indicating the existence of a characteristic pattern observed on the phase-plane constructed from the experimentally recorded signals of human postural oscillations.

2. METHODS

2.1 Subjects, Apparatus, and Procedures

During a biped stance, the feet of a subject apply distributed forces on the ground in three directions. The ground reaction equilibrating this distributed force system can be measured by means of a force platform while the subject is standing on it. The ground reaction actually consists of three force components and three moment components but we will limit our study to the motion in the sagittal plane. The vertical axis passes through the *Center of Pressure* (CoP). In this study, three components of the ground reaction force (F_x, F_y, F_z) and the moment causing rotation in the sagittal plane (M_y) are measured with a Bertec® force plate in the Biomechanics Laboratory of the Department of Mechanical Engineering at the Middle East Technical University (METU). Force plate signals are first pre-amplified internally and then sent to an external amplifier in which a filter with a pre-set cut-off frequency of 500 Hz is employed. Filtered analog signals are fed to the computer after being digitized by an A/D converter (DAS 1202 Keithley MetraByte®). Force-Plus ALPHA Version 1.00 software (Bertec Corp.) is used to manipulate the signals to obtain the ground reaction forces and the moment at a sampling frequency of 50 Hz.

The analysis is confined to the sagittal plane. Accordingly, variations in the magnitude of the horizontal frictional force (F_x) and in the position of the center-of-pressure (CoP_x) are used to identify the postural sway. It should be noted that the problem considered is planar in xz-plane with the two force components F_x and F_z, and the moment M_y. CoP_x is obtained from F_z and M_y as $CoP_x = - M_y / F_z$.

Table1. Data Acquisition Protocol

Time (Minutes)	Record (i^{th})
Just before alcohol intake	1st
0th	85 gr. alcohol intake
10th	2nd
25th	3rd
40th	4th
70th	5th
100th	6th
160th	7th

Seven sets of 275-second time records of CoP_x are collected from a healthy adult due to a protocol presented below while the subject is instructed to stand still in upright posture. Sensorial non-linearities associated with the upright posture are provoked by the introduction of alcohol intake to the subject. 85 grams of 60% diluted ethyl alcohol are consumed by the subjects at the 0th minute of recording where as, the 1st time-record is received just before alcohol intake (see Table 1).

2.2 Analyses

Phase-plane representation; In order to construct the phase plane representation of the CoP_x signal, the velocities corresponding to the related CoP_x positions are also needed. As the only measured variable related to the center-of-pressure is the time variation of the position of the center-of-pressure, the unknown corresponding velocities are obtained by numerical differentiation. Forward finite difference formula is used for the numerical differentiation from the time series of the CoP_x signal; i.e.,

$$\frac{d}{dt}CoP_x(t_n) = \frac{CoP_x(t_{n+1}) - CoP_x(t_n)}{t_{n+1} - t_n} \qquad (1)$$

where, $CoP_x(t_n)$ is the nth data recorded at the time series of the signal CoP_x and the time interval between two successive data points was 20 milliseconds.

Mathematical modeling; The whole body posture is modeled as an inverted pendulum (Peterka, 2001; Mergner and Becker, 2003). The system presented in Fig. 1 is a damped, driven, inverted pendulum which can be assumed to behave in a linear fashion for small angular displacements by assuming $\sin\theta \approx \theta$. Nevertheless, the same inverted pendulum can present a complex dynamical behavior in a nonlinear case. The nonlinear behavior of the system for small amplitude perturbations is created by using receptor thresholds (Mergner *et al.*, 2003). In order to represent these receptor thresholds, dead-zone type static nonlinearities are employed for both position and velocity sensors.

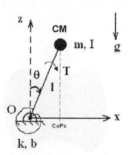

Fig. 1. The human posture modeled as an inverted pendulum.

The equation of motion of the inverted pendulum presented in Fig. 1 is given as:

$$I\ddot{\theta} + f(\theta,\dot{\theta}) - mgL\sin(\theta) = T \qquad (2)$$

where; m and I are the body mass and the moment of inertia of the body with respect to the ankle joint (O), respectively. L is the distance from the ankle joint, O to the center of mass (CM) of the pendulum. g is the gravitational constant. T is the input torque and defined as:

$$T = A\sin(\omega t) \qquad (3)$$

where; A is the peak perturbation amplitude and ω is the driving frequency. t is the independent variable, time. CoPx is the projection of CM on the x-axis and is defined as:

$$CoPx = l\sin(\theta) \qquad (4)$$

The position and velocity sensor thresholds ($\theta_{th}, \dot{\theta}_{th}$; respectively) are introduced to the system as the sources of nonlinear behavior. Under this condition, the nonlinear function $f(\theta,\dot{\theta})$ in the equation (2) is defined as:

$$f(\theta,\dot{\theta}) = \begin{cases} 0 \dots\dots\dots\dots\dots\dots\dots\dots\dots\dots\dots\dots\dots |\theta| \le \theta_{th} \, and \, |\dot{\theta}| \le \dot{\theta}_{th} \\ k(\theta - \text{sgn}(\theta)\cdot\theta_{th})\dots\dots\dots\dots\dots |\theta| > \theta_{th} \, and \, |\dot{\theta}| \le \dot{\theta}_{th} \\ b(\dot{\theta} - \text{sgn}(\dot{\theta})\cdot\dot{\theta}_{th})\dots\dots\dots\dots\dots |\theta| \le \theta_{th} \, and \, |\dot{\theta}| > \dot{\theta}_{th} \\ k(\theta - \text{sgn}(\theta)\cdot\theta_{th}) + b(\dot{\theta} - \text{sgn}(\dot{\theta})\cdot\dot{\theta}_{th})\dots |\theta| > \theta_{th} \, and \, |\dot{\theta}| > \dot{\theta}_{th} \end{cases} \dots\dots(5)$$

where; total stiffness and damping about the ankle joint (O) are modeled as k and b, respectively.

The linear dynamical behavior of the system is expected to reach a steady-state after the initial transients die out. However, the transients may continue forever for a nonlinear case and the system behavior could never reach a steady-state. The reason of this bounded but aperiodic dynamical behavior is *chaos* which can be revealed by computing the largest Lyapunov exponent (LLE) of the system (Nayfeh and Balachandran, 1995; Robinson, 1999). LLE of a dynamical system is an estimate about the fate of a perturbation given to the system trajectories. LLE of the system with a positive sign points to a divergence of the perturbed phase point from the neighboring system trajectories while a negative sign implies a converging behavior of the same phase point (Baker and Gollub, 1990).

3. RESULTS

3.1 Experimental data

Figure 2 presents two samples of CoP$_x$ time signals at the 0th and 10th minutes of data acquisition (see data acquisition protocol). The fast Fouriér transforms (FFT) of the seven sets of 275-second time series are presented in Figure 3. The phase-plane representation of the 0th and 10th minute 275-second time-records are presented in Figure 4.

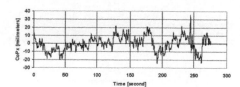

Fig. 2a. Time record taken at the 0th minute

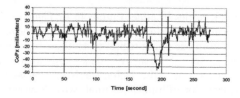

Fig. 2b. Time record taken at the 10th minute

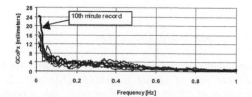

Fig. 3. FFT of the seven sets of 275-second time records of CoP$_x$ signal

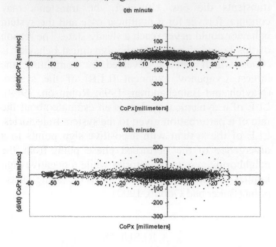

Fig. 4a and b. Phase-plane representation of the CoP$_x$ time series for 0th and 10th minutes respectively

If the trajectories in the vicinity of the gravity vertical at the phase-plane constructed from the CoP$_x$ time signal recorded at the 0th minute is zoomed (Figure 5), a similar topological representation is observed like the one presented in Figure 4b.

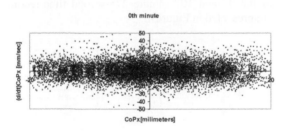

Fig. 5. Trajectories zoomed in the vicinity of the gravity vertical for 0th minute

The trajectories in either Figure 4b or Figure 5 show a typical rim shaped structure at the edges formed by jumps from one phase region to another. These jumps form a set of recursive dark and light bands introduced as the characteristic phase-plane representation of human postural sway. Nevertheless, the system trajectories do not visit the space at equal frequencies with respect to the gravity vertical; presenting an anti-symmetric distribution about the origin in the antero-posterior direction.

3.2 Exemplar model simulations

The system described in Fig. 1 is simulated for two different sets of sensor thresholds (Mergner, 2002; Gurses et al., 2005). In the first case, only a position sensor threshold (θ_{th}=0.46°) is used; whereas, in the second case, a larger value for the position sensor threshold (θ_{th}=0.69°) and also a velocity sensor threshold ($\dot{\theta}_{th}$=0.57°/s) are introduced to the system. This is believed to simulate the alcohol intake case. Model parameters are set to match reported values in the physiological range of mass and total stiffness of the whole body posture and the resonance frequency is set near 1 Hz (Gurses, et al. 2001; Gurses, 2002; Creath, et al., 2005).

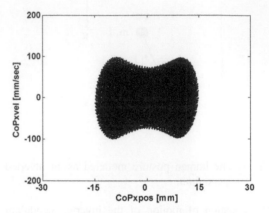

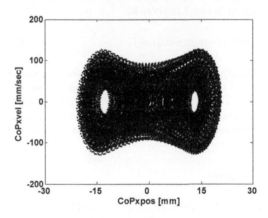

Fig. 6a and b. Model simulation outputs for case 1 (up) and case 2 (down) by using physiological system parameters published (Gurses, 2002; Creath, et al., 2005).

Fig. 6 presents the simulated outputs for the two cases. Input and system parameters for the two cases are: T = 5 N.m, ω = 0.5 Hz, m = 75 kg, k = 8768 N.m/rad, b = 3 N.m.s/rad. The mass moment of inertia (I) with respect to the center of mass and the length (L) are 25 kg.m^2 and 1 m, respectively. The time step used in numerical integration is 0.01 s for all simulations and simulations last for 275 s. The top plot (6a) represents the case 1 where θ_{th} = 0.008 rad. The bottom plot (6b) represents the simulation output for the case 2 where θ_{th} = 0.012 rad and $\dot{\theta}_{th}$ = 0.01 rad/s.

Characteristic phase-plane pattern observed in each simulation outputs is due to the jumps between the equilibrium points of the system. The stability of the equilibrium points changes sign when the pendulum approaches to the equilibrium, due to the threshold assigned to the sensors through which control torques of the system are generated. The absence of the control torque near the vicinity of the equilibrium point induces a jump towards to the other equilibrium when the system is perturbed. This nonlinear mechanism is believed to cause the characteristic sway pattern of the human posture.

The LLE of the system is computed in for each case (Wolf *et al.*, 1985; Gurses, 2002) and found to be 1.2 [1/s] for both. This shows that the system behaves in a chaotic manner in both of the simulated cases. Increasing the threshold value of the position sensor causes the system to behave in a similar manner at a larger scale. It is worth to note that a velocity sensor threshold is also added to the system in the second case.

4. DISCUSSION

Human upright posture is inherently unstable and utilizes different senses in order to get stabilized by means of a central controller. Sensory and motor processes are nonlinear in nature (Goldberg, 1992; Mergner, 2002). In this study, it is attempted to reveal the nonlinear characteristics of the human postural sway through its characteristic phase plane pattern. Chaotic character of sway has been diagnosed by computing the LLE of the postural control system through the recorded experimental data (Yamada, 1995; Gurses, 2002). One well-known mechanism in the route to chaos is period-doubling cascades (Moon, 1987; Baker and Gollub, 1990). This mechanism causing side banded-behavior on the way to chaos eventually ends up with a frequency spectrum which is continuous and broadband inducing nonstationary characteristics to the signal (Nayfeh and Balachandran, 1995). Non-stationary properties and time-varying spectral characteristics of human postural sway during quiet stance have already been reported (Carroll and Freedman, 1993; Schumann, *et al.*, 1995; Loughlin, *et al.*, 1996 and 2001). Furthermore, sensory thresholds inducing low frequency trends in the head-neck stabilization causing chaotic head oscillations at low frequency and small amplitude perturbations have recently been reported (Gurses, *et al.*, 2005). The non-linearity causing the chaotic behavior of the postural oscillations is apparently provoked by the alcohol intake of the subject making the system sluggish; triggering slow harmonics (see Fig. 3). It is a quite well known fact that the sensorial thresholds are easily affected by alcohol intake; pointing out one of the probable sources of non-linearity in the dynamics of the postural control system. These findings led an inverted pendulum with positional and velocity thresholds to be used to simulate the characteristic phase plane pattern of the human postural sway.

Topological similarity between the trajectories of Figure 4b and 5 may be due to the same fractal structure of the human postural sway. The existence of long range correlations in the human postural oscillations has been shown to cause a fractal structure (Duarte and Zatsiorsky, 2001). It is attempted to simulate the self-similar structure in the dynamics of a nonlinear inverted pendulum by increasing the threshold of its position and velocity sensors. The self-similarity for the characteristic phase plane pattern of the two different cases of the nonlinear inverted pendulum is demonstrated by computing the LLE of each case.

5. CONCLUSION

One of the reasons for the everlasting complex oscillatory behavior of the human upright posture is proposed as the sensorial thresholds which cause the characteristic phase-plane pattern of the system trajectories. This fact is provoked experimentally by recording from alcohol intake subjects.

Simulation results by using a nonlinear inverted pendulum with both position and velocity sensor thresholds resemble the charactcristic phase plane pattern of human postural sway. Furthermore, the self-similarity of the two phase plane patterns generated by increasing thresholds of the inverted pendulum sensors is shown through computing the LLE of the dynamical system for each of the two cases.

REFERENCES

Baker G.L. and J.P. Gollub (1990). *Chaotic Dynamics*, Cambridge University Press, New York.

Carroll J.P. and W. Freedman (1993). Nonstationary properties of postural sway. *J. Biomechanics*, **26**, 409-416.

Chiari L., A. Cappello, D. Lenzi and U.D. Croce (2000). An improved technique for the extraction of stochastic parameters from stabilograms. *Gait and Posture*, **12**, 225-234.

Collins J.J. and C.J. De Luca (1994). Random Walking during Quiet Standing. *Physical Review Letters*, **73**, Number 5, 764-767.

Creath R., T. Kiemel, F. Horak, R. Peterka and J. Jeka (2005). A unified view of quiet and perturbed stance: simultaneous co-existing excitable modes. *Neuroscience Letters*, **377**, 75-80.

Duarte M. and V.M. Zatsiorsky (2001). Long-range correlations in human standing. *Physics Letters A*, **283**, 124-128.

Duarte M. and V.M. Zatsiorsky (2000). On the fractal properties of natural human standing. *Neuroscience Letters*, **283**, 173-176.

Goldberg, J. (1992). Nonlinear Dynamics of Involuntary Head Movements. In: *The Head-Neck Sensory Motor System* (A. Berthoz, P.P. Vidal, W. Graf (Eds)), Chapter 61, 400-403, Oxford University Press, New York

Gurses S., Y. Dhaher, T.C. Hain and E.A. Keshner (2005). Perturbation parameters associated with nonlinear responses of the head at small amplitudes. *Chaos*, **15**, 023905-1 – 023905-10.

Gurses S. (2002). *Postural Dynamics and Stability*, Ph.D. dissertation, Department of Engineering Sciences, Middle East Technical University, Ankara, Turkey.

Gurses S., S.T. Tumer, B.E. Platin and N. Akkas (2001). Characteristic frequencies of human postural sway. *XVIIIth Congress of the International Society of Biomechanics*, ETH-Zurich.

Ishida A., S. Imai and Y. Fukuoka (1997). Analysis of the Posture Control System under Fixed and Sway-Referenced Support Conditions. *IEEE Transactions on Biomedical Engineering*, **44**, No., 5, 331-336.

Johansson R., M. Magnusson and M. Akesson (1988). Identification of Human Postural Dynamics. *IEEE Trans. Biomed. Eng.*, **35**, No., 10, 858-869.

Loughlin P.J. and M.S. Redfern (2001). Spectral characteristics of visually induced postural sway in healthy elderly and healthy young subjects. *IEEE Trans. Neural Syst. Rehabil. Eng.*, **9**, 24-30.

Loughlin P.J., M.S. Redfern and J.M. Furman (1996). Time-varying characteristics of visually induced postural sway. *IEEE Trans. Rehabil. Eng.*, **4**, 416-424.

Massion J. (1998). Postural Control Systems in Developmental Perspective. *Neuroscience and Biobehavioral Reviews*, **22**, No. 4, 465-472.

Mergner T. and W. Becker (2003). A Modeling Approach to the Human Spatial Orientation System. *Ann. N. Y. Acad. Sci.*, **1004**, 303-315.

Mergner T., C. Maurer and R.J. Peterka (2003). A multisensory posture control model of human upright stance. In: *Progress in Brain Research* (Prablanc C., D. Pelisson and Y. Rosetti (Eds.)), **142**, Chapter 12, 189-201.

Mergner T. (2002). The Matryoshka Dolls principle in human dynamic behavior in space: A theory of linked references for multisensory perception and control of action. *Current Psychology of Cognition*, **21 (2-3)**, 129-212.

Moon C.F. (1987). *Chaotic Vibrations*, John Wiley & Sons, Inc., New York.

Nayfeh A.H. and B. Balachandran (1995). *Applied Nonlinear Dynamics: Analytical, Computational, and Experimental Methods*, John Wiley & Sons, Inc., New York.

Newell K.M., S.M. Slobounov, E.S. Slobounova and P.C.M. Molenaar (1997). Stochastic processes in postural center-of-pressure profiles. *Exp. Brain Res*, **113**, 158-164.

Peterka R.J. (2002). Sensorimotor Integration in Human Postural Control, *J. Neurophysiol.*, **88**, 1097-1118.

Robinson C. (1999). *Dynamical Systems: Stability, Symbolic Dynamics, and Chaos* (2nd Edition), Chapters 8 and 9. CRC, Boca Raton, Florida.

Schumann T., M.S. Redfern, J.M. Furman, A. El-Jaroudi and L.F. Chaparro (1995). Time-frequency analysis of postural sway. *J. Biomechanics*, **28**, 603-607.

Slobounov S.M., E.S. Slobounova and K.M. Newell (1997). Virtual Time-to-Collision and Human Postural Control. *Journal of Motor Behavior*, **29**, No. 3, 263-281.

Wolf A., J.B. Swift, H.L. Swinney and J.A. Vastano (1985). Determining Lyapunov Exponents From A Time Series. *Physica D*, **16**, 285-317.

Yamada N. (1995). Chaotic swaying of the upright posture. *Human Movement Science*, **14**, 711-726.

THE GLUCOSE MINIMAL MODEL: POPULATION VS INDIVIDUAL PARAMETER ESTIMATION

Alessandra Bertoldo, Paolo Vicini, Claudio Cobelli

Department of Information Engineering, University of Padova, Italy
Department of Bioengineering, University of Washington, Seattle, WA, USA

Abstract: Glucose minimal model parameters are commonly estimated by applying weighted nonlinear least squares separately to each subject's data. Because of the model's nonlinearity. the parameter precision of the single-compartment minimal model is not always satisfactory, especially in presence of a reduced sampling schedule. In the current work, the use of population analysis through nonlinear mixed effects models is evaluated and its performance tested against the parameter estimates obtained by the standard individual approach through weighted nonlinear least squares. *Copyright © 2006 IFAC*

Keywords: Modeling, Parameter estimation, Nonlinear models, Physiological models, Sampling frequency.

1. INTRODUCTION

The single-compartment minimal model method (Bergman, *et al.*, 1979) is widely used in clinical and epidemiological studies to estimate metabolic indexes of glucose effectiveness (S_G) and insulin sensitivity (S_I) from an intravenous glucose tolerance test (IVGTT). Use of the minimal model for S_G and S_I determination requires the injection of a glucose bolus at time 0, and subsequently sampling for 3 or 4 hr. As typical in physiological and metabolic modeling, minimal model parameters are commonly estimated by applying weighted nonlinear least squares separately in each subject. After having obtained individual estimates for each subject, the sample mean and the variance of all the model parameter estimates are calculated and assumed to approximate the first- and the second-order moment (expected value and variance) of the subject population distribution. However, due to its complexity, the parameter precision of the single-compartment minimal model is not always satisfactory, especially in presence of a reduced sampling schedule ("data poor" situation). Of note is that a reduced sampling scheme is highly desirable, both for ethical and practical reasons, above all when clinical trials are performed in a large number of subjects: a reduced sampling scheme allows to minimize experimental invasiveness.

To derive accurate and precise individual estimates and, consequently, description of the subject population also in presence of a data poor situation, maximum a posteriori Bayesian estimation has been evaluated (Sparacino, *et al.*, 2000). The drawback of this estimation method is that it requires some independent a priori statistical (i.e., mean, variance, covariance) knowledge on the model parameters. This drawback can potentially heavily compromise the parameter estimation process, when a priori information is unavailable or poor quality. However, other estimation approaches focused on ensembles of individuals, like population kinetic analysis through mixed effects models (Beal and Sheiner, 1982), have only recently been applied in this context (De Gaetano, *et al.*, 1996) and have still to be thoroughly evaluated.

Population analysis aims at quantitative assessment of model parameters, taking advantage of the entire collection of measures obtained from a population of individuals. Population analysis directly estimates statistical features of the data set, and finds its natural application in quantification of data poor studies, e.g. when the number of samples available for each individual subject is rather small in comparison with model complexity. It is widely used in the analysis of pharmacokinetic studies. Among all available kinetic data analysis methods, population approaches using nonlinear mixed effects models have become an increasingly important tool, since they not only allow one to quantify both population and individual parameters, but also to identify the biological sources of between- and within-subject variability.

In this work, we will describe the use of population analysis through nonlinear mixed effects model to identify single-compartment minimal model parameters in a population of subjects composed of healthy and young adults. The performance of the population approach will be tested against the parameter estimates obtained by the standard individual approach, where each subject is analyzed individually by weighted nonlinear least squares. While others have looked at applications of nonlinear mixed effects to minimal modeling in a simulation context (Erichsen, et al., 2004), we have chosen a "data rich" situation for this evaluation. By comparison with the standard estimates, we will evaluate the most common parametric nonlinear mixed effects modeling approaches. By selecting the one performing best, we will have developed an important estimation tool for handling of sparse sampling protocols used in physiological and metabolic modeling.

2. MATERIALS AND METHODS

2.1 Subjects

Standard IVGTT [dose 330 mg/kg] studies were performed on 58 nondiabetic young subjects (mean age 23±3 and mean BMI 24.5±2.9 kg/m^2) in the Clinical Research Center at the Mayo Clinic, Rochester, MN, USA. Subjects received the glucose bolus at time 0,. Blood samples were collected at -120, -30, -20, -10, 0, 2, 4, 6, 8, 10, 15, 20, 22, 25, 26, 28, 31, 35, 45, 60, 75, 90, 120, 180, and 240 min for measurement of glucose and insulin concentrations.

2.2 The Minimal Model

The classic one-compartment minimal model (Bergman, et al., 1979) can be described by:

$$\dot{Q}(t) = -[S_G + X(t)]Q(t) + S_G Q_b \quad Q(0) = D/V + G_b \quad (1)$$
$$\dot{X}(t) = -p_2 X(t) + p_2 S_I [I(t) - I_b] \quad X(0) = 0$$
$$G(t) = Q(t)/V$$

where D is the glucose dose, Q(t) (mg/kg) is glucose mass in plasma with Q_b denoting its basal value, G(t) (mg/dl) is plasma glucose concentration, I(t) (μU/ml) is insulin concentration, G_b and I_b are their basal values, and X(t) is insulin action (min^{-1}). The model has four uniquely identifiable parameters: S_G (min^{-1}), glucose effectiveness, S_I (min^{-1} μU^{-1} ml), insulin sensitivity, p_2 (min^{-1}), the insulin action parameter, and V (dl/kg), the glucose distribution volume per unit of body mass. The model parameters are estimated by assuming I(t) as a known input (forcing) function.

2.3 The Individual Standard Estimation Approach

We used weighted nonlinear least squares as implemented in SAAM II (Barrett, et al., 1998). Assuming that the observed data are statistically related to the individual true parameters p_j through the measurement equation: $G_j(t_i) = G(p_j, t_i) + \varepsilon_j(t_i)$; the cost function to be minimized is:

$$WRSS(p_j) = \sum_{i=1}^{N} \frac{[G_j(t_i) - G(p_j, t_i)]^2}{\sigma_{i,j}^2} \quad (2)$$

where N is the number of glucose samples, $G_j(t_i)$ is the ith time point for the jth of M subjects, $\sigma_{i,j}^2$ is the variance of the measurement error of the ith data point, and $G(p_j, t_i)$ is the minimal model prediction of glucose concentration. Measurement error was assumed to be additive, uncorrelated, Gaussian, zero mean, and with a standard deviation given by:

$$\sigma_{i,j} = 0.02 \cdot G_j(t_i) \quad (3)$$

After obtaining all the individual estimates, we calculated for each parameter, the sample mean of all the individual parameter estimates and the corresponding sample covariance.

2.4 Population Analysis: the Nonlinear Mixed-Effects Model Approach

Unlike the estimation approach discussed above, a more elaborate statistical model is required by the nonlinear mixed-effects model approach. In particular, the observed data are again supposed to be related to the individual true parameters p_j thought Eq. 3, but, in addition, it is assumed that the individual parameters p_j are characterized by some attributes that do not change across the population of M subjects (fixed effects, i.e. values that are common to all subjects) and some others that do (random effects, i.e. values typical of a specific subject). Mathematically, this can be written as:

$$p_j = d(\theta, \eta_j) \quad (4)$$

where d is a known function that describes the expected value of p_j as a function of the fixed effects, θ, and the random effects, η_i. More specifically, the individual parameter can be written as:

$$p_j = d(\theta, a_j, \eta_j) \quad (5)$$

with a_j being known individual specific covariates such as weight, age, body mass index, etc.

Parametric mixed-effects modeling requires to postulate at least some characteristics of the population probability distribution for the random effects (e.g. whether it is Gaussian or lognormal). We assume the random effects to be independent, with:

$$\eta_j \in N(0, \Omega) \qquad (6)$$

with Ω being a diagonal positive definite matrix, and:

$$p_j = \theta e^{\eta_j} \qquad (7)$$

Note that, under the assumption of normality of the random effects, the vector of minimal model parameters p_j defined as in Eq. 7 belong to a lognormal distribution.

The last step required to perform nonlinear mixed-effects modeling is to choose an appropriate method to obtain estimates of both fixed and random effects. Most of the nonlinear mixed-effects model methods estimate the parameters by the maximum likelihood approach. Due to the nonlinear dependencies, it is computationally taxing or impossible to calculate the appropriate likelihood function, and thus several approximate methods have been proposed in the pioneering work of Sheiner and Beal.

The most frequently used are the First-Order (FO) and the First-Order Conditional Estimation (FOCE) methods (Beal and Sheiner, 1992). FO approximates the model function for subject j around zero random effects by using a first-order Taylor series expansion of the model function (Beal and Sheiner, 1992). FOCE is a more sophisticated method where the Taylor expansion is carried out around a conditional estimate of the individual random effects, instead of zero.

We used both first order and first order conditional approaches, assuming the measurement error to be additive, uncorrelated, Gaussian, zero mean, and with a standard deviation:

$$\sigma_{i,j} = \xi \cdot G_j(t_i) \qquad (8)$$

with ξ being an additional parameter to estimate. We also evaluated the methods' performance assuming a fixed ξ value equal to 0.02 (as in Eq.3). Note that, since all the expected values and variances in the model are estimated simultaneously, the choice of whether to have proportional error be an additional parameter (like in Eq. 8) may have an impact on the estimated distributions: this is different from individual weighted least squares, where measurement error variance is calculated a posteriori, and is thus uncorrelated from the other model parameters.

The implementation of first order and first order conditional likelihood approximations we used (Bell, 2001) is the one available in SPK, the System for Population Kinetics, which is being developed by the Resource for Population Kinetics (RFPK, http://www.rfpk.washington.edu), a NIH / NIBIB research resource in the Department of Bioengineering at the University of Washington.

2.4 Comparison

To quantify in each subject the agreement between the results obtained with population and individual standard estimation methods, we calculated the mean absolute percentage deviation between the estimates as:

$$|\Delta p| = \frac{1}{M} \sum_{j=1}^{M} \frac{\left| p_j^{\text{Individual}} - p_j^{\text{Population}} \right|}{p_j^{\text{Individual}}} \times 100 \qquad (9)$$

where j is the jth subject and M the total number of subjects. In addition, to quantify the goodness of model fit, we also calculated for each subject and each estimation method the sum of the squared residual:

$$\text{SRES}_j = \sum_{i=1}^{N} \left[G_j(t_i) - G(p_j, t_i) \right]^2 \qquad (10)$$

where N is the number of glucose samples.

The parameter estimates obtained in each subject are also shown by using boxplots, where the horizontal line across each box is the median value for the parameter, while the whiskers represent the spread between the highest and lowest values, excluding outliers (represented in the plots by the symbol "+").

3. RESULTS

Table 1 shows the individual standard estimation approach (IND) and population results.

Table 1. Population description provided by IND, FO-fixed, FO-free, FOCE-fixed, and FOCE-free

	IND	FO fixed	FO free	FOCE fixed	FOCE free
S_G					
(min^{-1})	0.0197	0.0235	0.0273	0.0210	0.0195
%SD	24%	1%	40%	13%	15%
S_I					
(min^{-1} mU^{-1} ml)	9.98E-05	8.01E-05	2.29E-05	8.41E-05	8.72E-05
%SD	48%	65%	349%	58%	55%
p_2					
(min^{-1})	0.0455	0.0457	0.1030	0.0466	0.0444
%SD	40%	32%	316%	14%	33%
Vol					
(dl/Kg)	1.65	1.60	1.66	1.62	1.64
%SD	13%	5%	13%	6%	10%

In particular, Table 1 shows the description derived from IND as sample mean and %standard deviation of the individual estimates, together with the fixed effects and their %standard deviation obtained with FO and FOCE, both when ξ is fixed (FO-fixed & FOCE-fixed) to 0.02 (2%) or also estimated (FO-free & FOCE-free).

When estimated, ξ was 0.05 (5%) both with FO and FOCE.

There is a relevant difference between FO-free population estimates and IND results, above all for S_G and p_2 mean values and their %SD. In comparison with IND, the population variance of S_G and p_2 obtained with FO-fixed is heavily underestimated (regression to the mean), a slight underestimation for p_2 population variance holds with FOCE-fixed, while FOCE-free results are fully comparable with IND, both for means and variances.

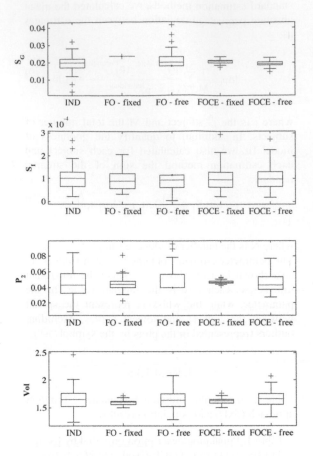

Fig. 1. Boxplots of individual parameter estimates obtained with IND, FO (free & fixed value for ξ), and FOCE (free & fixed value for ξ). The horizontal line across each box is the median value; the boxes contain 50% of the values (interquartile range); the whiskers are lines extending from each end of the boxes to show the extent of the rest of the estimates, excluding outliers, which are plotted with the symbol "+".

Moving from the description of the population to the single individual results, the boxplots of all the single-subject results (Fig. 1) confirm and highlight the consistently superior performance of the conditional linearization likelihood approximation, mainly when the standard deviation of the measurement error is fixed, but also when it is estimated separately.

This is supported by the differences between IND and FO in the median and interquartile ranges shown in the boxplots. The boxplots also illustrate that the use of FOCE-free results in a statistical picture of the estimates more comparable with IND, even if the interquartile ranges are narrower (Fig. 1).

The boxplots also show that the FOCE-free performance is very close to IND, resulting in individual results having substantially the same median and interquartile range, with the only exception provided by the variation of S_G estimates, which is lower with FOCE-free.

Table 2 The mean absolute percentage deviation between the parameter estimates of all the subjects

	ΔS_G	ΔS_I	Δp_2	ΔVol
FO fixed	39	12	37	9
FO free	28	13	35	3
FOCE fixed	29	11	49	8
FOCE free	21	7	26	3

This superior performance of FOCE-free in comparison with the other population methods is also detectable from Table 2, where the mean absolute percentage deviation between the individual estimates is shown for each used population estimation method.

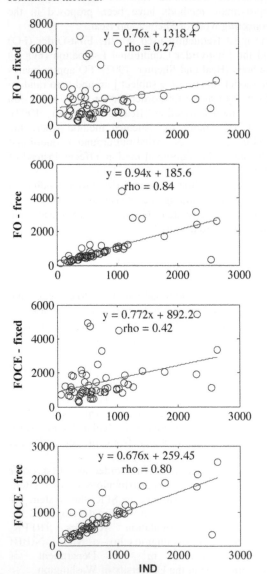

Fig. 2. IND sums of squared residuals for each subject are compared with the corresponding values obtained by using FO and FOCE population estimation methods. Rho values reported are Spearman rank correlation results.

In fact, from Table 2, FOCE-free results in the lowest deviation from IND estimates at the single subject level, while FO-fixed shows the worst performance also at the single subject identification level.

To investigate the discrepancy between goodness of model fit provided by IND and that obtainable with population modeling, we compared the sum of the squared residual of each subject via linear regression (Fig. 2). When proportional measurement error ξ is fixed to 0.02, FO and FOCE both result in a very low correlation rank (rho=0.27 with P=0.04 for FO and rho=0.42 with P<0.001 for FOCE), while a higher value is found for FO-free and FOCE-free (rho=0.84 with P<0.0001 for FO and rho=0.80 with P<0.0001 for FOCE). Even if FO-free seems to perform slightly better than FOCE-free when considering SRES values, the mean and SD values for SRES show a lower variability of SRES for FOCE-free in comparison with FO-free and a mean value very close to that of IND (744.6 ± 579.8 for IND vs 762.8 ± 505.6 for FOCE-free and 889.5 ± 816.2 for FO-free).

4. DISCUSSION

We have evaluated on real data the performance of nonlinear mixed effects population analysis methods applied to minimal modeling of IVGTT data, and compared them with the "gold standard" of minimal model parameter estimation, individual model identification via weighted nonlinear least squares. From these results, it appears that the first-order model approximation that is at the heart of the FO method is detrimental to minimal model parameter estimation. The higher order approximation provided by FOCE is likely more respectful of the complexity of the time-variant equations used in the glucose minimal model, and returns parameter estimates that are closer to individual analysis, especially when measurement error parameters are also estimated. While IND is expected to provide inflated estimates of between-subject variation (Davidian and Giltinan, 1995), it appears that population methods show regression to the mean for some parameters, sometimes substantial (FO-fixed and FOCE-fixed). Further work would be needed to elucidate this, perhaps by considering a full population covariance matrix, instead of assuming uncorrelated parameters. Based on these results, population analysis methods are promising in the context of minimal model IVGTT analysis, and warrant further investigation as potential tools to reduce required intensive sampling and perhaps shorten experimental duration.

Acknowledgements: This study was partially supported by NIH grant P41 EB-001975.

REFERENCES

Barrett PH, BM Bell, C Cobelli, H Golde, A Schumitzky, P Vicini, and DM Foster (1998). SAAM II: Simulation, Analysis, and Modeling Software for tracer and pharmacokinetic studies. *Metabolism*.47: 484-92.

Beal SL, and LB Sheiner (1982). Estimating population kinetics. *Crit Rev Biomed Eng*. 8: 195-222.

Beal SL, and LB Sheiner (1992). NONMEM Users Guide. NONMEM Project Group, UCSF, San Francisco, CA.

Bell B.M. (2001). Approximating the marginal likelihood estimate for models with random parameters. *Appl. Mathem. Comput.*, 119: 57-75.

Bergman R.N., Y.Z. Ider, C.R. Bowden, and C Cobelli (1979). Quantitative estimation of insulin sensitivity. *Am J Physiol*. 236: E667-E677.

Davidian M, and D. Giltinan. *Nonlinear Models for Repeated Measurement Data*. New York: Chapman and Hall, 1995.

De Gaetano A., G. Mingrone, M. Castagneto (1996). NONMEM improves group parameter estimation for the minimal model of glucose kinetics. *Am J Physiol* 271(5 Pt 1): E932-937.

Erichsen L, O.F. Agbaje, S.D. Luzio, D.R. Owens, and R. Hovorka (2004). Population and individual minimal modeling of the frequently sampled insulin-modified intravenous glucose tolerance test. *Metabolism*.53: 1349-54.

Sparacino G, C Tombolato, and C Cobelli (2000). Maximum-likelihood versus maximum a posteriori parameter estimation of physiological system models: the C-peptide impulse response case study. *IEEE Trans Biomed Eng*. 47: 801-11.

METHODS FOR IMPROVING RELIABILITY OF GLLS FOR PARAMETRIC IMAGE GENERATION

Hon-Chit Choi[1], Lingfeng Wen[1,2], Stefan Eberl[1,2], Dagan Feng[1,3]

*Biomedical and Multimedia Information Technology (BMIT) Group, School of
Information Technologies, University of Sydney, Sydney, Australia[1]
PET and Nuclear Medicine Dept., Royal Prince Alfred Hospital, Sydney, Australia[2]
Center for Multimedia Signal Processing, Department of Electronic and Information
Engineering, the Hong Kong Polytechnic University, Hong Kong[3]*

Abstract: The computationally efficient generalized linear least square (GLLS) algorithm has been successfully applied in positron emission tomography (PET) for constructing parametric images from dynamic data. Recently, we have applied GLLS to substantially more noisy single photon emission computed tomography (SPECT) data. Due to the nature of the data, GLLS sometimes failed to provide physiologically meaningful estimates. In this work, we investigated two potential methods to improve the reliability and success rate of GLLS for estimating kinetic parameters from noisy data:- incorporation of the volume of distribution (V_d) prior into GLLS and applying the bootstrap Monte Carlo method. Our simulation results show that both methods can improve the parameter estimation reliability at the expense of extra computation time. *Copyright © 2006 IFAC*

Keywords: Modelling, biomedical systems, parameter estimation, Monte Carlo simulation

1. INTRODUCTION

Parametric images, where pixel values represent quantification of physiological parameters of tracer kinetics, can provide an insight into in vivo physiological and biochemical processes, which can be imaged by positron emission tomography (PET) and single photon emission computed tomography (SPECT). Formation of parametric images requires fitting of a kinetic model to tissue time activity curves (TTACs) for a given input function (IF) for each voxel in the 3D data set.

The nonlinear least square (NLS) method is typically used to fit TTACs derived from regions of interest, and is regarded as the 'gold standard'. However, it is computationally expensive, requires reasonable initial parameter estimates close to the correct solution and is prone to be trapped in local minima for very noisy curves. Graphical approaches (Logan, Fowler et al. 1990), (Patlak, Blasberg et al. 1983), (Yokoi, Iida et al. 1993) are computationally efficient and relatively insensitive to noise and have thus been successfully applied for generating parametric images. However, they provide only a limited number of parameters (typically 2) and frequently make assumptions about the underlying model, which may not be valid for a given data set.

The generalized linear least square (GLLS) method was proposed by Feng, *et. al*(Feng, Huang et al. 1996) as an unbiased, computationally efficient algorithm for kinetic model parameter estimation and it does not require initial parameter estimates. GLLS has been successfully applied to PET data in the brain (Feng, Huang et al. 1996; Cai, Feng et al. 1998), heart (Chen, Lawson et al. 1998) and liver (Choi, Chen et al. 2006). Recently, Wen et al have applied GLLS to dynamic SPECT data (Wen, Eberl et al. 2003a). However, the considerably higher noise intrinsic in SPECT data, especially for the voxel-wise TTACs, can result in physiologically meaningless parameter estimates, such as negative rate constants, with the GLLS method. Efforts to improve parameter estimation of GLLS for SPECT include clustering (Choi, Wen et al. 2006) and optimum sampling schedule(Wen, Eberl et al. 2003b). In this paper, we proposed two approaches to improve GLLS and evaluated their performances with Monte Carlo simulations. The first method reduces the parameter estimation space for GLLS by using a set of predetermined volume of distribution V_d values. The second approach utilizes the Bootstrap Monte Carlo resampling method to eliminate unsuccessful fits.

2. METHODS

2.1 Traditional 3-compartment-4-parameter GLLS

The basic theory and derivation of GLLS for a 3-compartment and 4-parameter kinetic model has been discussed in (Feng, Huang et al. 1996). The second order differential equation is:

$$c_T''(t) = P_1 c_p'(t) + P_2 c_p(t) + P_3 c_T'(t) + P_4 c_T(t) \quad (1)$$

where $P_1 = K_1$, $P_2 = K_1(k_3+k_4)$, $P_3 = k_2+k_3+k_4$, $P_4 = k_2 k_4$.

The 3-compartment and 4-parameter GLLS estimate is stated as follows,

$$\vartheta_{GLLS-3C-4P} = \left[Z^T Z \right]^{-1} Z^T r \quad (2)$$

where, t_1, t_2, ..., t_n are the corresponding times for sampling frame, $\vartheta_{GLLS\text{-}3C\text{-}4P} = [P_1, P_2, P_3, P_4]^T$,

$$r = \begin{bmatrix} c_T(t_1) + \hat{P}_3 \psi_1 \otimes c_T(t_1) + \hat{P}_4 \psi_2 \otimes c_T(t_1) \\ c_T(t_2) + \hat{P}_3 \psi_1 \otimes c_T(t_2) + \hat{P}_4 \psi_2 \otimes c_T(t_2) \\ \vdots \\ c_T(t_n) + \hat{P}_3 \psi_1 \otimes c_T(t_n) + \hat{P}_4 \psi_2 \otimes c_T(t_n) \end{bmatrix}$$

$$Z = \begin{bmatrix} \psi_1 \otimes c_P(t_1) & \psi_2 \otimes c_P(t_1) & \psi_1 \otimes c_T(t_1) & \psi_2 \otimes c_T(t_1) \\ \psi_1 \otimes c_P(t_2) & \psi_2 \otimes c_P(t_2) & \psi_1 \otimes c_T(t_2) & \psi_2 \otimes c_T(t_2) \\ \vdots & \vdots & \vdots & \vdots \\ \psi_1 \otimes c_P(t_n) & \psi_2 \otimes c_P(t_n) & \psi_1 \otimes c_T(t_n) & \psi_2 \otimes c_T(t_n) \end{bmatrix}$$

$$\psi_1 = \frac{\lambda_2 e^{-\lambda_2 t} - \lambda_1 e^{-\lambda_1 t}}{\lambda_2 - \lambda_1} \quad \psi_2 = \frac{e^{-\lambda_1 t} - e^{-\lambda_2 t}}{\lambda_2 - \lambda_1} \quad \lambda_{1,2} = \frac{\hat{P}_3 \pm \sqrt{\hat{P}_3^2 + 4\hat{P}_4}}{2}.$$

where $\hat{P}_3$ and $\hat{P}_4$ are estimated parameters from the previous iteration and their initial values are obtained by linear least square (LLS) fitting (Feng, Huang et al. 1996).

2.2 V_d aided GLLS

Given a 3-compartment and 4-parameter model, V_d is defined to be equal to the ratio of P_2 and P_4 in equation (3).

$$V_d = \frac{K_1}{k_2}\left(1 + \frac{k_3}{k_4}\right) = \frac{P_2}{P_4} \quad (3)$$

The differential equation (1) can be rewritten as follows:

$$c_T''(t) = P_1 c_p'(t) + P_3 c_T'(t) + P_4 (c_T(t) + V_d c_p(t)) \quad (4)$$

If one initial $\hat{V}_d$ can be found to be close to the true value, equation (2) can be simplified to equation (5), reducing the number of parameters to be estimated and potentially enhancing the reliability of estimating the remaining, reduced number of parameters.

$$\vartheta_{GLLS-V_d} = \left[Z^T Z \right]^{-1} Z^T r \quad (5)$$

where, $\vartheta_{GLLS\text{-}Vd} = [P_1, P_3, P_4]^T$,

$$r = \begin{bmatrix} c_T(t_1) + \hat{P}_3 \psi_1 \otimes c_T(t_1) + \hat{P}_4 \psi_2 \otimes c_T(t_1) \\ c_T(t_2) + \hat{P}_3 \psi_1 \otimes c_T(t_2) + \hat{P}_4 \psi_2 \otimes c_T(t_2) \\ \vdots \\ c_T(t_n) + \hat{P}_3 \psi_1 \otimes c_T(t_n) + \hat{P}_4 \psi_2 \otimes c_T(t_n) \end{bmatrix}$$

$$Z = \begin{bmatrix} \psi_1 \otimes c_p(t_1) & \psi_1 \otimes c_T(t_1) & \psi_2 \otimes c_T(t_1) + \hat{V}_d \psi_2 \otimes c_p(t_1) \\ \psi_1 \otimes c_p(t_2) & \psi_1 \otimes c_T(t_2) & \psi_2 \otimes c_T(t_2) + \hat{V}_d \psi_2 \otimes c_p(t_2) \\ \vdots & \vdots & \vdots \\ \psi_1 \otimes c_p(t_n) & \psi_1 \otimes c_T(t_n) & \psi_2 \otimes c_T(t_n) + \hat{V}_d \psi_2 \otimes c_p(t_n) \end{bmatrix}$$

The reliability of parameter estimation increases for simpler models with fewer parameters. Thus an approximate estimate of volume of distribution, V_{d0} can be reliably estimated using GLLS applied to a 2-compartment, 2 parameter model.

The higher order, 3-compartment, 4-parameter model fit with GLLS is then performed according to equation 5 where $\hat{V}_d$ is varied between 0.8 and 1.6 times of V_{d0} with 100 increments between this range. The range was determined empirically based on the observed bias in V_d estimated with the lower order model.

Of the fits with the 100 sets of $\hat{V}_d$ the optimum fit was selected as the fit for which all rate constants were positive and which had the smallest weighted residual sum of square (WRSSQ) between the estimated curve and original curve. The weight w was chosen to be proportional to the scan interval.

$$WRSSQ = \sum_{i=1}^{N} w \left\| C_{T(Original)}(t_i) - C_{T(Estimated)}(t_i) \right\|^2 \quad (6)$$

2.3 Bootstrap aided GLLS

Bootstrap Monte Carlo method(Press, Teukolsky et al. 1997) was used to generate "Bootstrap" curves for each TTAC. Given a curve of n data points, for each bootstrap Monte Carlo iteration, n points are randomly selected from the curve, with some points duplicated and others not selected for a particular sample. The model is then fitted to the n randomly selected points.

Two methods were used to select optimum fit and parameters from the set of bootstrap curves. Method 1 (BS_RSSQ) was the same as used for V_d aided GLLS, i.e. the fit which provided positive parameters and had the smallest WRSSQ when compared against the original, unsampled curve. The second method (BS_MEAN) used the mean of the parameters of the first 10 successful (i.e. positive rate constants) bootstrap fits.

2.4. Generation of Simulated Curves

Computer simulations were performed to test the proposed methods. The TTAC $C_T(t)$ was generated from typical kinetic parameters for cerebellum, frontal cortex and thalamus of the SPECT nicotinic receptor tracer 5-[^{123}I]-iodo-A-85380 according to equation (1). The parameters used are listed in Table.1. For each TTAC, there were 36 sampling intervals. Gaussian noise was added to $C_T(t)$ with variance σ^2 given by equation (7) and noise level α ranging from 0.1 to 1.0. Fig. 1 plots several simulated curves for the cerebellum.

$$\sigma^2(t_i) = \frac{\alpha * c_T(t_i)}{\Delta t_i} \qquad (7)$$

Table 1 Typical SPECT parameter sets for regions of interest in the brain

Cortex	K_1	k_2	k_3	k_4
Cerebellum	0.275	0.063	0.029	0.035
Frontal cortex	0.277	0.059	0.038	0.037
Thalamus	0.284	0.061	0.143	0.041

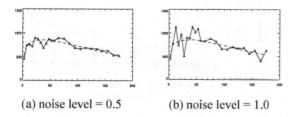

(a) noise level = 0.5   (b) noise level = 1.0

Fig.1. Typical simulated noisy curves with noise level (a) 0.5, (b) 1.0. Noisy curves are represented by solid line whereas the noiseless curve for cerebellum is represented by dashed line.

2.5. Evaluation of accuracy and reliability

For each set of parameters in Table 1, 200 curves were simulated. The proposed methods were used to derive the mean ($\overline{P}$) and standard deviation ($SD_{\overline{P}}$). Percentage bias (8) as well as the coefficient of variation (CV) (9) were then derived according to the reference values (P_{True}) in table 1.
The formula for CV and bias are stated as follow,

$$Bias = \left| \frac{P_{True} - \overline{P}}{P_{True}} \right| X100\% \qquad (8)$$

$$CV_{\overline{P}} = \frac{SD_{\overline{P}}}{\left| \overline{P} \right|} X100\% \qquad (9)$$

3. RESULTS

Fig. 2 and Fig. 3 show the percentage bias and percentage CV of parameter estimates K_1 and V_d for the cerebellum and thalamus, respectively. Overall,

both the V_d aided and the two bootstrap methods showed an improvement in estimating parameters, particularly at high noise levels, compared to the original GLLS method. The BS_MEAN method provided consistently low CV values and was least sensitive to noise. It also performed well and consistently in terms of bias and hence overall shows the best performance.

There are a number of unexpected peaks for the BS_RSSQ method such as at noise level 0.8 and 0.9 in Fig. 3d and noise level 0.3 and 0.5 in Fig. 4c and 4d. These unexpectedly high bias and CV values are due to sets of parameter estimates with extremely small positive k_4 values (in the order of 10^{-5} or 10^{-6}), which resulted in extremely large V_d estimate. This illustrates that the smallest RSSQ may not necessarily provide the best and most reliable estimate of the parameters. This was not observed with the V_d aided method as in that method, V_d is inherently constraint to a range of reasonable values.

The BS_MEAN method overcomes the sensitivity of outlier parameter estimates of the BS_RSSQ method, by taking the average from 10 successful fits. Moreover, since BS_MEAN stops as soon as 10 successful fits are found, the running time is greatly reduced. According to our experience, for a simulation study which consisted of all 20 noise levels as detailed in section II, BS_MEAN required only one-third of the time required by the BS_RSSQ and V_d methods. Thus while BS_RSSQ and V_d methods are about 100 times slower than the original GLLS, the computation time penalty for BS_MEAN is only about a factor of 30.

4. SUMMARY and CONCLUSIONS

The study evaluated 2 methods to overcome higher SPECT noise to improve the performance of the GLLS. The two methods are:

1) Use a predetermined set of volume of distribution (V_d) values in GLLS in order to reduce the parameter space, and
2) apply bootstrap Monte Carlo technique to eliminate unsuccessful fits.

For the bootstrap technique, we further investigated the performance of two selection criteria including 1) minimizing RSSQ (BS_RSSQ) and 2) taking the mean of the first 10 successful fits (BS_MEAN).

Our simulation results suggest that the BS_MEAN method not only provides parameter estimates with the lowest bias and CV, but also is also computationally the most efficient of the methods investigated. Therefore, the BS_MEAN method is recommended.

5. ACKNOWLEDGEMENT

This work was partially supported by the Australian Research Council (ARC) and Research Grant Council of Hongkong (RGC).

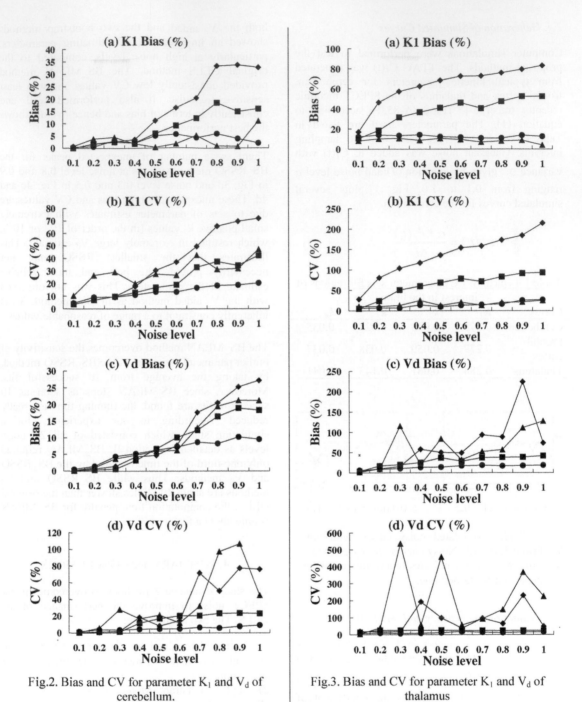

Fig.2. Bias and CV for parameter K_1 and V_d of cerebellum.

Fig.3. Bias and CV for parameter K_1 and V_d of thalamus

◆ Original ■ Vd ▲ BS_RSSQ ● BS_MEAN

Original – original GLLS method, V_d – V_d aided GLLS method, BS_RRSQ – Bootstrap Monte Carlo using minimum WRSSQ and BS_MEAN – Mean of 10 successful Bootstrap Monte Carlo fits

REFERENCES

Cai, W., D. Feng, et al. (1998). A fast algorithm for estimating FDG model parameters in dynamic PET with an optimised image sampling schedule and corrections for cerebral blood volume and partial volume. *Proceedings of the 20th Annual International Conference of the IEEE Engineering in Medicine and Biology Society*.

Chen, K., M. Lawson, et al. (1998). "Generalized linear least squares method for fast

generation of myocardial blood flow parametric images with N-13 ammonia PET." *Medical Imaging, IEEE Transactions on* **17**(2): 236-243.

Choi, H.-C., S. Chen, et al. (2006). "Fast parametric imaging algorithm for dual-input biomedical system parameter estimation." *Computer Methods and Programs in Biomedicine* **81**(1): 49-55.

Choi, H.-C., L. Wen, et al. (2006). Fuzzy C-mean clustering on kinetic parameter estimation with generalized linear least square algorithm in SPECT. *Medical Imaging 2006:*

Image Processing, San Diego, CA, USA, SPIE.

Feng, D., S.-C. Huang, et al. (1996). "An unbiased parametric imaging algorithm for nonuniformly sampled biomedical system parameter estimation." *Medical Imaging, IEEE Transactions on* **15**(4): 512-518.

Logan, J., J. Fowler, et al. (1990). "Graphical analysis of reversible radioligand binding from time-activity measurements applied to [N-11C-methyl-(-)-cocaine PET studies in human subjects." *J Cereb Blood Flow Metab* **10**(5): 740-747.

Patlak, C., R. Blasberg, et al. (1983). "Graphical evaluation of blood-to-brain transfer constants from multiple-time uptake data." *J Cereb Blood Flow Metab* **3**: 1-7.

Press, W. H., S. A. Teukolsky, et al. (1997). Quick-and-Dirty Monte Carlo: The Bootstrap Method. *Numerical Recipes in C: The art of scientific computing*, Cambridge university press: 691-692.

Wen, L., S. Eberl, et al. (2003a). A Reliable Voxel-by-Voxel Parameter Estimation for Dynamic SPECT. *Proceeding of World Congress on Medical Physics and Biomedical Engineering*, Sydney, Australia.

Wen, L., S. Eberl, et al. (2003b). An improved optimal image sampling schedule for multiple ROIs in dynamic SPECT. *IFAC Modelling and Control in Biomedical Systems*, Melbourne, Australia.

Yokoi, T., H. Iida, et al. (1993). "A new graphic plot analysis for cerebral blood flow and partition coefficient with iodine-123-iodoamphetamine and dynamic SPECT validation studies using oxygen-15-water and PET." *J Nucl Med* **34**(3): 498-505.

MEDICAL IMAGE SEGMENTATION TECHNIQUES FOR VIRTUAL ENDOSCOPY

László Szilágyi[*,], Balázs Benyó[*], Sándor M. Szilágyi[**], Zoltán Benyó[*]**

*Department of Control Engineering and Information Technology
Budapest University of Technology and Economics
Magyar tudósok krt. 2, 1117 Budapest, Hungary*

**Faculty of Technical and Human Science
Sapientia – Hungarian Science University of Transylvania
Târgu Mureş, Romania*

Abstract: Virtual endoscopes give internal views of the human body without penetrating it, based on a set of parallel cross-sections produced with any computer tomography method. This paper presents some ideas concerning the design and implementation of a software system, which acts like a virtual endoscope. It takes into account the general requirements of the system, gives a solution that uses a multi-step algorithm, and finally shows the resulting 3-D images. Most of the algorithmic steps have several possible solutions. Our virtual endoscope establishes 3-D internal views based on sets of 2-D slices, which originate from magnetic resonance imaging devices. The chain of the applied image processing methods consists of the followings: (1) Adequate pre-filtering to eliminate the low-frequency intensity non-uniformity (INU) artifact, and high-frequency "salt-and-pepper" disturbances; (2) Segmentation of the stack of MRI slices using an enhanced fuzzy C-means algorithm; (3) 3-D surface recovery algorithm based on level set methods and fast marching methods; (4) Interactive visualization using modern computer graphics technologies, providing the possibility to measure distances, areas, volumes as well. The quality of service provided by the chosen method mainly depends on the resolution of input images. *Copyright © 2006 IFAC*

Keywords: image segmentation, fuzzy logic, image reconstruction, medical applications, computer tomography.

1. INTRODUCTION

Traditional endoscopes penetrate the human body in order to provide high-resolution internal views of cavities and hollow organs. Even though such examinations are mostly considered non-invasive, the procedure causes pain, or at least discomforts the patient, who consequently needs some kind of sedation or anesthesia.

Magnetic resonance imaging (MRI) is a non-invasive diagnostic tool that views the internal anatomy of the human body in 2-D cross sections called slices. A virtual endoscope establishes 3-D internal views based on these sets of 2-D slices, using modern image processing techniques and computer graphics

as well. Besides the comfort provided, another relevant advantage is the fact, that it can create images of any body part, not only the hollow ones.

This paper presents a new concept of the virtual endoscope, developed in the Biomedical Engineering Laboratory at TU Budapest. During the development process, MRI brain images are used for testing the methods, but the algorithm is capable to process other kinds of medical images, too. Consequently the virtual endoscope will have several medical applications.

In order to create a virtual endoscope based on magnetic resonance images, the following image processing tasks need to be performed (see Fig. 1.):

(1) filtering the initial MR images; (2) segmentation of the 2-D slices, classification of their pixels into a set of clusters, whose cardinality is set according to the requirements of medical scientists; (3) a shape recovery algorithm is applied to reconstruct the 3-D image of the object; (4) visualization via modern computer graphics tools.

Fig. 1. Main steps of image processing

2. METHODS

2.1. Magnetic resonance imaging

Magnetic resonance imaging provides parallel cross sections of the investigated part of the human body. This study is based on a set of 171 slices of the human brain, each of them having 256×256 pixels, thus having a resolution around 1 pixel per mm.

2.2. Filtering methods

Magnetic resonance images tend to have two main noise types, having several possible sources for each.

High frequency noise manifests as isolated white and black pixels scattered over the whole set of cross sections. They are generally referred to as salt-and-pepper noise. Several implementations use low-pass averaging filtering techniques in order to eliminate these noises (Ahmed *et al*, 2002). This technique really works fast, it considerably reduces the noise level, but also erects an obstacle to the segmentation as it hides the sharp edges behind an introduced blur. In spite of its slightly higher computational needs, the median filter is a better choice, because it completely eliminates the isolated noisy pixels unless more then 5% of the image pixels are contaminated.

Low frequency noises are caused by the unwanted presence of an intensive bias field that turns some parts of the MR images darker than others. Efficient adaptive methods have been introduced in order to estimate the distribution of the bias field (Pham, and Prince, 1999; Liew, and Yan, 2003).

2.3. Segmentation of MRI brain slices using a modified fuzzy C-means (FCM) algorithm

The standard FCM algorithm presented by Bezdek and Pal (1991), groups the values x_k, $k = 1..N$ into a number of c clusters, using the objective function

$$J_B = \sum_{i=1}^{c} \sum_{k=1}^{N} u_{ik}^p (x_k - v_i)^2 , \qquad (1)$$

where v_i represents the prototype value of the i th cluster, u_{ik} represents the fuzzy membership of the k th voxel with respect to cluster i, and p is a weighting exponent. By definition, for any k we have: $\sum_{i=1}^{c} u_{ik} = 1$. To minimize the objective function, it is necessary to assign high membership values to those voxels, whose intensities are situated close to the prototype values of their particular clusters.

Ahmed *et al* (2002) proposed a modification to the original objective function by introducing a term that allows the labeling of a voxel to be influenced by the labels in its immediate neighborhood. This effect acts as a regularizer, and biases the solution toward piecewise-homogeneous labeling. The modified objective function is given by:

$$J_A = \sum_{i=1}^{c} \sum_{k=1}^{N} \left[u_{ik}^p (x_k - v_i)^2 + \frac{\alpha}{N_k} \sum_{r=1}^{N_k} u_{ik}^p (x_{k,r} - v_i)^2 \right] \quad (2)$$

where $x_{k,r}$ represents the neighbor voxels of x_k, and N_k stands for the number of voxels in the neighborhood of the k th voxel. The parameter α controls the intensity of the neighboring effect. This combination of filtering and segmentation made it possible to estimate the contaminating bias field, but considerable reduced its performance against the clock.

In the followings, we will introduce some modifications to this algorithm, in order to reduce its computational needs. It is obvious, that a set of MR brain image slices contains approximately 10^7 voxels. The intensity of the voxels is generally encoded with 8 bit resolution, that is, there are only 256 possible levels of intensity for each voxel. If we perform a median filtering preceding the fuzzy classification, then the formula of this latter does not have to treat each voxel separately. We only need to know, how many voxels of each existing gray level are present in the whole stack of filtered slices. This information is reflected by the histogram. This technique is not applicable using the formulation of Ahmed *et al*, (2002).

So the proposed enhanced fuzzy C-means algorithm consists of the following steps:

Step 1. First we apply a median filtering to each pixel, using a 3×3 neighborhood. This means, that the nine intensity values situated in the vicinity of the given pixel are sorted increasingly, and the filtered value will be the one situated in the middle. Let us denote by ξ_k the filtered intensity level of the k th voxel.

Step 2. Let us denote the number of intensity levels by q. As it was previously stated, q is much smaller than N. We denote by γ_l the number of voxels from the whole stack of filtered slices, having the intensity equal to $\xi_k = l$, where $l = 1..q$ and $k = 1..N$. By definition, we have: $\sum_{l=1}^{q} \gamma_l = N$. In the followings, ξ_l will denote the intensity level corresponding to color l.

Step 3. The objective function used for the segmentation of the filtered image will be:

$$J_S = \sum_{i=1}^{c} \sum_{l=1}^{q} \gamma_l u_{il}^p (\xi_l - v_i)^2 . \qquad (3)$$

We need to find those values of the parameters u_{il} and v_i, for which this objective function has the minimal value. Let us consider the Lagrange multiplier:

$$F_S = \sum_{i=1}^{c} \sum_{l=1}^{q} \left[\gamma_l u_{il}^p (\xi_l - v_i)^2 \right] + \sum_{l-1}^{q} \lambda_l \left(1 - \sum_{i=1}^{c} u_{il} \right). \qquad (4)$$

Step 4. Taking the derivative of F_S with respect to u_{il}, and equaling it to 0, we get:

$$\frac{\delta F_S}{\delta u_{il}} = p \gamma_l u_{il}^{p-1} (\xi_l - v_i)^2 - \lambda_l = 0 , \text{ so}$$

$$u_{il} = \left(\frac{\lambda_l}{p \gamma_l} \right)^{\frac{1}{p-1}} (\xi_l - v_i)^{\frac{-2}{p-1}} . \qquad (5)$$

From $\sum_{j=1}^{c} u_{jl} = 1$, we obtain:

$$\lambda_l = p \gamma_l \left[\sum_{j=1}^{c} (\xi_l - v_j)^{\frac{-2}{p-1}} \right]^{1-p} , \text{ and so}$$

$$u_{il} = \left[\sum_{j=1}^{c} \left(\frac{\xi_l - v_i}{\xi_l - v_j} \right)^{\frac{2}{p-1}} \right]^{-1} . \qquad (6)$$

Step 5. Taking the derivative of F_S with respect to v_i, and equaling it to 0, we get:

$$\frac{\delta F_S}{\delta v_i} = -2 \cdot \sum_{l=1}^{q} \left(\gamma_l u_{il}^p (\xi_l - v_i) \right) = 0 , \text{ so}$$

$$v_i = \left(\sum_{l=1}^{q} \gamma_l u_{il}^p \xi_l \right) \left(\sum_{l=1}^{q} \gamma_l u_{il}^p \right)^{-1} . \qquad (7)$$

The proposed modified FCM algorithm for 2-D segmentation is summarized in Fig. 2.

The enhanced FCM algorithm for MR brain image segmentation can be summarized as follows:

a. Determine the values of $\{\gamma_l\}_{l=1}^q$, select initial cluster prototypes $\{v_i = (2i-1)/(2c)\}_{i=1}^c$.

b. Update membership function values according to formula (6).

c. Apply formula (7) to compute the new values for cluster prototypes.
d. Repeat b-c until the Euclidean norm of the change of the prototype vector is smaller then a previously set small positive number ε.

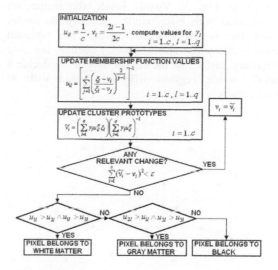

Fig. 2. The algorithm of the 2-D segmentation

Attempts for further development of the standard FCM algorithm, in the direction of local and adaptive processing, are presented in Pham *et al* (1999) and Ardekani *et al* (2002).

2.4. 3-D surface reconstruction methods

Three dimensional shape recovery is the key problem of this whole image processing tool. A traditional and widely used solution is to apply the marching cube algorithm, because it is easily understandable and gives acceptable results. Alternative experiments use elastic surfaces to estimate the 3-D shape of the investigated objects. All these methods rely on the results and side-products of the 2-D segmentation.

Any voxel k in the investigated volume ($k = 1..N$) has a probability of belonging to the 3-D region named class i equal to the fuzzy membership function value u_{ik}. Based on these values, we can define the region indicator scalar spaces R_i, having the value at voxel k given by the formula $R_{ik} = 1 - 2u_{ik}$. The region indicator will be negative inside the region, positive outside the region, and the boundary surface of the region will be the zero level set of this scalar space.

The marching cube algorithm. The marching cube algorithm divides the whole investigated volume into unitary sized cubes, having at its corners 2×2 adjacent pixels of two neighbouring slices. Based on the region indicator values of these 8 voxels, it determines whether the zero level set intersects this cube and if so, it also locates the intersection. As any of the 8 voxels can be either inside or outside the 3-D region we wish to detect, there are $2^8 = 256$ different cases. Symmetry assigns these cases to 14 different topologies (Lorensen, and Cline, 1987), which are shown in Fig. 3. Voxels inside the region are represented with black circles, while white circles show the voxels situated outside. The obtained surface elements unambiguously define the 3-D boundary surface of the region only if we decide a priori, which regions will be treated with 6-connectivity.

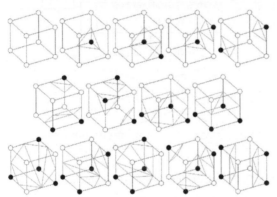

Fig. 3. The fourteen different topologies of the marching cube algorithm

The surface elements compose a high-resolution 3-D view with a considerable accuracy. That is why even nowadays several medical imaging systems are being developed using this concept.

Elastic surfaces. The zero level set of the region indicator R_i is the ideal surface boundary of the 3-D region classified in class i. Our task is to define a propagating closed surface within the region and then to make this surface approximate the zero level set as accurate as possible. The accuracy will mainly depend on the gradient values around the zero level, because sharper edges are easier to localize. A stopping force is needed so that the propagating surface stops at the appropriate place.

Gradient driven stopping force was introduced by Caselles *et al.* (1993) and Malladi *et al.* (1995). Their solution had a significant weakness with the pulling back feature, that is, when a front crossed the aim

boundary, it could not come back. To avoid this problem, Kichenassamy *et al.* (1996) and Yezzi *et al.* (1997) introduced their additional stopping force term due to edge strength. To improve the boundary leak characteristics, Siddiqui *et al.* (1998) added another extra stopping term due to area minimization. The most recent advance in the domain is the usage of curvature dependent stopping forces (Malladi, and Sethian, 1996; Lorigo, *et al.*, 2000).

The complete summary of elastic surface based 3-D shape recovery methods is presented in (Suri, *et al.*, 2002).

2.5. Visualization issues

Visualization issues generally refer to development tasks. In our case an OpenGL-based user interface is needed, which provides interactivity facilities in order to perform the virtual penetration, and instantly shows the internal view of the investigated organ.

3. RESULTS AND DISCUSSION

3.1. Filtering

The median filter vs. averaging low-pass filter has significant advantages, namely: (1) it acts less sensitively to severe contamination with salt-and-pepper noise; (2) it does not blur the sharp edges; (3) it also has a shape regularizer effect.

3.2. Fuzzy segmentation

Due to medical requirements, the brain images are generally segmented in three classes: white matter, gray matter, and black. The fuzzy C-means classification performs a quick convergence. Fig. 4 shows, that the number of necessary cycles mainly depends on the initialization of cluster prototypes, but the resulting prototypes values do not vary. So the initial values of cluster prototypes may be random values with the constraint that they differ from each other (Szilágyi, and Benyó, 2003; Szilágyi, 2004). Fig. 5 presents the obtained fuzzy membership functions.

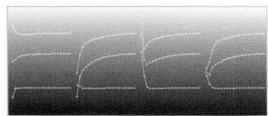

Fig. 4. Converging cluster prototypes with different initializations. The necessary number of computation cycles may depend on the initialization values, but the cluster prototypes converge to the same values.

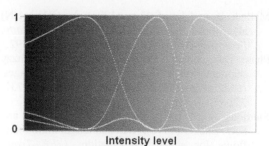

Intensity level

Fig. 5. The fuzzy membership functions of the three clusters

Fig. 6 uses three brain cross sections to show the result of the fuzzy clustering. On the left side we can see an original MR brain slice, in the middle the output of the median filter is presented, while the one on the right side is the output of the fuzzy segmentation. Fig. 7 shows a cross section of the region indicator scalar spaces corresponding to the white matter and gray matter (Szilágyi *et al*, 2005).

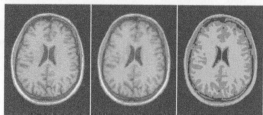

Fig. 6. MR brain cross sections: original (left), after preprocessing with median filter (middle), segmented using the proposed version of FCM (right)

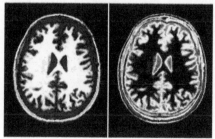

Fig. 7. Intensity plots of white (left) and gray matter (right) probabilities

3.3. 3-D surface reconstruction

Fig. 8 shows some 3-D endoscopic images obtained using the described methods. They show the boundary surface resulting from the region indicator data of white matter. The clarity of the boundary surface demonstrates the efficiency of the presented methods.

4. CONCLUSION

The proposed algorithms provide fast image processing and lead to smooth boundaries between the black, gray, and white matter. The obtained 3-D

image still has to improve, but results are promising. In order to visualize smaller details of the human body with the right accuracy, higher-resolution MR images will be needed. The presented algorithms are capable to support a virtual brain endoscope.

ACKNOWLEDGMENT

This research has been supported by the Hungarian National Research Funds (OTKA), Grants No. T042990 and F046726, Communitas Foundation, Pro Progressio Foundation, Domus Hungarica Scientiarum et Artium, and Sapientia Institute for Research Programmes (KPI).

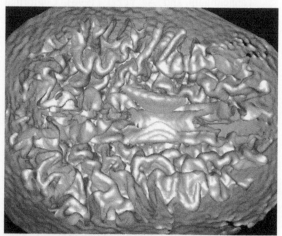

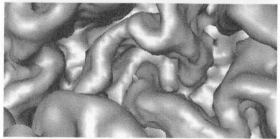

Fig. 8. 3-D brain surface obtained using the proposed method

REFERENCES

Ahmed, M.N., S. M. Yamany, N. Mohamed, A.A. Farag and T. Moriarty (2002), A Modified Fuzzy C-Means Algorithm for Bias Field Estimation and Segmentation of MRI Data, *IEEE Transactions on Medical Imaging*, **21**, No. 3, pp. 193-199.

Ardekani, S., H. Kangarloo and U. Sinha (2002), Region Based Fuzzy Clustering for Automated Brain Segmentation, Proc. 2nd Joint IEEE EMBS/BMES Conference, Houston pp. 1041-1042.

Bezdek, J.C. and S.K. Pal (1991), *Fuzzy Models for Pattern Recognition, Piscataway*, NJ: IEEE Press.

Caselles, V., F. Catte, T. Coll and F. Dibos (1993), A geometric model for active contours, *Numer. Math.*, **66/1**, pp. 1–31.

Kichenassamy, S., A. Kumar, P. Olver, A. Tannenbaum and A. Yezzi (1996), Conformal curvatures flows: From phase transitions to active vision, *Arch. Rational Mech. Anal.*, **134/3**, pp. 275–301.

Liew, A.W.C. and H. Yan (2003), An Adaptive Spatial Fuzzy Clustering Algorithm for 3-D MR Image Segmentation, *IEEE Trans. Medical Imaging*, **22/9**, pp. 1063-1075.

Lorensen, W.E. and H.E. Cline (1987), Marching Cubes: a High Resolution 3D Surface Construction Algorithm, *Computer Graphics*, **21/4**, pp. 163-169.

Lorigo, L.M., W. Grimson, L. Eric, O. Faugeras, R. Keriven, R. Kikinis, A. Nabavi and C.F. Westin (2000), Two geodesic active contours for the segmentation of tubular structures, *Proc. Comput. Vision Pattern Recognition*, pp. 444–451.

Malladi, R., J.A. Sethian and B.C. Vemuri (1995), Shape modeling with front propagation, *IEEE Trans. Pattern Anal. Machine Intell.*, **17/2**, pp. 158–175.

Malladi, R. and J.A. Sethian (1996), An O(N log N) algorithm for shape modeling, *Appl. Math., Proc. Nat. Academy Sci.*, **93/18**, pp. 9389–9392.

Pham, D.L. and J.L. Prince (1999), Adaptive fuzzy segmentation of magnetic resonance images, *IEEE Trans. Medical Imaging*, **18/9**, pp. 737-752.

Siddiqui, K., Y.B. Lauriere, A. Tannenbaum and S.W. Zucker (1998), Area and length minimizing flows for shape segmentation, *IEEE Trans. Image Processing*, 7, pp. 433–443.

Suri, J.S., K. Liu, S. Singh, S. Laxminarayan, X. Zeng and L. Reden (2002), Shape Recovery Algorithms Using Level Sets in 2-D/3-D Medical Imagery: A State-of-the-Art Review, *IEEE Transactions on Information Technology in Biomedicine*, **6.**, No. 1., pp. 8-28.

Szilágyi, L. and Z. Benyó, (2003), Magnetic Resonance Brain Image Segmentation Using an Enhanced Fuzzy C-Means Algorithm, *Proc. WC2003 World Congress on Medical Physics and Biomedical Engineering*, Sydney, paper #4406, pp. 1-4.

Szilágyi L. (2004), Virtual Brain Endoscopy Based on Magnetic Resonance Images, *Periodica Politechnica, TU Timişoara, Trans. Automatic Control and Computer Science*, **49/63**, pp. 47-50.

Szilágyi, L., S.M. Szilágyi and Z. Benyó (2005) Medical Image Segmentation for Virtual Endoscopy, *Proc. 16th IFAC World Congress*, Prague, paper #1775, pp. 1-5..

Yezzi A., S. Kichenassamy, A. Kumar, P. Olver and A. Tannenbaum (1997), A geometric snake model for segmentation of medical imagery, *IEEE Trans. Medical Imaging*, vol. **16**, pp. 199–209.

FUZZY FUSION SYSTEM FOR BRAIN MRI IMAGE SEGMENTATION

Su Ruan [a] , **Weibei Dou** [b,c] , **Daniel Bloyet** [b] , **Jean-Marc Constans** [d]

[a] *CReSTIC,9 Rue de Québec, 10026 Troyes France*
[b] *GREYC-CNRS UMR 6272, 6 Boulevard, Maréchal Juin, 14050 Caen, France*
[c] *Department of Electronic Engineering Tsinghua University 100084, Beijing China*
[d] *Unité d'IRM, EA3916, CHRU, 14033Caen, France*

Abstract: *A fuzzy data fusion scheme is proposed in this paper to automatically segment different tumor areas of human brain from multispectral Magnetic Resonance Imaging (MRI) images. The information obtained from the segmentation allows then to help doctors to make the diagnostic. The proposed framework consists of four stages: a registration of the multispectral images, a fuzzification using a priori knowledge based fuzzy models, a fuzzy fusion and a post treatment by means of a fuzzy region growing. The comparison between results of the proposed method and hand-labels of a radiology expert shows that this automatic scheme is efficient. Copyright © 2006 IFAC*

Keywords: image processing, fuzzy modeling, data fusion, segmentation, medical system.

1. INTRODUCTION

Accurate and robust brain tissue segmentation from Magnetic Resonance Imaging (MRI) is a very important issue in many applications of medical image system for quantitative studies and particularly in the study of some brain disorders (Michael Kaus, *et al*., 2001). One example is to analyze and estimate quantitatively the growth process of brain tumors, and to evaluate effects of some pharmaceutical treatments in clinic. A brain tumor segmentation consists of separating the different tumor tissues such as solid tumor, edema and necrosis from the normal brain tissues such as Gray Matter (GM), White Matter WM) and Cerebro- Spinal Fluid (CSF). Since MRI can provide various information about brain tissues from a variety of excitation sequences, it is a powerful tool in clinic to improve diagnostic. The different types of MR images obtained from the different of excitation sequences, also called multispectral images, can provide different image intensity information for a given anatomical region and subject. As a tumor consists of different biologic tissues, one type of MRI cannot give complete

information about abnormal tissues. Therefore, radiology experts always combine the multispectral MRI information of one patient to take a decision on the location, extension, prognosis and diagnosis of the tumors. At least 3 types of MRI, generally T1-weighted (T1), T2-weighted (T2) and the proton density (PD) are used as the routine sequences in the clinic. These three types are used in our study.

As known, manual tracing by an expert of a tumor in 3D for all types of MR modalities involved in studies is not only exceedingly time consuming, but also exhausting for experts leading to human errors. Therefore, an automatic segmentation is necessary. A lot of studies of brain segmentation have been carried out and are reported in the literature. The methods based on elastic registration using elastic matching techniques, or deformable models (Pitiot, *et al*., 2002) have proven the efficiency for small and local shape changes, especially for normal tissue segmentation. The methods based on statistical models, such as Gaussian intensity models (Styner, *et al*., 2000), explicit models (Leemput, *et al*., 2003), Markov random field models (Ruan, et al., 2002) work well in case of normal tissue segmentation. In the pathological cases, the methods based on supervised or unsupervised classification integrating anatomical templates (Warfield, *et al.*, 2000) have shown their robustness. Level set methods are also used for brain tumor segmentation (Ho, *et al.* 2002) with some successes. Mancas and Gosselin (2003) used the iterative watersheds to segment the brain tumor with a given initialization. Gibbs, *et al.* (1996) combine morphological and region growing for tumor volume determination. Cabral, *et al.* (1993) proposed an interactive segmentation of brain tumor based on a three dimensions (3D) region growing. Clark, et *al.* (1998) have introduced knowledge-based techniques to make classification and segmentation more intelligent. Based on the concept of fuzzy logic, Udupa, et *al.,* (2002), Saha and Udupa (2001) used the fuzzy clustering or the fuzzy connectedness for addressing the problem of abnormal tissue segmentation and classification. In spite of the power of this kind of approaches, some of them need a manual tracing.

In conclusion, the full automatic segmentation of tumor tissues is still a difficult problem for two key reasons: one is that it exists a large number of tumor types which are very different in size, shape, location, tissue composition and tissue homogeneity, and usually their frontiers with the normal tissues cannot be very well defined on the images. It's even difficult for radiology experts to delineate them due to the low contrast. The other one is the consequence of the partial volume effects (one pixel may be composed of multiple tissue types) and the noise due to the MRI acquisition system. Taking into account these problems, a knowledge based technique and a fuzzy segmentation are adopted for coping with these difficulties. This technique can provide a possibility value of belonging to the brain tumor for each voxel.

We present in this paper a fuzzy information fusion framework for an automatic segmentation of tumor tissues from multiple MR image sequences. This framework consists of the registration of the multispectral images, the fuzzyfiction of the three images volumes (based on a priori knowledge), the fuzzy fusion and a post treatment by a fuzzy region growing. The paper is organized as follows: firstly an overview of the proposed method is presented in section 2. Then section 3 shows fuzzy modeling methods for establishing mathematical relationships between the knowledge about tumor tissues provided by radiology experts and the multispectral image signals. Some fuzzy combination operators are suggested in section 4 to fuse the multispectral information extracted by the fuzzification to obtain a coarse segmentation. In section 5, a post treatment based on fuzzy region growing, is introduced to ameliorate the final results. Some experiment results using three routine MRI sequences T1, T2 and PD features images are shown in section 6. We finally conclude in section 7.

2. OVERVIEW OF THE FUZZY SEGMENTATION SYSTEM

Let us first describe with more details the proposed method which is based on the knowledge of experts and the fuzzy concept. According to descriptions of radiology experts, the type of glial tumor gives very bright signals, in both T2 images and PD images, but dark signal in T1 images. We have summed up in Table 1 the descriptions given by the radiology experts about image signals relative to the different brain tissues in the three types of MR images. The symbol '+' represents a hyper-signal meaning a signal intensity very high, while the symbol '-' presents a hypo-signal, meaning a signal intensity very low. The symbol '-+' means that the signal intensity is higher than hypo-signal, and '+-' means that it is darker than hyper-signal. '–' means that the signal intensity is lower than the standard hypo-signal, and '++' means that it is brighter than the standard hyper-signal. From table 1, we can say that the signal intensity of tumor is neither very bright nor very dark (except for necrosis) in T1 (intensity between the GM and CSF), but it is very bright in T2 and PD (GM and CSF are bright in both images). These concise descriptions are very fuzzy in term of image signals, but very helpful for us to know about relative signals of tumors in different types of MR sequences. This *a priori* knowledge is a linguistic description (Table 1). It's very fuzzy. Transformations of this description into fuzzy mathematics models are proposed in order to benefit of them. As we use multispectal MRI images, one fuzzy model for one modality is built. The fuzzy segmentation can be then considered as a fuzzy fusion problem after the fuzzification of the data.

Table 1 Descriptions of intensity characteristics of brain tissues on MR images.

Image Type	CSF	GM	WM	Tumor	Edema
T1	--	-	++	-+	-+
T2	++	+	--	++	+-
PD	+-	++	--	++	-+

The proposed framework consists of four steps. The first step, registration or matching of the multispectral images, allows to align the different source data in a common coordinate system. Because the acquisition time for the routine MRI images (T1, T2, PD types) needs about 20 minutes, the alignment of them is necessary to correct head rigid movements. Linear Image Registration Tool (FMRIB, http://www.fmrib.ox.ac.uk/fsl) is chosen in our approach, which gives satisfying results.

The second step combines information from a priori knowledge and information from image intensities to built fuzzy membership functions relative to tumors. These fuzzy membership functions are considered as fuzzy models in which the used parameters are defined automatically by using information of image intensities. The fuzzification consists of using the fuzzy models, to transform MR images into fuzzy feature spaces (fuzzy sets). Three fuzzy sets corresponding to three types MRI images can be then obtained. The following section will describe in details this issue.

The third step then fuses these fuzzy spaces to lead to a fuzzy tumor space Fμ. From Fμ, a decision can be taken on to obtain the final tumor segmentation (defuzzification). However the obtained results are not enough precise, due to noise or low contrast around the contours. A post treatment is added (the fourth step) to ameliorate the results by using a fuzzy region growing. The final result is represented by a fuzzy volume in which the value of each voxel corresponds to its possibility to belong to the tumor.

3. FUZZY MODEL BUILDING

A fuzzy set has been defined as a collection of some objects with membership degrees (Pedrycz and Gomide, 1998). A membership function represents a mapping of the elements of a universe of discourse to the unit interval [0, 1] in order to determine the degree to which each object is compatible with distinctive features to collect. A membership function, considered as a fuzzy model, is used to obtain a corresponding fuzzy set. Pedrycz and Gomide (1998) have given an exhaustive analysis for experimental methods to determine membership functions. Boundaries and shapes of membership functions must correspond to an interpretation for an observation. Since our objective is to segment the brain tumor, the membership functions are relative to the brain tumor signals observed in MR image.

Many mathematical functions can be used as membership functions such as Rectangular-like functions, Trapezoidal-like functions, Parabolalike functions, Gaussian-like functions, etc... According to tumor characteristics in MRI images, some mathematical functions are proposed here, which are suitable to model the fuzzy information of tumor tissues presented in table 1. The membership functions corresponding to T1, T2 and PD are noted M_{T1}, M_{T2} and M_{PD}, respectively. They are defined by the following equations :

$$M_{T1}(s) = \begin{cases} 0 & s \leq a_1 \\ \frac{1}{2} + \frac{1}{2}\sin\left[\left(\frac{\pi}{a_2 - a_1}\right)\left(s + \frac{a_1 + a_2}{2}\right)\right], & a_1 < s \leq a_2 \\ 1 & a_2 < s \leq a_3 \\ \frac{1}{2} - \frac{1}{2}\sin\left[\left(\frac{\pi}{a_4 - a_3}\right)\left(s - \frac{a_3 + a_4}{2}\right)\right], & a_3 < s \leq a_4 \\ 0 & s > a_4 \end{cases} \quad (1)$$

$$M_{T2}(s) = \frac{1}{2} + \frac{1}{2}\sin\left[\left(\frac{\pi}{b_2 - b_1}\right)\left(s - \frac{b_2 + b_1}{2}\right)\right], b_1 < s \leq b_2 \quad (2)$$

$$M_{PD}(s) = \begin{cases} 0 & s \leq c_1 \\ \frac{1}{2}\left(\frac{s - c_1}{c_2 - c_1}\right)^2, & c_1 < s \leq c_2 \\ 1 - \frac{1}{2}\left(\frac{s - c_1}{c_2 - c_1}\right)^2, & c_2 < s \leq c_3 \\ 1 & c_3 < s \end{cases} \quad (1) \quad (3)$$

where s represents the intensity value of T1, T2 and PD images. The constants **a**, **b** and **c** are boundary parameters of M_{T1}, M_{T2} and M_{PD}, respectively.

From table 1, the boundary of M_{T1} should be taken within the intensity mean of CSF and that of GM in T1 MR, and the boundaries of both M_{T2} and M_{PD} should be taken within the maximum intensity of image and the means of WM in T2 and PD images, respectively. If the intensity means of the three tissues are known, we can easily find these boundary parameters. The fuzzy Markovian segmentation method proposed in (Ruan, *et al.*, 2002) can successfully segment three main brain tissues, WM, GM and CSF, and their mixtures (partial volume effects) from T1 weighted images. The intensity of mixtures depends on the mix percentages. The sum of the mix percentages should be 1. For example, a CSF-GM mixture can consist of 80% CSF and 20% of GM. It can be observed in T1 images a little brighter than the pure CSF, and much darker than the pure GM. Boundary parameters can then be found from the intensity means of the pure tissues and their mix-tissues. From table 1, the tumor is brighter than CSF. The parameter a_1 is then defined by the mean of the mixture with 90% of CSF and 10% of GM. It is a little brighter than CSF. The parameters a_2 and a_3 are defined by both mixtures with 30% of CSF and 40% of CSF. Voxels with intensity values within the interval [$a2$, $a3$] certainly belong to the tumor. As the tumor is darker than GM, a_4 is defined by the mixture of 90% GM. To deal with T1 and T2 images, we just need to project the result of T1 into them to obtain the corresponding segmentation, since all types of MRI images are aligned in a same space system. By the same way, we can also find the parameters *b* and **c**. As shown in table 1, intensities of the tumor in T2 images are brighter than GM, and of the same brightness as CSF. Here CSF is the brightest. Therefore, b_1 is defined by the mixture of 90% GM and 10% of CSF, b_2 by the mean of CSF. Intensities of the tumor in PD images are also taken within the interval between the mean of GM and that of CSF, but there are some differences compared to intensities of T2 images. GM is the brightest in PD images, while CSF is the brightest in T2 images. Intensities of the tumor can be darker than GM, and brighter than CSF in PD images. The corresponding of the parameter c_1 is chosen by the mixture of 40% of GM, c_2 by the mixture of 60% of GM, and c_3 by the mixture of 90% of GM. Thanks to the *a priori* knowledge, these parameters can be easily chosen. Using these three fuzzy membership functions the three MRI image volumes can be transformed into 3 fuzzy sets. In fact the parameters are not very sensible to influence the final results, because there are two steps after this fuzzification: fusion allowing to cancel some ambiguities and a post treatment which takes into account the spatial information to ameliorate the result .

Fig. 1. Proposed membership functions of the tumor tissue in MRI images corresponding to equation 1 (left), to equation 2 (middle), to equation 3 (right).

4. FUZZY DATA FUSION

Due to complexities of tumor tissues, they are more or less observed on the three types of MRI. But they cannot be all observed by only one type of MRI. Therefore the use of the three types of images is a benefit to have complete information about the tumor. That is why we use the data fusion. The obtained fuzzy models, M_{T1}, M_{T2}, and M_{PD}, allow us to transform the three types of MRI volumes into three fuzzy feature spaces, noted as μ_{T1}, μ_{T2}, and μ_{PD}, respectively, whose values represent their possibilities belonging to the tumor, because a fuzzy space can also be considered as a possibility space. Fusion of the three spaces can then give one fuzzy space, noted $F\mu$. which is more precise than one of μ_{T1}, μ_{T2}, and μ_{PD}.

Many works have been done in the field of fuzzy information fusion. Waltz (2001) presented three basic levels of image data fusion: pixel-level, feature-level and decision level, which correspond to three processing architectures. Registration-based methods are considered as pixel-level fusion, such as MRI-/PET (positron emission tomography) data fusion (Behloul, et al., 1998) and the fusion of multi-modality images in (Aguilar and New, 2002). Some techniques of knowledge-based segmentation can be considered as the feature-level fusion such as the methods proposed in (Barra and Boire, 2001). Some belief functions, uncertainty theory, Dempster-Shafer theory are often used for the decision-level fusion such as in (Lefevre, et al., 2000).

In our case, the fusion is considered as the feature-level, since the feature spaces μ_{T1}, μ_{T2}, and μ_{PD} are obtained after the step of fuzzifiction. The fusion is carried out on each voxel to obtain $F\mu(v)$ (v: co-ordinates of a voxel). Fuzzy fusion operators presented in (Pedrycz and Gomide 1998), such as fuzzy intersection operators, average operators or fuzzy t-norm, are tested and compared. Zadeh intersection operator, Yager intersection operator, Hamacher intersection operator, and geometric mean were used in our study. Both Yager intersection operator and Hamacher intersection operator use parameters allowing to adjust the membership degrees. However, it's difficult for us to choose optimal values. Zadeh's operator, selecting the minimum membership degree among the three fuzzy sets, is so strict that obtained membership degrees are very low comparing with others operators. The geometric mean operator compromises well these three memberships. In addition, it doesn't need any

parameter. As a result, it was chosen in our method. The definition is given by the following equation:

$$F\mu(v) = (\mu_{T1}(v) \cdot \mu_{T2}(v) \cdot \mu_{PD}(v))^{1/3} \qquad (4)$$

5. FUZZY REGION GROWING

Region growing is one of region-based segmentation methods in the domain of image processing. Region homogeneity, usually used as the main growing criterion, can be based on gray level, color, texture, shape, and model when using semantic information.

A fuzzy region growing algorithm is proposed here to improve the obtained the fuzzy set $F\mu$ after the fusion step. Spatial information, meaning that voxels belonging to the tumor should be connected, is considered in this step. It is a region connection processing based on the similarity of membership degrees and the neighborhood positions of the regions in 3D space. $F\mu$ is firstly divided into N fuzzy subsets according to different intervals of membership degrees. Different regions can then be obtained corresponding to the N subsets. Adjacent voxels whose membership values belong to the same set are merged into a region. Seeds of growing are the regions where each voxel has the membership degree =1. In the case of several regions (several seeds), the largest surface region is chosen with the assumption that only one tumor is presented in the brain. The growing procedure connects the adjacent regions using 6-connectivity with N-1 growing steps. The growing procedure performs with a decreasing membership degree in each step. The false regions which have high membership degrees due to noise or artifacts, can then be taken off. The final results are represented by a fuzzy set in which voxels have the membership degrees >0, and are spatially connected.

6. EVALUATION AND EXPERIMENTATION

4 patients with a glial cerebral tumor are considered in this paper. MRI images of each of the 4 patients are acquired on a 1.5T GE (General Electric Co.) machine using an axial 3D IR (Inversion Recuperation) T1-weighted sequence, an axial FSE (Fast Spin Echo) T2-weighted and an axial FSE PD-weighted sequence. The total number of slices is 124 for T1 images with a voxel size of $0.94 \times 0.94 \times 1.5 mm^3$; 20 slices for T2 and PD images with a voxel size of $0.47 \times 0.47 \times 5 mm^3$.

Three slices MRI, T1, T2 and PD images of patient-1 (one of the 4 patients), are shown in Fig.2 after having been registered. The three fuzzy models shown in Fig. 1 are applied to the corresponding registered MRI volumes to obtain the fuzzy spaces, presented in Fig.2. We can observe that no one space can give correctly the tumor region. The fusion operator, the geometric mean shown in the above section, is used for combining the three fuzzy spaces. Fig. 3 shows that the results after the fusion are better than anyone of the three precedent results. However due to the noise, artifacts, and imperfections of the fuzzy models, some regions are falsely detected as tumor region. The fuzzy region growing is applied to the fused result Fμ to chose only one tumor region. Fμ was divided here into 10 subsets with an equal interval 0.1. The growing seed is shown in Fig.3. Results of the growing steps are shown in Fig.4. Different brightness values represent different tumor membership degrees. The brighter intensity presents the higher membership degree. The obtained results are represented by a fuzzy space whose values represent the possibility of belonging to the tumor. Comparing to the original images, different pathological tissues can be distinguished by different fuzzy membership degrees. Two types of them can be identified clearly: tumor and edema. The intensity of the tumor is higher than that of edema in T1. In the region growing procedure, the edema is connected in the last steps due to its lower memberships. An *alpha*-cut set can separate these two tissues.

For evaluating quantitatively the proposed framework, hand traced results of the 4 patients obtained by a neuro-radiologist are used as the gold standard. Here the radiologist traced only the tumor tissues, shown in Fig. 5. The ratio of correct detection Pc and false detection Pf, used frequently for measuring the absolute errors, are used here as evaluation criteria. They are defined as follows:

$$Pc = \frac{N_{truepositif}}{N_{total}} \qquad (5)$$

where $N_{truepositif}$ is the number of voxels segmented as true positive, and N_{total} is the number of total voxels of the tumor region.

$$Pf = \frac{N_{false}}{N_{total}} \qquad (6)$$

where N_{false} is the number of voxels segmented as false positive.

To obtain the tumor tissue region (crisp result) for the comparison with the hand-traced region, •-cut is performed to the fuzzy result with •= 0.8. The obtained results of the four patients are shown in Fig.5. Visually, they are satisfying for all the four patients in spite of their different shapes and locations. The comparison results show a good Pc with an average of 96% and a weak Pf with the average 5% for the 4 patients.

7. CONCLUSION

We have presented in this paper a fuzzy segmentation method based on knowledge based fuzzy models and fuzzy fusion, in order to automatically segment tumor areas of human brain from multispectral MR images. Three fuzzy models are introduced to represent tumor tissue features for different MR image sequences. They allow to built fuzzy spaces in which fuzzy membership values represent the possibility belonging to the tumor. The

geometric mean is chosen as the fusion operator through our experiments, because it allows to correctly take into account the three fuzzy spaces by a simple way. The fuzzy region growing using the fuzzy connection technique improves the fused result. The defuzzification uses a *alpha*-cut set, allowing to obtain crisp results from the fuzzy results, such as, tumor tissue region or edema region. The comparison between the hand-labelling by one neuro-radiologist on four patients and the automatically obtained results, shows an average correct detection ratio is 96% and the average false detection ratio is 5%.

In a further work, we will continue to develop fuzzy modeling of tumors and to study fuzzy information fusion operators for other types of brain tumors. More experts will be asked to help us to evaluate the results.

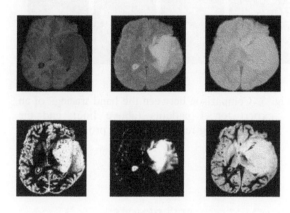

Fig. 2. One slice of a T1 volume (left at the above line), the corresponding slices of the registered T2 (middle) and of the registered PD (right). Fuzzy feature spaces of the corresponding images of T1 , T2, and PD from left to right at the bottom line.

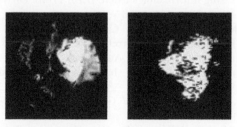

Fig. 3. The fused fuzzy space (left) and the tumor seed with $\mu F\mu(v)$= 1 (right).

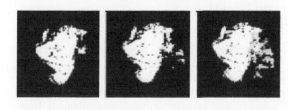

Fig.4. Steps of the fuzzy region growing with decreasing membership degrees (from left to right):$\mu F = 0.9, 0.8, 0.7$ (above line), 06 , 0.5 , 0.4 (bottom line).

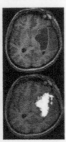

Fig. 5. Comparison between the hand tracings of an expert for 4 patients (above line), and the corresponding results using the proposed method (bottom line).

REFERENCES

Aguilar, M., New,J.R (2002). Fusion of Multi-Modality Volumetric Medical Imagery. *ISIF pp.*1206–1212.

Barra, V., Boire, J(2001). Automatic Segmentation of Subcortical Brain Structures in MR Images Using Information Fusion. *IEEE Trans. On Med. Imag.* **20**, pp.549–558.

Behloul, F., Janier, M., Croisille, P., Poirier, C., Boudraa, A., Unterreiner, R., Mason, J.C., Revel, D. (1998). Automatic assessment of myocardial viability based on PETMRI data fusion. IEEE-*EMBS, Proceedings of the 20th Annual International Conference.* **1**, pp. 492–495.

Cabral, J.E., White, K.S., Kim, Y. and. Effmann, E.L(1993). Interactive segmentation of brain tumors in MR images using 3D region growing. *Medical Imaging: Image Processing*, **1898**, pp.171–181.

Clark, M.C., Hall, L.O., Goldgof, D.B., Velthuizen, R. Murtagh, F.R., Silbiger, M.S (1998). Automatic Tumor Segmentation Using Knowledge-Based Techniques. *IEEE Trans. on Med. Imag.*17, pp.187–201.

Gibbs, P., Buckley, D., Blackband, S. and Horsman, A (1996). Tumour volume determination from MR images by morphological segmentation. *Phys Med Biol.*, **13**, pp. 2437–2446.

Ho, S., Bullitt, E., and Gerig, G (2002). Level set evolution with region competition: Automatic 3-D segmentation of brain tumors. *International Conference on Pattern Recognition*, **1**, pp.532–535.

Michael Kaus, Simon K. Warfield, Arya Nabavi, Peter M. Black, Ferenc A. Jolesz, and Ron Kikinis (2001). Automated Segmentation of MRI of Brain Tumors. *Radiology* **218** pp. 586–591.

Pitiot, A., Toga, A.W., Thompson, P.M (2002). Adaptive Elastic Segmentation of Brain MRI via Shape Model Guided Evolutionary Programming. *IEEE Trans .on Med.Imag.* **21**, pp. 910–923.

Leemput, K.V., Maes, F., Vandermeulen, D., Suetens, P (2003). A Unifying Framework for Partial Volume Segmentation of Brain MR Images. *IEEE Trans. On Med. Imag.* **22**, pp. 105–119.

Lefevre, E., P. Vannoorenberghe, P.and Colot, O. (2000). About the use of Dempster-Shafer theory for color image segmentation. *CGIP'2000,First International Conference on Color in Graphics and Image Processing.* Saint-Etienne, France.

Mancas, M. and Gosselin, B (2003). Iterative watersheds and fuzzy tumor visualization. *Proceedings of the IEEE Visualization Conference.*

Pedrycz, W. and Gomide, F (1998). An introduction to fuzzy sets analysis and design. The MIT Press.

Ruan, S., Moretti, B., Fadili, J., Bloyet, D (2002). Fuzzy Markovian Segmentation in Application of Magnetic Resonance Images. *Computer Vision and Image Understanding.* **85**, pp.54–69.

Saha, P.K., Udupa, J.K (2001). Fuzzy Connected Object Delineation: Axiomatic Path Strength Definition and the Case of Multiple Seeds. *Computer Vision and Image Understanding.* **83**, pp. 275–295.

Styner, M., Brechb¨uhler, C., Sz´ekely,G., Gerig,G (2000). Parametric estimate of intensity inhomogeneities applied to MRI. *IEEE Trans. On Med. Imag.* **19**, pp. 153–165.

Udup, J.K., Saha, P. K., Lotufo, R.A (2002). Relative Fuzzy Connectedness and Object Definition: Theory, Algorithms, and Applications in Image Segmentation. *IEEE Trans. On Pattern Analysis and Machine Intelligence.* **24 (11)**, pp. 1485–1500.

Waltz, E.D. The principles and practice of image and spatial data fusion (1995). *Proceedings of the 8th National Data Fusion Conference.* pp. 257–278, Dallas, Texas.

Warfield, S. K., Kaus, M., Jolesz, F.A., Kikinis, R (2000). Adaptive, Template Moderated, Spatially Varying Statistical Classification. *Medical Image Analysis.* **4(1)**, pp.43–55.

TUMOR SEGMENTATION FROM PET/CT IMAGES USING LEVEL SETS METHOD

Sonia Khatchadourian* Stéphane Lebonvallet*
Michel Herbin** Jean-Claude Liehn*** Su Ruan*

* CReSTIC, 9 rue de Québec, Troyes 10024
** CReSTIC, rue des Crayères, Reims 51000
*** Institut Godinot, 1 rue du général Koenig, Reims 51056

Abstract: In the framework of detection, diagnostic and treatment planning of tumors, the Positron Emission Tomography (PET) examination coupled with a Computed Tomography (CT) have become recently the most efficient technique. Manual segmentation of regions of interest (ROI) could be time consuming and this is necessary to obtain information about patient pathology. The aim of our study is to propose an automatic solution to this problem. This paper presents an approach of tumor segmentation based on a level set method. One critical step, the algorithm stopping, is automatic. The results obtained by the proposed method dealing with PET-CT images are encouraging. Copyright © 2006 IFAC

Keywords: Image, Partial differential equations, Segmentation

1. INTRODUCTION

PET (Positron Emission Tomography) and CT (Computed Tomography) scans are both standard imaging tools that physicians use to pinpoint disease states in the body. A PET scan demonstrates the biological function of the body before anatomical changes take place, while the CT scan provides information about the body's anatomy such as size, shape and location. By combining these two scanning technologies, a PET/CT scan enables physicians to more accurately diagnose and identify cancer, heart disease and brain disorders, and also to determine how much cancer has spread, and how well cancer treatment is working. Accurate and automatical tumor segmentation is an important issue in many applications of medical image system for quantitative studies. As known, manual tracing by an expert of a tumor in 3D is not only exceedingly time consuming, but also exhausting for experts. Therefore, an automatical segmentation is necessary.

Many segmentation methods have already been used in medical imaging field. A simple method is the thresholding. (Malyapa *et al.*, 2002) used a binary threshold to segment tumorous areas in the pelvis region. This method allows the user to obtain results very quickly but it is not accurate. The seeded region growing is one of segmentation methods. It consists of choosing seeds, and growing them according to a criteria. (Adams and Bischof, 1994) choose the seeds as the local extrema and then to grow them until the regions touch themselves. But when one need to delineate just one region, one cannot venture to fill the entire image. That is why (Zoroofi *et al.*, 2004) have chosen the seeds upon the histogram and then let grow until the criteria was no longer verified. This work has been used to the segmentation of a non-necrotic femoral head. (Mancas and Gosselin, 2004) proposed a segmentation based on watersheds (Roerdink and Meijster, 2001) to segment PET /CT images. The principle of the watershed technique is to transform the gradient of a greyscale image into a topographic surface. (Mancas and Gosselin, 2004) used an iterative watersheds. A very common way to segment medical images is to use an atlas of the human body as a priori knowledge. (Bondiau et al., 2005), (Ehrardt et al., 2001) and (Lorenzo-Valdez et al., 2004) have used such approach respectively on the brain, the hip and the heart atlases. The statistical methods have been also studied to deal with the medical images, because of noise presenting in images. (Ruan et al., 2000) propose a statistical segmentation based on Random Markov Fields to segment brain RM images. The fuzzy segmentation offers an interesting point of view to take into account ambiguities of objects to segment. As shown in (Dou et al., 2002), membership functions are modeled to express the fuzzy signals of the brain tumor observed in different types of images. Among various image segmentation techniques, active contour model [2] has emerged as a powerful tool for semi-automatic object segmentation. The basic idea is to evolve a curve, subject to constraints from a given image,for detecting interesting objects in that image. It consists of the resolution of systems of partial differential equations for which interface propagation phenomenon has to be described. The active contour models are often implemented based on level set method (Sethian, 1999), which is a powerful tool to capture deforming shape. But it has the disadvantage of a heavy computation requirement even using the narrow band evolution. The fast marching method is proposed for monotonically advanced fronts (Sethian, 1999), and is extremely faster than level set evolution. Generally, there are three key problems needed to be solved to implement the curve evolution methods. The first one is the initialization of the seed points. The second one is the formulation of the speed function. And the last one is the determination of the stopping criterion.

The level set methods have been widely applied in medical imagery (Suri et al., 2002) in different domains : the brain (Xie et al., 2005), the bone (Morigi and Sgallari, 2004), the vascular trees (Farag et al., 2004) and so on... The most common way to initialize the level set is the manual selection of a ROI which seems to be relevant ((Xu et al., 2000), (Farag et al., 2004) and (Xie et al., 2005)). Sometimes a simple mouse click combined with a fast marching approach (Fan, n.d.) is used. In this case the final contour determined by the fast marching step is the initial front of the level set. Those methods are semi-automated while we are focused on the automated methods. (Morigi and Sgallari, 2004) proposed an automated method but the imaging system is not the same as the subject of our study.

Our work consists of detecting tumors from the whole body image volume acquired by a PET/CT device. We have no a priori knowledge on the tumor location. A contour evolution model using a level set method with an initialization based on thresholding is proposed in this paper.

The paper is organized as follows. Firstly, an overview of our study is described. Secondly, the level set method and its implementation will be exposed. The different steps of our approach and the associated results are then presented. Finally we will conclude and give some perspectives.

2. OVERVIEW OF THE STUDY

2.1 PET-CT imaging system

PET/CT combines the functional information from a PET with the anatomical information from a CT into one single examination. Registration between both images is not needed. A PET detects changes in cellular function: how cells are utilizing nutrients like sugar and oxygen. Since these functional changes take place before physical changes occur, PET can provide information that enables physician to make an early diagnosis. A CT scanner uses a combination of x-rays and computers to give the radiologist a non-invasive way to see inside a human body. One advantage of CT is its ability to rapidly acquire multiple two-dimensional image slices of the anatomy.

For giving an optimal treatment, physicians carry out usually manual segmentations to obtain information about sizes, location and image signals of tumors. The objective of our work is to provide a system allowing to automatically segment tumors with a good precision. Since the PET pinpoints increased metabolic activity in cells, tumorous areas can be better observed. Hence, the tumor segmentation is carried out in PET images. Then the segmented regions are projected into CT images to obtain an anatomical localization.

2.2 Segmentation framework

Most previous works which have been carried out on the topic of segmentation only considered a part of the body of the patient. Our aim is at detecting the tumorous areas from the whole body. Any a priori knowledge about locations of the tumors are taken into account. As the PET images are usually noisy and bad contrasted, the methods based on the image intensity or gradient are not efficient in these cases. The statistical methods cannot be neither used efficiently due to the small size of the tumor : they are too small to get statistical properties comparing with all images. The solution of the evolving contours is interesting in this case because they can grow to the expected size of the tumorous areas with help of geometrical and intrinsic properties.

To segment the 3D images, we process the 2D images slice-by-slice. The proposed framework consists of 3 steps: seed detection giving a set of seeds susceptible to belong to the tumor; seed selection allowing to delete aberrant seeds and to consider the left as the initial tumor contours; contour evolution according to an active contour model.

The seed detection consists of finding ROIs using intensity information. The areas of high glucose activity lead to high gray levels observed in PET images. A thresholding of images can be carried out to obtain the ROIs. The problem is how to choose the threshold. As known, the histogram can give the information about the distribution of grey levels. The maximum of the histogram is firstly found, which represents body tissues. Supposing that the number of pixels belonging to tumor regions has less than that of the pique of histogram. The threshold is then defined as the gray level on which the number of pixels equals to the maximum multiplied by a proportionality factor α which is given by experiences.

After the thresholding of images, several seeds are obtained in which some of them do not belong to the tumor. Not only the small regions which could be tumorous, are detected as seeds, but also the big regions representing some anatomical regions (heart for example) which give high intensity. The big regions can be easily moved out from the seeds if their sizes, compared to the size of the patient body, are significant. An erosion, morphological mathematics operator, is carried out to decrease the sizes of seeds. Thus, the initial contours of those plausible ROIs are preserved. This seed selection step allows us to delete aberrant seeds and to keep that of tumorous areas. From the obtained initial contours (seeds), a level set method is used to grow them to find the tumor contours. In the next section, this method is presented in details.

3. CONTOUR EVOLUTION BASED ON LEVEL SET METHOD

The level set method has been introduced by (Osher and Sethian, 1988) to solve the partial differential equations. It refers to the theory of the curve evolution. The algorithm proposed by Sethian (Sethian, 1999) has been widely applied to many domains ((Fan, n.d.), (Xu *et al.*, 2000))

3.1 Theory

Considering a curve represented by a level set function Φ. For a point p, $\Phi(p)$ is the signed minimum distance from p to the contour :

- if $\Phi > 0$, p is outside the contour,
- if $\Phi = 0$, p is on the contour,
- if $\Phi < 0$, p is inside the contour.

From a geometric point of view, the evolution of a contour can be described as follows :

$$\frac{\partial x}{\partial t} = VN \qquad (1)$$

with x a point of the contour, V the speed function, N the normal vector of the curve at x. The evolution of the curve depends on the normal vector N of the curve and the curvature K at each point of the curve, with :

$$N = \frac{\nabla \Phi}{|\nabla \Phi|}$$

$$K = \nabla \frac{\nabla \Phi}{|\nabla \Phi|} = \frac{\Phi_{xx}\Phi_y^2 - 2\Phi_x\Phi_y\Phi_{xy} + \Phi_{yy}\Phi_x^2}{(\Phi_x^2 + \Phi_y^2)^{3/2}}$$

To describe the evolution of the curve we need to define the initial curve as zero level set :

$$\Phi((x(t)), t = 0) = 0 \qquad (2)$$

To associate the zero level set to the evolving curve at each time and to derive the motion equation for this level set function, the zero level set has to be re-initialized at each time step :

$$\Phi((x(t)), t) = 0 \qquad (3)$$

After derivation of the equation 3 :

$$\Phi_t + V \nabla \Phi((x(t)), t) = 0 \qquad (4)$$

where $V = x'(t) \cdot N$ is defined as a speed function and $\nabla \Phi$ is the gradient of the level set function Φ. This speed function is the key of the implementation of the level set method.

3.2 Speed function

The speed function V depends on :

- local properties given by local geometrical information (curvature, normal of the curve),
- global properties depending on the form and the position of the front,
- independent properties defined as a fluid velocity that transport passively the front.

Based on these properties, the speed function can be expressed as follows :

$$V = V_{prop} + V_{curv} + V_{adv} \qquad (5)$$

with $V_{prop} = V_0$ constant speed propagation

$$V_{curv} = -\epsilon K \quad \text{curvature dependent speed}$$
$$V_{adv} = U(x, y, t) \cdot N \quad \text{advection speed}$$

Since the speed function decreases to zero at the boundary of the area to segment, the components of the speed function are proposed as follows:

$$\epsilon = \epsilon_c V_{pij} \quad \text{with } \epsilon_c \text{ constant ,} \qquad (6)$$

$$V_{pij} = \frac{1}{1 + G_{ij}} \quad \text{with } G_{ij} \text{ the image gradient} \qquad (7)$$
$$\text{at pixel } (i, j) ,$$

$$U_{ij} = \beta \nabla V_{pij} \quad \text{with } \beta \text{ constant .} \qquad (8)$$

ϵ_c introduces a viscosity notion around the contour and β controls the attraction force. The bigger is ϵ_c, the slower is the evolution of the contour. The bigger is β, the faster is the evolution of the contour. Those parameters are to be defined according to used images. For further details on the implementation of the speed function, see (Sethian, 1999) and (Xu *et al.*, 2000).

The stopping criteria depends on the speed function, therefore indirectly on the intrinsic parameters of the images. The evolution of contours stops when the speed function $V = 0$.

3.3 The narrow band

The problem of this method is that it takes a long time to compute if the update of the level set function is made on the entire image. The solution proposed by (Chopp, 1993) is to compute the level set function in a narrow band around the front. The level set function is only updated when it reaches the boundary of the narrow band. This narrow band approach can reduce importantly the computing time. It has been used in shape recognition by (Malladi *et al.*, 1994) and analyzed by (Adalsteinsson and Sethian, 1995) with success. Therefore, the narrow band is also adopted in our method. The width of the narrow band used is 3 pixels around the contour because of the small size of the tumors.

4. EXPERIMENTAL RESULTS

4.1 Data

The data, we use for our experimentation, consist of PET-CT image volumes corresponding to three patients who have tumors. The size of the images is of 144x144 pixels, for a resolution of 7mm per pixel for PET images. One volume is composed of about 190 slices. Visually, the tumors observed in images are well segmented, confirmed by hospital experts. One of them is presented in this paper to show the efficiency of our method.

4.2 Choice of parameters

Different values of the parameters have been studied and tested before validating these ones : $\alpha = 0,0025$ for the seed detection, $\epsilon_c = 0,05$ and $\beta = 0,005$ for the level set. Those values are chosen according to the images to be dealt with. They can be kept if the images to be treated are acquired from the same PET-CT imaging machine.

4.3 Segmentation

Ten PET slices of a patient who has a lung tumor are presented here (figure 1). For a good visualization, the gray levels are inverted. The high activity in glucose regions appears dark. The darker region in the middle of the image is the heart. The muscular tissues are brighter : the arms and the ribcage can be seen as the border of the patient body. The brightest regions represent the lungs. The tumor to detect is on the right part of the image, on the lung area near the ribcage.

The different steps of the segmentation are:

- seed detection (figure 2),
- seed selection (figure 3),
- tumor segmentation (figure 4).

The seed detection (figure 2) allows us to determine ROIs which could be contained by tumorous areas. It is achieved thanks to the gray level information of the entire image volume. We know that higher gray levels represent areas of higher glucose activity and the tumors have abnormal glucose activity. But as foreseen the ROIs obtained are not necessarily tumors. The seed selection can help the decision of seed as explained previously. On the figure 3, it remains only the plausible seeds to initialize the segmentation.

The level set method is carried out image by image for all the volume from the initialization given by the seed selection. We can see on figure 4 that the tumor is well segmented. Unfortunately, the tumor is not the only region segmented because of the seed detection which is not robust enough.

5. CONCLUSION AND FUTURE WORKS

This paper presents a work on the automatic segmentation of tumorous areas from whole body information. The tumors are well segmented even if it remains in the results some false regions. Two possibilities have been evoked to solve this :
- Improving the seed detection by using a multi-scale binarization method ((Jolion, 1994) and (Trier and Taxt, 1995)) for example. Indeed the question of seed detection has been briefly considered to test the level set method.

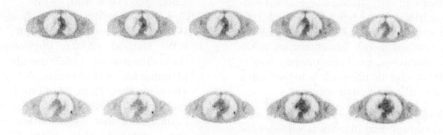

Fig. 1. Patient 3 stack sample illustrating a lung tumor. White matter is the lunge, in darker the muscular tissues, and in dark the heart in the middle and the tumor on the right lung.

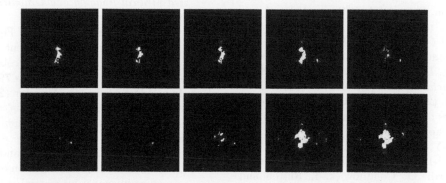

Fig. 2. Seed detection on this sample.

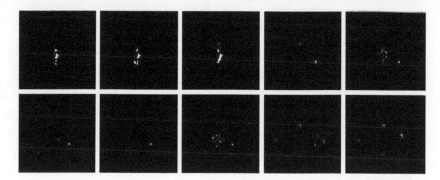

Fig. 3. Seed selection.

Fig. 4. Level set segmentation. The red contours represent the potential tumorous areas.

- Implementing a robust classification method to select the tumor contours among all obtained contours. If the initialization step is not robust, the classification step is necessary. A SVM classification, already studied in our laboratory on medical image classification, gave encouraging results (AitAouit, 2004). Our future work is to perform a SVM to obtain only the tumor contours.

Finally the level set should be implemented as a real 3-dimensional method in order to consider the whole 3D information. That allows to improve the performances of the contour evolution.

REFERENCES

Adalsteinsson, D. and J.A. Sethian (1995). A fast level set method for propagating interfaces. *Jour. of Comp. Phys.* **118**, 269–277.

Adams, R. and L. Bischof (1994). Seeded region growing. *IEEE Transaction on Pattern Analysis Machine Intelligence* **16**, 641–647.

AitAouit, D. (2004). Classification d'images par la mthodes des support vector machines (svm): tude et applications.

Bondiau, P-Y., G. Malandain, S. Chanalet, P-Y. Marcy, J-L. Habrand, F. Fauchon, P. Paquis, A. Courdi, O. Commowick, I. Rutten and N. Ayache (2005). Atlas-based automatic segmentation of mr images: Validation study on brainstem in radiotherapy context. *Int. J. Radiation Oncology Biol. Phys.* **61**, 289–298.

Chopp, D.L. (1993). Computing minimal surfaces with level set curvature flow. *Jour. of Comp. Phys.* **106**, 77–91.

Dou, W., Q. Liao, S. Ruan, D. Bloyet, J.M. Constans and Y. Chen (2002). Automatic brain tumor extraction using fuzzy information fusion. *Proc. SPIE* **4875**, 604–609.

Ehrardt, J., H. Handels, T. Malina, B. Strahmann, W. Pltz and S.J. Pppl (2001). Atlas-based segmentation of structures to support virtual planning of hip operations. *International Journal of Medical Informatics* **64**, 439–447.

Fan, D. (n.d.). www.cs.wisc.edu/~fan/levelset/.

Farag, A.A., H. Hassan, R. Falk and S.G. Hushek (2004). 3d volume segmentation of mra data sets using level sets. *Academic Radiology* **11**, 419–435.

Jolion, J-M. (1994). Analyse multirsolution du contraste dans les images numriques. *Traitement du Signal* **11**, 245–255.

Lorenzo-Valdez, M., G.I. Sanchez-Ortiz, A.G. Elkington, R.H. Mohiaddin and D. Rueckert (2004). Segmentation of 4d cardiac mr images using a probabilistic atlas and the em algorithm. *Medical Image Analysis* **8**, 255–265.

Malladi, R., J.A. Sethian and B.C. Vermuri (1994). Evolutionnary fronts for topology-independent shape modeling and recovery. *Proceedings of Third European Conference on Computer Vision* **800**, 3–13.

Malyapa, R.S., S. Mutic, D.A. Low, I. Zoberi, W.R. Bosch, R. Laforest, T.R. Miller and P.W. Grigsby (2002). Physiologic fdg-pet three-dimensional brachytherapy treatment planning for cervical cancer. *Int. J. Radiation Oncology Biol. Phys.* **54**, 1140–1146.

Mancas, M. and B. Gosselin (2004). Towards an automatic tumor segmentation using iterative watersheds. *Proc. of the Medical Imaging Conference of the International Society for Optical Imaging (SPIE Medical Imaging)*.

Morigi, S. and F. Sgallari (2004). 3d long bone reconstruction based on level sets. *Computerized Medical Imaging and Graphics* **28**, 377–390.

Osher, S. and J.A. Sethian (1988). Fronts propagating with curvature-dependent speed : algorithms based on hamilton-jacobi formulations. *J. Computational Physics* **79**, 12–49.

Roerdink, J.B.T.M. and A. Meijster (2001). The watershed transform: Definitions, algorithms parallelization strategies. *Fundamenta Informaticae* pp. 187–228.

Ruan, S., C. Jaggi, J. Xue, J. Fadili and D. Bloyet (2000). Brain tissue classification of magnetic resonance images using partial volume modeling. *IEEE Transactions on Medical Imaging* **19**, 1179–1187.

Sethian, J.A. (1999). *Level Set Methods and Fast Marching Methods*. Cambridge Univerity Press.

Suri, J., K. Liu, S. Singh, S. Laxminarayana and L. Reden (2002). Shape recovery algorithms using level sets in 2-d/3-d medical imagery: A state-of-the-art review. *IEEE Transaction on Information Technology in Biomedicine* **6**, 8–28.

Trier, O.D. and T. Taxt (1995). Evaluation of binarization methods for document images. *IEEE Trans. Pattern Anal. Mach. Intell.* **17**, 312–315.

Xie, K., J. YANG and Y.M. ZHU (2005). Semiautomated brain tumor and edema segmentation using mri. *European Journal of Radiology*.

Xu, C., D. L. Pham and J. L. Prince (2000). Medical image segmentation using deformable models. In: *Handbook of Medical Imaging – Volume 2: Medical Image Processing and Analysis* (J.M. Fitzpatrick and M. Sonka, Eds.). pp. 129–174. SPIE Pres.

Zoroofi, R.A., Y. Sato, T. Nishii, N. Sugano, H. Yoshikawa and S. Tamura (2004). Automated segmentation of necrotic femoral head from 3d mr data. *Computerized Medical Imaging and Garphics* **28**, 267–278.

A STUDY OF PARTIAL VOLUME EFFECTS
ON CLUSTERING-AIDED PARAMETRIC IMAGES

Lingfeng Wen*,***, Stefan Eberl*,**, Dagan Feng*,***, Michael Fulham*,**

* School of Information Technologies, University of Sydney, NSW 2006, Australia
** Dept. of PET & Nuclear Medicine, Royal Prince Alfred Hospital, Missenden Road,
Camperdown, NSW 2050, Australia
*** Center for Multimedia Digital Signal Processing, Dept. of Electronic &
Information Engineering, Hong Kong Polytechnic University, Hung Hom, Kowloon,
Hong Kong

Abstract: Cluster analysis has been applied in functional imaging to derive parametric images with improved signal to noise ratio. However, the impact of partial volume effects (PVE) on the parametric images aided by clustering is still uncertain. Computer simulations were performed to generate simulated dynamic data at various noise levels. Reconstructed data were processed by cluster analysis. The generalized linear least squares (GLLS) method was used to estimate parametric images. The results were compared with the parametric images generated without clustering. The results demonstrate that clustering does not enhance PVE, but reduces PVE. Furthermore, clustering-aided parametric images are shown to be insensitive to noise. *Copyright © 2006 IFAC*

Keywords: Monte Carlo Simulation, Parameter Estimation, Physiological Model, Quantitative analysis, Computer Tomography

1. INTRODUCTION

Molecular functional imaging techniques, such as positron emission tomography (PET), can detect subtle biochemical and physiological changes well before structural changes are apparent on anatomical imaging, like computed tomography (CT) and magnetic resonance (MR). More recently, single photon emission computed tomography (SPECT) has also been shown to potentially achieve quantitative functional imaging (Almeida, Ribeiro et al. 1999).

Molecular functional imaging is capable of deriving physiological parameters which explicitly depict the tracer kinetics such as influx rate and receptor binding potential. To estimate the parameters of the appropriate model describing the tracer kinetics, a plasma time activity curve (PTAC) is obtained as the input function through measuring the tracer concentration in blood plasma over the duration of the study. The acquired dynamic projection data are reconstructed to derive tissue time activity curves

(TTAC) for each voxel or the region of interest (ROI) as the output function. Parameters are estimated by the appropriate curve fitting method. Fig.1 shows an example of a three-compartment and four-parameter kinetic model for a neuronal receptor tracer with specific binding.

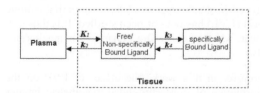

Fig 1. Definition of rate constants for 3-compartment and 4-parameter model

Compared to the traditional manual delineation of ROIs, voxel-wise generation of parametric images has the advantage of avoiding operator dependency in defining the correct anatomical region. Parametric images may also potentially visualize subtle changes, which may be lost due to the averaging inherent in ROI based analysis.

Nonlinear least square (NLS) fitting is regarded as the method of choice for providing parameter estimates with optimum statistical accuracy (Huang, Phelps et al. 1980). However, the NLS method relies on good initial estimates of the parameters, particularly for noisy voxel TTACs and is impractical to generate parametric images due to its heavy computational burden. Thus graphical approaches are commonly employed to generate parametric images through linear or multi-linear regression analysis of transformed and linearized data (Patlak, Blasberg et al. 1983; Logan, Fowler et al. 1990; Yokoi, Iida et al. 1993; Ichise, Ballinger et al. 1996). However, graphical methods provide only a limited number of parameters, typically no more than two. In addition, some of their underlying assumptions may give rise to bias in the parametric images. Feng et al. have proposed the generalized linear least square (GLLS) method to provide unbiased estimates of multiple parameters of interests without requiring careful and optimized choice of initial parameters (Feng, Huang et al. 1996; Chen, Lawson et al. 1998; Wong, Feng et al. 1998).

One of the challenging issues of PET and SPECT is the low signal to noise ratio (SNR), which can lead to instability of the parameters estimates. Efforts have been made to improve SNR for more reliable parametric images such as the optimal sampling schedule (Li, Feng et al. 1996; Li, Feng et al. 2000; Wen, Eberl et al. 2003b), wavelet-aided parameter estimate (Turkheimer, Banati et al. 2000; Cselenyi, Olsson et al. 2002). Cluster analysis is one approach to classify and organize TTACs into clusters according to their similarities (Kimura, Hsu et al. 1999; Wong, Feng et al. 2002). Cluster analysis assumes that the complicated functional imaging data can be represented by a limited number of cluster centroid curves without loss of quantitative accuracy.

Cluster-aided methods have been applied to process dynamic PET data for parametric image generation (Kimura, Hsu et al. 1999) and image segmentation (Wong, Feng et al. 2002). Recently, clustering has also been applied to dynamic SPECT (Bal, DiBella et al. 2003; Wen, Eberl et al. 2003a). However, the impact of clustering on the quantitative accuracy achieved in small structures subject to partial volume effects (PVE) has not yet been studied. It is thus still unclear whether clustering enhances or ameliorates PVE.

Therefore, in this work, the effect of PVE on the performance of clustering-aided parametric images was investigated with computer simulations of dedicated phantoms. High count Monte Carlo simulations were performed to generate the dynamic data at various noise levels. Kinetic parameters and reliability for the dynamic data with and without clustering were estimated to evaluate the impact of PVE.

2. METHODS

2.1 Cluster analysis

While there are a number of similarity measures used in cluster algorithms (Xu and Wunsch 2005), the classical Euclidean distance was chosen in this work, due to its applicability to data with multiple temporal samples. The cluster analysis was performed for the dynamic reconstructed data with a weighted Euclidean distance (1).

$$E(z_i, \overline{u}_j)_w = \sum_{t=1}^{p} \left| z_i(t) - \overline{u}_j(t) \right|_w^2 \qquad (1)$$

E_w is the obtained weighted Euclidean distance, z_i represents the corresponding TTAC for the ith voxel, $\overline{u}_j$ is the centroid TTAC of the jth cluster and p is the total number of frames in the dynamic studies. The weights w were chosen to be proportional to the frame duration divided by the whole scan duration, which resulted in the higher weights for the frames with longer duration and hence better counting statistics, and lower weights for the shorter frames with low SNR.

The TTACs for each voxel are classified automatically into the nearest cluster C_k with the minimum weighted least-square distance according to the criterion given by equation (2).

$$\left. \begin{array}{l} \min(E(z_i, \overline{u}_j)) < \Delta d \\ \overline{u}_j \in U \end{array} \right\} \Rightarrow z_i \in C_k \qquad (2)$$

In the equation (2), U is the set of centroid TTACs for all obtained cluster, Δd is the threshold, which is derived from the histogram analysis of the whole image set, to determine whether the TTAC of the candidate z_i satisfies the maximum allowable weighted Euclidean distance requirement. If so, the corresponding voxel is added to cluster C_k, and the cluster's centroid is updated to reflect the contribution of TTAC of ith voxel. Otherwise, a new cluster is formed to represent this voxel which does not fulfil the criterion (2).

Clustering was performed according to the hierarchical analysis (Wong, Feng et al. 2002; Wen, Eberl et al. 2003a), which has an advantage over other clustering algorithms such as K-means and fuzzy C-means as it avoids having to specify the number of clusters a priori. The cluster analysis was iterated until the number of clusters no longer varied.

2.2 Computer simulation

Five cylindrical phantoms with spherical hot lesions of various sizes were simulated to evaluate the impact of PVE. The cylindrical phantoms consisted of a 10-mm-thick outer rim representing grey matter and 120-mm-diameter central cylinder representing white matter within a 140-mm-diameter and 140-mm-long cylinder. The hot spheres, whose diameters varied from 10mm to 50mm, were located in the center of each phantom. The transaxial and coronal views are shown in the Fig.2 for the phantom with a 30-mm-diameter spherical hot lesion.

High count static projection data for individual structures of the phantoms were generated by the SimSET Monte Carlo package (Lewellen, Harrison et al. 1998). The effects of attenuation, scatter, limited detector collimator spatial resolution and energy resolution were included in the simulation. The camera parameters were based on a Triad XLT triple head gamma camera (Trionix Research Laboratories, Twinsburg, OH, USA).

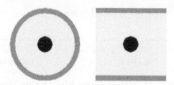

Fig.2 Transaxial and coronal views through the center of one phantom with a 30-mm-diameter spherical hot lesion.

2.3 Simulation of the dynamic data

The dynamic projection data were generated through the combination of individual structures in the phantoms and their corresponding activities for each frame duration of the sampling schedule. TTACs from studies with the neuronal nicotine acetylcholine receptor tracer 5-[^{123}I]-iodo-A-85380 (Kassiou, Eberl et al. 2001) were used in the simulation. Five different levels of realistic noise were added in the scaled projection data, while one projection data set was generated without noise added for comparison.

Table 1 The reference parameter sets for simulations

Cortex	K_1	k_2	k_3	k_4
White Matter*	0.05	0.025		
Grey Matter	0.277	0.059	0.038	0.037
Lesion	0.284	0.061	0.143	0.041

* Two-compartment and two-parameter model fit

The dynamic projection data sets were reconstructed with the OS-EM iterative reconstruction method (Hudson and Larkin 1994). The reconstructed data were corrected for attenuation and scatter. The reconstructed spatial resolution was about 12 mm full width at half maximum (FWHM) with a voxel size of 2.2 mm $\times$ 2.2 mm $\times$ 2.2 mm.

Two sampling schedules were used in the investigation. The conventional sampling schedule (CSS) consisted of fifteen 60s scans, nine 300s scans and twelve 600s scans (Kassiou, Eberl et al. 2001). The optimum image sampling schedule (OISS) for the multiple regions of interests was four scans with the durations of 7.3, 21.8, 81.3 and 69.7 minutes (Wen, Eberl et al. 2003b).

2.4 Parameter estimation

TTACs of reconstructed data were fitted voxel-by-voxel with the GLLS method (Feng, Huang et al. 1996), Yokoi (Yokoi, Iida et al. 1993) and Logan graphical methods (Logan, Fowler et al. 1990). The influx rate of K_1 and the volume of distribution of V_d

(3) were chosen as the parameters of interests for the evaluation.

$$V_d = \frac{K_1}{k_2}\left(1 + \frac{k_3}{k_4}\right) \qquad (3)$$

To conform to the underlying two-compartment and two-parameter model for the Yokoi method, the same model was used to estimate K_1 when the GLLS method was applied. V_d was estimated using the three-compartment and four-parameter model (as shown in Fig.1) for the GLLS and Logan methods. The reconstructed data were processed by the cluster analysis. K_1 and V_d were estimated with the GLLS method for each cluster centroid curve prior to the generation of cluster-aided parametric images.

Volumes of interests (VOI) were defined for the spherical hot lesion. Percentage bias (4) was derived for each VOI to evaluate the accuracy across 20 Monte Carlo simulation data sets. Coefficient of variations (CV) (5) were also derived to compare the reliability of the obtained parametric images.

$$Bias = \frac{1}{M}\left[\sum_{i=1}^{M}\sum_{j=1}^{N}\frac{p_{i,j}-p_o}{N}\right]/p_o \times 100\% \qquad (4)$$

$$CV = \frac{1}{p_0}\sqrt{\frac{\sum_{i=1}^{M}(\sum_{j=1}^{N}\frac{p_{i,j}}{N})^2 - M(\sum_{i=1}^{M}\sum_{j=1}^{N}\frac{p_{i,j}}{N})^2}{M-1}}$$
$$\times 100\% \qquad (5)$$

In equations (4) and (5), $p_{i,j}$ is the estimated parameter for the jth voxel in the corresponding VOI for the ith simulation data set, p_o is the reference value of the TTAC used in the simulation (Table 1), M is the number of simulation data sets for each of noise levels, and N is the total number of voxels for the VOI.

3. RESULTS

3.1 Partial volume effects on parameter estimates

The percentage biases of estimated parameters are plotted as a function of hot lesion sphere diameters at the highest level of noise in Fig.3. Not unexpectedly, all the studied methods suffered from PVE which led to the pronounced underestimation of parameters with biases exceeding -70% for K_1 and -80% for V_d for the 10-mm-diameter lesion due to the lesion size being smaller than the 12mm FWHM resolution of the simulated camera systems.

For the parametric images of K_1, the methods without clustering had very similar trends as a function of the sphere diameter, with the bias increasing with decreasing sphere diameters. In contrast, the bias due to PVE was reduced and less affected by sphere diameter when clustering was included to process the CSS and OISS data. The GLLS method achieved less bias for OISS data over the CSS data due to improved SNR with the longer frame durations. The clustering-aided methods only suffered from pronounced bias at the smallest sphere diameter of 10 mm.

For V_d, clustering did also reduce PVE despite of a more pronounced effect than observed for K_1. Interestingly, the clustering-aided GLLS method achieved approximately equivalent estimates of V_d for the CSS and OISS data. The Logan method applied to OISS data showed the least bias, which may be due to the limited number of only four frames for OISS resulting in a higher slope and hence less bias.

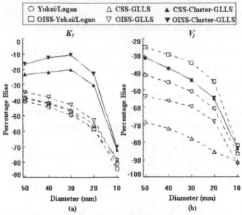

Fig.3 Plots of percentage bias as a function of hot spheres diameter. Yokoi/Logan (open circle) – Yokoi or Logan method applied to CSS data, CSS-GLLS (open triangle) – GLLS applied to CSS data without clustering, CSS-Cluster-GLLS (solid triangle) – GLLS applied to the clustered CSS data, OISS-Yokoi/Logan (open square) – Yokoi or Logan methods applied to OISS data, OISS-GLLS (open inverted triangle) – GLLS applied to OISS data without clustering, OISS-Cluster-GLLS (solid inverted triangle) – GLLS applied to OISS data with clustering

High reliability was achieved for all the methods for estimating K_1 with CVs less than 2.0% for the diameter of 30 mm at the highest level of noise, expect the Yokoi method with CVs of 4.0% and 2.9% respectively for CSS and OISS data. The reliability of V_d was slightly worse than K_1, but still acceptable with the CVs less than 5% for all the methods for the 30-mm-diameter sphere at the highest level of noise. Thus the results demonstrate that clustering does not increase bias due to PVE in the functional imaging, and in fact reduces bias.

3.2 Noise effect on the parameter estimates

The percentage biases of estimated parameters were plotted as a function of the increasing noise level for the 30-mm-diameter lesion in Fig.4.

The estimated K_1 of all the studied methods was observed to be relatively insensitive to the noise level. However, the methods without clustering suffered from higher bias for CSS and OISS data, with bias ranging from -35.1% to -47.2%. In contrast, clustering-aided methods reduced the bias to -19.1% and -9.9% for CSS and OISS data, respectively.

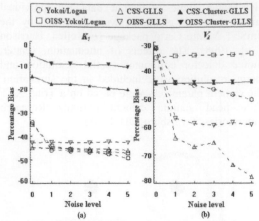

Fig.4 Plots of percentage bias as a function of increasing noise level. Legends are the same as for Fig.3

For V_d, strong noise influences were observed for the GLLS method without clustering. The bias exceeded -77.8% and -59.4% for CSS and OISS data at the highest noise level. This is expected due to the increased number of voxels with unsuccessful GLLS fitting for the noisy TTACs. The Logan method suffered slightly from noise for the CSS data, whose biases were somewhat lower than those with GLLS (-50.6% at the highest noise level). Almost constant estimates were achieved with the GLLS method for the clustered CSS and OISS data, and the Logan method for the OISS data, regardless of the noise level. Interestingly, almost identical estimates of -44.6%±0.2% and -44.3%±0.1% were achieved with the GLLS method for the clustered CSS and OISS data, which demonstrated that clustering was the main contributing factor to the constant estimates of V_d. The graphical methods also benefited from the OISS method to give the least biased estimates.

Reliable parameter estimates were achieved, with CVs for all the methods lower than 6%. Especially for the clustered data, high reliability was achieved for V_d (CV<0.8%) as well as the Logan method for CSS and OISS data. Therefore, clustering was efficient in reducing the noise effect on the parameter estimates and provided almost noise-insensitive estimates over the range of noise studied.

3.3 Noise effect on the cluster analysis

Table 2 shows the cluster numbers as well as the obtained thresholds in the clustering for CSS and OISS data. Despite of the slight decreased thresholds for clustering, the obtained cluster numbers were approximately constant and independent of noise level.

The consistent cluster numbers explains why the clustering-aided parametric images could provide the noise-insensitive estimates. Automated determination of threshold in this work is superior to the constrained cluster number or cluster member due to the self-adaptive threshold acquisition from the images. Sufficient cluster numbers guarantee that the cluster centroid curves represent the range of TTACs and kinetics in the data, thus reducing noise without loss of quantitative accuracy.

Table 2 The mean and standard deviation of the obtained threshold values and cluster numbers

Noise level	1	2	3	4	5
CSS-TH	379 ±9	376 ±11	369 ±7	363 ±7	360 ±9
CSS-NUM	199 ±17	200 ±13	205 ±14	196 ±12	196 ±17
OISS-TH	401 ±9	396 ±8	395 ±9	391 ±7	393 ±14
OISS-NUM	209 ±11	215 ±17	219 ±19	226 ±23	214 ±14

CSS-TH: thresholds for CSS data, CSS-NUM: cluster numbers for CSS data, OISS-TH: threshold for OISS data, OISS_NUM: cluster numbers for OISS data

4. CONCLUSION

In this paper, partial volume effects on the performance of the clustering-aided parametric images were systematically investigated through Monte Carlo simulation for one triple head camera system of the kinetics of the neuronal nicotine acetylcholine receptor tracer 5-[^{123}I]-iodo-A-85380. The clustering method was shown not to enhance, but to reduce the partial volume effects. The simulation data demonstrates that clustering was efficient in reducing the estimated biases for parameters of interests with noise-insensitive estimates. The study also shows that the clustering method is promising to aid the GLLS method applied to voxel-wise parameter estimations.

5. ACKNOWLEDGEMENT

This work was partially supported by the Australian Research Council (ARC), Research Grant Council of Hongkong (RGC), and Australian Department of Education, Science and Training (DEST).

REFERENCES

Almeida, P., M. J. Ribeiro, et al. (1999). Absolute quantitation of iodine-123 epidepride kinetics using single-photon emission tomography: comparison with carbon-11 epidepride and positron emission tomography. *Eur. J. Nucl. Med.* **26**(12): 1580-1588.

Bal, H., E. V. R. DiBella, et al. (2003). Parametric image formation using clustering for dynamic cardiac SPECT. *IEEE Trans. Nucl. Sci.* **50**(5): 1584-1589.

Chen, K., M. Lawson, et al. (1998). Generalized linear least squares method for fast generation of myocardial blood flow parametric images with N-13 Ammonia PET. *IEEE Trans. Med. Imaging* **17**: 236-243.

Cselenyi, Z., H. Olsson, et al. (2002). Wavelet-aided parametric mapping of cerebral dopamine D-2 receptors using the high affinity PET radioligand C-11 FLB 457. *Neuroimage* **17**(1): 47-60.

Feng, D., S. C. Huang, et al. (1996). An unbiased parametric imaging algorithm for nonuniformly sampled biomedical system parameter estimation. *IEEE Trans. Med. Imaging* **15**: 512-518.

Huang, S. C., M. E. Phelps, et al. (1980). Noninvasive determination of local cerebral metabolic rate of glucose in man. *Am. J. Physiol.* **238**: E69-E82.

Hudson, H. M. and R. S. Larkin (1994). Accelerated image reconstruction using ordered subsets of projection data. *IEEE Trans. Med. Imaging* **13**: 601-609.

Ichise, M., J. R. Ballinger, et al. (1996). Noninvasive quantification of dopamine D2 receptors with iodine-123-IBF SPECT. *J. Nucl. Med.* **37**: 513-520.

Kassiou, M., S. Eberl, et al. (2001). In vivo imaging of nicotinic receptor upregulation following chronic (-)-nicotine treatment in baboon using SPECT. *Nucl. Med. Biol.* **28**: 165-175.

Kimura, Y., H. Hsu, et al. (1999). Improved signal-to-noise ratio in parametric images by cluster analysis. *Neuroimage* **9**(5): 554-561.

Lewellen, T. K., R. L. Harrison, et al. (1998). The Simset Program in *Monte Carlo Calculations in Nuclear Medicine*. M. Liungberg, S. E. Strand and M. A. King: 77-92, Institute of Physics Publishing, Bristol.

Li, X., D. Feng, et al. (1996). Optimal image sampling schedule: A new effective way to reduce dynamic image storage space and functional image processing time. **15**(5): 710-719.

Li, X., D. Feng, et al. (2000). Optimal image sampling schedule for both image-derived input and output functions in PET cardiac studies. **19**(3): 233-242.

Logan, J., J. S. Fowler, et al. (1990). Graphical analysis of reversible radioligand binding from time-activity measurements applied to [N-11C-methyl]-(-)-cocaine PET studies in human subjects. *J. Cereb. Blood Flow Metab.* **10**: 740-747.

Patlak, C. S., R. G. Blasberg, et al. (1983). Graphical evaluation of blood-to-brain transfer constants from multiple-time uptake data. *J. Cereb. Blood Flow Metab.* **3**: 1-7.

Turkheimer, F. E., R. B. Banati, et al. (2000). Modeling dynamic PET-SPECT studies in the wavelet domain. *J. Cereb. Blood Flow Metab.* **20**(5): 879-893.

Wen, L., S. Eberl, et al. (2003a). A Reliable Voxexl-by-Voxel Parameter Estimation for Dynamic SPECT. *Proceeding of World Congress on Medical Physics and Biomedical Engineering*.

Wen, L., S. Eberl, et al. (2003b). An improved optimal image sampling schedule for multiple ROIs in dynamic SPECT in *Modelling and Control in Biomedical Systems 2003*. D. Feng and E. Carson: 139-143, Elsevier, Oxford.

Wong, K. P., D. Feng, et al. (2002). Segmentation of dynamic PET images using cluster analysis. *IEEE Trans. Nucl. Sci.* **49**(1): 200-207.

Wong, K. P., D. Feng, et al. (1998). Generalized linear least squares algorithm for non-uniformly sampled biomedical system identification with possible repeated eigenvalues. *Comput. Meth. Programs Biomed.* **57**(3): 167-177.

Xu, R. and D. Wunsch (2005). Survey of clustering algorithms. *IEEE Trans. Neural Netw.* **16**(3): 645-678.

Yokoi, T., H. Iida, et al. (1993). A new graphic plot analysis for cerebral blood flow and partition coefficient with Iodine-123-Iodoamphetamine and Dynamic SPECT validation studies using Oxygen-15-water and PET. *J. Nucl. Med.* **34**(3): 498-505.

EFFICIENT AND AUTOMATIC ABDOMINAL IMAGE REGISTRATION BASED ON ACTIVE CONTOUR

Xiu Ying Wang[1,3]**, Cherry Ballangan**[1,4]**, David Feng**[1,2]

1 Biomedical and Multimedia Information Technology (BMIT) Group
School of Information Technologies, F09
The University of Sydney, NSW 2006, Australia
2 Center for Multimedia Signal Processing
Department of Electronic and Information Engineering
Hong Kong Polytechnic University
3 School of Computer Science and Technology
Heilongjiang University, Harbin 150080, P.R.China
4. Informatics Department
Petra Christian University, Indonesia

Abstract: Image registration is critical for making diagnostic decision and essential for image-guided surgery. To improve the quality and accuracy of healthcare, efficient registration is highly demanded. However, because of the non-rigid deformations caused by heartbeat and breath, abdominal image registration remains a challenging task. To address these issues, an automatic and elastic registration for abdominal images is proposed. The algorithm is divided into three steps: efficient non-iterative affine registration; elastic motion field extraction based on active contours; elastic registration based on motion field. The validation of the method on monomodality and multimodality abdominal images has demonstrated that the algorithm is reliable and efficient. *Copyright © 2006 IFAC*

Keywords: image registration, affine, transformations, mean-square error, computer vision.

1. INTRODUCTION

Medical imaging modalities can be divided into two major categories: anatomical modalities and functional modalities. Anatomical modalities, mainly emphasizing morphology, include X-ray, computed tomography (CT), magnetic resonance imaging (MRI), and Ultrasound (US). Functional modalities, primarily providing information on the biochemistry, include single photon emission computed tomography (SPECT), and positron emission tomography (PET). With the quick advances in imaging techniques, these diverse imaging modalities are playing a more and more important role in improving the quality and efficiency of healthcare. In clinical practice, to improve the optimization and precision of clinical decision and to achieve better, faster, and more cost-effective healthcare, a considerable amount of medical imaging data from multimodalities or over time intervals need to be collected, integrated, and analyzed. However, how to fully make use of the widely available and complementary multimodal images to provide the connection of structural information with functional information is a challenging and important issue (Wang, 2005). Biomedical image registration aims to solve this issue by combining the most meaningful information and facilitating the smart use of the embedded knowledge.

Registration is the process to match two datasets that may differ in time of acquisition, image properties, or viewpoints (Brown, 1992). Because of its essential role in assisting clinical training, surgery simulation and planning, and improving patient safety and healthcare benefits, medical image registration has been extensively studied and investigated decades, which has resulted in numerous of algorithms (Brown, 1992; Zitova and Flusser, 2003; Bankman, 2000; Maintz and Viergever, 1998; Hill *et al*, 2001).

According to the registration feature space, principally, medical image registration can be distinguished into intensity-based registration and feature-based registration. Directly and fully exploiting the image intensity information, the intensity-based registration algorithms have the advantages of no segmentation required and few user interactions involved, and most importantly, these methods have potentials to achieve fully automated registration. However, the computation of this category of schemes is not efficient.

The other principal medical image registration category is based on corresponding features (points, curves, or surfaces) that can be extracted manually, interactively, or automatically. One main advantage of feature-based registration is that the transformation often can be stated in analytic form, which leads to efficient computational schemes. However, in the feature-based registration methodologies, the preprocess step is needed and the registration results are highly dependent on the result of this preprocess.

In medical image registration, a matching transformation must be determined. Depending on the characteristics of the differences between the medical images to be registered, generally, the registration transformations can be divided into rigid and non-rigid transformations. The rigid transformations can be used to cope with rotation and translation differences between the images. But due to complex displacements of patient postures, tissue structures, and the shapes of the organs, elastic or non-rigid registrations are required.

In biomedical image registration community, most of efforts have been devoted to brain image registration and great progresses have been achieved in this area. However, the abdominal image registration still remains a challenge because of more complex, non-rigid, and involuntary motions caused by breath and heartbeat. Elastic deformations of organ structures and volume changes make the task even more difficult. Moreover, more efficient registration is required for clinical applications.

In this paper, an efficient, automatic, and elastic registration algorithm for abdominal images is proposed to address the above issues.

2. HIERARCHICAL REGISTRATION SCHEME

The proposed abdominal registration method can be divided into three steps (Figure 1).

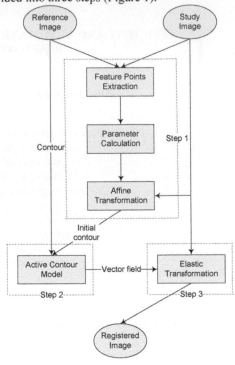

Fig. 1: Efficient and Automatic Registration Algorithm

Firstly, on the basis of automatically selected feature points, affine parameters can be directly derived by minimizing the mean-square error (MSE) and affine registration can be achieved; then, on the basis of the initial estimation provided by affine registration, the image contour can be extracted automatically and the deformation vector field can be obtained by using active contour algorithm; finally, based on the deformation field, elastic transformation is performed and elastic displacements can be corrected.

2.1 Step 1: Efficient Affine Registration

Usually, an optimization algorithm is needed to serve as a search strategy in the registration procedure. However, the iterative optimization procedure is time-consuming and sometimes, the registration will be trapped into local minimum. In order to improve registration efficiency, a non-iterative and automatic affine registration method is proposed.

Automatic Feature Extraction. As mentioned previously, landmark-based registration has the advantage of high computation efficiency. The landmark can be intrinsic or extrinsic. Abdominal image registration based on extrinsic landmarks maybe invasive or less accurate due to elastic motion of abdomen. While intrinsic landmark based registration is a challenging and ongoing topic.

In this paper, to get affine transformation parameters, corresponding feature points in the images need to be extracted from both statistical and geometrical properties. As the statistical properties, affine-invariant moment-based features, including the centroids and the focuses of the ellipse that have the same second order moment as each image, are extracted from the images. Besides, to get consistent and evenly distributed feature points, some boundary points are detected as the geometrical properties with respect to particular angles between the maximum axes of the images.

Another option to obtain the feature points is based on the intensity characteristic of the images. For example, in some images, the salient objects might have significant changes in intensity compared to their neighborhood. This nature can be useful to acquire the corresponding points between two images. However, this intensity-based feature point extraction approach is not robust in multimodal registration due to different intensity characteristics in multimodal images.

In the experiment of this paper, both geometrical feature points and intensity-based feature points are used for monomodal registration, while in multimodal registration, intensity-based points will not be detected as registration features.

Affine Transformation Parameter Derivation. In order to improve the registration efficiency, instead of using the traditional iterative optimization method, affine registration parameters are directly derived by minimizing Mean Squared Error (MSE). This direct transformation parameter derivation not only can provide efficient computation but also can generate the smallest difference between the two images to be registered.

Let $X = \{x_1, x_2, ..., x_n\}$ and $Y = \{y_1, y_2, ..., y_n\}$ be corresponding points in the study image and reference image respectively. MSE can be defined as:

$$e^2(R, t, c) = \frac{1}{n} \sum_{i=1}^{n} \|y_i - (cRx_i + t)\|^2 \qquad (1)$$

Where: R is rotation parameters; t is translation parameters; and c is scaling parameters.

Umeyama (1991) presented a solution to directly derive these affine transformation parameters from

MSE and this efficient method is adopted in the affine registration procedure.

2.2 Step 2: Automatic Active Contour Extraction

After affine registration, the simple deformations can be corrected, however, because of complex changes and deformations of abdominal images, elastic registration is required to further improve registration performance. In this paper, the results of affine registration will be used as the initial contour estimation in the active contour based elastic registration procedure. The reason that the active contour algorithm is adopted in this paper is that it can automatically produce the motion field that will be used to perform the elastic transformation, by an efficient computation.

Active contour or Snake is an energy minimizing spline developed by Kass et al (1988). The classic snake model attracts initial contour to some image features and minimizes the object energy function as presented in Equation 2.

$$E_{snake}^* = \int_0^1 E_{snake}(v(s))ds$$
$$= \int_0^1 E_{int}(v(s)) + E_{image}(v(s)) + E_{con}(v(s))ds \qquad (2)$$

An active contour can be represented by a curve $v(s) = [x(s), y(s)]$. The contour coordinates (x, y) can be expressed as the function of arc length s. The snakes are influenced by internal forces, image forces, and external constraint forces.

- The internal forces caused by stretching and bending, serve as a smoothness constraint to keep the contour from discontinuity or bending too much. The internal energy responsible for the smoothness and deformation of the contour can be expressed as:

$$E_{int} = \frac{1}{2}\left(\alpha(s)\left|\frac{dv}{ds}\right|^2 + \beta(s)\left|\frac{d^2v}{ds^2}\right|^2\right) \qquad (3)$$

Where: $\alpha(s)$ and $\beta(s)$ are the measure of elasticity and stiffness of the snake.
- The second term of Equation 2 is image forces responsible for attracting the snake to the true edge of the image.
- The third term of Equation 2 comes from external constraints imposed either by a user or some other higher level process which may force the snake toward or away from particular features.

The classic active contour model above is flexible since it maintains the shape as a curve and the final form of the contour can be influenced by feedback from a higher level process. However, this classic snake is sensitive to the initial contour guess and cannot deal with concavity. Some approaches have been proposed to solve these problems, for example, balloon (Cohen, 1991) and gradient vector flow (Xu and Prince, 1998).

2.3 Step 3: Elastic Transformation

The spatial differences between the initial contour and the deformed contour from the active contour algorithm specify the displacement vectors that can be used to warp the study image to fit into the reference image.

If (x,y) is a point in an image, elastic transformation can be achieved by using the equation proposed by Pielot *et al* (2000):

$$T(x,y) = (x,y) + \frac{\sum_{k=1}^{m} w_k(x,y)[(xs,ys)-(xi,yi)]}{\sum_{k=1}^{m} w_k(x,y)} \quad (4)$$

Where: (xi, yi) is the initial contour; (xs, ys) is the deformed contour; and $w_k(x, y)$ is the distance weighting function of a single point (x, y), given by:

$$w_k(x,y) = e^{-\beta(|x-xi|+|y-yi|)} \quad (5)$$

Where: β is the weighting factor.

3. EXPERIMENTAL VALIDATION

To validate the proposed algorithm, experiments on registration of monomodality abdominal images, multimodality abdominal images, intra-subject images, and inter-subject images have been carried out. The parameters used in this experiment are $\alpha = 0.1$ and $\beta = 0.1$ for the active contour and $\beta = 0.04$ (weighting factor) for the elastic transformation.

3.1 Monomodality Abdominal Image Registration

Registration of abdominal computed tomography (CT) images plays an essential role in checking injury, determining liver disease, detecting tumors, and evaluating the response to a therapy. The proposed algorithm has been validated on the experiments of both intra-subject registration and inter-subject registration.

Intra-subject Registration. To facilitate the diagnosis, usually, the same subject needs to undergo different medical check over time intervals. In the first series of experiments, abdominal images (512*512) of the same subject have been carried out.

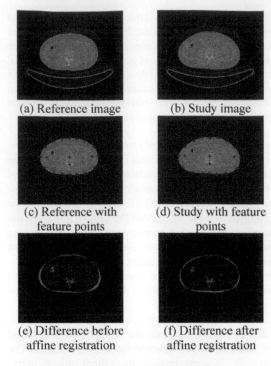

(a) Reference image   (b) Study image

(c) Reference with feature points   (d) Study with feature points

(e) Difference before affine registration   (f) Difference after affine registration

Fig. 2: Affine Registration for Abdominal CT Images

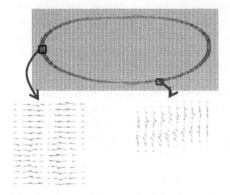

Fig. 3: Gradient of the Reference Image

Fig. 4: Motion Field of the Contours

After the affine registration which is shown in Figure 2, the active contour model is used to calculate gradient (Figure 3) and the motion field of the contours can be obtained. Some part of this motion field has been enlarged and shown in Figure 4.

The motion field obtained is used as the input to calculate the elastic transformation. The result of this whole elastic registration is shown in Figure 5. After the elastic registration, the study image has been deformed to fit to the reference image (Figure 5(d)).

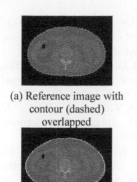 

(a) Reference image with contour (dashed) overlapped

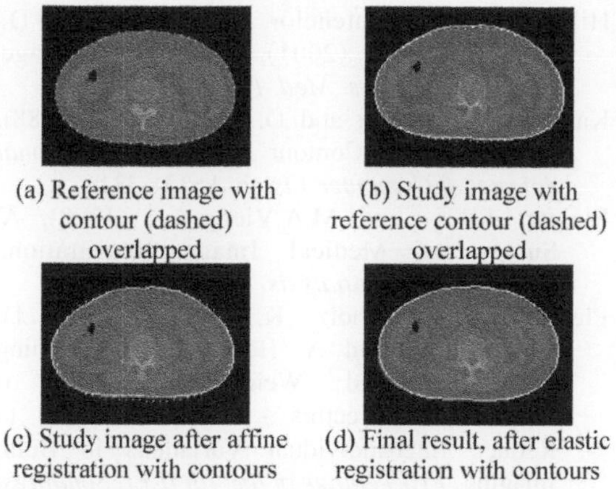

(b) Study image with reference contour (dashed) overlapped

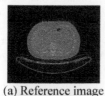 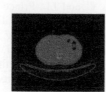

(c) Study image after affine registration with contours

(d) Final result, after elastic registration with contours

Fig. 5: Elastic Registration Results

Inter-subject Registration. Inter-subject registration is important in specific disease identification and atlas construction by involving images from different subjects. From the images in Figure 6, it can be seen that the difference between these images is relatively significant. Compared to the previous experiments, during the active contour convergence procedure, this experiment needs more iterations, it is mainly because the two images used in this experiment have much more difference.

(a) Reference image

(b) Study image

(c) Difference before affine registration

(d) Difference after affine registration

(e) Reference image with contour overlapped

(f) Study image with reference contour (dashed) overlapped

(g) Study image after affine registration with reference contour (dashed) and its own contour

(h) Final result, after elastic registration

Fig. 6: CT-CT Inter-subject Abdominal Image Registration

(a). Reference image (CT) with feature points

(b). Study image (PET) with corresponding feature points

(c) Reference image with contour overlapped

(d) Study image with reference contour (dashed) overlapped

(e) Study image after affine registration with reference contour (dashed) and its own contour

(f) Final result, after elastic registration

Fig. 7: CT to PET Image Registration Process

3.2 Multimodality Abdominal Image Registration

CT images provide high quality anatomical details while PET images provide functional information. Through the proper registration of functional information provided in PET with anatomical background of CT scanning, physiological functional regions can be located more precisely and surgeon can optimize the operation with minimal damage to the health organs. Such functional-to-anatomical data registration is very useful for clinical diagnosis and surgical operation, especially for telesurgery.

The experiments on CT and PET images have been carried out to test the proposed approach in the multimodal abdominal registration (Figure 7). It can be seen that the reference image and the study image have significant difference (Figure 7(d)) that might result in a slow active contour convergence. However, because of the affine registration step, the difference between the two images can be reduced significantly (Figure 7(e)) which makes the active contour converge relatively fast.

To further test the performance of the proposed elastic registration algorithm, a series of experiments have been carried out and MSE of 19 feature point pairs is calculated before registration, after affine registration, and after elastic registration. The experimental results are shown in Table 1. From this table, it can be discovered that the affine registration can decrease MSE greatly while elastic registration can be used to further improve the registration performance.

Table 1: MSE of CT-PET Image Registration

Images to be registered	Before registration	Affine Registration	Elastic Registration
Pair 1	162.0094	14.9679	4.9769
Pari2	164.0058	12.8577	4.3821
Pair3	162.4365	14.3552	5.1078
Pair4	159.7266	13.3452	5.5559
Pair5	160.2521	16.6090	6.8262
Pair6	164.4082	13.7143	5.4592

4. CONCLUSION

To improve the efficiency and effectiveness of abdominal image registration, in this paper, an efficient, automatic, elastic registration method is proposed. The proposed method is divided into three main steps: non-iterative and automatic affine registration, active contour generation procedure, and elastic registration procedure. Experiments on monomodality and multimodality images validate that the proposed method is reliable to produce good registration. Besides, the proposed approach has the advantage of high registration efficiency, because firstly during the affine registration procedure, the transformation parameters can be derived directly from MSE and the time-consuming iterative optimization procedure can be avoided; secondly, the initial contour estimation provided by the affine registration for the active contour algorithm is close to the reference contour, which can dramatically accelerate vector field extraction. Furthermore, elastic registration can be achieved by deriving contour motion fields from active contour models. This method can be applied to 2D and be extended to 3D monomodal and multimodal registration, intra-subject and inter-subject registration as well.

5. ACKNOWLEDGEMENTS

This work is supported by the ARC of Australia, RGC of Hong Kong, HLJNSF and HLJE of China.

6. REFERENCES

Bankman, I.N. (2000). *Handbook of medical imaging: processing and analysis*. Academic Press.

Brown, L.G. (1992). A survey of image registration techniques. *ACM Computing Surveys*, **24**(4), 325-376.

Cohen, L. D. (1991). On active contour models and balloons. *Computer Vision, Graphics, and Image Processing: Image Understanding*, **53**(2), 211-218.

Hill, D.L.G., P.G. Batchelor, M.H. Holden, and D. J. Hawkes. (2001). Medical image registration. *Phys. Med. Biol.*, **46**(1), 1-45.

Kass, M., A. Witkin and D. Terzopoulos. (1988). Snakes: Active Contour Models. *International Journal of Computer Vision*, **1**, 321-331.

Maintz, J.B.A. and M.A.Viergever. (1998). A Survey of Medical Image Registration. *Medical Image Analysis*, **2**(1), 1-36.

Pielot, R., M. Scholz, K. Obermayer, E. D. Gundelfinger and A. Hess. (2000). Warping with Optimized Weighting Factors of Displacement Vectors - A New Method to Reduce Inter-individual Variations in Brain Imaging. *Proceedings of the 4th IEEE Southwest Symposium Image Analysis and Interpretation*, 264-268.

Umeyama, S. (1991). Least-Squares Estimation of Transformation Parameters Between Two Point Patterns. *IEEE Transactions on Pattern Analysis and Machine Intelligence*, **13**(4).

Wang, X. and D. Feng. (2005) Biomedical Image Registration for Diagnostic Decision Making and Treatment Monitoring. Chapter 9 in R. K. Bali (Ed.) Clinical Knowledge Management: Opportunities and Challenges. *Idea Group Publishing*, 159-181.

Xu, C. and J.L. Prince. (1998). Snakes, Shapes, and Gradient Vector Flow. *IEEE Transactions on Image Processing*, **7**(3), 359-369.

Zitova, B. and J. Flusser. (2003). Image Registration Methods: A Survey. *Image and Vision Computing*, **21**, 977-1000.

A NOVEL INTEGRATIVE BIOINFORMATICS ENVIRONMENT FOR ENCODING AND INTERROGATING TIMELAPSE MICROSCOPY IMAGES

I. A. Khan[1], C. J. Hedley[1], N. S. White[2], R. Ali[3], M. J. Chappell[3], N. D. Evans[3], L. Campbell[4], N. Marquez[4], J. Fisher[4], P. J. Smith[4] and R. J. Errington[5].

[1] *Biostatistics and Bioinformatics Unit, School of Medicine, Cardiff University, Cardiff, CF14 4XN, UK.* [2]*Sir William Dunn School of Pathology, University of Oxford, Oxford, OX1 3RB, UK.* [3]*Department of Engineering, University of Warwick, Coventry, CV4 7AL U.K.* [4]*Department of Pathology, School of Medicine, Cardiff University, Cardiff, CF14 4XN, UK.* [5]*Department of Medical Biochemistry and Immunology, Cardiff University, Cardiff, CF14 4X, UK.*

Abstract: Image-derived kinetic cell-based assays, where time is the quality parameter, demand unique solutions enabling image encoding and interrogation of spatio-temporal cellular events. Our overall strategy is to derive integrated data mining tools and predictive models capable of producing *in-silico* cell response fingerprints for use in drug screening, experimental therapeutics and hypothesis-testing for the design of treatment regimens. Critical to realizing this aim is the development of bioinformatics and visualisation tools to address problems of cellular heterogeneity, stochasticity and scaling for the impact of drugs on cell populations and to use these tools in making fundamental advances in our understanding of drug targeting in complex neoplastic systems. *Copyright © 2006 IFAC*

Keywords: timelapse microscopy, lineage tracking, bioinformatics encoding, Quercus data mining, predictive signatures.

1. INTRODUCTION

Exploring and exploiting the enormous potential for pharmacological modulation of the mammalian cell cycle are key goals for basic research and drug discovery. A formidable challenge in drug discovery is the establishment of suitable preclinical screens which inform on mechanism of action and provide proof of principle. High-through-put and indeed high-content cell-based screening systems, incorporating elegant reporter assays, have been effectively used to profile drugs based on simple stimulus-response readouts, however the design of current high-throughput instrumentation, discards biological heterogeneity and most assays never contend with dynamic processes. In the absence of detailed kinetic information, simple snap-shot or static high-content-assays that measure drug effects provide an over simplified and often skewed view of the nature of resistant and sensitive cells. Currently there is no software available that encodes kinetic data derived from image sources and consequently permits a coherent analysis of drug-induced perturbations in complex populations. Bearing this in mind, we have designed and developed a novel integrative bioinformatics software suite, termed 'Quercus', designed to encode kinetic data from raw images of any generic perturb situation and subsequently builds parametised database, which later can be queried for hypothesis driven data mining. In relation to drug-induced perturbed situation, the database provides a rich repository for pharmacokinetic (PK) and pharmacodynamic (PD) modelling and validation.

1.1 Cell-based assays for understanding pharmacodynamic effects of anti-cancer drugs

Timelapse microscopy, provides a route to tracking individual cellular events or cellular responses in a population context (Chu *et al.*, 2004; Marquez, *et al.*, 2003). The resolution, and hence type of event, is determined by the contrast mode which include phase, differential interference contrast, dark field and fluorescence imaging (White and Errington, 2005). Transmission phase offers a probeless and non-perturbing contrast mode providing low resolution but highly informative outputs on cell behaviour (e.g. cell shape and cell position), the changes in these two basic features facilitate assays describing critical global cell pharmacodynamic responses such as cell division, cell death (Allman *et al* 2003) and cell motility (Stephens, *et al.*, 2004). At the core of these macro-pharmacodynamic assays is the implementation of timelapse microscopy to link the initial cell cycle position during acute exposures to anti-cancer agents with the proliferation consequences for individual cells. An anticancer drug often exerts its effect at specific phases of cell cycle resulting in a modified cell cycle traverse. The timelapse approach enables the determination of single cell cycle traverse, delay, arrest and checkpoint breaching in response to drug perturbations (Marquez, *et al.*, 2004) and can be considered as the basis for time-encoded cell-based assays.

1.2 Addressing tumour heterogeneity: single cell lineages underlie the basic assay concept

Many drugs and X-irradiation (Forrester, 1999) differentially target across the cell cycle, therefore this heterogeneity in cellular responses presents a clear route for cell cycle-mediated drug resistance. Lineage analysis provides an elegant, non-invasive assay for determining the evolving and complex interplay for tumour survival at the single cell level. In experimental terms a cell lineage is defined as descent in a line from a common progenitor that was exposed to a given influence for a discrete period. The behaviour of both the progenitor and the descending line of offspring reveal the time-integrated pharmacodynamic response (e.g. changes in inter-generation cell division time or cell death). For example, this would have direct relevance to how viable populations, representing resistant fractions, might be maintained in drug-treated tumour cell populations.

1.3 The bioinformatics challenge

Interpreting and encoding simple timelapse sequences is not a trivial undertaking. Systematic and objective practice must underlie the process where the encoding of the cell behaviour using image analysis sits along side other basic assay descriptors. The overall aim is to provide an integrated environment which can efficiently encode image data into a parametised database and also enables robust hypothesis-driven data-mining and drug signature queries. Quercus, written in Perl and Java has been developed to provide this type of integrated environment. This suite of software presents a novel advance for cell-based screening of drug action- the temporal monitoring of cell cycle progression, enabling the tracking of single cell lineage progression and checkpoint transitions in a non-invasive manner even within heterogeneous populations.

2. DESIGN AND DEVELOPMENT OF QUERCUS

2.1 Acquiring the time-lapse sequence-an illustrative experiment

Timelapse microscopy is the repeated collection of a single field of view from a microscope at discrete time intervals through which dynamics of cell division can be captured. Human osteosarcoma U-2 OS cells were grown for 24 h in a 6-well plate using standard cell culture conditions. Cells were then treated with the anticancer agent topotecan (TPT) (Feeney *et al* 2003) for 1h, after which the drug was washed out. TPT interferes with a vital enzyme for DNA metabolism and generate damage that can stall cell cycle progression. Post-treatment the culture plate was immediately mounted onto an x, y positioning stage of an Axiovert 100 time-laspe microscope fitted with an incubating enclosure held at 37^0 C and 5% CO_2. An ORCA-ER 12-bit CCD camera (Hamamatsu, Reading, UK), then captured bright-field phase images every 15 min for 5 days to follow the long-term consequences of drug treatment. At the end of the experiment the images were stacked and saved as *.stk or *.AVI format. MetaMorph (Molecular Devices, California, USA) was used to view the image files and Quercus in conjunction with MetaMorph was used to encode the images into a parametised database.

2.2 Defining multilayer descriptors for each cell

For every screen, all parameters are recorded in an accessible but simple screen file (eg*.txt or *.xls). The screen file acts as a digital laboratory notebook where all experimental descriptors for all drug screens are recorded with some details being recorded manually while many, such as the progenitor cell coordinate derived from the raw images, were acquired semi-automatically via image analysis (e.g. MetaMorph and a Perl script). The principal objective of this screen file is to attribute a unique encryption tag for each original or starting cell within the screen. This is critical, since the complexity evolves as each starting cell divides or dies and hence produces progeny which populate a full lineage. Therefore every subsequent event within the lineage can be rooted or associated to the progenitor cell and the tagging associated with it. This approach ensures comprehensive indexing within the Lineage Database.

2.3 Derivation of Quercus and interlinking with the image analysis software

Quercus is the botanical genus to which oak belongs. Like seed of a tree, each progenitor cell generates a lineage. The encoding part of Quercus was written in Perl. The software is divided into three interlinked parts. The first part interacts with the digital laboratory notebook and directs users to a specific progenitor cell location, this part of the programme also generates the tag through which the progenitor cell will be indexed in the database. The second part interacts with Metamorph and draws the evolving lineage into the canvas. Finally, the third part writes the image derived parameters associated with each cell of the lineage into the lineage database.

The image analysis software (MetaMorph) is interfaced with Quercus through a log file. For a selected region-of-interest (ROI) on the image, MetaMorph can extract 24 parameters from the image. Users only needs to select the ROI and type of event manually and all regional parameters and event information are sent to a log file when user presses the 'Log data' button in MetaMorph. Consequently, in Quercus all parameters and event information from the log file become associated with the appropriate cell node and according to the event type the node changes colour and the event consequences are drawn dynamically on the canvas.

For each event, a ROI measurement is performed twice - (at the start and end of each event), so 24 paired parameters are selected for each event as follows: Image Name, Image Plane, Image Date and Time, Elapsed Time, Stage Label, Wavelength, Z Position, Region Label , Area , Distance, Angle, Left, Top, Width, Height, Threshold Area, Threshold Area %, Threshold Distance, Average Intensity, Intensity Standard Dev, Intensity Signal/Noise, Integrated Intensity, Minimum Intensity and Maximum Intensity. Among these 24 pairs of parameters - time, position and intensity parameters are important for a wide range of cell based assays. In addition to the aforementioned parameter pairs, 5 further parameters are also stored for each event these include cell name, event type, step number, canvas coordinates. 5 blank spaces are also stored for each cell so that future annotation can easily be incorporated on the existing database. Altogether

these 58 parameters, for each cell, provide a comprehensive map of cell behaviour as well as maintaining lineage relationships through the use of unique cell nomenclature. Together with seed or progenitor cell tagging, we have made a basic but generic data structure that can encompass a wide spectrum of cell cycle dynamics studies.

2.4 From image to numbers

Quercus dynamically interacts with the digital screen file and guides user to select a progenitor cell. For example, when a particular experiment been chosen by the user, Quercus interacts with the screen file and both reads and display all information regarding each well within the specific screen the process continues up till the selection of cell level. When the tagging is complete, a cell is created in the canvas of Quercus, the raw image counter part of this newly created cell is located in the Metamorph video window and tracked manually within the sequence. When an event occurs for the selected cell, the appropriate event type must be allocated from the "Label log data" feature of MetaMorph. Then the ROI is placed on the nucleolus of the cell and all regional measurements recorded in the log file. When the event ends the same procedure is repeated. Once the data related to start and end of an event for the selected cell is logged, the data is streamed back over to the Quercus canvas and according to the event that has been logged the event is appended to the existing lineage display, a colour is assigned according to the type of event, therefore the user has a dynamic lineage map continually updated during the acquisition, providing orientation in the data set.

Quercus provides complete flexibility as it can map lineages based on all possible outcomes of a cell division, for example unusual circumstances such as the generation of three or four daughters due to abnormal cytokinesis, or the generation of a polyploidy cell. Quercus also assigns to each cell within a lineage a unique identifier. The start or beginning cell is named as 'B' if this cell divides into two daughter cell then the two daughters are named as 'BN' and 'BS' respectively. For a re-fused or polyploidy outcome the designation is 'BE'. Three individual daughters are named 'BN','BE' and 'BS' while four daughters are named 'BN','BU','BL' and 'BS' respectively. This identification pattern also establishes the relationship between different cells within a lineage. Once data related to all the cells for a track within a lineage have been logged, users can easily locate the last bifurcation or node point of the lineage in the raw image by clicking on the node in the Quecus canvas.

This semi-automated and user directed fashion of lineages encoding from the raw images is indeed time consuming, depending upon the size of the lineage, expertise of the user and cell density in the image, it may take few minutes to an hour to encode a lineage. This semi-automated manner of encoding is undeniably the rate limiting step but user's interaction ensures the highest precision of the data. A combination of automated and user-interactive bioinformatics software is what suggested by recent review (Taylor and Giuliano, 2005) as the challenge and opportunity for next generation high content screening. Once the encoding of a lineage is complete, the completed lineage dataset is placed into the Lineage Database.

2.5 Lineage Database (LDB)

All lineage data are stored in text file format. One lineage constitutes one text file and the name of the text file is the tag assigned to the progenitor cell. The tag or name of a lineage has 23 parameters associated with it, which makes it distinguishable from all other lineages of the database. Within a text file, i.e. lineage, each cell constitutes a row and 58 columns of data corresponding to 58 parameters mentioned earlier. The nomenclature of the cells within a lineage enables any computer language to access the data with a relationship and moreover the nomenclature of the lineage itself facilitates lineage classification based on user defined conditions, e.g. drug dose. All lineages accumulated into the LDB have passed through an automated but rigid quality control check which ensures that all lineage are stored in the correct data structure. Adapting this text file format was purely on an adhoc basis, work is in progress to transform these txt files to a formal relational database structure.

3. QUERCUS AND *IN-SILICO* ANALYSIS

3.1 Graphical visualization of cell lineages

Any complete or partially encoded lineage can be visualized just by selecting the appropriate lineage text file from the LDB and we have also developed a range of data mining features for visualisation and quantification of the dynamic relationship that exists within the underlying heterogeneous population.

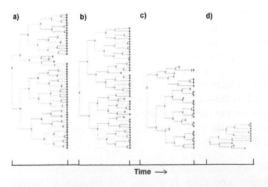

Fig. 1. Visualisation of four cell lineages selected randomly from the LDB a) control cell exposed to b) 0.001µM TPT c) 1µM TPT d) 10 µM TPT.

Our present database consists of lineages, up to 5 generations, derived from more than 600 encoded progenitor cells obtained from timelapse microscopy sequences for a screen of the pharmacodynamic effects of the anticancer agent topotecan (TPT).

3.2 Validation of control lineages

Quality control for important parameters of any *in vitro* assay model system is an essential step. For instance, the duration between sequential generations or InterMitotic Time (IMT) has been identified as a fundamental readout of cell cycle traverse time for individual cell lineage. It is well recognised that in cell cultures (eg primary fibroblast cell cultures) during the course of the experiment overcrowding would result in 'contact inhibition' and culture quiescence which affects cell movement and the ability to re-establish substrate connections following cell division. Therefore we investigated the effect of mobility restriction on IMT. Restriction was determined by the extent of cellular translocation between events. The InterMitotic Displacement (IMD) index is termed as the displacement (in pixels) from origin for each mitotic event.

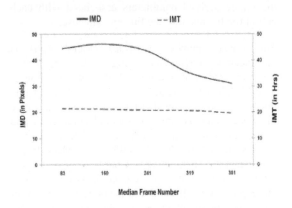

Fig. 2. Stability of the IMT (dotted) and IMD (solid) parameters over the course of the lineage assay.

When mean IMD and IMT values for five generations were plotted in a two axis graph against the median frame number (1 frame = 15 minutes for this experiment), it was revealed that the IMD decreased 30.54% over a five generations assay period and the decrease starting after a total of 4 days in culture. However the IMT did not change significantly during the whole assay period. The graph validates the point that due to the effect of overcrowding, movements of cells in later generations decreases but the mean cell cycle duration remains 20.2 hrs (0.74 SD) over the course of the entire experiment. We are therefore confident that the assay design provides a robust platform for investigating the impact of drugs on the cell cycle over 5 generations.

3.3 Measuring mitotic event kinetics for 'searchable' lineages.

Event (mitosis, apoptosis) curves provide a simple investigation route in timelapse image analysis to reveal the effect of drug. The cumulative number of events occurring in each frame is counted manually and at the end normalized with the number of cells at the start. In current counting protocols, a common unavoidable error is counting events for cells which at the start of the experiment were outside the image field view and hence adds a low level of noise to the event counter. However, when counting using lineage data from LDB, this error is totally removed, since Quercus only counts events encoded within a given original lineage. This would provide for important applications in situation where mixed cell populations are being analysed (eg fibroblast stromal elements within a tumour cell population).

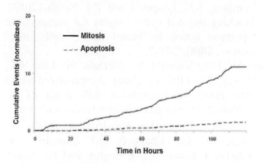

Fig. 3. Dose (10 μM topotecan) dependent mitosis (solid) and apoptosis (dotted) for a sub- population where the first mitosis has to occur within the first eight hours, thereby classifying the cells as located in the late cell cycle.

Figure 3 shows a typical event curve for lineages that have been classified using some of the basic searchable descriptors in the database. The query was to seek the lineages derived from cells exposed to 10 μM topotecan and then select further a sub-class of lineages in which the original cell delivered to mitosis with the first eight hours. These lineages were found to be an important sub-class with a good drug resistance capacity and from which very few cell death occurred.

As mentioned earlier, timelapse microscopy is the repeated collection of a single field of view from a microscope at discrete time intervals, however some cells, especially those in the edge of the field of view, get out of the field of view at a time point due to inherent motility nature of living cells. These cells are designated as 'lost' cell by Quercus and depicted as end node of a track in the canvas. This experimental effect introduces noise to any event base analysis and as such demands statistical manipulation. Currently we are exploring different statistical and mathematical approach to circumvent this issue.

3.4 CestLAView – viewing and measuring drug effect through multivariate analysis

The duration of the IMT, monitored from generation to generation after an insult, is a good indicator of the time dependent perturbation of cell cycle traverse in response to cell cycle delay-inducing drugs. The pattern of this delay from generation to generation could provide a dose and drug class-dependent signature. We have developed a novel approach to visualize and measure this relationship within a screening format. Written in Java 3D, this feature of Quercus illustrates the asymmetry in a 3D view with clustering perspective, where for each track of a lineage, the X axis represents the first InterMitotic Time (IMT1), Y axis the IMT2 and Z axis IMT3. A set of lineages can be selected or searched based on particular descriptors from the LDB based on the user-defined criteria, which are usually drug dose and/or progenitor cell cycle phase. Each cell belonging to a 3rd generation population has unique IMT1, IMT2 and IMT3 values associated with it and is depicted as a point within the box.

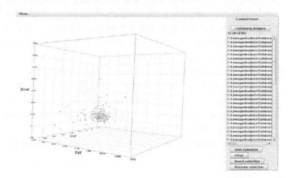

Fig. 4. Clustering view of cell cycle traverse over 3 generations (shown on left hand side 3D box) for a set of lineages (shown in right hand side window) selected by user-defined query.

Through this approach it is possible to visualize the cell cycle related heterogeneity that exists under different experimental conditions without having any prior knowledge about the number of cells that initially existed at the start of the experiment. The data generated are used for multivariate analysis to quantify the effect of drug on cell cycle delay. The method and results in this perspective are beyond the scope of this paper.

4. CONCLUDING REMARKS

The Quercus toolbox provides a step change in our ability to encode, visualise and access information on dynamic cell behaviour. Our hypothesis is that kinetic measurements provide an essential route to revealing important time windows and informative cells to study the mechanism of action of individual agents and their response pathways. Fundamental to the Quercus concept is that the encoding process encapsulating the critical features of cell-cell heterogeneity and time-dependent events. The multi-level descriptors and parameters attributed to each node within the resultant cell lineage maps provide a unique framework for applying bioinformatics-like query algorithms such as those used for genomic databases. The lineage map importantly provides a generation and cell functional layer upon which other information can be linked, such as proteomic and genomic expression data. We suggest that lineage mapping could be used to identify and select informative cells or clusters when sectoring of a biological response occurs within a lineage causing a possible blurring of protein expression patterns as monitored by proteomics technologies. The approach may also address the significant challenge of tracking the evolution of clonal variation in tumour cell populations using micro-array approaches.

Establishing the Quercus tools in such a generic way has allowed us to adapt to any type of high-content screening assay, work is underway to interlink multi scalar data generated from different assay techniques. Furthermore we are using the Quercus tool-enabled analyses to search for drug response fingerprints to inform the temporal windows for a simplified analysis of drug action suitable for micro-scale formats on optical biochip platforms. A significant challenge for us is to convert Quercus into an automated encoding programme while maintaining the current highly robust event identification element. This is not a trivial undertaking and will require some novel cell tracking algorithms appropriate for transmission microscopy images.

The Quercus database provides a rich data repository for pharmacokinetic (PK) and pharmacodynamic (PD) modelling and validation. Our next challenge for the Quercus programme of work is to develop bioinformatics derived predictive algorithms which link our 'real' screen data with our mathematical models describing drug-target interaction and cellular driven resistance mechanisms at the PK and PD level. (Evans, et al., 2004). Importantly, the biological outputs from our lineage databases translate directly to clinically relevant indicators of the therapeutic response of tumour cell populations in terms of initial response, growth delay and the appearance of surviving ('resistant') cells with distinct progenitor characteristics or evolving phenotypes.

5. ACKNOWLEDGEMENTS

The authors acknowledge grant support from the Research Councils UK Basic Technology Research Programme (GR/S23483) and the Biotechnology and Biological Sciences Research Council (75/E19292).

REFERENCES

Allman, R., R.J. Errington and P.J. Smith (2003). Delayed expression of apoptosis in human lymphoma cells undergoing low-dose taxol-induced mitotic stress, *Br J Cancer*, **88(10)**, 1649-58.

Chu K, Teele N, Dewey MW, Albright N, Dewey WC (2004). Computerized video time lapse study of cell cycle delay and arrest, mitotic catastrophe, apoptosis and clonogenic survival in irradiated 14-3-3sigma and CDKN1A (p21) knockout cell lines. Radiat Res. Sep;**162(3)**:270-86.

Evans, N.D., R.J. Errington, M. Shelley, G.P. Feeney, M.J. Chapman, K.R. Godfrey, P.J. Smith and M.J. Chappell (2004). A mathematical model for the in vitro kinetics of the anti-cancer agent topotecan, *Math Biosci*, **189(2)**, 185-217.

Feeney, G.P., R.J. Errington, M. Wiltshire, N. Marquez, S.C. Chappell and P.J. Smith (2003). Tracking the cell cycle origins for escape from topotecan action by breast cancer cells, *Br J Cancer*, **88(8)**, 1310-7.

Forrester HB, Vidair CA, Albright N, Ling CC, Dewey WC (1999). Using computerized video time lapse for quantifying cell death of X-irradiated rat embryo cells transfected with c-myc or c-Ha-ras. Cancer Res. Feb 15;**59(4)**:931-9.

Marquez, N., S.C. Chappell, O.J. Sansom, A.R. Clarke, J. Court, R.J. Errington and P.J. Smith (2003). Single cell tracking reveals that Msh2 is a key component of an early-acting DNA damage-activated G2 checkpoint, *Oncogene*, **22(48)**, 7642-8.

Marquez, N., S.C. Chappell, O.J. Sansom, A.R. Clarke, P. Teesdale-Spittle, R.J. Errington and P.J. Smith (2004). Microtubule stress modifies intra-nuclear location of Msh2 in mouse embryonic fibroblasts, *Cell Cycle*, **3(5)**, 662-71.

Stephens, P., P. Grenard, P. Aeschlimann, M. Langley, E. Blain, R.J. Errington, D. Kipling, D. Thomas and D. Aeschlimann (2004). Crosslinking and G-protein functions of transglutaminase 2 contribute differentially to fibroblast wound healing responses, *J Cell Sci*, **117(Pt 15)**, 3389-403.

Taylor, D.L. and K.A. Giuliano (2005). Multiplexed high content screening assays create a systems cell biology approach to drug discovery. *Drug Discov Today: Technologies*, **2(2)**, 149-154.

White N.S. and R.J. Errington (2005). Fluorescence techniques for drug delivery research: theory and practice, Adv Drug Deliv Rev, **57(1)**, 17-42.

METHOD FOR ANALYSIS OF VOLUME PROGRESSION TISSUES IN HEMIPLEGIC SUBJECT

Antonio PINTI [1], Patrick HEDOUX [2], Abdelmalik TALEB-AHMED [1]

(1) LAMIH – CNRS UMR 8530
Université de Valenciennes - Le Mont Houy - 59313 Valenciennes Cedex 9 - France
Tel: (+33) 03-27-51-14-29 - Fax : (+33) 03-27-51-13-16

(2) ACFY – D1 – 92T rue Roger Salengro – 59300 Famars - France
Tel: (+33) 06-88-80-20-98 – www.acfy.fr

Abstract: The goal of this study was to develop a new method for a quantitative analysis of lower limb soft tissues evolution in hemiplegic subjects. The study was performed from 2 MRI recordings on each of 8 male and 2 female volunteers suffering from hemiplegia. The first recording was performed on the day subjects entered the rehabilitation center; the second was carried out 6 months later. The method allowed for the determination of tissue volume evolution and the instantaneous volume difference between the two lower limbs during the rehabilitation period. *Copyright © 2006 IFAC*

Keywords: Image analysis, MRI, Handicap, Hemiplegia, Lower limbs.

1. INTRODUCTION

Every year in France, about 150,000 people are victims of a stroke accident (CVA). Patients disabled due to its aftermath are estimated to be 500,000. The average age at which CVAs occur is between 50 and 60. Right or left side hemiplegia is one of the consequences of a CVA. Hemiplegia is characterized by total or partial body part paralysis, with consecutive muscular atrophy. After a hospitalization period of about one month, during which the patient stays mostly lying down, a rehabilitation program adapted to the handicap is proposed. During rehabilitation the internal and external morphology of the lower limbs is modified. External morphology can be determined non-invasively with a three-dimensional (3D) infrared scanner (Norton, et al, 2002) or with 3D optical measurement systems such as the Symcad system. The objective of this study was to assess the internal morphology, especially the evolution of the main soft tissue volumes during the rehabilitation period. This in order to provide supplemental information for the therapist who already has objective indicators concerning the hemiplegic subject's functional recovery (Pelissier, et al, 1997).

This paper presents a method for quantitative analysis of lower limb soft tissues evolution. Medical magnetic resonance imaging (MRI) was used to quantify soft tissue volume changes of healthy and pathological limbs during functional rehabilitation in subjects after stroke. The first part explains the method used to quantify the progression of tissue volume. The second part shows results obtained from 10 hemiplegic subjects. The conclusion discusses the limits of the study and presents some research perspectives.

This study was performed with the agreement of the "Comité Consultatif de Protection des Personnes dans la Recherche Biomédicale" (CCPPRB) of Lille, France, written informed consent was obtained from patients prior to testing.

2. MATERIAL AND METHOD

2.1 MEDICAL IMAGING SYSTEM.

Digital medical imaging is an in-vivo technique for human body internal structure study. X-ray scanners and MRIs allow anatomic volumes to be obtained from two-dimensional digital image sequences (Fig. 1).

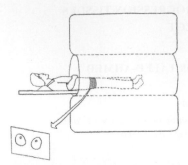

Fig. 1: Acquisition of axial MRI slices.

Pixels of these images represent elementary volumes called voxels. From these data, volumes in 3D can be reconstructed and analyzed with computerized data processing (Sonka and Fitzpatrick, 2000; Monziols, et al, 2005) and image synthesis algorithms (Foley, et al, 1992). MRI was selected for this study over classical techniques such as X-ray scanner because it is a non-invasive and non-radiating technique which has no known side effects, and only limited contra-indications, such as use of pacemaker and presence of ferromagnetic implants in the body (Hédoux, et al, 2005).

MRI slices were recorded using a GE SIGNA MRI system (1 T) and a PHILIPS INTERAT 1.5 Tesla. The MRI parameters were set up by an expert in order to reach a compromise between anatomical precision, signal to noise ratio and acquisition time were as follows:

- Spin-echo technique;
- T1 weighting;
- Axial slices;
- Repetition time (TR): 500 or 560 ms;
- Echo time (TE): 13 ms;
- Slice thickness (Es): 10 mm;
- Inter-slice gap (Ei): 1 mm;
- Field of view (Fv): 48 cm;
- Matrix size (Ms): 512 x 512;
- No change of reference between sequences.

MRIs were recorded in the DICOM medical format in 256 gray scale. Subject lower limbs' analysis requires the acquisition of 100 slices in 3 successive sequences. Acquisition time was approximately half an hour during which subjects remained still.

2.2 ACQUISITION PROTOCOL

An acquisition protocol was defined in agreement with all involved in the study. The first MRI recording was performed when the subject entered the rehabilitation center; the second one was performed six months later. This waiting period allowed evaluation of patients' tissue volume progression that had occurred during rehabilitation.

Recordings were performed on 8 male and 2 female Caucasian hemiplegic volunteers aged 45-70 years. Their admission in the rehabilitation center took place one month after the occurrence of their CVA.

2.3 SEGMENTATION

Lower limbs were divided into three segments: foot, leg and thigh. Segmentation methods applied for this study was the one proposed by Fujikawa (figure 2) (Fujikawa, 1963).

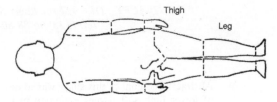

Fig. 2: Segmentation of lower limb proposed by Fujikawa.

Segmentation from MRI slices requires an expert to intervene in order to define slices segmentation, i.e. the first and last images for the foot and the leg. For the thigh, the expert defined the crossing point of the thighs then the position of the femoral heads.

2.4 IMAGE ANALYSIS

MRI analysis can be processed manually or in a semi-automatic or automatic manner. Many authors developed manually or semi-automatic methods for MRI analysis (Todd and Wang, 1996; Cheng, et al, 2000). In this study, MRI recordings were processed sequentially in an automated manner. An original image analysis technique was developed for this study, and was described elsewhere (Hédoux, et al, 1999).

Four body tissues were classified: spongy bone, cortical bone, muscle and fatty tissue. One class was associated with each tissue, respectively called T1, T2, T3 and T4. An additional class called T0 is for pixels that do not belong to the body. For each class Ti corresponded an arbitrary gray level. Each pixel of the resulting image was coded according to its class Ti. The first processing step (Pinti, et al, 2000) permitted the classification of for each MRI pixel. For this study, tissues of interest were muscle and fatty tissue. Fig. 3 shows the result on a slice taken from the thigh.

☐ Spongy bone
☐ Fatty tissue
☐ Muscle
■ Cortical bone

Fig. 3: Result of classification.

The second processing step allowed for the computation of the tissue volumes. Each image pixel was thus converted to an elementary voxel Ve defined by the following equation:

$$V_e = E_h * E_v * E_c$$

with $E_h = E_v = \dfrac{F_v}{M_s}$ and $E_c = E_s + E_i$

where:
E_h, E_v were the horizontal and vertical sampling of the fields of view in mm;
E_c was the voxel thickness in mm;
V_e was the elementary voxel volume in mm3;
E_s was the slice thickness;
E_i was the inter-slice gap;
F_v was the field of view;
M_s was the matrix size.

Each voxel $v_{ij}(x,y,z)$ belonged to a class T_i ($i \in \{0;1;2;3;4\}$) and to a unique segment j ($j \in \{1;2;3\}$).

The volume V_{ij} of a tissue of class T_i belonging to the body segment j was determined using the following equation:

$$V_{ij} = \sum_{x=1}^{nbx} \sum_{y=1}^{nby} \sum_{z=1}^{nbc} v_{ij}(x,y,z)$$

where:
nbx is the number of pixels in the image along the x axis;
nby is the number of pixels in the image along the y axis;
nbc is the number of segment slices.

2.5 REPEATABILITY

Measures repeatability was assessed through 2 consecutive lower limb acquisitions on the same patient. The second acquisition was performed on the same day after patient was asked out of the MRI device and in again.
MRI slice volumes were computed for each trial. Figure 4 shows volume's evolution along lower limbs for both acquisitions (Hédoux, 2004).

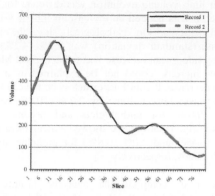

Figure 4: comparison of MRI slice volumes along lower limbs in two consecutive acquisitions (slice 1, proximal: pelvis – slice 80, distal: ankle).

Both curves are almost superimposed, presenting a maximum volume difference of 0,4%. The present method was, consequently, repeatable.

3. RESULTS

Volume progression shown in table 1 was computed using the following equation:

$$\%V = (\frac{V_{final}}{V_{initial}} - 1) * 100$$

where:
V_{final} was the volume of the limb or of the tissue at the end of the observation period;
$V_{initial}$ was the volume of the limb or of the tissue at the beginning of the observation period;
$\%V$ was the volume progression.

Table 1 Volume evolution.

	Healthy side			Pathological side		
S	%Vt	%Vm	%Vf	%Vt	%Vm	%Vf
1	+6.3	+9.9	-0.4	+8.1	+9.8	+6.1
2	+2.0	+1.2	+3.5	-0.1	+1.9	-4.1
3	-2.4	+5.5	-7.6	+4.0	+13.4	-1.4
4	+8.7	+8.7	+9.1	+12.0	+12.0	+13.0
5	+0.2	+1.8	-1.8	+1.8	+9.2	-8.0
6	+11.0	+13.3	+8.1	+10.2	+8.8	+12.0
7	+3.1	+10.8	-8.3	+4.0	+14.7	-8.0
8	-6.1	+1.4	-13.0	-3.7	+4.0	-9.2
9	-10.3	+2.5	-17.1	-9.4	+13.0	-22.8
10	+2.7	+6.5	-1.8	+4.1	+6.2	+0.7
Mean	+2.0	+6.2	-2.4	+3.1	+9.3	-2.2
Std	6.8	4.7	9.0	6.4	4.2	10.8

where:
S, the subject's number;
%Vt, the volume evolution of the limb;
%Vm, the volume evolution of the muscle;
%Vf, the volume evolution of the fatty tissue.

Lower limb volume evolution was different for each subject. It was noticed an increase in muscle volume in all patients. On pathological side, the mean increase (standard deviation) was 9.3% (4.2%). On healthy side, mean increase was 6.2% (4.7%). Muscle volume increase could not be explained by a fatty tissue decrease. It could nevertheless be noticed a loss in the mean fatty volume by 2.2% (10.8%) and of 2.4% (9.0%) for pathological and healthy sides, respectively. Total volume showed a mean increase of 3.1% (6.4%) and 2.0% (6.8%) for pathological and healthy sides, respectively.

In order to complete the analysis, healthy and pathological sides of the same subject were compared at the same period of rehabilitation. This instantaneous index was studied at both recording times. Volume differences between pathological and healthy sides of each subject were computed in percentage in the following way:

$$\%V_d = (\frac{V_{patho}}{V_{healthy}} - 1)*100$$

where:
V_{patho} is the total volume of the pathological limb;
$V_{healthy}$, is the total volume of the healthy limb;
$\%V_d$ is the volume differential.

Table 2 Volumes differences between pathological and healthy sides.

| | Month 0 | | | Month 6 | | |
S	%Vdt	%Vdm	%Vdf	%Vdt	%Vdm	%Vdf
1	-8.0	-12.4	+0.1	-6.5	-12.5	+6.6
2	+11.7	+24.1	-6.4	+9.3	+25.0	-13.2
3	-4.5	-13.0	+1.1	+1.7	-6.6	+7.8
4	-10.3	-12.8	-5.8	-7.6	-10.2	-2.5
5	+2.3	+7.9	-4.1	+4.0	+15.8	-10.1
6	-1.7	-2.0	-1.0	-2.4	-5.9	+2.6
7	-4.3	-11.5	+5.9	-3.1	-8.4	+6.2
8	-6.9	-16.2	+1.4	-4.5	-14.0	+5.8
9	+4.1	+13.7	-1.0	+5.2	+25.4	-7.8
10	+2.8	+12.8	-9.7	+4.1	+12.5	-7.4
Mean	-1.5	-0.9	-2.0	+0.0	+2.1	-1.2
Std	6.7	14.4	4.6	5.6	15.7	7.9

where:
S, the subject number;
$\%V_{dt}$, the volume difference of the limb;
$\%V_{dm}$, the volume difference of the muscle;
$\%V_{df}$, the volume difference of the fatty tissue.

It can be noticed that mean muscle volume on pathological side has become more important than on healthy side during rehabilitation. Indeed, at Month 0, mean (standard deviation) $\%V_{dm}$ was -0.9% (14.4%) and 2.1% (15.7%), at month 6. The same pattern was noticed for $\%V_{dt}$, that changed from -1.5% (6.7%) to 0.0% (5.6%). The same effect was noticed for $\%V_{df}$ that changed from 2.0% (4.6%) to -1.2% (7.9%).

4. DISCUSSION

Lower limb volume progression of hemiplegic subjects could be determined from several MRI acquisitions with preset interval. Measurement precision depends on the image quality and slice sampling. With respect to image quality, the spin-echo technique and T1-weighting permitted to have a good contrast ratio in order to differentiate four principal lower limb tissues (spongy bone, cortical bone, muscle, and fat tissue).

In this study, lower limb volumes varied differently for the 10 subjects. Muscle and fatty tissue volumes for all subjects were modified by rehabilitation. Table 1 showed that subjects generally lost fatty tissue volume to the benefit of muscle volume. Total volume difference could be explained by fatty and muscle volume modifications considering that bony volume remained the same in our study. Table 2 showed that pathological limb volume increased relative to healthy limb for the mean subject.

5. CONCLUSION

This work is the starting point of a new tool for analysis and evaluation of functional rehabilitation of hemiplegic patients. A quantification method for assessing lower limb tissue volume evolutions was achieved. It was based on the analysis of medical volume images. This new way of analysis was used to measure main lower segment tissue volume progression in 10 hemiplegic subjects during the first six months of their functional rehabilitation in a specialized rehabilitation center. However, the lack of subjects has not made it possible yet to evaluate the influence of rehabilitation methods and to explain the reasons of positive or negative tissue volume evolutions of the lower limbs.
The method of quantitative analysis is an interesting complement to available indicators such as gait analysis (Pelissier, et al, 1997).
This method could also be used for athletes to evaluate specific training programs, or to study specific diet effects. This new method of non-invasive quantitative analysis could therefore be used in many experiments in biomechanics and in human rehabilitation. One limit of this tool is the low number of non-radiating imaging systems such as MRI available in France. Moreover, highly qualified personnel is required to perform image acquisition sequences (manipulators and radiologists) thus limiting the number of studies with large subject samples.

ACKNOWLEDGEMENTS

The authors extend their warm thanks to the administration staff and personnel of the hospitals of Wattrelos and Tourcoing (France).

REFERENCES

Cheng CK, Chen HH, Chen CS, Lee CL, Chen CY. (2000) Segment inertial properties of Chinese adults determined from magnetic resonance imaging. Clinical Biomechanics; 15: 559-566.

Foley JD, Van Dam A, Feiner ST. (1992) Hughes JF. *Computer Graphics principles and practice*, Addison-Wesley Publishing Company.

Fujikawa K. (1963) The center of gravity in the parts of human body, Okajimos Folia Anat. Jap., 39(3), 117-126.

Hédoux P, Watelain E, Pinti A, Barbier F, Boluix B, Kemoun G. (1999) Automatic analysis of lower limb MRIs of hemiplegic patients for biomechanic parameter calculation. *Arch Physiol Biochem*; 107 Suppl: 110.

Hédoux P. (2004) Détermination de paramètres biomécaniques personnalisés à partir d'imagerie médicale – Application aux sujets hémiplégiques –, PhD Thesis, Université de Valenciennes, France.

Hédoux P, Pinti A, Rambaud F. (2005) Volume determination compared between CT and MRI: application to hemiplegic subjets. Assistive technology: from virtuality to reality, *IOS Press*, 129-132.

Monziols M, Collewet G Mariette F, Kouba M, Davenel A. (2005) Muscle and fat quantification in MRI gradient echo images using a partial volume detection method. Application to the characterization of pig belly tissue. Magnetic Resonance Imaging; 23: 745 – 755.

Norton J, Donaldson N, Dekker L. (2002) 3D whole body scanning to determine mass properties of legs. *J Biomech*; 35: 81-6.

Pelissier J, Perennou D, Laassel EM. (1997) Analyse instrumentale de la marche de l'hémiplégique adulte: revue de la littérature. *Ann. Réadaptation phys*; 40: 297-313.

Pinti A, Hédoux P, Watelain E, Kemoun G, Boluix B. (2000) Comparaison à partir d'I.R.M. de caractéristiques biomécaniques de membres inférieurs sains et pathologiques, *Journal Européen des Systèmes Automatisés*; 34 (6-7) : 845-58.

Sonka M, Fitzpatrick JM. (2000) Medical Image Processing and Analysis. Vol 2. SPIE Press.

Todd BA, Wang H. (1996) A Visual Basic program to pre-process MRI data for finite element modelling. Comput Biol; 26(6): 489-495.

GA-BACKPROPAGATION HYBRID TRAINING AND MORPHOMETRIC PARAMETERS TO CLASSIFY BREAST TUMOURS ON ULTRASOUND IMAGES

André Victor Alvarenga[1], Wagner C. A. Pereira[2], Antonio Fernando C. Infantosi[2] and Carolina M. de Azevedo[3]

[1] *Laboratory of Ultrasound, Division of Acoustics and Vibration Metrology, Directory of Scientific and Industrial Metrology, National Institute of Metrology, Standardization, and Industrial Quality, Duque de Caxias, Rio de Janeiro, Brazil.*

[2] *Biomedical Eng. Program/COPPE, Federal University of Rio de Janeiro, Rio de Janeiro, Brazil*

[3] *Radiology Department/Brazilian National Cancer Institute (INCa) Rio de Janeiro, Brazil*

avalvarenga@inmetro.gov.br, victor@peb.ufrj.br

Abstract: This work presents a multilayer perceptron (MLP) network, trained with backpropagation algorithm, to classify breast tumours as malign or benign ones. Seven morphometric parameters, extracted from the convex polygon and the normalised radial length techniques, are used as MLP input. A genetic-based selection procedure helps backpropagation training scheme to select the best input parameters and best training set, as well. To achieve this aim, an objective function is proposed. The best values of accuracy (97.4%), sensitivity (98.0%) and specificity (96.2%) were achieved with a set of five parameters, despite the training set sizes tested: 30% and 50% of the total samples. *Copyright © 2006 IFAC*

Keywords: Hybrid training, morphometric parameters, genetic algorithm, neural network, backpropagation, breast cancer, ultrasound.

1. INTRODUCTION

Breast cancer is one of the major causes of death by cancer in human female population in Brazil. Besides, the Brazilian Health Ministry (MS), through The Cancer National Institute (INCa), estimated that almost 50.000 new breast cancer cases would take place in 2006 (INCa, 2005).

Mammography is the screening modality used to breast cancer early diagnosis. Nevertheless, a considerable number of suspicious solid masses are usually recommended for surgical biopsy (Dennis *et al.*, 2001) although only 10 % to 30 % of them are malignant (Horsch *et al.*, 2002). Ultrasound (US) breast image has been used, in addition to mammography, to improve the diagnostics and reduce the number of unnecessary biopsies for patients with palpable mass and inconclusive mammograms (Huber *et al.*, 2000; Rahbar *et al.*, 1999; Skaane, 1999).

Malignant breast tumours tend to present irregular or ill-defined contour due the infiltration on surrounding tissue (Chou *et al.*, 2001). Therefore, from the tumour contour it is possible to establish a diagnostic hypothesis (Chou *et al.*, 2001; Huber *et al.*, 2000; Skaane, 1999; Rahbar *et al.*, 1999). Besides, researchers have demonstrated the morphometric parameters could help in distinguishing malign from benign breast tumours on US images (Alvarenga *et al.*, 2005; Chou *et al.*, 2001).

Computer Aided Diagnosis (CAD) has been largely studied to help radiologists give more accurate diagnostics in breast cancer and Artificial Neural Networks (ANN) has been applied to solve this kind of classification problem (Drukker *et al.*, 2004; Chen *et al.*, 2003; Bakic and Brzakovic, 1997). However, the selection of ANN input parameters (Zhang and Sun, 2002; Kim and Shin, 2000; Komosinski and Krawiec, 2000; Su and Wu, 2000) and training set (Harpham *et al.*, 2004), as well, is a tricky task, whereas both of them should represent the typical behaviour of the phenomenon.

Several multivariate statistical methods such as the Linear Discriminant Analysis (LDA) or Principal Component Analysis (PCA) can be applied to evaluate the parameters discrimination potential used as ANN input (Lafuente *et al.*, 1997). However, general statistical discriminant methods usually assume the normal distribution for the input data. The method using an optimization approach, such as Genetic Algorithm (GA), disregards the assumption of a normal distribution (Su and Wu, 2000).

Considering the training set selection, generally, due to a limited number of samples, the performance evaluation is typically carried out using one of the three methods - cross-validation, jack-knife (leave-one-out), and bootstrap (Bakic and Brzakovic, 1997). Moreover, GA can also be applied to find an optimal training set (Harpham *et al.*, 2004).

This work presents a multilayer perceptron (MLP) network, trained with backpropagation algorithm, to classify breast tumours as malign or benign ones. Morphometric parameters, extracted from the convex polygon and the normalised radial length techniques, are used as MLP input. A GA selection procedure helps the backpropagation training scheme to select the best input parameters and best training set, as well. To achieve this aim, an objective function is proposed and the results are compared to the ones presented in a previous work, where the MLP input parameters were selected using LDA (Alvarenga *et al.*, 2005).

2. MATERIAL AND METHODS

2.1 MLP Network and GA-Backpropagation Hybrid Training

The MLP network is implemented with three layers (Fig. 1). The sigmoid activation function is used for each of the nodes in the hidden layer and for the output layer of the network. The input layer consists of the input parameters (normalised between 1 and –1) and the hidden layer was all connected to the input layer. It was also connected to an output layer of a single neuron producing a normalised value in the range of 0 (malign) to 1 (benign).

The proposed hybrid training uses GA to simultaneously select the best input parameters and the best training set, while the MLP is trained by the classical backpropagation algorithm. In the GA initial population, the first genes of each the chromosome represent the input parameters (p_i) and the other ones represent the training sets (t_i). The chromosomes lengths are defined by the number of input parameters added to the number of samples desired in the training set. An example of an initial

population with four chromosomes, five input parameters (p_1 to p_5), nine samples (t_1 to t_9) and a restricted number of five samples in the training set, is presented in Fig. 2. Note that input parameters that are not used on a specific training iteration are set to zero. Besides, the samples not used in the training sets are used in the test sets (for example, t_3, t_4, t_6 and t_8 to the first chromosome in Fig. 2).

The objective function (f_o) defined as:

$$ f_o = \left(\left| S_{train} - S_{test} \right| + \left| E_{train} - E_{test} \right| \right) * k , \qquad (1) $$

attempts to maximise sensitivity (S_{train} and S_{test}) and specificity (E_{train} and E_{test}) of training and test sets at the same time. The k factor, employed to balance the number of false positive (FP) and false negative (FN) samples in training and test sets, is defined as:

$$ k = \left(\frac{FP_{train} + FN_{train} + rp}{size_{train}} + \frac{FP_{test} + FN_{test} + rp}{size_{test}} \right) \qquad (2) $$

where $size_{train}$ and $size_{test}$ are the number of samples in each set. The rp factor, which carries the information about the number of parameters used during the training, is defined as:

$$ rp = \frac{nps}{npt} \qquad (3) $$

where npt is the total number of parameters (five in the previous example – Fig. 2) and nps is the number of input parameters selected (for example, three – p_1, p_3 and p_4 – for the first chromosome in Fig. 2).

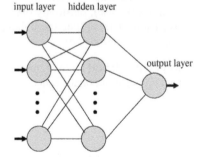

Fig. 1. Neural network general structure. The number of neurons in input and hidden layers is equal and depends on the number of input parameters selected on the hybrid training. One neuron is used in the output layer.

p_1	0	p_3	p_4	0	t_1	t_2	t_5	t_7	t_9
0	p_2	p_3	p_4	0	t_2	t_3	t_4	t_7	t_8
p_1	0	p_3	0	p_5	t_3	t_4	t_6	t_7	t_8
p_1	p_2	p_3	p_4	p_5	t_1	t_2	t_4	t_6	t_7

Fig. 2. Example of four chromosomes representing an initial population with five input parameters (p_1 to p_5), a total of nine samples (t_1 to t_9) and five samples in the training set.

The GA-Backpropagation hybrid training was implemented in MATLAB® (Mathworks Inc., Natick, MA) and based on the following steps:

1. Randomly create an initial population of chromosomes, where the first genes are integer numbers ranging from 1 to the number of input parameters and the subsequent ones as integer numbers ranging from 1 to number of samples. The later represents the possible samples in training sets. The chromosome length is defined as the number of input parameters added to the number of samples desired in training set;

2. Each chromosome is applied to the backpropagation algorithm to train MLP. Sensitivity (S_{train}) and specificity (E_{train}) of trained MLP to each chromosome are calculated;

3. The remaining samples from the training set (test set) are applied to the trained MLP and sensitivity (S_{test}) and specificity (E_{test}) are also calculated;

4. The objective function is calculated to each chromosome (1);
5. Sixty percent of chromosomes with best values of f_o are selected to generate the offspring by (a) reproduction, (b) crossover and (c) mutation operations;
(a) Reproduce an existing chromosome by copying it into the new population.
(b) Create two new chromosomes from two existing ones by using the crossover operation at a randomly chosen starting point.
(c) Create a new chromosome from an existing one by randomly mutating a gene, each three generations.

6. Calculates f_o from offspring.

7. If the convergence criteria have not been reached, return to step 2.

8. The chromosome that has given the optimum value is designated as the one containing the best input parameters and the best training set, as well. The remaining samples are defined as the best test set and the weights determined from backpropagation training as the ideal ones. Figure 3 presents the previous steps as a flowchart.

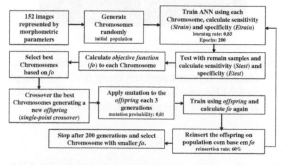

Fig. 3. Hybrid training flowchart.

In this work, the learning rate and the number of epochs are fixed in 0.85 and 200, respectively, to the backpropagation algorithm (Hudson & Cohen, 2000). In addition, the number of chromosomes and the number of generations are set as 300 and 200 (Harpham *et al.*, 2004), correspondingly.

The hybrid training evaluation is performed considering training set sizes of 30% and 50% of samples and the performances are assessed considering as figures of merit: sensitivity (*Se*), specificity (*Sp*), accuracy (*Ac*), positive predictive value (*ppv*) and negative predictive value (*pnv*) (Hudson & Cohen, 1999).

2.2 Database

The database consists of 152-breast tumour US images from patients of the National Cancer Institute (Brazil - Rio de Janeiro), acquired with a 7.5 MHz US (*Sonoline – Sienna* ®Siemens) and stored in TIF format. The sonograms depicted 100 malign and 52 benign tumours that were histopathologically proven.

The tumour contour was estimated by the semi-automatic contour procedure (SAC), based on morphological operators (Alvarenga *et al.*, 2003). Application of this procedure is illustrated for a malign (Fig. 4b) and benign (Fig. 4d) breast tumour. It is worth emphasising that there is no statistical significant difference between the SAC and the contour established by radiologists (Alvarenga *et al.*, 2002).

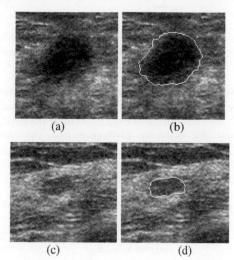

Fig. 4. Examples of (a) malign and (c) benign breast tumour on US images and respective contours (b and d) established by SAC.

2.3 Morphometric Parameters

For each SAC-defined contour, the Normalized Radial Length (NRL) is calculated as (Chou *et al.*, 2001):

$$d(i) = \frac{\sqrt{(x(i) - X_0)^2 + (y(i) - Y_0)^2}}{\max(d(i))}, 1 \le i \le N \quad (4)$$

where (X_0, Y_0) and $(x(i),y(i))$ are respectively the coordinates of the centroid and the boundary pixel at the *i*-th location, N is the number of contour pixels and $\max(d(i))$ is the maximum value of the radial length. Three parameters were calculated from $d(i)$: standard deviation (D_{NRL}), area ratio (RA) and the roughness index (R). The D_{NRL} defined as (Chou *et al.*, 2001):

$$D_{NRL} = \sqrt{\frac{1}{N-1}\sum_{i=1}^{N}(d(i)-\overline{d(i)})^2}, \qquad (5)$$

where $\overline{d(i)}$ is the average value of $d(i)$. This parameter gives a measure of the contour macroscopic irregularities (Chou *et al.*, 2001).

The area ratio (*RA*), defined as:

$$RA = \frac{1}{\overline{d(i)} \cdot N}\sum_{i=1}^{N}(d(i)-\overline{d(i)}), \qquad (6)$$

where

$$d(i)-\overline{d(i)}=0 \quad \forall\, d(i) \leq \overline{d(i)}, \qquad (7)$$

computes the percentage of tumour outside the circular region defined by $\overline{d(i)}$. The more irregular is the contour, the higher the value of *RA*.

The roughness index (*R*) defined as (Chou *et al.*, 2001):

$$R = \frac{1}{N}\sum_{i=1}^{N}|d(i)-d(i+1)|, \qquad (8)$$

gives the average distance between neighbour pixels over the entire contour. Irregular contours provide high values of roughness index.

Convex polygon (Castleman, 1996) is the geometric shape that circumscribes the contour established by SAC. As exemplified in Fig. 5, the more irregular the contour, the more the difference from the convex polygon. This difference can be quantified using two parameters: overlap ratio (*RS*) and normalised residual mean square value (*nrv*).

The parameter *RS* is defined by (Horsch *et al.*, 2002):

$$RS = \frac{Area(S_o \cap S_m)}{Area(S_o \cup S_m)}, \qquad (9)$$

with S_m, the binary image determined from SAC and S_o, the binary image of its respective convex images. The symbols $\cap$ and $\cup$ indicate the areas intersection and union, respectively. Therefore, if the areas have the same shape and size and are in the same position, the overlap ratio is the unity.

The parameter *nrv* application is based on the determination of a residue S_r defined as (Infantosi *et al.*, 1998):

$$S_r = Area|(S_m \cup S_o)-(S_m \cap S_o)| \qquad (10)$$

If areas are identical (shape and size) and in the same position, $S_r = 0$, *nrv* is defined as (Infantosi *et al.*, 1998):

$$nrv = \frac{\psi_r^2}{\psi_o^2}, \qquad (11)$$

where ψ_r^2 is the squared average value of S_r and ψ_o^2 is the squared average value of contour perimeter P_o.

We have also tested ψ_o^2 as the squared average value of the area but it resulted in less sensibility (Alvarenga *et al.*, 2003).

Two other parameters were also calculated: the circularity (*C*) and the morphological-closing area ratio (*Mshape*). The former has demonstrated as an important parameter for the correct classification of breast tumours (Chou et al., 2001) and is defined as:

$$C = \frac{P^2}{A}, \qquad (12)$$

where *P* is the perimeter and *A* the area of the SAC-segmented tumour. The perimeter was measured by summing the number of pixels on the tumour contour, and the area was the number of pixels inside the contour.

Mshape is defined as the ratio between the *S* area and its morphological-closing area. This morphological operator allows filling small holes and gaps (possible missing data) (Soille, 1999) on SAC-defined contour. By applying this operator, the morphological-closing area (white in Fig. 6) tends to be greater than the *S* area (grey in Fig. 6). Hence, the more irregular is the contour, the smaller is *Mshape*.

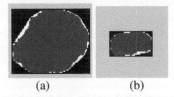

(a)   (b)

Fig. 5. Convex polygons (in white) from (a) malign and (b) benign tumour and their respective areas (in grey) defined by SAC. Note the difference between the areas is higher on malign tumour.

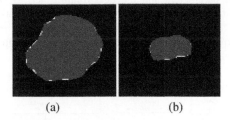

(a)   (b)

Fig. 6. Morphological-closing area (in white) of the segmented breast tumours using SAC: (a) malign and (b) benign. Notice the difference between the areas is slightly bigger on malign tumour.

3. RESULTS

From the seven parameters presented to the MLP input, the GA-Backpropagation hybrid training selected, as the best set to classify breast tumours on ultrasound images, the following five parameters: normalised residual mean square value (*nrv*), circularity (*C*), roughness index (*R*), standard deviation of NRL (D_{NRL}) and morphological-closing area ratio (*Mshape*) (Table 1). This set was the same for the two different training set sizes tested: 30% and 50%. Moreover, the values of accuracy (97.4%), sensitivity (98.0%) and specificity (96.2%) achieved to the test step (Table 1) were also exactly the same.

The number of malign (M: 25) and benign (B: 24) samples selected to the training set of 30% were almost identical. However, for the training set of 50%, the number of malign samples (M: 41) was higher than benign ones (B: 26).

An example of the GA-Backpropagation hybrid training behaviour (training set size of 50%) can be seen on Fig. 7, in terms of objective function (f_o) and backpropagation squared error values.

Table 1 Performance of the GA-Backpropagation hybrid training considering set sizes of 30% and 50%. The numbers of malign and benign samples are represented by M and B, respectively

Training size	≈ 30%		≈ 50%	
Parameters	nrv, C, R, D_{NRL} & $Mshape$		nrv, C, R, D_{NRL} & $Mshape$	
	Training	Test	Training	Test
Ac (%)	98.0	97.4	97.0	97.4
Se (%)	100.0	98.0	97.6	98.0
Sp (%)	95.8	96.2	96.2	96.2
ppv (%)	96.2	98.0	97.6	98.0
pnv (%)	100.0	96.2	96.2	96.2
Number of samples	M: 25 B: 24	M: 75 B: 28	M: 41 B: 26	M: 59 B: 26

The backpropagation error curve (Fig. 7 – dotted line) presents high oscillations during the initial generations (solid arrow). This behaviour occurs because the initial chromosomes are essentially random and the MLP weights are constantly been corrected searching for a lower error. As soon as the chromosomes converge to a stable population (dashed arrow), the backpropagation error curve oscillations decrease and the ANN tend to converge. Furthermore, oscillations in objective function curve (Fig. 7 - solid line) are related to chromosome mutations, which are attempts to achieve better solutions (dotted arrow).

4. DISCUSSION

The GA-Backpropagation hybrid training performance in classifying breast tumours on US images achieved high values of accuracy, sensitivity and specificity, considering different training set sizes. This result point out that the proposed hybrid training, and its respective objective function (1), achieved its aim in reducing the number of input parameters (from seven to five) and selecting the best samples to two different training sets.

In a previous work, a similar objective function was applied, but the best MLP input parameters selection was performed off-line, using Linear Discriminate Analysis. The best performance was reached joining the parameter nrv, calculated from convex polygon, to the roughness (R), calculated from NRL, and the circularity (C). However, lower values of accuracy

(90.0%), sensitivity (90.0%) and specificity (90.0%) were achieved (Alvarenga et al., 2005).

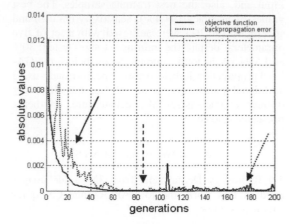

Fig. 7. GA-Backpropagation hybrid training behaviour considering training set size of 50%. The solid and dotted curves represent the objective function and the backpropagation squared error behaviours, respectively. The arrows point to specific phenomena that occurs during the training as: high oscillations (solid arrow) and convergence (dashed arrow) of the backpropagation error curve, besides the oscillations in objective function curve related to chromosome mutations (dotted arrow).

The best set of parameters selected by hybrid training includes, beside the nrv, C and R, the standard deviation of NRL (D_{NRL}) and the morphological-closing area ratio ($Mshape$). Chou et al. (2001) have reported that D_{NRL}, combined to C and R, presented the best performance in classifying breast tumours as malign or benign ones. On the other hand, $Mshape$, which presented the worst individual performance ($Ac = 60.5\%$, $Se = 95.7\%$, $Sp = 6.7\%$), when applied to LDA classifier (Alvarenga et al., 2005), appear among the set of five best parameters selected in this work.

The global improvement achieved on the classification seems to be associated to the exploratory scheme, based on GA, which select the input parameters and the training set at the same time. It is worth to emphasize that the GA-Backpropagation hybrid training does not rely on monotonic behaviour (Fig. 7 - solid line and dotted arrow) what can occur in traditional approaches. Moreover, the rp factor (3), which was added to the previous objective function (Alvarenga et al., 2005), contributed to the input parameter selection and reduction.

Finally, the performance obtained by the proposed hybrid training is comparable to the ones presented on literature (Chang et al., 2005; Chen et al., 2003)

5. CONCLUSION

This work presented a multilayer perceptron (MLP) network using a GA-Backpropagation hybrid training to classify breast tumours as malign or benign ones. Seven morphometric parameters, extracted from the convex polygon and the normalised radial length techniques, were used as MLP input and the hybrid training selected the best parameters used in the MLP input and, also, the best training samples. The best values of accuracy (97.4%), sensitivity (98.0%) and specificity (96.2%) were achieved with a set of five parameters, despite the training set sizes tested: 30% and 50% of the total samples. Nevertheless, the GA-Backpropagation hybrid training performance using additional parameters, principally to quantify other tumour characteristics like echotexture, are being presently studied.

ACKNOWLEDGEMENTS

To Radiology Department from INCa for images used in this work and to FAPERJ and CNPq for financial support.

REFERENCES

Alvarenga, A.V., A.F.C. Infantosi, W.C.A. Pereira and C.M. Azevedo (2005). Classification of Breast Tumours on Ultrasound Images using Morphometric Parameters. In: *IEEE International Symposium on Intelligent Signal Processing*, **1**, 1-5

Alvarenga, A.V., A.F.C. Infantosi, C.M. Azevedo, W.C.A. Pereira (2003). Application of Morphological Operators on the Segmentation and Contour Detection of Ultrasound Breast Images. *Brazilian Journal of Biomedical Engineering*, **19**, 91-101.

Alvarenga, A.V., A.F.C. Infantosi, W.C.A. Pereira and C.M. Azevedo (2002). Contour Detection of Breast Ultrasound Tumor Images Using Morphological Operators. In: *Proc. of the IFMBE 12th Nordic Baltic Conference on Biomedical Engineering and Medical Physics*, Reykjavik, Iceland, **2**, 78-79.

Bakic, P.R. and D.P. Brzakovic (1997). Application of Neural Networks in Computer Aided Diagnosis of Breast Cancer, URL: http://citeseer.ist.psu.edu/404677.html.

Castleman, K.N. (1996). *Digital Image Processing*. Prentice-Hall International, New Jersey, New York.

Chang, R.F., Wu, W.J., Moon, W.K. and Chen, D.R. (2005). Automatic Ultrasound Segmentation and Morphology Based Diagnosis of Solid Breast Tumors". *Breast Cancer Research and Treatment*, **89**, 179-185.

Chen, C.M., Chou, Y.H., Han K.C., Hung G.S., Tiu, C.M., Chiou H.J. and Chiou S.Y. (2003). Breast Lesion on Sonograms: Computer-Aided Diagnosis with Nearly Setting-Independent Features and Artificial Neural Networks. *Radiology*, **226**, 504-514

Chou, Y.H., C.M. Tiu, G.S. Hung, S.C. Wu, T.Y. Chang and H.K. Chiang (2001). Stepwise Logistic Regression Analysis of Tumour Contour Features for Breast Ultrasound Diagnosis. *Ultrasound in Medicine & Biology*, **27**, 1493-1498.

Dennis, M.A., S.H. Parker, A.J. Klaus, A.T. Stavros, T.I. Kaske and S.B. Clark (2001). Breast Biopsy Avoidance: The Value of Normal Mammograms and Normal Sonograms in the Setting of a Palpable Lump. *Radiology*, **219**, 168–191.

Drukker, K., M.L. Giger, C.J. Vyborny and E.B. Mendelson (2004). Computerized Detection and Classification of Cancer on Breast Ultrasound. *Academic Radiology*, **11**, 526-535.

Harpham, C., C.W. Dawson, M.R. Brown (2004). A Review of Genetic Algorithms Applied to Training Radial Basis Function Networks. *Neural Comput. & Applic.*, **13**, 193–201.

Horsh, K., M.L. Giger, L.A. Venta, and C.J. Vyborny (2002). Computerized Diagnostic of Breast Lesions on Ultrasound. *Medical Physics*, **29**, 157-164.

Huber, S., J. Danes, I. Zuna, J. Teubner, M. Medl, S. Delmore (2000). Relevance of Sonographic B-Mode Criteria and Computer-aided Ultrasonic Tissue Characterization in Differential Diagnosis of Solid Breast Masses. *Ultrasound in Medicine & Biology*, **26**, 1243–1252.

Hudson, D.L. and M.E. Cohen (2000). *Neural Networks and Artificial Intelligence for Biomedical Engineering*, IEEE Press, New York, NY.

INCa, Rio de Janeiro, Instituto Nacional de Câncer. URL: http://www.inca.gov.br/cancer/mama/.

Infantosi, A.F.C., J.L. Silva Jr, C.J. Tierra-Criollo and D.M. Simpson (1998). Performance Evaluation of Interpolation Techniques for Brain Mapping Using Simulations. *Brazilian Journal of Biomedical Engineering*, **14**, 71-96.

Kim, S.H. and S.W. Shin (2000). Identifying the Impact of Decision Variables for Nonlinear Classification Tasks. *Expert Systems with Applications*, **18**, 201–214.

Komosinski, M., K. Krawiec (2000). Evolutionary Weighting of Image Features for Diagnosing of CNS tumors. *Artificial Intelligence in Medicine*, **19**, 25–38.

Lafuente, R., J.M. Belda, J. Sanchez-Lacuesta, C. Soler, J. Prat (1997). Design and Test of Neural Networks and Statistical Classifiers in Computer-Aided Movement Analysis: a Case Study on Gait Analysis. *Clin Biomech*, **13**, 216–229.

Rahbar, G., A.C. Sie, G.C. Hansen, J S. Prince, M.L. Melany, H.E. Reynolds, *et al.* (1999). Benign versus Malignant Solid Breast Masses: US Differentiation, *Radiology*, **213**, 889-894.

Skaane, P. (1999). Ultrasonography as Adjunct to Mammography in the Evaluation of Breast Tumors. *Acta Radiologica Supplementum*, **40**, 1-47.

Soille, P. (1999). *Morphological Image Analysis*, Springer-Verlag, Heidelberg, Berlin.

Su, F.C. and W.L. Wu (2000). Design and Testing of a Genetic Algorithm Neural Network in the Assessment of Gait Patterns. *Medical Engineering & Physics*, **22**, 67–74.

Zhang, H. and G. Sun (2002). Feature Selection Using Tabu Search Method. *Pattern Recognition*, **35**, 701-711

2–D PANORAMAS FROM CYSTOSCOPIC IMAGE SEQUENCES AND POTENTIAL APPLICATION TO FLUORESCENCE IMAGING

Yahir Hernández Mier * **Walter Blondel** *
Christian Daul * **Didier Wolf** *
Geneviève Bourg-Heckly **

* *CNRS UMR 7039 – CRAN*
Centre de Recherche en Automatique de Nancy
2, avenue de la Forêt de Haye, 54516
Vandœuvre–Lès–Nancy Cedex, France
** *CNRS UMR 7033 – BioMoCeTi*
Laboratoire de Biophysique Molculaire, Cellulaire et
Tissulaire. Université Paris VI GENOPOLE Campus 1,
Site SERONO, RN 7, 91030 Evry cedex, France

Abstract: This work describes an algorithm for the automatic construction of 2–D panoramas from sequences of images taken from a cystoscopic exam. During a cystoscopy, the existent distance between the cystoscope and the bladder walls allows the clinician to observe only a reduced region of the zone of interest. A panoramic representation of this zone could represent a better visual support to the clinician in the localization of eventual lesions and in the application of further exams. We also explore the application of this algorithm to endoscopic fluorescence imaging, one of the main procedures used in the detection of epithelial cancers. *Copyright © 2006 IFAC.*

Keywords: image registration, image mosaicing, bladder, fluorescence endoscopy.

1. INTRODUCTION

Cystoscopy is a clinical exam that allows the clinician to observe the internal walls of the bladder by inserting a thin instrument (cystoscope) trough the urethra. Cystoscopes, and the associated devices, can generate and store sequences of images in form of a video. However, when a cystoscopy is being carried–out, the existent distance between the cystoscope and the walls of the bladder authorizes the observation of only a reduced area of the zone being studied. A panoramic representation of the bladder under a cystoscopic procedure, would be an innovative visual support for the clinician in the localization of eventual lesions, post–operative observations or to guide further exams. Furthermore, building this panoramic representation in a period of time compatible with the duration of a clinical exam, i. e. when the patient is still under examination, would be of valuable interest. A popular method to increase the window of observation of a scene of interest, while preserving

[1] We thank Jean–Marie Munier for his contribution to the instrumental development of the device used in this work and Céline Frochot (DCPR - UMR CNRS 7630, Nancy) for providing us with the fluorescent marker. We specially thank the CNRS (STIC department) and "La ligue régionale de lutte contre le cancer (CD54)" for its financial support.

spatial resolution, is image mosaicing. It consists in extracting images from a moving scene, registering (finding geometric transformation between images) and stitching them to construct a larger image (a panorama). Image mosaicing has been widely used in different disciplines, from consumer photography (Sawhney et al., 1998)(Realviz S. A., 2002) to several fields in medicine (Can et al., 2002)(Asmuth et al., 2001)(Aiger and Cohen-Or, 2000), but its application to endoscopy (cystoscopy) has not been yet developed. This paper describes our methodology to build, in an automatic and efficient way, 2–D panoramas from cystoscopic image sequences taken during a real clinical exam. The first step in the proposed algorithm applies a band–pass filter over the sequence of images. The second step registers the filtered images using correlation in the frequency domain and minimization of intensity difference between images. The last step stitches images to form a 2–D panorama. Visual results and computation times in constructing the 2–D panorama for each sequence and each process are presented.

Endoscopy (fluorescence endoscopy) is also one of the main procedures used in the detection of epithelial cancers (trachea, bronchi, bladder, colon). In this modality of macroscopic fluorescence imaging, the fluorophores of the tissue are excited with violet light (390–460 nm) and ratio images in two different wavelength bands are formed. Considering that normal and cancerous lesions are characterized by different autofluorescence spectra, this modality is well adapted to improve the clinical sensibility of cancer detection and some devices are available and have been commercialized since a few years (Xillix Corporation, 2005), (PENTAX Corporation, 2005), (KARL STORZ ENDOSKOPE, 2005).

In this work, we propose to combine white light images with spatially localized fluorescence information acquired in blue light by "merging them" in one image. Acquiring experimentally two sets of images (white and blue light) we formed two 2–D panoramas and then we combined them to have fluorescence information superposed to a white light image.

2. METHODOLOGY

2.1 Mosaicing algorithm

The first step in constructing the proposed algorithm is the elimination of illumination differences between the center of the image and the borders (vignetting) and the reduction of blurring caused by the movement of internal walls of the bladder and objects passing in front of the cystoscope. To do so, a band–pass filter was applied over images by subtracting two low–pass versions of the same image. To reduce the effects caused by a weak radial distortion (not corrected in this work), a central square of 256 x 256 pixels was selected as region of interest (ROI). Once a sequence of images was preprocessed, the registration algorithm was used. As a first step, the well known phase correlation registration algorithm (Kuglin and Hines, 1975) was used to obtain, in a fast way, a first approach of the translation parameters between images at a pixel level. This algorithm is based on the fact that a displacement in the spatial domain corresponds to a linear change in the Fourier domain, as indicated by the shift property of the Fourier transform. This is, if an image $I_0(\mathbf{x})$, where $\mathbf{x} = (x, y)^T$, differ only by a translation $\mathbf{x_0} = (x_0, y_0)^T$ from image $I_1(\mathbf{x})$ [i.e., $I_1(\mathbf{x}) = I_0(\mathbf{x} - \mathbf{x_0})$], their Fourier transform, denoted by $F_0(\mathbf{u})$ and $F_1(\mathbf{u})$, where $\mathbf{u} = (u, v)^T$ is the spatial frequency vector, are related by:

$$F_1(\mathbf{u}) = e^{-j2\pi(\mathbf{u} \cdot \mathbf{x_0})} F_0(\mathbf{u}). \qquad (1)$$

Computing the correlation function between Fourier transforms, we have:

$$R(\mathbf{u}) = \frac{F_0(\mathbf{u}) F_1^*(\mathbf{u})}{|F_0(\mathbf{u})||F_1(\mathbf{u})|}, \qquad (2)$$

where * denotes the complex conjugate.

By taking the inverse Fourier transform of R we obtain a Dirac's delta function, where the position of the peak value indicates the pixel translation in the spatial domain (Reddy and Chatterji, 1996):

$$r(\mathbf{x}) = \delta(\mathbf{x} - \mathbf{x_0}). \qquad (3)$$

But translation is not the only transformation found in a cystoscopic sequence. Discarding radial distortion in images and considering the 3D movements of the cystoscope, a projective transformation model was chosen as the more appropriate model to register adjacent images in the sequence. The displacement obtained by the phase correlation algorithm was used to initialize an iterative process to find the projective transformations, at sub–pixel level, between each adjacent pair of images. The iterative process is based on the efficient inverse composite registration algorithm developed in (Baker and Matthews, 2002), which objective is to align an image $I_1(\mathbf{x})$ to a template image $I_0(\mathbf{x})$. This algorithm is a generalization of the Lucas–Kanade algorithm (Lucas and Kanade, 1981) to parametric motion models. A projective transformation T of parameters $\mathbf{p} = (p_0, p_1, \ldots, p_8)^T$ is applied over the pixel coordinates of image I_1, i. e. $I_1(T(\mathbf{x}; \mathbf{p}))$, to take its pixel values to the coordinates of their corresponding pixel values in image I_0. This algorithm assumes that the current transformation parameters $\mathbf{p}$ are known and then iteratively minimizes

$$\sum_x [I_0(T(\mathbf{x}; \Delta\mathbf{p})) - I_1(T(\mathbf{x}; \mathbf{p}))]^2, \qquad (4)$$

with respect to an increment $\Delta\mathbf{p}$ of the transformation parameters. The summation is done over the defined ROI. At every iteration, the transformation function is updated by a bilinear combination (denoted by the ∘ operator) of the parameters of $T(\mathbf{x};\mathbf{p})$ and $T(\mathbf{x};\Delta\mathbf{p})$.

$$T(\mathbf{x};\mathbf{p})_{new} = T(\mathbf{x};\mathbf{p})_{old} \circ T(\mathbf{x};\Delta\mathbf{p})^{-1}. \quad (5)$$

A full explanation of this algorithm can be found at (Baker and Matthews, 2002). The transformation parameters obtained for every image are stored and then used to stitch all images to form a 2–D panorama. The stitching process is performed by assigning a weighted average value to overlying pixels by a Gaussian function,

$$w_1 = 0.9e^{-\frac{r}{2\sigma^2}} + 0.1; \quad (6)$$
$$w_0 = 1 - w_1,$$

where w_1 is the weight of pixels of the image to stitch and w_0 is the weight of the existing panoramic image; r is the radial distance of a pixel measured from the center of the image and σ is the opening of the Gaussian function. These weights are then multiplied by the intensity values of the pixels in the image being stitched, $I_1(\mathbf{x})$, and the intensity values of the existing panoramic image $I_m(\mathbf{x})$,

$$I_{pano}(\mathbf{x}) = w_1 I_1(\mathbf{x}) + w_0 I_m(\mathbf{x}), \quad (7)$$

where $I_{pano}(\mathbf{x})$ is the new panoramic image, including $I_1(\mathbf{x})$. This was applied $\forall\, I_1(\mathbf{x}), I_m(\mathbf{x}) \neq 0$. This process strongly attenuates visual artifacts at image borders.

The previous algorithms were programmed in Matlab. To test the mosaicing algorithm, three image sequences, containing 80, 162 and 193 images were extracted from video acquired during a cystoscopy. To extract the images, a minimal overlap of 70% was considered. Execution times of registration and stitching processes, for the three sequences, were computed on a PC 2GHz 1Gb RAM.

2.2 Application to fluorescence imaging

To form a white light panoramic image combined with fluorescence information, two sets of 27 images (a set in white light and a set acquired in the 500–600 nm band, after excitation at 400–430 nm), were acquired with an endoscope using the positioning system shown in figure 1. We used an endoscope instead of a cystoscope because of availability issues. Image quality of endoscopically acquired images is lower compared to cystoscopic images and radial distortion is greater. Thus, a radial distortion correction is applied over acquired images using the algorithm described in (Miranda-Luna *et al.*, 2004). This was an extra

Fig. 1. Positioning testing set–up used to acquire the test sequence. This device allows a micrometric control over translation movements.

step that was applied over acquired images. To simulate the texture found in a clinical exam, we used a high–quality bladder photography. To induce fluorescence, we applied a little quantity of a fluorescent marker (coumarin). The acquisition was performed over a defined path and to simulate the movements of a cystoscopy exam, the acquisition involved three directions of displacement: a translation movement (15 images) over $\overrightarrow{x}$, a diagonal translation (7 images) over $\overrightarrow{x}$ and $\overrightarrow{y}$, and a diagonal translation with 2° rotations and 2° perspective rotations of the endoscope between images (5 images). The first sequence was acquired under white light where fluorescence cannot be observed. The same process (same positions) was repeated over the same photography, but this time under fluorescence excitation violet light. A schematic representation of the process is shown in figure 2. The white spot represents the region where the fluorescent marker was applied. The registration and stitching algorithm was then applied to images acquired in white light to find the transformations between them to build the 2–D panorama. Then, these transformations were applied over the set of fluorescence images and a second panoramic image was constructed. By thresholding the 2–D fluorescence panorama, the fluorescent region was extracted and then superposed to the white light 2–D panorama.

3. RESULTS

3.1 Mosaicing algorithm

Figures 3, 4 and 5 show the panoramic views constructed from 80, 162 and 193 images respectively. The algorithm is robust enough to find a good visual correspondence between images even if blurring and illumination inhomogeneities are present. After application of the weighting average

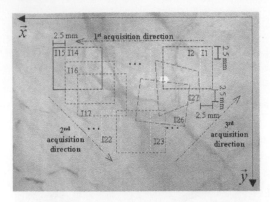

Fig. 2. Schematic representation of the image acquisition path performed over a photography of pig bladder (internal surface). I1, I2,..., I27 are the first, second,..., twenty-seventh acquired image. The white spot represents the region where the fluorescent marker was applied.

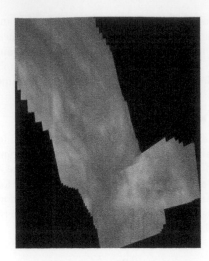

Fig. 3. Panoramic view (959 x 671 pixels) from a sequence of 80 images. The vessels and a suspicious structure (bottom right) in the panoramic view are easily identifiable.

function, visual artifacts between images persist, but only when strong illumination changes between images are involved. Table 1 shows computation times for each constructed panoramic view and for each pair of images processed. Computation times were measured separately for registration and stitching processes because stitching time varies with the transformation complexity and image size after transformation. The maximum displacement recovered for the sequences presented here was 96 pixels. Table 1 shows that the required computation time allows the panoramic image to be constructed in a few minutes. This computation time could be compatible with the duration of a cystoscopic exam (15–20 min). Stitching time in sequence 3 shows a considerable increase. This is due to the complexity of the transformations obtained for the last images (bottom region) and their large size after transformation.

Table 1. Timing results in seconds for each process and for each constructed panoramic view.

Seq.	Imgs.	Regist.	Stitch.	Total	p/pair
1	80	155.62	25.85	181.47	2.29
2	162	310.23	30.70	340.93	2.11
3	193	376.52	426.54	803.06	4.18

3.2 Application to fluorescence imaging

Figure 6 shows the 2–D panorama built from images acquired under white light. The spot of the fluorescent marker is hardly visible. Fluorescence 2–D panorama is shown in figure 7. The region where the fluorescent marker was applied is clearly visible. The superposition of the fluorescent information over the white light 2–D panorama is shown as a red spot in figure 8. This combined

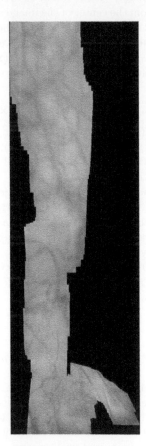

Fig. 4. Panoramic view (1651 x 482 pixels) from a sequence of 162 images (vertical scan of the bladder).

image has now a greater information content for fluorescence imaging that the single white light and fluorescence images.

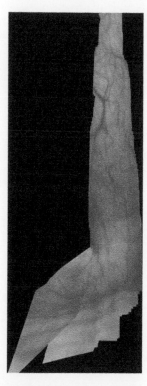

Fig. 5. Panoramic view (4883 x 1697 pixels) from a sequence of 193 images (vertical scan of the bladder).

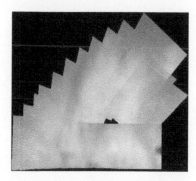

Fig. 6. 2–D panorama (450 x 503 pixels) constructed from images acquired over a bladder photography under white light, using the endoscopic set–up shown in Figure 1. The fluorescent maker is hardly visible.

4. CONCLUSION

Visual characteristics of the constructed panoramic views are well preserved and authorize an easier observation of the zone of interest by providing a wider observation window. Timing results showed the possibility of obtaining a panoramic image in a few minutes. This computation time could be compatible with the duration of a clinical cystoscopy. In addition, the presented algorithm is robust enough to deal with blurring, illumination inhomogeneities and remaining radial distortion in images. We also explored the possibility of combining information of images used in the detection

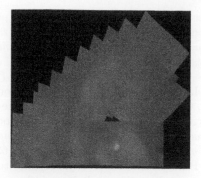

Fig. 7. 2–D panorama (450 x 503 pixels) constructed from images acquired under blue light. The white spot indicates the region where the fluorescent marker was applied.

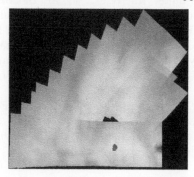

Fig. 8. This image shows the superposition of the fluorescent region (in red), extracted by thresholding of the fluorescence 2–D panorama, over the white light panorama.

of cancer by autofluorescence. The information from the fluorescence 2–D panorama was easily extracted and then superposed to the white light panorama. These results showed us that this algorithm could be used without modifications in a fluorescence imaging application. Complementary test over new clinical sequences are being performed for the evaluation of the proposed algorithm.

REFERENCES

Aiger, D. and D. Cohen-Or (2000). Mosaicing ultrasonic volumes for visual simulation. *IEEE Computers Graphics and Applications* **20**(2), 53–61.

Asmuth, J., B. Madjarov, P. Sajda and J. W. Berger (2001). Mosaicking and enhacement of slit lamp biomicroscopic fundus images. *British Journal of Ophtalmology* **0**(85), 563–565.

Baker, S. and I. Matthews (2002). Lucas–Kanade 20 years on: A unifying framework: Part 1. Technical Report CMU-RI-TR-02-16. Robotics Institute, Carnegie Mellon University. Pittsburgh, PA.

Can, A., C. V. Stewart, B. Roysam and H. L. Tanenbaum (2002). A feature-based, robust, hierarchical algorithm for registering pairs of images of the curved human retina. *IEEE Transactions on Pattern Analysis and Machine Intelligence* **24**(3), 347–364.

KARL STORZ ENDOSKOPE (2005). D–Light/AF. http://www.karlstorz.com/.

Kuglin, C. D. and D. C. Hines (1975). The phase correlation image alignment method. In: *Procceedings of the 1975 IEEE International Conference Cybernetics Society.* pp. 163–165.

Lucas, B. D. and T. Kanade (1981). An iterative image registration technique with an application to stereo vision (darpa). In: *Proceedings of the 1981 DARPA Image Understanding Workshop.* pp. 121–130.

Miranda-Luna, R., W. C. P. M. Blondel, Ch. Daul, Y. Hernandez-Mier, R. Posada and D. Wolf (2004). A simplified method for endoscopic image distortion correction based on grey level registration. In: *2004 International Conference on Image Processing, ICIP2004.* Vol. 5. pp. 3383–3386.

PENTAX Corporation (2005). SAFE–3000. http://www.pentax.com/.

Realviz S. A. (2002). *Stitcher 3.x main tutorial.* HTTP://www.realviz.com/.

Reddy, B. S. and B. N. Chatterji (1996). An fft-based technique for translation, rotation, and scale-invariant image registration. *IEEE Transactions on Image Processing* **5**(8), 1266–1271.

Sawhney, H., R. Kumar, G. Gendel, J. Bergen, D. Dixon and V. Paraganoet (1998). VideoBrushTM: Experiences with consumer video mosaicing. In: *4th IEEE Workshop on Applications of Computer Vision (WACV'98).* p. 56.

Xillix Corporation (2005). Xillix Onco–LIFE. http://www.xillix.com/.

PARAMETRIC IMAGING OF ACETYLCHOLINESTERASE ACTIVITY WITH PET: EVALUATION OF DIFFERENT METHODS

Giampaolo Tomasi, Alessandra Bertoldo, Claudio Cobelli

Department of Information Engineering, University of Padova, Italy

Abstract: C-11-labeled N-methyl-4-piperidin acetate ([11C]MP4A) is used for the quantitative measurement of acetylcholinesterase activity with positron emission tomography (PET). In this study, two new methods, i.e. simplified ridge regression with spatial constraint (SRRSC) and its generalized formulation (GRRSC), are evaluated to quantify, without arterial measurements, [11C]MP4A images at pixel level. Their performance is assessed against state of art quantification methods for [11C]MP4A by Monte Carlo simulations. Although characterized by a little bias, GRRSC emerges as the most reliable and computationally efficient algorithm to generate parametric images of [11C]MP4A when an arterial input function is not available. *Copyright © 2006 IFAC*

Keywords: Image analysis, Modelling, Monte Carlo simulations, Algorithms, Mean square error, Bias, Parameter estimation.

1. INTRODUCTION

Acetylcholinesterase (AChE) activity, a marker for degeneration of the central cholinergic system, is a suitable in vivo indicator for the diagnosis and assessment of progression of some neurodegenerative disorders - Alzheimer's disease in particular. The quantification of AChE activity may also be crucial for evaluating the therapeutic effect of a drug and/or understanding which are the areas mostly damaged by any brain disease related to AChE modifications.

In recent years, C-11-labeled N-methyl-4-piperidin acetate ([11C]MP4A), an acetylcoline analog, has been developed for in vivo imaging with positron emission tomography (PET) of AChE activity. [11C]MP4A enters the brain by diffusion and is hydrolyzed by AChE to a hydrophilic metabolite which is trapped into the brain according to the distribution of AChE activity. The different steps of [11C]MP4A kinetics can be adequately quantified by using a three-compartment three-rate constant model (Namba, *et al*, 1994; Iyo, *et al*, 1997; Tanaka, *et al*, 2001; Herholz, *et al*, 2001) with K_1 representing the rate of tracer influx into the brain, k_2 the rate of outflux from the brain, and k_3 the rate of tracer hydrolysis.

The gold-standard method to estimate local hydrolysis rate of [11C]MP4 by AChE is weighted nonlinear least squares (NLLS) with the arterial tracer concentration as input function (AIF – arterial input function) to the model. This method requires measurements of arterial concentration of the tracer and of its plasma metabolites. However, these measurements are invasive to patients and require also considerable technical expertise, thus reducing the diffusion of PET as a method for quantification of AChE activity in clinical practice.

It is therefore of crucial importance to be able to reliably estimate kinetic parameters of the tracer without the use of the arterial input function. Several methods have been developed for [11C]MP4 (Herholz, *et al*, 2001; Zundorf, *et al*, 2002; Nagatsuka, *et al*, 2001; Tanaka, *et al*, 2001). In the present study, two novel methods for [11C]MP4 quantification are tested and validated on simulated data and results compared to those obtained by using NLLS and three state of art methods developed to quantify [11C]MP4 without arterial input function, i.e. the method of Herholz and co-workers(2001), its modification developed by Zundorf and co-workers (2002), and shape analysis (Tanaka, *et al*., 2001).

2. MATERIALS AND METHODS

2.1 Simulation

Two simulated [^{11}C]MP4A dynamic images were constructed to reproduce, respectively, a healthy subject and an Alzheimer patient. In both cases, pixel activities were generated assuming the three-compartment three-rate constant model proposed in (Namba, et al, 1994) and negligible presence at pixel level of vascular contribution. The parametric maps of K_1, k_2 and k_3 obtained by quantifying [^{11}C]MP4A images of one normal subject and one Alzheimer patient using arterial input function and NLLS, were filtered by a 2D-Gaussian filter. Error-free time activity curves (TACs) for each pixel and subject were then generated using these resulting smoothed parametric maps and the corresponding known plasmatic input functions. In particular, error-free TACs were generated at the midtimes of the frames of the scanning protocol used for the two original subjects: 6x0.5min, 2x1min, 2x2.5min, 10x5min, for a total of 20 frames. For each pixel, a set of 100 noisy TACs were generated adding to the error-free TACs Gaussian noise with zero mean and standard deviation $\sigma_i = \sqrt{\alpha / \Delta t_i}$ where Δt_i denotes the duration of the i-th scan interval, and α is a parameter quantifying the amount of noise. To choose reliable values for α - constant for each pixel but varying from pixel to pixel due to differences in the spatial position- α maps were generated during the quantification of the [^{11}C]MP4 images of the normal subject and the Alzheimer patient by computing for each pixel:

$$\alpha = \frac{\text{NLSS}(\hat{p})}{N - P} \qquad (1)$$

where $\text{NLSS}(\hat{p})$ is the value of the cost function evaluated at the minimum, N the number of scans and P the number of model parameters (3, in our case). These maps were then used in the process of noise generation. In this way, simulated activity curves resemble real ones not only as to the amount of noise but also as to the differences in noise according to pixel position.

2.2 NLLS & AIF

The total concentration, C_T, of [^{11}C]MP4A and its metabolite [^{11}C]MP4AOH, can be expressed as a function of the arterial plasma tracer concentration, C_{pl}, by assuming a three-compartment three-rate constant model structure:

$$C_T(t) = \frac{K_1 k_2}{k_2 + k_3} \int_0^t C_{pl}(x) e^{-(k_2+k_3)(t-x)} dx + \frac{K_1 k_3}{k_2 + k_3} \int_0^t C_{pl}(x) dx \qquad (2)$$

with K_1, k_2, and k_3 having the same previous meanings. Parameters were estimated with NLLS from Eq.2, assuming the arterial tracer concentration as input function (AIF) of the model and with inverse of scan durations used as weights. It is of note that NNLS with arterial input function (NNLS & AIF) is

the gold standard for quantitative functional imaging with PET.

2.3 Reference Least Squares

Reference Least Squares (RLS) method is based on the linear approach proposed by Blomquist (Blomquist, et al., 1984) than can be applied to any three-compartment irreversible model to estimate kinetic parameters according to:

$$C_T(t) = K_1 \int_0^t C_{pl}(x) dx + K_1 k_3 \int_0^t \int_0^\phi C_{pl}(x) dx d\phi + \qquad (3)$$

$$- (k_2 + k_3) \int_0^t C_T(x) dx$$

The idea allowing to avoid the use of C_{pl} for [^{11}C]MP4A in Eq.3 is the following: [^{11}C]MP4A molecules incorporated into cerebellum are rapidly transformed into the hydrophilic metabolite [^{11}C]MP4OH because AChE activity is very high in this regions. In addition, cerebellum TAC shows a rapid increase after tracer injection and a plateau level which begins when plasma [^{11}C]MP4A radioactivity is almost zero, suggesting that it could be used to approximate the time integral of the arterial input function according to:

$$C_R(t) = K_1^{REF} \int_0^t C_{pl}(x) dx \qquad (4)$$

(Nagatsuka, et al, 2001) where C_R denotes cerebellum activity (cerebellum is also named reference region), and K_1^{REF} is the value of K_1 in this region. By using Eq.2 and Eq.3, one gets:

$$C_T(t) = p_1 C_R(t) + p_2 \int_0^t C_R(x) dx + p_3 \int_0^t C_T(x) dx \qquad (5)$$

with $p_1 = \frac{K_1}{K_1^{REF}} = K_R$, $p_2 = K_R k_3$, and

$p_3 = -(k_2 + k_3)$. By using weighted linear regression, one can estimate p_1, p_2 and p_3 and from these determine K_R, k_2, and k_3.

Weights were chosen as the inverse of scan durations and coefficient of variation (CV) were computed as $\text{std}(\hat{p}_i)/\hat{p}_i$, where $\text{std}(\hat{p}_i)$ denotes the standard deviation associated with the estimated model parameter $\hat{p}_i$.

2.4 Herholz's method

Another method which does not require an arterial input function has been proposed by Herholz and co-workers (Herholz, et al, 2001). In reference tissue (denoted by C_R) as cerebellum, hydrolysis is extremely rapid, so that the reference TAC can be approximated by means of Eq.4. In addition, due to the very rapid fall of non-hydrolysed tracer activity in plasma, Herholz assumed that C_{pl} can be approximated by monoexponential decline:

$$C_{pl}(t) = C_0 e^{-k_p t} \qquad (6)$$

Then, it can be shown that tissue TACs relative to reference activity can be described by:

$$C(t) = \frac{C_T(t)}{C_R(t)} = A e^{-kt} + B \qquad (7)$$

with $A=\dfrac{K_1}{K_1^{REF}}\dfrac{k_2}{k_2+k_3}$, $B=\dfrac{K_1}{K_1^{REF}}\dfrac{k_3}{k_2+k_3}$, $k=k_2+k_3$.

By using weighted nonlinear least squares, one can estimate A, B and k and, successively, derive K_1/K_1^{REF}, k_3, and k_2. Weights were chosen as for RLS.

2.5 Zundorf's method

To avoid the approximation of the plasmatic tracer concentration with a mono-exponential function, Zundorf (Zundorf, et al., 2002) assumes as in Herholz (Herholz, et al., 2001) and RLS (Nagatsuka et al, 2001) that the reference TAC can be approximated by means of Eq.4 so that the tissue TACs relative to reference activity is described by:

$$C(t)=\frac{C_T(t)}{C_R(t)}$$

$$=\frac{K_1}{K_1^{REF}}\frac{k_2}{k_2+k_3}\frac{\int_0^t C_{pl}(x)e^{-(k_2+k_3)(t-x)}dx}{\int_0^t C_{pl}(x)dx}+ \qquad (8)$$

$$+\frac{K_1}{K_1^{REF}}\frac{k_3}{k_2+k_3}$$

By using Eq.4 and Eq.8, one gets:

$$C(t)=\frac{C_T(t)}{C_R(t)}=A\left[1-k\frac{\int_0^t C_R(x)e^{-k(t-x)}dx}{C_R(t)}\right]+B \qquad (9)$$

$$=A\omega_k(t)+B$$

with $A=\dfrac{K_1}{K_1^{REF}}\dfrac{k_2}{k_2+k_3}$, $B=\dfrac{K_1}{K_1^{REF}}\dfrac{k_3}{k_2+k_3}$, $k=k_2+k_3$.

To obtain parameter estimates, $\omega_k(t)$ is first calculated by numerical integration from a set of different k that covers the entire physiological range. A and B are then estimated by weighted linear regression from Eq.9. and $\omega_k(t)$ which gives rise to the smallest weighted sum of residuals is selected. Weights were chosen as for RLS.

2.6 Shape analysis

Shape analysis (SA) can be applied to any irreversible tracer and is based on the assumption that the tracer in tissue is not metabolized at the start and completely hydrolyzed at the end of the study. The equations used are:

$$C_T(0)=C_{REV}(0) \qquad (10)$$
$$C_{IRR}(i)-C_{IRR}(i-1)=k_3\Delta t_i C_{REV}(i-1) \qquad (11)$$
$$C_T(n)=C_{IRR}(n) \qquad (12)$$

where $C_{REV}(i)$, $C_{IRR}(i)$ and $C_T(i)$ denote respectively the concentration of the tracer in the reversible and irreversible compartments and their sum at a generic frame i, and n stands for the last frame. One has to use Eq.10 as a starting point and Eq.12 to update compartment concentration estimations to get in the end a value for $C_{IRR}(n)$; if

this value is sufficiently close to $C_T(n)$, measured from PET data, the current value of k_3 is accepted, otherwise it is appropriately updated and the procedure repeated. The assumption that the tracer is completely hydrolyzed at the end of the study is critical and so is the final value of the time-activity curve. The indications given by Tanaka and co-workers (Tanaka, et al., 2001) who studied the optimal settings of parameters for this method were followed. 19 frames out of 20 -corresponding to 50 minutes -were used for calculation, with the last 13 frames of the each time radioactivity curve fitted to a steadily decreasing bi-exponential function with negativity constraint for the exponents. PET data consisting of observed (first 6 frames, corresponding to the first 3 minutes) and fitted (last 13 frames) were then linearly interpolated to yield an 8-fold increase in the number of data points before shape analysis calculation. No weights were used for parameter estimation.

2.7 Ridge Regression

Two novel quantification methods have been developed based on the Ridge Regression with Spatial Constraint method proposed by Zhou and co-workers (Zhou, et al 2001; Zhou et al 2002;Zhou et al 2003) and in the current study implemented in its Simplified (SRRSC) and Generalized (GRRSC) forms. The main idea behind this class of methods is to improve the precision of parametric images and to reduce estimation variability due to noise by penalizing local spatial variation of parameters. First, parameters are estimated for each pixel in the conventional way by minimizing the function:

$$(\mathbf{Y}\text{-}\mathbf{X}\beta)^T\mathbf{W}(\mathbf{Y}\text{-}\mathbf{X}\beta) \qquad (13)$$

where $\mathbf{W}$ denotes a matrix containing appropriate weights, $\mathbf{Y}$ is an n×1 observation matrix, $\mathbf{X}$ is an n×m matrix defining the model, and β is a m×1 parameter vector to be estimated. With our simulated data set, weights were chosen as for RLS. The parametric maps so obtained are then smoothed, typically using for each pixel a window of size 5x5 or 3x3 with equal weights in it, so that an estimate β_0 of the parameter vector β is obtained for every pixel. Parameter estimation is then performed again, but this time a term derived from the previous smoothing process is added to the cost function in order to incorporate spatial information into the fit. The function to minimize becomes:

$$(\mathbf{Y}\text{-}\mathbf{X}\beta)^T\mathbf{W}(\mathbf{Y}\text{-}\mathbf{X}\beta)+(\beta-\beta_0)^T\mathbf{H}(\beta-\beta_0) \qquad (14)$$

with $\mathbf{H}$ determining the weight of the Bayesian term. The diagonal ridge matrix H is calculated for SRRSC as:

$$h_i=m\sigma^2/(\beta-\beta_0)^T(\beta-\beta_0) \quad i=1,2,...m \qquad (15)$$

and for GRRSC:

$$h_i=\sigma^2/(\beta_i-\beta_{i0})^2 \quad i=1.,2,...m \qquad (16)$$

where σ^2 is the noise variance of the data estimated for each pixel from the residuals of the weighted linear regression, and m is the number of parameters. GRRSC, therefore, makes use of different weights for each parameter while SRRSC does not; both methods were applied to RLS assuming the same configuration of the three-compartment three-rate constant model for $[^{11}C]MP4A$ quantification.

2.8 Performance Indices

For each method, parameter estimates were compared with the true values at each pixel. In particular, percentage average bias and percentage average mean squares errors were computed for the kinetic parameter k_3 since it is by far the most important parameter for AChE study. The indices used in evaluating the performance of each algorithm were BIAS and MSE averaged over all the pixels of each slice:

$$BIAS = \frac{\frac{1}{N}\sum_{i=1}^{N}(p_i - p_{TRUE})}{p_{TRUE}} \times 100 \qquad (17)$$

$$MSE = \frac{1}{p_{TRUE}}\sqrt{\frac{\sum_{i=1}^{N}(p_i - p_{true})^2}{N}} \times 100 \qquad (18)$$

For each pixel and iteration percentage bias higher than 100% or lower than -100% were bounded to 100% and -100% respectively and MSEs were corrected accordingly: this was done to avoid outliers from significantly affecting global results.

3. RESULTS

The rate of tracer hydrolysis, k_3, is the most interesting and informative parameter obtainable from $[^{11}C]MP4$ quantification. Consequently, only k_3 CV, BIAS and MSE are shown. Moreover, it is of note that results refer to occipital cortex (slice #11) and to simulated slice #27, which contains both for the healthy subject and for the Alzheimer patient a significant amount of cerebral cortex. The reason for this choice is that cerebral cortex is the most interesting brain tissue for AChE study, especially in Alzheimer disease.

Table 1 and 2 summarize MSE and BIAS for the healthy and Alzheimer simulated data set, respectively.

Table 1. MSE and BIAS for k3 averaged over all pixels and all the 100 runs for the healthy simulated data set in a full slice (#27) and in the occipital cortex of slice #11

	Slice #27		Occipital cortex (Slice #11)	
	MSE	BIAS	MSE	BIAS
NLLS&AIF	19.8	-1.6	22.5	0.7
RLS	26.0	-6.5	33.6	-13.6
Herholz	83.0	-16.8	81.8	-10.6
Zundorf	17.1	4.2	17.1	-0.2
SA	73.9	3.6	65.8	-13.4
GRRSC	16.7	-3.1	19.4	-9.3
SRRSC	21.1	-4.7	22.4	-11.7

Table 2. RMSE and BIAS for k3 averaged over all pixels and all the 100 runs for the Alzheimer simulated data set in a full slice (#27) and in the occipital cortex of slice #11

	Slice #27		Occipital cortex (Slice #11)	
	MSE	BIAS	MSE	BIAS
NLLS&AIF	36.4	-0.4	33.3	1.8
RLS	39.4	-22.4	37.0	-19.8
Herholz	103.2	8.1	89.7	-0.8
Zundorf	24.1	-0.2	22.2	-5.2
SA	89.9	13.9	81.8	17.3
GRRSC	25.7	-18.4	24.9	-16.9
SRRSC	27.7	-21.0	28.0	-18.5

From Table 1 and Table 2, NLLS&AIF shows to be the method globally characterized by the lowest BIAS (almost 0%, as expected). Thus NLLS&AIF is the best choice for $[^{11}C]MP4$ quantification when arterial plasma tracer concentration is available and computational time is not an issue. However, when AIF is not measured and/or a less time-consuming method than NLLS&AIF is required one of the other considered method has to be evaluated. Among the non-invasive alternatives considered, Zundorf's method always provided the best results both in terms of MSE and BIAS, which was almost absent, outclassing even NLLS&AIF in terms of MSE (MSE higher of 3%-13% for NLLS&AIF). Zundorf's method, however, has a high computational cost, triggered by the series of fit performed for each values of k_2+k_3 in the physiological range (in our simulation 0.1-0.25 min^{-1}, uniformly spanned with step 0.01 min^{-1}) for each pixel. This makes Zundorf's method hardly usable for parametric imaging. In addition, the choice of the interval for values of k_2+k_3 is not irrelevant affecting MSE and BIAS. The interval we used (0.1- 0.25 min^{-1}) seems optimal since, globally, it yielded average bias that were very close to zero and low MSE; increasing the second extreme of the spanned interval triggers slight overestimations of k_3, whereas decreasing it produces systematic underestimation. The use of a smaller step than 0.01 min^{-1}(0.001 min^{-1}) yielded negligible improvements in performances whereas it significantly increased computational time. GRRSC, on the other side, is very fast due to linearity of RLS itself. Besides, although characterized by a negative bias (ranging from -2% to -18%) that is the obvious consequence of the bias affecting RLS, this method provided very low MSE, smaller than those computed through NLLS and less than 3% higher than those computed through Zundorf's method. SRRSC gave results very similar but always slightly worse than GRRSC: this was expected since SRRSC is a simplification of GRRSC and therefore meant to yield poorer results.

The negative bias that characterizes RLS is a known result (Nagatsuka, *et al*, 2001). A striking fact is the significant improvement triggered by the use of GRRSC: MSE decreases ranged from 30% to 40% applying general ridge regression to reference least squares with a negligible increase of computational time. It is of note that, leaving aside Herholz's method and SA that were the least reliable, results concerning the Alzheimer data set show with all the methods an average increase of MSE, ranging from 4% to 16%.

Fig. 1 shows an example of the modifications produced by the use of GRRSC to RLS. In particular, Fig. 1 shows parametric maps of k_3 for slice #27 of both the healthy subject (upper panel) and the Alzheimer patient (lower panel). Images represent the simulated "true" k_3 parameters (left) and the corresponding maps obtained through RLS (middle) and GRRSC (right). Notice how GRRSC images are smoother than the spotted images in the centre, and much more similar to the 'real' maps.

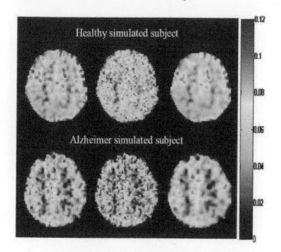

Fig. 1. Parametric maps of k_3 for slice #27 of the simulated healthy subject(upper part) and of the Alzheimer patient (lower part). Real maps, RLS maps and GRRSC maps are displayed on the left centre and right respectively.

GRRSC is superior to Zundorf's method in terms of CV. CV averaged over all pixel and all the 100 runs are shown in Table 3 (healthy subject) and in Table 4 (Alzheimer patient).

GRRSC provided the lowest CVs: this reduction of uncertainty of estimates is expected since GRRSC is a Bayesian estimation approach.

Table 3 CV averaged over all pixels and 100 runs for healthy simulated subject

	Slice #27	Occipital cortex(Slice #11)
NLLS&AIF	18.4	19.2
Zundorf	21.2	21.4
GRRSC	5.1	5.8

Table 4 CV averaged over all pixels and 100 runs for Alzheimer simulated subject

	Slice #27	Occipital cortex(Slice #11)
NLLS&AIF	19.7	20.3
Zundorf	22.0	22.4
GRRSC	5.8	5.9

4. CONCLUSION

In the present study, two novel methods for quantification of [11C]MP4A images without arterial input function were evaluated. Their performances were also compared to those of the four principal other different methods available for estimating $[^{11}C]MP4A$ kinetic parameters without the use of the arterial tracer concentration. Comparison of the methods were performed by simulations at pixel level, since pixel-by-pixel maps are particularly interesting in the process of diagnosis of the precise diffusion of Alzheimer's disease into the various cerebral regions. Among the non-invasive alternatives considered, Zundorf's method always provided the best results both in terms of mean square error MSE and BIAS, which was almost absent. This approach, however, has a very high computational cost, triggered by the series of fit performed for values of k_2+k_3 in the physiological range at each and every pixel. The method could be used at region of interest (ROI) level - when the number of 'elements' considered is rarely higher than a dozen for each subject and therefore computation burden is limited – but when interest is addressed in pixel-by-pixel mapping, GRRSC is preferable, providing results only slightly inferior in a more efficient fashion. Shape analysis (SA) and Herholz's method poorly performed. In particular, even when all settings are optimal, average MSE for SA is high indicating that one or more of the hypothesis this method is based upon may not hold. Herholz's method, on the other side, is based on a non-linear fit and is therefore unsuitable in pixel-by-pixel analysis, where noise of pixels' time activity curves may trigger unreliable estimates of kinetic parameters if this procedure is used. As to RLS, its performances were good but significant improvements in terms of MSE can be obtained through the use of GRRSC with negligible increase of computational time, i.e. MSE decreased from 30% to 40%, with slight improvements in terms of BIAS too. SRRSC results are similar but always worse than GRRSC. Differences between methods were also significant in terms of uncertainty of estimates, with GRRSC yielding the lowest CV. Even if outclassed by NLLS&AIF in terms of BIAS, GRRSC provides excellent results in terms of MSE and CV, besides being very fast due to linearity of RLS itself and therefore suitable to application at pixel level. GRRSC is therefore the optimal choice among all the non invasive alternatives for $[^{11}C]MP4A$ quantification at pixel level.

REFERENCES

Blomqvist, G. (1984) On the construction of functional maps in positron emission tomography *J Cereb Flow And Metabol* 4:629-632.

Herholz, K., Lercher, M., Wienhard, K., Bauer, B., Lenz, O., Heiss, W.D. (2001) PET measurement of cerebral acetylcoline esterase activity without blood sampling *Eur J Nucl Med* 28:472-477.

Irie, T., Fukushi, K., Namba, H., Iyo, M., Tamagami, H., Nagatsuka, S., Ikota, N. (1996) Brain acetylcolinesterase activity:validation of a PET tracer in a rat model of Alzheimer's disease *J Nucl Med* 37:649-655

Iyo M., Namba, H., Fukushi, K., Shinotoh, H., Nagatsuka, S., Suhara, T., Sudo, Y., Suzuki, K., Irie, T. (1997) Measurement of acetylcolinesterase by positron emission tomography in the brains of healthy controls and patients with Alzheimer's disease *Lancet* 349: 1805-1809.

Namba, H., Irie, T., Fukushi, K., Iyo, M. (1994) In vivo measurement of acetylcolinesterase activity in the brain with a radioactive acetylcoline analog *Brain Res* 577:112-120.

Namba, H., Tanaka, N., Matsuura, H., Fukushi, K., Shinotoh, H., Nagatsuka, S., Aotsuka, A., Ota, T., Tanada, S., Irie, T. (2002) Pixel-by-pixel mapping of acetylcholinesterase activity in human brain with [^{11}C]MP4A/PET. In: *Brain Imaging using PET* (Senda M., Kimura Y. and Herscovitch P. eds), pp 55-61, New York, NY, Elsevier Science

Nagatsuka, S., Fukushi, K., Shinotoh, H., Namba, H., Iyo, M., Tanaka, N., Aotsuka, A., Ota, T., Tanada, S., Irie, T. (2001) Kinetic analysis of [^{11}C]MP4A using a high radioactivity brain region that represents an integrated input function for measurement of cerebral acetylcolinesterase activity without arterial activity using N-[^{11}C]methylpiperidin-4-yl acetate without arterial blood sampling. *J Cereb Blood Flow and Metab* 21: 1354–1366.

Tanaka N., Fukushi, K., Shinotoh, H., Nagatsuka, S., Namba, H., Iyo, M., Aotsuka, A., Ota, T., Tanada, S., Irie, T. (2001) Positron emission tomography measurement of brain acetylcholinesterase activity using N-[^{11}C]methylpiperidin-4-yl acetate without arterial blood sampling: methodology of shape analysis and its diagnostic power for Alzheimer's disease. *J Cereb Blood Flow and Metab* 21:395-406

Zhou, Y., Huang, S.C., Bergsneider, B. (2001) Linear ridge regression with spatial constraint for generation of parametric images in dynamic positron emission tomography studies *IEEE Transactions on Nuclear Science* 48: 125-130.

Zhou, Y., Huang, S.C., Bergsneider, B., Wong, D. (2002) Improved parametric image generation using spatial-temporal analysis of dynamic PET studies *Neuroimage* 15:697-707.

Zhou, Y., Endres, C., Brasic, J.R., Huang, S.C., Wong, D.F. (2003) Linear regression with spatial constraint to generate parametric images of ligand-receptor dynamic PET studies with a simplified reference tissue model, *Neuroimage* 18:975-989.

Zundorf, G., Herholz, K., Lercher, M., Wienhard, K., Bauer, B., Weinsenbach, S., Heiss, W.D. (2002) PET functional parametric images of aceylcholine esterase activity without blood sampling. In: *Brain Imaging using PET* (Senda M., Kimura Y. and Herscovitch P. eds), pp 41-46, New York, NY, Elsevier Science

Copyright © IFAC Modelling and Control in Biomedical Systems
Reims, France, 2006

BOLUS TRACKING USING LOCAL DENSITY INFORMATION

Z. Cai * **J. Bennett** ** **D. Lu** ** **J. Liu** **
M. Sharafuddin ** **H. Bai** *** **G. Wang** ** **E. Bai** *

* *Dept. of Elec & Compu Eng, University of Iowa*
** *Dept. of Radiology, University of Iowa*
*** *Dept. of Compu Eng, Iowa State University*

Abstract: In this paper, a bolus tracking algorithm was proposed for the Computed Tomography Angiography (CTA) under a realistic constraint, bolus density is monitored through a narrow temporal window. The objective of the control is to predict the bolus peak position so the synchronization of temporal window and bolus peak position can be obtained. *Copyright © 2006 IFAC*

Keywords: Computer Tomography, Trajectories, Estimation algorithms, Local control, Tracking application

1. INTRODUCTION

In recent years, computed tomography (CT) has been widely used. It has become one of the most popular medical diagnostic tools due to its noninvasive and accurate nature and also faster scanning capabilities (Rubin *et al.*, 1998; Saito, 1998; Wang *et al.*, 2000*a*) . In some cases, computed tomography angiography (CTA) is preferred to conventional angiography in the evaluation of vasculature, lesions and tumors (Bae *et al.*, 2000; Sheafor *et al.*, 1998; Tublin *et al.*, 1999). In order to better define those tissues, a contrast medium (contrast bolus) is injected into a vein before the CT scanning. Scanning the peak enhancement of the bolus through entire period of image acquisition is highly desirable for the purpose of image processing and display. Therefore, synchronization of contrast administration and CT imaging becomes a crucial issue in the CT scanning due to the shortened scan interval and image acquisition time of future CT machine.

Currently, bolus synchronization is achieved by using arrival monitoring with CT fluoroscopy. Subsequently, the patient table moves at a constant velocity which becomes problematic. Peak bolus velocity is rarely uniform due to various blood velocity (see Table 1 summarized by Evans and et al. (1989); Zierler and et al. (1992)), so a fixed table speed is unable to follow the bolus peak position. In severe cases, a retake is needed.

There are three methods to overcome this problem (Schweiger *et al.*, 1998): (1) test bolus timing, (2) ROI threshold triggering, and (3) visual cue triggering. The first method may decrease lesion conspicuity due to equilibration by test bolus (Hubener *et al.*, 1982; Kopka *et al.*, 1996). The other two methods are vulnerable to patient motion, usually related to breathing, which may displace the target organ or vessel from scan plan (Kopka *et al.*, 1996; Schweiger *et al.*, 1998; Silverman *et al.*, 1996). All of three methods do not match the table translation to bolus propagation, and do not consider that blood velocities variations.

---

[1] Supported by NIH/NIBIB EB004287

A large amount of clinical studies on CT contrast enhancement has been published (Bae et al., 1998a; Bae et al., 1998b; Bae et al., 1998c; Berland, 1995; Kopka et al., 1996; Sheafor et al., 1998), and some works are related to the investigation of bolus geometry and dynamics (Bae et al., 1998b; Blomley and Dawson, 1997; Claussen et al., 1998; Reiser, 1984; Fleischmann and Hittmair, 1999; Fleischmann et al., 2000)(see for (Cademartiri et al., 2000) for detail). In (Bae et al., 1998b), a physiologic model of contrast bolus was developed to predict organ-specific contrast enhancement and an optimal bolus injection protocol was obtain in (Bae et al., 2000). In (Fleischmann and Hittmair, 1999), a mathematical model of contrast bolus was obtained by computing transfer function from input (test bolus) to output (enhancement response), where the system was assumed to be time-invariant and linear. Optimized bolus injection method was obtained after substituting the desired bolus enhancement response. However, the optimization of bolus geometry approach is far from ideal due to several reasons: 1) contrast bolus geometry and dynamics are very complex influenced by many factors, such as patient characteristics, contrast injections, etc. The method has to assume some over-simplified conditions; 2) optimization of bolus could increase the dose of contrast medium. Another practical way to obtain optimal imaging is to use bolus chasing technique (Wang et al., 2000b). In (Wu and Qian, 1998; Bennett et al., 2003) and (Bai and Huang, 2000), bolus chasing method was proposed to be used in X-Ray peripheral Angiography and MRA, respectively. However, both methods used a wide window monitoring, in which the bolus peak position can be found at current time. Unfortunately, during the CT scanning, the bolus peak position is usually not available and the only information is the bolus density monitored through the narrow temporal window (CT gantry).

This paper is organized as follows: in Section 2, the bolus geometry and dynamics is studied in order to find a control-friendly parametric model, followed by problem statement. In Section 3, the tracking algorithm is presented based on bolus local density information as well as convergence analysis and modified algorithm, where the parametric model developed in Section 2 was used. Section 4 gives the simulation results using real bolus peak position trajectory extracted from DSA data. The results show that bolus peak position is tracked well by applying the presented algorithm, which means a higher image quality can be obtained in CTA without increasing the dosage of contrast material. Conclusion and future work are given in Section 5.

Table 1. Blood velocity variation for normal adult.

Blood Velocities (in artery)	Peak Velocity (cm/sec)	Mean Velocity (cm/sec)
Aorta	150 ± 30	27 ± 8.9
Common Iliac	$125 \pm NA$	13.5 ± 4.0
External Iliac	119 ± 21.7	10.5 ± 5.0
Common Femoral	114 ± 24.9	10.2 ± 4.8
Superficial Femoral	90.8 ± 13.6	8.8 ± 3.5
Popliteal	68.8 ± 3.5	4.9 ± 2.9
Posterior tibial	61 ± 20	4.4 ± 3.3
Dorsalis pedis	NA	3.6 ± 3.8

2. BOLUS PROPAGATION MODEL

In this section, a bolus propagation model will be reviewed and discussed in order to develop a control-friendly model. When injected, the contrast medium will be dispersed as it flows through blood vessels. The bolus dispersion can be characterized either at fixed position with respect to time (temporal profile) or at fixed time along the distance (spatial profile). In actual CT scanning, it is nearly impossible to have a dispersion profile at a fixed time along the distance. Most research rely on the contrast density at fixed points of travel path with respect to time. In (Jacobs and Williams, 1993), a model based dosing algorithm was proposed to obtain the targeted effect compartment drug concentration, which is similar to but different from the bolus chasing CTA. In (Bae et al., 1998b; Wang et al., 2000b), bolus propagation model is described by a set of partial differential equations which contains a large number of patient and circulatory stage-dependent parameters. Unfortunately, those parameters are related to individual patient characteristic and are unknown. Therefore, the model has little use in practice for adaptive bolus tracking, though it could be accurate if those parameters were available. Another well known bolus propagation model, called the lagged normal model, was given by Bassingthwaite et al., (Bassingthwaighte et al., 1966).

$$b(t,y) = b(t,0) * \frac{1}{\sigma\sqrt{2\pi}} e^{-\frac{(t-t_c)^2}{2\sigma^2}} * \frac{1}{\tau} e^{-\frac{t}{\tau}} \quad (1)$$

where $*$ denotes the convolution. In (1), $b(t,0)$ is the injection pattern of the bolus, and $b(t,y)$ is contrast density observed at a down-stream vessel location y, while parameters t_c, σ, and τ depend on the location y and no explicit relations have been found. If one wants to transform temporal profile into spatial profile, relations of three parameters in (1) and location y must be known a priori.

In CT scanning, bolus contrast density data is required as a time sequence at different fixed points. However, in bolus tracking implementation, the model that characterizes the spatial dispersion at different time is more interesting. Few paper investigates this topic (Hawkes et al., 1994; Hoffmann *et al.*, 1991; Wu and Qian, 1998). In (Wu and Qian, 1998), spatial profile is transformed from lagged-normal model.

In this paper, the bolus dispersion model is assumed to be Gaussian and the bolus peak enhancement decay as a product of a linear and an exponential functions. Thus, the complete bolus dynamics, as shown in Figure 1, is given by

$$b(t,y) = p(0)(1 - a_1 t)e^{-a_2 t}e^{-\frac{(y - m_y)^2}{\sigma}}, \quad (2)$$

where a_1, a_2 are constants, and $p(0)$ denotes the initial peak enhancement.

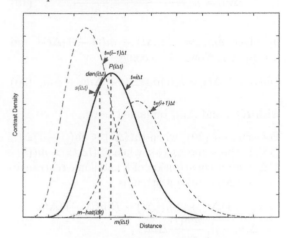

Fig. 1. Spatial bolus profiles at different times.

Suppose that bolus density function is given by $b(t,y)$. During the CT scanning, the only information available is the bolus density $b(t,y)$ through CT gantry of body position y at time t, which is the local density information of the bolus. Though bolus dynamics is very complicated, it has several properties that are helpful to control algorithm.

- Bolus dispersion profile is smooth and it only has one major peak enhancement for uniphase injection (Blomley and Dawson, 1997; Reiser, 1984).
- Although bolus peak velocity is rarely uniform, it is bounded. (see Table 1).
- Bolus peak enhancement is decreasing during the CT scanning.

To facilitate control algorithm, spatial profile is used. Let Δt be the sampling interval. $m(i\Delta t)$ and $p(i\Delta t)$ denote the bolus peak position and bolus maximum enhancement value at time $i\Delta t$, respectively, which implies

$$p(i\Delta t) = b(i\Delta t, m(i\Delta t)) = \max_y b(i\Delta t, y). \quad (3)$$

An estimate of $m(i\Delta t)$ is denoted by $\hat{m}(i\Delta t)$, and further the observed bolus enhancement is denoted by

$$den(i\Delta t) = b(i\Delta t, \hat{m}(i\Delta t)). \quad (4)$$

Another important element is the dynamics of patient table. Since most existing control systems use AC or DC stepping motor, it is assumed that CT table is driven by AC or DC servo system, which makes CT table motion very simple provided that the motor has enough torque. Let $\hat{m}(i\Delta t)$ be the table position at time $i\Delta t$. The table position at time $(i+1)\Delta t$ is given by

$$\hat{m}((i+1)\Delta t) = u(i\Delta t) + \hat{m}(i\Delta t). \quad (5)$$

where $u(i\Delta t)$ is the input to the servo system determined by the control law. Therefore, in this paper, it is focused on the estimation of bolus peak position under the constraint that only local bolus density is measurable.

3. ESTIMATION AND CONTROL ALGORITHM

3.1 Algorithm

Assume bolus peak enhancement is available and slope at the observe point is measurable. The bolus peak position prediction algorithm is given by

$$\hat{m}((i+1)\Delta t) = \hat{m}(i\Delta t) + \mu sign(s(i\Delta t))\frac{[p(i\Delta t) - den(i\Delta t)]}{p(i\Delta t)} \quad (6)$$

where μ is a constant, and $s(i\Delta t)$ is the slope at observe point $\hat{m}(i\Delta t)$. In (6), no information about the bolus velocity and peak position are needed. As mentioned before, CT scanning will not start until bolus arrival is monitored. Thus, it is assumed that the initial observed enhancement is equal to peak enhancement and accordingly initial peak position could be set to zero. To improve robustness, the *sign* function instead of the slope is used. $p(i\Delta t)$ in the denominator normalizes the enhancement which also makes the algorithm robust.

3.2 Convergence Analysis

In (6), using the mean value theorem to $L(i\Delta t) := p(i\Delta t) - den(i\Delta t)$, it gives

$$L(i\Delta t) = \underbrace{\frac{\partial b}{\partial y}|_{y=y'}}_{h(i\Delta t)}(m(i\Delta t) - \hat{m}(i\Delta t)) \quad (7)$$

where $y' = \lambda\hat{m}(i\Delta t) + (1 - \lambda)m(i\Delta t)$, and $0 \leq \lambda \leq 1$.

Define estimation error as

$$\tilde{m}(i\Delta t) = \hat{m}(i\Delta t) - m(i\Delta t). \quad (8)$$

Substituting (6) into (8) and taking advantage of (7), it follows

$$\tilde{m}((i+1)\Delta t) = K(i)\tilde{m}(i\Delta t) + \Delta m_i \qquad (9)$$

where

$$K(i) = 1 - \mu sign(s(i\Delta t))h(i\Delta t), \qquad (10)$$

and $\Delta m_i = m(i\Delta t) - m((i-1)\Delta t)$.

The solution of the above equation is given by

$$\tilde{m}((i+1)\Delta t) = (\prod_{l=0}^{i} K(l))\tilde{m}(0) + \qquad (11)$$

$$+ \sum_{l=0}^{i-1} (\prod_{j=l+1}^{i} K(j))\Delta m_l + \Delta m_i.$$

From (11), it is seen that if $|K(l)| < 1 (l = 0, \cdots, i)$, the error is stable. The question is how to choose μ so that $|K(l)| < 1 (l = 0, \cdots, i-1)$.

If bolus dynamics is given by (2), which means bolus profile is Gaussian along the distance at a fixed time, then $h(i\Delta t)$ in (7) is given by

$$h(i\Delta t) = -2p(i\Delta t)\frac{y' - m_y}{\sigma}e^{-\frac{(y'-m_y)^2}{\sigma}}. \qquad (12)$$

From Bolus Property 1, $sign(s(i\Delta t))(y' - m_y) = -|y' - m_y|$ can be derived. Then by using (12), (10) can be rewritten as

$$K(i) = 1 - 2\mu\frac{|y' - m_y|}{\sigma}e^{-\frac{(y'-m_y)^2}{\sigma}} \qquad (13)$$

$|K(i)| < 1$ leads to

$$|1 - 2\mu\frac{|y' - m_y|}{\sigma}e^{-\frac{(y'-m_y)^2}{\sigma}}| < 1. \qquad (14)$$

Using the fact

$$0 \le \frac{|y' - m_y|}{\sigma}e^{-\frac{(y'-m_y)^2}{\sigma}} \le \sqrt{\frac{1}{2e\sigma}}, \qquad (15)$$

μ is upper bounded by $\sqrt{2e\sigma}$. Furthermore, if a fast convergence rate for estimation error is expected, which means $K(i)$ should be kept around zero, it implies

$$2\mu\frac{|y' - m_y|}{\sigma}e^{-\frac{(y'-m_y)^2}{\sigma}} \cong 1. \qquad (16)$$

Take advantage of (15), μ is bounded below by $\sqrt{\frac{e\sigma}{2}}$. Finally, μ is given by

$$\sqrt{\frac{e\sigma}{2}} \le \mu \le \sqrt{2e\sigma} \qquad (17)$$

3.3 Modified Algorithm with compensation

As analyzed before, Δm_i is the major error for step i. If Δt is small, Δm_i will be kept small since bolus profile is smooth. In the case that Δm_i is not small, a compensation term could be added. Let

$$\hat{m}((i+1)\Delta t) = \hat{m}(i\Delta t)$$
$$+\mu sign(s(i\Delta t))\frac{[p(i\Delta t) - den(i\Delta t)]}{p(i\Delta t)} + \hat{\Delta}m_i \qquad (18)$$

where

$$\hat{\Delta}m_i = \mu_1\frac{(\delta m_i + |\delta m_i|)}{2}\frac{den(i)}{p(i)}, \qquad (19)$$

in which $\delta m_i = \hat{m}(i\Delta t) - \hat{m}((i-1)\Delta t))$ and $0 < \mu_1 < 1$. Now, (9) becomes

$$\tilde{m}((i+1)\Delta t) = K(i)\tilde{m}(i\Delta t) + \Delta m_i + \hat{\Delta}m_i \qquad (20)$$

with $K(i)$ and Δm_i remained same.

Focusing on (20), when $\hat{m}(i\Delta t) \le \hat{m}((i-1)\Delta t)$, (18) is the same as (6); when $\hat{m}(i\Delta t) > \hat{m}((i-1)\Delta t)$, after substitution of 8 and some rearrangements, (20) can be written as

$$\tilde{m}((i+1)\Delta t) + A\tilde{m}(i\Delta t) + B\tilde{m}((i-1)\Delta t)$$
$$= \Delta m_i - \mu_1\frac{den(i)}{p(i)}\Delta m_{i-1} \qquad (21)$$

where $A = -K(i) - \mu_1\frac{den(i)}{p(i)}$, $B = \mu_1\frac{den(i)}{p(i)}$ and $\Delta m_{i-1} = m((i-1)\Delta t) - m((i\Delta t)$. Obviously, $|B| < 1$ and $|A| < 1 + B$ if $|K(i)| < 1$, therefore, this second order system is stable without the additional term on right side.

$\hat{\Delta}m_i$ is selected as (19) based on the following reasons.

- Track closely when bolus peaking position is increasing. Assume at step i, the estimate peak position is right on the real peak trajectory, that is $\hat{m}(i\Delta t) = m(i\Delta t)$. According to algorithm (6), the next estimate position $\hat{m}((i+1)\Delta t) = \hat{m}(i\Delta t)$, which is not true when bolus peak position is increasing and it will be a big lag proportional to the bolus velocity at step $i+1$. To overcome this, it is assumed that bolus velocity does not change much, therefore the difference of $\hat{m}((i-1)\Delta t)$ and $\hat{m}(i\Delta t)$ will be used as the primary step size for step $i+1$.
- Reduce the tracking error at each step. From the bolus property, it is known that $\Delta m_i = m(i\Delta t) - m((i+1)\Delta t) < 0$, so $\hat{\Delta}m_i$ is kept be greater than or equal to zero all the time to make tracking error smaller at step.
- Avoid over-compensation. When $b(i\Delta t)$ is smaller, which means $\hat{m}(i\Delta t)$ is further away from $m(i\Delta t)$, step size is dominated by the

second term at right side of (6), and the corresponding compensation is smaller. On the other hand, if $b(i\Delta t)$ is bigger, compensation term will contribute more. Combined with $0 < \mu_1 < 1$, $\hat{\Delta}m_i$ will avoid overcompensation.

4. SIMULATION

In the simulation, bolus peak position trajectory is extracted from real patient DSA data(see (Bai *et al.*, 2005)), and bolus dispersion is assumed to be Gaussian as discussed before. Time interval Δt was 0.35 according to the current common CT technique (three frames per second). As for $s(i\Delta t)$, it is obtained in the following way: assume that at each estimate position $\hat{m}(i)$, bolus enhancement $den(i\Delta t)$ and $den_{\delta x}(i)$ at $\hat{m}(i)$ and $\hat{m}(i)+\delta x$ can be measured simultaneously. This is completely feasible due to the multi row property of current CT. $s(i\Delta t)$ is approximated by

$$s(i\Delta t) = \frac{den_{\delta x}(i\Delta t) - den(i\Delta t)}{\delta x} \quad (22)$$

In the simulation, δx was set to 0.5 cm, which is reasonable for current CT machines. Control gains μ and μ_1 were selected as 5 and 2/3, respectively. Clearly, the control performance will be better if Δl is smaller or δx is relatively bigger, since small Δt means that estimation error will be corrected fast, and relatively big δx will make $sign(s(i))$ robust to the noise.

Three patient data sets were used in simulations and the results are showed in Fig. 2 and Fig. 3, where solid lines denote the actual bolus peak trajectories, and $'*'$ is the controlled table positions at each step. It shows that the controlled table position follows the bolus peak position well. Table 4 summaries the tracking error for each patient. It is seen that the mean error for algorithm with compensation is smaller than algorithm (6). However, the standard deviation is bigger, which means that estimate positions are around real positions (see Fig 3), not only just behind them uniformly (see Fig 2).

Table 2. Tracking errors.

Tracking Errors	Mean (cm) Algorithm (6)/(18)	Std. Dev. (cm) Algorithm (6)/(18)
Patient 1	0.88/0.49	1.90/2.09
Patient 2	0.47/0.12	0.64/0.65
Patient 3	0.52/0.13	0.87/1.20

5. CONCLUSION

In this paper, a bolus tracking algorithm was proposed based on local density information of contrast bolus. The tracking algorithm is simple but

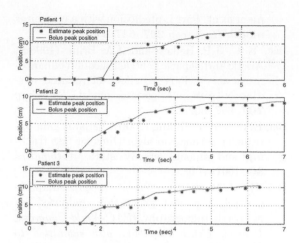

Fig. 2. Bolus tracking result for 3 patients using algorithm (6) .

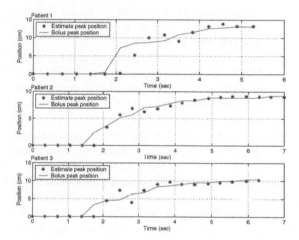

Fig. 3. Bolus tracking result for 3 patients using algorithm (18).

robust. Simulation results show that bolus peak position can be estimated well with the real bolus peak position trajectory extracted from DSA data. Future work will be focused on validating the algorithm in a clinical environment.

REFERENCES

Bae, K.T., H.Q. Tran and J.P. Heiken (2000). Multiphasic injection method for uniform prolonged vascular enhancement at ct angiography: pharmacokinetic analysis and experimental porcine model. *Radiology* **216**, 872–880.

Bae, K.T., J.P. Heiken and J.A. Brink (1998*a*). Aortic and hepatic contrast medium enhancement at ct: effect of contrast medium injection rate-pharmacokinetic analysis and experimental porcine model. *Radiology* **206**, 455–464.

Bae, K.T., J.P. Heiken and J.A. Brink (1998*b*). Aortic and hepatic contrast medium enhancement at ct: Part i. prediction with a computer model. *Radiology* **207**, 647–655.

Bae, K.T., J.P. Heiken and J.A. Brink (1998c). Aortic and hepatic contrast medium enhancement at ct: Part ii. effect of reduced cardiac output in a porcine model. *Radiology* **207**, 657–662.

Bai, E.W. and Y. Huang (2000). Variable gain parameter estimation algorithms for fast tracking and smooth steady state. *Automatica* **36**, 1001–1008.

Bai, H., J. Bennett and el al. (2005). Adaptive control of a next generation computed tomograph angiography. *IFAC World Congress, Prague, Czech Republic, also submitted to IFAC Control Engineering Practice*,.

Bassingthwaighte, J.B., F.H. Ackerman and E.H. Wood (1966). Application of the lagged normal density curve as a model for arterial dilution curves. *Circulation Research* **XVIII**, 398–415.

Bennett, J., E.W. Bai, J. Halloran and G. Wang (2003). A preliminary study on adaptive field of view tracking in peripheral digital subtraction angiography. *J. of X-ray Science and Technology* **11**, 149–159.

Berland, L.L. (1995). Slip-ring and conventional dynamic hepatic ct: Contrast material and timing considerations. *Radiology* **195**, 1–8.

Blomley, M.J.K. and P. Dawson (1997). Bolus dynamics: theoretical and experimental aspects. *Br. J. Radiol.* **70**, 351–359.

Cademartiri, F., Aad van der Lugt and et al. (2000). Parameters affecting bolus geometry in cta: A review. *J. of Computer Assisted Tomography* **26**, 598–607.

Claussen, Claus D., Dietrich Banzer, C. Pfretzchner and et al. (1998). Bolus geometry and dynamics after intravenous contrast medium injection. *Radiology* **207**, 645–655.

Fleischmann, D. and K. Hittmair (1999). Mathematical analysis of arterial enhancement and optimization of bolus geometry for ct angiography using the discrete fourier transform. *J. Computer Tomography* **23**, 474–484.

Fleischmann, D., G.D. Rubin, A.A. Bankier and et al. (2000). Improved iniform of aortic enhancement with customized contrast medium injection protocols at ct angiography. *Radiology* **214**, 363–371.

Hawkes, D.J., A.M. Seifalian and et al. (1994). Validation of volume blood flow measurements using three-dimensional distance-concentration function derived from digital x-ray angiograms. *Investigative Radiology* **29**, 434–442.

Hoffmann, K.R., K. Doi and L.E. Fencil (1991). Determination of instantaneous and average blood flow rate from digital angiograms of vessel phantoms using distance-density curves. *Investigative Radiology* **26**, 207–212.

Hubener, K.H., W.A. Kalender and H.F. Metzger (1982). Fast digital recording of x-ray dilution curves: A preliminary evaluation. *Radiology* **145**, 545–547.

Jacobs, J.R. and E.A. Williams (1993). Algorithm to control "effect compartment" drug concentrations in pharmacokinetic model-driven drug delivery. *IEEE Transactions on Biomedical Engineering* **40**, 993–999.

Kopka, L., J. Rodenwaldt, U. Fischer and et al. (1996). Helical ct of the liver: Effects of bolus tracking and different volumes of contrast material. *Radiology* **201**, 321–326.

Reiser, Ulrich J. (1984). Study of bolus geometry after intravenous contrast medium injection: Dynamic and quantitative measurements (chronogram) using an x-ray ct device. *J. of Computer Assisted Tomography* **8**, 251–262.

Rubin, G.D., D.S. Paik, P.C. Johnston and et al. (1998). Measurement of the aorta and its branches with helical ct. *Radiology* **206**, 823–829.

Saito, Y. (1998). Multislice x-ray ct scanner. *Medical Review* **66**, 1–8.

Schweiger, G.D., P.C. Chang and B.P. Brown (1998). Optimizing contrast enhancement during helical ct of the liver: A comparison of two bolus tracking techniques. *A.J.R.* **171**, 1551–1558.

Sheafor, D.H., M.T. Keogan, D.M. DeLong and et al. (1998). Dynamic helical ct of the abdomen: Prospective comparison of pre- and postprandial contrast enhancement. *Radiology* **206**, 359–363.

Silverman, P.M., S.C. Roberts, I. Ducic and et al. (1996). Assessment of a technology that permits individualized scan delays on helical hepatic ct: A technique to improve efficiency in use of contrast material. *A.J.R* **167**, 79–84.

Tublin, M.E., F.N. Tessler, S.L. Cheng and et al. (1999). Effect of injection rate of contrast medium on pancreatic and hepatic helical ct. *Radiology* **210**, 97–101.

Wang, G., C.R. Crawford and W.A. Kalender (2000a). Multirow detector and cone-beam spiral/helical ct. *IEEE Trans. Med. Imaging* **19**, 817–821.

Wang, G., G. Raymond, Y. Li and et al (2000b). A model on intervenous bolus propagation for optimization of contrast enhancement. **3978**, 436–447.

Wu, Zhenyu and Jian-Zhong Qian (1998). Realtime tracking of contrast bolus propagation in x-ray peripheral angiography. *IEEE Workshop on Biomedical Image Analysis* pp. 164–171.

FUZZY ADVISOR ALGORITHM FOR GLUCOSE REGULATION IN TYPE 1 DIABETIC PATIENTS ON A MULTI–DOSES REGIME

D.U. Campos–Delgado [*]
M. Hernández–Ordoñez [**,1] **R. Femat** [***]
E. Palacios [*,2]

* Fac. de Ciencias, UASLP, S.L.P., México,
ducd@fciencias.uaslp.mx, epalacios@fciencias.uaslp.mx
** CIEP, Fac. de Ing., UASLP, S.L.P., México,
mar@uaslp.mx
*** Div. Mat. Aplicadas y Sistemas, IPICYT, S.L.P.,
México, rfemat@ipicyt.edu.mx

Abstract: This study presents an advisory/control algorithm for a type 1 diabetes mellitus (TIDM) patient, in a chronic stage, under an intensive insulin treatment based on a multiple daily injections regimen (MDIR). In order to incorporate expert knowledge about the treatment of this disease, the design methodology is carried out using Mamdani–type fuzzy logic controllers to regulate the blood glucose level (BGL). The overall control strategy is based on a two–loop feedback strategy to overcome the variability in the glucose–insulin dynamics from patient–to–patient. In this way, it is pursued to compute the correct amounts of insulin required to maintain the glucose in the euglycemic interval. In order to analyze the performance of the control algorithm, extensive closed-loop simulations are illustrated using a detailed nonlinear model of the subcutaneous insulin-glucose dynamics in a TIDM patient with meal intake. *Copyright © 2006 IFAC.*

Keywords: Diabetes Control, Fuzzy Logic, Multi–Doses Insulin Regime

1. INTRODUCTION

Inside the human body, there are plenty of feedback loops in charge of maintaining homeostasis in the human body. The failure or malfunction of one of these loops can induce severe illnesses with short and long–term complications. In this context, the insulin is a hormone responsible of processing the glucose (energy) by the body cells. As a result, this hormone has a regulatory effect in the blood glucose, and prevents high (hyperglycemia) glucose concentrations beyond the euglycemic (normal) level (ADA, 2002), (Lebovitz, 1998).

The type 1 diabetes mellitus (TIDM) is characterized by absence or death of the β-cells in the pancreatic islets of Langerhans. Since the β-cells produce the insulin by the pancreas, external insulin infusions are needed by the patient in order to maintain regulated the blood glucose. Due to continuous variations in the blood glucose concentration, the diabetes can produce short and long term

[1] Acknowledges the support provided by CONACYT (No.158330) through a doctoral scholarship.
[2] This research is supported in part by a grant from PROMEP.

illnesses (nephropathy, retinopathy, and other tissue damage) (Bode, 2004), (Lebovitz, 1998). However, the results of the Diabetes Control and Complications Trial (DCCT) (DCCT, 1993) showed that an intensive insulin therapy can reduce the incidence of these illnesses in the long–term. Moreover the benefits of an intensive therapy have been shown in multiple experimental trials for children and adults (Lalli et al., 1999), (Weintrob et al., 2003). On the other hand, it was also noticed in (DCCT, 1993) that a possible side effect of an intensive therapy is the propensity to hypoglycemic scenarios in the patient. With this consideration, if an intensive therapy is followed by the patient, the prescribed insulin treatment must be carefully studied by the physician, and it has to be constantly updated according with the results achieved. Thus, it is appealing the idea of an automatic advisory system for the patient in order to update each daily dose of insulin continuously (Bellazzi, 2003), (Campos et al., 2004), (Miyako et al., 2004), (Ruiz et al., 2004). Consequently, an intensive therapy is encouraged for TIDM patients prescribed either by a continuous–infusion pump (CIP), or a multiple daily injection regimen (MDIR) depending on the patient's necessities. In this research, the latter one is studied, which is the most common scenario in chronic patients, due to the high cost and availability of portable CIP's.

The intensive insulin therapy based on a MDIR consists of a combination of rapid/short and intermediate/long acting insulin (RSAI and ILAI), scheduled before each meal (3 doses per day). It is assumed that the patient is in a chronic stage and has prescribed a diet regimen by a physician (Bode, 2004). In previous approaches reported in (Bellazzi et al., 1995), (Hovorka et al., 1999), the control algorithms assume the information of the equivalent carbohydrates intake by each meal. This information is difficult to compute by the patient and can be a source of major uncertainty. Thus, the approach proposed in this work pursues to eliminate the dependence on this information. Moreover, the algorithm does not rely on a direct glucose prediction or estimation to evaluate the insulin adjustments as in previous approaches, and the two-loop feedback architecture adds robustness to the overall control scheme.

The document is organized as follows. Section 2 presents the insulin types and characteristics. The problem statement and proposed control structure is introduced in Section 3. Section 4 shows the closed–loop simulation results. Finally, Section 5 presents concluding remarks.

2. INSULIN TYPES AND CHARACTERISTICS

In a healthy subject, a constant basal insulin's rate of approximately 22 mU/min is produced by the pancreas (Sorensen, 1985). However, in order to assimilate the glucose absorbed by the gut through meals, this basal rate is temporarily increased (post–prandial peaks) (Lebovitz, 1998). Therefore, ideally this insulin release pattern should be imitated by the MDIR in order reduce the risk of future diseases. To achieve this goal, a combination of different types of insulin is applied (Dickerson, 1999).

In general, the insulin is classified according with its origin: bovine, porcine, and human; and with its action: rapid (Aspart and Lispro), short (Regular), intermediate (NPH and Lente), and long (Ultralente, Glargine and Detemir) (APhA, 2001). For some types of insulin, in (Berger and D. Rodbard, 1989), (Wilinska et al., 2005) a mathematical model was proposed to reproduce the assimilation pattern after a subcutaneous injection. However, there were not provided the simulation parameters for Lispro insulin. Moreover, the structure of this model was also validated with experimental data for Lispro insulin by Wilinska et al. (2005). Therefore, the authors followed the parameters reported by Wilinska et al. (2005) for Lispro insulin. The simulated time evolution of Lispro, Regular, NPH, Lente and Ultralente insulins after a 10 U infusion is shown in Figure 1. In this investigation a combination of a

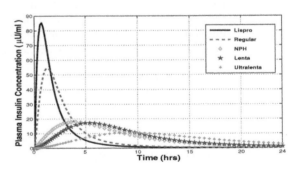

Fig. 1. Time Evolution of Plasma Insulin Concentration after a Subcutaneous Insulin Infusion of 10 U.

Lispro and NPH is applied. As it was reported in (Lalli et al., 1999), this combination results in less frequent hypoglycemic scenarios and effective glycemic control. However, the approach could also be fitted to a different combination of RSAI and ILAI.

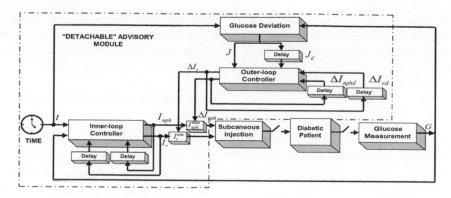

Fig. 2. Control Diagram for Blood Glucose Regulation in Type 1 Diabetes Patients by Subcutaneous Route.

3. PROBLEM STATEMENT AND CONTROL METHODOLOGY

Three meals are taken per day: breakfast (7 to 10 hrs), lunch (13 to 15 hrs) and dinner (20 to 22 hrs); where the lunch has the largest carbohydrates content of the day. Roughly, there is a time interval of 6 hrs among each meal of the day. However, the control algorithm introduced can be extended to different meal customs. The insulin doses are programmed previous to each meal.

In the proposed approach, the ILAI provides the basal insulin, and the transient effects after each meal (post–prandial peaks) are regulated by the RSAI. Due to the slow absorption process of the basal insulin, the lunch doses for ILAI are skipped, and only RSAI is injected. Thus, the control objective is stated as: *regulate the BGL around a target level (ADA, 2002),(Bode, 2004), defined as: $TGL = 90-130$ mg/dl, using three daily doses of a preparation of RSAI and ILAI.*

The definition of the target glucose level (TGL) is consistent with the pre–prandial targets in an adult patient suggested by (ADA, 2002). Furthermore, it is desired to reach this objective minimizing the amount of insulin by the patient. In this control scheme, at least three glucose measurements are assumed daily, which are taken just before injecting the insulin preparation.

On the other hand, in the control field, the fuzzy logic has emerged as a powerful methodology to incorporate expert knowledge about the systems into the controllers design (Driankov et al., 1996), (Wang, 1997). Similar to (Bellazzi et al., 1995), a two–loop structure is adopted for the control scheme in order to improve the glucose regulation due to variability of the human metabolism, where the inner and outer–loop controllers are designed using a Mamdani–type of fuzzy structure.

3.1 Inner–Controller Characteristics

The inner–loop computes the RSAI (I_r) and ILAI (I_{nph}) insulin doses given to the patient before each meal, where the input variables to this inner controller are:

- Time of the day (t): the information of time is used to define the meal characteristics by the patient, and estimate the carbohydrates load.
- Glucose measurement (G): the information of the instantaneous pre–prandial BGL is acquired by blood samples.
- Previous RSAI dose (I_{rd}): the RSAI dose evaluated in the previous meal is used to analyze the glycemic control.
- Previous ILAI insulin dose (I_{nphd}): due to the absorption process of the ILAI, its dose in the morning or evening (lunch–time dose is omitted) is considered to evaluate glycemic control.

The two outputs RSAI (I_r) and ILAI doses (I_{nph}) are normalized to the interval [0, 1], and the actual injection preparation is calculated when the amplitudes are scaled according to the values I_r^{max} (maximum RSAI insulin dosing) and I_{nph}^{max} (maximum ILAI insulin dosing). Since, the time–scales of the insulin applied change drastically, as seen in Figure 1, the previous values I_{rd} and I_{nphd} are selected following Table 1.

Table 1. Previous Values Selection for RSAI and ILAI Used for the Inner–loop Controller

Type	Morning	Lunch	Evening
I_{rd}	Previous Evening	Morning	Lunch
I_{nphd}	Previous Evening	No Doses	Morning

3.2 Outer–Controller Characteristics

The outer–loop controller optimizes and regulates the amounts of insulin given to the patient by evaluating the glycemic control in a days time–scale. According with glucose measurements, the systemic glucose deviation from the TGL can be measured as:

$$J = \frac{1}{n} \sum_{k=1}^{n} \phi(k) \qquad (1)$$

where n is the number of measurements used for evaluation, and $\phi(k)$ (pointwise deviation from TGL) is defined as

$$\phi(k) = \begin{cases} G(k) - 130 \ mg/dl, & G(k) > 130 \ mg/dl \\ \Gamma \cdot (G(k) - 90) \ mg/dl, & G(k) < 90 \ mg/dl \\ 0, & 90 \le G(k) \le 130 \ mg/dl \end{cases} \qquad (2)$$

where $\Gamma \geq 1$ is a constant that includes an additional weight for low glucose concentrations. The number of BGL measurements n can be a minimum of three, or more if they are available. As mentioned in (Strowig and P. Raskin, 1998), an increase in the frequency of blood glucose testing has been correlated with a better glycemic control. Note that this measurements can be made from blood samples extraction or non–invasive blood glucometers.

Consequently, the outer controller must adjust the insulin dosing in three global scenarios: increase it if an hyperglycemic condition is detected, decrease it in the case of an hypoglycemic condition, and maintain it for a normal condition. These dosing adjustments are performed in a time scale of days, where they could be specified per day or week according with the physician advise. This time evaluation should change with the metabolism variability of each patient. However, the adjustment is done each morning by modifying the scaling factors I_r^{max} and I_{nph}^{max} using an integral–type of updating rule:

$$I_r^{max}(i) = I_r^{max}(i-1) + \Delta I_r$$
$$I_{nph}^{max}(i) = I_{nph}^{max}(i-1) + \Delta I_{nph} \qquad (3)$$

where ΔI_r and ΔI_{nph} are the increments/decrements given by the outer–loop controller. The index $i-1$ refers to the old scaling factor and i to the new adjusted one. The input information used by the outer controller includes details of the glycemic control during the previous days and the previous insulin adjustments, this is:

- The glucose deviation (J) in (1)
- Memory of the previous deviation (J_d)
- The previous adjustments ΔI_{rd} and ΔI_{nphd}

The objective of this strategy is to detect tendencies in the behavior of the BGL. Here both controllers are synthesized using physician knowledge (ADA, 2002), (Bode, 2004) by applying a Mamdani–type fuzzy logic structure. Note that the outer–loop controller runs at a much slower time–scale that the inner–loop controller. So, the outer–loop controller can be seen as a **supervisor** of the inner–loop controller.

4. CLOSED–LOOP SIMULATION RESULTS

4.1 Meals Description

The meals carbohydrate intakes were calculated according with the following patient profile (Bode, 2004),(Lebovitz, 1998): a male with 30 years old, 70 kg of weight, 1.7 m height and 2275 $Kcal/day$. It is assumed that 50 % $Kcal$ are coming from carbohydrates, and 4 $Kcal$ are equivalent to 1 g of carbohydrates (CH). Consequently, it is needed 284.3 g of carbohydrates per day. It is assumed a distribution of the total amount of carbohydrates in three meals: 35 % breakfast, 45 % lunch and 20 % dinner. As a result, in the next meal distribution of carbohydrates is obtained: breakfast with 99.5 g, lunch with 127.93 g and dinner with 56.86 g carbohydrates. Therefore, the lunch is the heaviest meal of the day. During the simulation time (14 days), the amount of carbohydrate intake per meal was varied randomly $\pm 10\%$ (uniform distribution) around the nominal values calculated previously, but with an average of $\approx 2275 \ Kcal/day$ during the simulation time.

4.2 Simulations Scenarios

Three simulation scenarios were tested used the purposed two–loop control structure:

(1) **Case 1**: the patient starts with small scaling factors for both types of insulin, producing small insulin doses and high glucose levels. The algorithm looks for adjusting the insulin dosages in order to reach a TGL. Since it is not considered a variation in the carbohydrates intake per meal. For this scenario, a ± 15 % error (typical error in commercial devices) in each of the glucose measurements is assumed. 25 simulations were tested using different random perturbations in each case.

(2) **Case 2**: the patient varies his carbohydrate intakes during meals by ± 25 % from the nominal ones, and the meal time is also perturbed randomly ± 30 min using an uniform distribution for both factors. Hence total daily intakes are not constant in carbohydrates content and meal time. This scenario looks to represent a typical meals distribution for a TIDM patient in chronic condition, since a tight carbohydrates count and time schedule in each meal is difficult for any patient. Thus, 25 simulations were analyzed using different random perturbations.

Table 2. Simulation Summary Results for 25 Evaluations of Each Case.

Case	ABGL		A_{1c}	
	mean	STD	mean	STD
	(mg/dl)	(mg/dl)	(%)	(%)
1	129.91	3.63	5.82	0.100
2	123.04	1.12	5.62	0.031
3	131.04	8.58	5.85	0.240

(3) **Case 3**: the insulin–glucose dynamics vary drastically from patient to patient. In previous studies (Parker et al., 2000), (Ramprasad et al., 2004), it was shown that the parameters related to the hepatic and peripheral glucose uptake, and fractional hepatic insulin clearance presented the largest impact in the blood glucose concentration. Thus, in order to analyze this scenario, these parameters were perturbed ±40 % and ±20 % respectively, in order to achieve the largest sensitivity, 25 combinations of parameters were simulated at the start of the simulation.

In the results of the DCCT (DCCT, 1993), the glycosylated hemoglobin (A_{1c}) test was recognized as a valuable source of information to identify possible risks for diabetic complications. The A_{1c} is a weighted average of blood glucose over a period of 120 days (Bode, 2004), (Lebovitz, 1998), hence it provides an estimation of euglycemic control over the preceding 6 − 10 weeks. It can be estimated following the relation

$$A_{1c} = \frac{ABGL + 77.3 \ mg/dl}{35.6 \ mg/dl} \qquad (4)$$

where ABGL stands for average blood glucose level during the simulation time. It is important to point out that the previous estimate in (2) gives only an indication of the A_{1c} level, if the simulated blood glucose profile is maintained for 6−10 weeks (Lehmann, 2001). This parameter will be used to evaluate the glycemic control during the simulation tests, note that for a TIDM patient is recommended $A_{1c} < 7$ % (Bode, 2004),(DCCT, 1993).

Figures 3 present one of the simulations for Case 1: meal carbohydrates intakes, plasma glucose, insulin doses, insulin plasma concentration, glucose deviation function, and insulin scaling factors for Case 1. The Cases 2 and 3 are not showed due to space limitations. However, a summary of the simulation results is shown in Table 2 for all the 25 evaluations in each case.

The mean and standard deviation (STD) for the ABGL and A_{1c} indexes are illustrated. For all cases, the control algorithm is able of successfully regulate the plasma glucose to the TGL despite initially low scaling factors (Case 1), variable meal time and carbohydrates intakes (Case 2), and variability in the insulin–glucose dynamics (Case 3).

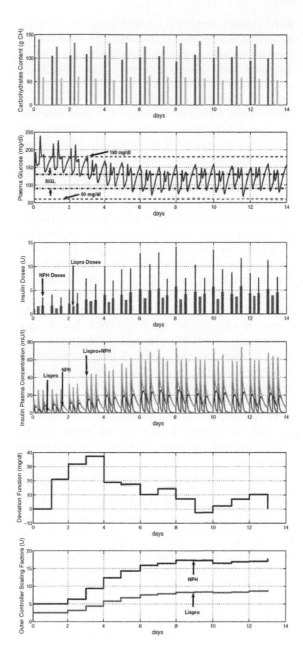

Fig. 3. Closed–Loop Simulation for a 14-Days Period: **Case 1**.

Hence the calculated glycosylated hemoglobin A_{1c} was always lower than 7 % in average indicating good euglycemic regulation. Moreover, the standard deviation was also small, representing low variability in the results. Consequently, the results present good robustness in the two–loop control structure proposed in this work.

5. CONCLUSIONS

In this research, the methodology for a two–loop control scheme for TIDM patients in a chronic stage is detailed. The treatment strategy is based on a three daily dose of a preparation of RSAI and

ILAI (Lispro and NPH), which is applied through a subcutaneous route. In order to incorporate knowledge about patient treatment, the inner–loop and outer–loop controllers are designed using a Mamdani–type fuzzy scheme. It is important to mention that the control algorithm is in essence model–free, because the algorithm does not rely on a direct glucose prediction or estimation to evaluate the insulin adjustments as in previous approaches. Simulation results with a physiological model of the TIDM patient show the effectiveness of the two–loop structure for blood glucose regulation. Moreover, it has the potential of being implemented in a microcomputer for home treatment. Besides, it can be adapted to another combination of insulin, or another route of application to the patient, like inhaled insulin. On the other hand, the information of periodic A_{1c} testing could also be incorporated in the outer–loop (supervisory) controller to scale the RSAI and ILAI doses. As shown in this paper, the fuzzy–logic has the potential to synthesize expert knowledge to treat diseases. Therefore, the approach and methodology introduced could also be visualized as a alternative for type 2 diabetic patients, and it could be a valuable tool for educational purposes. Moreover, it is considered as future work, the inclusion of an exercise regime in the overall model of the TIDM patient, in order to have a more realistic simulation.

REFERENCES

American Diabetes Association (2002). Standards of Medical Care for Patients with Diabetes Mellitus. *Diabetes Care*, 25, 533–549, Supplement 1.

APhA Special Report (2001). New Approaches to Insulin Therapy for Diabetes. *http:// www.pharmacist.com / pdf / insulin-therapy-sr.pdf*, American Pharmaceutical Association.

Bellazzi. R. (2003). Electronic Management Systems in Diabetes Mellitus: Impact on Patient Outcomes. *Disease Management & Health Outcomes*, 11(3): 159–171.

Bellazzi R., C. Siviero, M. Stefanelli, and G. De Nicolao (1995). Adaptive Controllers for Intelligent Monitoring, *Artificial Intelligence in Medicine*, 7, 515–540.

Berger M. and D. Rodbard (1989). Computer Simulation of Plasma Insulin and Glucose Dynamics after Subcutaneous Insulin Injection. *Diabetes Care*, 12, 725–736.

Bode B.W. (2004). Medical Management of Type 1 Diabetes. *American Diabetes Association*, Fourth Edition.

Campos–Delgado D.U., R. Femat, M. Hernández–Ordoñez and A. Gordillo–Moscoso (2004). Self-tuning Insulin Adjustment Algorithm for Type I Diabetic Patients Based on Multi-Doses Regime. *Int. Symp. on Robotics and Automation*, Queretaro, México, 25–27 August.

Dickerson L.M. (1999). Insulin Therapy in the Treatment of Diabetes Mellitus. *http:// www.musc.edu / dfm / pharmd / Med%20Resident / insulin.pdf*.

Driankov D., H. Hellendoorn and M. Reinfrank (1996). An Introduction to Fuzzy Control. *Springer-Verlag Berlin Heidelberg*, 2nd Edition.

Hovorka R., R.S. Tudor, D. Southerden, D.R. Meeking, S. Andreassen, O.K. Hejlesen and D.A. Cavan (1999). Dynamic Updating in DIAS-NIDDM and DIAS Causal Probabilistic Networks. *IEEE Transactions on Biomedical Engineering*, 46(2), 158–168.

Lalli C., M. Ciofetta, P. Del Sindaco, E. Torlone, S. Pampanelli, P. Compagnucci, M. Giulia Cartechini, L. Bartocci, P. Brunetti and G.B. Bolli (1999). Long-Term Intensive Treatment of Type 1 Diabetes with the Short-Acting Insulin Analog Lispro in Variable Combination with NPH Insulin at Mealtime. *Diabetes Care*, 22, 468–477.

Lebovitz H.E. (1998). Therapy for Diabetes Mellitus and Related Disorders. *American Diabetes Association*, Third Edition.

Lehmann E.D. and T. Deutsch (1992). A Physiological Model of Glucose-Insulin in Type I Diabetes Mellitus. *Journal of Biomedical Engineering*, 14, 235-242.

Lehmann E.D (2001). The freeware AIDA interactive educational diabetes simulator - http://www.2aida.org - (2) Simulating glycosylated haemoglobin (HbA_{1c}) for AIDA v4.3. *Med. Sci. Monit.*, 7(3), 516-525.

Miyako K., R. Kuromaru, H. Kohno and T. Hara (2004). Improved Diabetes Control by Using Close Adjustment Algorithms. *Pediatrics International*, 46, 678–684.

Parker R.S., F.J. Doyle III, J.H. Ward, and N.A. Peppas (2000). Robust H_∞ Glucose Control in Diabetes Using a Physiological Model. *AIChE Journal*, 46, 2537–2549.

Ramprasad Y., G.P. Rangaiah, and S. Lakshminarayanan (2004). Robust PID Controller for Blood Glucose Regulation in Type I Diabetics. *Industrial Engineering Chemistry Research*, 43, 8257–8268.

Ruiz–Velazquez E., R. Femat and D.U. Campos-Delgado (2004). Blood Glucose Control for Type I Diabetes Mellitus: A Robust Tracking H_∞ Problem. *Control Engieering Practice*, 12(9), 1179–1195, September.

Sorensen J.T. (1985). A Physiologic Model of Glucose Metabolism in Man and its Use to Design and Assess Improved Insulin Therapies for Diabetes. Ph.D. Dissertation, Chemical Engineering Department, MIT, Cambridge.

Strowig S.M. and P. Raskin (1998). Improved Glycemic Control in Intensively Treated Type 1 Diabetic Patients Using Blood Glucose Meters with Storage Capability and Computer–Assisted Analyses. *Diabetes Care*, 21, 1694–1698.

The Diabetes Control and Complications Trial Reserach Group (1993). The Effect of Intensive Treatment of Diabetes on the Development and Progression of Long-term Complications in Insulin-dependent Diabetes Mellitus. *N. Engl. J. Med.*, 329, 977–986.

Wang L.X. (1997). A Course in Fuzzy Systems and Control. *Prentice Hall*, Upper Saddle River, NJ.

Weintrob N., H. Benzaquen, A. Galatzer, S. Shalitin, L. Lazar, G. Fayman, P. Lilos, Z. Dickerman and M. Phillip (2003). Comparison of Continuous Subcutaneous Insulin Infusion and Multiple Daily Injection Regimens in Children with Type 1 Diabetes: A Randomized Open Crossover Trial. *Pediatrics*, 112, 559–564.

Wilinska M.E., L.J. Chassin, H.C. Schaller, L. Schaupp, T.R. Pieber and R. Hovorka (2005). Insulin Kinetics in Type-1 Diabetes: Continuous and Bolus Delivery of Rapid Acting Insulin. *IEEE Transactions on Biomedical Engineering*, 52(1), 3–11.

AN FES-ASSISTED GAIT TRAINING SYSTEM FOR HEMIPLEGIC STROKE PATIENTS BASED ON INERTIAL SENSORS

N.-O. Negård [*,**] **T. Schauer** [**] **R. Kauert** [***] **J. Raisch** [**,*]

** Max Planck Institute for Dynamics
of Complex Technical Systems, Sandtorstr. 1, D-39106
Magdeburg, Germany
E-mail: negaard@mpi-magdeburg.mpg.de*

*** Technische Universität Berlin,
Fachgebiet Regelungssysteme,
D-10587 Berlin, Germany*

**** HASOMED GmbH, Paul-Ecke-Straße 1,
39114 Magdeburg, Germany*

Abstract: An inertial sensor mounted on the foot of the affected body side represents an alternative to traditional foot switches in Functional Electrical Stimulation (FES)-assisted gait rehabilitation systems. The inertial sensor consisting of 3 gyroscopes and 3 accelerometers can be utilised to detect gait phases which can be applied to synchronise the electrical stimulation with the gait. Additionally, the sensor can be applied to estimate orientation and 3 dimensional movement of the foot. Based on the estimated orientation and linear position several movement parameters can be defined. The most important are the foot clearance, which is defined as maximal distance between foot and ground, and the sagittal angle of the foot in relation to the ground at the time as the heel hits the ground. In this paper we describe a practical system for FES-assisted gait training based on inertial sensors where the electrical stimulation is triggered by the gait phase detection and the stimulation intensity is automatically tuned by feedback of movement parameters. Copyright ©2006 IFAC

Keywords: Electrical stimulation, Inertial sensing, Biomedical systems.

1. INTRODUCTION

The impact of stroke on the life of an individual can be dramatic both mentally and physically. Physically the motor control of one body side may be detoriated. Such detoriated motor functions can be improved by training. Electrical current pulses can be used to excite intact peripheral nerves, and then cause muscles to contract. This muscle contraction will generate muscle forces and a corresponding joint torque leading to a body movement. Normally, these activations are controlled by the brain or the spinal cord. In cases of dysfunction, like in individuals with stroke or in some other types of upper motor neuron lesion, this normal activation is not possible. In such cases, the activation can be generated artificially as described. Use of electrical stimulation with the intention to restore useful body movements is called Functional Electrical Stimulation (FES). Since Liberson *et al.* (1961) for the first time applied electrical stimulation to elicit the withdrawal reflex during the swing phase, many systems for FES-assisted gait training and Drop

Foot Stimulator (DFS) systems have been designed. In order to trigger the stimulation gait phases must be detected, either as a simple detection of heel-off or a more refined detection of several phases.

Gait Phase Detection (GPD) systems have already been developed where the gait cycle is divided into several phases. The number of these phases can vary as well as the definitions of these. There is no standard terminology in the literature but the definition by Perry (1992) is the most used. By her definition the gait is divided in eight phases for each leg. These eight phases are divided according to functional tasks of the gait and consist of initial contact, loading response, mid stance, terminal stance, pre-swing, initial swing, mid-swing and terminal swing. In gait phase detection systems the sensors used force a limitation of the phases which are possible to detect, and normally a less refined detection with typically four phases is applied: stance, pre-swing, swing and loading response.

In methodology, there are mainly two different approaches to gain the gait phases, the first one is a rule based approach where the gait phases are defined as states of a finite state machine and the transitions between states are logic functions of the sensory input (Papas et al., 2001; Dai et al., 1996; Willemsen et al., 1990; Sabatini et al., 2005; Kotiadis et al., 2004). The second approach is from the methodology completely different, instead of clearly defined rules for transitions, the detection system is represented as a black box where the gait phase is the output and sensory information is the input (Williamson and Andrews, 2000; Ng and Chizeck, 1997). Such black-box systems are usually related to machine learning technics, fuzzy logic systems or neural networks. The advantage of such systems is that they can be trained to accurately and robustly detect gait phases for one subject. The disadvantage is that the system has to be trained for each subject separately with some sort of reference detection system, possibly by foot switches or manually by a hand switch. This is a time-consuming procedure that has to be redone as the gait rehabilitation progresses and consequently the gait changes.

Different sensors have been used to detect gait phases. Foot switches based on Force Sensitive Resistors (FSR) have traditionally been applied for triggering stimulation. Usually, the foot switch is attached under the heel and triggers the stimulation as the heel lifts of the ground. Later, combinations of several foot switches attached to different positions underneath the foot have been applied (Papas et al., 2001) in order to improve the robustness of the detection. Because of the short life span and lack of mechanical robustness of foot switches, other sensors have been investigated as replacement. In Willemsen et al. (1990) four accelerometers were used to measure the radial and tangential acceleration of the shank segment. A rule based algorithm was developed to detect four distinct

gait phases with the emphasis on detecting heel off as this is essential in a peroneal nerve stimulator. This algorithm worked fine for three out of four patients, but for the fourth patient the heel-strike was constantly detected too early due to disturbances. Other alternatives for triggering stimulation like goniometers measuring hip-, knee- and ankle-joint angles (Ng and Chizeck, 1997) have also been proposed. Recently, the interest in using a combination of gyroscopes and accelerometers has grown for the purpose of detecting gait phases. Kotiadis et al. (2004) was using an inertial sensor. Although measuring with a complete inertial sensor, only the 2 accelerometers in the sagittal plane and a gyroscope measuring angular velocity in the sagittal plane were considered in that work. Contrary to our work, the sensor was fixated on the shank segment just below the knee. A similar placement of tilt sensors in (Dai et al., 1996) showed that this sensor configuration leads to a bad differentiation between gait movement and standing up/sitting down. A similar study was done by Sabatini et al. (2005) where additionally spatial gait parameters were estimated. To the authors' knowledge no GPD system utilising all gyroscopes and accelerometers in an inertial sensor unit has been developed until now.

Although two accelerometers and one gyroscope are collecting the most valuable information, the remaining sensors might improve the robustness and accuracy. Furthermore, an inertial sensor unit provides more information than a reduced sensor leading to a more accurate estimation of the foot velocity and position. These derived signals can also be used in a gait phases detection system, possibly making it more robust. When using a full inertial sensor, another advantage arises; how the sensor is attached to the foot does not influence the performance of the gait phase detection system anymore, as the sensor is able to find its own orientation.

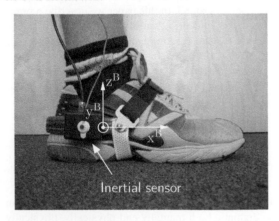

Figure 1. Experimental setup: Inertial sensor attached to the foot segment by a bracket.

In this paper, a practical FES-assisted gait training system is described. Algorithms for estimating foot movement and detecting gait phases as well as strategies for electrical stimulation are presented.

2. METHODS

A prototype FES-assisted gait training system has been developed. An inertial sensor system is used as sensory input, namely the RehaWatch system consisting of two miniature Inertial Measurement Units (IMU) and a Digital Signal Processing (DSP) unit. An IMU consists of three accelerometers and three gyroscopes measuring angular rate and acceleration about three orthogonal axes. The sensor system was developed by the Fraunhofer Institute for Factory Operation and Automation (IFF), Magdeburg (Germany), and the company HASOMED GmbH. Sensor signals are sampled with a frequency of 500 Hz. The algorithms described in this section do only assume one sensor on the disabled body side.

Before sampling, the signals are filtered through an analogue Butterworth filter with a cut-off frequency of 100 Hz. The measurement range of the accelerometers is ±4 g and the range of operation of the gyroscopes is ±700 [deg /s]. The measurements are transfered onto a laptop through an USB-interface.

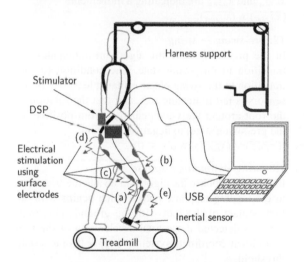

Figure 2. The muscles and nerves stimulated during FES-assisted gait training: (a) peroneal nerve, (b) quadriceps, (c) hamstrings, (d) gluteus maximus and (e) tibialis anterior.

A 8-channel stimulator[1] is connected through an USB-interface and is controlled by a special protocol called ScienceMode[2].

For straightforward testing of new stimulation strategies a MATLAB/SIMULINK user interface was written where new stimulation patterns can be easily realised. The algorithms described in the following sections have been implemented in C++ and are running on a laptop with Linux as operating system.

[1] http://www.rehastim.de/
[2] http://sciencestim.sourceforge.net/

2.1 Orientation estimation

Position and orientation of the foot can be estimated from an IMU when attached to the foot (cf. Fig. 1). The rotation of the sensor/foot can be found by integration of the angular velocity measured with the gyroscopes. It is important to have an accurate estimate of the orientation because this is the basis for calculation of the foot movement. As the pure integration will unavoidably drift off after a short time, a Kalman filer has to be applied to avoid drift (Negård *et al.*, 2005a).

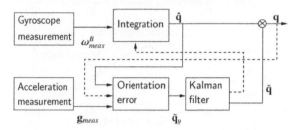

Figure 3. Block structure of the indirect Kalman filter

The structure of the Kalman filter is shown in Fig. 3. The filter is an indirect filter where the states are the error in orientation and biases of the angular velocity measurement. The accelerometers measure the gravity vector as long as the sensor is not accelerated which is nearly the case in the stance phase. The gravity can be used to estimate the orientation and this is later compared with the orientation estimate from the angular velocity integration giving the measurement input $\tilde{\mathbf{q}}_y$ to the Kalman filter. In the Kalman filter the bias of the gyroscopes and the orientation error $\tilde{\mathbf{q}}$ are calculated. This estimate is used to correct the orientation $\hat{\mathbf{q}}$ obtained by simple integration. From the orientation $\mathbf{q}$ of the sensor, angles between the foot and the ground in the sagittal and the coronal plane can be easily extracted.

2.2 Movement parameters

By use of the obtained orientation, the acceleration can be transformed into a global coordinate system and the foot movement can be estimated through a double integration of the transformed acceleration. For every stride the integration is started at heel off and continued until the foot flat event. In order to improve the accuracy, constraints on the integration are introduced. The velocity of the sensor is assumed to be zero at the beginning and at the end of a step. Furthermore, the position in the vertical direction is zero before and after a step by the assumption that the subject is walking on a horizontal surface. These constraints can be imposed on the integration by the introduction of an artificial bias on the acceleration measurement and more accurate position estimates can be calculated. In Fig. 4, position and orientation trajectories calculated from an inertial sensor unit for a healthy subject are plotted against the gait cycle percentage for three steps

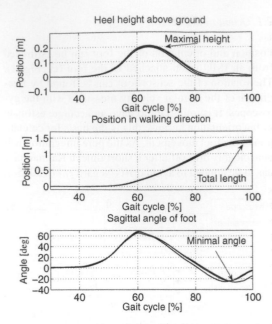

Figure 4. The upper graph shows position above the ground estimated from inertial sensor measurement. The middle graph shows the position in the walking direction, and the lower graph shows the estimated angle between the foot and the ground in the sagittal plane.

(during pre-swing and loading response phase). Movement parameters can be defined from the orientation and the position estimates as follows:

- *Foot clearance*: the maximal distance between heel and ground in the vertical direction during swing phase
- *Step length*: the total length of one step in the walking direction
- *Foot angle at heel-strike*: the angle between foot and ground in the sagittal plane at the moment as the heel hits the ground.

2.3 Gait phase detection

A gait phase detection algorithm has been developed where the gait cycle is divided into four distinct gait phases: stance, pre-swing, swing and loading response. These phases can be represented as a state machine with four states similar to the state machine described in (Papas *et al.*, 2001). The difference to that paper is the type of sensors applied, with the consequence that the transitions between states are different. The algorithm allows 6 transitions between the states (cf. Fig. 5).

Based on the angular velocity measurement a coarse detection is done whether the sensor is at rest or if it is moving. The same detection is also done for robustness purposes using the acceleration measurement. These binary variables are denotes as $x_{a,rest}$ for the accelerometers and $x_{g,rest}$ for the gyroscopes. The logic value one is indicating that the sensor is at rest

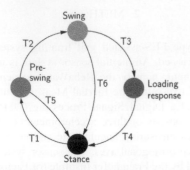

Figure 5. Gait phase detection system represented as a state machine. The gait phases are represented as 4 states where 6 transitions between the states are possible.

and zero is indicating that the sensor is moving. The transitions between the states have the following conditions:

T1: stance → pre-swing
In the stance phase, the only transition which can occur is to the pre-swing state. This is done when both $x_{a,rest}$ and $x_{g,rest}$ are indicating a movement:
$(\overline{x_{a,rest}}) \wedge (\overline{x_{g,rest}})$.

T2: pre-swing → swing
In the pre-swing state the algorithm anticipates the transition to the swing state. The condition for the transition to the swing phase is that at least one of the sensors is not indicating rest, and that the rotation of the foot around the y-axis changes from positive (in the pre-swing state) to negative direction:
$((\overline{x_{a,rest}}) \vee (\overline{x_{g,rest}})) \wedge (\dot{\omega}_y < 0)$.

T3: swing → loading response
In the swing phase the algorithm awaits the transition to the loading response phase which begins with the first contact of the foot with the ground. This transition is detected if the total acceleration of the foot in a global coordinate system is bigger than a certain threshold.

T4: loading response → stance
After the loading response the next phase is stance which begins when both front and rear part of the foot touch the ground. This event is detected when both the accelerometers and the gyroscopes are indicating rest. The transition condition becomes
$(x_{a,rest}) \wedge (x_{g,rest})$.

T5: pre-swing → stance
If the subject lifts the heel and then put it back on the ground, is this event detected as a transition from pre-swing back to stance. This transition is detected when both the accelerometer and the gyroscopes are indicating rest. The transition condition becomes
$(x_{a,rest}) \wedge (x_{g,rest})$.

T6: swing → stance
In certain gait patterns where the proband hits the ground very softly, the transition T3 does not occur. When this is the case, a direct transition from swing to

stance is useful. This event is detected when both the accelerometers and the gyroscopes are indicating rest. Further requirements are that the rotational velocity around the y- axis and its derivative are close to zero. The transition condition becomes

$$((x_{a,rest}) \wedge (x_{g,rest})) \wedge (\|\dot{\omega}_y\| < \delta_1 \wedge \|\omega_y\| < \delta_2).$$

2.4 Stimulation strategy

As the FES training system is implemented on a PC platform, different frequencies can easily be realised. Orientation estimation and gait phase detection are performed with the same sample time used in the inertial sensor unit (typically 500 Hz). After a completed step, detected by the gait phase detection system, the 3D movement trajectory of the foot is calculated following the algorithm described in Section 2.2 using buffered sensory data of the last step.

After a completed step, temporal information of the gait like cadence is calculated and then averaged over the last three steps and the result is used in the pattern generator. Different patterns can be programmed where transitions of phases are used to trigger the stimulation, and duration can be easily programmed to be a percentage of certain gait phases. The amplitude can either be chosen to be constant or to follow an arbitrary curve scaled to the desired duration. In Fig. 6, a typical stimulation pattern is shown. The peroneal nerve stimulation is triggered by the detection of preswing and lasts until the loading response. Hamstrings stimulation is also triggered by the detection of preswing phase but is turned off earlier as the peroneal nerve stimulation. Furthermore, quadriceps can either be stimulated in the swing phase in order to improve the knee extension or in the stance phase to improve the stability. The gluteus maximus can in some cases be stimulated during the stance phase in order to stabilise the hip.

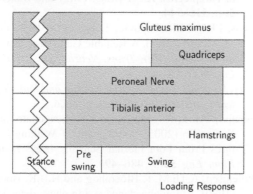

Figure 6. A typical stimulation pattern for FES-assisted gait training. Stimulation periods are indicated by grey bars.

Another possible stimulation configuration is the stimulation of the peroneal nerve in combination with the tibialis anterior whereas the latter is stimulated at the end of the swing phases. Peroneal nerve stimulation takes place with a frequency of 60Hz while muscles are stimulated with 20 Hz.

2.5 Feedback control

The movement parameters defined in Section 2.2 can be used to estimate the quality of the foot movement and to determine the required stimulation intensity. For normal gait these parameters vary between persons depending on height, gender and individual gait style, but remain fairly constant for one specific person. By assuming a relationship between a specific stimulation channel and one movement parameter, the possibility arises to control the gait movement by varying the stimulation intensity on a gait cycle basis. This is done by keeping the stimulation intensity constant during one step and updating it before the next step by evaluating the movement parameter. Foot clearance can be controlled by adjusting the stimulation intensity of the hamstrings, and the angle of the foot before touching ground is controlled by stimulation of tibialis anterior. A discrete-time PI-controller was designed for adjusting the pulse width for the above mentioned stimulation channels by using the movement parameters as feedback. In this scheme the duration, frequency and current are set to constant values, and only the pulse width is controlled by feedback. The relation between pulse width and the related movement parameter can be considered to be a linear relation

$$y[k] = bu[k] \tag{1}$$

where $u[k]$ is the normalised non-saturated pulse width and $y[k]$ is the controlled movement parameter of the gait cycle k. A discrete PI-controller can be described like this

$$u[k] = u[k-1] + q_0 e[k] + q_1 e[k-1] \tag{2}$$

with

$$e[k] = r[k] - y[k], \quad q_0 = K(1 + \frac{1}{2\tau_i}), \quad q_1 = K(-1 + \frac{1}{2\tau_i}) \tag{3}$$

where $r[k]$ is the reference value of the movement parameter, K is the control gain and τ_i is the integration constant.

3. RESULTS

Gait phase detection and movement parameter estimation have been validated with intact subjects and stroke patients. The estimated movement parameters, e.g. foot clearance and step length, were compared with a reference measurement system, and a mean error of less than 5 % and standard deviation of the error less than 5 % were shown for 2 hemiplegic subjects walking on a treadmill. Furthermore, the gait phase detection system also showed a very good performance as all steps were successfully detected for both patients (Negård *et al.*, 2005*a*). It must be mentioned that these results are preliminary and more data must be collected in order to confirm them.

The proposed feedback strategy in Section 2.5 has been tested in simulations by using a mathematical model of the free swinging leg. To illustrate the performance of the controller the reference value for the foot clearance was changed after 20 cycles. The results from this simulation trial are shown in Fig. 7. A more detailed explanation of the model and the results can be found in (Negård *et al.*, 2005*b*). In the simulations,

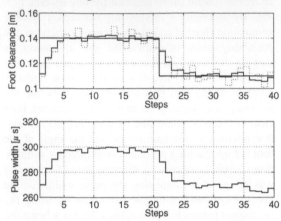

Figure 7. This figure shows the results of a simulation trial. The upper graph shows the foot clearance, the solid lines are the real foot clearance and its reference while the dashed line is the measured noisy foot clearance. The lower graph shows the stimulation pulse width.

the foot clearance could be controlled quite accurately by stimulation of the hamstring muscle group even in the presence of noisy measurements. When a step in the reference value was applied, it took about five cycles before the foot clearance was settled to the new reference value.

4. DISCUSSION AND CONCLUSIONS

Real-time control of intensity and automatic tuning of stimulation pattern have received little attention in the clinically applied FES-assisted gait rehabilitation. Any practical system must be easy to operate by physiotherapists and/or patients. Therefore, the choice of the sensors is important. Foot switches have been the de facto standard until now, but they do not provide any useful information for feedback control of stimulation intensity. Goniometers are more useful in that respect, but a time-consuming procedure has to take place to attach them and to calibrate the angular measurement before it can be used in any feedback loop. On the other hand, inertial sensors can replace foot switches for triggering purposes, and can be applied for feedback control. The system described in this paper does not require any extensive and time-consuming calibration of the sensors before taken into

use. The algorithms are not depending on an exact initial orientation as long as the sensors are rigid mounted to the foot. The Kalman filter automatically detects the orientation of the sensor by use of the gravity measurement and will consequently deliver correct movement parameters. An extensive platform for testing feedback algorithms and stimulation strategies in FES-assisted gait training has been developed, but more experiments with stroke patients have to be performed in order to validate the algorithms described in this paper.

REFERENCES

Dai, R., R.B. Stein, B.J. Andrews, K.B. James and M. Wickler (1996). Application of Tilt Sensors in Functional Electrical Stimulation. *IEEE Trans. Rehab. Eng.* **4**(4), 62–72.

Kotiadis, D., H. Hermens, P.Veltink and P. Slyke (2004). Inertial gait phase detection system: Design. In: *Proceedings of the 9th Ann. IFESS Conference*. Bournemouth, UK.

Liberson, W.T., H.J. Holmquest, D. Scot and M. Dow (1961). Functional Electrotherapy: Stimulation of the Peroneal Nerve Synchronized with the Swing Phase of the Gait of Hemiplegic Patients. *Arch. Phys. Med. Rehabil.* **42**, 101–105.

Negård, N.-O., R. Kauert, S. Andres, T. Schauer and J. Raisch (2005*a*). Gait phase detection and step length estimation of gait by means of inertial sensors. In: *Proc. of the 3rd European Medical & Biological Engineering Conference*. Prague, Czech Republic.

Negård, N.-O., T. Schauer and J. Raisch (2005*b*). Control of FES-aided gait by means of inertial sensors. In: *Proc. of the 4th Wismar Symposium on Automatic Control*. Wismar, Germany.

Ng, S.K. and H.J. Chizeck (1997). Fuzzy Model Identification For Classification of Gait Events in Paraplegics. *IEEE Trans. Fuzzy and Systems* **5**(4), 536–544.

Papas, I.P.I., M.R. Popovic, T. Keller, V. Dietz and M. Morari (2001). A Reliable Gait Phase Detection System. *IEEE Trans. Neural Syst. Rehabil. Eng.* **9**(2), 113–125.

Perry, J. (1992). *Gait Analysis: Normal and Pathological Function*. SLACK Incorporated.

Sabatini, A.M., C. Martelloni, S. Scapellato and F. Cavallo (2005). Assessment of Walking features From Foot Inertial Sensing. *IEEE Trans. Biom. Eng.* **52**(3), 486–494.

Willemsen, A.Th.M, F. Bloemhog and H.B.K. Boom (1990). Automatic stance-swing phase detection from accelerometer data for peroneal nerve stimulation. *IEEE Trans. Biom. Eng.* **37**(12), 1201–1208.

Williamson, R. and B. Andrews (2000). Gait Event Detection for FES Using Accelerometers and Supervised Machine Learning. *IEEE Trans. Rehab. Eng.* **8**(3), 312–319.

ELSEVIER
IFAC
PUBLICATIONS

CONTROL ARCHITECTURE OF A 3-DOF UPPER LIMBS REHABILITATION ROBOT

Alexandre Denève, Saïd Moughamir, Lissan Afilal, Jérémy Lesieur, Janan Zaytoon

*Centre de Recherche en Sciences et Technologies de l'Information et de la Communication
Université de Reims Champagne-Ardenne, BP 1039, 51687 Reims Cedex 2, France*

Abstract: This paper presents the control system of a rehabilitation and training robot for the upper limbs. This system is based on the execution of sequence of switching control laws (position, force, impedance and force/impedance) corresponding to the required training configuration. Some illustrative results for a particular rehabilitation mode are discussed. *Copyright © 2006 IFAC*

Keywords: Biomedical systems, control system synthesis, fuzzy control, man/machine interaction, robot control.

1. INTRODUCTION

In terms of rehabilitation and muscular reinforcement, the resort to robots constitutes a notable progress. These robots can free the physiotherapist from certain tasks and make it possible to increase performance by introducing original rehabilitation and training modes (Krebs, *et al.*, 1998; Cozens, 1999; Reinkensmeyer, *et al.*, 2000).

The 3-degrees-of-freedom (dof) robot for upper limbs rehabilitation and training developed in our research center allows the execution of physiological movements (Fig. 1) in horizontal and vertical planes. The development of this robotized arm benefits from our previous experience related to the specification and the design of rehabilitation and training machines for the lower limbs (Moughamir, *et al.*, 2002).

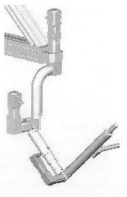

Fig. 1. Robotized arm with 3 degrees of freedom.

Robot mechanical design and performance differ according to the control paradigm used: admittance or impedance control. Admittance controlled robots can render high stiffnesses, very small frictions and modulate their apparent inertia because they use an active force feedback (Clover, 1999; Van der Linde and Lammertse, 2003). Their design is simpler and larger workspaces can be used while maintaining an isotropic apparent inertia. Thus, admittance control robots are very suitable for gradual rehabilitation and training in many degrees of freedom. For these reasons, our robotized arm is intrinsically designed to use an admittance control paradigm.

This robot can carry out different rehabilitation modes (*Isometric, Isokinetic, Steering, Isotonic, Physiokinetic, Assisted* and *Active-Assisted*) whose definitions are give in (Moughamir, 1999; Zaytoon, *et al.*, 1996). In order to command these rehabilitation modes, four control laws are used: position, force, impedance and force/impedance control laws. During a specific rehabilitation or training session, a corresponding switching sequence of these control laws is necessary to perform the required movement patterns.

This paper presents the control system of the robotized arm; the synthesis of the switching control laws is particularly emphasised. We also focus on the *Active-Assisted* rehabilitation mode that is performed thanks to a fuzzy weighted hybrid force/impedance control. Some illustrative simulation results of the *Active-Assisted* rehabilitation mode are presented and discussed to validate the robot control system before its implementation.

2. CONTROL SYSTEM

The architecture of the system is depicted on Fig. 2. The robot includes 3-rotoïd joints actuated by brushless DC geared motors. These motors are equipped with absolute encoders. Each motor torque is controlled by a servo drive which transmits position and velocity information on a CAN bus (CANopen protocol). At the robot end-effector, a 3-dof strain gauge-type transducer sends force information on a CAN Bus via a force transmitter. According to the position, velocity and force information and for a given training configuration, a target PC issues the corresponding torque reference to servo drives. At the higher level of the control architecture, a Host PC uses Matlab/Simulink/Stateflow as development software. Programs are compiled and loaded directly on the target PC. During execution a constant dialog between the Host PC and the Target PC allows a real time tuning of different control laws parameters.

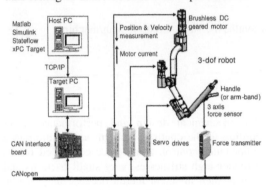

Fig. 2. Architecture of the system.

A human-machine interface allows users to choose a training exercise from a pre-established database. In order to facilitate the correct execution of the exercise, a screen provides visual information about measured forces and the execution of the real movement trajectory compared to the desired one.

The control system of our robot belongs to the class of switching systems. The established medical specifications have shown that four control laws (position, force, impedance, force/impedance) are required to carry out the different movements. The switching sequence between these control laws depends on the nature of the exercise to be realized and the sensory information (robot end-effector position, velocity, and patient's force). The hierarchical control structure (Fig. 3) is inspired from the generic framework, proposed in (Moughamir, *et al.*, 2002) for the specification and design of any training and rehabilitation machine. This hierarchal structure comprises two parts: a sequential controller divided into 3 levels and the switching control laws.

A rehabilitation session (Fig. 3) is used to co-ordinate the rehabilitation (or training) modes and the consecutive phases forming the session. A phase is given by a succession of training series separated by a period of muscular relaxation. Each series comprises a number of repetitions of a particular *forward* movement pattern followed by a particular

backward movement pattern. Many dedicated movement patterns were developed to drive the upper limb(s) between two coordinate points of the robot workspace. Each of these patterns invokes one or more switching control laws and a predefined trajectory. These trajectories are selected thanks to a pre-recorded database.

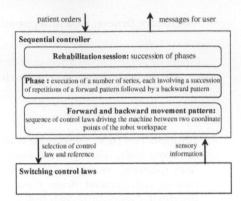

Fig. 3. Hierarchical control structure.

The switching control scheme depicted in Fig. 4 shows the four control laws: position (L_p), force (L_f), impedance (L_i) and force/impedance (L_{fi}). The activation of these control laws depends on the variable i (i ∈ {1,2,3,4}) delivered by the Sequential controller.

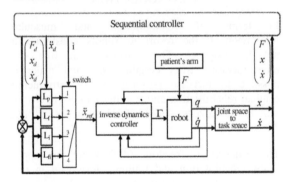

Fig. 4. Switching control scheme.

In this control scheme, all control laws define a desired robot end-effector dynamics and generate the corresponding reference acceleration, $\ddot{x}_{ref}$, in task space.

In joint space, the Lagrangian dynamics of a manipulator constrained by the environment are given by:

$$\Gamma = A(q)\,\ddot{q} + n(q,\dot{q}) + J^T F \qquad (1)$$

where q represents the angle position vector, Γ the torque vector, A the matrix of inertia, n the vectorial sum of the centrifugal and Coriolis torques, gravitation torque and viscous friction torque, J the Jacobian matrix, F the vector of contact forces and torques supported by the robot end-effector.

The joint space acceleration is related to the task space acceleration in the following way:

$$\ddot{q} = J^{-1}(\ddot{x} - \dot{J}\dot{q}) \qquad (2)$$

In order to impose the desired dynamics to the robot end-effector, the relations (1) and (2) are used to compute the inverse dynamics control:

$$\Gamma = A(q)\,J^{-1}(q)(\ddot{x}_{ref} - \dot{J}(q)q) + n(q,\dot{q}) + J^T F \qquad (3)$$

This well-known nonlinear feedback control (Freund, 1975; Zabala-Iturralde, 1978), ensures a good tracking of the trajectory if the parameters of the dynamic model are known with sufficient accuracy. Despite the complexity of this control scheme, in terms of architecture and computation, its implementation is feasible thanks to the advent of increasingly fast microprocessors.

The four control laws, depicted in Fig.4, are discussed in the next section.

3. CONTROL LAWS

3.1 Position control law

The position control law, L_p, is used in *Isometric* training mode where a patient needs to apply a maximal force around a fixed number of positions determined by the physiotherapist. This control law is also applied near extreme positions of training movements to realize smooth decelerations.

A well-known PD control with a feedforward acceleration is used to calculate the task space reference acceleration:

$$\ddot{x}_{ref} = \ddot{x}_d + K_{pp}(x_d - x) + K_{pv}(\dot{x}_d - \dot{x}) \qquad (4)$$

where x_d represents the desired position vector, K_{pp} and K_{pv}, the proportional and derivative gains.

The desired trajectory is completely predefined offline.

3.2 Force control law

This control is used to execute free movements. It allows physiotherapist to record the desired trajectories by guiding patient's arm along prescribed paths. Thus, the obtained trajectories are specific to each patient anatomy and the physiotherapist can select movements which are appropriate for each pathology.

The task space reference acceleration is given by:

$$\ddot{x}_{ref} = K_{fp}(F_d - F) + K_{fi}\int(F_d - F)dt \qquad (5)$$

where F_d is the desired force vector, K_{fp} and K_{fi}, the proportional and integral gains.

Here, a proportional-integral form has been preferred to a proportional derivative to prevent resonance oscillations induced by derivative control of the noisy force signal (Volpe and Khosla, 1993).

3.3 Impedance control law

The impedance control law (Hogan, 1985), usually employed in the human-robot interactions for its advantages in term of safety, is used for *Isotonic* and *Physiokinetic* rehabilitation modes. The desired impedance of the robot end-effecter is given by:

$$F = K(x - x_d) + B\dot{x} + M\ddot{x} \qquad (6)$$

When contact forces arise, the real position x deviates from the desired position x_d to satisfy (6) and, hence, to establish a compromise between force and position according to the matrix of stiffness K, damping B and inertia M.

From equation (6), we obtain the task space reference acceleration $\ddot{x}_{ref}$:

$$\ddot{x}_{ref} = M^{-1}\left[K(x_d - x) - B\dot{x} + F\right] \qquad (7)$$

3.4 Force/impedance control law

The Force/impedance control law, L_{fi}, is used for the *Active-Assisted* rehabilitation mode. This control is based on a weighted sum of a force and an impedance control:

$$\ddot{x}_{ref} = \alpha\ddot{x}_f + (I - \alpha)\ddot{x}_i \qquad (8)$$

where $\ddot{x}_f$ and $\ddot{x}_i$ represents respectively the force and impedance control acceleration, and α is a diagonal weighting matrix.

The next section explains the requirements of the *Active-Assisted* rehabilitation mode and clarifies the elements of relation (8).

4. ACTIVE-ASSISTED REHABILITATION MODE

The first requirement of the *Active-Assisted* mode is to let the robot end-effector behave like a simple inert mass. The goal of the control law is thus to assign the following dynamics to the end-effector:

$$\ddot{x}_f = \frac{1}{M_d}(F - M_d.g) \qquad (9)$$

where M_d is the matrix of desired inertia, and g, the vector of gravity acceleration. The resulting control is similar to a force controller. The measured force, F, is compared with the reference value, $M_d.g$, to determine the movement dynamics. The integration of relation (9) into the inverse dynamics control confers to the robot a similar behaviour to that of an ideal weight machine, with the additional advantage of being able to execute complex movements without frictions (Moughamir, *et al.*, 2002).

The second requirement of the *Active-Assisted* mode is to avoid a large movement deviation from the desired trajectory. In order to fulfil this requirement, we use the impedance control already defined in section 3.3:

$$\ddot{x}_i = M^{-1}\left[K(x_d - x) - B\dot{x} + F\right] \quad (10)$$

The two requirements of the *Active-Assisted* mode are combined by taking the weighted sum of relations (9) and (10). Thus, we obtain the task space reference given by relation (8) where α is used to fix the respective weights of the contributions of force and impedance.

For the 3-dof robot: $\alpha = \begin{bmatrix} \alpha_1 & 0 & 0 \\ 0 & \alpha_2 & 0 \\ 0 & 0 & \alpha_3 \end{bmatrix}$

In a previous study (Moughamir, *et al.*, 2005), this weighting (α, $I - \alpha$) was computed in the following manner :

$$\alpha_i = \frac{\tilde{x}_{i\max} - \left|\tilde{x}_i\right|}{\tilde{x}_{i\max}} \qquad \tilde{x}_{i\max} > 0 \quad (11)$$

where α_i is the weighting along direction i and $\tilde{x}_{i\max}$ is the upper limit of the position error in the considered direction.

This method exhibits satisfactory results in simulation but some contained oscillations are noticed. In order to solve this problem and obtain a smoother human/robot interaction, we propose next to determine α_i by fuzzy logic, using not only position error $\tilde{x}_i$ but also velocity error $\dot{\tilde{x}}_i$ as input variables. Sugeno's inference method (Takagi and Sugeno, 1985) is used with three fuzzy sets of input variables: negative (N), zero (Z) and positive (P). In our case, six inference rules, based on Active-Assisted rehabilitation mode objectives, are sufficient to improve the performance significantly:

IF $\tilde{x}_i$ is N AND $\dot{\tilde{x}}_i$ is NOT P THEN $z_1 = 0$
IF $\tilde{x}_i$ is N AND $\dot{\tilde{x}}_i$ is P THEN $z_2 = 0.5$
IF $\tilde{x}_i$ is Z AND $\dot{\tilde{x}}_i$ is NOT Z THEN $z_3 = 0.5$
IF $\tilde{x}_i$ is Z AND $\dot{\tilde{x}}_i$ is Z THEN $z_4 = 1$
IF $\tilde{x}_i$ is P AND $\dot{\tilde{x}}_i$ is N THEN $z_5 = 0.5$
IF $\tilde{x}_i$ is P AND $\dot{\tilde{x}}_i$ is NOT N THEN $z_6 = 0$

z_j is the output membership function of the rule j. Because a zero-order Sugeno model is used, z_j is equal to a constant c. In order to determine the output α_i of the fuzzy controller, z_j is weighted by w_j, the firing strength of the rule j:

$$\alpha_i = \frac{\sum_{j=1}^{6} w_j z_j}{\sum_{j=1}^{6} w_j} \quad (12)$$

The three triangular membership functions for position error and velocity error are shown in Fig. 5.

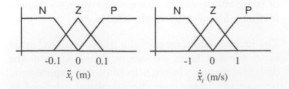

Fig. 5. Membership functions.

The parameter $\tilde{x}_{i\max}$ defines the subject's workspace in the considered direction. The larger this parameter is, the lower the assistance provided by the robot is. If this parameter is identical in all directions ($x_{i\max} = x_{\max} \quad \forall i$), the workspace at instant t is reduced to a sphere centred on the desired position $x_d(t)$ nearest to the real position $x(t)$ (Fig. 6).

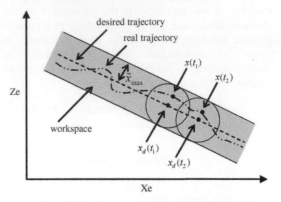

Fig. 6. Workspace in the sagittal plane (Xe, Ze).

The proposed controller forces the subject to remain in this space, which gradually forms a safety space. To maintain the subject in this workspace, the position error is required to satisfy the following condition:

$$\left|\tilde{x}_i(t)\right| < \tilde{x}_{i\max} \quad (13)$$

The satisfaction of this inequality depends obviously on the control parameters m_i, k_i and b_i, but also on the capacity of the subject to carry out the desired task. By considering (8),(9) and (10), it is advantageous to choose the matrix M equals to M_d to ensure a good compromise between the contributions of force and impedance and to render the inertia felt by the subject equal to the desired inertia irrespective of the position error. The choice of the control parameters k_i and b_i is more delicate, because the control must be sufficiently compliant to guarantee the subject's safety while ensuring a good trajectory correction. In (Moughamir, *et al.*, 2005) we proposed a method to determine the parameters k_i and b_i which fulfil this requirement.

For obvious safety reasons, the suggested control must be tested exhaustively before experimentation. We propose to compare the two weighting methods and illustrate the potentialities of the controller in terms of dynamic performance and medical interest. Simulation results are presented in the following section.

5. SIMULATION

To simplify the presentation, we consider the movement of flexion/extension in the sagittal plane, which brings into play only two of the robot's three degrees of freedom. We neglect small displacements in the horizontal direction when the movement is carried out in a natural way.

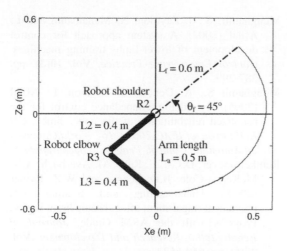

Fig. 7. Initial robot's position and desired trajectory.

The initial position of the robot as well as the desired trajectory is depicted in Fig. 7. This desired trajectory takes into account the displacements of the shoulder (glenohumeral) joint (Walmsey, 2001). The intersection of the two axis of rotation of the robot's shoulder ($X_e=0$, $Z_e=0$) is chosen as a reference mark. The estimated initial position of the glenohumeral rotation centre of the subject coincides with this reference mark. In the initial position, the subject's arm, of length $L_a = 50$ cm, is directed downwards. In the final position, $\theta_f = 45°$, the length between the origin of the reference mark and the robot end-effector (handle or arm-band) is: $L_f = 60$ cm. Thus, we suppose that the rotation axis misalignment of the subject's shoulder relatively to the rotation axis of the robot's shoulder, R2, entails a 10 cm increase of the length L for this motion range of 135°. L2 and L3 are both fixed at 40 cm. Any proximity with the singular position of the robot (tended arm) is thus impossible since the sum of these two lengths largely exceed the length of the subject's arm.

If one neglects the effect of the sampling ($Te = 1$ms), the robot's dynamic model is completely compensated. The desired isotropic mass is fixed at 1kg and the acceleration of gravity at $9{,}81$m.s^{-2}. For all directions, we consider that the subject cannot exert forces higher than $f_{i\ max} = 100$N. To simulate his/her behaviour, we suppose that the subject exerts a force of 1N towards the desired trajectory and entirely compensates the gravity force:

$$F(t) = \frac{1}{\left\| x_d^+ - x(t) \right\|}\left(x_d^+ - x(t)\right) - Mg \qquad (14)$$

where x_d^+ is a sample point of the desired trajectory located some centimetres ahead the subject current position $x(t)$.

In order to study the control reactions with respect to abrupt force variations, we add a sinusoidal disturbance (with a frequency of 3 Hz and an amplitude of 20 N in the vertical direction) to relation (14). This disturbance roughly simulates an action tremor of patient's upper limb.

Figure 8 depicts the simulation results for the two weighting methods. The subject workspace is fixed at 10cm. The other control parameters are selected according to the method proposed in (Moughamir, *et al.*, 2005) and are given by:

$$M = M_d \qquad B\left[Nm^{-1}s\right] = 98.I \qquad K\left[Nm^{-1}\right] = 1000.I$$

For both weighting methods, the movement is completely achieved inside the assigned subject workspace. However, we notice that the tracking of the desired trajectory is better with the fuzzy weighting method. The average norm of weighting matrix α informs us about the average rate of force control preponderance versus impedance control. This index is of medical interest within the framework of a gradual rehabilitation since it provides a quantification of the quality of movement execution. A higher percentage (about 85% has been obtained with the fuzzy method and 71% with the non-fuzzy one) indicates a better accuracy of movement execution and a lower assistance provided by the robot.

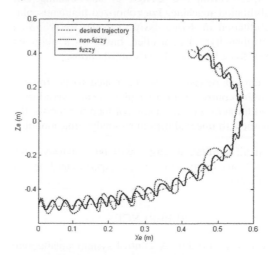

Fig. 8. Flexion/extension movement

Another simulation was conducted to test the dynamic and static performances of the proposed control scheme and to compare the two weighting methods. We simulated the release and grab of the handle in vertical direction (Fig. 9). Subject workspace is fixed at 10 *cm*. The release occurs at $t = 0$ *s* and the grab at $t = 1$ *s*.

Results show limited static errors, which are the same for both methods since the limits of position error membership function (Z) (Fig. 5) was chosen equal to subject workspace. Notice that these static errors are easy to cancel because force control is dominating for this weak position errors. Dynamic errors are different according to the weighting method used. Fuzzy method presents much less oscillations than non-fuzzy one with a dynamics hardly slower. Thus, fuzzy method allows a safer human/machine coupling.

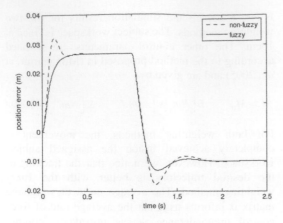

Fig. 9. Release and grab of the handle.

6. CONCLUSION

This paper has presented the control architecture of a 3-dof rehabilitation robot for the upper limbs. This structure is inspired from a generic framework for the specification and design of any training and rehabilitation machine. For robotized neuromuscular rehabilitation in *Active-Assisted* mode, we proposed an original hybrid controller, based on a weighted sum of force and impedance contributions.

Our current research work is related to the inverse dynamics controller. In particular, we are considering the addition of a position control loop to improve the robustness to uncertainties in robot dynamic model.

When all simulation stages will be conclusive, the overall control structure will be experimented on our 3-dof robot.

REFERENCES

Clover, C.L. (1999). A control-system architecture for robots used to simulate dynamic force and moment interaction between humans and virtual objects. *IEEE Transactions on Systems, Man, and Cybernetics - Part C: Applications and Reviews*, **Vol. 29(4)**, pp. 481-493.

Cozens, J.A. (1999). Robotic assistance of an active upper limb exercise in neurologically impaired patients. *IEEE Transactions on Rehabilitation Engineering*, **Vol. 7(2)**, pp. 254-256.

Freund E. (1975). The structure of decoupled nonlinear systems. *Int. Journal of .Control.*, **vol. 21(3)**, pp. 443-450.

Hogan, N. (1985). Impedance control: An approach to manipulation: Part I, part II, part III. *ASME Journal of Dynamic Systems, Measurement and Control*, **Vol. 107**, pp. 1-24.

Krebs, H.I., N. Hogan, M.L. Aisen and B.T. Volpe (1998). Robot-aided neurorehabilitation. *IEEE Transactions on Rehabilitation Engineering*, **Vol. 6(1)**, pp. 75-87.

Moughamir, S. (1999). Conception et développement d'une machine de rééducation et d'entraînement des membres inférieurs. *Ph.D Thesis of University of Reims Champagne-Ardenne, France.*

Moughamir, S., J. Zaytoon, N. Manamanni and L. Afilal (2002). A system approach for control development of lower-limbs training machines. *Control Engineering Practice*, **Vol. 10(3)**, pp. 287-299.

Moughamir S., A. Denève, J. Zaytoon, L. Afilal (2005). Hybrid force/impedance control for the robotized rehabilitation of the upper limbs, *CD ROM Proc. of IFAC 2005 – 16ᵗʰ World Congress on Automatic Control, Prague, Tcheck Republic.*

Reinkensmeyer, D.J., L.E. Kahn, M. Averbuch, A.N. McKenna-Cole, B.D. Schmit and W.Z. Rymer (2000). Understanting and treating arm movement impairment after chronic brain injury: Progress with the ARM Guide. *Journal of Rehabilitation Research and Development*, **Vol. 37(6)**, pp. 653-662.

Takagi T. and M. Sugeno (1985). Fuzzy identification of systems and its application to modeling and control. *IEEE Transactions on Systems, Man and Cybernetics*, **Vol. 15(1)**, pp. 116-132.

Van der Linde, R.Q. and P. Lammertse (2003). HapticMaster – a generic force controlled robot for human interaction. *Industrial Robot*, **Vol. 30(6)**, pp. 515-524.

Volpe R. and P. Khosla (1993). A theoretical and experimental investigation of explicit force control strategies for Manipulators. *IEEE Transactions on Automatic Control*, **Vol. 38(11)**, pp. 1634-1650.

Walmsey, R.P. (2001). Movement of the axis of rotation of the glenohumeral joint while working on the Cybex II dynamometer. Part I. Flexion/Extension. Part II. Abduction/Adduction. *Isokinetics and Exercise Science*, **Vol. 9**, pp. 16-25.

Zabala-Iturralde J. (1978). Commande des robots manipulateurs à partir de la modelisation de leur dynamique. *Ph.D Thesis of Paul Sabatier University of Toulouse, France.*

Zaytoon J., E. Richard, S. Moughamir and L. Angelloz (1996). A formalism for complex control system: Application to a machine for training and re-education of lower limbs. *In Proc. CESA'96 IMACS/IEEE Symposium on Discrete Events & Manufacturing Systems, Lille, France*, pp.789-794.

ELSEVIER
IFAC
PUBLICATIONS

ADAPTIVE CONTROL OF COMPUTED TOMOGRAPH ANGIOGRAPHY

R. McCabe ** H. Bai * J. Bennett * T. Potts **
M. Sharafuddin *** J. Halloran **** M. Vannnier †
G. Wang * E.W. Bai **,‡

Dept. of Radiology, University of Iowa
**Dept. of Electrical & Computer Engineering, University
of Iowa*
***Dept. of Surgery*
****Dept. of Interventional Radiology, Cedar Vally Medical
Specialists, Waterloo, Iowa*
†*Dept. of Radiology, University of Chicago, Chicago*
‡*Corresponding Author, er-wei-bai@uiowa.edu*

Abstract: In this paper, an adaptive scheme is proposed and tested for a next generation Computed Tomograph Angiography (CTA). The purpose of the control is to estimate the contrast bolus position so its variations can be compensated by controlling the patient table. This improves the imaging quality and reduces the amount of harmful contrast injection and radiation exposure. The convergence result has been achieved and the experimental results are very promising. *Copyright C 2006 IFAC*

Keywords: Adaptive Control, Medical Applications, Biomedical Systems, Estimation Algorithms, Biomedical Control

1. INTRODUCTION

In the recent years, CT (Computed Tomography) angiography has become one of the most popular medical diagnostic tools (Rubin *et al.*, 1998) due to its non-invasive nature and faster scanning capabilities. In CT angiography, contrast material is often administrated to allow a narrow temporal window to obtain optimal visualization of vessels, lesions and tumors (Sheafor *et al.*, 1998; Tublin *et al.*, 1999). The quality of scans depends on the ability to synchronize patient table position with the relatively narrow aperture of the imaging system during propagation of a contrast bolus after intravenous injection. Contrast bolus synchro-

nization is achieved by using arrival monitoring with CT fluoroscopy. However, arrival monitoring synchronizes only the initial peak of contrast and the subsequently assumed linear table velocity becomes problematic as time increases.

Peak bolus velocity is rarely uniform. Therefore synchronization of the bolus with a fixed, preset table transport often results in less-desirable vascular enhancement. Lack of synchronization may be more problematic when scanning speed is fast, contrast volume is small, injection rate is high (leading to reduced peak duration), and/or variable vessel lumen diameter. Even for a normal individual, it is common that the contrast bolus velocity is rapid in the torso and relatively slow in the legs. Moreover, if asymmetric peripheral

---
[1] supported in part by NIH/NIBIB EB004287-01

Table 1. Blood velocity variation for normal male adult.

Blood Velocities (in artery)	Peak Velocity (cm/sec)	Mean Velocity (cm/sec)
Aorta	150 ± 30	27 ± 8.9
Common Iliac	125 ± NA	13.5 ± 4.0
External Iliac	119 ± 21.7	10.5 ± 5.0
Common Femoral	114 ± 24.9	10.2 ± 4.8
Superficial Femoral	90.8 ± 13.6	8.8 ± 3.5
Popliteal	68.8 ± 3.5	4.9 ± 2.9
Posterior tibial	61 ± 20	4.4 ± 3.3
Dorsalis pedis	NA	3.6 ± 3.8

vascular disease exists, there may also be substantial variability in flow velocity between the opposite legs. Scanning too early may result in overestimation of stenosis, while scanning too late may result in venous opacification. The published data shows that even in a normal person, the bolus velocities at different body section can vary by 8 times, see Table 1. Obviously, adaptive bolus chasing techniques are relevant to CT angiography because of the impact on image quality, as well as the need to limit contrast dose and radiation exposure.

The aim is to develop an adaptive bolus chasing CT angiography technique. The idea is illustrated in Figure 1. The control system consists of an imaging acquiring, processing and reconstruction part, an adaptive algorithm to estimate and predict future bolus position and a controller that moves the patient table to compensate the bolus variations. Works reported here are the algorithm development and experimental results in a clinical environment based on the actual patients data. The convergence of the algorithm has been

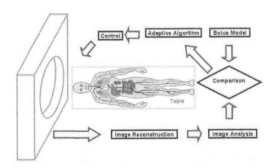

Fig. 1. Control scheme illustration

2. BOLUS DATA EXTRACTION

Adaptive control of a bolus chasing CTA requires an understanding of contrast bolus dynamics under normal and diseased conditions. Properties such as ECG gating delay, peak bolus velocity,

and average bolus velocity are essential to development of a robust adaptive control system. Furthermore, variations in contrast bolus dynamics secondary to vascular disease categories must be understood to allow for experiments under realistic clinical conditions.

While a through investigation of the bolus dynamic is beyond the scope of this control paper, actual patient data is necessary. The patient data was obtained from routine diagnostic peripheral angiograms on a Siemens AXIOM-Artis utilizing iodinated contrast agent. The scans are generally performed at 15 frames per second (fps) and the sampling rate for the ECG signal is 400 samples per second. The data sets were saved in the Digital Imaging and Communications in Medicine (DICOM) Format, a medical standard in most modalities for transfer of images, movies, and other diagnostic data. Each DICOM patient data file was opened with RUBO. Then, the movie information was extracted and saved as a Windows Media Video Clip (AVI). The ECG data (native format is in the hexadecimal base) was manually retrieved from the XML file. The algorithm developed in LabVIEW extracts every frame in the cine sequence and processes these images for analysis of bolus dynamics. First, the image was converted from a RGB image (pixel is associated with three intensity values: Red, Green, Blue) into a gray scale image (pixel with only one intensity value). Then, the image was defined to a region of interest without significant interfering features. A process called Digital Subtraction was used to remove any stationary artifacts. For example, if each pixel in the current frame is subtracted from its counterpart pixel in the mask frame, stationary objects in the sequence will be suppressed. This will increase the conspicuity of the moving structures, i.e., the contrast bolus, in each frame of the sequence. Figure 2 illustrates the effects.

(a) (b) (c)

Fig. 2. (a) First frame of a cine scene, (b) the nth frame and (c) the resultant subtracted image

Over one hundred of patient data sets were studied. A representative ECG signal and bolus peak position as functions of time is shown in Figure 3. Alignment of the bolus propagation and the ECG

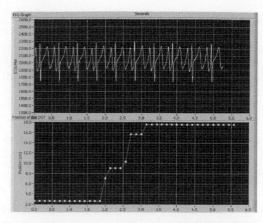

Fig. 3. Bolus peak position and ECG signal

graphs provides an interesting observation. The ECG graph (top graph) is a plot of the cardiac electrical potential versus time. Both of the graphs have the same starting point and time scale. It clearly shows that the bolus peak position is pulsatory. It surges in the first phase of the systole stage and is relatively stationary in the diastole stage. This pulsatory and non-smooth nature of the bolus peak position increases the difficulty for adaptive control.

3. ESTIMATION AND CONTROL ALGORITHMS

The control goal is to move the patient table by the exact amount as the bolus but in opposite direction so that the bolus peak position and the imaging aperture are synchronized.

As illustrated conceptually in Figure 2, the overall control system consists of 4 components. The first part is imaging acquiring and processing that provides real time bolus position. The second part is a predictor. Based on some bolus dynamics models and observed measurements, it predicts future bolus positions. Since the bolus dynamics is unknown, the model inevitably involves some unknown parameters. Thus, the estimator is the third part that estimates unknown parameters on-line. The final part is a patient table driven by a motor. The motor takes information from the predictor and moves the table so that the imaging aperture and the bolus are synchronized.

Both the CT table and the bolus dynamics are involved and have to be understood. For the CT table, most existing control systems use an AC or DC stepping motor servo system to move the table. Mechanically and electronically speaking, the system is very complicated for patient comfort and safety. Because of the stepping motor servo system, however, the mathematical equation that describes the CT table motion is surprisingly simple provided that the motor has enough torque.

Let Δt be the sampling interval and $p_T(i\Delta t)$ be the table position at time $i\Delta t$. The table position at time $i\Delta t + \Delta t$ is given by

$$p_T(i\Delta t + \Delta t) = u(i\Delta t) \qquad (1)$$

where $u(i\Delta t)$ is the control input at time $i\Delta t$ to the motor servo system informing the stepping motor how many revolutions it should turn that translates into the table linear distance. If the bolus peak position $p_b(i\Delta t + \Delta t)$ were available at time $i\Delta t$, one could set

$$u(i\Delta t) = p_b(i\Delta t + \Delta t)$$

that guarantees

$$p_T(i\Delta t + \Delta t) = p_b(i\Delta t + \Delta t)$$

a perfect synchronization between the bolus peak position and the imaging aperture. This would solve the adaptive control problem. Unfortunately, the future bolus peak position $p_b(i\Delta t + \Delta t)$ is unknown at time $i\Delta t$, and a model is needed that estimates and predicts the future bolus peak position.

Clearly, an accurate estimation and prediction of the future bolus peak position $p_b(i\Delta t + \Delta t)$ based on the current and past bolus information $p_b(k\Delta t), k \leq i$ is essential. The success of the proposed strategy depends on how accurately the model can predict. Therefore, modeling is an important step in estimating and predicting the bolus position.

3.1 Full model

It was shown (Wang *et al.*, 2000*b*) that bolus propagation is governed by a set of partial differential equations which contains a large number of patient and circulatory stage-dependent parameters. The model is fairly accurate provided that all parameters are available. Because these parameters are unknown, this full model has a little use in practice for adaptive bolus chasing CT angiography. It is known in the adaptive community that partial differential equations are not easy to deal with. Morover, online estimation of such a large number of parameters in a very short time (typically CT angiography lasts about 20-30 seconds) is impossible. Another commonly used model to describe bolus dynamics is the compartmental model (Bae *et al.*, 1998) that is also of little use for adaptive bolus chasing CT angiography. Again, the model is a set of equations involving a large number of unknown parameters that are patient and circulatory stage dependent. Obviously, parameters about the patient conditions, e.g., vessel radius at each stage of the vascular tree, are difficult to have in advance. Also, disease-state related parameters are impossible to be quantified prior to an angiogram. Further, the compartmental model describes contrast enhancement specific to a compartment (organ or vessel) (Bae *et al.*, 1998) instead of predicting the bolus dynamic as a function of time.

3.2 Approximate linear model

To overcome the complexity problem based on a full mode, some linear models of the bolus dynamics have been investigated. At a fixed location of the body y (Bassingthwaighte *et al.*, 1966), the bolus dynamics can be described by convolutions of three functions

$$b(t, y) = c(t) * \frac{1}{\sigma(y)\sqrt{2\pi}} e^{-\frac{(t-t_c(y))^2}{2\sigma^2(y)}} * \frac{1}{\tau(y)} e^{\frac{t}{\tau(y)}}$$

where the function $c(t)$ is determined by the injection of the bolus and the parameters t_c, τ and σ depend on the location y, i.e., the body section. There are several difficulties with this linear model. First, the model only considers the average bolus motion and does not consider the pulsatility of the bolus dynamics. It has little use in tracking the bolus peak position which is pulsatory. Secondly, the unknown parameters t_c, τ and σ depend on the patients' conditions which are unknown. Even assuming all the unknown parameters are available, one has to switch from one linear model to another depending on the body section. This adds complexity to the model and requires additional physilogical measurements.

3.3 Non-parametric model

The complete dynamics of the bolus are not necessary, instead only the next bolus position is needed. Though the bolus velocity varies greatly, with current computer and CT techniques, the difference of the bolus peak positions at two consecutive sampling instances is small provided that the sampling rate is high. In fact, the bolus velocity may be considered as a constant between two sampling instances if the sampling interval Δt is small. With the knowledge of the current bolus velocity which is the difference between the current and the immediate past bolus positions divided by the sampling interval, the next (future) bolus peak position can be fairly accurately predicted. To estimate the velocity, only one parameter, the bolus position at the current time that is patient and circulatory stage-dependent, needs to be estimate. Moreover, this information can be readily obtained in modern CT systems (Wang *et al.*, 2000a; Wang *et al.*, 2000c). Therefore, based on this very simple adaptive nonlinear model, the future bolus peak position can be estimated and predicted.

Again the idea is that the bolus velocity $v(i\Delta t)$ depends on i and is unknown, with a very short sampling period Δt, two consecutive $v(i\Delta t)$ and $v((i-1)\Delta t)$ are however close and differ by only a very small amount. Suppose there exists a small $\delta > 0$ so that

$$v((i-1)\Delta t) - v(i\Delta t) = \Delta_i, \quad |\Delta_i| \leq \delta \quad \forall i$$

Now, let $\hat{v}(i\Delta t)$ and $\hat{p}_b(i\Delta t)$ denote the estimates of the bolus velocity and position $v(i\Delta t)$ and $p_b(i\Delta t)$ at time $i\Delta t$, respectively. Clearly,

$$p_b(i\Delta t) = p_b((i-1)\Delta t) + v((i-1)\Delta t)\Delta t$$

Now, the adaptive estimation algorithm can be defined as follows

$$
\begin{aligned}
\hat{v}(i\Delta t) &= \hat{v}((i-1)\Delta t) + \mu[p_b(i\Delta t) \\
&\quad - p_b((i-1)\Delta t) \\
&\quad - \hat{v}((i-1)\Delta t)\Delta t] \\
\hat{p}_b((i+1)\Delta t) &= p_b(i\Delta t) + \hat{v}(i\Delta t)\Delta t
\end{aligned}
\tag{2}
$$

where $\mu > 0$ is the gain. Note that $p_b(i\Delta t)$ and $p_b((i-1)\Delta t)$ are measurements, noises are unavoidable. Denoted the noise by $e(i\Delta t)$, the actual implemented algorithm is

$$
\begin{aligned}
\hat{v}(i\Delta t) &= \hat{v}((i-1)\Delta t) \\
&\quad + \mu[p_b(i\Delta t) - p_b((i-1)\Delta t) \\
&\quad + e(i\Delta t) - \hat{v}((i-1)\Delta t)\Delta t] \\
\hat{p}_b((i+1)\Delta t) &= p_b(i\Delta t) + \hat{v}(i\Delta t)\Delta t
\end{aligned}
$$

The hope is that $\hat{p}_b(i\Delta t)$ converges to $p_b(i\Delta t)$ if $e(i\Delta t), \delta = 0$ and is close to $p_b(i\Delta t)$ if $e(i\Delta t)$ and δ are not zero but small.

Let the estimation errors at time $i\Delta t$ be,

$$
\begin{aligned}
\tilde{v}(i\Delta t) &= \hat{v}(i\Delta t) - v(i\Delta t) \\
\tilde{p}_b(i\Delta t) &= \hat{p}_b(i\Delta t) - p_b(i\Delta t) \\
&= (p_b((i-1)\Delta t) + \hat{v}((i-1)\Delta t)\Delta t \\
&\quad -(p_b((i-1)\Delta t) - v((i-1\Delta t)\Delta t \\
&= \tilde{v}((i-1)\Delta t)\Delta t
\end{aligned}
$$

Then, the error equations are given by

$$
\begin{aligned}
\tilde{v}(i\Delta t) &= (1 - \mu\Delta t)\tilde{v}((i-1)\Delta t) + \Delta_i \\
&\quad + \mu e(i\Delta t) \\
\tilde{p}_b((i+1)\Delta t) &= (1 - \mu\Delta t)\tilde{p}_b(i\Delta t) + \Delta_i\Delta t \\
&\quad + \mu\Delta t e(i\Delta t)
\end{aligned}
$$

Consider the adaptive algorithm (2). Suppose $|1 - \mu\Delta t| < 1$. Then,

(1) In the absence of noise, the estimation error $\tilde{p}_b(k\Delta t)$ asymptotically satisfies

$$|\tilde{p}_b(k\Delta t)| \leq \frac{\delta}{\mu}$$

(2) If the noise is iid with zero mean and variance σ_e^2, then

$$|\mathbf{E}\tilde{p}_b(k\Delta t) \leq \frac{\delta}{\mu}$$

and

$$\mathbf{E}\tilde{p}_b(i\Delta t)^2 \leq (\frac{\delta}{\mu})^2 + \frac{\mu\Delta t\sigma_e^2}{2 - \mu\Delta t}$$

where $\mathbf{E}$ stands for the expectation operator.

Remarks:

(1) The estimate $\hat{p}_b(k\Delta t)$ is biased but the bias is very small ($\leq \frac{\delta}{\mu}$). This bias is unavoidable if the variations Δ_i's of v_k's unknown.

(2) To make the bias $\frac{\delta}{\mu}$ small $\Longrightarrow \mu$ large.

(3) To increase the convergence rate $\Longrightarrow 1-\mu\Delta t$ small $\Longrightarrow \mu\Delta t$ close to 1.

(4) To make $\frac{\mu\Delta t\sigma_e^2}{2-\mu\Delta t}$ small $\Longrightarrow \mu\Delta t$ small.

Thus, there is a compromise in choosing the gain μ. Once the estimate $\hat{v}_i$ is available, the next bolus position can be estimated

$$\hat{p}_b((i+1)\Delta t) = p_b(i\Delta t) + \hat{v}(i\Delta t)\Delta t$$

and the controller moves the table to $\hat{p}_b((i+1)\Delta t)$ at time $(i+1)\Delta t$ by setting

$$u(i\Delta t) = \hat{p}_b(i\Delta t + \Delta t)$$

The block diagram of overall control system is shown in Figure 4.

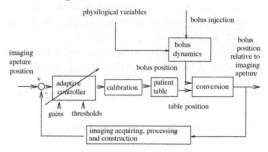

Fig. 3. Block diagram of the adaptive control

3.4 Nonlinear (extended Hammerstein) Model

The experiments results will show that the non-parametric model works well, in particular, in the diastole stages. In the aortic areas during the systole stages, however, the bolus velocity surges and this sudden jump may cause some tracking errors. To this end, a nonlinear (extended Hammerstein) model could be used which predicts the surges of the bolus. Let $s(i)$ denote the S phase of the ith ECG signal, the idea of the nonlinear model can be described as

$$\hat{p}_b(k\Delta t + dt) = \begin{cases} p_b(k\Delta t) & s(i)+q(i) \leq k \leq s(i+1) \\ p_b(k\Delta t)+c & s(i) = k < s(i)+q(i) \end{cases}$$

for some tunable variables $q(i)$ and c, where c captures the jumps of the bolus velocity during the systole stages. After a small time interval $q(i)$, the bolus becomes stationary again. On top of the increased complexity, a disadvantage of the nonlinear model is that it requires additional signals, e.g., ECG signals, to monitor and predict the arrival of the systole stages.

4. EXPERIMENTAL RESULTS

The proposed adaptive control algorithm based on the non-parametric model discussed in the previous section has been implemented on a prototype

Table 2. Tracking errors

Tracking errors (cm)	Constant velocity CTA		Adaptive CTA	
	Maximum	Mean	Maximum	Mean
Patient 1	19.63	9.18	1.33	0.07
Patient 2	7.09	4.22	1.89	0.20
Patient 3	4.97	2.95	1.09	0.34

CT scanner shown in Figure 5. This prototype consists of four elements: a Master Flex Pump 7550-30, a movable table controlled by a Vexta α stepping motor AS46, a Pulnix-6700 camera and a PC (personal computer). The pump is controlled by the PC that simulates a person's heart which drives the bolus through plastic tubings. The bolus velocity can be arbitrarily assigned by computer programs. The stepping motor takes commands from the PC through a serial port. This simulates the patient table. The camera, connected to the PC by a PCI card, provides the real time bolus peak position that simulates the CT imaging device. The imaging acquiring and processing are carried by NI IMAQ VISION DEVELOPMENT MODULES. In fact, all the algorithms are implemented by using the NI Labview software which is widely available.

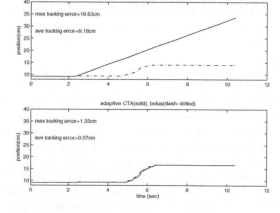

Fig. 5. Experimental setup

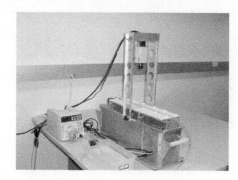

Fig. 4. Patient 1

To carry out the experiments and compare the proposed adaptive control techniques with the current constant velocity CTA technology, actual bolus propagation data sets were collected from

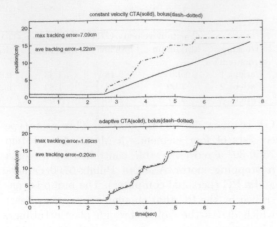

Fig. 5. Patient 2

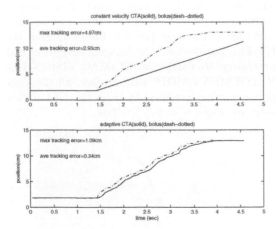

Fig. 6. Patient 3

8 patients. Then, the collected actual bolus positions and velocities were implemented on the prototype CT scanner with the proposed adaptive techniques and the current constant velocity CTA technology respectively. For the current constant CTA, a constant velocity must be pre-determined before CT. In the experiment, an velocity of 30mm per second was used which is typical in practice. Figures 7-14 show experimental results for all 8 patients. In all figures, the actual bolus peak positions are described by dash-dotted lines. The top diagrams are the CT table positions in solid lines based on the current constant velocity technology. The bottom diagrams are the CT table positions in solid lines using the proposed adaptive scheme. It is clear that with the constant velocity, the CT table follows the bolus peak poorly that results in large tracking errors. On the other hand, the proposed adaptive CTA follows the unknown bolus peak satisfactorily as predicted. This translates into a better quality imaging and a reduction in contrast injection and radiation exposure. The Table 2 summaries the tracking errors for each patient.

5. CONCLUDING REMARKS

In this paper, theoretical and experimental results have been obtained for adaptive control of a next generation of CT scanner. The control scheme combines the imaging techniques, adaptive estimation algorithms and controls. The experimental data shows that the bolus position can be accurately estimated and tracked by using a simple non-parametric model which does not requires much computations. Currently, the proposed method is being implemented on a Toshiaba Cliker CT scanner.

REFERENCES

Bae, KT., JP. Heiken and JA. Brink (1998). Aortic and hepatic contrast medium enhancement at ct: Part iii. effect of contrast medium injection rate - pharmacokinetic analysis and experimental porcine model.. *Radiology* **207**, 647–655.

Bassingthwaighte, FH. Ackerman and EH. Wood (1966). Application of the lagged normal density curve as a model for arterial dilution curves. *Circulation Research* **XVIII**, 398–415.

Rubin, GD., DS. Paik, PC. Johnston and S. Napel (1998). Measurement of the aorta and its branches with helical ct. *Radiology* **206**, 823–829.

Sheafor, DH., MT. Keogan, DM. DeLong and RC. Nelson (1998). Dynamic helical ct of the abdomen: Prospective comparison of pre- and postprandial contrast enhancement. *Radiology* **206**, 359–363.

Tublin, ME., FN. Tessler, SL. Cheng, TL. Peters and PC. McGovern (1999). Effect of injection rate of contrast medium on pancreatic and hepatic helical ct. *Radiology* **210**, 97–101.

Wang, G., CR. Crawford and WA. Kalender (2000a). Multirow detector and cone-beam spiral/helical ct. *IEEE Trans. Med. Imaging* **19**, 817–821.

Wang, G., G. Raymond, Y. Li, D. Schweiger, K. Sharafuddin, A. Stolpen, S. Yang, Z. Li, J. Bassingthwaighte, B. James and M. Vannier (2000b). A model on intervenous bolus propagation for optimization of contrast enhancement. *Proceedings of SPIE - The International Society for Optical Engineering* **3978**, 436–447.

Wang, G., GM Raymond, Y. Li, GD. Schweiger, MJ. Sharafuddin, AH. Stolpen and et al (2000c). A model of intravenous bolus propagation for optimization of contrast enhancement. *SPIE*.

NONLINEAR CONTROL OF HIV-1 INFECTION
WITH A SINGULAR PERTURBATION MODEL

M. Barão* J. M. Lemos**

INESC-ID/Univ. of Évora, Lisboa, Portugal,
mjsb@ramses.inesc.pt
**INESC-ID/IST, Lisboa, Portugal, jlml@inesc.pt*

Abstract: Using singular perturbation techniques, a nonlinear state-space model of HIV-1 infection, having as state variables the number of healthy and infected CD4+ T cells and the number of virion particles, is simplified and used to design a control law. The control law comprises an inner block that performs feedback linearizing of the virus dynamics and an outer block implementing an LQ regulator that drives the number of virion particles to a number below the specification. A sensitivity analysis of the resulting law is performed. *Copyright © 2006 IFAC*

Keywords: HIV-1, feedback linearizing control, singular perturbations

1. INTRODUCTION

Strategies for the counteracting of HIV infection designed using control methods are receiving an increased attention. Detailed studies show that the initial infection phase may be represented using simple nonlinear state models (Perelson and Nelson, 1999). This fact boosted the production of an increasing number of papers where therapy strategies are derived from control principles. Examples include nonlinear control using decomposition in strict feedback form and backstepping (Gee *et al.*, 2005), state drive using bang-bang control (Chang *et al.*, 2004), adaptive control (Cheng and Chang, 2004) and Optimal Control (de Souza *et al.*, 2000).

This paper proposes a strategy which combines model reduction using singular perturbations, feedback linearization and LQ regulation. A robustness study is performed with respect to model parameter variation.

The paper is organized as follows. After this introduction, the reduced complexity model is derived in section 2. Section 3 characterizes reduced model properties, *viz.* equilibrium points and controlla-

bility. Section 4 presents feedback linearization and section 5 the control strategy. Section 6 draws conclusions.

2. HIV-1 DYNAMIC MODEL

The model used to describe the HIV-1 infection (Craig *et al.*, 2004) is a deterministic model with the following three state variables: x_1, Concentration of healthy cells; x_2, Concentration of infected cells; x_3, Concentration of virions (free virus particles). The equations connecting these variables read as follows:

$$\dot{x}_1 = s - dx_1 - (1 - u_1)\beta x_1 x_3$$
$$\dot{x}_2 = (1 - u_1)\beta x_1 x_3 - \mu x_2 \qquad (1)$$
$$\dot{x}_3 = (1 - u_2)kx_2 - cx_3.$$

In the first equation, s represents the production rate of healthy cells, the coefficient d the natural death of the cells and β the infection rate coefficient. The infection rate of healthy cells is proportional to the product of healthy cells x_1 and free virus x_3. This process can be influenced by drugs (Reverse Transcriptase Inhibitors) that reduce the virus performance. This influence is

Parameter	Value	Units
d	0.02	s^{-1}
k	100	s^{-1}
s	10	$mm^{-3}s^{-1}$
β	2.4×10^{-5}	$mm^{3}s^{-1}$
μ	0.24	s^{-1}
c	2.4	s^{-1}

Table 1. Model parameters.

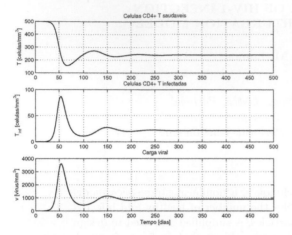

Fig. 1. Time response to an infection without medication

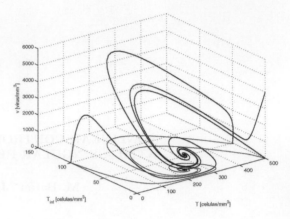

Fig. 2. State trajectories, starting from different initial conditions and their projections on the plane $[T, T_{inf}]$.

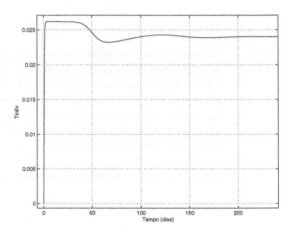

Fig. 3. Time evolution of the relation x_2/x_3.

represented by the manipulated variable u_1, in which $u_1 = 0$ corresponds to absence of drug and $u_1 = 1$ to a drug efficiency in preventing infection of 100%. Actually, with the available drugs, the efficiency is below 100%, and u_1 is constrained to the interval $[0, u_{\max}]$ with $u_{max} < 1$. The second equation comprises two terms that represent, respectively, the transition of healthy cells to infected cells and the death of infected cells. An infected cell liberates free virus. This process is represented in the third equation, where the first term represents the liberation of virus by infected cells and the second the "death" of free virus. The manipulated variable u_2 represents the action of drugs (Protease Inhibitors – PI) that prevent infected cells to produce free virions.

Figure 1 shows the transient time response to an HIV-1 infection. The parameters used (Craig *et al.*, 2004) are the ones of table 1. The initial conditions correspond to an healthy person infected with a virus concentration of 1 copy per mm^3.

Figure 2 shows some state trajectories obtained with different initial infection conditions (together with their projections on the $[x_1, x_2]$ plane. Although not all the initial conditions correspond to realistic infections, this plot provides insight into the type of dynamic behavior of (1).

In particular, it is seen that the trajectories approach fast a plane before converging in spiral to an equilibrium point. This observation reveals the existence of two time scales for the system states, one fast and one slow, and suggests the use of

Singular Perturbation methods. After the extinction of the fast transient, the variables x_2 and x_3 become approximately proportional. Figure 3 shows the relation x_2/x_3, where it is apparent that, after a transient lasting about 2 or 3 days, the quotient of these variables is close to 0.024 with an initial small deviation.

2.1 Reduced dynamic model

By looking at the third state equation in x_3 it is seen that this defines a stable linear system with input x_2 and time constant $\tau_v = 1/c \approx 0.42$ days. The equilibrium corresponds to the solution of the equation

$$0 = (1 - u_2)kx_2 - cx_3 \qquad (2)$$

or

$$x_3 = (1 - u_2)\frac{k}{c}x_2 \qquad (3)$$

Since this equation is stable and converges fast to the equilibrium, the controller does not need to control this equation explicitly and the model can be reduced to a second order model.

Equilibrium point:	$\begin{bmatrix} 240.0000 & 21.6667 \end{bmatrix}^T$
Eigenvalues:	$-0.0208 \pm 0.0690j$
Stability:	asymptotically stable
Equilibrium point:	$\begin{bmatrix} 500.0000 & 0.0000 \end{bmatrix}^T$
Eigenvalues:	$-0.0200, \quad 0.2600$
Stability:	unstable

Table 2. Stability of the equilibrium points of the reduced model.

Replacing (3) in the state model (1), and assuming just one manipulated variable, yields the reduced second order model:

$$\dot{x}_1 = s - dx_1 - (1-u)\frac{\beta k}{c} x_1 x_2$$
$$\dot{x}_2 = (1-u)\frac{\beta k}{c} x_1 x_2 - \mu x_2. \tag{4}$$

3. MODEL PROPERTIES

3.1 Equilibrium points

The analysis of equilibrium points and corresponding stability properties of the full model (1) has been performed in (Craig et al., 2004). The reduced model is considered hereafter.

In the absence of therapy, $u = 0$, the reduced model has as equilibrium points the solutions of the algebraic equations

$$0 = s - dx_1 - (1-u)\frac{\beta k}{c} x_1 x_2 \tag{5}$$

$$0 = (1-u)\frac{\beta k}{c} x_1 x_2 - \mu x_2. \tag{6}$$

with respect to the state variables x_1 and x_2. These equilibrium points are

$$x_1 = \frac{s}{d}, \quad x_2 = 0 \tag{7}$$

corresponding to an healthy person, and

$$x_1 = \frac{\mu c}{\beta k(1-u)}, \quad x_2 = \frac{s}{\mu} - \frac{dc}{\beta k(1-u)} \tag{8}$$

corresponding to an infected individual.

The stability analysis of these equilibrium points is made by computing the eigenvalues of the Jacobian matrix $\tilde{A} = \partial f / \partial x$, given by

$$\tilde{A} = \begin{bmatrix} -d - \dfrac{\beta k}{c} x_2 & -\dfrac{\beta k}{c} x_2 \\ \dfrac{\beta k}{c} x_2 & \dfrac{\beta k}{c} x_1 - \mu \end{bmatrix}_{x=x_{eq}} \tag{9}$$

By using the model parameters of table 1, the results of table 2 are obtained. These results are similar to the ones obtained for the full model, but in which the fast mode is absent.

3.2 Controlability

The reduced nonlinear model (4), may also be written as

$$\dot{x} = f(x) + g(x)u \tag{10}$$

with obvious definitions for the vector functions f and g. It can be linearized around an equilibrium point (x_1^*, x_2^*) yielding a linear model $\dot{x} = Ax + Bu$. The corresponding controllability matrix is given by

$$C = \begin{bmatrix} B & AB \end{bmatrix} = \frac{\beta k}{c} x_1 x_2 \begin{bmatrix} 1 & -d - \dfrac{\beta k}{c}(x_2 - x_1) \\ -1 & \dfrac{\beta k}{c}(x_2 - x_1) + \mu \end{bmatrix} \tag{11}$$

and it is seen that

$$\text{rank}(C) = \begin{cases} 2 \text{ if } d \neq \mu, & x_1 \neq 0, & x_2 \neq 0 \\ 1 \text{ if } d = \mu, & x_1 \neq 0, & x_2 \neq 0 \\ 0 \text{ if } x_1 = 0 \text{ or } x_2 = 0 \end{cases} \tag{12}$$

Since $d \neq \mu$ and $x_1 > 0$, it is concluded that the controllability matrix has rank 2 for $x_2 \neq 0$ (infected individual) and rank 0 for $x_2 = 0$ (healthy individual).

When the linearized system is not controllable, it may still be possible to control the nonlinear system. The controllability analysis of a nonlinear system is much more complex than in the linear case and, since there are no global results, the controllability in the non-linear case can only be studied locally.

The reachable set $R^V(x_0, T)$, with T finite, is defined as the set of states x for which there is an admissible control input $u(t)$ that drives the state $x(t)$ from the initial state $x(0) = x_0$ t0 the final state $x(T) = x$, satisfying simultaneously $x(t) \in V, t \in [0, T]$. It is proved in (Nijmeijer and van der Schaft, 1990) that if, for a given x_0, the Lie algebra $C(x_0)$ generates a space of dimension n then, in any neighborhood V of x_0 and $T > 0$, the reachable set $R_T^V(x_0) = \cup_{\tau < T} R^V(x_0, \tau)$ contains a non-empty open subset of the state pace. In this case the system is said to be locally reachable from x_0.

In (12), and under realistic conditions, it can be verified that for $x_2 \neq 0$ the local linearization is controllable, and the doubt remains only on the situation in which $x_2 = 0$. The following question may then be posed: Is there any state x with $x_2 \neq 0$ such that the reachable set from that state contains a final state with $x_2 = 0$? In clinical terms, this question reads: Is it possible that an individual, once infected, gets again rid of the infection? The answer to this question is negative, as shown bellow.

Computing the Lie Algebra in all the points of the state space with $x_2 \neq 0$ it is seen that the accessibility rank condition is 2 (it is enough to verify that $f(x)$ and $g(x)$ are linearly independent), and hence this region is locally reachable. On the other way, computing the Lie Algebra for the states $x = (x_1, 0)$, and since, for these states

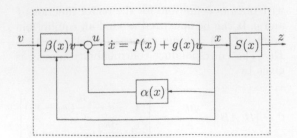

Fig. 4. Feedback linearization

$$f(x) = \begin{bmatrix} 10 - 0.02x_1 & 0 \end{bmatrix}' \qquad (13)$$
$$g(x) = \mathbf{0} \qquad (14)$$

all the Lie brackets of higher order vanish and the rank reachability condition is 1. The nonlinear system is then locally non-reachable in the region $\{x | x_2 = 0\}$, meaning that it is not possible to pass an healthy individual to the state of being infected by drug administration (a fact that is expected).

Much more interesting is to prove that there is not a trajectory in the opposite sense. By considering the second state equation in (4)

$$\dot{x}_2 = \underbrace{(1 - u)}_{>0} \underbrace{\frac{\beta k}{c}}_{>0} \underbrace{x_1 x_2}_{\geq 0} - \mu x_2 \qquad (15)$$

it is observed that, since the first term is non-negative, then x_2 never vanishes and, hence, it is never possible to eliminate the infection.

4. FEEDBACK LINEARIZATION

The system is not linearizable by performing a state transformation only. However, it is possible to yield a linear system by the combined use of the transformations $u = \alpha(x) + \beta(x)v$ and $z = S(x)$, obtaining the linear system

$$\dot{z} = Az + Bv. \qquad (16)$$

with the structure

$$\dot{z} = \begin{bmatrix} 0 & 1 & & 0 \\ & & \ddots & \\ & & & 1 \\ 0 & \cdots & \cdots & 0 \end{bmatrix} z + \begin{bmatrix} 0 \\ \vdots \\ 0 \\ 1 \end{bmatrix} v. \qquad (17)$$

Figure 4 shows a block diagram of these transformations.

In the case at hand, it can be shown (details are omitted due to lack of space) that the transformations performing linearization are

$$\beta(x) = \frac{c}{\beta k x_1 x_2 (\mu - d)} \qquad (18)$$

$$\alpha(x) = \frac{-ds + d^2 x_1 + \mu^2 x_2 + (d - \mu)\frac{\beta k}{c} x_1 x_2}{(d - \mu)\frac{\beta k}{c} x_1 x_2} \qquad (19)$$

$$S(x) = \begin{bmatrix} \varphi(x) \\ s - dx_1 - \mu x_2 \end{bmatrix} \qquad (20)$$

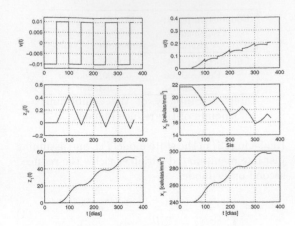

Fig. 5. Time response of the linearized system to a virtual rectangular system (virtual signal on the left, actual signal on the right).

With these transformations, the system around x_0 is transformed in the linear system (17). Figure 5 shows the response of the linearized system to a rectangular virtual input (*i. e.* the input v before the transform). This simulation assumes that all parameters are exactly known and the transform is applied to the full model (1).

It is remarked that, during the initial period, the signal $v(t)$ is negative and causes $u(t)$ to saturate. for that reason, the linearized system does not behave like a double integrator during that interval of time.

5. HIV-1 VIRAL LOAD CONTROL

This section shows how to develop a control law for the system linearized by feedback. This is done both under the hypothesis of perfect (in the first stage) and partial knowledge of the system parameters.

5.1 Control with known parameters.

Assume that the concentration of infected cells x_2 is to be driven to a reference value r and kept there. At the equilibrium defined by $x_2 = r$ one has

$$(1 - u) = \frac{\mu dc}{\beta k(s - \mu r)} \qquad (21)$$

and

$$x_1 = \frac{s - \mu r}{d} \qquad (22)$$

In terms of the linearized system (that operates with transformed variables) this results in the equilibrium point $z = S(x)$, *i. e.*:

$$\begin{bmatrix} z_1 \\ z_2 \end{bmatrix} = \begin{bmatrix} \frac{s - \mu r}{d} + r + \frac{c}{\beta k}(d - \mu) - \frac{s}{\mu} \\ 0 \end{bmatrix} =: T(r) \qquad (23)$$

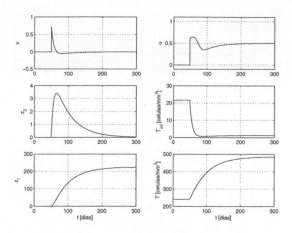

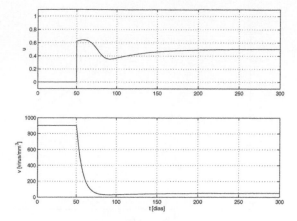

Fig. 6. Changing the reference in the number of infected cells.

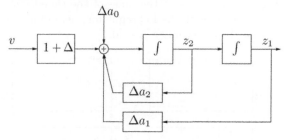

Fig. 7. Evolution of viral load.

It is then possible to design a LQ controller, using the linearized dynamics, that keeps the system at the desired reference value r.

The transformation $T(r)$ allows to compute the equilibrium point in terms of the variables (z_1, z_2). The controller is designed by minimizing the quadratic cost:

$$J = \int_0^{+\infty} z^T Q_z z + \rho v^2 \mathrm{d}t \qquad (24)$$

where Q_z and ρ adjust the contribution of the variables $z(t)$ and $v(t)$. Since these variables are virtual (corresponding to transformed states) it is difficult to develop heuristic choices of their values. Thus it was decided to adjust the weights Q_x for the state variables x and then compute the corresponding Q_z. Using a linear approximation, it is possible to show that

$$Q_z = \left(\frac{\partial S^{-1}}{\partial z}\right)^T Q_x \left(\frac{\partial S^{-1}}{\partial z}\right). \qquad (25)$$

With the following choice of the weights

$$Q_x = \begin{bmatrix} 0.01 & 0 \\ 0 & 23 \end{bmatrix}, \qquad \rho = 10^3 \qquad (26)$$

the results shown in figures 6 and 7 are obtained. The simulation has been performed using the full, third order, model. Figure 6 shows in the three left graphics the variables of the linearized system (virtual input v and states z_1, z_2), and on the three graphics of the right the actual variables (input u and states x_1, x_2). Fig. 7 shows the body concentration of free virus. Its value decays fast, such as the one of infected cells, as shown in fig. 6. The specification consists in reducing the number of virus to 50 copies per mm^3 in a period of less then 50 days.

5.2 Control with uncertain parameters

Consider now the problem of control design by feedback linearization in the presence of struc-

Fig. 8. *Quasi*-linearized system (Remark that with $\Delta = 0$ the double integrator is recovered).

tured uncertainty in the model. Assume that there is multiplicative uncertainty in parameter β, *i. e.*, the actual system uses $\beta(1+\Delta)$, with Δ unknown, while the linearization assumes the nominal model ($\Delta = 0$). Thus, the actual model is described by the state equation

$$\dot{x} = f(x, \Delta) + g(x, \Delta)u \qquad (27)$$

while the linearization uses the nominal model given by

$$\dot{x} = f(x, 0) + g(x, 0)u \qquad (28)$$

By applying the feedback linearization transformations yielded by the nominal model in the actual model, it is expected that the final result is no longer exactly a double integrator. In this case the following "*quasi*-linearized system" is obtained:

$$\begin{aligned} \dot{z}_1 &= z_2 \\ \dot{z}_2 &= v + \Delta \left(a_0 + a_1 z_1 + a_2 z_2 + v\right) \end{aligned} \qquad (29)$$

where

$$\begin{aligned} a_0 &= \frac{d\mu c}{\beta k} - s \\ a_1 &= d\mu \\ a_2 &= d + \mu \end{aligned} \qquad (30)$$

Figure 8 shows the structure of the system thereby obtained.

The additional term due to the uncertainty Δ does not change the linear characteristic of the *quasi*-linearized system. There is only a pole displace-

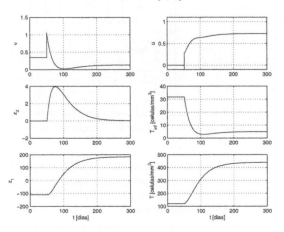

Fig. 9. Root-locus of the poles of the closed loop system (with the LQ regulator), as a function of the uncertainty $\Delta \in [0, 2]$.

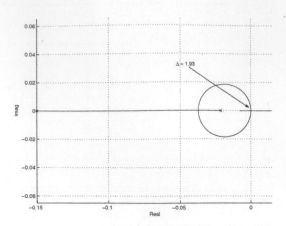

Fig. 10. Control performance with uncertainty on the parameter β. ($\Delta = 1$, *i. e.*, the true β is twice the nominal value).

ment, variation of the loop gain and an additive disturbance at the input.

In closed-loop, and with the LQ regulator designed above the closed loop podes are as in fig. 9.

It is possible to compute analytically that the closed-loop remaisn stable for values of $\Delta \in$ $]-1, 1.93[$. This ensures the robustness of the controller design with rrespect to uncertainty on parameter β. Figures 10 and 11 show simulations with $\Delta = 1$ and $\Delta = -0.5$.

6. CONCLUSION

The paper studies nonlinear control of HIV-1 infection. Using singular perturbation methods, a reduced model is first obtained and used to show that it is not possible to completely eliminate the infection resorting only to the available manipulated variable.

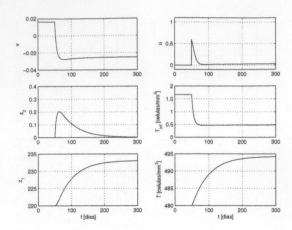

Fig. 11. DControl performance with uncertainty on the parameter β. ($\Delta = -0.5$, *i. e.*, the true, β is half the nominal value).

In order to constrain the infection level to be bellow a specified level (50 virus copies/mm^3 in the plasma) a nonlinear controller is proposed, comprising two nested loops. The inner loop performs the exact feedback linearization of the system, while the outer loop is a LQ regulator.

A sensitivity study of the effect of the variations of one of the parameters has been performed, showing that the closed-loop system remains stable within reasonably large bounds of uncertainty.

REFERENCES

Chang, H. J., H. Shim and J. H. Seo (2004). Control of immune response of hiv infection model by gradual reduction of drug dose. *Conference on Decision and Control*.

Cheng, C.-F. and C.-T. Chang (2004). Viral load analysis of a biodynamical model of hiv-1 with unknown equilibrium points. *Proc. 2004 IEEE Int. Conf. Control Applications, Taipei, Taiwan* pp. 557–561.

Craig, I., X. Xia and J. Venter (2004). Introducing hiv/aids education into electrical engineering curriculum at the university of pretoria. *IEEE Trans. on Education* **47**(1), 65–73.

de Souza, J. F., M. Caetano and T. Yoneyama (2000). Optimal control applied to the antiviral treatment of aids. *Proc. 39th IEEE CDC, Sydney, Australia* pp. 4839–4844.

Gee, S., Z. Tian and T. Lee (2005). Nonlinear control of a dynamikc model of hiv-1. *IEEE Trans. Biomedical Eng.* **52**(3), 353–361.

Nijmeijer, Henk and Arjan van der Schaft (1990). *Nonlinear Dynamical Control Systems*. Springer-Verlag.

Perelson, A. and P. Nelson (1999). Mathematical analysis of hiv-1 dynamics in vivo. *SIAM Review* **41**(1), 3–44.

INSULIN + NUTRITION CONTROL
FOR TIGHT CRITICAL CARE GLYCAEMIC REGULATION

**J. Geoffrey Chase*, Jason Wong*, Jessica Lin*, Aaron LeCompte*,
Thomas Lotz*, Timothy Lonergan*, Michael Willacy*,
Christopher E. Hann[*] and Geoffrey M. Shaw****

*Centre for Bioengineering, University of Canterbury, Christchurch, New Zealand
***Department of Intensive Care Medicine, Christchurch Hospital,
Christchurch, New Zealand*

Abstract: A new insulin and nutrition control method for tight glycaemic control in
critical care is presented from concept to clinical trials to clinical practice change. The
primary results show that the method can provide very tight glycaemic control in critical
care for a very critically ill cohort. More specifically, the final clinical practice change
protocol provided 2100 hours of control with average blood glucose of 5.8 +/- 0.9
mmol/L for an initial 10 patient pilot study. It also used less insulin, while providing the
same or greater nutritional input, as compared to retrospective hospital control for a
relatively very critically ill cohort with high insulin resistance. *Copyright © 2006 IFAC*

Keywords: Biomedical Control, Control Algorithms, Non-Linear Models, Physiological
Models, Physiology, Medical Systems.

1. INTRODUCTION

Hyperglycaemia is prevalent in critical care, and
worsens outcomes, increasing the risk of severe
infection, myocardial infarction, neuropathy, and
multiple organ failure (Krinsley, 2003; Van den
Berghe *et al.*, 2001). Tight glucose control can
reduce mortality by up to 45%. However, insulin-
mediated control, is severely challenged in critical
care by very high effective insulin resistance
(McCowen *et al.*, 2001; Mizock, 2001).
Glycaemic reductions are thus limited by insulin
effect saturation at high concentrations (Prigeon *et
al.*, 1996). Next, high glucose content nutritional
support exacerbates hyperglycaemia (Weissman,
1999) and studies with lower glucose nutrition
alone saw large reductions in glucose levels
(Patino *et al.*, 1999).

2. MODELS and METHODS

This research presents the development of an
insulin nutrition method for tight glycaemic
control in critical care. First, a virtual cohort is
used to develop the method in simulation. Second,
the methods are tested in limited proof of concept
clinical trials. Finally, a paper-based method that

mimics the computerised controller is introduced
as a clinical practice change for long-term testing
to validate the overall concept.

2.1 Control Model

Chase et al (2005a) used a system model that that
included insulin utilisation, losses and saturation.

$$\dot{G} = -p_G G - S_I (G + G_E)\frac{Q}{1+\alpha_G Q} + P(t) \quad (1)$$

$$\dot{Q} = -kQ + kI \quad (2)$$

$$\dot{I} = -\frac{nI}{1+\alpha_I I} + \frac{u_{ex}(t)}{V} \quad (3)$$

$$P(t_i < t < t_{i+1}) = \overline{P}_{i+1} + (\overline{P}_i - \overline{P}_{i+1})e^{-k_{pd}(t-t_i)} \text{ where } \overline{P}_{i+1} < \overline{P}_i \quad (4)$$

$$P(t_i < t < t_{i+1}) = \overline{P}_{i+1} + (\overline{P}_i - \overline{P}_{i+1})e^{-k_{pr}(t-t_i)} \text{ where } \overline{P}_{i+1} > \overline{P}_i \quad (5)$$

where $G(t)$ [mmol/L] is the plasma glucose above
an equilibrium level, G_E [mmol/L]. $I(t)$ [mmol/L]
is plasma insulin concentration resulting from
exogenous insulin input, $u_{ex}(t)$ [mU/min]. $Q(t)$
[mU/L] is interstitial insulin concentration and k
[1/min] accounts for the effective life of insulin in
the system. Patient endogenous glucose clearance
and insulin sensitivity are p_G [1/min] and S_I

[L/(mU.min)], respectively. V [L] is the insulin distribution volume and n [1/min] is the constant first order decay rate for insulin from plasma. Total plasma glucose input is denoted $P(t)$ [mmol/(L.min)]. k_{pr} is the rise rate of rate of plasma glucose input from enterally administered feed [1/min]. k_{pd} is the decay rate of rate of glucose input into plasma from enterally administered feed [1/min]. $\overline{P}_i$, $\overline{P}_{i+1}$ are stepwise consecutive enteral glucose feed rates [mmol/L.min]. Michaelis-Menten functions model saturation, with α_I [L/mU] for the saturation of plasma insulin disappearance, and α_G [L/mU] for the saturation of insulin-dependent glucose clearance. In this research, k, n, α_G, α_I and V are identified from generic population values. Details of the model, its development, and control analyses presented for it and similar models models can be found in (Chase, et al., 2005a).

2.2 Control Method

In this study, non-steady stepwise enteral glucose fluxes are employed for control and modelled using the 2-compartment model in Eqs. (4-5). The exponential rates for total glucose rate of appearance (GRa) rise (k_{pr}) and decay (k_{pd}) model the effect of transient net hepatic glucose output and glucose disposal. Impaired splanchnic and peripheral glucose uptake imply a slow decay rate in total GRa following nutritional feed reduction (Kiwanuka et al., 2001). Conversely, the rate of peripheral appearance of oral glucose is approximately equal to the intestinal absorption rate, implying a rapid rise following a nutritional increase (Radziuk et al., 1978). Thus, k_{pr} and k_{pd} are set to $0.0347\,min^{-1}$ and $0.0068\,min^{-1}$ (half-lives of 20 and 100mins) to reflect this data.

The controller targets 10-15% hourly glycaemic reduction to 5mmol/L using a combination of insulin bolus, infusion and/or feed rate change. The goal is blood glucose in the 4-6mmol/L band. Thus, insulin sensitivity, S_I, is fitted from the prior hours' data before each intervention (Hann et al., 2005) and endogenous clearance, p_G, is set to $0.01\,min^{-1}$, a value found to be insensitive across this type of cohort (Hann et al., 2005). Finally, the required combination of insulin bolus, insulin infusion rate and/or nutritional feed rate to achieve the hourly target glucose is determined iteratively using the updated S_I, value and Eqs. (1)-(5).

2.3 Virtual Cohort and Simulated Trials

The patient cohort includes 17 patients from a 201 patient data audit plus 2 patients from a hyperglycaemia control clinical trial (Chase et al., 2005b). It represents a general cross-section of ICU population, in medical subgroup, APACHE II score, age, sex and mortality. Each record has glucose measurements every 3h or less. The average length is 3.9 days (range: 1.4-18.8). The

cohort details are in Table 1. Ethical consent was granted by the Canterbury Ethics Committee.

Virtual trials use the retrospective fitted patient profiles of S_I and p_G, to simulate physiological patient response. It assumes these parameters are independent of the control inputs administered, creating a virtual patient response for any glucose or insulin inputs. Normally distributed error of ±7% is added to measured glucose values to include typical glucometer measurement error.

Table 1: Long-Term Virtual Trial Patient Cohort

Patient number	Medical subgroup	Apache II score	Age	Sex	Mortality	Diabetes
1	Sepsis	17	56	M		Type 2
2	Sepsis	24	64	M		
24	Other medical	25	47	M	Y	Type 1
87	Other medical	26	62	F		
130	Trauma	11	21	M		Type 1
229	Cardiac	15	73	F		
289	Cardiac	18	70	M		
468	General surgical	32	76	M		
484	Other medical	34	30	F		
486	General surgical	22	76	F		Type 2
519	General surgical	29	69	M		Type 2
554	Other medical	26	20	F		Type 1
666	Cardiac	8	44	F		Type 2
847	Other medical	17	67	F		
1016	General surgical	20	37	F		Type 2
1025	Pulmonary	36	48	M		Type 2
1090	General surgical	Unknown	37	F		
1099	Pulmonary	Unknown	24	M	Y	
1125	Other medical	Unknown	72	F	Y	

Each patient is tested using the control method. Results are compared to retrospective hospital data and an insulin-only control protocol (Chase et al., 2005a). The control method uses three basic steps:

- Measure glucose every 30 minutes
- Every hour fit SI based on prior hours data
- Determine the insulin and nutritional changes to meet target reduction

Frequent measurement ensures tight control and safety. Hence, these trials are used for proof of concept testing of the insulin plus nutrition control concept. Less frequent measurement would be required for long-term clinical care.

2.4 Clinical Trials Method

The methods developed virtually are tested in short 10-hour proof-of-concept trials and one 24-hour trial. Inclusion criteria: in situ enteral feeding tube; random glucose level >8mmol/L; age >16 years; and an in situ cannula. Exclusion criteria: delayed gastric emptying; moribund; neuromuscular blockade; and morbid obesity (BMI>35kgm^{-2}).

Patients are fed enterally with RESOURCE™ Diabetic (Novartis Medical Nutrition, USA) up to 700kcal/day of glucose using a Ross Products Patrol Enteral Pump (Abbott Laboratories, Abbott Park, Illinois, U.S.A.). Actrapid™ insulin (Novo Nordisk, Bagsvaerd, Denmark) is infused with a 3500 syringe pump (Graseby Medical Limited, Colonial Way, Herts, UK). Ethical approval was obtained from the Canterbury Ethics Committee.

The overall trial protocol is shown in Figure 1. During the 2-hour pre-trial period, the insulin infusion is kept constant to estimate the onboard insulin level in steady state. The blood glucose level at 0900h is taken as the equilibrium blood glucose, G_E. At 0900h, feed rate is decreased by 30-40% depending on current glucose level and feed rate as an initial challenge. Hourly glucose targets are set for a 10-15% reduction to a 5mmol/L minimum. Insulin sensitivity, S_I, is re-evaluated every hour using the prior hours' data. The controller prescribes insulin bolus size, insulin infusion rate, and feed rate to achieve the target.

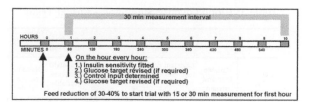

Fig.1: Clinical Trial Procedure

Note that glucose is only measured hourly for the 24-hour trial. This trial tests the ability of the controller to use less frequent measurements as a final step towards clinical, long-term testing.

Insulin is limited to 6U/hr to minimise saturation and saturated, ineffective insulin is limited to 30mU/L. The minimum feed rate is 280kcal/day of glucose or 40% of maximum for a total caloric intake of 778kcal/day (Novartis, 2005). This level exceeds the level found to avoid increased risk of bloodstream infections (Rubinson *et al.*, 2004).

2.5 Clinical Trials Cohort

The clinical trial patient cohort ($n = 8$) represents a heterogeneous cross-section in age and sex, as shown in Table 2. The median APACHE II score is 23 with inter-quartile range [19, 25]. The mean age is 64.8 ± 7.8 years.

Table 2: Clinical Trial Patient Cohort

Patient number	Medical subgroup	APACHE II score	APACHE II ROD (%)	APACHE III	SAPS II	SAPS II ROD (%)	Age	Sex	Mortality	Diabetes
1	Sepsis	17	14.3	40	15	2	56	M	N	Type 2
2	Sepsis	24	49.7	59	35	16.7	64	M	N	
3	Pulmonary	31	73.3	85	45	34.8	60	M	N	
4	Sepsis	26	59.7	91	62	71.9	75	F	N	
5	Sepsis	21	33.2	58	34	15.3	73	M	N	Type 2
6	Other medical	17	14.3	44	44	32.6	57	M	N	
7	General surgical	23	62.3	84	57	61.9	73	F	N	Type 2
8	Other medical			Not available			60	M	N	

2.6 Long-term Testing – The SPRINT Protocol

The clinical methods are developed and tested, first virtually and then in short proof of concept case studies. The final step is long-term clinical testing of this nutrition and insulin control approach. However, the measurement frequency must be reduced to 1-2 hourly for clinical ease of use. In addition, the methods must be removed from a computer and made paper based for easy uptake by clinical staff.

The SPRINT (Specialised Relative Insulin Nutrition Tables) protocol is designed to nearly exactly mimic the computerised trial protocol, as an easy-to-use equivalent. It consists of two wheels dedicated to enteral nutrition and insulin bolus administration, as shown in Figure 2. Instructions are printed on the wheels and hourly blood glucose measurements are used to determine the next hour's intervention.

The instructions on the "Feed Wheel" are used to determine the rate of feed as a percentage of the patient's clinically determined goal feed. The result is based on the previous hour's feed level, the current blood glucose concentration and whether blood glucose is rising or falling. The percentage goal feed is converted into an absolute feed rate (in ml/hr) using a patient-specific conversion sticker. The "Insulin Wheel" is then used to determine the insulin bolus size based on the previous insulin bolus size, the current blood glucose level and whether the blood glucose has decreased by more than 1.5mmol/L. The method is effectively fully automated once clinical staff take the hourly glucose measurement.

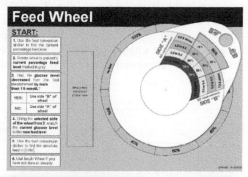

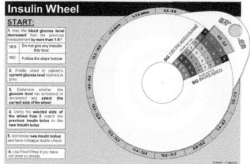

Fig.2: SPRINT feed and insulin wheels.

Hourly blood glucose measurements are used to ensure tight control. Two-hourly measurements are used when the patient is stable, defined as 3 consecutive measurements in the 4-6 mmol/L band. For two-hourly measurements, the feed rate is maintained and the same insulin bolus administered on the hour between measurements. Two-hourly measurements are continued until the patient leaves the 4-6 mmol/L band. SPRINT is stopped when the patient is stable, and normoglycaemic, defined as 6 or more hours in the 4-6.1mmol/L band, with over 80% of goal feed rate and a maximum of 2U per hour of insulin. Finally, insulin is always administered via bolus for patient safety, avoiding infusions being left on.

The specific wheel layout resulted from extensive consultation. ICU staff were proficient in minutes and reported the system as very easy to use. A nursing survey reported that 25 of 27 respondents viewed the wheels as satisfactory or better, with 13 rating it very good or higher. The covered wheel reduces table complexity, which reduces error.

3. RESULTS and DISCUSSION

3.1 Virtual Trial Results

Figure 3 shows Patient 87 from retrospective hospital data, the insulin-only protocol (Chase *et al.*, 2005a), and the variable feed and insulin protocol developed. Tight control in the 4-6mmol/L desired band is clear with the variable nutrition protocol compared to the other protocols. The total insulin administered by the variable nutrition protocol is 38.5% less than the insulin-only protocol (410.5U versus 667.0U). From the retrospective data, the total insulin infused was 248.0U, indicating another source of poor control. Time spent in the desired 4-6mol/L band was 89% versus 21.8% for the insulin-only protocol and 10.7% for hospital control. Finally, the results are achieved with total enteral glucose administered identical to the retrospective patient data (1284g versus 1286g).

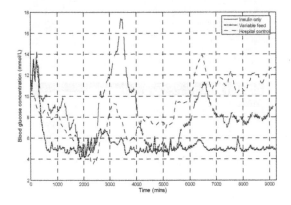

Fig.3: Patient 87 Virtual Trial Results

A summary of the results for all patients is shown in Table 3. The variable nutrition and insulin controller increased the time spent in the 4-6mmol/L band by 240% compared to the insulin-only protocol and 312% versus the retrospective data. Time above 6mmol/L is reduced by 231% and 237%. No hypoglycaemic events occurred for any virtual trial protocols. Figure 4 summarises these results plotting percentage time in the 4-6mmol/L band versus log mean fitted S_I.

Figure 4 shows that percentage time-in-band and mean blood glucose level decrease for all protocols with decreasing insulin sensitivity. With insulin alone, performance is highly dependent on the patients' effective insulin resistance ($R=0.90$, $p<0.001$) due to saturation limitations (Chase *et al.*, 2005a). The variable feed rate and insulin protocol provided tighter blood glucose control across the range of observed insulin sensitivities with significantly higher time-in-band ($R=0.57$, $p<0.02$). The insulin-only protocol only reached similar levels only at high insulin sensitivities, and with significantly more administered insulin. For hospital control, greater variation in blood glucose control was recorded, as expected ($R=0.49$, $p<0.04$), and showed tighter control than the insulin-only protocol only at low insulin sensitivities, where clinically selected feed reductions have affected the comparison.

Table 3: Blood Glucose Summary – Virtual Trials

Controller Type / Patient No.	Mean Blood Glucose			Percentage of time in 4-6mmol/L band (%)		
	Variable feed and insulin	Constant feed-rate, variable insulin	Hospital sliding-scale	Variable feed and insulin	Constant feed-rate, variable insulin	Hospital sliding-scale
1	6.0	12.1	9.3	66.8	1.6	10.2
2	5.9	9.8	7.8	78.4	0.9	3.6
24	6.6	12.4	12.2	80.1	0.0	0.0
87	5.4	8.4	8.8	89.1	21.8	10.7
130	7.0	13.2	11.2	60.1	0.0	10.3
229	5.4	7.7	7.5	84.6	30.2	15.5
289	5.3	5.5	6.8	80.8	79.8	13.2
468	8.5	10.4	7.4	43.4	0.0	18.5
484	7.5	12.3	11.5	70.0	0.0	0.0
486	6.5	9.4	8.9	60.7	10.6	12.0
519	5.6	7.8	6.3	78.6	51.4	33.9
554	6.0	7.6	6.9	66.5	36.1	20.9
666	7.2	12.4	5.3	35.7	0.0	74.9
847	6.2	6.2	7.3	75.5	75.7	21.7
1016	7.5	9.4	7.2	24.7	0.0	10.7
1025	6.4	7.9	8.0	59.5	41.3	21.0
1090	5.2	5.3	3.9	84.4	82.6	46.8
1099	5.3	5.5	6.5	88.6	82.4	35.8
1125	5.9	7.3	5.4	61.0	21.8	51.8
Mean	6.3	9.0	7.8	67.8	28.2	21.7
S. D.	0.9	2.6	2.2	17.9	31.8	19.3
Range	3.3	7.9	8.3	64.4	82.6	74.9

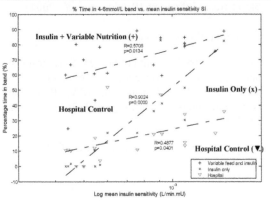

Fig.4: Mean Insulin Sensitivity, S_I, versus Time in the 4-6mmol/L Band

In summary, these results all indicate the effectiveness of using nutrition as an added control input. In particular, high APACHE II score, very critically ill patients are generally highly insulin resistant. Thus, this added control path may represent the only means to maintain euglycaemia, as well as one that is not saturable as is the insulin path.

3.2 Clinical Trial Results

The main goal of the clinical trials was to prove the insulin and nutrition control concept by illustrating the potential for tight control. Tight control is shown by accurately reducing glucose levels to pre-set target values. Hence, the target error is the main performance criteria for evaluation.

The mean target error for all trials is 9.3% (0.52mmol/L), absolute range [0, 2.9] mmol/L, and 41.9% of targets are achieved within ±5% with a mean target error of 2.6% (0.15mmol/L). Mean target error for errors >5% is 14.3% (0.79mmol/L). Out of 86 targets, only seven had errors >20%, so that 90.7% of all measurements are within ±20% of targets. More specifically almost 90% of target errors are explainable by measurement errors (Weitgasser *et al.*, 1999). Outliers are attributed to significant and rapid changes in patient condition observed, such as atrial fibrillation. Model prediction errors at a 60min glucose measurement frequency (Trial 8) were not statistically discernible from the other trials.

Figure 5 presents a bootstrapped linear regression model applied to the achieved and target glucose values using 6000 bootstrap samples. Also shown are the non-parametric 95% confidence intervals (CI) for the prediction of achieved glucose values for a given target. A correlation coefficient between 0.7695 and 0.8983 can be stated with 95% confidence.

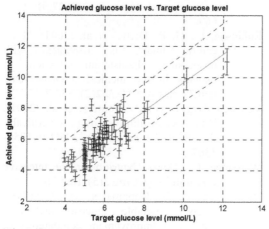

Fig.5: Target Error Summary

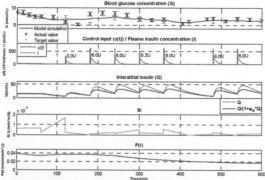

Fig.6: Patient 2 Clinical Trial Progression

Finally, Figure 6 shows a typical trial result for Patient 2. This trial highlights a common difficulty in critical care glycaemic control, the highly dynamic patient with rapidly evolving condition. The glucose measurement at 150mins was on course for the 5mmol/L target at 180mins. However, the recorded measurement at 180mins was 8.5mmol/L. The patient experienced atrial fibrillation at approximately 200mins, indicating that the change may have been due to adrenergic surge preceding the cardiac event. From that point, effective insulin resistance increased, requiring greater insulin input and feed rate reductions compared to the initial 60-120mins. The controller adapted to this not uncommon event, tracking the glucose measurements accurately within the next hour and the 300min target with 5.1% error.

3.3 SPRINT Results

The SPRINT protocol was implemented as a clinical practice change in the Christchurch Hospital ICU. The entry requirement was 2 successive random glucose measurements over 8 mmol/L. this limit ensures only the relatively more critically ill, and thus potentially more insulin resistant, patients are considered.

An initial pilot study of 10 patients was performed to test SPRINT over long term clinical care. The cohort had an average age of 54 (range: 44-80), average APACHE II score of 23 (range: 11-37) and an average APACHE III score of 70 (range: 34-108). There were 6 males and 4 females.

The total controlled time is 2103 hours with 1579 measurements indicating that 49.8% of the controlled time was on 2-hourly measurement as the patients were glycaemically stable. The average length of control for each patient was 210 hours (8.75 days), also indicating a significantly critically ill cohort.

The overall control results can be summarised:

- Average Blood Glucose = 5.8 +/- 0.9 mmol/L
- Average Insulin = 2.5 U/hour
- Average Feed Rate = 64% (1279 kcal/day)
- Time Feed Rate > 50% of goal feed = 70%

However, more relevant performance is time in glycaemic band and any hypoglycaemic events. The primary bands are the 4.-6.1 mmol/L band defined by van den Berghe et al and the 4-7.75 mmol/L band defined by Krinsley. More importantly, these bands are associated with reductions in mortality of 45% and 20-30% respectively, as well as significant reductions in other negative clinical outcomes. The overall glycaemic performance is thus summarised:

- Time in the 4-6.1 mmol/L band = 64%
- Time in the 4-7.0 mmol/L band = 89%
- Time in the 4-7.75 mmol/L band = 97%
- Number measurements < 4 mmol/L = 23 (1.5%)
- Number Measurements < 3 mmol/L = 0
- Minimum Blood Glucose = 3.2 mmol/L

Thus, the results indicate that SPRINT provided very tight glycaemic regulation. The values for time in the glycaemic bands from the landmark studies on hyperglycaemia and mortality are also very high. This latter result indicates that glycaemic levels were not only tightly controlled on average, but that their variation was also very limited. This result is backed up by the narrow 0.9 mmol/L standard deviation. Overall, the results indicate that modulating nutrition and insulin, in combination with frequent measurement, can provide very tight control for a very critically ill cohort.

4. CONCLUSIONS

This paper has presented the development, from concept to clinical practice change, of a nutrition plus insulin control methodology for maintaining euglycaemia in critical care. The methods are developed from a model-based virtual study to proof of concept clinical trials using a model based controller. The control method is then made paper based through a system that effectively mimics the model-based control methods, and implemented as a clinical practice change. Thus, the overall methodology of using retrospective data through to clinical change is also presented as an approach to developing this type of model-based control therapy.

The overall results indicate that modulating nutrition and insulin is an effective approach to controlling hyperglycaemia in critical care. In particular, the more critically ill cohorts with higher APACHE II scores are typically more insulin resistant and this path may offer the only approach to lowering glucose levels to within a desired level or band. Also apparent in the need for higher measurement frequency to ensure that dynamic patients are well monitored and that inappropriate interventions of nutrition or insulin are not maintained when patient condition evolves significantly.

REFERENCES

Chase, J. G., G. M. Shaw, et al. (2005a). "Adaptive bolus-based targeted glucose regulation of hyperglycaemia in critical care." *Med Eng Phys* **27**(1): 1-11.

Chase, J. G., X. W. Wong, et al. (2005b). *Clinical Trials of Active Insulin and Nutrition Control in Critically Ill Patients*. Proc. of the 12th International Conf on Biomedical Engineering (ICBME 2005), Singapore.

Hann, C. E., J. G. Chase, et al. (2005). "Integral-based parameter identification for long-term dynamic verification of a glucose-insulin system model." *Comput Methods Programs Biomed* **77**(3): 259-70.

Kiwanuka, E., R. Barazzoni, et al. (2001). "Glucose kinetics and splanchnic uptake following mixed meal ingestion in cirrhotic-diabetic subjects." *Diabetes Nutrition & Metabolism* **14**(6): 315-324.

Krinsley, J. S. (2003). "Association between hyperglycemia and increased hospital mortality in a heterogeneous population of critically ill patients." *Mayo Clin Proc* **78**(12): 1471-1478.

McCowen, K. C., A. Malhotra, et al. (2001). "Stress-induced hyperglycemia." *Crit Care Clin* **17**(1): 107-24.

Mizock, B. A. (2001). "Alterations in fuel metabolism in critical illness: hyperglycaemia." *Best Pract Res Clin Endocrinol Metab* **15**(4): 533-51.

Patino, J. F., S. E. de Pimiento, et al. (1999). "Hypocaloric support in the critically ill." *World J Surg* **23**(6): 553-9.

Prigeon, R. L., M. E. Roder, et al. (1996). "The effect of insulin dose on the measurement of insulin sensitivity by the minimal model technique. Evidence for saturable insulin transport in humans." *J Clin Invest* **97**(2): 501-507.

Radziuk, J., T. J. McDonald, et al. (1978). "Initial Splanchnic Extraction of Ingested Glucose in Normal Man." *Metabolism-Clinical and Experimental* **27**(6): 657-669.

Rubinson, L., G. B. Diette, et al. (2004). "Low caloric intake is associated with nosocomial bloodstream infections in patients in the medical intensive care unit." *Crit Care Med* **32**(2): 350-7.

Van den Berghe, G., P. Wouters, et al. (2001). "Intensive insulin therapy in the critically ill patients." *N Engl J Med* **345**(19): 1359-1367.

Weissman, C. (1999). "Nutrition in the intensive care unit." *Crit Care* **3**(5): R67-75.

Weitgasser, R., B. Gappmayer, et al. (1999). "Newer portable glucose meters - Analytical improvement compared with previous generation devices?" *Clinical Chemistry* **45**(10): 1821-1825.

STOCHASTIC INSULIN SENSITIVITY MODELS FOR TIGHT GLYCAEMIC CONTROL

J. Geoffrey Chase*, Jessica Lin*, Dominic S Lee**, Jason Wong*, Christopher E. Hann* and Geoffrey M. Shaw***

*Centre for Bioengineering, University of Canterbury, Christchurch, New Zealand
*Dept of Mathematics & Statistics, University of Canterbury, New Zealand
***Department of Intensive Care Medicine, Christchurch Hospital,
Christchurch, New Zealand

Abstract: Hyperglycaemia is prevalent in critical care, and tight control reduces mortality. Targeted glycaemic control can be achieved by frequent fitting and prediction of a modelled insulin sensitivity index, S_I. However, this parameter varies significantly in the critically ill as their condition evolves. A 3-D stochastic model of hourly S_I variability is constructed using retrospective data from 18 critical care patients. The model provides a blood glucose level probability distribution one hour following an intervention, enabling accurate prediction and more optimal glycaemic control. *Copyright © 2006 IFAC*

Keywords: Biomedical Control, Non-Linear Models, Physiological Models, Physiology, Stochastic Modelling, Markov Models, Medical Systems.

1. INTRODUCTION

Hyperglycaemia and severe insulin resistance are prevalent in the critically ill, and tight control can reduce mortality up to 45% (Van den Berghe et al., 2001). Chase et al. (2005a) clinically verified a targeted control algorithm that accounts for inter-patient variability and evolving physiological condition. The adaptive control approach identifies patient dynamics, particularly insulin sensitivity, to determine the best control input. Hence better understanding and modelling of patient variability in the ICU can lead to better glycaemic management.

Therefore, the ultimate goal of this study is to produce model-base blood glucose confidence bands to optimise glycaemic control. These bands are based on stochastic models developed from clinically observed model-based variations, and allow targeted control with user specified confidence on the glycaemic outcome.

2. METHODS

2.1 Glucose-Insulin System Model

This study uses a patient-specific glucose-insulin system model from Chase et al. (2005a). It accounts for time-varying insulin sensitivity and endogenous glucose removal, and two saturation kinetics.

$$\dot{G} = -p_G G - S_I (G + G_E) \frac{Q}{1 + \alpha_G Q} + P(t) \quad (1)$$

$$\dot{Q} = -kQ + kI \quad (2)$$

$$\dot{I} = -n \frac{I}{1 + \alpha_I I} + \frac{u_{ex}(t)}{V_I} \quad (3)$$

where G and I denote the glucose above an equilibrium level, G_E, and the plasma insulin from an exogenous insulin input. Insulin utilization over time is Q, with effective insulin decay rate k. Endogenous glucose removal and insulin sensitivity are p_G and S_I. Insulin distribution volume is V_I, and n is plasma insulin decay. External nutrition and insulin input are $P(t)$ and $u_{ex}(t)$. Michaelis-Menten saturation in plasma insulin disappearance and insulin-stimulated glucose removal are defined by α_I and α_G.

Insulin sensitivity, S_I, is the critical parameter that drives the dynamic system response to exogenous insulin. This value changes with the severity of illness, and thus captures the evolution of the patient's insulin resistance and condition. Hence, identifying S_I over time is critical to providing safe, tight glycaemic control. It will also enable better prediction of the outcome of an intervention. However, no such models or data currently exist.

2.2 Stochastic Model

Patient-specific parameters, p_G and S_I, are fitted to long term retrospective clinical data from 18 patients from a 201-patients data audit (Shaw et al., 2004). Parameter identification is performed with an integration-based method developed by Hann et al. (2005). Each patient record spans at least one day with data every three-hours or less. This cohort broadly represents the cross section of patients seen in the ICU, regarding medical condition, age, sex, APACHE II scores and mortality.

Zero order piecewise linear functions are used to define p_G and S_I, with a discontinuity every two hours for p_G and every hour for S_I because greater variability in S_I is previously identified (Hann et al., 2005). Table 1 shows the parameter values (Chase et al., 2005a).

Table 1: Generic parameter values

Parameter	Unit	Value
α_G	L/mU	1/65
α_I	L/mU	0.0017
n	min^{-1}	0.16
k	min^{-1}	0.0198
V_I	L	3.15

The fitted p_G and S_I data reveals that the variability of both parameters is dependent on its present value. The distribution of fitted S_I is shown by the dots in Figure 1. The probability distribution of potential S_I, shown by the probability bands, clearly varies with its value across the horizontal axis.

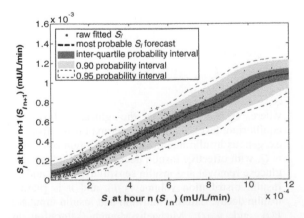

Figure 1: Fitted S_I and probability intervals

Thus, the variations in S_I can be treated as a Markov process. A Markov process has the property that the conditional probability distribution of future states of the process, given the present state, depends only upon the current state. Therefore, using the Markov property of the stochastic behaviour of S_I, the conditional probability distribution of $S_{I\,n+1}$ taking on a value y can be calculated by knowing $S_{I\,n} = x$:

$$P(S_{I\,n+1} = y \mid S_{I\,n} = x) = \frac{P(S_{I\,n} = x, S_{I\,n+1} = y)}{P(S_{I\,n} = x)} \quad (4)$$

Considering the fitted S_I in a 2-D space, as shown in Figure 1, the joint probability function across the x-y ($S_{I\,n}$ - $S_{I\,n+1}$) plane is defined by the fitted values shown by the dots whose coordinates are x_i and y_i,

$$P(x, y) = \frac{1}{n} \sum_{i=1}^{n} \frac{\phi(x; x_i, \sigma_{x_i}^2)}{p_{x_i}} \frac{\phi(y; y_i, \sigma_{y_i}^2)}{p_{y_i}} \quad (5)$$

$$p_{x_i} = \int_0^\infty \phi(x; x_i, \sigma_{x_i}^2) \quad (6)$$

$$p_{y_i} = \int_0^\infty \phi(y; y_i, \sigma_{y_i}^2) \quad (7)$$

Effectively, the 2-D joint probability function is the normalised summation of normal probability distribution functions $\phi(x; x_i, \sigma_{x_i}^2)$ centred at individual data points.

To illustrate a 3-D map in the mind, consider this numerical operation as a sand building exercise. If the first quadrant of the x-y ($S_{I\,n}$ - $S_{I\,n+1}$) plane, as shown in Figure 1, is where the sand box is confined in, and that a pile of sand of a cubic unit is dropped onto every dot in Figure 1, then the resulted sand sculpture is the simple representation of the joint probability $P(x, y)$ on the x-y ($S_{I\,n}$ - $S_{I\,n+1}$) plane. In Equations (5)-(7), the variance σ at each data point is a function of the local data density in a centred and orthonormalised space of x and y. Putting Equations (6) and (7) into Equation (5) normalises each $\phi(x; x_i, \sigma_{x_i}^2)$ and $\phi(y; y_i, \sigma_{y_i}^2)$ in the positive domain. This, in the sand building exercise example, effectively puts boundaries along $x = 0$ and $y = 0$, confining sand to stay in the first quadrant, and therefore forces physiological validity in S_I values.

In Equation (4), the right hand side denominator can be calculated by integrating Equation (5) with respect to y. Hence, Equation (5) can be calculated:

$$P(S_{I\,n+1} = y \mid S_{I\,n} = x) = \sum_{i=1}^{n} \omega_i(x) \frac{\phi(y; y_i, \sigma_{y_i}^2)}{p_{y_i}} \quad (8)$$

$$\omega_i(x) = \frac{\phi(x; x_i, \sigma_{x_i}^2)/p_{x_i}}{\sum_{j=1}^{n} \phi(x; x_j, \sigma_{x_j}^2)/p_{x_i}} \quad (9)$$

Thus, knowing $S_{I\,n} = x$ at hour n, the probability of $S_{I\,n+1} = y$ at hour $n+1$ can be calculated using Equations (8) and (9). The probability intervals shown in Figure 1 are also calculated from integrating Equation (8). Plotting Equation (8) across the x-y ($S_{I\,n}$ - $S_{I\,n+1}$) plane, the resulting 3-D stochastic model is shown in Figures 2 and 3.

The same numerical operations described in Equations (4)-(9) also apply to p_G, producing similar results. However the probability density across the x-y plane is highly concentrated along the line $y = x$, almost to the exclusion of other points. This result reinforces the idea that p_G is effectively constant, even though patient specific (Hann et al., 2005). Hence, variability of p_G is neglected in this study and $p_G = 0.01$ used (Hann et al., 2005).

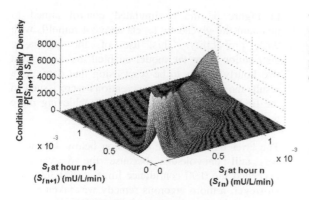

Figure 2: Three-dimensional S_I stochastic model

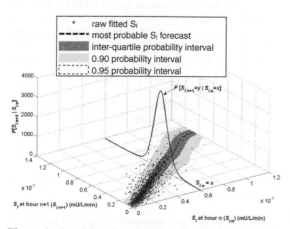

Figure 3: Conditional probability distribution

The stochastic parameter model developed can be integrated into the model of Equations (1)-(3), defining the blood glucose level probability distribution one hour following a known insulin and/or nutrition intervention. This distribution can then be used to adjust a target glucose value for the subsequent hour to ensure a probability of excedance for the resulting glucose level. The stochastic model therefore enables more knowledgeable predictions

with defined probability distributions for the outcomes of glycaemic control inputs.

2.3 Model Validation with Clinical Trial Data

The stochastic model developed from the 18-patients cohort is evaluated on 8 clinical control trials (Wong et al., 2006). This data is independent from the cohort used to develop the stochastic model. The trials performed consisted of hourly cycles of the following steps:

1. Measure blood glucose levels.
2. Fit p_G and S_I to the measured blood glucose.
3. Determine new control intervention to achieve a blood glucose target level.
4. Implement control intervention.

To asses the stochastic model, these 8 trials are numerically re-enacted with control interventions as given in the trial but with step 3 of the trial cycle modified to include the use of the model and confidence bands it generates for an intervention:

3a. Generate potential S_I probability intervals from the time-average identified S_I of the fitted time interval using the stochastic model.
3b. Calculate blood glucose confidence intervals with respect to the S_I probability intervals using the numerical model in Equations (1)-(3).

This test allows validation of the model in a clinical control scenario. The resulting outputs are validated based on how well the resulting clinical data fit the predicted distributions for the clinical trial patient. More specifically, it is a means of assessing whether, for example, the 90% confidence band delivered by the model captures 90% of the results.

2.4 Application as Virtual Patient

Finally, the model can be used to create virtual patients by using the Markov model to create a time-varying profile for S_I. In combination with the mdel of Equations (1)-(3) this stochastic model can then be used, with constraints on the limits for S_I, to test or develop control protocols in simulated clinical trials. All that is required is an initial value and a validated stochastic model to ensure realistic behaviour for the virtual patients.

3. RESULTS AND DISCUSSION

3.1 Comparison to Clinical Trial Data

Blood glucose probability intervals were produced at each control intervention in the 8 clinical trials and compared to measured blood glucose levels one hour later. The results are shown in Table 2. Detailed results from Trial 4 are shown Figure 4.

Table 2: Retrospective probabilistic assessment on clinical control trials

Clinical control patients	Number of interventions made	Measurement error within inter-quartile probability interval		Measurement error within 0.90 probability interval	
1	9	6	(67%)	9	(100%)
2	9	5	(56%)	7	(78%)
3	9	5	(56%)	8	(89%)
4	9	5	(56%)	7	(78%)
5	9	9	(100%)	9	(100%)
6	9	9	(100%)	9	(100%)
7	9	8	(89%)	9	(100%)
8	23	16	(70%)	23	(100%)
total	86	63	(73%)	81	(94%)

The top panel of Figure 4 displays blood glucose, where the crosses are the actual clinical measurements with 7% measurement error, the solid line is the fitted blood glucose profile, and the circles are the most likely probabilistic blood glucose predictions following control interventions. The 90% band and inter-quartile probability ranges are shown by the bars. The bottom panel shows the fitted S_I value, its most probable value, and its probabilistic bounds, as produced by the stochastic model. Note that only the prior hour's value of S_I is required to find the distribution.

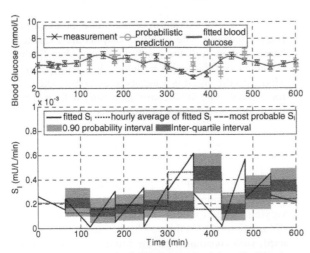

Figure 4: Simulated clinical control trial on Patient 4

Patient 4's blood glucose briefly dropped below 4 mmol/L during the trial at approximately 360mins, which was not accounted for in the probabilistic forecast. Given the identified Patient 4 S_I profile, different control interventions were explored. In particular, the S_I stochastic model and 90% bounds are used to assist decision making. A comparison between the clinical trial and simulated new control intervention results is shown in Figure 5.

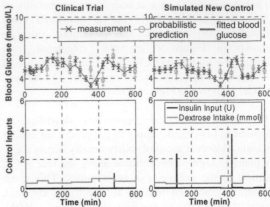

Figure 5: Clinical trial vs. simulated new control results on Patient 4

In Figure 5, the re-simulated control aimed to maintain the glycaemic levels above 4 mmol/L with 90% probability. This use of the stochastic distribution from the model enabled the subsequent two hourly targets to be reset using that data. As a result, more aggressive interventions were issued in the first half of the simulated trial, achieving more tightly controlled glycaemic levels.

The brief blood glucose excursion below 4 mmol/L was still unavoidable because the S_I variation exceeded the 0.90 confidence limit at 300-360mins. However, a more vigorous remedy was taken at 360 minutes in the simulated trial to obtain a 0.90 confidence in blood glucose above 4 mmol/L in an hour. This first intervention was a large feed change as seen in Figure 4. It was followed by an aggressive insulin bolus to counter the sudden feed change the hour prior. Overall, the S_I stochastic model can be used to deliver tighter, safer glycaemic management and improve control intervention selection.

Across all 8 patients, the S_I stochastic model successfully captures the identified S_I variation trend, accounting for 94% of measurements over time within the 0.90 confidence band, and 73% with a 0.50 confidence. Hence, the model may be slightly conservative in this respect where the 7% measurement error is considered.

However, if just the measured values are used from the trials the results are closer to exact. Specifically, 48% of explicit measurement values were in the 0.50 band and 87% were in the 0.90 band. Thus, without accounting for measurement error the model is slightly in error, which may be due to the limited number of measurements, the first order Markov model employed, or both.

Overall, it is worth noting that when S_I increases, the blood glucose level probability interval tightens, as seen in Figures 1-2. The wider range of uncertainties in blood glucose levels associated with low S_I reflects the risk of hypoglycaemic events for highly insulin resistant patients under intensive insulin therapy (Amiel et al., 1987). This situation was specifically seen in Patient 4, whose identified S_I profile is in the lower physiological range.

3.2 Virtual Trial Application and Analysis

"Virtual patients" with p_G and S_I following the stochastic behaviour of the Markov model developed reflect typical critical care patient conditions. A virtual cohort of n = 200 patients was created and tested in simulated trials. Initial conditions for these virtual patients, including starting blood glucose levels, initial S_I levels, insulin infusion, dextrose infusion etc., were randomly chosen to represent typical critical care situations. Resulting blood glucose probability intervals from control inputs are produced with each control intervention. The simulated trials each span 24 hours. Therefore, 23 hourly blood glucose measurements (excluding the starting blood glucose levels) were analysed against the probability intervals. The results from the simulated trials are summarised in Table 3.

Table 3: Virtual patient trials summary

	Glucose < 4 mmol/L	Glucose in 50% band (%)	Glucose in 90% band (%)
Max	22%	96%	100
Mean	2.5%	77%	95%
Min	0%	52%	78%
SD	4%	9%	4.5%

The virtual cohort produced results that are similar to the 8 clinical trials. The inter-quartile confidence intervals covered 77% of blood glucose measurements, and the 0.90 confidence intervals covered 95%. The defined hypoglycaemic level for the trials was 4 mmol/L.

All control interventions maintained a minimum of 0.90 confidence level in the resulting blood glucose levels being above 4 mmol/L. Across the 200 virtual patients cohort, 2 measurements (0.04%) fell below 3 mmol/L, and 111 (2.5%) fell below 4 mmol/L. These slightly hypoglycaemic events all occurred when S_I took a sudden rise that exceeded the 0.90 probability intervals in S_I.

The loss of control with large swings outside the 90% likelihood of occurrence, further illustrates the meaning of this bound. In particular, the size of such swings, especially at low insulin sensitivity, indicates the size of the change required to be outside the 90% likelihood of occurrence. In contrast, the width of these bounds also indicates that 10% of the time patients can take sudden, quite drastic swings in

insulin sensitivity. These quite drastic swings would be due to equally significant changes in patient condition. Hence, the metric may be worth monitoring on its own as a guide to patient condition. From a control standpoint, the targeted, confidence interval based control algorithm was able to maintain blood glucose levels within the 4-6 mmol/L band 70% of the time once the blood glucose levels were brought into this range. This value exceeds clinical simulations without confidence bands (Wong et al., 2005). For those patients whose blood glucose levels were reduced to 4-6 mmol/L (n = 159) during the 24-hour simulated trial, 125 (78.62%) stayed in the band more than 50% of the time, and 78 (50.94%) stayed in the band more than 75% of the time.

More notably, out of the cohort of 200 virtual patients, 41 (20.50%) never achieved normoglycemia in the 4-6 mmol/L band at any instance during the 24 hours trial due to insulin resistance and insulin effect saturation. These patients have virtual S_I profiles generally in the very low physiological range. Consequently, insulin-stimulated glucose removal was constantly saturated with high insulin doses, and the blood glucose confidence bands are also wide.

These results indicated that to always maintain a 0.90 confidence level against a hypoglycaemic event, the achievable blood glucose reduction is limited in some cases. In particular, very low insulin sensitivity and wide 0.90 bands will hinder the ability to remain in the 4-6 mmol/L band under control, while also ensuring a 90% confidence of no hypoglycaemic events. As a result, the glucose levels are higher. These results match clinical observations that blood glucose levels under control are more volatile in highly insulin resistant patients (Chase et al., 2005b; Hann et al., 2005; Wong et al., 2006).

The average number of hours taken for the blood glucose levels to be reduced to within 4-6 mmol/L from the start of the trial was 8.3 (SD ±8.91) hours. Hence, the time taken to get into the band for a hyperglycaemic patient can be quite high if they are highly insulin resistant. This result highlights the need to take early action at the emergence of hyperglycaemia in critical care.

3.3 Results and Discussion Summary

The glucose-insulin system model, together with the integral-based parameter identification, can effectively capture critical care patient behaviour. In addition, the stochastic model further enhances the ability to predict, as well as imitate, typical critical care patient dynamics. The incorporation of the stochastic model into the numerical glucose-insulin system can also be used to create "virtual patients", creating a platform to experiment with different clinical control protocols based on clinically observed patient dynamics and evolution.

Overall, higher identified S_I levels result in tighter blood glucose probability intervals, making tighter control easier with less control effort. It is worth noting that less critically ill patients, by APACHE II or other score, are also typically less insulin resistant and hyperglycaemic (e.g. Christiansen et al., 2004; Mentula et al., 2005). Therefore, a less critically ill cohort is potentially much more likely to be easier to control in terms of variability. This result could thus be used to help compare results of different protocols on different types of patient cohorts.

4. CONCLUSIONS

The stochastic model presented defines the variation of critical care patient insulin sensitivity for the system model presented. As a result, the distribution of blood glucose levels one hour following a known insulin and/or nutrition intervention can be determined and used to enhance control, by enabling more knowledgeable and accurate prediction. The stochastic model thus acts as a tool to assist clinical intervention decisions, maximising the probability of achieving the desired tight glycaemic regulation while maintaining patient safety. The same stochastic model can also be used to create realistic, validated virtual patients for developing new control protocols.

More generally, application of this model also offers new insights. In particular, the model shows that less critically ill cohorts, who are also less insulin resistant, have tighter variation in insulin sensitivity. Such cohorts would be easier to control and shed light on the different results obtained in landmark glycaemic control studies with very different cohorts in terms of APACHE II score and level of critical illness. Overall, the model allows the impact of control inputs on blood glucose levels to be statistically assessed, providing further confidence in the effectiveness of the control protocol utilised against evolving patient dynamics.

REFERENCES

Amiel, S. A., Tamborlane, W. V., Simonson, D. C. and Sherwin, R. S. (1987). "Defective glucose counterregulation after strict glycemic control of insulin-dependent diabetes mellitus." N Engl J Med 316(22): 1376-83.

Chase, J. G., Shaw, G. M., Lin, J., Doran, C. V., Hann, C., Lotz, T., Wake, G. C. and Broughton, B. (2005a). "Targeted glycemic reduction in critical care using closed-loop control." Diabetes Technol Ther 7(2): 274-82.

Chase, J. G., Shaw, G. M., Lin, J., Doran, C. V., Hann, C., Robertson, M. B., Browne, P. M., Lotz, T., Wake, G. C. and Broughton, B. (2005b). "Adaptive bolus-based targeted glucose regulation of hyperglycaemia in critical care." Med Eng Phys 27(1): 1-11.

Christiansen, C., Toft, P., Jorgensen, H. S., Andersen, S. K. and Tonnesen, E. (2004). "Hyperglycaemia and mortality in critically ill patients - A prospective study." Intensive Care Medicine 30(8): 1685-8.

Hann, C. E., Chase, J. G., Lin, J., Lotz, T., Doran, C. V. and Shaw, G. M. (2005). "Integral-based parameter identification for long-term dynamic verification of a glucose-insulin system model." Comput Methods Programs Biomed 77(3): 259-70.

Mentula, P., Kylanpaa, M. L., Kemppainen, E., Jansson, S. E., Sarna, S., Puolakkainen, P., Haapiainen, R. and Repo, H. (2005). "Early prediction of organ failure by combined markers in patients with acute pancreatitis." British Journal of Surgery 92(1): 68-75.

Shaw, G. M., Chase, J. G., Lee, D. S., Bloomfield, M., Doran, C. V. and Lin, J. (2004). How high ARE blood glucose levels in intensive care? ANZICS ASM, Wellington, New Zealand.

Van den Berghe, G., Wouters, P., Weekers, F., Verwaest, C., Bruyninckx, F., Schetz, M., Vlasselaers, D., Ferdinande, P., Lauwers, P. and Bouillon, R. (2001). "Intensive insulin therapy in the critically ill patients." N Engl J Med 345(19): 1359-67.

Wong, X. W., Chase, J. G., Shaw, G. M., Hann, C. E., Lin, J. and Lotz, T. (2005). Comparison of Adaptive and Sliding-Scale Glycaemic Control in Critical Care and the Impact of Nutritional Inputs. Proc. of the 12th International Conf on Biomedical Engineering (ICBME 2005), Singapore.

Wong, X. W., Shaw, G. M., Hann, C. E., Lotz, T., Lin, J., Singh-Levett, I., Hollingsworth, L., Wong, O. S. and Chase, J. G. (2006). "Optimised Insulin and Nutrition Delivery via Model Predictive Control for Tight Glycaemic Regulation in Critical Care." Diabetes Technology & Therapeutics 8(2): 174-90.

STRATEGIES FOR HAEMODYNAMIC CONTROL OF EXTRACORPOREAL CIRCULATION

Berno J.E. Misgeld * Jürgen Werner *
Martin Hexamer *

* Department for Biomedical Engineering, Ruhr-University
Bochum, Bochum, Germany

Abstract: Three different control strategies for haemodynamic control of extracorporeal circulation were developed, tested and compared to each other for the total cardiopulmonary bypass case. The controllers were tuned on robust stability and performance with a detailed model of the vascular system and the heart-lung machine. The control strategies were validated in simulation studies and on a haemodynamic vascular system simulator. All controllers were stable during simulations and in-vitro experiments in stationary and pulsatile control. An arterial blood flow controller with arterial pressure boundary control extension shows the best result. *Copyright © 2006 IFAC*

Keywords: Robust haemodynamic control, extracorporeal circulation, cardiopulmonary bypass, heart-lung machine

1. INTRODUCTION

Cardiopulmonary bypass (CPB) with heart-lung machine (HLM) support has been established as a routine treatment in extracorporeal circulation (ECC) for several decades now. To guarantee the cardiothoracic surgeon a bloodless, motionless operating field the human heart and lung are put into a resting condition. Since the circulation of blood is stopped and thus oxygen and nutrients delivery, tissue and brain damage would occur in the course of minutes. The HLM as an artificial organ keeps the blood circulating (heart) and takes over oxygenation and carbon dioxide removal (lung). The HLM is connected to the systemic vascular system (VS) by cannulation.

Due to the artificial environment, the anaesthetisation and the resting lung and heart, some of the haemodynamic physiological autoregulation mechanisms are suspended for the time of CPB. Therefore, trained perfusion technicians are

needed, who are responsible for the monitoring and manual control of the HLM by means of various pressures and flows, blood gases, etc. The advantages of an automatic control strategy for these vital variables can help to remove workload from the perfusion technicians and improve the patient's safety. Regarding haemodynamics during CPB, an almost physiological pressure and flow distribution as well as minimum blood traumatisation would be desirable.

This paper contributes to stationary and pulsatile haemodynamic control strategies, where a rotary (centrifugal) blood pump (RPB) is used as the control actuator. In order to guarantee robust performance and stability with a time-varying nonlinear system, advanced modelling and control approaches are required. The developed control strategies were validated in a simulation and an experimental study with a HLM machine and a hydrodynamic system simulator. Finally, this paper ends with a discussion.

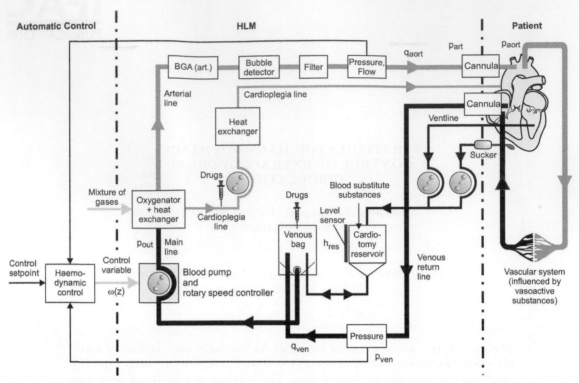

Fig. 1. Outline of a cardiopulmonary bypass with a heart-lung machine, with regard to haemodynamic aspects (BGA: blood-gas-analysis, ventline: ventricle drainage).

2. CONTROL STRATEGY

Different strategies of haemodynamic feedback-control in ECC exist in literature (Soejima *et al.*, 1983; Beppu *et al.*, 1995; Nishida *et al.*, 1995). These varieties are due to the many variables, which up to present have been manually observed and controlled. Fig. 1 shows a diagram of the HLM/patient, with regard to haemodynamic aspects and a feedback-control example. Typical variables that can be considered for feedback-control are arterial or venous pressure and flow and the amount of blood in the venous reservoir. The reason for automatic control depends on the operating conditions for the variable. Variables of main importance are, in the case of haemo-dynamics, the arterial flow and pressure. Table 1 shows the different variables with conditions for control. Total and boundary values are taken from ECC literature (Kay and Munsch, 2004) and from cardiovascular hospital guidelines for ECC. Venous flow, pressure and reservoir height should be continually monitored to prevent highly blood damaging venous conditions, for example on a clearing of the reservoir ("venous chatter"). The suggested feedback-control for the arterial haemodynamics is depicted in Fig. 2. In cases (a) and (b) the plant output is the arterial flow and the arterial pressure. The control setpoint can be either stationary or pulsatile. Since a simultaneous control of both arterial flow and pressure with the

Table 1. Haemodynamic variables and conditions for control.

Variable	Control conditions
arterial flow q_{aort}	continually updated
	may be pulsatile
	$\approx 2.4\ l/min/m^2$ mean flow/
	body surface area
aortic pressure p_{aort}	may be pulsatile
	$40 \leq p_{aort} \leq 60\ mmHg$
venous flow q_{ven}	should be monitored
venous pressure p_{ven}	should be monitored
reservoir height h_{res}	should be monitored

RPB as an actuator is not possible Fig. 2 (c) shows a cascaded pressure boundary control, which will be described in detail below.

3. THE MODEL

The requirement for a fast responding control with optional pulsatility requires a control-loop incorporating high bandwidth. For robust stability and performance a detailed time-varying non-linear model describing the HLM and the vascular system (VS) of the patient was developed and validated (Misgeld *et al.*, 2005). The HLM was modelled in terms of a nonlinear model with a RPB (Deltastream, Medos AG, Stolberg, Germany), DC-motor and rotary speed control, the oxygenator, the arterial filter and the arterial cannula. Special importance was given to the mod-

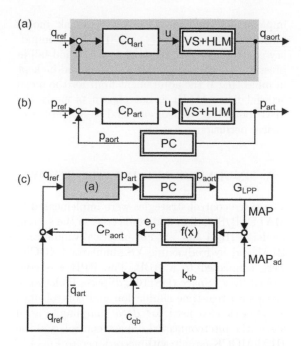

Fig. 2. Haemodynamic control strategies, with flow (a) and pressure (b) controllers $C_{q_{art}}$ and $C_{p_{art}}$. (c) shows the MAP boundary control strategy. PC is the pressure correction (refer to section 4.3 for details).

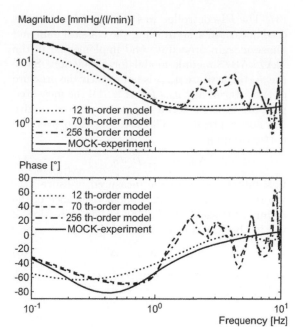

Fig. 3. Frequency response of the VS models compared to a MOCK.

$$G_p(z) = \frac{P_{aort}(z)}{\omega_{aort}(z)} \quad (2)$$

$$G_q(z) = \frac{Q_{aort}(z)}{\omega_{aort}(z)}, \quad (3)$$

where ω_{aort} is the revolution speed of the RPB.

4. CONTROL

4.1 Arterial Blood Flow Control

With the TF (2), three different discrete controllers were designed and tuned for blood flow control (BFC) (Misgeld et al., 2005). A proportional plus integral (PI) controller was tuned with the worst case linearised system using the classical gain and phase margin procedure. A $\mathcal{H}_\infty$-controller was tuned with the worst case linearised system using the $\mathcal{H}_\infty$-optimal approach, incorporating frequency shaping functions for performance and additional uncertainty specification (Morari and Zafiriou, 1989). And as a third controller a self-tuning general predictive controller (GPC) including a Kalman-Filter was tuned with the worst case linearised system. The PI- and the $\mathcal{H}_\infty$- and the GPC controller with incorporated Kalman filter were implemented in the MAT-LAB/Simulink model for the simulation study.

4.2 Arterial Pressure Control

In the case of arterial blood pressure control (BPC) a PI-controller was tuned with the TF

elling of the VS, for which three models varying in complexity were compared to each other. The haemodynamics of the VS were modelled with the Navier-Stokes equations. By using the finite difference method, blood vessels or blood vessel areas were described in compartmental form (Misgeld and Hexamer, 2005). A high order 128-compartment model was implemented in MAT-LAB/Simulink, reduced from 256th to 70th order and compared to a 5-compartment 12th order model. These models were initialised with different patients' vascular parameter data (Reul et al., 1975; Avolio, 1980) and compared to physiological data in the frequency domain. Fig. 3 shows the frequency response of the vascular impedance

$$G(j\omega) = \frac{P_{aort}(j\omega)}{Q_{aort}(j\omega)}. \quad (1)$$

In addition the frequency response of a hydrodynamic VS simulator (MOCK) is shown in Fig. 3 that will be described below.

The model of HLM and 12th-order VS was implemented in MATLAB/Simulink and extended with volume and mass transport equations for vasoactive drugs (Rideout, 1972). For robust control the model was linearised by state perturbation algorithms at a range of operating points. The two model transfer functions (TF) for arterial blood flow and pressure control are in the z-domain

(3). The PI-controller was tuned with the worst case linearised system using the classical gain and phase margin procedure and implemented in the MATLAB/Simulink model for simulation. Since the aortic pressure p_{aort} is not exactly the pressure of the arterial line p_{art} (see Fig. 1), the measured pressure of the arterial line was corrected to give the aortic pressure. The pressure drop over the aortic cannula

$$\Delta p_c = q_{aort} R_C(q_{aort}) \qquad (4)$$

was subtracted from the measured pressure p_{art}, where R_C is the flow-dependent resistance of the cannula (Misgeld *et al.*, 2005). The correction of the fed back aortic pressure results in

$$p_{aort} = p_{art} - \Delta p_c, \qquad (5)$$

and is shown in the pressure correction (PC) block in Fig. 2 (b).

4.3 Mean Arterial Pressure Boundary Control

During automatic BFC an adequate pressure in the VS prevents venous blood vessels from collapsing, but leads to the formation of oedema if it is too high. The mean arterial pressure (MAP) should be kept in boundaries (Table 1) to satisfy these conditions. However, during automatic BFC the pressure in the VS can only be influenced by means of changing the total peripheral resistance (TPR, i.e. by vasoactive drugs). For that reason a cascaded control structure was developed, which adjusts the mean value of the BFC setpoint up to ± 2 l/min. In stationary and pulsatile BFC conditions the MAP boundary control functions as follows. The corrected pressure (5) is fed back and low-pass filtered, by a filter of the form

$$G_{LPP}(s) = \frac{MAP(s)}{p_{aort}(s)} = \frac{1}{T_{LPP}s + 1}. \qquad (6)$$

The MAP is then compared with the adjusted reference mean arterial pressure (MAP_{ad}), determined from the flow operating point to

$$MAP_{ad} = k_{qb}(\bar{q}_{aort} - c_{qb}), \qquad (7)$$

in which k_{qb} is a conversion gain and c_{qb} is a constant, corresponding to the BFC setpoint adjustment. A function $f(x)$ maps the absolute difference $x = MAP - MAP_{ad}$ to the control error e_p. Function $f(x)$ is a hyperbolic weighting of the form

$$e_p = f(x) = \frac{1}{k_g} \sinh(x - c_g), \qquad (8)$$

with the gain k_g and the normal operating point for pressure c_g, at which the control input error goes to zero. Equations (4)-(8) were combined with a PI-controller $C_{p_{aort}}$ in Fig. 2 (c). This PI-controller was tuned with the worst case linearised model of the closed-loop arterial BFC system and

implemented in the MATLAB/Simulink model together with equations (4)-(8). The MAP boundary control is able to respond to a rise and fall in pressure by adjusting the MAF. It should be kept in mind that if the adjustment limit for the mean arterial flow (MAF) is not chosen properly the MAP boundary control can lead to an unphysiological perfusion.

5. SIMULATION AND IN-VITRO STUDY

The three control strategies were implemented in MATLAB/Simulink and connected to the system model of HLM and VS. For practical validation a HLM and hydrodynamic VS simulator (MOCK) were connected to a RBP. The RPB was controlled by a dSpace (DS1104, dSpace, Paderborn, Germany) real-time simulation and control unit, which was also used for data sampling. Fig. 4 shows the interconnected dSpace control- and the HLM-MOCK-circuit with accordance to Fig. 1.

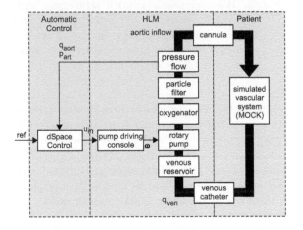

Fig. 4. Experimental setup for the haemodynamic control strategies, with automatic control unit, HLM and vascular system simulator.

The hydrodynamic simulation circuit consisted of a flow resistance (tube clamping), a compliance chamber and the tubing system. To simulate the rheologic properties of blood, a water-glycol mixture (70%/30%) was used (Reul *et al.*, 1975). Both elements, TPR and compliance of the MOCK were adjustable and computer controlled (Nagel, 2004). TPR, compliance, MOCK pressure and flow data were sampled with the MOCK computer at a sampling time of $T_{s,MOCK}$. Computer adjustments for the TPR and the compliance could be made in ranges $C_{art} \approx [0.8 \ldots 2]$ ml/mmHg and $R_{TPR} \approx [5 \ldots 40]$ mmHg/(l/min), to simulate the VS of different patients, as well as the effects of different vasoactive drugs.

The three control approaches of section 4 were tested in simulations and in experimental test series. For stationary control, step responses were

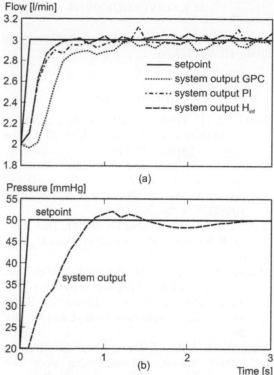

(a)

(b)

Fig. 5. Experimental result for a setpoint change with (a) the three BFC's and (b) BPC.

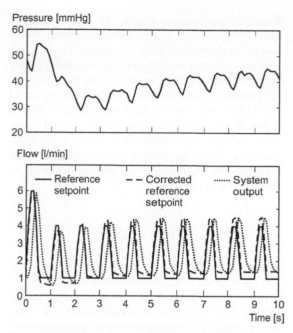

Fig. 6. Experimental result for MAP boundary control with pulsatile setpoint and a pressure disturbance at t = 0.5 s.

applied over the whole operating range and at varying vascular parameter conditions. Fig. 5 shows a step response for a) the three arterial blood flow controllers and b) the arterial blood pressure.

For pulsatile control the control setpoint was made out of three distinct variables: mean flow, heart rate and pulsatility index (Misgeld *et al.*, 2005). The result for the pulsatile reference setpoint are sinusoidal halfwaves. As in stationary control the controllers were tested over the whole operating range and the VS was initialised with different parameter values. Fig. 6 shows the closed-loop system response of a pulsatile in-vitro experiment with the MAP boundary control. The system output flow follows the arterial blood flow reference setpoint. At the time when a disturbance to the pressure occurs, the MAP boundary control adjusts the blood flow and drives the MAP back into boundaries. The limits for the MAP boundary control intervention on the arterial blood flow reference value is the adjustment limit of up to ±2l/min. In order not to risk unphysiological flow conditions a remaining error in MAP therefore has to be tolerated.

6. RESULTS

Three different haemodynamic control strategies were developed and designed for total CPB with HLM support. The automatic control strategies were tested with a model of ECC and in in-vitro experiments using a HLM and a hydrodynamic VS simulator. The three control strategies including all controllers were stable over the whole operating range in simulations, in-vivo test series and in pulsatile control conditions.

Of the three blood flow controllers, the self-tuning general predictive controller with Kalman-Filter was near instability in operating regions of greater nonlinear static gain. The $\mathcal{H}_\infty$-controller showed the best result of the three controllers. Automatic BFC shows robust performance and a fast responding control compared to literature, for example (Nishida *et al.*, 1995). Pressure variations of up to 30 mmHg in the ascending aorta were possible with pulsatile automatic control (note that during in-vivo ECC mostly arterial post-oxygenator pressure is measured, which does not correspond to the pressure in the aortic arch because of the pressure drop over the a. cannula).

The control-response time of the BPC to a step-input is longer compared to that of the three blood flow controllers. This is because of the higher time constant in the TF (3). In dependance on the flow resistance of the HLM elements and the TPR, the arterial flow can take on very unphysiological values. The same is true for pulsatile pressure control. Examples for a flow resistance change during ECC are the changes of TPR induced by anaesthetics and the clotting of the oxygenator with blood. Therefore an adequate arterial blood flow for sufficient oxygen supply cannot be guaranteed during BPC.

As an extension of the automatic blood flow control circuit, the MAP boundary control circuit was able to maintain the pressure in the pre-described boundaries (Table 1). By choosing a limit of up to ± 2 l/min for the arterial blood flow an unphysiologic flow is avoided. The control-response time for MAP boundary control depends on the pre-filter time-constant (6) for the arterial pressure measurement. During measurements the MAP boundary control circuit was able to respond fast enough to all kinds of fluid resistance changes and responds in about 5s to step-like direct disturbances on the measured arterial pressure (for example at the partial occlusion of the arterial line).

7. DISCUSSION

The complex autoregulation system of heart and VS determines and accomplishes the haemodynamic changes needed in physiological perfusion. During ECC with the application of CPB, these autoregulation mechanisms are no longer guaranteed. In this paper different control strategies were analysed, which can automate the regulation of haemodynamics in the ECC case. Venous pressure and flow should be observed during the ECC procedure but appear unimportant for direct control. The arterial flow and pressure on the other hand are important variables for a physiological perfusion. Even though a stationary and pulsatile blood pressure control is possible, arterial blood flow control is of superior importance since it determines the functions with more benefit to the patient. These are especially oxygen delivery and the prevention of oedema formation. The suggested MAP boundary control, which intervenes in the MAF reference setpoint appears to be best suited for haemodynamic regulation with the RBP as the only actuator. The limit of this control strategy is of course pressure disturbance dependent and can be overcome by the introduction of an additional actuator (i.e. vasoactive drugs). The developed haemodynamic control strategies can be further extended with additional safety mechanisms and interconnected with new automatic regulations, for example blood gas control in the oxygenator. This will be the subject of future research.

Appendix A. CONSTANTS

Table A.1. Model and control parameters

Symbol	Value/Unit	Parameter
T_{LPP}	$1/\pi$ s	Filter time constant
k_{qb}	5 mmHg/(l/min)	MAF conversion gain
c_{qb}	3 l/min	MAF constant
k_g	1/80	MAP error gain
c_g	50 mmHg	MAP operating point
$T_{s,MOCK}$	540 msec	MOCK sampling time

ACKNOWLEDGEMENT

Supported by the German Research Foundation Grant HE 2713/5 - 1.

REFERENCES

Avolio, A. P. (1980). Multi-branched model of the human arterial system. *Med. Biol. Eng. Comput.* **18(6)**, 709–718.

Beppu, T., Y. Imai and Y. Fukui (1995). A computerized control system for cardiopulmonary bypass. *J. Thorac. Cardiovasc. Surg.* **109**(3), 428–38.

Kay, P. H. and C. M. Munsch (2004). *Techniques in Extracorporeal Circulation*. Arnold. London.

Misgeld, B. J. E. and M. Hexamer (2005). Modellierung und Regelung des arteriellen Blutflusses während der extrakorporalen Zirkulation. *Automatisierungstechnik* **53(9)**, 454–461.

Misgeld, B. J. E., J. Werner and M. Hexamer (2005). Robust and self-tuning blood flow control during extracorporeal circulation in the presence of system parameter uncertainties. *Med. Biol. Eng. Comput.* **43**, 589–598.

Morari, M. and E. Zafiriou (1989). *Robust Process Control*. Prentice-Hall International, Inc.. Englewood Cliffs, NJ.

Nagel, M. (2004). Aufbau eines Versuchsstandes zur Simulation des menschlichen Kreislaufs unter den Bedingungen der extrakorporalen Membranoxygenation (ECMO). Master's thesis. Dortmund University.

Nishida, H., T. Beppu, M. Nakajima, T. Nishinaka, H. Nakatani, K. Ihashi, T. Katsumata, M. Kitamura, S. Aomi, M. Endo and et al. (1995). Development of an autoflow cruise control system for a centrifugal pump. *Artif. Organs* **19**(7), 713–8.

Reul, H., H. Minamitani and J. Runge (1975). A hydraulic analog of the systemic and pulmonary circulation for testing artificial hearts. *Proc. ESAO II* **2**, 120–127.

Rideout, V. C. (1972). Cardiovascular system simulation in biomedical engineering education. *Trans. Biomed. Eng.* **19(2)**, 101–107.

Soejima, K., Y. Nagase, K. Ishihara, Y. Takanashi, Y. Imai, K. Tsuchiya and Y. Fukui (1983). Computer-assisted automatic cardiopulmonary bypass system for infants. In: *Progr. Artif. Organs* (K. Atsumi, M. Maekawa and K. Ota, Eds.). pp. 918–922. ISAO Press, Cleveland, OH.

THE BENEFITS OF USING GUYTON'S MODEL
IN HYPOTENSIVE CONTROL SYSTEM

Chi-Ngon Nguyen, Olaf Simanski, Ralf Kähler,
Agnes Schubert, Bernhard Lampe

Institute of Automation
Department of Computer Science and Electrical Engineering
University of Rostock, Germany
nguyen-chi.ngon@ uni-rostock.de
Tel./Fax: +49 381 498 3556/3563

Abstract: In order to improve the applications of intraoperation and internal medicine, this paper presents a method of hypotensive control. The mean arterial pressure (MAP) is decreased and maintained at a low level during anaesthesia by controlling sodium nitroprusside (SNP) infusing rate. In this system, a new dynamical model of MAP response to SNP is modified based on Guyton's model of cardiovascular dynamics. The resulting model is not only useful to design a PID controller, but also for studying the behaviors of patients under anaesthesia condition, such as the perfusion of organs and the reaction of the body at hypotensive state. A fuzzy gain scheduler (FGS) is online updated for tuning the PID gains during control activities to handle the behaviors of the body. Simulation results prove the benefits of using Guyton's model, and indicate the safety and stability of the control system. *Copyright © 2006 IFAC*

Keywords: Fuzzy control, fuzzy logic, PID control, scheduling algorithms, medical systems, medical applications, blood pressure.

1. INTRODUCTION

In medical applications, maintaining the MAP at a low level has several advantages. During cardiac surgery, it can limit intraoperative bleeding, which causes a lot of side effects, such as increased risk of sepsis and organ failure (Furutani *et al.*, 1995, 2004). In postsurgery at Intensive Care Unit, it can promote healing, especially after cardiac surgery (Slate and Sheppard, 1982; Er and Gao, 2003; etc.). Since sodium nitroprusside (SNP) became commercially available in 1974, the drug has been used in the treatment of hypertension (Isaka and Sebald, 1993). However, automatic control of blood pressure (BP) is required to handle the wide range of patient sensitivities to the drugs. Because an overdose of SNP could, however, cause toxic side effects (Chen

et al., 1997; Er and Gao, 2003). When used and designed properly, the automatic control systems can improve the quality of patient care and also reduce the amount of work for physicians and nurses (Isaka and Sebald, 1993).

From the mid 1970's through the early 1980's, a number of BP control systems were developed to regulate BP by SNP infusion and were tested in simulation, in animal experiments, or on human patients (Isaka and Sebald, 1993). However, due to the nonlinear nature of the input-output response, the interaction of drugs, the variation of response from patient to patient and the variation in the same patient under different conditions, modelling the BP response to SNP is a problem. Most of previous studies developed the dynamical models based on the

Table 1 A comparison between some selected papers on BP control

Research groups	Patient's model[*]	Medical applications[**]	Hypotensive agents
(Slate et al., 1980; 82), (Ganbing, 1988)[+] (Behbehani et al., 1991)[+], (Chen et al., 1997)[+], (Ma et al., 2000)[+], (Ying et al., 1988,90,92,94)	SISO model (FOPDT)	Hypertensive control	SNP
(Meier et al., 1992)[+], (Akpolat et al., 2003)[+]	SISO model (FOPDT)	Normotensive control	Isoflurane
(Yu et al., 1992)	MIMO model (FOPDT)	Hypertensive control	SNP and Dopamine
(Held and Roy, 1995)[+], (Rao et al., 2000)	Physiological MIMO model	Hemodynamic and anesthetic states	SNP and Dopamine
(Er and Gao, 2003)[+]	Fuzzy-Neural network SISO	Hypertensive control	SNP
(Furutani et al., 1995; 2004)	SISO model (FOPDT)	Normotensive control	Trimethaphan camsilate
This paper	Physiological SIMO model	Hypotensive control	SNP

[*]: Model of MAP response to hypotensive agents;
[+]: Simulation studies
[**]: Hypotensive control – BP is decreased from hypertension to normal value for promoting healing; Normotensive control – BP is reduced from high or normal value to a low level for blood loss purposes; Hypotensive control – BP is decreased to a deep level (e.g., MAP=40mmHg) for intraoperative applications.

first-order plus dead time (FOPDT), which will be compared together as given in Table 1. These models were useful to design the hypertensive and normotensive control systems. But, applying to hypotensive control, they cannot present the reaction of the body, which is caused by eight mechanics of BP autoregulation (Guyton et al., 1972a; b; 1996).

The aim of this work is to improve a recent hypotensive control system in (Nguyen et al., 2005) by using a complex model, which is modified based on Guyton's model of cardiovascular dynamics. The resulting model is not only useful for tuning a fuzzy PID controller, but also in studying a lot of physiological parameters in the circulation of patient.

2. MODELLING OF MAP RESPONSE TO HYPOTENSIVE DRUG

2.1 Problem motivation

In order to model the effects of SNP on MAP, we measured BP on 7 pigs by AS/3 monitoring system. In each experiment, the SNP infusion rate was maintained at a constant level during its infusion period. Fig.1 illustrates the response of MAP to SNP on one pig (Kähler et al., 2004), which ΔMAP is the change of MAP from initial value. After getting steady state, the MAP is increased by the behaviors of patient, called body reaction, especially at deep hypotension. This is a problem for modelling, which was not recognized in previous BP control systems.

Table 1 summaries some papers in BP control with its dynamical model of MAP response to hypotensive agents. Slate and Sheppard proposed a linear single-input single-output (SISO) model based on FOPDT (Slate, 1980; Slate and Sheppard, 1982). A low

amplitude pseudorandom binary signal was used to obtain the impulse response, thus the model produced is valid only for small signal (Held and Roy, 1995). In the complete system, Slate and Sheppard also considered the body reaction as the impact of respiration, the random variations due to sympathetic stimulation and the angiotensin reflex. However, being linear, the model cannot accurately represent nonlinear and time-varying features of the relation (Ying and Sheppard, 1994).

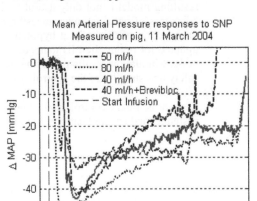

Fig. 1. MAP responses to SNP.

To improve the system of Slate and Sheppard, many researchers subsequently designed intelligent controllers instead of improving the model, such as adaptive controller (Ganbing, 1988; Behbehani and Cross, 1991; Ma et al., 2000), fuzzy controller (Ying et al., 1988, 1990, 1992, 1994), neural network controller (Chen et al., 1997), etc. Furutani et al. also proposed a SISO model based on FOPDT but the response time constant of FOPDT is changed due to BP is decreasing or increasing. The model was useful in normotensive control with trimethaphan camsilate hypotensive drug for reducing intraoperative bleeding during cardiac surgery (Furutani *et al.*, 1995, 2004). Yu *et al.* presented a multi-input multi-output (MIMO) model of patient responses to two kinds of drugs, included SNP and Dopamine (Yu *et al.*, 1992). This MIMO model was also constructed based on FOPDT. Held and Roy showed that all above linear models could not be able to accurately mimic a physiologic system of human circulation (Held and Roy, 1995). Instead of developing the model, Er and Gao considered it as an unknown system. They developed a fuzzy neural network model of the system inverse dynamics for simulating a neural-fuzzy adaptive controller (Er and Gao, 2003). However, the neural network is sensitive with noises, thus it may not be able to accurately work under different clinical conditions. For regulating the hemodynamic and anesthetic states, a physiological MIMO model was studied and applied by (Held and Roy, 1995) and (Rao *et al.*, 2000). This physiological model presents the body reaction by a baroreflex mechanism. However, Guyton *et al.* showed that arterial pressure is not autoregulated by a single pressure feedback system, but, instead by multiple feedbacks (Guyton *et al.*, 1972a).

There exist eight important mechanisms of autonomic regulation of arterial blood pressure (Guyton *et al.*, 1972a, 1996). And all of them were integrated in Guyton's model of cardiovascular dynamics (Guyton *et al.*, 1972b, 1993). Therefore, we purpose to modify Guyton's model for modelling the effects of SNP on the circulation.

2.2 Reconstruction of Guyton's model

Guyton's model consists of 18 modules containing about 600 physiological parameters and variables. It was originally written in FORTRAN, but was later translated into "C" by Guyton and his colleagues (Guyton *et al.*, 1993, Werner *et al.*, 2002). In this study, Guyton's model of cardiovascular dynamics was reconstructed in Simulink version.

2.3 Modelling the effects of SNP on the circulation

BP is a product of cardiac output and vascular resistance. A popular means to reduce BP is to reduce vascular resistance by infusing a vasodilating drug. When administered intravenously, SNP relaxes the muscle of the peripheral vascular, causing a reduction in BP (Isaka *et al.*, 1993). Indeed, in systems analysis of Guyton's model, when the vascular resistances are reduced the blood volume in systemic arteries is decreased, and thus the arterial pressure is also decreased. So, reducing vascular resistance is the main idea for modelling the effects of SNP on the circulation. To carry out this idea, the

main module of circulatory dynamics in Guyton's model was modified to insert 2 inputs of *REN* and *REM* and 1 output of *ΔMAP*. Where, *REM* and *REN* denote the "effect of SNP on vascular resistance in muscle tissues" and the "effect of SNP on vascular resistance in non-muscle, non-renal tissues", respectively. *ΔMAP* is the change of MAP from initial value. When vascular resistances are reduced, blood flows in the circulation are decreased causing a reduction of *ΔMAP*. Fig.2 presents how to modify the effects of SNP on vascular resistances with all of notations can be found in the appendix.

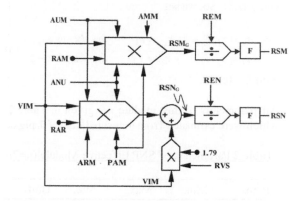

Fig. 2. The effect of SNP on vascular resistances.

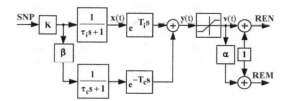

Fig. 3. SNP effective module.

Let RSM_G and RSN_G be the original vascular resistances in muscle tissues, and in non-muscle, non-renal tissues of Guyton's model, respectively. The modified vascular resistances are given in (1); where F is a low pass filter.

$$RSM = F\left(\frac{RSM_G}{REM}\right)$$
$$RSN = F\left(\frac{RSN_G}{REN}\right) \quad (1)$$

Two coefficients of *REM* and *REN* are determined by a SNP effective module given in Fig.3. This module can be described by (2) and (3).

$$\frac{y(t)}{SNP} = K\left(\frac{e^{-T_i s}}{\tau_i s + 1} + \frac{\beta e^{-T_c s}}{\tau_c s + 1}\right)$$
$$v(t) = \begin{cases} y(t), & y(t) \ge 0 \\ 0, & y(t) < 0 \end{cases} \quad (2)$$
$$REN = 1 + v(t)$$
$$REM = 1 + \alpha v(t)$$

where K is the gain of the body. T_i and T_c present the initial transport delay and the transport delay of body reaction, respectively. τ_i and τ_c are the response time constants. β is a factor of the body reaction. The lower limit of $v(t)$ is set to zero to ensure that REM and REN are not less than one. α presents the ratio of different effect of SNP on vascular resistances in muscle and in non-muscle, non-renal tissues.

In addition, the transport delays and response time constants are themselves different in decrease of MAP and in increase of MAP due to the sign of dx/dt (see Fig.3). So, we set

$$\begin{cases} \tau_i = \tau_1, T_i = T_1, \tau_c = \tau_3 & \text{for } dx/dt > \xi \\ \tau_i = \tau_2, T_i = T_2, \tau_c = \tau_4 & \text{for } dx/dt < -\xi \end{cases} \quad (3)$$

with $\xi = 0.025$.

All parameters of this module are given in Table 2, which were estimated from measured data of 7 pigs.

Table 2 Parameters of SNP Effective Module (n=7)

Paras.		Min.	Max.	Ave.	Units
K		0.01	2.2	0.2	1/ml/h
β		-0.3	-0.9	-0.6	-
T_i	T_1	25	195	60	sec
	T_2	1	25	5	sec
T_c		5	14	7	min
τ_i	τ_1	15	75	30	sec
	τ_2	1	6	3	min
τ_c	τ_3	6	20	8	min
	τ_4	1	25	5	sec
α		1	3	1.75	-

2.4 Model simulation

Simulation parameters of SNP effective module for simulation were selected as follows: K=0.21(1/ml/h), β=-0.65, T_1=185(s), T_2=5(s), T_c=425(s), τ_1=30(s), τ_2=65(s), τ_3=17(min), τ_4=5(s), and α=1.75. The result is demonstrated in Fig.4 that is also compared with measured MAP on pig. The average values in Table 2 are set as default parameters for the model, which is used for controller design.

3. CONTROLLER DESIGN

3.1 Control structure

The structure of the system is presented in Fig.5. This is a PID control system with a fuzzy gain scheduler (FGS). In this diagram, the patient's block is the resulting model described in section above. The observer supervises the current infusion rate and the response of MAP (i.e., ΔMAP) for online updating the FGS during operation (see 3.3).

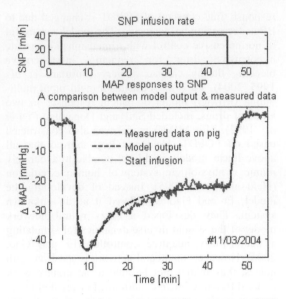

Fig. 4. A simulation result of MAP response to SNP.

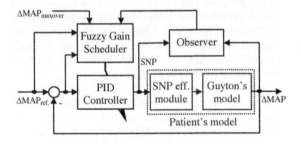

Fig. 5. The structure of control system.

It is assumed that the PID gains K_p, K_d and K_i are in prescribed ranges $[K_{pmin}, K_{pmax}]$, $[K_{dmin}, K_{dmax}]$, and $[K_{imin}, K_{imax}]$, respectively (Zhao et al., 1993). The appropriate ranges are determined experimentally and will be given in (4). The role of FGS is to adjust for the suitable values of K_p, K_d and K_i of the PID controller in these ranges.

3.2 Fuzzy gain scheduling of PID controller

The FGS has two inputs and three outputs. Selecting the fuzzy output ranges in (4), respectively for K_p, K_d and K_i, requires an early estimation method to detect the dead time L and early slope R of the output response curve that was explained in (Kähler et al., 2004). After estimating R and L, the initial gains of K_p^*, K_d^* and K_i^* are calculated as showing in Table 3 and Table 4 (with $K_d^*=K_p^*T_d^*$, and $K_i^*=K_p^*/T_i^*$). These parameters are used to determine (4), which is experimentally obtained through simulations.

The fuzzy set of first input $e(k)$, for the error between output and setpoint, is arranged in $[E_{min}, E_{max}]$. The fuzzy set of second input $\Delta e(k)$, for the change of the error, is within $[\Delta E_{min}, \Delta E_{max}]$. They are calculated due to the setting values of the operator. Let ΔMAP_{ref}

be the setpoint and $\Delta MAP_{maxover}$ be acceptable maximum overshoot. The ranges of input fuzzy sets are modified in (5).

$$K_p \in [1.75K_p^*,\ 0.25K_p^*]$$
$$K_d \in [2K_d^*,\ 0.5K_d^*] \qquad (4)$$
$$K_i \in [2K_i^*,\ 0.25K_i^*]$$

$$\begin{cases} E_{min} = \Delta MAP_{ref} - \Delta MAP_{maxover} \\ E_{max} = \Delta MAP_{maxover} \qquad\qquad (5) \\ \Delta E_{min} = -1; \qquad \Delta E_{max} = 1 \end{cases}$$

Table 3 Calculating T_d^* and T_i^* due to dead time L

L (sec)	[min-30]	(30-60]	(60-90]	(90-max]
T_d^*	0.75L	0.35L	0.2L	0.1L
T_i^*	$3.5T_d^*$	$3.5T_d^*$	$4T_d^*$	$4T_d^*$

Table 4 Calculating K_p^* due to early slope R

-R	[min-.05]	(.05-.4]	(.4-1]	(1-max]
K_p^*	2/RL	6/RL	8/RL	12/RL

The FGS has 35 fuzzy rules for tuning the PID controller, which can be found in (Nguyen *et al.*, 2005). It is also online updated during operation by a supervising algorithm.

3.3 Supervising algorithm

As mentioned above, the fuzzy output ranges in (4) are experimentally obtained through simulations. Therefore, to optimize them, a supervising algorithm is also developed based on (Isaka *et al.*, 1993). During operations, when the MAP response does not reach the target, the output ranges [K_{min}, K_{max}] (i.e. output fuzzy sets) will be updated for making the controller acts stronger. And when the overshoot appears, they will be changed to act weaker. This algorithm was described in (Nguyen *et al.*, 2005).

4. RESULTS

Simulation result 1: In Fig.6, the MAP is reduced and maintained at a setpoint-bank for 60 min. The setpoint-bank is defined by a range of 5mmHg upper and lower the setpoint. The results indicate that the output response reaches the target within 5min without overshoot. When ΔMAP is out of the bank, the supervising algorithm updates the FGS due to the behaviors of patient for driving it back to this range.

Simulation result 2: Using Guyton's model is useful in simulation of many other physiological parameters such as the changes of heart rate, cardiac output, plasma volume, and so forth. It is also available for simulating the response of patient after hypotensive

control. An example is illustrated in Fig.7, which presents a fluctuation within 20 mmHg around normal value of MAP after stop the infusion pump.

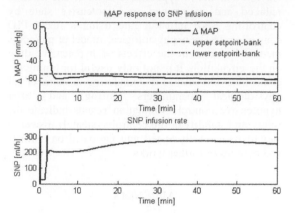

Fig. 6. Result 1 – Hypotensive control.

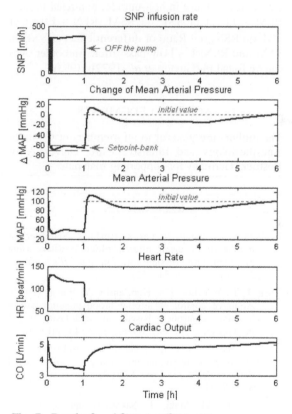

Fig. 7. Results 2 – After stop the pump.

5. DISCUSSION

Using Guyton's model is a suitable solution for modelling the effects of SNP on the circulation. However, Guyton's model contains a lot of sensitive parameters (Guyton *et al.*, 1993), so it is not easy to validate the model. Mapping this model to blood pressure control system is difficult because of many positive feedbacks. Therefore it is also not so easy to tune the controller. However, it is very useful for simulating several different medical conditions.

6. CONCLUSIONS

The paper summarizes the advantages of using Guyton's model in hypotensive control. The MAP is reduced and maintained at hypotensive state by controlling SNP infusion rate using a fuzzy PID controller. The new physiological model of patient is modified to present the effects of hypotensive drug on the circulation. It is not only useful for tuning the controller, but also for simulating a number of physiological parameters during and after hypotensive control. Simulation results indicate the safety and stability of the control system. However, it should be carefully tested and validated on animals and patients in further works.

APPENDIX

The notations of SNP effective module in Fig.2 are: RSM – Vascular resistance in muscle tissues; RSN – Vascular resistance in non-muscle, non-renal tissues; REM – Effect of SNP on RSM; REN – Effect of SNP on RSN; α – Ratio of different effect of SNP on RSM and RSN; F – Low pass filter. And other ones can be found in (Guyton et al., 1972b; 1993).

ACKNOWLEDGMENTS

The authors are grateful to all members of Clinic of Anesthesiology and Intensive Care, University of Rostock, Germany for supporting materials.

REFERENCES

Behbehani, K. and R. R. Cross (1991). A controller for regulation of mean arterial blood pressure using optimum nitroprusside infusion rate. *IEEE Trans. Biomed. Eng.*, **38**, 513-521.

Chen, C.T., W.L.Lin, T.S. Kuo, and C.Y. Wang (1997). Adaptive control of arterial blood pressure with a learning controller based on multilayer neural networks. *IEEE Trans. Biomed.Eng.*, **44**, 601-609.

Er, M. J. and Y. Gao (2003). Adaptive control strategy for blood pressure regulation using a fuzzy neural network. *IEEE Int. Conf. Syst., Man and Cybernetics*, **3**, 2120-2125.

Furutani, E., M. Araki, T. Sakamoto and S. Maetani (1995). Blood pressure control during surgical operations, *IEEE Trans. Biomed.Eng.*, **42**, 999-1006.

Furutani, E., M. Araki, S. Kan, T. Aung, H. Onodera, M. Imamura, G. Shirakami and S. Maetani (2004). An automatic control system of the blood pressure of patients under surgical operation. *Inter. J. Control, Automat., and Syst.*, **2**, 39-54.

Ganbing W., (1988). Adaptive Controller of Blood Pressure using Model with Fraction time delays. Proc. *IEEE 10th Conf. Med.Biology*, 1309-1310.

Guyton, A.C., T.G. Coleman, A.W. Cowley, Jr J.F. Liard, Jr R.A. Norman and Jr R.D. Manning (1972a). Systems analysis of Arterial Pressure Regulation and Hypertension. *Annals of Biomed. Eng.*, **1**, 254-281

Guyton, A.C., T.G. Coleman and H.J. Granger (1972b). Circulation: Overall Regulation, *Annual Rev. Physiology*, **4**, 13-46.

Guyton, A.C., T.G. Coleman and J.P. Montani (1993). *Annotation of large circulatory model*, University of Mississippi Medical Center.

Guyton, A.C. and L.E. Hall (1996). Unit IV – The Circulation, *in: Textbook of medical physiology*, W.B. Saunders, Philadelphia, 159-294.

Held, C.M., R.J. Roy (1995). Multiple Drug Hemodynamic Control by Means of a Supervisory-Fuzzy Rule-based Adaptive Control System: Validation on a model. *IEEE Trans. Biomed. Eng.*, **42**, 371-385.

Isaka, S. and A. V. Sebald (1993). Control strategies for arterial blood pressure regulation. *IEEE Trans. Biomed. Engineering*, **40**, 353-363.

Kähler, R., M. Janda, C. Beck, O. Simanski (2004). Kontrollierte Hypotension mit Natrium nitroprussid, *Proc. 11. Sym. Maritime Elektro., Elektronik und Informat., Universität Rostock*, **534-04**, 145-151.

Ma, J., K.Y. Zhu, and S.M. Krishnan (2000). Automatic Postoperative Blood Pressure Control, *IEEE 22nd Annual EMBS*, July 23-28, Chicago IL, 817-820.

Meier, R., J. Nieuwland, A.M. Zbinden, and S.S. Hacisalihzade (1992). Fuzzy control of blood pressure during anesthesia, *IEEE Control Syst. Magazine*, **12**, 12-17.

Nguyen, C.-N., O. Simanski, A. Schubert, R. Kähler, and B. Lampe (2005). An online Fuzzy Gain Scheduling for Blood Pressure Regulation. *Proc. 16th IFAC World Congress*, Prague, Czech Republic, July 4-8, 2005, Th-A19-TO/3.

Rao, R.R., B.W. Bequette, R.J. Roy (2000). Simultaneous regulation of Hemodynamic and anesthetic states: a simulation study, *Annals Biomed. Eng.*, **28**, 71-84.

Slate, J. B. (1980). *Model-based design of a controller for infusion sodium nitroprusside during postsurgical hypertension*. PhDThesis, Uni.ofWisconsin-Madison.

Slate, J. B. and L. C. Sheppard (1982). Automatic control of blood pressure by drug infusion, *IEEE Proc., Pt. A.*, **129**, 639-645.

Werner, J., D. Böhringer and M. Hexamer (2002). Simulation and prediction of cardiotherapeutical phenomena from a pulsatile model coupled to the Guyton circulatory model, *IEEE Trans. Biomed. Eng.*, **49**, 430-439.

Ying, H., L. Sheppard and D. Tucker (1988). Expert-system-based fuzzy control of arterial pressure by drug infusion. *Medical Progress Through Technology*, **13**, 203–215.

Ying, H., M. McEachern, D.W. Eddleman, and L.C. Sheppard (1992). Fuzzy Control of Mean Arterial Pressure in Postsurgical Patients with Sodium Nitroprusside infusion. *IEEE Trans. Biomed. Eng.*, **39**, 1060-1070.

Ying, H. and L.C. Sheppard (1994). Regulating Mean Arterial Pressure in Postsurgical Cardiac Patients. A fuzzy logic system to control administration of sodium nitroprusside. *IEEE Eng. in Medicine and Biology*, **13**, 671-677.

Yu C., R.J. Roy, H. Haufman, and B.W. Bequette (1992). Multiple-Model Adaptive Predictive Control of Mean Arterial Pressure and Cardiac Output. *IEEE Trans. Biomed. Eng.*, **39**, 765-778.

Zhao, Z. Y., M. Tomizuka and S. Isaka (1993). Fuzzy gain scheduling of PID controllers. *IEEE Trans. on Syst., Man and Cybernetics*, **23**, 1392-1398.

KINEMATIC TRAJECTORY GENERATION IN A NEUROMUSCULOSKELETAL MODEL WITH SOMATOSENSORY AND VESTIBULAR FEEDBACK

Kamran Iqbal[a], Anindo Roy[b]

[a]*Department of Systems Engineering, University of Arkansas, Little Rock, AR, USA*
[b]*Department of Mechanical Engineering, Massachusetts Institute of Technology, Cambridge, MA, USA*

Abstract: Mechanisms of posture and movement control in the human body are investigated via a four-segment neuro-musculoskeletal model characterizing the action of the central nervous system (CNS). The model includes position, velocity, force, and vestibular feedback, the intrinsic stiffness properties of the muscle, and the physiological latencies of the motor servo-system. Prediction of limb kinematics is achieved through a combination of analytical methods and computer simulations. Our simulation results confirm that the anatomical arrangement, active muscle stiffness, force and vestibular feedback, and physiological latencies of the body segments play a major role in shaping motor control processes in the human body. *Copyright © 2006 IFAC*

Keywords: biomechanics, musculoskeletal model, dynamic stability, PID controller.

1. INTRODUCTION

The use of dynamic systems theory to provide insight into neurophysiology has a long history. Posture and movement in the human body are the outcomes of a complex control system that monitors a very large number of inputs, related to the orientation of the body segments, to produce an adequate output as muscle activation. Complexity arises because of the very large number of correlated inputs and outputs. The finite contraction and release time of muscles and the neural control loop delays make the problem even more difficult. The human postural control system receives information from proprioceptive, visual, vestibular, and perhaps other sensors, and it controls a musculoskeletal structure with over 200 degrees of freedom (DOFs) powered by approximately 750 muscles (Barin, 1989).

The motivation for this work is to develop a simple yet physiologically accurate model of human biomechanics and use it to study fundamental aspects of CNS control of posture and movement. Specifically, we are interested to explore answers to the following questions: a) how can a simple CNS control models be integrated into the mathematical description of the body derived from anatomy and physiology, and b) how does proprioception involving position, velocity, and force feedback facilitate control of posture and movement. To answer these questions, we consider a simplified characterization of the postural control system that broadly speaking has two components: one, representing the musculoskeletal dynamics in the sagittal plane, the other representing the sensors (muscled spindle, GTO, and the vestibular system), and the CNS. The model includes important physiological parameters such as muscle (active and passive) stiffness properties, force feedback from the Golgi tendon organ (GTO), length and velocity feedback from the muscle spindle, vestibular feedback from the Otolith system, and transmission latencies in the neural pathways, which are often overlooked in the motor control models (He *et al.*, 1991). A neural PID controller is assumed to represent the CNS analogue in the model theoretic framework for posture and movement regulation.

The proposed model presented in this paper makes a few simplifying assumptions such as: 1) the inertial dynamics are linearizable about an operating point (He *et al.*, 1991; Barin, 1989); 2) the foot segment is stationary (Kuo, 1995); and, 3) the transmission delays can be approximated in the linear analysis.

The paper is organized as follows: In Section 2 we develop the four-link neuro-musculoskeletal model and derive its closed-loop dynamics. In Section 3 we derive limb kinematics of point-to-point voluntary movement and provide simulation results illustrating the applicability of the modelling framework. Finally, conclusions are drawn in Section 4.

2. FORMULATION OF THE MULTI-SEGMENT BIOMECHANICAL MODEL

In this section we develop mathematical model of a multi-segment neuro-musculoskeletal system based on the dynamics of the constituent components.

The human body is modelled as a multi-segment structure comprising of skeletal, muscular, and sensory subsystems. The musculoskeletal system model consists of four planar rigid-body segments connected by single-degree-of-freedom joints that approximate the sagittal plane biomechanics (Fig. 1). The segments represent a bilateral symmetrical arrangement of the feet, legs, thighs, and head-arm-trunk (HAT) with stationary foot segment. The model parameters, i.e., the segment length, mass, centre of gravity and moment of inertia, are based on gross anatomical properties of the human body (Stroeve 1999). The length of the stationary foot segment defines the base of support (BOS) in the anterior-posterior direction. The leg, thigh, and HAT each have a single-rotational degree of freedom.

The CNS commands and active force generation in the muscle are represented by torques applied at the ankle, knee, and hip joints. The joint torques each comprise of a feedforward and a feedback component, the feedback component representing the action of passive and active viscoelasticity in the muscle tendon and the CNS response to proprioceptive feedback from the muscle spindle and GTO in the lower level motor servo. It follows from experiments (Kirsch *et al.*, 1993) that the feedback gains are task-dependant, and can be adapted by supraspinal pathways to suit task conditions.

The corresponding block diagram for postural control and movement regulation is shown in Fig. 2. In the following, $I \triangleq I^{n \times n}$ represents an identity matrix of dimension n and $\mathbb{R}^{n \times 1}$ represents a real vector of dimension n, where $n = 3$ is the DOF.

The Muscle Spindle Model. The muscle spindle dynamics are characterized by a constant gain and a first order lag (Chen and Poppele, 1978):

$$\tilde{G}_1(s) = \frac{g}{\tau_1 s + 1} I, \quad \tilde{G}_1^*(s) = \frac{\beta g}{\tau_1^* s + 1} I \qquad (1)$$

where $\tilde{G}_1^*$ and $\tilde{G}_1^*$ refer to the spindle transfer characteristics with respect to position and velocity inputs, and β is the ratio of the muscle length and rate sensitivities and lies in a fixed interval [0.06, 0.14] for most impedance levels.

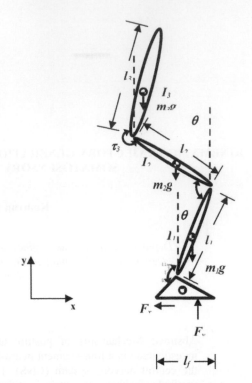

Fig.1. Schematic of the multi-segment biomechanical model over stationary base of support (BOS). In the figure, m_i and l_i are the masses and lengths of the ankle, knee, and hip, respectively; k_i is the location of segment centres of mass (COM) above BOS, θ_i are the segment angles measured from the vertical; I_i are the moments of inertia for the three segments; τ_i are the ankle, knee, and hip torques, respectively; and g is the acceleration due to gravity (Iqbal and Pai, 2000).

In this study, a value of $\beta = 0.15$ is assumed. We note that the spindle dynamics can be neglected without significantly affecting the response, since: 1) While simple models for muscle spindles are in general, unrealistic, they are expedient and justifiable for small perturbations around an operating point (Loeb and Mileusnic 2003); 2) Researchers have often used linear models of the muscle spindles in the literature (e.g. He at al., 1991); and finally, 3) It has been shown that intrafusal fibres are slow twitch fibres. Fast dynamic behaviour would in fact distort the equality of this information, and would in any case not be useful in regard of the time-delays for the neural transport and processing times, which dominate the dynamic behaviour. Therefore, simplification of the muscle spindle to a linear gain accompanied by a time delay seems to be justified. The constant gain representation is given as: $\tilde{G}_1(s) = gI$, $\tilde{G}_1^*(s) = \beta gI$, where it is assumed, purely for simplicity, that the spindle gains for the ankle, knee, and hip muscles have equal magnitude.

The Muscle Model. A Hill-based muscle model is assumed. Such a model typically contains three elements (Fig. 3). The parallel elastic element (PE) models the force generated under passive conditions. The contractile element (CE) produces the active force, which is transmitted through the series elastic element (SE) to the point of attachment.

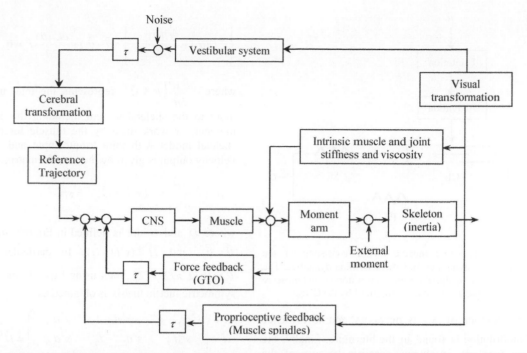

Fig. 2. Conceptual block diagram of the four-link human musculoskeletal system with inherent muscle stiffness and viscosity, and including physiological latencies in position, velocity, force, and vestibular feedback.

The combination of the CE and SE elements is referred to as the muscle-tendon-unit. The inputs to the muscle model are the neural input, and the muscle-tendon-unit length. One output is the total force, which is the sum of the active and passive forces. The second output is the CE length, which must be available if the muscle spindles are to be modelled in parallel with the CE.

For this work a second-order muscle model (Winters and Stark, 1985) is used. It consists of a component representing the excitation dynamics from the motor control signal to the neural signal, the activation dynamics representing transfer from the neural signal to the active state, and the contraction dynamics that characterizes the force velocity relation, in combination with the fibre force-length, and series elastic (SE) force-length relation. Without loss of the essential dynamic features, the model can be linearized, in which the excitation and activation dynamics are each modelled as first-order lags. The dynamic contribution of the SE element is significant only for frequencies above 4 Hz (van der Helm and Rozendaal, 2000) and therefore can be neglected. The linearized force-length and force-velocity relations can be regarded as part of the skeletal system, affecting the joint stiffness and viscosity. Hence, the muscle activation dynamics can be described by the transfer matrix given as:

$$\tilde{G}_m(s) = G_{exc}(s)G_{act}(s)\tilde{F}_{max} \qquad (2)$$

where $G_{exc}(s) = 1/(\tau_e s + 1)$, $\tau_e > 0$ represents the model of the excitation dynamics; $G_{act}(s) = 1/(\tau_a s + 1)$, $\tau_a > 0$ represents the model of the activation dynamics; $\tilde{F}_{max}$ is a diagonal matrix of the maximal isometric muscle forces, which depend on the physiologic cross-sectional area (PCSA)

including the intrinsic muscle properties, the pennation angles, and the myofiber length of the muscles in the ankle, knee, and hip, given as: $\tilde{F}_{max} = \text{diag}(F_{max_1}, F_{max_2}, F_{max_3})$, and τ_e and τ_a are the excitation and activation time constants.

The active and passive muscle stiffness and viscosity are modelled as intrinsic muscle impedance. The intrinsic stiffness model is given as (Stroeve, 1999):

$$\tilde{K}_{ms}(s) = \frac{K_{ce}K_{se}}{K_{ce} + K_{se}} \frac{s/\tau_1 + 1}{s/\tau_2 + 1} + K_{pe},$$ where the

frequency constants are given as: $\tau_1 = K_{ce}/B_{ce}$, $\tau_2 = (K_{ce} + K_{se})/B_{ce}$, K_{ce} and B_{ce} are the stiffness and viscosity of the CE, K_{se} is the stiffness of the SE, and K_{pe} is the stiffness of the PE.

The Force Feedback. Golgi tendon organs (GTO) are mechanoreceptors that sample the active muscle force. The force feedback signal from the GTO has been commonly modelled as a force sensor with a static nonlinearity preceding the linear dynamics (Crago *et al.*, 1982). However, there is sufficient evidence in the literature (e.g. van der Helm and Rozendaal, 2000) that the dynamic effects of the GTO are negligible, so the force feedback can be represented by a constant gain followed by a time delay. Therefore, the force feedback from GTO is modelled as a pure gain, i.e., $\tilde{G}_{gt}(s) = K_f I$, where it is assumed that the feedback gains are the same for ankle, knee, and hip.

The force feedback is very effective in increasing the frequency bandwidth of the muscle activation dynamics (van der Helm and Rozendaal, 2000). Additionally, force feedback gain is not affected by the dynamics of the skeletal system. Furthermore,

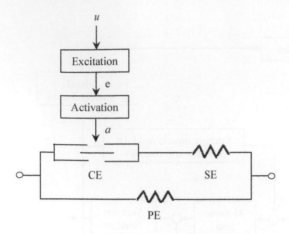

Fig. 3. A Hill-type muscle model consisting of the excitation dynamics and the activation dynamics. The motor control signal u represents a normalized measure of the muscle activation a specified by the CNS.

no modulation of K_f is necessary and no evidence of modulation is found in the literature. Finally, the force feedback is always negative because of the presence of an inhibitory interneuron present in the projection of the GTO to the α-motor neuron.

The Musculoskeletal Dynamics. The linearized model of the musculoskeletal dynamics is derived as follows: let θ_i be the set of segment angles in inertial reference frame; $\tilde{\dot{\theta}}_i \in \mathbb{R}^{3\times1}$ be the vector of segment velocities; $\tilde{\ddot{\theta}}_i \in \mathbb{R}^{3\times1}$ be the vector of segment accelerations; τ_i be the set of net joint moments; d_{ii} be the set of components of the inertia matrix; f_i be the set of gravitational moment components; then, the dynamics of the multi-segment model supported on a fixed BOS can be derived using Euler-Lagrangian dynamics (Iqbal and Pai, 2000). This non-linear matrix differential equation is given as:

$$\tilde{D}(\theta)\ddot{\theta} + \tilde{B}(\theta,\dot{\theta})\dot{\theta} + \tilde{G}(\theta) = \tilde{E}\cdot\tilde{\tau} \qquad (3)$$

where $\tilde{\theta}(0) \triangleq \tilde{\theta}_i$ and $\tilde{\dot{\theta}}(0) \triangleq \tilde{v}_i$ are the initial conditions; $\tilde{E} \in \mathbb{R}^{3\times3}$ is the input matrix; $\tilde{D} \in \mathbb{R}^{3\times3}$ is the inertia matrix, $\tilde{B} \in \mathbb{R}^{3\times3}$ is the Coriolis component, and $\tilde{G} \in \mathbb{R}^{3\times1}$ is the gravitational component.

The nonlinear body dynamics of the skeleton have been demonstrated to be fairly linear in certain regions (Hemami and Jaswa, 1978; Kuo, 1995), and for a given perturbation, the closed-loop system comprised of both the neural controller and the body dynamics appear to be linear (Barin, 1989). By using multi-input multi-output (MIMO) transfer matrix, the musculoskeletal dynamics can be analyzed using the rich set of tools from linear system theory. The corresponding linearized transfer function model about the stance position ($\tilde{\theta} = \tilde{\theta}_e$) can be obtained by substituting $\tilde{\theta} = \tilde{\theta}_e$ in Eq. (3) and is given as:

$$\left\{ s^2\tilde{D}(\tilde{\theta}_e) + \left.\frac{\partial\tilde{G}(\tilde{\theta})}{\partial\tilde{\theta}}\right|_{\theta=\theta_e} \right\}\cdot(\tilde{\theta}-\tilde{\theta}_e) + \frac{\partial\tilde{L}^T(\tilde{\theta})}{\partial\tilde{\theta}}\tilde{F} = 0 \quad (4)$$

where $\dfrac{\partial\tilde{L}^T(\tilde{\theta})}{\partial\tilde{\theta}}\tilde{F} \triangleq \tilde{M}_{tot}$ represents the total moment input to the skeletal system including the external moment, or work done by the muscle forces. The skeletal model with joint torque input and angular velocity output is given by the transfer matrix:

$$\tilde{G}_I(s) \triangleq \frac{s\tilde{\theta}}{\tilde{M}_{tot}} = s(s^2\tilde{D}+\tilde{G})^{-1} \triangleq s\tilde{H}^{-1} \qquad (5)$$

where $\tilde{D}$ and $\tilde{G}$ are as defined in Eq. (4) and (5) at $\tilde{\theta} = \tilde{\theta}_e$, and $\tilde{H} \triangleq (s^2\tilde{D}+\tilde{G})$. In particular, when $\tilde{\theta}_e = [\pi/2\ \pi/2\ \pi/2]'$, then using Eqs. (3) and (4) the symmetric inertia matrix is obtained as:

$$\tilde{H} = \begin{pmatrix} s^2d_{11}-f_1 & s^2d_{12} & s^2d_{13} \\ s^2d_{12} & s^2d_{22}-f_2 & s^2d_{23} \\ s^2d_{13} & s^2d_{23} & s^2d_{33}-f_3 \end{pmatrix} = \tilde{H}' \qquad (6)$$

where the prime symbol denotes transpose operation.

Neural PID Controller Model. The CNS control of the postural stabilization process is represented by three autonomous PID controllers (Roy and Iqbal, 2005b), one each for the ankle, knee, and hip joints. The PID controller is chosen to characterize the control action of the CNS for the following reasons: 1) In biomechanics, researchers have often used an inverted-pendulum model to identify human postural dynamics (Johansson *et al.*, 1988). Such models generally include a simple spring-damper servomechanism that naturally develops into PID control action; 2) Experimentally observed gain and phase data in human postural control fits an inverted-pendulum postural control model with a PID controller (Peterka, 2002); and 3) PID control action is a simple feedback structure that implements all three fundamental modes of control. The neural controller model used in this study is given as:

$$\tilde{G}_c = \begin{pmatrix} n_{c_1}(s)/s & 0 & 0 \\ 0 & n_{c_2}(s)/s & 0 \\ 0 & 0 & n_{c_3}(s)/s \end{pmatrix} \qquad (7)$$

where $n_{c(i)}(s) \triangleq K_{d(i)}s^2 + K_{p(i)}s + K_{I(i)}$ denotes the numerator polynomial of the PID controllers.

Physiological Latencies. The feedback delays in position, velocity, force, and vestibular feedback are assumed to be time-invariant, and lumped together such that Padé approximation can be used, leading to a non-transcendental form of the characteristic polynomial of the closed-loop system. The latencies in the muscle spindle and GTO feedback loops are given as:

$$e^{-\tilde{\Delta}s} = \begin{pmatrix} e^{-\Delta_1 s} & 0 & 0 \\ 0 & e^{-\Delta_2 s} & 0 \\ 0 & 0 & e^{-\Delta_3 s} \end{pmatrix} \simeq (I - s\tilde{\Delta})(I + s\tilde{\Delta})^{-1} \quad (8)$$

where $\tilde{\Delta} = \mathrm{diag}(\Delta_i)$ represents a transmission delay (muscle spindle or GTO loop).

Muscle Moment Arms. The muscle moment arms represent the mapping between the muscle and the joint. In general, the moment arm model can be obtained from the change in the muscle-tendon-unit length, i.e., $\tilde{R}(\tilde{\theta}) \triangleq \partial \tilde{l}_m / \partial \tilde{\theta}$, where $\tilde{l}_m$ is the muscle-tendon-unit length vector and $\tilde{\theta}$ is the joint angle vector. We assume that the muscle moment arm matrix is invariant to the changes in the joint angles. The resulting muscle moment arm matrix is given as:

$$\tilde{R}(\tilde{\theta}) = \tilde{R} \triangleq \begin{pmatrix} r & 0 & 0 \\ -r & r & 0 \\ 0 & -r & r \end{pmatrix}, \ r > 0. \quad (9)$$

The Vestibular System Model. The vestibular system is the sensory apparatus that provides the dominant input about movement and orientation in space. The dynamics of the vestibular system are characterized by a lead-lag filter (Borah *et al.*, 1988), given as: $G_{vesti} = k(s + c_1)/(s + c_2)$. For humans, the frequency constants c_1 and c_2 are approximately 0.1 Hz and 0.2 Hz, respectively.

Closed-loop System Dynamics. The closed-loop transfer matrices of the biomechanical model are defined between the reference trajectory $\tilde{\theta}^*$ and joint angle $\tilde{\theta}$. The closed-loop matrix is derived using block diagram reduction (Roy and Iqbal, 2005b):

$$\tilde{G}_{CL(track)} \triangleq \frac{\tilde{\theta}}{\tilde{\theta}^*} = \{\tilde{H} + (K_{\theta p} + B_{\theta p}s)I + \tilde{R}'\tilde{T}\tilde{R}\}^{-1}$$
$$\cdot \tilde{R}'(I + \tilde{L}_g)^{-1}\tilde{G}_m\tilde{G}_c \quad (10)$$

The closed-loop characteristic polynomial can be computed by evaluating the matrix inverse in Eq. (10) whose determinant is given as $\psi(s)/\delta(s)$, where $\delta(s)$ and $\psi(s)$ are polynomials in s. Thus the closed-dynamics for movement control as:

$$\begin{pmatrix} \theta_{ankle} \\ \theta_{knee} \\ \theta_{hip} \end{pmatrix} = \frac{\delta(s) \cdot M(s)^{adj}}{\psi(s)} \tilde{R}'\tilde{T}^*\tilde{\theta}^*. \quad (11)$$

We note that analytical characterization of stabilizing PID controllers for general biomechanical models was discussed in Roy and Iqbal (2005a).

3. COMPUTATION OF LIMB KINEMATICS

In this section, we analytically compute limb

kinematics for point-to-point voluntary movement, based on the closed-loop equations developed earlier.

3.1. Reference Movement Trajectories

One of the most commonly used forms for the reference trajectories is the sigmoid function whose many variants can be found in the literature (Stroeve, 1999). One form of the sigmoid function is given as:

$$\theta^*(t) = \frac{2}{\pi}\tan^{-1}\left(\frac{c\pi(t - t_0)}{2}\right), \ c, t_0 \geq 0, \forall t \in [0, t_f) \quad (12)$$

We note that the Laplace transform of $\theta^*(t)$ does not exist as the function is nonlinear, however, using series expansion, an approximate sigmoid can be used, which is valid for $t \in [0, t_0 + 2/c\pi)$:

$$\theta^*_{approx}(t) \cong \frac{2}{\pi}\sum_{n=0}^{\infty}\frac{(-1)^n(c\pi)^{2n+1}(t - t_0)^{2n+1}}{2^{2n+1}(2n+1)} \quad (13)$$

$$\theta^*_{approx}(s) \cong \frac{2}{\pi}e^{-t_0 s}\sum_{n=0}^{\infty}\frac{(-1)^n(c\pi/2)^{2n+1}(2n)!}{s^{2n+2}} \quad (14)$$

We also note that a suitable reference trajectory can be realized at the output of a filter transfer function when the input is a step function, i.e.,

$$\tilde{\theta}^*(s) = \begin{pmatrix} \theta^*_{ankle} \\ \theta^*_{knee} \\ \theta^*_{hip} \end{pmatrix} = \frac{1}{s(\tau_{ref}s + 1)^n}\begin{pmatrix} \varphi_1 \\ \varphi_2 \\ \varphi_3 \end{pmatrix} \triangleq \Theta(s)\begin{pmatrix} \varphi_1 \\ \varphi_2 \\ \varphi_3 \end{pmatrix} \quad (15)$$

where φ_i ($i = 1, 2, 3$), represents the desired steady-state posture (in radians) of the ankle, knee, and hip, respectively; τ_{ref} is the time-constant (in ms); and n is the order of the filter. The above reference trajectory is characterized by a nonzero slope at $t = 0$, that corresponds to the impulsive action of the muscles at the initiation of the movement.

3.2. Movement Kinematics

In order to calculate the point-to-point movement profiles in response to a desired reference trajectory, we make use of the closed-loop dynamics for movement control (Eq. 10). The resulting limb kinematics of the ankle, knee, and hip are given as:

$$\begin{pmatrix} \theta_{ankle} \\ \theta_{knee} \\ \theta_{hip} \end{pmatrix} = r\sum_{i=1}^{3}\varphi_i\begin{pmatrix} \Lambda_i^{ankle} \\ \Lambda_i^{knee} \\ \Lambda_i^{hip} \end{pmatrix} \quad (16)$$

where Λ_i, are the unit step responses of the relevant transfer functions defined by Eqs. (10) and (15), and φ_i, is steady-state posture (in rad). We note that an arbitrary initial posture can be embedded into the framework by adding a non-zero initial condition vector in the closed-loop tracking dynamics, i.e.,

$$\begin{pmatrix} \theta_{ankle} \\ \theta_{knee} \\ \theta_{hip} \end{pmatrix} = r \sum_{i=1}^{3} \varphi_i \begin{pmatrix} \Lambda_i^{ankle} \\ \Lambda_i^{knee} \\ \Lambda_i^{hip} \end{pmatrix} + r^{-1} \begin{pmatrix} \varphi_1^0 \\ \varphi_2^0 \\ \varphi_3^0 \end{pmatrix} \qquad (17)$$

where φ_i^0 are the initial posture of the ankle, knee, and hip, for $i = 1, 2, 3$, respectively. We note that there are two biomechanical constraints on the movement: 1) overshoot, and 2) speed of the response as characterized by the settling time. Low values of both are desirable to reduce undesirable body sway. The higher order kinematics (e.g. velocity and acceleration) are computed as: $\dot{\tilde{\theta}}(s) \triangleq s\tilde{\theta}(s)$ and $\ddot{\tilde{\theta}}(s) \triangleq s^2\tilde{\theta}(s)$.

3.3. Simulation Results

For illustration, let the initial posture be given by $\varphi_i^0 = 0.15 \times [\pi/6 \ -\pi/3 \ \pi/12]'$ rad and suppose we desire the final posture to be $\varphi_i = [\pi/8 \ -\pi/4 \ \pi/16]'$ rad; such a trajectory may, for example, represent stand-to-sit movements (Fig. 4a). The inertia model was linearized about the upright posture $\tilde{\theta}_e = [\pi/2 \ \pi/2 \ \pi/2]'$ rad and a first-order Padé approximant was used for the spindle and GTO latencies. The resulting limb trajectories are plotted in Fig. 4b. It can be seen that the kinematics are dynamically stable and attain the desired steady-state posture. Further, the movement has negligible overshoot ($\sim 0.1\%$), and a low settling time (≤ 1 sec).

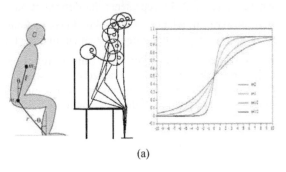

(a)

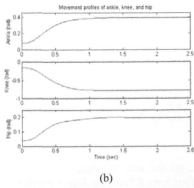

(b)

Fig. 4. (a) Reference trajectories for different time constants (right) and its physiological significance (left); (b) limb trajectories in response to a third-order reference trajectory with time constant $\tau = 100$ ms.

4. CONCLUSIONS

The multi-segment biomechanical model presented in this study displays several physiological attributes such as musculoskeletal dynamics, Hill-type muscle behaviour, proprioceptive feedback, neural PID controllers, latencies, and a vestibular system model. Analytical and computational results display stability and performance aspects of the closed-loop system.

REFERENCES

Barin, K., 1989, "Evaluation of a generalized model of human postural dynamics and control in the sagittal plane," *Biol. Cyb.*, **61**, 37-50.

Borah, J., Young, L.R., and Curry, R.E., 1988, "Optimal estimator model for human spatial orientation," *Ann. NY Acad. Sci.*, **545**, 51-73.

Chen, W.J., and Poppele, R.E., 1978, "Small-signal analysis of response of mammalian muscle spindles with fusimotor stimulation and a comparison with large-signal responses," *J. Neurophysiology*, **41**, pp. 15-27.

Crago, P.E., Houk, J.C., and Rymer, W.Z., 1982, "Sampling of total muscle force by tendon organs," *J. Neurophysiology*, **47**, 1069-1083.

He, J., Levine, W.S., and Loeb, G.E., 1991, "Feedback Gains for Correcting Small Perturbations to Standing Posture," *IEEE Trans. Autom. Control*, **36**, 322-332.

Hemami, H., and Jaswa, V.C., 1978, "On a three-link model of the dynamics of standing up and sitting down," *IEEE Trans. Sys., Man, and Cyb.*, **8**, 115-120.

Iqbal, K., and Pai, Y.C., 2000, "Predicted region of stability for balance recovery: motion at the knee joint can improve termination of forward movement," *J. Biomech.*, **33**, 1619-1627.

Johansson, R., Magnusson, M., and Akesson, M., 1988, "Identification of Human Postural Dynamics," *IEEE Trans. Biomed. Eng.*, **35**, 858-869.

Kirsch, F.K., Kearney, R.E., and MacNeil J.B., 1993, "Identification of time-varying dynamics of the human triceps surae stretch reflex: I Rapid isometric contraction," *Exp. Brain Res.*, **97**, 115-127.

Kuo, A.D., 1995, "An optimal control model for analyzing human postural balance," *IEEE Trans. Biomedical Eng.*, **42**, 87-101.

Loeb, G.E., and Mileusnic, M., 2003, "A Model of the Mammalian Muscle Spindle," *Soc. Neuroscience*, **278.2**.

Peterka, R.J., 2002, "Sensorimotor integration in human postural control," *J. Neurophys.*, **88**, 1097-118.

Roy, A., and Iqbal, K., 2005a, "Synthesis Of Stabilizing PID Controllers Using Generalized Hermite-Biehler Theorem," *IFAC World Cong.*, 1, 1-6, Czech Rep.

Roy, A., and Iqbal, K., 2005b, "Theoretical framework for the dynamic stability analysis and trajectory generation of a multi-segment biomechanical model," submitted to *ASME J. Biomechanical Eng.*

Stroeve, S., 1999, "Impedance characteristics of a neuromusculoskeletal model of the human arm. I. Posture control," *Biol. Cybern.*, **81**, 475-495.

van der Helm, F., and Rozendaal, L., 2000, "Musculoskeletal Systems with Intrinsic and Proprioceptive Feedback," in *Biomechanics and Neural Control of Movement and Posture*, Springer-Verlag, Chapter 11, 164-174.

Winters, J.M., and Stark, L., 1985, "Analysis of fundamental human movement patterns through the use of indepth antagonistic muscle models," *IEEE Trans. Biomed. Eng.*, **32**, 826-839.

A NONLINEAR MODEL FOR VASOCONSTRICTION

John Ringwood* Violeta Mangourova*
Sarah-Jane Guild** Simon Malpas**

* Dept. of Electronic Eng., NUI Maynooth, Ireland
** Dept. of Physiology, Uni. of Auckland, New Zealand

Abstract: The control of blood pressure is a complex mixture of neural, hormonal and intrinsic interactions at the level of the heart, kidney and blood vessels. While experimental approaches to understanding these interactions remain useful, it remains difficult to conduct experiments to quantify these interactions as the number of parameters increases. Thus modelling approaches can offer considerable assistance. Typical mathematical models which describe the ability of the blood vessels to change their diameter (vasoconstriction) assume linearity of operation. However, due to the interaction of multiple vasocontrictive and vasodilative effectors, there is a significant nonlinear response to the influence of neural factors, particularly at higher levels of nerve activity (often seen in subjects with high blood pressure) which leads to low blood flow rates. This paper proposes a nonlinear mathematical model for the relationship between neural influences (sympathetic nerve activity (SNA) and blood flow, using a feedback path to model the predominently nonlinear effect of local vasoactive modulators such as Nitric Oxide, which oppose the action of SNA. The model, the structure of which is motivated by basic physiological principles, is parameterised using a numerical optimisation method using open-loop data collected from rabbits. The model responses are shown to be in good agreement with the experimental data. *Copyright C 2006 IFAC.*

Keywords: Biomedical systems, mathematical model, blood flow, nonlinear analysis, numerical optimisation.

1. INTRODUCTION

The regulation of blood pressure is critical in maintaining nutrient and oxygen supply to the various perfused organs. Blood pressure is determined according to the (Ohm's Law) relationship:

$$MAP = CO.TPR \qquad (1)$$

where:

MAP is the mean (of the systolic and diastolic) pressure (measured in mmHg),

CO is cardiac output, evaluated as the product of heart rate and stroke volume (in l/s), and

TPR is the total peripheral resistance as seen by the heart (in mmHg s/l).

This study will focus on those components which mediate the resistance to blood flow, with the primary pump, the heart, assumed to have a relatively constant output. Blood flow may be differentially regulated according to physiological needs at any particular time via a variety of hormonal, neural and intrinsic factors.

In particular, the emphasis is on TPR and how it mediates blood flow/pressure on a relatively short timescale i.e. seconds. Central to this timescale, with a time delay between stimulation and response of 0.6s (Guild *et al.*, 2001), is the neural control of blood pressure, with sympathetic innervation of a number of major organs and areas of the vasculature, allowing rapid control of resistance via the central nervous system. Such sympathetic nerve activity (SNA) causes the release of neurotransmitters which, in general, cause the smooth muscle surrounding small arteries and arterioles to constrict (DiBona and Kopp, 1997).

The distribution of sympathetic innervation throughout the vasculature (and the nature of the local receptors i.e. whether they cause vasoconstriction or vasodilation) determines the action that will take place at any particular site. However, in addition to neural control, several other mechanisms have significant effect on resistance, including:

- Hormones, which circulate throughout the system and can effect both vasodilation or vasoconstriction, depending on the particular hormone and the type of receptor it binds to (typical hormones include Epinephrine, Antidiuretic Hormone, Angiotensin II and Cortisol (Sorensen *et al.*, 2000; Bellomo *et al.*, 1999)),
- Intrinsic factors (myogenic autoregulation), which regulate blood vessel compliance and, for example, produce a vasoconstrictive action in the smooth muscle in response to a distorting force on the walls of blood vessels due to blood pressure (Navar, 1998),
- Paracrines, which are humoral substances that are secreted by cells in the endothelium (the area between the circulating blood and the vascular smooth muscle) and affect neighboring cells. Paracrines can have both vasodilatory (e.g. Prostacyclin, Nitric Oxide) and vasoconstrictive effects (e.g. Thromboxane, Endothelin-1), with some paracrines having both dilatory and constrictive potential (e.g. Endothelin-1 (Boulanger and Vanhoutte, 1998)), depending on the receptors they bind to.
- Metabolic factors, which can elicit vasoaction in response to local metabolic demands. Typical mediators include oxygen (constriction).

Fig.1 (adapted from (Richardson *et al.*, 1998)) attempts to summarise the various factors involved in mediating vasoaction. The vasoactive mechanisms can be loosely grouped into systemic effects (e.g. SNA, hormones) and local effects (paracrines, tissue metabolites). The vasoaction at any particular site is therefore likely to be a combination of both factors, dependent on:

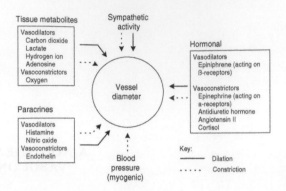

Fig. 1. Summary of vasoactive mechanisms

- The systemic requirements (mainly regulation of blood pressure), and
- Local requirements, including metabolic needs.

The study in this paper examines the renal vasculature in particular and attempts to build a mathematical model relating blood flow to SNA, with hormones, paracrines, etc. as mediating factors.

Mathematical models can be used to develop understanding of the system under study if the structure, and parameters, of the model can be validated by good agreement between model output and experimental data. In order to achieve this structural information, the emphasis should be on models which attempt to exploit the physical system description, rather than adopting a 'bulk' black box modelling approach. While the latter approach can give a very good model fit for specific experimental data, it does little to reveal the generic structure of the system under study.

To date, a number of attempts have been made to model the blood flow response to SNA. However, most techniques focus on linear models, which fail to capture essential aspects of the response. For example, the paper by Eppel *et al.* (2003) considers only broad magnitude changes in renal blood flow (RBF) in response to SNA stimulation, while the paper by Leonard *et al.* (2000) fits an unparameterised frequency response to the RBF/SNA relationship. Navakatikyan *et al.* (2000) fit a first-order (pole-only) model to the response, with Guild *et al.* (2001) using a frequency-domain approach to fit a linear 4th order (4 poles and 2 zeros plus delay) model to the data. While the linear model of Guild *et al.* (2001) gives a good fit at relatively low SNA amplitudes, the response match deteriorates as higher SNA stimulation evokes reactionary responses in (local) vasodilatory mechanisms.

2. MODEL DEVELOPMENT

The essential model structure is shown in Fig.2. The neural control of the renal vasculature is considered central to the model for two reasons:

(1) It is the most significant (and 'independent') input to the model i.e. most other mechanisms are considered reactionary on a more local level, and

(2) The experimental data on which the model will be validated is 'open-loop' as far as neural control of the vasculature is concerned. This is achieved via transection of the renal sympathetic nerve and artificial (electrical) stimulation of the renal nerves using a suitable excitation signal.

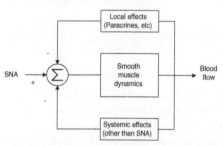

Fig. 2. Feedforward/feedback configuration

The two feedback paths represent the effects that both local and systemic blood pressure/flow control mechanisms have in response to SNA-based activation of renal blood flow. Since the renal vasculature is just one component which regulates blood pressure, the response from systemic mechanisms is unlikely to be nearly as significant as the response from local mechanisms. Therefore, a single feedback block will be employed in the structure as shown in Fig.2. This single block could incorporate systemic effects, but is configured to mainly model local effects. The model structure is based on the following physiological premise. Above a certain (threshold) value of (normal) blood flow, the response of blood flow to SNA is relatively linear. However, when blood flow drops below a certain value, local myogenic factors and paracrines work progressively harder (as blood flow decreases) to maintain an acceptable level of local blood flow. This combination of threshold and progressive response is captured by the 'activation level' block in Fig.3. The 'local dynamics' block in Fig.3 captures the speed of response of these local reactionary mechanisms. Finally, the 'smooth' muscle dynamics' block represents the dynamic response of the smooth muscle to a stimulus from an appropriate receptor.

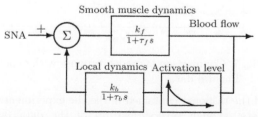

Fig. 3. Block diagram of proposed model structure

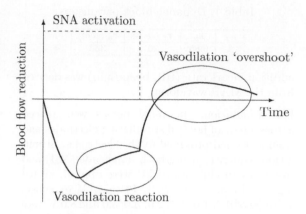

Fig. 4. Typical 'large-signal' response to SNA activation

Fig.4 shows the typical type of response obtained from the model. The initial response to a step activation in SNA is roughly first order exponential, but as soon as blood flow reduction reaches a certain level, local (opposite) effects temper the response dramatically. Following release of the SNA activation, the response returns rapidly to the original level, assisted by the local paracrines, etc. which are still active and have not yet been dispersed. Finally, the blood flow overshoots its original value, due to the slow dispersal of these local vasodilatory effects.

From the above description, some aspects of the model can be clarified:

- The local vasodilatory response is not linear and has some 'threshold' of blood flow change above which it is activated,
- The response of the local vasodilatory reaction is significantly slower than that of the smooth muscle to the SNA stimulus (i.e. $\tau_b > \tau_f$), and
- The magnitude of the action (to SNA) and reaction (by the local vasodilatory mechanism) is comparable, at least to an order of magnitude.

3. DATA AVAILABILITY

Experiments were performed on 6 anaesthetized New Zealand white rabbits (Leonard *et al.*, 2000). A transit time flow probe (type 2SB; Transonic Systems, Ithaca, NY, USA), connected to a compatible flowmeter (T106, Transonic Systems) was used to measure RBF, with arterial pressure being monitored using a catheter inserted into the central ear artery and connected to a pressure transducer (Cobe, Arvarda, CO). The measured signals were sampled at 500Hz, digitized and saved continuously as 2s averages of each variable. In

Table 1. Dynamic block parameters

k_f	k_b	τ_f (secs)	τ_b (secs)
1	0.85	20	333

addition, heart rate (HR, beats/min) was derived from the MAP waveform.

For stimulation, the renal nerves were placed across a pair of hooked stimulating electrodes and then sectioned proximal to the electrodes. Stimulation sequences using both amplitude (AM) and frequency modulation (FM) were applied, all using a pulse width of 2mS. In the AM sequence, voltages of 0.5, 1.0, 1.5, 2.0, 3.0, 5.0 and 8.0 V were applied in random order at a constant frequency of 5Hz. For the FM sequence, frequencies of 0.5, 1.0, 1.5, 2.0, 3.0, 5.0 and 8.0 Hz were applied in random order using a voltage equal to that required to produce a maximal RBF response. For both AM and FM sequences, the stimulation interval was 3 min., with a 5 min. recovery period before delivering the next stimulus.

4. MODEL PARAMETERISATION

Given the intuitive nature of the model and the strong relationship with the underlying physiology, initial attempts focussed on tuning the model parameters by trial and error. One further component was added to the model of Fig.3 in order to correctly represent the relationship between the varying levels of steady state response to the frequency of SNA stimulation. This (mildly) nonlinear characteristic preceeds the model section shown in Fig.3 and is given by the transformation in Fig.5. The parameters of the dynamic feedfor-

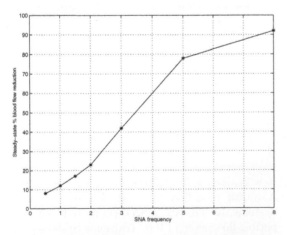

Fig. 5. Transformation for frequency stimulation

ward and feedback blocks are detailed in Table.1. Finally, the nonlinear feedback activation function is shown in Fig.6. A number of aspects of the model are noteworthy:

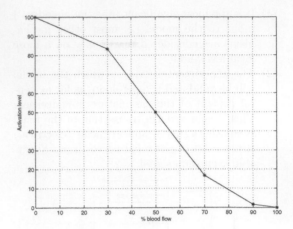

Fig. 6. Feedback activation function

- The feedback activation function has little effect below blood flow reduction levels of 30%.
- The feedback branch has a potential activation level which is comparable with that of the feedforward section, when the blood flow level suffers any significant decrease (say to about 60%, representing a reduction of 40%). Note that the nonlinear feedback characteristic has been normalised approximately to the SNA stimulation level (of 100) at the summation block. Therefore the values of k_f and k_b can be directly compared.
- The feedback (vasodilatory) mechanism has a time response which is an order of magnitude greater than that of the feedforward response. This, in the main, accounts for the characteristic step response of the system.

The performance of the model in comparison to the recorded experimental data may now be evaluated by reference to, by way of example, Fig.7. Clearly, the model has captured the essence

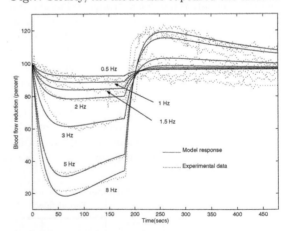

Fig. 7. Comparison of model response with experimental data

of the response contained in the the experimental data, though several features of the data fall outside the scope of the model, for example:

- The data contains a significant amount of noise, as is to be expected with physiological experimental data. It is not the intention of the model to capture this. Arguably a better comparison could be made if the experimental data had been filtered prior to plotting, but the filter would introduce dynamics of its own which may interfere with the parameter determination.
- There is some longer term drift in the data, most noticable at lower levels of SNA activation. This is due to longer term autoregulatory effects, which are numerous. Conceivably, such an effect could be built into the model, but it is difficult (from an experimental point of view) to isolate such effects in order to develop components which will provide a generic description of these mechanisms.

The experimental responses in Fig.7, for higher activation levels (e.g. 3Hz, 5 Hz and 8 Hz) show a good pattern match to the 'template' response of Fig.4. At lower levels of SNA activation, the response is broadly (first-order) exponential, with little participation of the feedback loop.

5. CONCLUSIONS

This paper has developed a large-signal model for neurally-induced vasoaction in the renal vasculature. The model is based on physiological principles and the resulting intuitive relationship between the model parameters and its response has enabled the parameters to be determined on a trial-and-error basis. A Gauss-Newton gradient search algorithm was used in an effort to provide a more objective means of determining an optimum parameter set, but there was no improvement as a result of this, due to the difficulties with multiple local minima and the resulting sensitivity to initial parameter values. Some future work will examine the effectiveness of stochastic and concurrent search algorithms in providing an optimal parameter set.

The model presented in this paper focusses on the renal vasculature only and caution must be exercised in any attempt to extend its applicability to other vasculature components or, indeed, to TPR in general. It is known (see Section 1) that different vasculature beds may respond differently to similar vasoactive mechanisms, depending on the particular receptors (or mix of receptors) contained in the various vascular beds. Therefore, it is not reasonable to attempt to generalise this model to other vascular beds until it can be validated with appropriate experimental data. However, the renal vasculature is a major component of innervated resistance (approximately 30%) and therefore the model has a not insignificant relevance to TPR.

The model developed has deliberately separated dynamic and nonlinear elements (with a Hammerstein structure in the feedback path) in an effort to make the model as transparent as possible and facilitate parameter tuning. However, it is likely that an integrated model could provide a better fit to the data, though presenting a greater challenge in parameter determination (only via optimisation techniques).

We believe that this model can also be helpful as part of the modelling effort to investigate the origins of low-frequency (circa 0.1 Hz in humans) oscillations in blood pressure. Current models utilise a relatively simple linear first-order dynamic element to represent the resistance component of the vasculature (Ringwood and Malpas, 2001) and while this representation is adequate for small-signal situations, it is known that oscillations of a significant amplitude can occur under certain physiological conditions e.g. haemorrhage (Malpas and Burgess, 2000). Inclusion of the counteractive vasodilatory mechanism in the model presented in this paper is likely to make a significant change to predictions of oscillation amplitudes (particularly at higher amplitudes) compared to current models utilising simple linear models.

There is considerable scope for further work. In addition to the investigation of different optimisation techniques for model parameter determination, some improvements to the basic model structure are possible. In particular, Fig.7 confirms that, notwithstanding the employment of different time constants for feedforward and feedback components, the responses in positive-going and negative-going directions occur at different rates, with the slower response during the recovery from stimulation. This is perfectly reasonable, since:

- Recovery from SNA activation is passive and the smooth muscle may take longer to relax than contract under forced activation, and
- Hormones, paracrines, etc. may take much longer to disperse than the rate at which they were formed, since they rely on other aspects of the physiology to dilute them.

Finally, it is also anticipated that a model can be built which can combine the effects of both amplitude and frequency SNA stimulation. However, some careful analysis of the equivalence between these two mechanisms is necessary and there is an inherent difficulty in quantifying 'amplitude' stimulation on SNA fibres, since there is uncertainty as to the number of fibres covered by stimulating electrodes (and the mechanism by which 'amplitude' modulation occurs is via the recruitment of more/less fibres, 'amplitude' level on a single fibre being approximately fixed).

REFERENCES

Bellomo, R., J.A. Kellum, S.R. Wisniewski and M.R Pinsky (1999). Effects of norepinephrine on the renal vasculature in normal and endotoxemic dogs. *Am. J. Respir. Crit. Care Med.* **159**, R1186–R1192.

Boulanger, C.M and P.M. Vanhoutte (1998). The endothelium: a modulator of cardiovascular health and disease. *Dialogues in Cardiovascular Medicine* **3**, 4.

DiBona, G.F. and U.C. Kopp (1997). Neural control of renal function. *Physiol. Rev* **77**, 75–197.

Eppel, G.A., K.M. Denton, S.C. Malpas and R.G. Evans (2003). Nitric oxide in responses of regional kidney perfusion to renal nerve stimulation and renal ischaemia. *Eur. J. Physiol* **447**, 205–213.

Guild, S.J., P.C. Austin, M. Navatikyan, J.V. Ringwood and S.C. Malpas (2001). Dynamic relationship between sympathetic nerve activity and renal blood flow: a frequency domain approach. *Am. J. Physiol. (Regulatory Integrative Comp. Physiol.)* **281**, R206–R212.

Leonard, B.L., R.G. Evans, M.A. Navakatikyan and S.C. Malpas (2000). Differential neural cotrol of intrarenal blood flow. *Am. J. Physiol. (Regul Ingr. Comp. Physiol)* **297**, R907–R916.

Malpas, S.C. and D.E. Burgess (2000). Renal sna as the primary mediator of slow oscillations in blood pressure during haemorrhage. *Am. J. Physiol.* **279**, R1299–R1306.

Navakatikyan, M.A., B.L. Leonard, R.G. Evans and S.C. Malpas (2000). Modeling the neural control of intrarenal blood flow. *Clinical and Experimental Pharmacology and Physiology* **27**, 650652.

Navar, L. Gabriel (1998). Integrating multiple paracrine regulators of renal microvascular dynamics. *Am. J. Physiol. (Renal Physiol.)* **274**, F433 F444.

Richardson, D.R., D.C. Randall and D.F. Speck (1998). *Cardiopulmonary System.* 1st ed.. Fence Creek Publishing.

Ringwood, J.V. and S.C. Malpas (2001). Control of renal blood flow - the case for a nonlinear model. *Am. J. Physiol.* **280**, R1105–R1115.

Sorensen, C.M., P.P. Leyssac, O. Skott and N.-H. Holstein-Rathlou (2000). Role of the renin-angiotensin system in regulation and autoregulation of renal blood flow. *Am. J. Physiol. (Regulatory Integrative Comp. Physiol.)* **279**, R1017–R1024.

INERTIAL GAIT PHASE DETECTION: POLYNOMIAL NULLSPACE APPROACH

Otakar Šprdlík [*,1] Zdeněk Hurák [**,2]

*Department of Control Engineering
Faculty of Electrical Engineering
Czech Technical University in Prague
**Center for Applied Cybernetics, FEE, CTU in Prague*

Abstract: Detection of gait phases (swing and stance or more detailed) is a usual mean of feedback in closed-loop control of Functional Electrical Stimulation (FES) used for improving gait of persons with some motor control disability in a lower extremity, e.g., drop-foot problem. This paper presents a use of linear fault detection technique based on polynomial matrices for detection of gait phases. Data collected from two-axial accelerometer placed on a shank is lead to detector producing a residual signal which indicates an event by getting away from zero. The residual generator relies on linearised model of accelerometer measurement during stance phase to detect rising heel. Detection of heel rise together with threshold detection of peaks in measured signals during heel-strike and several empiric constraints (e.g., timeouts) forms the gait phase detector. *Copyright © 2006*

Keywords: Accelerometers, Biomedical systems, Fault detection

1. INTRODUCTION

Accelerometers and rate gyroscopes have became small parts manufactured with employment of MEMS technology. They posses low power and high durability, which enables them to be used in portable or even implantable devices. In the medical field inertial sensors can extend or replace systems for clinical measurement of absolute position. They can also be fundamental parts of portable devices for rehabilitation assistance, day-long measurement, or for control of FES. To assist walking by FES it is essential to determine stage of gait cycle (gait phase).

As a part of introduction to the presented topic, gait cycle decomposition to phases, literature survey of gait phase detection by means of accelerometry and a polynomial matrix method of fault detection are shortly outlined. In the second section fault detection is proposed for the gait phase detection. Sections 3 and 4 include derivation of residual generator for heel-off detection and its use in gait phase detector, respectively. Last two sections bring experimental verification and conclusions.

[1] Partially supported by the Grant Agency of the Czech Republic under the project 102/03/H116
[2] The work of the second author was supported by the Ministry of Education of the Czech Republic under Project 1M0567

1.1 Gait phase detection

There are many ways to formally decompose a gait cycle, see fig. 1 for an example: Cycle begins at the moment of first foot contact with ground (initial contact, heel strike). Next, weight shifts from the second leg and toe is getting closer to the ground. When the whole opposite foot is off the ground, midstance phase begins. Approximately at this time whole foot is in contact with the ground (*foot-flat*). The moment heel begins to rise from ground (*heel-off*) separates the next phase, terminal stance or preswing, which switches to swing when no part of the foot is touching ground. It is possible to decompose swing phase to several subphases. In pathological gait, there may terminal stance be missing or heel is not the first part of the foot touching ground at initial contact.

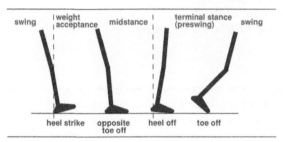

Fig. 1. Gait phases

This paper describes a method for detection of only two phases (separated by dashed lines in the figure):

- Heel touches ground = weight acceptance + midstance (= stance for short in the folowing)
- Heel above ground = preswing + swing (= swing in the folowing)

This division is sufficient to control peroneal nerve stimulation for patients with drop-foot problem.

In the most of current FES systems, there are hand switches, foot switches, or force-sensing resistors under the foot used for control. Inertial sensors (accelerometers, gyroscopes) placed on shank or thigh are an alternative way of measurement with several advantages over mentioned contact sensors,

- there is no need of instrumented footware,
- there is a possibility to implant them.
- foot switches and force-sensing resistors can produce false heel-off detections due to weight shifting during standing,
- mechanical switches are mechanical parts with low reliability and short durability,
- open-loop control with hand switches strains a patient by need of high degree of concentration,

Accelerometers have been investigated by several authors for the purpose of instrumented footware-free on-line detection of gait phases. Willemsen et al. (1990) used cross-correlation coefficients between measured and predefined time courses, Dai et al. (1996) compared tilt estimates (can be obtained from filtered accelerometric data) with thresholds, Williamson and Andrews (2000) used machine-learning techniques and training data sets to setup their detectors, Kotiadis et al. (2004) studied accelerometers and gyroscopes for the detection and then compared selected measured signals with thresholds. Shimada et al. (2005) used thigh-fixed accelerometer and machine learning.

1.2 Polynomial matrix approach to fault detection

Fault detection techniques use *residual generator*, i. e. system whose inputs are known signals from the investigated system and its output is a *residual*. Residual should be small or 0 when no fault is present and significantly greater in the presence of a fault. Usual requirement is that residual is decoupled from disturbances (unknown system inputs) and faults not in interest. Set of several residual generators sensitive to different faults and decoupling from others forms fault detection and isolation system able to detect faults and distinguish between them.

The detection method used (Frisk and Nyberg, 2001) is based on transformation of residual generation problem into a problem of finding polynomial basis for null-space of polynomial matrix. Consider a linear system with known inputs u, faults to be detected f and disturbances d including faults to be decoupled. If all faults can be described as unknown inputs, the system input-output description is

$$y = Gu + Hd + Lf,$$

where G, H, L are transfer functions from u, d, and f, respectively, and y is the system output. Problem of residual generator construction is the task of finding transfer matrix Q with output r satisfying requirements for residual as remarked above.

$$r = Q \begin{bmatrix} y \\ u \end{bmatrix}$$

Frisk and Nyberg (2001) introduced a method for finding residual generator $Q(s)$ of minimal order: $Q(s)$ must belong to left null space (LNS) of

$$M = \begin{bmatrix} G & H \\ I & 0 \end{bmatrix},$$

where I is identity matrix of suitable dimension. If there is no known input then $M = H$. Rational matrix problem of finding LNS of M ($\mathcal{N}_L(M)$)

can be transformed to polynomial matrix one by performing right matrix fraction description

$$M = M_1 D^{-1},$$

LNS of M is the same as LNS of polynomial matrix M_1. One of rows of minimal polynomial basis N_M of $\mathcal{N}_L(M_1)$ corresponds to a decoupling residual generator Q with minimal row degree. All rows of N_M parametrize all decoupling polynomial vectors (Q with one row only).

2. FAULT DETECTION VIEW OF GAIT PHASES

Gait phases can be considered as discrete states of a state machine, transition between them are related to events such as heel strike. To detect next phase an event detector can be run during active state. When an event is detected, machine switches to the new state. Fault detection constitutes a mature methodology for detection of such events.

It is necessary to obtain a model of inspected system or some relations between system signals to be able to use fault detection techniques. In the case of gait phase detection with the use of inertial sensors these relations are

- description of signals measured on segment(s) and relations between them,
- models of segments' movements or restrictions of movements during individual phases.

For the detection of heel-off the following model is used. Between foot-flat and heel-off, the longitudinal axis of the shank is considered to rotate around fixed point which is located near the ankle joint. See fig. 2 for simplified scheme of the situation. Distance between the rotation axis and the sensor is equal r. Angular position, velocity, and acceleration of the shank (φ, ω, ϵ) are vectors with dimension 3, one component of φ is pictured in fig. 2. Values a_{rad} and a_{tan} are two elements of three-dimensional vector of equivalent acceleration (= acceleration + component due to gravity) in sensor coordinate frame.

If shank movements satisfy rotational movement restriction, no matter what are values of φ, ω, and ϵ, output of residual generator should be close to 0. Angular acceleration can be viewed as unknown input which should be decoupled from residual. Restriction to rotational movements are broken when heel rises from ground. At beginning of heel rising an additional linear acceleration of ankle must occur, its direction is up from ground, we consider it approximately in the radial direction.

Only 2D (sagital) leg movements are considered in order we can assume two-axial accelerometer

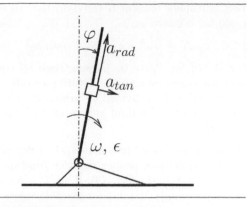

Fig. 2. Pendulum model of a shank

oriented in sagital plane is able to provide enough information for detection of broken restriction to rotational movements.

3. HEEL-OFF DETECTION

In 2D model, if accelerometer's axes are situated in the sagital plane and one of them (radial) cuts the rotation axis measured signals are described by

$$\begin{bmatrix} a_{rad} \\ a_{tan} \end{bmatrix} = \begin{bmatrix} -r\omega^2 + g\cos\varphi \\ r\epsilon - g\sin\varphi \end{bmatrix} \quad (1)$$

For application of linear fault detection a linearized model has to be used. Linearization is realized at nominal trajectory $x_0(t)$. Let $\tilde{x}$ denotes deviation from x_0 and d is disturbance input which should not be observed at the output of residual generator.

$$\tilde{x} = \begin{bmatrix} \tilde{\omega} \\ \tilde{\varphi} \end{bmatrix} \quad d = \epsilon$$

$$\dot{\tilde{x}} = A\tilde{x} + B_d d \quad \tilde{y} = C\tilde{x} + D_d d \quad (2)$$

$$A = \begin{bmatrix} 0 & 0 \\ 1 & 0 \end{bmatrix} \quad B_d = \begin{bmatrix} 1 \\ 0 \end{bmatrix}$$

$$C = \begin{bmatrix} -2r\omega_0 & -g\sin\varphi_0 \\ 0 & -g\cos\varphi_0 \end{bmatrix} \quad D_d = \begin{bmatrix} 0 \\ r \end{bmatrix}$$

Nominal trajectory is not a constant

$$x_0(t) = [\omega_0 \quad \varphi_0(0) + \omega_0 t]^{\mathrm{T}}$$

In other words φ_0 is drifting with constant velocity. Because ω isn't measured and long-time stance phases with bounded φ can occur between steps we assign $\omega_0 = 0$ to avoid unrealistic estimates of $\varphi_0(t)$.

Output effect of the disturbance is described by transfer function

$$H = C(sI_2 - A)^{-1}B_d + D_d = \begin{bmatrix} \dfrac{-g\sin\varphi_0}{s^2} \\ \dfrac{rs^2 - g\cos\varphi_0}{s^2} \end{bmatrix}$$

Left null space basis of H (trivially derived in this case) for nonzero $\sin \varphi_0$

$$N = \begin{bmatrix} rs^2 - g\cos\varphi_0 & g\sin\varphi_0 \end{bmatrix} \quad (3)$$

(or $\begin{bmatrix} 1 & 0 \end{bmatrix}$ for $\varphi_0 = 0$) parametrizes all transfer functions decoupling from disturbance ϵ. It can be multiplied and/or divided by arbitrary polynomials to obtain a residual generator with required dynamics.

We have to choose divisor $den(s)$ of degree 2 or greater to achieve proper transfer function Q in the case of N in the form (3). If one of poles of den is $-\sqrt{g\cos(\varphi_0)/r}$ (stable for possible values of φ_0 and r), it cancels the same pole of $rs^2 - g\cos\varphi_0$ in N and lowers degree of corresponding element of Q.

In the case of $\varphi_0 = 0$ we can use residual generator of lower order – when the generator is $\begin{bmatrix} 1 & 0 \end{bmatrix}$ detection changes to comparing $|a_{rad} - g|$ with a threshold. Because the premise is an additional (positive) acceleration occurs approximately in the direction of the a_{rad} axis of accelerometer $(a_{rad} - g)$ can be compared with a positive threshold only. Hence application of a threshold to a_{rad} is a modified special case of presented method of heel-off detection.

If $\tilde{y}$ is lead to the input of residual generator N/den and system behavior agrees with (2) zero is observed at the output. When an additional acceleration in the radial direction occurs it is transferred to the output of residual generator by $(rs^2 - g\cos\varphi_0)/den$ if (3) holds.

4. DETECTION ALGORITHM

Gait phase detector is constructed as shown in fig. 3.

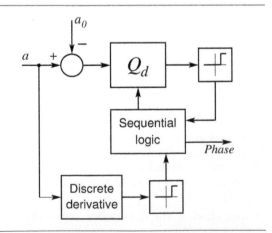

Fig. 3. Stance/swing detector

Nominal output a_0 (output of (1) at $x = x_0$, $\epsilon = 0$) is subtracted from measured signals a_{rad} and a_{tan}

filtered by 2nd order low-pass digital filter with 3dB attenuation at 16 Hz. This deviation signal is lead to the input of discretized residual generator

$$Q_d(z) = \text{discretized } N/den,$$

where 2nd order polynomial den was chosen experimentally on the basis of one of the trials such that one of its poles corresponds to frequency of approximately 1 Hz and the second to 4 Hz and adds more marked filtration.

Because only two acceleration components are measured and in reality they are not placed exactly in the sagital plane measured components of gravity acceleration do not form the whole gravity acceleration vector. To rectify this discrepancy between reality and formulas for residual generator and a_0 above there was used a simple solution – although still different from reality but more close: At still and comfortable standing a_{rad} and a_{tan} are recorded and euclidean norm of the 2-dimensional vector is computed and g is substituted by this norm in the formulas used for heel-off detection. This corresponds to hypothesis of constant tilt of sensor from vertical sagital plane during stance.

Recordings of a_{rad} and a_{tan} during still standing were also used to estimate φ_0.

$$\varphi_0 = -\arctan\left(a_{tan}/a_{rad}\right)$$

Angle φ at the time before heel-off is considered to be approximately the same as φ at still stance. Both vary from 0 to 10° in healthy subjects and normal gait. For typical ankle angles during normal gait see for example (Whittle, 2002).

Heel strike is detected by large values of numerically differentiated measured signals. Both the heel-off and heel strike detection are performed after a timeout elapse. Timeouts are used to avoid false detections just after previous event. During terminal stance and toe-off large acceleration changes occur and may cause false heel strike detections. After heel strike, there is a time before foot-flat and measurement unit trembles due to soft tissue for a while – this may cause false heel-off detection.

At the time heel-off is not in concern of detection there is Q_d adjusted to follow measured signals faster to avoid long responses of heel strike peaks in residual.

There are parameters that can be adjusted for detector set-up,

- φ_0 and a value g has to be substituted by – but they can be got from still standing measurements just before walking starts,
- den,
- thresholds,
- timeouts.

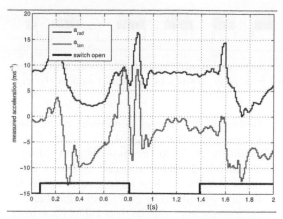

Fig. 4. Measured equivalent accelerations and heel-switch signal

5. EXPERIMENTAL VERIFICATION

5.1 Data acquisition

Accelerometric data were gained by an inertial measurement unit developed for low-encumbrance data acquisition without need of long wires. Digitized signals from ADXL202 accelerometer (Analog Devices, Inc.) is stored in data flash memory whose capacity enables storing several minutes of measured data gathered at 100 Hz. The measurement unit do not contain battery, it is connected by a short wire and may be fixed on the opposite side of the leg (medial or lateral). External battery mass do not extend measurement unit weight which is critical to tremble of the unit.

The unit was fixed on the lateral side of subject's shank just below the knee. This is the place where many peroneal stimulators are placed on. Mechanical switch was placed under the subject's heel to give a signal for comparison. Three trials was performed by three healthy subjects asked to walk at comfortable, but varying walking speed. All subjects were wearing their own footware. All trials consist of level walking with several turnings, the first trial includes stairs down and up walking. Static calibration was performed before trials. Measured signals from one gait cycle are shown in fig. 4.

Measured accelerations was violated by strong mechanical tremble of soft tissue – a motion not described by the pendulum model. To avoid false heel-off detections due to the tremble long limeout (0.4 s) was applied to delay heel-off detection. The timeout is longer than times when heel was on ground during downstairs walking in trial 1. Tremble can be reduced by suitable placement of measurement unit – for example on the frontal side of shank like (Williamson and Andrews, 2000) or on frontal/lateral side just at the tibia, but mechanical construction of our 2D measurement unit

Table 1. Detection statistics

Trial:	1	1 without stairs down	2	3
h-off avg	0.08	0.03	-0.06	-0.03
h-off std	0.11	0.07	0.04	0.08
h-off min	-0.08	-0.08	-0.13	-0.2
h-off max	0.3	0.25	0.0	0.06
h-s avg	-0.02	-0.02	0.02	-0.08
h-s std	0.06	0.06	0.07	0.07

don't provide required components of acceleration when fixed at these places.

5.2 Algorithm test

Detector was programmed in Matlab and Simulink (The MathWorks, Inc.) but it is simple enough to be implemented in a low-cost, low-power hardware.

Table 1 shows statistics of differences between heel-switch and accelerometric detection. First row contains average delay in seconds from heel-off detected by switch to the moment of accelerometric detection. Other rows contain standard deviation, maximum and minimum delay of heel-off detection and average and standard deviation of heel strike detection. Statistics of the first trial are influenced by late heel-off detections during walking downstairs due to long timeout. Next column contains statistics of trial 1 without downstairs walking.

See fig. 5 for an example of detection results. There is also displayed result of heel-off detection performed by comparing a_{rad} with a threshold. In the picture, there are two points with significant deviations of simple threshold detection from switch detection not seen in displayed result of presented method but contrary situations also occurred.

There is one missed heel strike in trial 3 and one false heel-off detection in trial 2, they are not covered by statistics.

6. DISCUSSION AND CONCLUSIONS

Fault detection based method for heel-off detection was proposed and used for gait phase detector design. Heel switch signal was recorded together with accelerometric data as a reference. Although nearly all events were detected there are large variations between results of accelerometric and switch-based detection (see tab. 1). All used detection methods (fault detection, simple threshold, and the switch) showed false or missed detections. Switching times of heel-switch depends on exact placement under the heel, for better verification of the proposed accelerometer-based detection more trials has to be done and a more accurate reference

Fig. 5. Comparison of heel-switch (highest bars, grey) and accelerometer based stance/swing detection. Black bars show the method described, the white ones show results of threshold applied to a_{rad}. Bars coincide with swing phase.

should be used, for example FSRs as a better alternative for switches or an accurate marker-based motion analysis system.

Simplifications were made in construction of residual generator for heel-off detection (linearization at one point, 2D movements,...), they induce differences between model and reality. Our hypothesis is that with accelerometer and, perhaps, a gyroscope a nonlinear hell-off detector can be constructed on the basis of the original 3D nonlinear model such that good performance should be ensured even when gait stale is changing dramatically during time – there is great (arbitrary) inter-cycle variance of shank orientations (irregular gait due to a disability, walking down/upstairs). The use of 3D measurement unit should enable placement in an arbitrary position around the shank to ensure as low mechanical tremble as possible.

More complicated models have to be used for fault detection design for other gait events because of more degrees of segments' freedom during other phases. This may make design of the detector more difficult or even enforce use of more sensors on the leg and therefore add a discomfort for the patient. Combination of other detection methods with the fault detection should form the core of the whole detector even if fault detection approach show efficient for detection of particular events and phases.

This paper do not intend to propose a fully functioning practical method for gait phase detection but rather we wanted to introduce some concepts from fault detection domain. To make the presented scheme practically usefull more work would to be invested. Whether or not this specific application could benefit from it cannot be said before.

REFERENCES

R. Dai, R. B. Stein, B. J. Andrews, K. B. James, and M. Wieler. Application of tilt sensors in functional electrical stimulation. *IEEE Transactions on Rehabilitation Engineering*, 4(2):63–72, 1996.

E. Frisk and M. Nyberg. A minimal polynomial basis solution to residual generation for fault diagnosis in linear systems. *Automatica*, 37:1417–24, 2001.

D. Kotiadis, H. J. Hermens, P. H. Veltink, and P. Slycke. Inertial gait phase detection system: Design. In *9th Annual Conference of the International FES Society*, 2004.

Y. Shimada, S. Ando, T. Matsunaga, A. Misawa, T. Aizawa, T. Shirahata, and E. Itoi. Clinical application of acceleration sensor to detect the swing phase of stroke gait in functional electrical stimulation. *Tohoku Journal of Experimental Medicine*, 207:197–202, 2005.

M. W. Whittle. *Gait Analysis: an introduction*. Butterworth Heinemann, third edition, 2002.

A. Th. M. Willemsen, F. Bloemhof, and H. B. K. Boom. Automatic stance-swing phase detection from accelerometer data for peroneal nerve stimulation. *IEEE Transactions on Biomedical Engineering*, 37(12):1201–8, 1990.

R. Williamson and B. J. Andrews. Gait event detection for FES using accelerometers and supervised machine learning. *IEEE Transactions on Rehabilitation Engineering*, 8(3):312–319, 2000.

A SUPERVISOR FOR VOLUME-CONTROLLED TIDAL LIQUID VENTILATOR USING INDEPENDENT PISTON PUMPS

[1]R. Robert, P. Micheau and H. Walti

[1]INOLIVENT, Université de Sherbrooke, Mechanical Engineering Department,
Sherbrooke, QC, J1K 2R1, Canada. Email : Philippe.Micheau@USherbrooke.ca

Abstract: Liquid ventilation using perfluorochemicals (PFC) offers clear theoretical advantages over gas ventilation, such as decreased lung damage, recruitment of collapsed lung regions and lavage of inflammatory debris. This paper presents the control of a total liquid ventilator (TLV) dedicated to ventilate patients with completely filled lungs with a tidal volume of perfluorochemical liquid. The two independent piston pumps are volume controlled and pressure limited. Measurable pumping errors are corrected by a programmed supervisor module, which modifies the inserted or withdrawn volume. Pump independence also allows easy FRC modifications during ventilation. The prototype was tested on 5 healthy term newborn lambs (<5 days old). *Copyright © 2006 IFAC.*

Keywords: pump control system, mechanical ventilation, tidal liquid ventilation.

1 INTRODUCTION

Liquid assisted ventilation (LAV) uses perfluorochemical (PFC) liquids to replace the common gas mixture during mechanical ventilation. These liquids are able to dissolve a sufficient quantity of O_2 and CO_2 at atmospheric pressure to support gas exchange in the lungs (Clark and Gollan, 1966). Liquid assisted ventilation can be performed either as partial or total liquid ventilation. During partial liquid ventilation (PLV), a fraction of the functional residual capacity (FRC) is filled with PFC liquid and a conventional mechanical gas ventilator ensures lung ventilation. In contrast, total (or tidal) liquid ventilation (TLV) necessitates a dedicated mechanical system in order to ventilate completely filled lungs with a tidal volume of PFC.

By eliminating the air-liquid interface, TLV allows recruitment of collapsed lung regions at lower pressure, hence decreasing the risk of lung injuries and ensuring more homogeneous alveolar ventilation

(Cox et al., 1996). Other potential advantages of TLV include a better washout of inflammatory debris from the lungs and in vivo anti-inflammatory, anti-oxidant and anti-bacterial effects of PFC (Wolfson et al, 1998). Many studies involving various experimental models of acute lung injury suggest clear benefits from TLV as compared to all other tested ventilation strategies, including conventional and high frequency gas ventilation and PLV (Hirschl et al, 2002). Diverse types of tidal liquid ventilators have been developed for conducting animal experiments (Pedneault and al, 1999). Regardless of the technologies used, a liquid ventilator must perform the following essential functions: insert and withdraw the tidal volume V_t of PFC from the lungs, oxygenate the PFC and maintain it at a desired temperature (usually the patient's temperature).

In order to insert and withdraw the tidal volume of PFC, some devices exploit gravity by placing reservoirs at different heights to force the PFC liquid in and out of the lungs. However, a pump is necessary to precisely control inspiratory and expiratory flows; hence the earlier use of ventilators and peristaltic pumps, bellow pumps, gear pump and piston pumps. The latter produces steady flows nearly exempted of pulsations, although the main interest of a piston pump is to achieve perfect volume-controlled ventilation. Moreover, it was shown that more PFC is drained from the lungs using a piston pump, comparatively to a peristaltic or gravimetric system (Meinhardt et al, 2003).

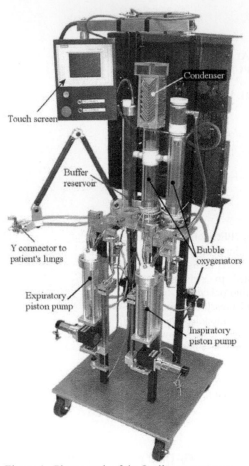

Figure 1. Photograph of the Inolivent prototype.

Two main problems must be considered in the control of the pump in TLV: avoiding airway closure (chocked flow) during expiration and controlling FRC in the lungs. Development of airway closure can be avoided by including pressure limits which manage (i.e. stop or slow down) the pump when an important negative pressure is reached. Measurement of FRC can be obtained by monitoring the patient's weight end-expiratory pressure or liquid volume in the ventilator (Degraeuwe et al, 2000).

The major problem was to control with high precision the volume of liquid to transfer in the lungs in spite of important measurement noises. Moreover, the speed of the pump must be slowly variable in spite of the noise, the pump disturbances and the possibility of collapse. This problem motivate the implementation

of a supervisor in the sense that it learns the input needed for reproducing a given output trajectory for performing a cyclic sequence in a specified finite time. It exist different forms of learning control for dynamic systems.

The Repetitive Control started to develop around the beginning of the 80's stores a whole period of the signal. From a theoretical point of view, the repetitive controllers are applications of the Internal Model Principle according to Wonham (1976): the reference-generating polynomial must be in the denominator of the open loop transfer. Hillerström applied it to control a peristaltic pump. However, even with really sophisticated filtering within the loop of the delay chain, the repetitive controller would not stabilize for full working range (Hillerström, 1996). The cyclic controller executes cycles defined by a series of points in the product space of states and controls to be attained at given time instants, with the first and last point coincident (Lucibello and Panzieri, 1998). Finally, the introduction of some open-loop improvements (with iterative learning control) leads to reduce the lower gain loops, and consequently improves the robustness (Bitmead, 2002).

Our first TLV prototype used learning control adapted to a peristaltic pump (P. Micheau et al, 2002). The foremost novelty of the presented ventilator is its independent expiratory and inspiratory piston pumps, which allow an optimized control of the ventilation profile and FRC (Robert et al, 2006).

Section 2 is a description of the overall ventilator, the integrated condenser-heater-oxygenator element, the pump system and its controller. The calibration tests presented in section 3 allowed to validate the system design. Finally, results obtained during in vivo testing in an experimental model of healthy newborn lambs are presented.

2 DESCRIPTION OF THE TIDAL LIQUID VENTILATOR

The prototype of tidal liquid ventilator, presented in figure 1, is designed for infants weighing up to 9 kg using a tidal volume V_t of 25 ml/kg of body weight. At any time, the clinician can change the ventilation parameters, e.g., phase time, tidal volume, ventilation profiles, and obtain information on the various ventilator components, e.g., PFC or condenser temperatures, airway pressure.

It is controlled by an industrial programmable logic computer (PLC) while a touch panel serves as a human-machine interface. As presented in figure 1, this TLV ventilator includes:
i) Two independent piston pumps to insert and withdraw PFC from the lungs;
ii) A gas exchanger to perform complete PFC oxygenation and CO2 removal. It includes a heating system to warm up and maintain the

desired PFC temperature, and a condenser to retrieve PFC vapours;

iii) Four pneumatic pinch valves to control the inspiratory and expiratory fluid circuit independently.

iv) A buffer reservoir to monitor the level of PFC in the ventilator.

v) A condenser to attenuate PFC losses by evaporation.

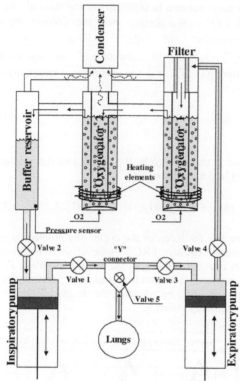

Figure 2. Schematic drawing of the TLV ventilator. The arrows indicate the liquid flows. The inspiratory circuit includes the inspiratory pump, valves 1 and 2. The expiratory circuit contains the expiratory pump, valves 3 and 4. The Y-connector contains a manual valve (5) to isolate the circuit from the patient's lungs.

Different cycles are available on the TLV ventilator. A preparation cycle allows the clinician to circulate the PFC liquid in a closed loop to warm and oxygenate the liquid. Then, a filling sequence can be used to fill the patient's lungs using one pump. Finally, the respiratory cycle is used to carry out TLV. This cycle is divided into four distinct phases:

1) Inspiration phase: valves 2 and 3 are closed, valve 1 is opened, and the inspiratory pump moves up to insert the inspiratory volume of PFC, V_i, into the lungs.

2) End-inspiration pause: valves 1 and 3 are closed. The positive end-inspiratory pressure, PEIP, is measured during this pause via a pressure sensor positioned in the endotracheal tube, 12 mm proximal to its ending.

3) Expiration phase: valves 1 and 4 are closed, valve 3 is opened, and the expiratory pump moves down to withdraw the expiratory volume of PFC, V_e, from the lungs.

4) End-expiration pause: valves 1 and 3 are closed. The positive end-expiratory pressure, PEEP, is measured during this pause via the endotracheal pressure sensor.

The expiratory pump and the inspiratory pump are the same, but are controlled individually. Pump independence is used to:

i) optimize PFC residing time in the gas exchangers by pushing the expired liquid as soon as possible in the oxygenators. In fact, this is done at the onset of the inspiration phase by opening valve 4 (valve 3 is closed) and by pushing the liquid present in the expiratory pump as fast as possible.

ii) improve pressure measurement in the buffer reservoir by waiting until the latest possible moment to fill the inspiratory pump with oxygenated PFC. In fact, at the end of the expiration phase, the PFC is pumped from the buffer reservoir by opening valve 2 (valve 1 is closed).

iii) modify FRC during ventilation according to the clinician's request. The requested correction of FRC, ΔV, is the PFC volume to retrieve from (if negative) or to add into (if positive) the lungs during one cycle (detailed in section 2.3).

iv) compensate for small pumping errors and to deal with an eventual exceptional stoppage of the cycle, caused when reaching either an upper or lower pressure limit detected by pressure measurement in the endotracheal tube.

2.1 Control system of the piston pumps

A schematic representation of the piston pumps used on the TLV ventilator, with all of its components, is given in figure 2. Figure 3 presents the complete control system implemented for the control of the two piston pumps. Three hierarchies must be considered: the control of the desired volumes (the controllers), the generation of inspiratory and expiratory volume references (the generators) and the volume supervisor (the Supervisor).

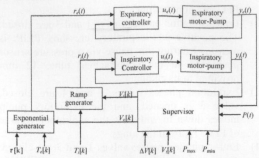

Figure 3. Schematic representation of the pump control system.

Each pump uses an individual proportional controller which independently commands the pump motor using a feedback loop control design. The objective of this feedback loop is to follow the volume reference ($y_e(t) \rightarrow r_e(t)$ for the expiratory pump, and $y_i(t) \rightarrow r_i(t)$ for the inspiratory pump) delivered by the corresponding (inspiratory or expiratory) generator, based on the volume measured in the pumps by the potentiometers.

The voltage applied to the servo-amplifier, $u(t)$, modulates the tension applied to the motor. The volume $y(t)$ is measured via the pump potentiometer. The volume reference, $r(t)$, and the desired volume of PFC to pump, $V[k]$, is delivered by the generator. The subscripts e and i denote the expiratory and the inspiratory circuit respectively. The clinician's commands are $T[k]$ the time of pumping, $\tau[k]$ the time constant, ΔV the correction of FRC, $V_t[k]$ the tidal volume, P_{max} the upper pressure, and P_{min} the lower pressure limits. The pressure measured in the trachea is $P(t)$.

2.2 The control problem

The references are computed to perform the desired volume, V_e and V_i and, during the specified time T_e and T_i. Two volume profiles illustrated in figure 4 are considered: the ramp for inspiration and the exponential for expiration. In the following, constant expiratory and inspiratory times are considered.

For inspiration, the ramp volume profile is generated with a 20% acceleration, 40% constant and 40% deceleration. However, at the end of inspiration (at the time $t = T_i$), the effective inspiratory volume may be different of the desired one, $y_i(T_i) \neq V_i$ because the controller of the inspiratory pump may introduce a volume error. We assume that the volume error of the inspiratory pump, $E_i = V_i - y_i(T_i)$, is function of an unknown function, $g_i(V_i, T_i)$, and the inspiratory measurement noise, b_i:

$$E_i = g_i(V_i, T_i) + b_i \qquad (1)$$

For expiration, the exponential volume profile is generated with the equation

$$r_e(t) = R_e\left(\exp\left(-\frac{t}{\tau}\right) - \exp\left(-\frac{T_e}{\tau}\right) \right) \qquad \text{where}$$

$R_e = \dfrac{V_e}{1 - \exp(-T_e/\tau)}$, τ is the time constant, and t the time (equal to zero at the beginning). However, at the end of expiration (at the time $t = T_e$), the effective expiratory volume is different of the desired one, $y_e(T_e) \neq V_e$. We assume that the volume error measurement of the expiratory pump, $E_e = V_e - y_e(T_e)$, is function of an unknown function $g_e(V_e, T_e)$ and the expiratory measurement noise, b_e:

$$E_e = g_e(V_e, T_e) + b_e \qquad (2)$$

Hence, cycle after cycle, the addition of the volume errors lead to drift the FRC:

$$FRC[k] = FRC[0] + k\big(g_i(V_i, T_i) - g_e(V_e, T_e)\big) \qquad (3)$$

where k is the index of the cycle. The problem is to maintain a constant FRC in spite of small additives errors due, (1) and (2), to the pump controllers. For this purpose, a supervisor was first designed to control the FRC by adjusting the desired inspiratory and expiratory volumes.

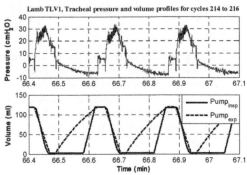

Figure 4. Typical pressure measurements in the trachea and volume variations in the pumps. In this experiment, the tidal volume was 120 ml. During inspiration, the ramp volume profile included a 20% acceleration time and a 40% deceleration time. The exponential profile was used during expiration.

2.3 The supervisor module

The supervisor module computes the inspiratory volume $V_i[k]$ and the expiratory volume $V_e[k]$ according to the clinician's requests with regard to tidal volume $V_t[k]$ and the FRC correction ΔV. In addition, the supervisor module compensates for errors in piston movement (presented in section 2.2).

The desired inspiratory volume is computed with $V_t[k]$ and ΔV (if it needs to be decreased):

$$V_i[k] = \begin{cases} V_t[k] & if \quad \Delta V \geq 0 \\ V_t[k] + \Delta V & if \quad \Delta V < 0 \end{cases} \qquad (4)$$

The desired expiratory volume $V_e[k]$ is computed based on the $V_t[k]$, ΔV (if it needs to be increased), $E_i[k]$, and the previous expiratory error $E_e[k-1]$:

$$V_e[k] = \begin{cases} V_t[k] - E_i[k] + E_e[k-1] & if \; \Delta V \leq 0 \\ V_t[k] - E_i[k] + E_e[k-1] - \Delta V & if \; \Delta V > 0 \end{cases}$$
$$(5)$$

This error management algorithm (equations 2 to 5) is stable and converges on a number of cycles depending on the form of the error (see section 2.3 for a complete demonstration).

2.4 Convergence analysis

The pumps and their controls imply tracking errors and measurement noises. One role of the supervisor module is to compensate such pumping errors. To demonstrate the convergence of the supervisor module, the following case is considered: a constant tidal volume $V_i[k] = V_t$, no compensation of FRC ($\Delta V = 0$) and constant expiratory and inspiratory times. The measured inspiratory and expiratory errors are:

$$E_i[k] = g_i + b_i[k] \qquad (6)$$
$$E_e[k] = g_e(V_e[k]) + b_e[k] \qquad (7)$$

where $b_i[k]$ is the inspiratory measurement white noise, g_i is a constant and g_e is a monotonous increasing positive function of V_e.

Because $\Delta V = 0$, the desired inspiratory volume given by (4) is $V_i[k] = V_t$, and the desired expiratory volume given by (5) is $V_e[k] = V_t - E_i[k] + E_e[k-1]$. Using relation (6) and (7) we obtain the following stochastic nonlinear equation:

$$V_e[k] = V_t - g_i + g_e(V_e[k-1]) + b[k] \qquad (8)$$

with $b[k] = b_e[k-1] - b_i[k]$. With $E\{b[k]\} = 0$, the expectance value of the equilibrium point, V_e*, is solution of $g_e(V_e*) = g_i$. The point V_e* is attractive, if and only if $-1 < \dfrac{dg_e}{dV_e} < 1$. Because $\dfrac{dg_e}{dV_e} > 0$, the stability condition implies to verify $\dfrac{dg_e}{dV_e} < 1$. Hence, in steady state condition, the

expiratory volume is corrected in order to compensate for inspiratory errors. This corrected volume ensures the same expected value of inspiratory and expiratory volume, thus a constant FRC during ventilation.

2.5 Pressure limitations

Lower and upper pressure limits are set to protect the patient's lung. If the upper pressure P_{max} is reached during the inspiration phase, $P(t) > P_{max}$, the inspiratory pump is stopped, and the cycle switches to the end-inspiratory pause. In this case, due to equation 3, only the volume instilled in the lungs will be expired. Also, if the lower pressure limit, P_{min}, is reached during the expiration phase with the risk of an airway closure, $P(t) < P_{min}$, the expiratory pump is stopped, and the cycle switches to the end-expiratory pause. In such a case, the desired inspiratory volume for the next inspiration is equal to the volume expired from the lungs during the stopped expiratory cycle, $V_i[k] = y_e[k-1]$. Hence, every time a pressure limit is reached, the volume inserted or expired from the lungs is adjusted to maintain the same FRC. Hence, each pump is time-limited, volume-controlled and pressure-limited.

3 EXPERIMENTATION

3.1 Calibration tests

The supervisor module was tested to determine whether the algorithm converges and manages measurable pumping errors. A dSpace acquisition station (DS1003 processor board, DS2201 I/O board) was used to precisely record the analog signals provided by the potentiometers of the expiratory and inspiratory pumps. Four V_t were chosen, from 75 to 150 ml, in order to reflect the weight range of a term newborn lamb. Over a two hour period, the differences between the inspired and expired volumes (ΔFRC) were summed. The results are presented as means $\pm$ SD range in table 1. Of note, the standard deviation of the inspired volume was close to the quantization error of the analog signal by the PLC to its discrete state, which is 0.14 ml. Thus, the supervisor module, presented with equations 2 to 5, thereby proved its effectiveness in managing measurable errors.

Secondly, to test the operating capabilities of the expiratory and inspiratory piston pumps and their overall system control, in vivo TLV was mimicked by replacing the lungs with a fixed reservoir. A pressure sensor placed at the bottom of the reservoir was used to determine the volume variations within the reservoir, as a surrogate for V_t, over a two hour period. As performed earlier, four V_t were chosen, from 75 to 150 ml, in order to reflect the weight range of a term newborn infant during the first weeks of life. The results presented in table II confirm that the measured V_t is within $\pm 2\%$ of the reference value.

Vt	V_t inspired measured	V_t expired measured	ΔFRC measured
75	75.06 ± 0.16	75.09 ± 0.16	-14.3
100	100.16 ± 0.15	100.19 ± 0.43	-15.8
125	125.19 ± 0.17	125.19 ± 0.34	1.0
150	150.22 ± 0.15	150.31 ± 0.28	-31.1

TABLE 1. Supervisor module tests results (values in ml and presented as mean ± SD). The ΔFRC measured is the diffence between the inspired and expired volumes, summed for a 2 hours period.

Vt	Vt delivered
75	76.13 ± 0.57
100	99.51 ± 0.48
125	124.05 ± 0.40
150	148.98 ± 0.44

TABLE 2. Pumping precision tests results (values in ml and presented as mean ± SD). The V_t delivered is the volume variation in the fixed reservoir.

3.2 In-vivo testing

The experimental protocol was approved by our institutional Ethics Committee for Animal Care and Experimentation. The results obtained in 8 healthy term newborn lambs demonstrate the efficiency and safety of our TLV ventilator in maintaining adequate gas exchange and normal acido-basis equilibrium during a short 2 hours TLV trial (Robert et al, 2006). Cardio-vascular stability was also maintained and was not different from results obtained in a similar gas-ventilated animal preparation (data not shown).

Furthermore, airway pressure, lung volumes and ventilation scheme were maintained in the targeted range including the absence of any observed perfluorothorax. Overall, the present results are in accordance with previous studies on TLV using healthy term newborn lambs and support further testing of our TLV ventilator in animal models of lung injury. Ongoing works are being done on a model of ARDS using newborn lambs.

4 CONCLUSION

The distinct advantage of our TLV prototype is its ability to control FRC using a system of independent pumps and the ability to estimate FRC via the buffer reservoir. Current developments will enable better control of FRC and reduction in airway collapse. These developments include a more accurate model of the airway system during TLV, thus improving pump control.

The TLV ventilator presented is also shown to be efficient and safe for volume controlled, pressure limited tidal liquid ventilation in 8 term newborn lambs with healthy lungs. Further TLV studies will be performed on experimental models of lung injury, especially acute respiratory distress syndrome.

ACKNOWLEDGMENT

The authors would like to thank Valerie Cardinal, J. Lebon, V. Provost, and C. Ouellet for their technical assistance supporting the in-vivo experiments. The authors would also like to thank R. Oddo, G. Drolet and O. Berbuer for their technical assistance and Pulsion Medical Systems AG which provided the acquisition software for the PiCCO.

REFERENCES

Bitmead, R.R., (2002), Open-loop iterative learning control, In Iterative Identification and Control, (P. Albertos and A. Sala (Eds.)),99-119, Springer, UK.

Clark, L. C., and Gollan, F., (1996) Survival of mammal breathing organic liquids equilibrated with oxygen at atmospheric pressure, Science, 152, pp. 1755–1756, June 1966.

Cox, C. A., Wolfson, M. R., and Shaffer, T. H., (1996) Liquid ventilation: A comprehensive overview, Neonatal Network, 15, no. 2, 31–43.

Degraeuwe, P. L. J., Dohmen, L. R. B., Geilen, J. M., and Blanco, C. E., (2000), A feedback controller for the maintenance of FRC during tital liquid ventilation: theory, implementation, and testing, Int. J. Artif. Organs, 23, no. 10, 680–688.

Hillerström, G., and Sternby, J., (1996), Robustness properties of repetitive controllers, International Journal of Control, 65(6), 939-961.

Hirschl, R. B., Croce, M., Gore, D., Wiedemann, H., Davis, K., Zwischenberger, J., and Bartlett, R. H., (2002), Prospective, randomized, controlled pilot study of partial liquid ventilation in adult acute respiratory distress syndrome, Am. J. Respir. Crit. Care Med., 165, no. 6, 781–787.

Lucibello, P., and Panzieri, S., (1998), Application of cyclic control to a two-link flexible arm, Automatica, 34(8), 1025-1029.

Meinhardt, J. P., Ashton, B. A., Annich, G. M., Quintel, M., and Hirschl, R. B. (2003), The dependency of expiratory airway collapse on pump system and flow rate in liquid ventilated rabbits, Eur. J Med. Res., 8, 212–220.

Micheau, P., Mazouzi, M., Cyr, S., Robert, R., (2002), Learning Control of a Pump Used in a Liquid Ventilator", T-Tu-M01, 15th World Congress of the IFAC, Barcelonna, 21-26 july.

Pedneault, C., Renolleau, S., Gosselin, R., Letourneau, P., and Praud, J.-P., (1999), Total liquid ventilation using a modified extracorporeal gas exchange circuit: Preliminary results in lambs, Pediatr. Pulmonol., 18, A241.

Robert, R., Micheau, P., Cyr, S., Lesur, O., Praud, J.P., Walti, H. (2006) A Prototype of Volume-Controlled Tidal Liquid Ventilator Using Independent Piston Pumps, submitted to ASIAO.

Wolfson, M. R., Greenspan, J. S., and Shaffer, T. H., (1998), Liquid assisted ventilation: An alternative respiratory modality, Pediatr. Pulmonol., 26, 42–63.

ELSEVIER

IFAC

PUBLICATIONS

A REAL-TIME PREDICTIVE SCHEME FOR CONTROLLING HYGROTHERMAL CONDITIONS OF NEONATE INCUBATORS

Gustavo H. C. Oliveira [*,1] Mardson F. Amorim [**]
Carlos Pacholok [***]

* PPGEPS/CCET/PUCPR
Rua Imaculada Conceição 1155 - Zip Code 80215-901
Curitiba/PR/Brazil
e-mail: gustavo.oliveira@pucpr.br
** PPGTS/CCET/PUCPR
e-mail: mardson@ppgia.pucpr.br
*** CCET/PUCPR

Abstract: This work is focused on hygrothermal control problem of closed newborn incubators. Such incubator promotes a controlled micro-climate, with small heat transfer between the premature and the environment, which promotes a healthful environment. In this context, the main hygrothermal informations are temperature, relative humidity and partial vapor pressure where the last one is closed related with the water loss by transpiration. A model predictive control scheme for this problem is presented and real time closed-loop control examples validate the proposed method in such a context. The identification procedure, a need in model based control schemes, is based on the use Laguerre functions and the experiments are performed on a laboratory pilot plant (full scale) which was built to evaluate control algorithms in incubators. Copyright © 2006 IFAC

Keywords: predictive control, constrained control, system identification, orthonormal basis functions, neonatal incubators, hygrothermal conditions

1. INTRODUCTION

From many years, incubators have been used to create a comfortable and healthful hygrothermal environment for neonates. The aim of such device is to keep the respiratory and epidermal water losses at a small level and to increase the body heat storage.

In closed-type incubators, the internal temperature can be completely controlled. This property decreases the neonate temperature variance due to large differences between the air and the skin temperatures. An appropriate thermal environment decreases the rate of preterm infant morbidity and mortality. It has already been reported a reduction of 22% in such indexes by using incubators with temperature control (Perlstein et al. 1976).

Furthermore, another media of heat exchange between the neonate and its environment is the water loss through the skin and by respiration. When the incubator air temperature is constant, an increase in the air relative humidity (RH) value reduces the skin cooling and increases the body heat storage. Air RH values close to 65% prevents excessive body water loss and improves the maintenance of body temperature. The evaporation

---

[1] Author for correspondence.

rate when the air is at 60% RH is approximately 40% lower than that observed at a lower relative humidity (*e.g.*, 40%) (Telliez *et al.* 2001). Therefore, some incubators have active or passive systems to control the internal humidity. Control schemes, built to deal with this issue, have been described (Bouattoura *et al.* 1998) (Guler and Burunkaya 2002). In fact, by controlling the relative humidity and the temperature, one is actually controlling the internal partial vapor pressure . In an incubator, the partial vapor pressure value has an important role in the neonate water losses by skin and respiration.

From a control system point of view, an incubator is a system where temperature and RH values (consequently, the partial vapor pressure value) are the main controlled variables. Oliveira *et al.* (2005) presented an actual pilot plant built to simulate the micro-clime found in neonate incubators; and an application of multiple model control based on Laguerre functions modelling is also described. The results motivate real-time implementation of such control schemes.

The present work recalls some ideas discussed in (Oliveira *et al.* 2005) and extends such work by using a different predictive control law (*i.e.*, a scheme based on single models) and by presenting real-time results of such scheme in terms of by temperature, RH and partial vapor pressure control by the above mentioned pilot plant.

In the next section, some details of the incubator prototype are presented. In Section 3, important points related with orthonormal basis modelling are reviewed. This is the modelling approach used to represent the incubator. In Section 4, the predictive control law is described and, in Section 5, simulation examples of temperature and RH closed-loop control illustrate the performance of the discussed algorithm. Finally, conclusions are addressed.

2. PROCESS DESCRIPTION

In order to research issues related with incubators temperature and RH control and to test the results discussed in this paper, a neonatal incubator prototype was constructed and described in (Amorim *et al.* 2004, Oliveira *et al.* 2005). The main points related with such equipment are mentioned in this section. The pilot plant has the following parts: an acrylic transparent box (50cm height × 80cm length × 40cm width); a domestic heater, a fan and a humidifier. The heater and the humidifier are modified to allow external control in such a way that four power levels are available, that is: 0, 1, 2, 3 (or off, low, medium, maximum). The humidifier is based on ultrasound. The fan is

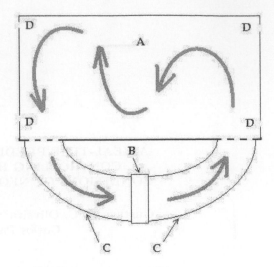

Fig. 1. Diagram with the main parts of the pilot plant.

Fig. 2. The neonatal incubator prototype.

on all the time. Ventilation ducts connect all the above-mentioned parts and allow air circulation inside the incubator. Fresh air supply is provided by the humidifier to guarantee some air renewal.

The process diagram is presented in Figure 1. In this figure, the acrylic box is represented by (A), the heating and humidifying devices by (B), the fan is also in the position (B), the ducts that form a closed circuit are represented by (C) and the orifices that simulate open spaces for catheters, ducts, wires, sensors, etc are in the position (D).

Figure 2 contains an incubator photograph. In this photo, one can notice the acrylic box, the two inner temperature sensors and the two humidity sensors (two small black boxes), the electronic actuator device (it is below the acrylic box) and the ventilation ducts (they are behind the incubator). Some orifices are placed in the incubator's side to promote air changes.

The software environment for supervision and digital control is implemented by using the virtual instrumentation software LabView / National Instruments. The sampling frequency for temperature and RH signals is 2 Hz.

3. ORTHONORMAL BASIS FUNCTIONS FOR SYSTEM MODELLING

A SISO linear causal and dynamic system can be described by its impulse response $h(k)$. If such system has finite memory, *i.e.*, $h(k)$ is absolutely integrable, it can be represented by a series of orthonormal functions, as follows:

$$h(k) = \sum_{i=1}^{\infty} c_i \phi_i(k) \qquad (1)$$

where $\{ \phi_i(k) \}_{i=1}^{\infty}$ is a base constructed with orthonormal functions and c_i is the i-th series coefficient. Assume that $\Phi_i(z)$ is the $\mathcal{Z}$ transform of $\phi_i(k)$ and $l_i(k)$ is the output of $\Phi_i(z)$ when the input signal is $u(k)$. By using these definitions, the model output $y(k)$, when the series is truncated at n terms, is given by:

$$y(k) = \sum_{i=1}^{n} c_i l_i(k) = \boldsymbol{c}^T \boldsymbol{l}(k) \qquad (2)$$

where the vectors $\boldsymbol{l}(k)$ and $\boldsymbol{c}$ are composed by the $l_i(k)$ signals and c_i coefficients. This model is linear in the parameters, so a least square algorithm can be used to estimate the c_i coefficients.

Although different orthonormal basis can be used in such a context, (see (Heuberger *et al.* 2005), for instance), the present work is focused on the Laguerre basis (Wahlberg and Makila 1996) since it represents a good tradeoff between the model quality and the *a priori* information required to build the basis. The model constructed with Laguerre basis (Laguerre Model) can be expressed as recursive functions, *i.e.*, the i-th function can be written using the $(i-1)$-th one. Thus, the signals $l_i(k); i = 1, \ldots, n;$ can be expressed by state equations and then the model is stated as follows:

$$\boldsymbol{l}(k+1) = A \boldsymbol{l}(k) + \boldsymbol{b}\, u(k-\tau) \qquad (3)$$

The matrix A and the vector $\boldsymbol{b}$ have constant coefficients which depend on a *a priori* selected pole p, which characterizes the Laguerre basis chosen to build the model. The size of such matrices is a function of the truncated series order n. τ is an approximate knowledge of the process time delay, which can be incorporated on the model as shown in equation (3).

The parametric identification properties of orthonormal based models, represented by equations (2) and (3), have been discussed by several authors in the literature (see, for instance, (Heuberger *et al.* 2005) and references included). This work highlights some properties and advantages of such system modelling approach. Some of them, related with the present paper, are recalled in (Oliveira *et al.* 2005).

4. PREDICTIVE CONTROL

Model predictive controllers (MPC) are defined by the following main steps: first, a model is used to compute the predicted process output. Next, a cost function related with the system closed loop performance is defined, and then, this cost function is minimized in relation to a set of future control signals. Finally, the first of these optimal control signals is applied to the process, *i.e.*, the receding horizon strategy. Several MPC algorithms have been proposed based on this scheme and the main difference between them is the strategy used to implement each step described above (Clarke 1994, Camacho and Bordons 1999).

Following, an MPC algorithm is presented. It is characterized by using Laguerre basis state-space models, as the one discussed in the previous section, and constraints in the control signal. The cost function of such MPC controller is:

$$J_k = \sum_{j=1}^{N_y} (\hat{y}(k+j|k) - w(k+j))^2 + \\ \sum_{j=0}^{N_u-1} \lambda \Delta u(k+j|k)^2 \qquad (4)$$

where N_y and N_u define the prediction and control horizon, respectively; λ is a weighting factor in the control signal; $w(k)$ is the set-point signal, $u(k+j|k)$ is the optimal control signal at time $k+j$ computed at time k; $\Delta u(k) = u(k) - u(k-1)$ and $\hat{y}(k+j|k)$ is the process output prediction at time $k+j$, computed at time k, by using the model composed by equations (2) and (3). The control law is obtained by minimizing the cost function (4) in relation to the future control signal variations $\Delta u(\cdot)$, that is:

$$\min_{\Delta u(k|k),\Delta u(k+1|k),\ldots,\Delta u(k+N_u-1|k)} J_k$$

s.to
$$\Delta u(k+j|k) = 0 \quad \forall\, j = N_u, \ldots, N_y \qquad (5)$$

In this scheme, the optimization problem has analytical solution. This problem can be rewritten by using a vector representation (see (Clarke 1994, Camacho and Bordons 1999)), which makes easy an implementation in Labview environment. The optimal control signal is computed by using the first optimal control variation, *i.e.*, $\Delta u(k|k)$, as follows: $u(k) = u(k-1) + \Delta u(k|k)$.

The problem's (5) solution space represented by $\{\Delta u(k|k), \Delta u(k+1|k), \ldots, \Delta u(k+N_u-1|k)\}$ is continuous, however, the actual one is discrete since the control signal $u(k)$ should receive integer values inside the interval $[0,3]$ (see Section 2, about the incubator construction). By using a control horizon equal to 1, the problem (5) becomes a one-variable convex function minimization problem. Since the control signal has lower and upper bounds, if the global solution is outside the bounds, the optimal constrained solution is at the bounds. Additionally, the near value of the optimal solution $\Delta u(k|k)$ is computed such that the control signal is integer, to respect the hardware limitations. The control $u(k)$ and control variation $\Delta u(k)$ signals actually applied in the plant are stored and used in the next control law computations. This introduces an anti-windup effect in the control law that reduces overshoot.

5. EXPERIMENTAL RESULTS

In this section, the performance of the hygrothermal control of the incubator described Section 2, by using the Laguerre model based predictive scheme is analyzed. First, the control problem is stated, followed by the incubator identification procedure. Then, real-time control results are presented and analyzed.

The Brazilian technical norm NBR IEC 60601-2-19 (NBR 1997) for neonate incubators indicates that: the set-point of the internal temperature should be inside the interval $[32,37]°C$, and the one for the RH signal should be inside the interval $[40,60]\%$, the temperature signal's first overshoot should be less than 2°C and, in the stead-state period, the temperature signal should be inside a band of $\pm0.5°C$ around the set-point signal.

Therefore, by using this guidelines, the problem is, starting from the environmental conditions, to lead the incubator hygrothermal conditions close to 35°C and 55%. The partial vapor pressure value is correlated with temperature and RH values So, these set-point values for temperature and RH guarantee that the partial vapor pressure is equal to 3006.33 Pa.

The available control signals for the heater and humidifier are integer numbers within the interval $[0,3]$.

For sake of comparison, the performance of an on-off control law strategy is presented in Figures 3 and 4. The on-off controller is set with no hysteresis zone. By means of these figures, it can be note that the on-off scheme is not able to keep the temperature inside a band smaller than $\pm1°C$ around the set-point. The closed loop RH band is $[54,58]\%$, where the mean value is above the specified set-point. The partial vapor pressure is also quite oscillatory (see Figure 10).

As discussed in Section 4, in other to build the predictive control law, a process model is need. The modelling approach proposed in the present paper for the incubator is the one presented in Section 3 and the steps are shown in following.

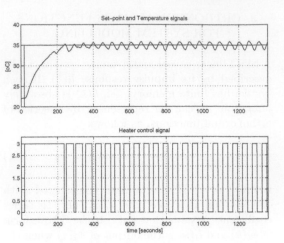

Fig. 3. Temperature control performance by using the on-off strategy.

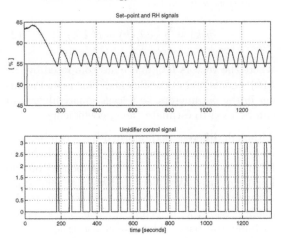

Fig. 4. Relative humidity control performance by using the on-off strategy.

The experiments are based on step response signals, and they are: A amplitude-1-step-shape signal (at time 23.5 seconds) in the heater, with no humidification; and a amplitude-1-step-shape signal (at time 161 seconds) in the humidifier, with the closed-loop temperature control active. Therefore, two step response curves representing the temperature and RH dynamics are obtained and showed in Figures 5 and 6.

By means of these signals, it can be noted that the temperature time-delay is 7 seconds (14 samples) and the RH time-delay is 10 seconds (20 samples). These time-delays are incorporated in the state-space Laguerre model as shown by equation (3). A 4-functions Laguerre model with pole equal to 0.99 (for temperature and RH models) are used and the series coefficients (see equation (2)) are

$$\{c_i\}_{i=1}^4 = \{0.4323, 0.1623, 0.0865, 0.0825\} \quad (6)$$

$$\{c_i\}_{i=1}^4 = \{0.3675, 0.3533, 0.1840, 0.0503\} \quad (7)$$

for the temperature and RH dynamics respectively. The k-step ahead prediction of the Laguerre models are also shown in Figures (5) and

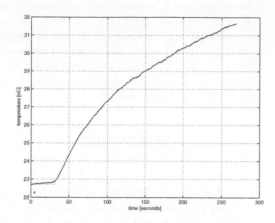

Fig. 5. Actual and model step response for temperature.

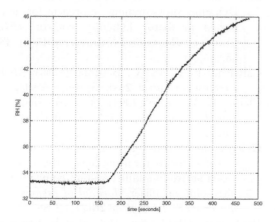

Fig. 6. Actual and model step response for RH.

(6). The curves (actual and model responses) are very close to each other and the MSE (Mean Square Error) of these approximations are 1.59×10^{-3} and 0.438, for temperature and RH models, respectively. A higher (than 4) number of functions could be used in the model, however, the improvement in the model quality is quite small.

The temperature and RH predictive controllers are constructed using the previously identified models as shown in Section 4. The temperature controller parameters are: $N_y = 24$, $N_u = 1$ and $\lambda = 0$; and the RH controller parameters are: $N_y = 30$, $N_u = 1$ and $\lambda = 0$.

The performance of the predictive control strategy is given by Figures 7 and 8. By means of these figures, it can be notice that the settling time for the temperature signal is small, i.e., close to 140 seconds. The performance of the predictive and on-off controller are similar in this index, since both uses the maximal power in such stage. The smaller settling time obtained by the predictive law is due to a bigger initial temperature of the incubator. Moreover, the predictive law presents no important overshoot. As for the RH signal, the

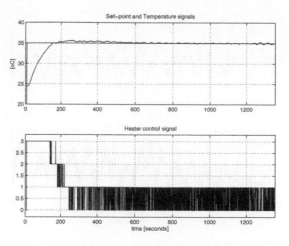

Fig. 7. Temperature control performance by using the Laguerre Predictive strategy.

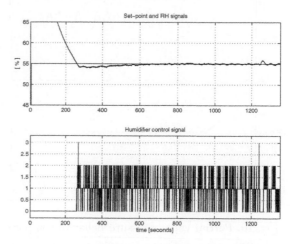

Fig. 8. Relative humidity control performance by using the Laguerre Predictive strategy.

idea is to compensate, through humidification, the drop in the RH due to the internal heating. The settling time in the RH signal is slightly bigger than the one observed for the temperature. However, the main advantage of the predictive control law is that the temperature and internal RH variation around the set-point value is quite smaller than the one provided by the on-off scheme. Note that these signals are within intervals close to $\pm 0.1^{\circ}$C and $\pm 0.2\%$, respectively (see Figure 9, for a zoom on Figures 7 and 8). Moreover, by improving the temperature and RH control, the control over partial vapor pressure is quite better than the one provided by the on-off strategy (see Figure 10).

These results show that the closed loop control behavior is quite good, mainly if one considers the actuator limitations due to a low cost hardware solution that lead to quite small resolution control signals. All these facts validate the control algorithm scheme.

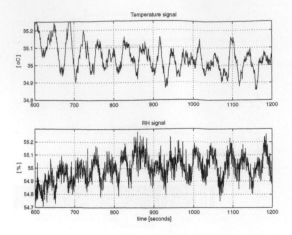

Fig. 9. Relative humidity control performance by using the Laguerre Predictive strategy.

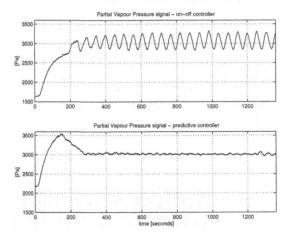

Fig. 10. Partial vapor pressure behavior comparison.

Oliveira *et al.* (2005) notice that the identified incubator model is different (mainly in the gain) if different amplitude steps are used in the modelling stage. However, by analyzing the control signal amplitude, it can be seen that the amplitude one is often used, so it justifies the choice of identification based on amplitude-1-step inputs.

6. CONCLUSIONS

This work has focused on hygrothermal conditions control, represented by temperature, RH and partial vapor pressure signals, of neonatal incubators. In this context, a full scale pilot plant, with a measurement of relevant signals, was used.

The proposed control law is the model predictive control. In order to perform the control synthesis, an identification procedure based on Laguerre functions for the incubator was performed. By the using real-time experiments, it was shown that both techniques revealed to be quite appropriate for such context. The use of Laguerre functions provided accurate models based on small process

information and it is based on input/output signals easy to be obtained. The predictive control law provided a good closed-loop control performance, by far respecting the norm requirements. Moreover, such good performance was obtained although the presence of actuator constraints created by the incubator characteristics.

REFERENCES

Amorim, M. F., G. H. C. Oliveira, D. S. R. Silva and L. M. Kiapuchinski (2004). Water vapour partial pressure control in neonatal incubator using prevision by multiple models. In: *Proc of the 25th Annual International Conference of the IEEE Engineering in Medicine and Biology Society.*

Bouattoura, D., P. Villon and G. Farges (1998). Dynamic programming approach for newborn's incubator humidity control. *IEEE Trans. on Biomedical Engineering* **45**(1), 48–55.

Camacho, E. F. and C. Bordons (1999). *Model Predictive Control.* 2 ed.. Springer Verlag.

Clarke, D. W., Ed.) (1994). *Advances in Model Based Predictive Control.* Oxford University Press.

Guler, I. and M. Burunkaya (2002). Humidity control of an incubator using the microcontroller-based active humidifier system employing an ultrasonic nebulizer. *Journal of Medical Engineering & Technology* **26**(2), 82–88.

Heuberger, P.S.C., den Hof, P.M.J. Van and Wahlberg, B., Eds.) (2005). *Modelling and Identification with Rational Orthogonal Basis Functions.* Springer Verlag.

NBR (1997). *Electro-medical equipments Part 2: Prescriptions for safety in neonate incubators (in Portuguese).* NBR IEC 60601-2-19 ed.. Brazilian Technical Norms Association. Rio de Janeiro.

Oliveira, G. H. C., M. F. Amorim and K. Latawiec (2005). Multiple model identification and control of neonate incubators using laguerre basis. In: *Proc. of the IFAC World Congress.* Prague/Czech Republic.

Perlstein, P. H., N. K. Edwards, H. D. Atherton and J. M. Sutherland (1976). Computer-assisted newborn intensive care. *Pediatrics* **57**, 494–501.

Telliez, F., V. Bach, S. Delanaud, A. Leke, M. Abdiche and K. Chardon (2001). Influence of incubator humidity on sleep and behaviour of neonates kept at stable body temperature. *Acta Paediatr* **90**, 998–1003.

Wahlberg, B. and P. M. Makila (1996). On approximation of stable linear dynamical systems using Laguerre and Kautz functions. *Automatica* **32**(5), 693–708.

MODELLING AND ANALYSIS PHYSIOLOGICAL MOTOR CONTROL USING BOND GRAPH

Asif M. Mughal[1] and Kamran Iqbal[2]

[1]*Dept. of Applied Science,* [2] *Dept of Systems Engineering*
University of Arkansas at Little Rock
Little Rock, Arkansas, USA

Abstract: - Human movement, postural stability and physiological models have been subjects of interest for several centuries. Physiological models for postural stability are studied in this paper with bond graph modelling and optimal control techniques. The bond graph models of a physiological motor control system provide a new prospective to analyze stability and movement of biomechanical models. The bond graphs of the musculoskeletal feedback system are used with linear H_2 optimal controller for analysis of different physiological parameters. Simulation results are obtained for various physiological parameters to analyze overall robustness of the model. These results demonstrate the applicability of bond graph modelling with robust control theory for physiological systems. *Copyright © 2006 IFAC*

Keywords: Bond Graphs, Optimal Control, Physiological Models, Robust Control, State Space Realization.

1. INTRODUCTION

Physiological functions and biomechanical movements have been object of interest for several centuries. Aristotle wrote a first book on the movement of animals –De Motu Animalium– and is titled as first biomechanician in the recorded history. There are many classical names such as Ibn Sina, Galaileo, Marcello Mappighi and Lenardo De Vincci, who all studied muscle, muscle structure and biomechanical systems with different prospective. Modern day biomechanical engineers, physiologists and scientists are still contributing to the development of this subject with new theories and application of modern tools. Hill (1938) proposed muscle structure as combination of contractile and stiff element in series or parallel connection. This model was studied extensively since last 50 years and different complexities have been added, such as Winter (1990) presented a nonlinear design for the neuromuscular activation in the muscular design with spindles and tendons. Linden (1995) studied the mechanical muscle by finite element method on muscle fibbers, which was further explained and elaborated by Huijing (1996). Recent researchers

(Crago, 2000; Kearny and Kirsch, 1997; Brown and Leob, 2003) worked with proprioceptors (muscle spindles and tendons) fibbers with neuro-musculoskeletal models. Davoodi *et al* (2003) developed a virtual muscle model with intrinsic and proprioceptive feedback. This model is comprehensive and useful for study of muscular response for different physiological testing conditions. Rozendaal (1997, 2000) presented a large scale musculoskeletal model in state space representation with feedback for analysis of human arm and also studied stability of shoulder with this model. Stroeve (1997) studied the similar neuromuscular model with feedback control and Mughal and Iqbal (2005) applied the optimal control methods for biomechanical sit to stand movement.

Muscular modelling involves mechanical, chemical, biological and electrical properties of the muscle structures. Bond graph modelling provides better solution when dealing with systems involving different kind of energy systems. Bond graph models deal with flow of power from one node to another. It uses generalized power and energy variables to track the flow of power. Sharpae and Brucewell (1993) presented a methodology to integrate interdisciplinary systems with bond graph modelling. K. Seo et al (1999) used bond graphs with genetic programming for automated design and Mughal & Iqbal (2004) used this approach for the master –slave tele-manipulation system and developed the bond graphs model of a human arm muscle model.

In this paper postural stability is studied with bond graph models of the muscle structure, Hill muscle models, muscle spindle and Golgi Tendon Organs (GTO). These models are then used for development of closed loop feedback neuro musculoskeletal system to analyze the various physiological parameters. After that H_2 controller design is used to analyze the model. Simulation results are provided for different variables of interest for postural stability.

2 BOND GRAPH MODELS OF PHYSIOLOGICAL SYSTEM

2.1 Bond Graph Muscle Models.

Hill muscle models (1938, 1950) are used by physiologists and researchers for the biomechanical modelling and development of the musculoskeletal control strategies. Muscles structure exhibits mechanical, electrical and chemical properties simultaneously. Fig. 1 shows a Hill muscle models and its respective bond graph is shown in Fig 2. General stiffness and viscous damping are represented by k and B respectively. In muscle model contractile elements are represented by B. Series and parallel elements are represented by stiffness component (spring constants) ks and kp respectively. Neural input is electrical signal provided by motor neurons (MN) units. Proprioceptive feed back and efferent inputs are added into motor neuron input as intrafusal inputs to the muscle.

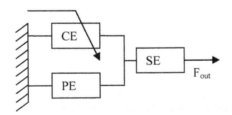

Fig 1. Hill Muscle Model

In classic testing conditions the neural input is used to study the behaviour of muscle with an impulse or a step response. However, this is a single direction input to the muscle and muscle behaviour doesn't affect this port of input. This neural input is represented by active bond which means that it is not representing flow of power at this port; however, either effort or flow excitation acts at this junction. It is possible to represent this active bond for either effort or flow excitation mechanism according to the requirement. The output port is represented by a

viscous damping element B_{out} which may have different values depending upon different testing conditions. This element is replaced by ports of the musculoskeletal structure when used with inertia or other proprioceptive elements. For series elements, forces are the same and extensions (velocities) add. In parallel elements, extensions (velocities) are the same and forces add.

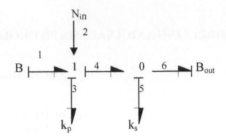

Fig 2. Bond graph of Hill Muscle Model

In these types of bond graph systems, state variables are usually chosen ports containing the stiffness components. The state equations for the system is then given as

$$\dot{x}_3 = \frac{x_3}{k_p \cdot B} + \frac{x_5}{k_s \cdot B} + N_{in} + S_V \qquad (1)$$

$$\dot{x}_5 = \frac{x_3}{k_p \cdot B} + \frac{x_5}{k_s \cdot B} - \frac{x_5}{k_s \cdot B_{out}} + N_{in} + S_V$$

$$F_{out} = \frac{x_5}{k_p} \qquad (2)$$

These models may change slightly according to the different testing conditions or after integration in large musculoskeletal system which can be done easily by adding ports appropriately.

2.2 Muscle Spindle Model

Muscle spindles are activated by neural inputs of dynamic (γd) and static (γs) fusiomotor input and mechanical inputs of fascicle length and fascicle velocity. The outputs of muscle spindle are primary and secondary afferent which add into the neural excitation of a muscle. Crago (2000), Mileusnic & Leob (2003) and Brown & Leob (2003) provided the model structure for muscle spindle with two intrafusal bags and chain. Structure of each intrafusal bag remains the same and output of bag 1 is the primary afferent and output of bag 2 & chain are the secondary afferent. These outputs are functions of extrafusal contractile length, dynamics of intrafusal fibbers, mechanical and neural inputs. Each of intrafusal bag and chain consists of a contractile element and series and parallel stiffness (spring) elements. Mechanical inputs are the fascicle length and velocity from musculoskeletal structure. The neural outputs or primary (Ia) and secondary afferent (II) from muscle spindle adds into neural excitation of muscle. General structure of the intrafusal bags and chain are given in Fig 3.

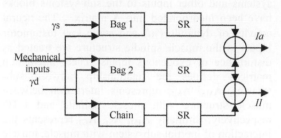

Fig 3. General Structure of Muscle Spindle

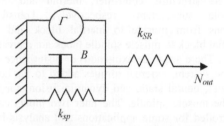

Fig 4. Structure of intrafusal bag & chains with sensory region (SR)

Components of muscle spindle and sensory region (SR) are shown in Fig 4. It consists of a parallel viscous element and a stiffness (spring) element. Neural input is represented by Γ. These elements may also be treated as linear as well as nonlinear elements and also combination of several terms (Mileusnic and Leob 2002). Contractile elements consist of fibbers and these can be modelled separately as well as combined into a equivalent effect shown by Brown & Loeb (1997). Bond graph model of this structure is shown in fig 5

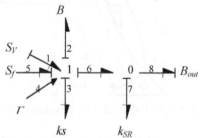

Fig 5. Bond Graph model of muscle spindle

Components shown in this model are a mechanical source of flow (S_V), neural inputs (port 4), stiffness (port 3), viscous damping (port 2) and sensory region stiffness (port 6). The output is measured at port 8 with viscous components representing output impendence. However, this can be replaced by other muscular structure at output. State equations of this bond graph model of muscle spindle is given as

$$\dot{x}_3 = \frac{1}{B}S_f - \frac{1}{B}\left(\frac{x_3}{k_{sp}} + \frac{x_6}{k_{SR}}\right) + \Gamma + S_V \qquad (3)$$

$$\dot{x}_7 = \frac{1}{B}S_f - \frac{x_3}{B \cdot k_{sp}} - \frac{x_7}{k_{SR}}\left(\frac{1}{B} - \frac{1}{B_{out}}\right) + \Gamma + S_V$$

The output force is at port 8 is given by

$$F_{out} = \frac{x_7}{k_{SR}} \qquad (4)$$

The combined effect of bags and chain for model representing in Fig 3 can be developed from the same model. This is sixth order model, with each intrafusal bag and a chain representing similar 2nd order system shown in Fig 5. There are two output ports (terminating at output impedance B_{01} and B_{02}) to produce the primary afferent and secondary afferent.

2.3 Golgi Tendon Organ Model

GTO responds to tensions in the muscle fibbers and send proprioceptive feedback to the muscle activation units. GTO is usually represented by gains and in bond graph detailed models of GTO can be implemented. In simple approach GTO can be modelled as only elastic spring element or combination of elastic element with viscous damping.

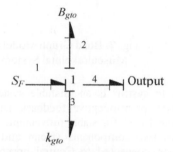

Fig 6. Bond Graph Model of GTO

In this figure, S_F is the source of force from muscle and Output is the output impedance terminating to the neural control system. This is the simplest one degree model of GTO. The state equation for this model is given as

$$\dot{x}_{gto} = \frac{x_{gto}}{k_{gto} \cdot B_{gto}} + \frac{1}{B_{gto}}S_F \qquad (5)$$

3 MUSCULOSKELETAL SYSTEM MODELING

The musculoskeletal systems with inertia, muscle, muscle spindle and GTO can be modelled using bond graphs. In this model we also need two port elements called transformers for conversion from translational to rotational motion or vice versa. Inertial equations of joint mechanics are usually represented in angles of rotation i.e. flexion of limbs (segments) at joints. Muscle equations are mechanical translational equation so a transformer is needed at every joint to convert muscle forces in to joints torques. Fig 7 shows the bond graph representation of a system with block diagrams of components. In Fig 7 muscle output force is transformed into torque for inertial block and added up to external torque for limb movement. Transformer ratio (r) is the length of a limb. Similarly angle and angular velocity from inertial block are fed back to muscle spindle by transforming these to fascicle length and fascicle velocity. The output angle and velocity from inertial block are represented by the vector bond graphs. The vector bond graphs are used when more than multiple variables are connecting one port to another identically. These are also used for representing assembly of sub-systems. The negative ratio (r) is used here because if force to moment is positive then resulting angular motion results in muscle shortening.

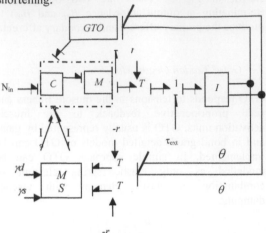

Fig. 7. Bond Graph Model of Musculoskeletal System

This whole system is an unstable system. Muscle block takes proprioceptive feedback and produces appropriate forces for stable movement. The muscle block has two components (Helm and Rozendaal 2000): one connected to Central nervous systems (CNS) and other producing controlled forces to inertial block. GTO also responds to the muscle forces and its feedback also changes the neural excitation. The muscle output forces are transformed into joint torques adding up with external or disturbance torques and then causes the movement in inertial block. The musculoskeletal feedback system can be combined into one state space representation for analysis and a robust design of a controller structure. This dynamic system takes effect of all physiological variables interacting with each other in closed loop response. The state variables of closed loop system are x_M, x_S, x_G and x_I represents the dynamics of muscle, muscle spindle, GTO and inertia respectively. The combined musculoskeletal model with the proprioceptive feedback loops and accompanying gains is given in Eq (6).

$$\begin{bmatrix} \dot{x}_M \\ \dot{x}_S \\ \dot{x}_G \\ \dot{x}_I \end{bmatrix} = \begin{bmatrix} A_M & A_{MS} & A_{MG} & 0 \\ 0 & A_S & 0 & A_{SI} \\ A_{GM} & 0 & A_G & A_{GI} \\ A_{IM} & 0 & 0 & A_I \end{bmatrix} \cdot \begin{bmatrix} x_M \\ x_S \\ x_G \\ x_I \end{bmatrix} + \begin{bmatrix} B_M \\ 0 \\ 0 \\ 0 \end{bmatrix} \cdot U \quad (6)$$

The order of the system is different in different problem depending upon order of each sub-system. The muscle structure and inertia are 2nd order system, GTO is 1st order system and muscle spindle is 6th order using 2 intrafusal bags and a chain system represented in Fig 3. The musculoskeletal system shown in Fig 7 is 11th order system and if a simplified 2nd order muscle spindle structure is used then system is reduced to 7th order. Only muscle structure is directly affected by the input through CNS and so in **B** matrix, there are zeros for other sub

systems and other inputs to the sub-systems blocks have been incorporated into **A** matrix. . The neural activity of dynamic (γd) and static (γs) fusiomotor inputs to the muscle spindle structure are treated as disturbance or exogenous inputs. There interaction matrices defines the relationship between sub-systems, A_{MS}, A_{MG} represents interaction between muscle structure with muscle spindle and GTO respectively. Similarly A_{IM}, A_{SI}, A_{GI} represents the interaction of inertial subsystem with muscle, muscle spindle and GTO. In Fig 7, M, C, I and MS are the muscle structure, controller, inertial and muscle spindle sub-systems respectively. Transformer actions from muscle to inertial block and from inertial block to muscle spindle block are represented by T. There are three exogenous or disturbance input in the system, external torques added to the control torques, neural static and dynamic fusiomotor input to the muscle spindle. The later two inputs can be controlled for some applications and analysis but in this system their effects are simulated for known signals used by Mileusnic et al (2002).

3.1 Postural Stability Model.

A single link inertial inverted pendulum biomechanical model for postural stability is shown in Fig 8. This model discussed in detail by Iqbal and Roy (2004) with a PID controller.

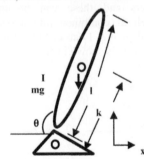

Fig 8. Single link model for postural stability.

This is 2nd order nonlinear model linearized at equilibrium positions, angle θ and angular velocity are the error state variables with respect to equilibrium position. This model is used in closed loop feedback model as x_I in Eq (6). The input torque at joint comes from muscle force transforming into torque and represented as A_{IM} in Eq (6). The outputs of this model are angle and velocity and these are transformed into fascicle length and fascicle velocity as inputs to the muscle spindle structure.

$$\begin{bmatrix} \dot{\theta} \\ \ddot{\theta} \end{bmatrix} = \begin{bmatrix} 0 & 1 \\ (I + mk^2)^{-1} & 0 \end{bmatrix} \cdot \begin{bmatrix} \theta \\ \dot{\theta} \end{bmatrix} + \begin{bmatrix} 0 \\ 1 \end{bmatrix} \tau \quad (7)$$

3.2 H_2 Optimal Controller.

The controller block in musculoskeletal system represents the CNS activity in the muscular structure. This controller gets feedback from proprioceptors and generates commands for muscle structure. This controller is designed for the analysis of the musculoskeletal system with only three measurements from the system. An input U is regulated through a H_2 optimal controller designed from the musculoskeletal system. There are three exogenous or disturbance inputs in the system, two are the static and dynamic fusiomotor input and one is external disturbance torque to the inertial sub-system. The overall system including measured and regulated variables is given as:

$$p = \begin{bmatrix} A & B_w & B_u \\ C_y & D_{yw} & D_{yu} \\ C_m & D_{mw} & D_{mu} \end{bmatrix} \quad (8)$$

In the **p** matrix, **A** and **B$_u$** are the same matrices given in Eq (6) as **A** and **B** matrices, and **Bw** is a matrix for external disturbances. It is obvious from Fig 7 that controller is only taking input from proprioceptive feedbacks and these are GTO output and primary and secondary afferent from the muscle spindle block, represented in **C$_m$** matrix. In this system one control input and five other state outputs are optimized, and these are muscle output, GTO output, primary afferent, inertial angle and velocity represented by **D$_{yu}$** and **C$_y$** matrices in the system. . In most general case **D$_{mu}$** and **D$_{yw}$** are zero matrices, while **D$_{mw}$** and **D$_{yu}$** must be full row rank and full column rank, respectively. The whole system **p** must also satisfy the following requirements

1. (**A,B$_u$**) is stablizable and (**C$_m$,A**) is detectable
2. (**A,B$_w$**) is stablizable and (**C$_y$,A**) is detectable.
3. $\mathbf{C_y^T D_{yu}} = \mathbf{0}$ and $\mathbf{B_w D_{mw}} = \mathbf{0}$, $\mathbf{D_{yu}^T D_{yu}} = \mathbf{I}$ and $\mathbf{D_{mw}^T D_{mw}} = \mathbf{I}$

A H_2 optimal controller **K** is obtained by minimizing the H_2-norm of the system for two Riccati equations X and Y given in Eq (9).

$$A'X + XA - XB_m B' + C_y' C_y = 0 \quad (9)$$
$$AY + YA' - YC_m' C_m Y - B_w B_w' = 0$$

The solution of X and Y leads to an optimal and unique controller K for the problem.

$$K = \begin{bmatrix} A - B_m B_m' X - YC_m' C_m & YC_m' \\ -B_m' X & 0 \end{bmatrix} \quad (10)$$

This method is discussed in detail by Doyle et al (1989), and possesses the equivalent LQG design discussed in Burl (1999). This is 11th order controller which takes three physiological measurements from the system and generates an output which is an input to the muscle structure.

4 SIMULATIONS

The bond graph diagram shown in Fig 7 is simulated in Matlab /Simulink for the linear musculoskeletal biomechanical model. There is only one controlled input in this case and there are two exogenous input to muscle spindle as static (γs) and dynamic (γd)

fusiomotor inputs and one external disturbance torque added to the torque supplied to the muscle block and this is the random noise of power 1e-11. The singular value plot for closed loop musculoskeletal system with controller and proprioceptive feedbacks is shown in Fig 9.

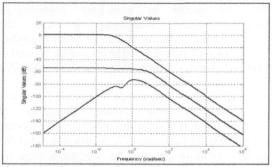

Fig 9. Singular Value plot of closed loop system with controller and proprioceptive feedbacks

The biomechanical model is disturbed from its rest (equilibrium) position angle $\pi/2$ to some error. In the first case, it is assumed that there are not any fusiomotor inputs present in the system and simulation results are shown in Fig 10. In the second case, model is simulated with feedback controlled input and with static and dynamic fusiomotor inputs used by Mileusnic et al (2002) and external disturbance torque. Simulation results are shown in Fig 11 and it is noted that the H_2 controller design doesn't affect much on the settling time and shape of dynamics. The amplitude of steady state response is directly dependent on amplitude of dynamic fusiomotor input and it has more effects on muscle output force and GTO output force then other variables. Similarly disturbance torque has more effect on inertial angle than other variables.

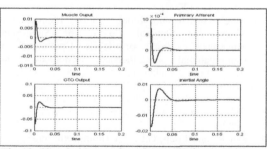

Fig 10. Simulation results of Muscle force, Primary afferent, GTO output and Inertial angle error

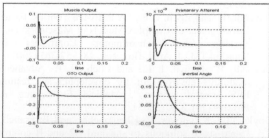

Fig 11. Simulation results of Muscle force, Secondary afferent, GTO output and Inertial angle error with fusiomotor inputs
(γs=0.1 and γd =0.1 @ 87 Hz).

5 CONCLUSIONS

Bond graph modelling and robust optimal control design techniques are used for the analysis of the musculoskeletal systems with physiological motor functions for proprioceptive feedbacks. Bond graphs are very useful in modelling physiological components and integrating it with the musculoskeletal systems, it also provides flexibility to track flow of power in different muscle activation levels. Postural stability is also studied with feed back control and in the presence of fusiomotor inputs and results shows their effects in muscle forces and other variables. The constant magnitude of fusiomotor inputs affects the dynamics of response and stability of the system. It is also noted that the optimal H_2 controller provides a better scheme for postural stability and can be applied to the other physiological analysis. In this scheme CNS controller is computed by using the whole system information including all proprioceptive feedbacks, physiological motor functions and desired measurements. This combined musculoskeletal model with proprioceptive feedback can be studied with other robust and adaptive control strategies to obtain better and more physiological relevant response. Similarly time and neural delays can be introduced in the system and fusiomotor inputs can be treated as neural feedback inputs.

REFERENCES

A. M Mughal and K. Iqbal, "A Bond Graph Model of Bilateral Master-Slave Tele manipulation", Proceedings of the Fifth IASTED International Conference on Modelling and Simulation, ISBN:0-88986-391-1, pp-362-367, Marina Del Rey, CA, March 1-3, (2004).

Asif Mughal and Kamran Iqbal, "A Fuzzy Biomechanical Model for Optimal Control of Sit-to-Stand Movement", Proc. of IEEE Conference on Computational Intelligence: Methods and Applications, Istanbul, Turkey, Dec 15-17, (2005).

Blake Hannaford: "A Design Framework for Teleoperators with Kinesthics Feedback", IEEE Transaction on Robotics and Automation, Vol.5, No.4, August (1989).

Davoodi R. and Loeb, G.E., "A Biomimetic Strategy for Control of FES Reaching",25rd Annual International Conference of the IEEE Engineering in Medicine and Biology Society, Cancun, Mexico, September 17-21 (2003).

Davoodi, R. and Loeb, G.E., "A Software Tool for Faster Development of Complex Models of Musculoskeletal Systems and Sensorimotor Controllers in SimulinkTM" J. Appl. Biomech, 18: 357-365 (2002).

Davoodi, R., Brown, I. E., and Loeb, G. E "Advanced modelling environment for developing and testing FES control systems", Medical Engineering & Physics (25) ,3-9, (2003).

Doyle, J.C., K. Glover, P. Khargonekar, and B. Francis, "State-space solutions to standard H2 and H control problems," IEEE Transactions on Automatic Control, vol. 34, no. 8, pp. 831-847, August (1989).

Hill, A. V. "The heat of shortening and the dynamic constants of muscle." Proc. Roy Society, 126B:pp136-195 (1938).

Hill, A. V., "The series elastic components of muscle", Proc. Roy. Soc., 137B:pp399-420 (1950).

Huijing, P.A. "Modeling of homogeneous muscle: It is realistic to consider skeletal muscle as a lumped sarcomere fiber." Chapter 6, pp92-96, Biomechanics and neural control of posture and movement: Springer-Verlag (2000).

JEE Sharpe, RH Bracewell - Proc IEEE international Conf. on Systems man and cybernetics Piscataway, NJ, USA (1993).

Jeffrey B. Burl, Linear Optimal Control, H_2 and H∞ Method", *Addison Wesley Longman Inc*, (1999).

K. Iqbal and A. Roy, "Stabilizing PID Controllers for a Single-Link Biomechanical Model with Position, Velocity, and Force Feedback," ASME Journal of Biomechanical Engineering, Dec. (2004).

K. Seo, E. Goodman, and R. Rosenberg, "First Steps toward Automated Design of Systems Using Bond Graphs and Genetic Programming", Proc. Genetic and Evolutionary Computation Conference, San Francisco, p. 189 (2001).

Kirsch R.F., Kearney R.E.: "Identification of time-varying stiffness dynamics of the human ankle joint during an imposed movement." Exp. Brain Res ,114: 71-85, (1997).

Lan, N., Fornwalt III, H.C., Mileusnic, M., Davoodi, R., Brown, I.E. and Loeb, G.E., "Biomimetic Design of FES Control Systems", 6th Annual Meeting of International Functional Electrical Simulation Society, Cleveland, Ohio, (2001).

Mileusnic, M. and Loeb, G.E., "Development of a Muscle Spindle Model", 7th Annual Conference of the International Functional Electrical Simulation Society, Ljubljana, Slovenia, (2002).

Patrick, E. Crago, "Creating Neuromusculoskeletal Models, Chapter 8, pp1199-133, Biomechanics and neural control of posture and movement: Springer-Verlag (2000).

Van der Helm FCT, Rozendaal LA . "Musculoskeletal systems with intrinsic and proprioceptive feedback". In: Winters JM, Crago P (Eds), Neural control of posture and movement, Springer-Verlag, NY,164-174. (2000).

Leonard Albert Rozendaal. "Stability of the Shoulder: Intrinsic muscle properties and reflexive control," PhD Thesis, TU-Delft (1997).

Sybert Stroeve, "Neuromuscular control of arm movements: A modelling approach", PhD Thesis, TU-Delft (1998).

Van der Linden, B.J.J.J, Meijer, K., Huijing, P.A.. Koopman, F.F.J.M., and Grootenboer, H.J. "Finite element model of anisotropic muscle: effect of curvature on fiber length distribution. Proc XVth congress of the International Society of Biomechanics, University of Jyvaskyla, Finland (1995).

Winters, J. M. and Woo, S.L-Y. "Hill-based muscle models: a systems engineering perspective". In Multiple Muscle System, Biomechanics and Movement Organization, Winter, J.M and Winters, J. M. and Woo, S.L-Y (eds), Ch-5, pp69-93, Springer-Velag, NY (1990).

Winters, Jack M. "Terminology and Foundations of Movement Science", Chapter 1, Biomechanics and neural control of posture and movement, Springer-Veralag (2000).

Yasuyoshi Yokokohji and Tsuneo Yoshikawa: "Bilateral Control of Master-Slave Manipulators for Ideal Kinesthetic Coupling - Formulation and Experiment", IEEE Transaction on Robotics and Automation, Vol. 10, No 5, October (1994).

TOWARDS MODELLING THE HUMAN SENSORY MOTOR SYSTEM

David Guiraud[1], Christine Azevedo[1], Ken Yoshida[2], Philippe Poignet[1], Mohammed Samer[1], Hassan El Makssoud[1]

[1] DEMAR Project, INRIA LIRMM,
161 Rue Ada 34392 Montpellier Cedex 5, France
[2] Center for Sensory-Motor Interaction (SMI),
Fredrik Bajers Vej 7 D-3 9220 Aalborg Denmark

Abstract: DEMAR aims at rehabilitation engineering using Functional Electrical Stimulation based on the automatic control theoretical approach but also on the physiology of the system studied, to obtain a useable and useful therapy for disabled people. To simulate, synthesize, and control movements of impaired limbs using Functional Electrical Stimulation, modelling is necessary. Living actuators, i.e. muscles, sensors, i.e. Golgi Tendon Organs and muscle spindles, need to be understood and modelled to perform realistic numerical simulations. The paper describes some results obtained in the DEMAR team. *Copyright © 2006 IFAC*

Keywords: Functional Electrical Stimulation (FES), Intra fascicular Electroneurograms (ENG), Muscle Modelling, Neuroprostheses.

1. INTRODUCTION

DEMAR project carries out research in the context of motor function rehabilitation *via* FES in Central Nervous System (CNS) injured persons. Lesions of the CNS induce a split-body situation delimited by the injury level where lower body remains functional but cannot communicate properly with upper body. Higher control centres influence on lower body actuators is partially or totally impossible and information from lower body sensors is not or is weakly transmitted to higher control centres. FES allows for restoring motor activity of paralyzed limbs by applying electrical stimulation to sensory-motor systems *via* electrodes which are placed on the skin, or implanted (epimysial, intramuscular, nerve cuff, intraneural); DEMAR focuses mainly on implanted FES. FES can be used either for acute clinical rehabilitation as for hemiplegics, and for chronic movement restoration for spinal cord injured (SCI) patients, mainly complete quadriplegics and paraplegics. The technique works well but the tuning of the stimulation sequences remains empirical (Kobetic *et al.* 1997), with some automatic control approach (Popovic *et al.* 1999, Riener and Fuhr, 1998, Hunt *et al.* 1998, Donaldson and Yu 1996)

when an accurate movement generation, a balance control, or fatigue compensation, is needed. Thus, measurements have to be performed and ENG recordings from the afferent muscle sensors could be an elegant and efficient solution. Modelling is then a necessary and important step, in order to apply the automatic control theory tools and results (Guiraud *et al.* 2003, Riener 1999). Different elements have to be modelled: i) actuators, i.e. muscles, ii) the main natural sensors directly involved in the movement. We do not explore brain sensory - motor cortical areas which complexity prevents from accurate modelling.

The paper describes how to handle models through examples, in order to perform simulations and analysis of sensory-motor system behaviours.

2. MOTOR AND EFFERENT PATHWAYS

As we want to control movement through FES, the minimum structure that can illustrate the validity of our approach is the modelling and then the control of a joint. Because the experimental setup is easy to provide, we studied the knee using quadriceps and hamstrings antagonist muscles.

2.1 Muscle modelling

We developed a series of models based as much as possible on the physiology so that parameters are meaningful (El Makssoud *et al.* 2004, Keener and Sneyd 2001). Moreover, the entry is the FES signal in order to use this model for FES control purposes as shown on figure 1.

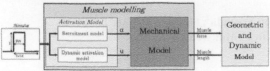

Fig.1. Global muscle model blocks.

Our muscle model is separated in two parts: i) activation block composed of the modelling of the chemical control - i.e. activation and relaxation phases through Ca^{++} dynamics, and action potential birth and propagation synchronised with the FES signal -, and the recruitment curve relating the FES parameters and the percentage of fired Motor Units in the muscle, ii) mechanical model dealing with the actin myosin force generation mechanism (Huxley 1957, Bestel and Sorine 2000) and passive tissues forces transmission (Hill 1938, Zahalak 1992). For our investigation of the knee joint, recruitment and Ca^{++} dynamics are not taken into account as the inputs are directly the chemical input u and the recruitment percentage α. The relationship between the FES parameters and α is static so that it is not important for simulation even though control is studied, but Ca^{++} dynamics could have an effect on the control strategies (see El Makssoud 2005 for details). Nevertheless, Ca^{++} dynamics mainly induces delay and non linear effects on short term contraction, such as impulse response whereas the simulation focuses on control strategies applied to long term control so that the time scales are significantly different. This dynamics is then neglected. As far as the mechanical model is concerned, the more general modelling is shown on figure 2 and is governed by a set of equations considering Ep as a non linear spring (equation 2), and all others passive elements as linear; that is two springs E_{s1}, E_{s2}, and two dampers A_1, A_2, that guaranty the stability of the system in isometric contraction.

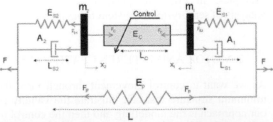

Fig. 2. Mechanical muscle model with masses and dampers.

The active contractile element Ec is governed by the state equations, obtained through the integration of the Huxley model (El Makssoud *et al.* 2004):

$$\begin{cases} \dot{k}_c = -k_c|u| + \alpha k_m(\varepsilon)|u|_+ - k_c|\dot{\varepsilon}_c| \\ \dot{F}_c = -F_c|u| + \alpha F_m(\varepsilon)|u|_+ - F_c|\dot{\varepsilon}_c| + L_{c0}k_c\dot{\varepsilon}_c \end{cases} \quad (1)$$

with u the chemical control, and α the recruitment input (figure 3). 0 indices denote constants at equilibrium.

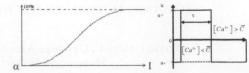

Fig. 3. α vs. stimulation current profile, and u command synchronised with the electrical stimulus with contraction (τ, u>0) and frequency dependant relaxation phases (u<0).

Km(ε) and Fm(ε) are respectively the maximum stiffness and force that the contractile element can produce. This is the force-length relationship. This model gives the output force Fc and the stiffness equivalent to the integration of the stiffness of each microscopic actin – myosin bridges. Depending on the experimental conditions and the aim of the simulation, different simplified models were developed sharing common subsets of parameters: i) studying isometric contractions need for masses and dampers but the parallel element Ep is not involved so that it is removed, ii) muscle used with skeleton can be simplified so that global masses of the limb, and reduced damping viewed from the joint are considered. In our simulation, we want to investigate the behaviour of a joint controlled by two antagonist muscles which parameters are quite different. Muscle's masses are neglected, and muscle's dampers are integrated in the joint damping factor. For our simulation, the muscle's masses and dampers were neglected, but we kept passive parallel and serial stiffness as shown on figure 4.

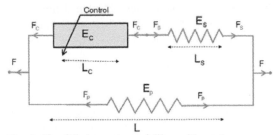

Fig. 4. Simplified muscle modelling without dampers and masses used for multi joint simulations.

This leads to the following state equations derived from equation 1 (2):

$$\begin{cases} \dot{k}_c = \left(s_a\alpha k_m(\varepsilon) - s_u k_c + s_v q \dfrac{s_a\alpha F_m(\varepsilon) - s_u F_c}{1 + pk_c - s_v q F_c}k_c \right)u - s_v\dfrac{ak_c}{1 + pk_c - s_v q F_c}\dot{\varepsilon} \\ \dot{F}_c = \dfrac{s_a\alpha F_m(\varepsilon) - s_u F_c}{1 + pk_c - s_v q F_c}u + \dfrac{bk_c - s_v aF_c}{1 + pk_c - s_v q F_c}\dot{\varepsilon} \\ \dfrac{dF_p}{d\varepsilon} = k_{p_1}F_p + k_{p_2} \end{cases}$$

where a, b p q are reduced parameters identified for each muscle, and s_v and s_u sign functions of the shortening speed and the command u respectively.

2.2 Joint modelling

Figure 5 shows the global modelling of the knee. The joint itself is simplified and assimilated to a one DOF rotation with simple links to the muscles.

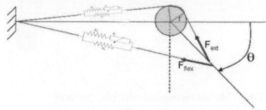

Fig 5. Knee modelling with the single joint actuation part of quadriceps and hamstrings.

They can be all resumed in the state space in order to design control scheme such as high order sliding modes (HOSM) (Mohammed *et al.* 2004) as follows:

$$\dot{\mathbf{x}} = \mathbf{f}(\mathbf{x}, t, \mathbf{U}) \qquad (3)$$

with $\mathbf{x} = [X_1 \dots X_6]^T = [k_{c1} \quad k_{c2} \quad F_{c1} \quad F_{c2} \quad \theta \quad \dot{\theta}]^T$ the state vector and $\mathbf{U} = [u_1 \quad \alpha_1 \quad u_2 \quad \alpha_2]^T$ the control vector. The variable θ represents the angle joint of the knee. The state variables k_{c1}, F_{c1} and k_{c2}, F_{c2}, and the command variables u_1, α_1 and u_2, α_2 are respectively the state and command variables of the quadriceps and hamstring related to equation 2. Parameters were taken from literature.

2.3 Simulations and discussion

The clinically used FES systems are mainly tuned empirically directly on the patient so that it is cumbersome and no one can guaranty the optimality of the tuning even though some experiments have been carried out to achieve closed loop or optimal control (Popovic et al. 1999, Riener and Fuhr, 1998, Hunt et al. 1998, Donaldson and Yu 1996, Durfee 1993). The design of complex control strategies needs modelling. For instance, figure 6 shows the use of HOSM control on the knee joint (Mohammed *et al.* 2004).

Performances can be evaluated and benchmarked through different simulations sets and in this example shows that HOSM is able to control the knee joint in position with good accuracy, stability and time response. The theoretical proofs of the performances remain difficult to state and thus to optimise. But simulations give the opportunity to get results on: i) various kind of control strategies, ii) movement synthesis with different optimisation criteria, iii) the effect of not well-known phenomena such as co contraction and joint stiffness control through muscle stiffness control (Mohammed *et al.* 2005, Matjacic 2001). In the latter case, modelling allows to observe the muscle stiffness and then the joint stiffness due to passive tissues but also due to muscle contractions. These studies show that with this kind of modelling, robustness, stability, and performances can be assessed through simulations while theoretical proofs could not always be obtained. Moreover, our model offers new

perspective such as stiffness control and thus co contraction study.

We try successfully to identify the muscle model (figure 2) through experiments on Gastrocnemius rabbit muscle in isometric conditions. Parameters identification using extended Kalman filter, and cross validation, demonstrate that the model is accurate enough to render impulse and step responses with parameter values closed to the measured ones; for instance on one sample (measured, estimated): u+ (--, $20s^{-1}$), u- (--, $15s^{-1}$), τ (5ms,--), ks (4500N/m, --), Lc0 (8cm, 7.9cm), Ls0 (3cm, 3.6cm), m (--, 17g), λ (--, 15 Ns/m). The modelling remains tricky when dealing with the identification not only because of the experimental setup, but also due to the convergence of the algorithms used in such a sensitive context. The validation on the patient himself is not easy to assess. Some other contributions to the movement such as voluntary movements of the upper body in paraplegics prevent from accurate modelling and then validations. Nevertheless, the aim could be to minimise voluntary contributions during the synthesis, or the make robust control to the voluntary movements. Then, the patient has to be taught to use correctly the system. We can guess that the design of useful movements will need to alternate between numerical simulations, experimental identification and patient learning.

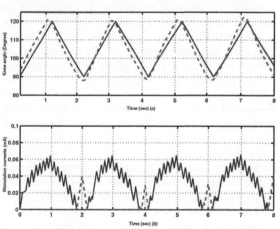

Fig. 6. HOSM applied to the control of the knee using the model of the knee joint; upper figure actual (dash line) and desired values of the angle; lower figure, quadriceps and hamstring (dash line) input commands.

3. SENSORY AND AFFERENT PATHWAYS

The framework of our research work is the rehabilitation of motor functions *via* implanted FES in CNS injured patients. To improve the efficiency and robustness of FES systems, it is necessary to move to closed-loop controllers. This implies the use of sensors whose type and number are highly constrained: the stimulation system has been implanted in order to simplify its use by the patient; it is therefore not possible to cover the person with various external apparatuses. An alternative to artificial sensors is to take advantage of natural sensors that are intact and active in the muscles below the spinal cord lesion.

3.1 Recording from muscle receptors

Muscles situated under the lesion remain functional; similarly, muscle receptors are intact and keep on sending information about muscle state to CNS. It should therefore be possible to use natural muscle sensitive fibre information as feedback for the FES controller. This implies to be able to online extract and interpret information from neural activity in a form usable by a closed-loop controller. In the past, researchers have worked on the interpretation of nerve firing patterns. Cutaneous mechanoreceptors (Goodall et al., 1993; Andreasen and Struijk, 2003), muscle spindles (Wise et al., 1999) and Golgi Tendon Organs (GTO) (Houk and Simon, 1967) have been studied. Some authors also demonstrated the feasibility to estimate joint position from recording from its two antagonist muscles (Simon et al., 1984). A simple corrector controller has been used to follow a desired joint angle trajectory despite application of external disturbance in cat (Yoshida and Horch, 1996; Jensen et al., 2002). Currently, muscle afferent activity is thought to be applicable as feedback in real-time closed-loop control in restrictive conditions. These results demonstrate that this research field is promising but remains challenging. Recently, it has been shown how populations of sensory receptors could encode limb position and how the firing of a small number of neurons can be used to decode the position of the limb (Stein et al., 2004). In this study, microelectrode arrays have been used to record impulses simultaneously from nerve cells in the dorsal root ganglia (DRG) of the cat. The drawback of this technique is the surgery needed to place the electrodes at the DRG. Recording activity from peripheral nerves is less invasive; it is classically done using cuff electrodes which sense the aggregate activity of the whole nerve fibers. We propose to use intra fascicular electrodes which allow solving the lack of selectivity of the cuff electrodes. The main difficulty with intra fascicular in comparison with DRG recordings is to identify the firing units and to isolate afferents from efferent fibers. We use Longitudinal Intra fascicular Electrode (LIFE), implanted longitudinally within individual peripheral nerve fascicles. LIFEs have been used to both activate and record from subsets of axons within a fascicle. When used for stimulation, topological selectivity in axonal recruitment as been demonstrated, and when used for recording, multiunit extra cellular recording was exhibited (Goodall et al., 1993; Malmstrom et al., 1998). These electrodes are more selective than cuff electrodes but remain multi-units.

3.2 Characterization of muscle in-vivo sensory responses to external stretches

A first study has been carried out to characterize the in-vivo sensory responses of rabbit skeletal muscle to passive external mechanical stretches (Azevedo and Yoshida, 2005). The left leg of anesthetized rabbits were anchored at knee and ankle joints to a fixed mechanical frame using bone pins placed through the distal epiphyses of the femur and tibia (fig.7).

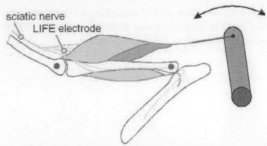

Fig. 7. Muscle mechanical stretching protocol.

Tendon of Medial Gastrocnemius muscle (MG) was attached to the arm of a motorized lever system. The position of the lever arm was controlled and both force and relative position were recorded. A LIFE was implanted in the tibial branch innervating MG muscle allowing us to record from this nerve activity (ENG). Results obtained in 2 rabbits are presented. After filtering ENG signal using a 5th order band pass Butterworth filter (300Hz-6kHz), we detected the peaks crossing a fixed threshold (Fig.8b). The threshold value was chosen in order to give statistical grounding as: **$\sigma=3.std(ENG)$**. Firing rate was computed by counting the number of peaks over a sliding time window. The window was then displaced 10% further and computation was repeated (fig.8c). This analysis has been repeated over the different frequency trials and a linear tendency for the relationship between firing rates (fig.8c) and length variation (fig.8a) was exhibited in the muscle stretching phase (fig.9). 2 main problems exist in using this approach: 1) no discrimination is made on peaks in order to estimate whether they correspond to an action potential or not. This induces that some of the detected peaks can be due to noise only. Therefore, the time window should be large enough to reduce noise influence, 2) the approach is not suitable for fast movements. Indeed, the approach is very sensitive to frequency of mechanical stimuli, as over a given time window, length can vary a lot from one type of stimulation to another. Finding a compromising generic time window is not easy as it should be ideally adapted to stimulation frequency, which is hardly usable in real-time conditions. We classified the peaks depending on their amplitude. We started with the first trial (1 sinusoidal period) of the stimulation sequence 100mHz. The first peak detected in the signal was labelled as belonging to first class. The following peak amplitudes were compared to first peak of class 1 and labelled as class 1 if their size was comprise between +/- 10% of peak 1 size. If the peak was rejected from class 1 it was labelled as reference peak for class 2 and the following peaks were classified in the same way as class 1 or 2 or defining a new class. We found 10 distinct classes for rabbit 1 and 11 distinct classes for rabbit 2. The classification was then used to classify peaks of all the trials for the 100mHz sequence as well as for the other sequences. For each set of classified peaks we computed the delay between two successive peaks. We then computed the firing rate frequency from the inter-delays. In figure 9 we present results obtained for one of the classes. The results obtained for firing rate are noisy but a clear tendency appears. Behaviour over the different frequencies is similar.

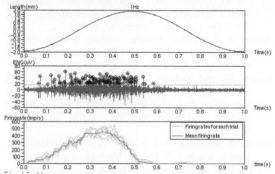

Fig. 8. Rabbit 2, 1Hz. Top to bottom: a) external mechanical stimulation (length variation), b) peak crossing threshold detection on preprocessed ENG signal (1 trial), c) firing rates computed in 5 trials (number of peaks over a 50ms sliding window overlapping 90%).

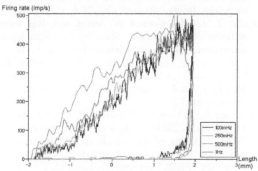

Fig. 9. Averaged firing rates over all trials in function of length variation in different frequency condition

It is possible to model the elicited unit response to stretching with a simple proportional relationship between firing rate **FR** and normalized length variation **Ln**: $FR = K3 + K4.Ln$ (4)
The same gains **K3** and **K4** can be used for the 5 different stimuli frequencies as shown in figure 10.

3.3 Towards online estimation of muscle state

We presented a simple approach to describe passive properties of muscle afferent nerve activity during passive sinusoidal stretches. We proposed a first approximation to do ENG signal spike separation based upon amplitude of detected peaks. Though not perfect, the estimated firing rate responses are consistent and an estimate of a relationship for the firing rate as a function of length could be found. It fits the behavior of the muscle lengthening and has the big advantage that it could be easily implemented for online application in order to estimate muscle length from ENG. The method could be used to generate a robust length estimator that maps the muscle afferent firing rate to a position. A possibility to improve robustness of muscle length estimation would be to work on several firing units instead of only one like done here. This could help to remove outlier detected spikes. The relevance of our findings will have direct application in FES: by observing the

ENG recordings corresponding to the antagonist muscle of a given electro-stimulated muscle one could estimate the length of the passively stretched muscle and therefore have some information on the corresponding joint angle. The next planned step of our work is to compare between the simple threshold technique presented here and more advanced technique, such as unsupervised learning for spike separation. Some issues remain, like migration of electrodes. We believe that the online analysis of afferent fiber activity could give us an indirect estimation of muscle fatigue and spasticity.

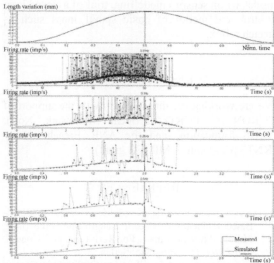

Fig. 10. Linearity of firing rate in function of length variation (Rabbit 2, K3=10, K4=50). From top to bottom: 1) Normalized length profile, Trials: 2) 10mHz, 3) 100mHz, 4) 250mHz, 5) 500mHz, 6) 1Hz.

4. CONCLUSION

Modelling such a complex system, with heterogeneous components is a top level research challenge. Indeed, it needs to precisely understand the physiology of the studied organs, i.e. muscles, natural sensors, and parts of the CNS circuitry. Then we describe these components using state equations where all the parameters are meaningful, i.e. related to physiological or physical entities. We have to face difficulties because simulations need as little sets of equations as possible; identification protocols need as few parameters as possible whereas physiology contains a great number of parameters.

Experiments not only account for parameters identification but also for model validation so that simulation errors could be hardly interpreted. Moreover, experimental setups are uneasy to design and run, and some experiments could be dangerous. This work demands that applied mathematicians, physiologists, medical doctor physiotherapists, automatic control theory specialists, micro electronic engineers work together on different aspects of the problem, which is another big challenge.

Nevertheless, modelling remains necessary and we begun to carry out research in order to achieve this long term goal. The first results obtained both on muscle modelling and natural sensors signal processing are encouraging and the first experimental validations show us the next issues to address. On the muscle modelling, we have now the structure able to evolve towards more complex muscle behaviours: i) accurate Ca++ dynamics to model short term muscle response, ii) 3D recruitment static function to understand and model the selective activation of fibre types and muscle regions, iii) slow and fast fibres discrimination, iv) fatigue phenomenon probably through ATP supply modelling. The next steps for the DEMAR team are: i) on muscle modelling validation of isometric contraction on humans, and integration of a fatigue model, ii) on sensors modelling, trial of a closed loop control and model of basic spinal loops such as stretch reflex.

ACKNOWLEDGEMENTS

We are working on those issues with the support of EURON (6th PCRD European framework, NoE), EADS foundation, and the ANR French agency (RNTS programme, MIMES grant).

REFERENCES

Azevedo, C. and Yoshida, K. (2005). Towards a Model-Based Estimator of Muscle Length and Force Using Muscle Afferent Signals For Real-Time FES Control, In: *EUROCON*, Belgrade, Serbia.

Andreasen, L.N.S. and Struijk, J.J.S. (2003). Skin Contact forces Extracted from Human Nerve Signals – A Possible Feedback Signal for FES Aided Control of Standing. In: *IEEE Trans. on Biomedical Engineering*. 50. 1320-1325.

Bestel J. and Sorine M. (2000), A differential model of muscle contraction and applications, In Schloessman *Seminar on Mathematical Models in Biology, Chemistry and Physics*, Max Planck Society, Germany.

Donaldson N. and Yu C.H. (1996), FES standing: Control by Handle Reactions of Leg Muscle Stimulation (CHRELMS), *IEEE Trans. Rehab. Eng.*, 4, 280-284.

Durfee W.K. (1993), Control of standing and gait using electrical stimulation: influence of muscle model complexity on control strategy, *Prog. Brain Res.*, 97, 369-381.

El Makssoud H., D. Guiraud, and P. Poignet (2004), Mathematical muscle model for functional electrical stimulation control strategies. *Proceedings of the International Conference on Robotics and Automation (ICRA)*, 1282-1287, New Orleans, USA.

El Makssoud H. (2005), Modelling and identification of the skeletal muscle under Functional Electrical Stimulation, University of Montpellier II, PhD Thesis.

Goodall, E.V. and Horch, K.W. and McNaughton, T.G. and Lybbert, C.M. (1993). Analysis of single-unit firing patterns in multi-unit Intrafascicular recordings. In: *Med.& Biol. Eng. & Comput*. 31. 257-267.

Guiraud D., P. Poignet, P.B. Wieber, H. El Makssoud, F. Pierrot, B. Brogliato, P. Fraisse, E. Dombre, J.L. Divoux, P. Rabischong (2003), Modelling of the human paralysed lower limb under FES. *ICRA*, special session on medical robotics.

Hill A. V. (1938), The heat of shortening and the dynamic constants in muscle. *Proceeding of the royal society, London, Sre.* B, 126, 136-195.

Houk, J. and Simon, W. (1967). Responses of Golgi tendon Organs to Forces Applied to Muscle Tendon. In: *J Neurophysiol*. 30-6. 1466-1481.

Hunt K.J., Munih M., Donaldson N. and Barr F.M.D. (1998), Optimal control of ankle joint moment : toward unsupported standing in paraplegia, *IEEE Trans. on Automatic Control*, 43, 6, 819-832

Huxley A. F. (1957), Muscle structure and theories of contraction. *Progress in Biophysics and Biophysical Chemistry*, 7, 255-318.

Jensen, W. and Sinkjaer, T. and Sepulveda, F. (2002). Improving signal reliability for on-line joint angle estimation from nerve cuff recordings of muscle afferents. In: *IEEE Trans Neural Syst Rehabil Eng*. 10-3. 133-139.

Keener J. and Sneyd J (2001). Systems physiology, Muscle, chapter 18, Part II. *Mathematical Physiology*. ed. J.E. Marsden, L. Sirovich & S. Wiggns.

Kobetic R., R. J. Triolo, E. B. Marsolais (1997), Muscle selection and walking performance of multichannel FES systems for ambulation in paraplegia, *IEEE Trans. on rehabilitation engineering*, 5, N1, 23-29.

Malmstrom, J.A. and McNaughton, T.G. and Horch, K. (1998). Recording properties and biocompatibility of chronically implanted polymer-based intrafascicular electrodes. In: *Ann. Biomed. Eng.* 26-6. 1055-1064

Matjačić Z. (2001), Control of Ankle and Hip Joint Stiffness for Arm-Free Standing in Paraplegia, International Neuromodulation Society, 1, 6, 37-46.

Mohammed S., P. Fraisse, D. Guiraud, P. Poignet, H. ElMakssoud (2005). Towards a Co-Contraction Muscle Control Strategy. CDC'05: Conference on Decision and Control.

Mohammed S., D. Guiraud, P. Fraisse, P. Poignet, and H. El Makssoud (2004), Using a complex, physiological based modelling of the muscle to perform realistic simulation and test control strategies: Closed loop controlled. *IFESS*, Bournemouth, England, 219-221.

Popović D., R.B. Stein, M. N. Oğuztöreli, M. Lebiedowska and S. Jonić (1999), Optimal Control of Walking with Functional Electrical Stimulation: A computer simulation study, *IEEE Trans. Rehab. Eng.*, 7, 69-79.

Riener R. & Fuhr T. (1998), "Patient-driven control of FES supported standing up: a simulation study", *IEEE Transactions on Rehabilitation Engineering*, 6, n°2, 113-124

Riener R. (1999), Model-based development of neuroprostheses for paraplegic patients", *The Royal Society*, 354, 877-894

Simon, J. and Wei, J.Y. and Randić, M. and Burgess, P.R. (1984). Signaling of Ankle Joint Position by Receptors in Different Muscles. In: *Somatosensory Research*. 2-2. 127-147.

Stein, R.B. and Weber, D.J. and Aoyagi, Y. and Prochazka, A. and Wagenaar, J.B.M. and Shoham, S. and Normann, R.A.. (2004). Coding of position by simultaneously recorded sensory neurones in the cat dorsal root ganglion. In: *J Physiol*, 560(3). 883-896.

Wise, A.K. and Gregory, J.E. and Proske, U. (1999). The Responses of Muscle Spindles to Small, Slow Movements in Passive Muscle and During Fusimotor Activity. In: *Brain Research*. 821. 87-94.

Yoshida, K. and Horch, K. (1996). Closed-Loop Control of Ankle Position Using Muscle Afferent Feedback with Functional Neuromuscular Stimulation. In: *IEEE Trans. Biomed. Engineer*. 43-2. 167-176.

Zahalak G.I. (1992), An overview of muscle modelling, *Neural prostheses - replacing motor function after disease or disability*, ed. R. Stein, H. Peckham & D. Popovic, pp. 17-57, New York and Oxford, Oxford University Press

JOINT TORQUES ESTIMATION IN HUMAN STANDING BASED ON A FUZZY DESCRIPTOR UNKNOWN INPUTS OBSERVER

Kevin GUELTON*, Sébastien DELPRAT** and Thierry Marie GUERRA**

*CReSTIC, URCA, Moulin de la House BP1039, 51687 Reims Cedex 2, France
**LAMIH, CNRS8530, UVHC, Le Mont Houy, 59313 Valenciennes Cedex 9, France
E-Mail : kevin.guelton@univ-reims.fr, {guerra, delprat}@univ-valenciennes.fr

Abstract: An alternative to inverse dynamics joint torques estimation in standing human is proposed by the use of an unknown input observer that allows the real time estimation of both the joint torques and the angular velocities from angular positions measurement. To design such observer, a state space descriptor dynamical model of the considered movement is proposed. Then, the considered model being non linear, we used Takagi-Sugeno fuzzy modeling to synthesis the non linear observer and to prove the convergence of the state (position, velocities and torques) estimation errors. *Copyright © 2006 IFAC*

Keywords: Human Torque Estimation, Human Standing, Double Inverted Pendulum, Descriptor Systems, Fuzzy Observers.

1. INTRODUCTION

Biomechanics draws from many different disciplines, applying the procedures and knowledge of these different sciences in original ways. In this article, we bring concepts drawn from automatic control theory and computer science to bear on a biomechanical problem: the evaluation of joint torques in human standing. Joint torques are classically estimated in biomechanics from the measurement of ground reaction force and of motion capture. The well known "bottom-up" inverse dynamics method is then used to solve Newton-Euler equation for each segment from the ground (bottom) where external forces are measured to the top one after another (Winter, 1990). The major drawback of this technique is that measurement errors are reported successively from the bottom to the top that leads to uncertainties on the estimation of joint torques (Zajac, 1993; Cahouet and Amarantini 2002). These measurement errors are partially due to the confrontation of two heterogeneous captors, the force plate and the motion capture device, and especially with the difficulties to make the two captors frames perfectly coincided in experimental studies (McCaw and De Vita, 1995). An objective to define an efficient joint torques estimation technique is to reduce the number of captor to its minimum, i.e. the motion capture device. Another source of error is the need to compute velocities from the segments positions that makes the inverse dynamics joint torques estimation highly noise sensitive and ruins real time estimations (Zajac, 1993; Hatze, 2001). An alternative to inverse dynamics is then proposed by the use of an unknown input observer that allows the real time estimation of both the joint torques estimation and the angular velocities from angular positions measurement. To design such observer, a state space descriptor dynamical model of the considered movement is developed. Among nonlinear control theory, the Takagi-Sugeno (TS) fuzzy model-based approach has nowadays become popular since it shown its efficiency to control complex nonlinear systems. Indeed, Takagi and Sugeno have proposed a fuzzy model to describe nonlinear models (Takagi and Sugeno, 1985) as a collection of linear time invariant models blended together with nonlinear functions. Therefore, this paper will deals with the application to joint torques estimation in human standing of a TS unknown inputs observer in descriptor form.

2. DOUBLE INVERTED PENDULUM MODELING OF HUMAN STANCE

When an individual is quietly standing in the sagittal plane, knees and neck movements are slower than ankles and hip movements. Thus, depending on the environment and certain pathological assumptions, two sway strategies can be defined: the "ankle" strategy and the "hip" strategy (Nashner and McCollum, 1985). Then, a planar double inverted pendulum has been chosen to model the human body in the sagittal plane, figure 1. The lower pendulum oscillates around a point A located at the ankle, and the upper pendulum around a point H at the hip. This model is based on two assumptions:

1) both inverted pendulum segments are rigid and connected by hinge joints
2) the neuromuscular system, i.e. the muscle actuators and the central nervous system, provides the necessary joint torques at the ankle u_1 and hip u_2 to stabilize quiet standing.

These torques are the inputs of the double inverted pendulum model, and the associated angular positions are its outputs. In figure 1, segment 1 represents the lower limbs, not including the feet; segment 2 represents the trunk, head and upper limbs. The inertial characteristics m_i, I_i and K for each segment can be estimated using anthropometric tables (Winter 1990). θ_i is the generalized angular coordinate of segment i with respect to the vertical axis.

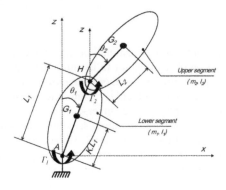

Fig. 1. A double inverted pendulum model of human standing.

The double inverted pendulum model is derived using Lagrange method and is given by:

$$M(y) \cdot \ddot{y} + S(y,\dot{y}) \cdot \dot{y} + G(y) \cdot y = Ru \qquad (1)$$

with $u(t) = \begin{bmatrix} u_1(t) & u_2(t) \end{bmatrix}^T$ the input vector,

$y(t) = \begin{bmatrix} \theta_1(t) & \theta_2(t) \end{bmatrix}^T$ the output vector,

$M(y) = \begin{bmatrix} a & c\cos(\theta_1 - \theta_2) \\ c\cos(\theta_1 - \theta_2) & b \end{bmatrix}$ the inertia matrix,

$S(y,\dot{y}) = \begin{bmatrix} 0 & c\dot{\theta}_2 \sin(\theta_1 - \theta_2) \\ -c\dot{\theta}_1 \sin(\theta_1 - \theta_2) & 0 \end{bmatrix}$ the anti-symmetric matrix,

$G(y) = \begin{bmatrix} d\dfrac{\sin\theta_1}{\theta_1} & 0 \\ 0 & e\dfrac{\sin\theta_2}{\theta_2} \end{bmatrix}$ the gravitational matrix,

$R = \begin{bmatrix} 1 & -1 \\ 0 & 1 \end{bmatrix}$ the matrix linking joint torque to generalized torque and $a = I_1 + m_1 K^2 L_1^2 + m_2 L_1^2$, $b = I_2 + m_2 L_2^2$, $c = m_2 L_1 L_2$, $d = (m_2 + m_1 K) g L_1$, $e = m_2 g L_2$.

Considering $x(t) = \begin{bmatrix} y^T(t) & \dot{y}^T(t) \end{bmatrix}^T$ the state vector of the system, (1) can be written as the following state space descriptor form:

$$\begin{cases} E(y(t))\dot{x}(t) = A(x(t))x(t) + Bu(t) \\ y(t) = Cx(t) \end{cases} \qquad (2)$$

with:

$$E(y(t)) = \begin{bmatrix} I & 0 \\ 0 & M(\theta_1, \theta_2) \end{bmatrix}, \quad B = \begin{bmatrix} 0 \\ R \end{bmatrix}, \quad C = \begin{bmatrix} I & 0 \end{bmatrix}$$

and $A(y(t)) = \begin{bmatrix} 0 & 0 \\ G(\theta_1, \theta_2) & -S(\theta_1, \theta_2, \dot{\theta}_1, \dot{\theta}_2) \end{bmatrix}$.

3. TS FUZZY DESCRIPTOR MODELS AND OBSERVERS

3.1 Notations.

With $v_k(z)$ (resp. $h_i(z)$) scalar functions and E_k, $k \in \{1, ..., e\}$ (resp. $Y_i, i \in \{1, ..., r\}$) matrices of the same dimensions, we will denote:

$$E_v = \sum_{k=1}^{e} v_k(z(t)) E_k, \quad Y_h = \sum_{i=1}^{r} h_i(z(t)) Y_i$$

and $Y_{hv} = \sum_{k=1}^{e} \sum_{i=1}^{r} v_k(z(t)) h_i(z(t)) Y_{ik}$.

Also for a function $\alpha(x) \in [\underline{\alpha} \quad \bar{\alpha}]$, $\underline{\alpha} = \min_x \alpha(x)$, $\bar{\alpha} = \max_x \alpha(x)$.

As usual, a star $(*)$ in a symmetric matrix indicates a transpose quantity.

3.2 TS modeling.

Let us consider the generic state space representation of a non linear descriptor model as:

$$\begin{cases} E(x(t))\dot{x}(t) = A(x(t))x(t) + B(x(t))u(t) \\ y(t) = C(x(t))x(t) \end{cases} \qquad (3)$$

where $x(t)$ is the state vector, $u(t)$ and $y(t)$ are respectively the inputs and the outputs vector. $E(x(t))$, $A(x(t))$, $B(x(t))$ and $C(x(t))$ are the non-constant nonlinear descriptor model matrices.

A fuzzy Takagi-Sugeno representation of (3) leads to a collection of LTI models in descriptor form that are interpolated with nonlinear functions (Taniguchi et al., 2000). Then, these models can be written as:

$$\begin{cases} \sum_{k=1}^{e} v_k\big(z(t)\big) E_k \dot{x}(t) = \sum_{i=1}^{r} h_i\big(z(t)\big)\big(A_i x(t) + B_i u(t)\big) \\ y(t) = \sum_{k=1}^{r} h_i\big(z(t)\big) C_i \dot{x}(t) \end{cases} \quad (4)$$

The functions $h_i\big(z(t)\big) \geq 0$, $i \in \{1,\ldots,r\}$, $v_k\big(z(t)\big) \geq 0$, $k \in \{1,\ldots,e\}$ satisfy the convex sum property, i.e. $\sum_{k=1}^{e} v_k(z) = 1$ (resp. $\sum_{i=1}^{r} h_i(z) = 1$).

Note that the TS descriptor is composed of $e \times r$ LTI descriptors. Recall that there is a systematic way to go from the nonlinear descriptor (3) to one of its TS representation (4). This way is called the sector non linearity approach (Tanaka and Wang, 2001), then the TS descriptor matches exactly the nonlinear model in a compact set of the state variables. Note also that infinity of TS models can represent a single nonlinear model (Taniguchi et al., 2001). Using the previous notations (4) becomes:

$$\begin{cases} E_v \dot{x}(t) = A_h x(t) + B_h u(t) \\ y(t) = C_h x(t) \end{cases} \quad (5)$$

Owing to that, the descriptor model of human stance (2) can be written in a TS descriptor form considering the following nonlinear functions contained in the matrices $E\big(x(t)\big)$ and $A\big(x(t)\big)$ with $x^T = \begin{bmatrix} \theta_1 & \theta_2 & \dot{\theta}_1 & \dot{\theta}_2 \end{bmatrix}$:

$$\omega(x) = \cos(\theta_1 - \theta_2), \quad \eta_1(x) = \frac{\sin(\theta_1)}{\theta_1},$$

$$\eta_2(x) = \frac{\sin(\theta_2)}{\theta_2}, \quad \eta_3(x) = \dot{\theta}_1 \sin(\theta_1 - \theta_2)$$

and $\eta_4(x) = \dot{\theta}_2 \sin(\theta_1 - \theta_2)$.

Each of these nonlinear terms can be bounded according to the minimum and maximum angles and velocities, i.e. $\omega(x) \in \begin{bmatrix} \underline{\omega} & \overline{\omega} \end{bmatrix}$, $\eta_1(x) \in \begin{bmatrix} \underline{\eta_1} & \overline{\eta_1} \end{bmatrix}$ and so on. Thus a possible TS descriptor model (matching perfectly the nonlinear model between the bounds that define a compact set for $x(t)$) will be composed of $2^1 \times 2^4 = 32$ LTI descriptors. Effectively, each bounded nonlinear term can easily be written according to two nonlinear functions satisfying the convex sum property, for instance:

$$\omega(x) = \frac{\overline{\omega} - \cos(\theta_1 - \theta_2)}{\overline{\omega} - \underline{\omega}} \cdot \underline{\omega} + \frac{\cos(\theta_1 - \theta_2) - \underline{\omega}}{\overline{\omega} - \underline{\omega}} \cdot \overline{\omega}.$$

In the following we will use a restricted TS descriptor with fewer LTI models. This reduction of models is done eliminating the nonlinearities $\eta_3(x)$ and $\eta_4(x)$. Note that the TS descriptor used will not match perfectly the nonlinear model. Two main reasons can be invoked. The first one is that these

functions, which are due to the Coriolis matrix, can be neglected because of the small range of the velocities in human standing. The second one is that for a theoretical aspect, it is easier to cope with TS descriptor with a premise vector $z(t)$ depending only on the measured variables $y(t)$ (Guerra et al., 2006). Both points will be discussed further with the experimental results presentation.

Therefore consider the six nonlinear functions $\omega^{(l)}$, $\eta_1^{(l)}$, $\eta_2^{(l)}$, $l = 1,2$ issued from the three nonlinearities $\omega(x)$, $\eta_1(x)$ and $\eta_2(x)$. The $2^1 \times 2^2 = 8$ LTI models are defined as follows $l, l_1, l_2 = 1,2$:

IF $\omega\big(x(t)\big)$ is $\omega^{(l)}$ AND $\eta_1\big(x(t)\big)$ is $\eta_1^{(l_1)}$ AND $\eta_2\big(x(t)\big)$ is $\eta_2^{(l_2)}$

THEN $\begin{cases} E_l \dot{x}(t) = A_{l_1 + l_2 - 1} x(t) + Bu(t) \\ y(t) = Cx(t) \end{cases}$

That leads to the simplified fuzzy TS descriptor model of human stance:

$$\begin{cases} \sum_{k=1}^{2} v_k\big(y(t)\big) E_k \dot{x}(t) = \sum_{i=1}^{4} h_i\big(y(t)\big) A_i x(t) + Bu(t) \\ y(t) = Cx(t) \end{cases} \quad (6)$$

with $v_k(y) = \omega^{(k)}(y)$, $h_{l_1 + l_2 - 1}(y) = \eta_1^{(l_1)}(y) \cdot \eta_2^{(l_2)}(y)$

and: $E_1 = \begin{bmatrix} I & 0 \\ 0 & \begin{bmatrix} a & c\overline{f_1} \\ c\overline{f_1} & b_2 \end{bmatrix} \end{bmatrix}$, $E_2 = \begin{bmatrix} I & 0 \\ 0 & \begin{bmatrix} a & c\underline{f_1} \\ c\underline{f_1} & b \end{bmatrix} \end{bmatrix}$,

$A_1 = \begin{bmatrix} 0 & I \\ \begin{bmatrix} d\overline{f_2} & 0 \\ 0 & e\overline{f_3} \end{bmatrix} & 0 \end{bmatrix}$, $A_2 = \begin{bmatrix} 0 & I \\ \begin{bmatrix} d\overline{f_2} & 0 \\ 0 & e\underline{f_3} \end{bmatrix} & 0 \end{bmatrix}$,

$A_3 = \begin{bmatrix} 0 & I \\ \begin{bmatrix} d\underline{f_2} & 0 \\ 0 & e\overline{f_3} \end{bmatrix} & 0 \end{bmatrix}$, $A_4 = \begin{bmatrix} 0 & I \\ \begin{bmatrix} d\underline{f_2} & 0 \\ 0 & e\underline{f_3} \end{bmatrix} & 0 \end{bmatrix}$.

3.3 Takagi-Sugeno observer descriptor structure.

The purpose of this section is to derive conditions of convergence for the estimation error of a TS observer defined as:

$$\begin{cases} E_v \dot{\hat{x}}(t) = A_h \hat{x}(t) + B_h u(t) + K_{hv}\big(y(t) - \hat{y}(t)\big) \\ \hat{y}(t) = C_h \hat{x}(t) \end{cases} \quad (7)$$

where $\hat{x}(t)$ and $\hat{y}(t)$ are respectively the estimated state vector and outputs vector. K_{hv} is the collection of observer gain matrices. Let us quote that the general case would imply the use of $\hat{z}(t)$, i.e. $h_i\big(\hat{z}(t)\big)$ and $v_k\big(\hat{z}(t)\big)$ instead of $h_i\big(z(t)\big)$ and $v_k\big(z(t)\big)$. This would lead to more complicated conditions of convergence (Guerra et al., 2006).

Summarizing for the present application, choosing an approximation of the nonlinear model of stance with 8 LTI models, instead of an exact one with 32 LTI models is a good compromise between model complexity (in terms of LMI resolution) and its reliability regarding to the application.

3.4 Estimation error convergence.

A way to obtain the convergence conditions fot TS fuzzy descriptor is to rewrite (4) using the augmented state $x^*(t) = \left[x^T(t), \dot{x}^T(t) \right]^T$:

$$\begin{cases} E^* \dot{x}^*(t) = A_{hv}^* x^*(t) + B_h^* u(t) \\ y(t) = C_h^* x^*(t) \end{cases} \quad (8)$$

where $E^* = \begin{bmatrix} I & 0 \\ 0 & 0 \end{bmatrix}$, $A_{ik}^* = \begin{bmatrix} 0 & I \\ A_i & -E_k \end{bmatrix}$, $B_i^* = \begin{bmatrix} 0 \\ B_i \end{bmatrix}$

and $C_i^* = \begin{bmatrix} C_i & 0 \end{bmatrix}$. In a similar way, the fuzzy TS observer (7) is written as:

$$\begin{cases} E^* \dot{\hat{x}}^*(t) = A_{hv}^* \hat{x}^*(t) + B_h^* u(t) + K_{hv}^* \left(y(t) - \hat{y}(t) \right) \\ \hat{y}(t) = C_h^* \hat{x}^*(t) \end{cases} \quad (9)$$

with $\hat{x}^*(t) = \left[\hat{x}^T(t), \dot{\hat{x}}^T(t) \right]^T$ and $K_{hv}^* = \begin{bmatrix} 0 & K_{hv} \end{bmatrix}^T$.

Let us define the augmented prediction error as $\tilde{x}^*(t) = \left[\left(x(t) - \hat{x}(t) \right)^T, \left(\dot{x}(t) - \dot{\hat{x}}(t) \right)^T \right]^T$, we can write its derivative as:

$$E^* \dot{\tilde{x}}^*(t) = \left(A_{hv}^* - K_{hv}^* C_h^* \right) \tilde{x}^*(t) \quad (10)$$

The following theorem ensure the convergence of the state reconstruction error for a suitable set of K_{ik}^*.

Theorem 1: Let us consider the fuzzy descriptor system (10). The convergence of the reconstruction error is ensured if there exists: $P_1 = P_1^T > 0$, P_3 and P_4 regular, K_{ik}, $k \in \{1, \ldots, e\}$, $i, j \in \{1, \ldots, r\}$, $j > i$, such that:

$$\Upsilon_{ii}^k < 0 \quad (11)$$

$$\Upsilon_{ij}^k + \Upsilon_{ji}^k < 0 \quad (12)$$

$$\gamma_{ij}^k = \begin{bmatrix} A_i^T P_3 + P_3^T A_i - C_i^T K_{ik}^T P_3 - P_3^T K_{jk} C_i & (*) \\ P_1 - E_k^T P_3 + P_4^T A_i - P_4^T K_{jk} C_i & -E_k^T P_4 - P_4^T E_k \end{bmatrix}$$

Proof: It is straightforward considering the Lyapunov candidate function $V \left(\tilde{x}^*(t) \right) = \tilde{x}^{*T}(t) E^{*T} P \tilde{x}^*(t)$, and the matrix $P = \begin{bmatrix} P_1 & 0 \\ P_3 & P_4 \end{bmatrix}$.

Let us point out that conditions (11) and (12) are only LMI in P_1, P_3 and P_4, i.e. provided K_{ik} are

given matrices. On the contrary, if K_{ik} and P_1, P_3, P_4 have to be searched together, it is necessary to render these conditions LMI. Some results, not presented here due to space reasons, are available in (Guerra et al., 2004). Note also that for the particular application presented, K_{ik} are computed apart using pole placement that ensures some performances, and theorem 1 conditions are only used to check the stability.

4. UNKNOWN INPUTS OBSERVER DESIGN

Let us recall that the primary objective of this study is the joint torques estimation. In human studies, measuring joint torque with external apparatus is ethically outlawed. To overcome this problem, we designed an unknown input observer under the assumption $\dot{u}(t) \approx 0$. This fy
pothesis states that the input dynamics is much slower than the observer state dynamics.

Defining the extended state vector $x^e(t) = \begin{bmatrix} x^T(t) & u^T(t) \end{bmatrix}^T$, the TS descriptor observer (7) reduces to:

$$\begin{cases} E_v^e \dot{\hat{x}}^e(t) = A_h^e \hat{x}^e(t) + K_{hv}^e \left(y(t) - \hat{y}(t) \right) \\ \hat{y}(t) = C^e \hat{x}^e(t) \end{cases} \quad (13)$$

where $E^e = \begin{bmatrix} E_v & 0 \\ 0 & I \end{bmatrix}$, $A_h^e = \begin{bmatrix} A_h & B \\ 0 & 0 \end{bmatrix}$, $K_{hv}^e = \begin{bmatrix} 0 \\ K_{hv} \end{bmatrix}$

and $C^e = \begin{bmatrix} C & 0 \end{bmatrix}$. In order to simulate the joint torques estimated by the unknown inputs observer, the whole nonlinear model needs to be stabilized. A linear state feedback control law is sufficient but it must be tuned properly. The state feedback dynamic have been chosen faster than the convergence of the estimation error one. A good compromise between fast dynamic and a nice convergence of the estimation has been found. For the state feedback control part, it corresponds to a control pole placement with four poles around −60 based on a LTI model obtained with the nonlinear model (1) by linearization around the erect position $\theta_1 = 0$ and $\theta_2 = 0$. For the convergence of the estimation error, the gains K_{ik} have been fixed using a pole placement of $E_k^{-1} \left(A_i - K_{ik} C \right)$ with two dominant poles at −18 and four auxiliary at −55.

The tuning has been validated on a flexion movement from the erect position $(\theta_1 = 0, \theta_2 = 0)$ to $(\theta_1 = -\pi/6, \theta_2 = \pi/3)$ with a realistic dynamics considering physiological constraints. Figure 2 shows the estimate state $\hat{x}(t)$ following the simulated trajectories $x(t)$ as well as the two joint torques estimation $\hat{u}(t)$ following the simulated ones $u(t)$.

Moreover, in order to illustrate the benefits of the TS unknown inputs observer (13), a comparison with a linear unknown inputs observer is performed. This linear observer is obtained based on a LTI model obtained with the nonlinear model (1) by linearization around the unstable equilibrium point $\theta_1 = 0$ and $\theta_2 = 0$, it is written as:

$$\begin{cases} E_L^e \dot{\hat{x}}^e(t) = A_L^e \hat{x}^e(t) + K_L^e \left(y(t) - \hat{y}(t) \right) \\ \hat{y}(t) = C^e \hat{x}^e(t) \end{cases} \quad (14)$$

K_L^* is then chosen using the same pole placement as the nonlinear observer. To point out the behavioural differences, "large" angles are used in order not to fulfil the linear approximation. A complex movement has been set up to reach and outrun human standing physiological limits, figure 3.

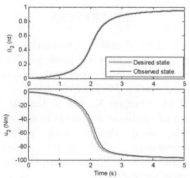

Fig. 2. Angular position and torques estimations at the hip following a simple trajectories simulation.

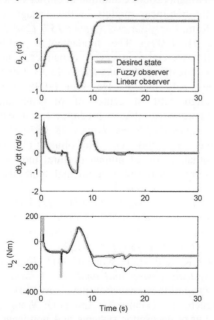

Fig. 3. Angular position and torques estimations following a complex trajectories simulation.

From $t = 10s$, the convergence error of the linear observer becomes significant since the angular position are high. Thus, low motion hypothesis is not respected and the linear observer failed to estimate the inputs. On the other hand, the convergence error of the fuzzy observer is acceptable excepted for the fastest transients of the joint torques, at $t = 0.5s$ and $t = 5s$. Of course this is due to the observer dynamic, but note also that these simulated torques are not physiologically possible.

Recall that the nonlinearities $\eta_3 \left(x(t) \right)$, and $\eta_4 \left(x(t) \right)$ have been removed from the whole descriptor. This assumption can be now examined. For the whole set of simulations, these neglected terms contributions remain always lower than 1% excepted for fast transient that are not physiologically possible. This confirms the choice made.

5. EXPERIMENTAL RESULTS

One 28 year-old male subject, weighing $69.8\,Kg$ and measuring $1.85\,m$ was asked to perform a combined trunk flexion/extension that disturbed the subject's equilibrium, provoking ankle and hip oscillation in the sagittal plane. Movements were captured at a frequency of $120\,Hz$ using an AMTI force-plate synchronized with a VICON 612 motion capture device (Figure 4). The 3-dimensional reconstruction error was evaluated at $0.6\,mm$. Reflective markers define 14 segments of the subject's body. The centre of mass and the inertia of both parts of the double inverted pendulum in the sagittal plane were determined as defined in(Winter, 1990).

To have indications on the accuracy of the observer based estimations (OE), the ankle and hip torques estimations were compared to those computed by the well-known bottom-up inverse dynamics (ID) technique that is classically used in biomechanics studies (Winter, 1990). The application of this method required to solve Newton-Euler equation for each segment from the ground (bottom) where external forces are measured to the top one after another as presented figure 5.

Figure 6 shows that the OE Joint torques estimations follow the same path as the ID ones. That is confirmed by the high values of the correlation coefficients given table 1 for both the ankle and hip joint torques. The standard error computed on both the ankle torques estimation is small $(2.83\,Nm)$.

Nevertheless, at the average of time $22s$, a difference between the two paths of the hip torques estimations can be noticed. This one is confirmed by a higher standard error ($6.29\,Nm$) than those obtained at the ankle torques. These estimation errors can be due to the fact that the "bottom-up" inverse dynamics require the use of two different apparatus that bring on the uncertainties (McCaw and De Vita, 1995). Moreover, it is also well known that inverse dynamics is subject to increasing uncertainties in proportion to the number of the considered links (Hatze, 2001). Consequently, unless using an internal measurement apparatus that is ethically outlaw, we do not have any measurement reference available to claim that using an unknown input observer is a better method to compute joint torques than using inverse dynamics. Nevertheless, when a dynamical model can be easily obtained and due to the fact that it only requires the segments positions measurements, we assume that the use of an unknown inputs observer is a suitable alternative to the use of inverse dynamics techniques in biomechanical studies.

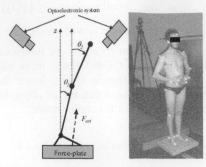

Fig. 4. Experimental devices

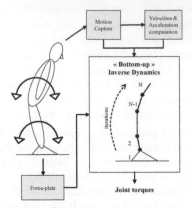

Fig. 5. Experimental devices for measuring angular position and external force

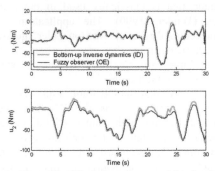

Fig. 6. ID and OE Joint torques obtained from experimental data.

Table 1. Quantitative comparison of the OE and ID joint torques estimations.

OE vs ID	Correlation coefficient	Standard error (Nm)
Ankle	0,98	2,83
Hip	0,98	6,29

6. CONCLUSION

A non linear model of human standing was proposed based on a double inverted pendulum. A fuzzy Takagi-Sugeno unknown inputs observer in descriptor form was then design to estimate both the joint torques and the velocities from only the angular position measurements. To establish the interest of designing such a non linear observer, the results were compared successfully in simulation to a linear observer. An experimental study has shown that unless using an internal measurement apparatus that is ethically outlaw, using an unknown input observer is a suitable method to compute joint torques than using inverse dynamics when a dynamical model is available. Moreover, classical inverse dynamics methods need a careful estimation of velocities and accelerations that are not easy when real time joint torques estimation is expected.

7. ACKNOWLEDGMENTS

This work was supported in part by the "Nord Pas-de-Calais" Region and the FEDER under the AUTORIS project and by the "Champagne-Ardennes" Region under the CPER SYS-REEDUC. The authors would like to thank Mr McAbey for his helpful advices within the experiments.

REFERENCES

Cahouët V., Luc M. and D. Amarantini (2002) Static optimal estimation of joint accelerations for inverse dynamics problem solution, *J of Biomechanics, 35 (11),1507-1513.*

Guerra T.M., Guelton K. and S. Delprat (2004) A class of nonlinear observers in descriptor form: LMI based design with application in biomechanics. *2nd IFAC Workshop on Advanced Fuzzy/Neural Control, Oulu, Finland, September16-17.*

Guerra T.M., Kruszewski A., Vermeiren L. and H. Tirmant (2006) Condition of output stabilization for nonlinear models in the Takagi-Sugeno's form. *Fuzzy Set and Systems 157, 1248-1259.*

Hatze H. (2001) The fundamental problem of myoskeletal inverse dynamics and its implications. *J of biomechanics 32, 109-115.*

McCaw S.T. and P. De Vita (1995) Errors in alignement of center of pressure and foot coordinates affecte predicts lower extremity torques. *J of Biomechanics, 28, 985-988.*

Nashner L. and G. McCollum (1985) The organization of human postural movements: a formal basis and experimental synthesis. *Behav Brain Sci 8,135-72*

Takagi T. and M. Sugeno (1985) Fuzzy identification of systems and its applications to modeling and control. *IEEE Trans. on System Man and Cybernetics, 15 (1), 116-132.*

Tanaka K. and H.O. Wang (2001). *Fuzzy control systems desing and analysis. A linear matrix inequality approach.* Wiley, New York.

Taniguchi T., Tanaka K. And H.O. Wang (2000). Fuzzy descriptor systems and nonlinear model following control. *IEEE Trans. on Fuzzy Systems, 8 (4), 442-452.*

Taniguchi T., Tanaka K. And H.O. Wang (2001). Model construction rule reduction and robust compensation for generalized form of Takagi-Sugeno fuzzy systems. *IEEE Trans. on Fuzzy Systems, 9 (4), 525-537.*

Winter, D.A. (1990) *Biomechanics and motor control of human movement.* Wiley, New York

Zajac F.E. (1993). Muscle coordination of movement: a perspective. *J of Biomechanics 26, 109–124.*

ELSEVIER

IFAC
PUBLICATIONS

A PRELIMINARY STUDY ON METABOLISM MODELLING WITH CAPILLARY

Huiting Qiao* Jing Bai*

Dept. of Biomedical Engineering, Tsinghua University, Beijing, 100084, China

Abstract: Substances transport and metabolism are essential for the maintenance of life. Some compartment models were proposed to describe the substances transport and metabolism in human body. However, they neglected the functions of capillary and could not show the effects of circulatory system. Capillary plays an important role in substances transport. In this paper, a novel mathematical model is presented for substances transport and metabolism. This model consists of two parts: one is substances transporting through capillary by Fick's conservation law; the other one uses a compartment model to describe the metabolism in tissue. This model is proved to be successful by numerical experimentation for brain. *Copyright © 2006 IFAC*

Keywords: Physiological Model, Parameter Estimation, Permeability, Computer Tomography, Numerical simulation

1. INTRODUCTION

Human body consists of several complex physiological systems. Circulatory system, also called as the transport system, transports oxygen and nutrients to reach whole body and carries away waste material to emunctories. Nutrients such as glucose and oxygen are metabolized by the biochemical process to produce energy for maintenance of living cells.

In the studies of metabolism modelling, compartment models are common to be applied in quantitative analysis of tracer kinetic modelling for functional imaging like positron emission tomography (PET). Several groups have developed compartment model techniques for human organ such as brain (Huang, *et al.* 1980), skeletal muscle (Bertoldo, *et al.* 2001), and liver (Chen and Feng 2004). Recently Hays, *et al* (2001) have developed a whole-body metabolic model to study tracer 2-[18F]fluoro-2-deoxy-D-

glucose (FDG), which is a radioligand to visualize in vivo metabolism of glucose. Compartment models are simple and efficient to demonstrate tracer kinetics with certain fundamental or physiologically reasonable assumptions. However it is insufficient to describe transport process of metabolic substances (Muzic and Saidel 2003). Most of past studies lacked of the consideration of real contribution of circulatory system.

Capillary is the smallest blood vessel and most closely interact with tissue. Nutrition molecules such as oxygen, glucose and lipid are transported to each organ in whole body by circulatory system, and then those molecules can pass through capillaries by diffusion and enter to the tissue, where metabolism is occurring. Capillary bridges circulatory system and tissue, and determines how fast and how much molecule can pass through. To our knowledge, only a few works have considered effect of capillary in their modelling. Sharan and *et al.* have developed models for oxygen transport in tissue capillaries (Sharan, *et al.*, 1995, 2002). Microvascular was used to modify compartment model for liver (Munk 2003).

In this paper a preliminary model is proposed to integrate transport and metabolism of metabolic substance in human body. This model consists of two components. One component describes the process of substance transport from circulatory system to tissue through capillary. The other describes the metabolism in tissue by a two-compartment model. The objective of this work was to model the transport and metabolism in human body with the consideration of capillary, which is expected to be extended to the whole-body metabolism modelling. The model was evaluated by the computer simulation for glucose tracer of FDG.

2. MODEL DESCRIPTION

The proposed model is based on mass balances and tracer kinetics. The transport component is established by the diffusion theory, which describes metabolic substance diffusion into tissue through capillary. The metabolism part applies kinetic parameters to describe metabolism in the tissue.

There are several assumptions in the model. Firstly distribution of FDG in tissue or blood is still assumed to be homogeneous. The second assumption is that all the amount of blood flow passes by capillary. Thirdly, the concentration uniformity in blood does not take time. Finally, structure of capillary net is assumed to be parallel without the geometrically complex and vastly inter-connected structures

2.1 Traditional 3-compartmnet model for FDG modelling

Figure.1 shows the traditional compartment model of 3-compartment and 4-parameter model for the cerebral study of glucose tracer of FDG. Free FDG in plasma transfers to tissue (the second compartment), followed by phosphorylating into FDG-6-P (the third compartment). For glucose, Glucose-6-phosphate is further metabolised in the glycolytic pathway to produce energy.

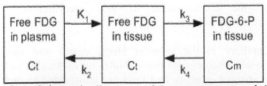

Fig.1. Schematic diagrams of 3-compartment and 4-parameter model, k_1, k_2, k_3 and k_4 are rate constants between each compartment.

The compartment model is based on principle of dynamic, lumped mass equilibrium between the assumed compartments. The mass flow from plasma

is simply modelled by two rate constants, k_1 and k_2, between the first and second compartments. The effect factors of transport process are inconspicuous. That is why a model on the base of capillary's function is supported.

2.2 Transport through capillary

Capillary can be treated as conduit with permeability, through which one part of substances flow with blood from artery to vena, while the other part of substances leave circulatory system and come into tissue by the permeability of capillary. Fick's first law of diffusion (Eq. 1) states that, the net flow across a unit membrane area is proportional to the concentration differential (Lassen, 1979; Truskey, 2004).

$$j_x = -D\frac{\partial c}{\partial x} \qquad (1)$$

D is the dispersion coefficient of capillary wall, c is the concentration of substance interested, and x is the dispersion distance in axial. Solute flow, the number of solute molecules crossing a unit membrane area per second:

$$j_s = n\pi a^2 D\frac{\partial c}{\partial x} = P\triangle c \qquad (2)$$

Where $P = n\pi a^2 \dfrac{D}{\triangle x}$, namely membrane permeability, $n\pi a^2$ is the effective area of permeability, $\triangle c$ is the difference between the concentration of FDG in capillary and that in tissue around the capillary.

The concentration gradient is formed along the axis in capillary, $\triangle c(x)$ presents the difference between concentration in capillary and in tissue at distance x from arteriole (equation 3). c_a is the concentration of FDG in artery. c_v is the concentration of FDG at the entrance of vena (equation 4). c_t is the concentration of FDG in tissue. c_a, c_v and c_t are time-varying. Thus the quantity of FDG is derived which demonstrates the amount enters tissue through capillary in unit time (equation 5).

$$\triangle c(x) = \triangle c(0)e^{-\frac{2P}{vr}x} \qquad (3)$$

$$c_v = c_a e^{-\frac{2Px}{vr}} + (1 - e^{-\frac{2Pl}{vr}})c_t \qquad (4)$$

$$q = Q(c_a - c_v) = Q(c_a - c_t)(1 - e^{-\frac{2Pl}{vr}}) \qquad (5)$$

Where v is the velocity of blood flow in capillary, r is the radius of capillary, l is the length of capillary.

2.3 Metabolism in tissue

q, the quantity of FDG entering tissue, is divided into two parts, one contributes the free-FDG in tissue, and the other is captured by cell and becomes FDG 6-phosphate (FDG-6-P). The metabolism can be described by two compartment model (fig.2). Rate constants k_3 and k_4 of compartment model are used to describe metabolism in tissue. While Chen (2004) used one-parameter model, where ^{18}F-FDG dephosphorylation was ignored (i.e. k_4=0), to character the relationship of FDG and FDG-6-P. Comparing one-parameter model with two-parameter model, the two-parameter model is taken, in which $k_4 \neq 0$.

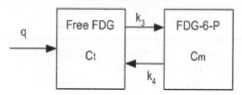

Fig.2. Two-parameter model for metabolism.

$$\frac{dc_m}{dt} = k_3 c_t - k_4 c_m$$

$$\frac{dc_t}{dt} + \frac{dc_m}{dt} = q/V_t \qquad (6)$$

Where V_t is the volume of the tissue. The change of concentration can be got, dividing q by V_t.

2.4 Whole transport-metabolism Model

To simplify the model equations, parameter K is defined to be a synthetical parameter. K is not just a abstract rate constant. It includes the influences of blood flow, tissue volume and parameters of microvascular (equation 7).

The whole model is shown in figure 3. The difference between FDG concentration in plasma and that in tissue is multiplied by synthetical parameter K to get q the quantity of FDG in permeability. q can effect the concentration in plasma, and also effect the concentration in tissue. c_v, c_t and part of c_a form the data, that can be got from PET.

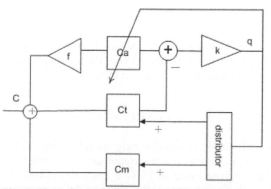

Fig. 3. The schematic diagrams of whole model.

$$K = \frac{Q(1 - e^{\frac{-2Pl}{vr}})}{V_t} \qquad (7)$$

According to equation (5) and (7), the following equations could be derived.

$$q = KV_t(c_a - c_t) \qquad (8)$$

$$\frac{dc_t}{dt} = \frac{q(t)}{V_t} - R \qquad (9)$$

Where R is the metabolic rate of glucose in a local region, and R is the net rate of phosphorylation.

$$R = k_3 c_t - k_4 c_m \qquad (10)$$

$$c_t = \frac{K}{\beta_2 - \beta_1}((k_4 - \beta_1)e^{-\beta_1 t} + (\beta_2 - k_4)e^{-\beta_2 t}) \otimes c_a \qquad (11)$$

$$c_m = \frac{Kk_3}{\beta_2 - \beta_1}(e^{-\beta_1 t} - e^{-\beta_2 t}) \otimes c_a \qquad (12)$$

$$\beta_1 = (k_3 + k_4 + K - \sqrt{(k_3 + k_4 + K)^2 - 4Kk_4})/2 \qquad (13)$$

$$\beta_2 = (k_3 + k_4 + K + \sqrt{(k_3 + k_4 + K)^2 - 4Kk_4})/2 \qquad (14)$$

$$c = c_t + c_m + fc_a \qquad (15)$$

Where c(t) is the total 18F activity in tissue, which can be measured with PET (equation 15). It includes free FDG, phosphorylated FDG and the contribution of tracer within vascular. f is the fraction of blood. $\otimes$ denotes the operation of convolution.

3. MODEL SIMULATION

3.1 Simulation strategy

To avoid the noise, ideal PTAC(plasma time-activity curve) is used to produce simulated data. One function of four exponential functions(equation 16) is used to derive PTAC (Muzic (2000)).

$$c_a(t) = 650e^{-6.7t} + 146e^{-0.25t} + 105e^{-0.03t} + 21e^{-0.0001t} \qquad (16)$$

The parameters of compartment are used to produce simulated output (TTAC). The parameters used are listed in Table. 1, which are taken from Huang (1980), with the first row for grey matter, the second row for white matter and the third row for intermediate tissue.

Table 1 Parameters used to generation TTAC

	k_1 min^{-1}	k_2 min^{-1}	k_3 min^{-1}	k_4 min^{-1}
1	0.102	0.13	0.062	0.0068
2	0.054	0.109	0.045	0.0058
3	0.078	0.1195	0.0535	0.0063

The simulated output is obtained from traditional compartment model with the known parameters for the sampling schedule (12*15, 4*30, 3*60, 1*120, 22*300 seconds frames) and PTAC(16). The fraction of blood is zero in simulation. The simulated curves are generated respectively for grey matter and white matter in human brain

Parameters of transport-metabolism model are estimated by fitting outputs of this model to the outputs of compartment models, in least-squares principle. Fitting is performed using COMKAT provided by Muzic (2001).

Then to evaluate whether the proposed model can be as practical as the conventional compartment model, the model outputs are chosen for the comparison, i.e. the tissue time activity curve (TTAC) for a region of interest (ROI).

3.2 Comparison between one-parameter and dual-parameter metabolic models

Our transport-metabolism model uses Eqs.(9), (10), which are derived from compartment model, to present the conversions between FDG and FDG-6-P. Though compartment model has been widely used, there are different opinions of that whether k_4 equal to zero. In the models of Chen (2004), Bertoldo (2001), k_4 was zero, while in models of Munk (2001), Laffon (2005) back conversion from FDG-6-P was not ignored. The weighted residual sum of squares (WRSS), Akaike Information Criteria (AIC), Schwarz Criteria (SC), see (Munk, 2001), of two forms of model are compared, when $k_4=0$ and $k_4 \neq 0$, using three groups simulated data.

$$WRSS = \sum_{i=1}^{N} w_i \left[c(t_i) - z(t_i) \right]^2 \qquad (17)$$

Where z is the PET measurement, w is the weight for time interval.

$$AIC = N \ln(WRSS) + 2M \qquad (18)$$

$$SC = N \ln(WRSS) + M \ln N \qquad (19)$$

M is the number of parameters in model, and N is the number of data points.

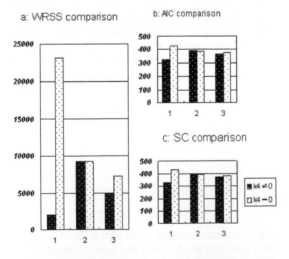

Fig.4. WRSS, AIC and SC are compared between 1-P model and 2-P model. (a) comparison of WRSS, (b) comparison of AIC, (c) comparison of SC.

Smallest WRSS (17) is not the only criteria for the choice of best model. AIC (18) and SC (19) are used to evaluate which model is better. The small values

of AIC and SC should be preferred for the better model fitting.

Figure.4 plots the WRSS, AIC and SC for the four sets of parameter (table.1) to compare the transport-metabolism model with or without k_4. The model with k_4 was observed with the lower values for the three evaluated criteria.

Table 2 Obtained parameters for transport-metabolism model

	K min⁻¹	k_3 min⁻¹	k_4 min⁻¹
1	0.0943	0.0443	0.00518
2	0.0419	0.0144	0
3	0.0682	0.0277	0.00235

3.3 Comparisons of TTAC

Using the parameters listed in table. 1, the compartment model produced three sets of TTAC. Least-squares principle is used to fit the transport-metabolism model outputs to this data set. Parameters for transport-metabolism model are listed in Table.2 in orders corresponding Table. 1.

Outputs comparison of the one data set is shown in figure.5. The transport-metabolism model can simulate the data of compartment model very well.

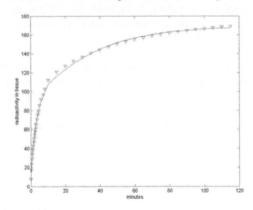

Fig. 5. Comparison of outputs from two models. Solid line for compartment model, and triangle for transport-metabolism model.

4. CONCLUSION

In this paper, one preliminary model is proposed to model the transport and metabolism at the same time. The glucose tracer of FDG is used to evaluate the model. The transport-metabolism model incorporates the function of capillary into the traditional kinetic model. Fick's conservation law is used to describe the transport progress through capillary, while compartmental model is used to describe metabolism process in tissue. A number of parameters have been taken into account when establishing this model, i.e.

blood-flow, permeability, parameters of micro-circulation and rate constants of conversions. By comparisons, rate constant of dephosphorylation k_4 could not be ignored, which is identical to the complicated process of glucose in tissue.

Three sets of data of compartment model are used to produce TTAC, using typical PTAC. According to the TTAC and PTAC, parameters of transport-metabolism model are estimated, by fitting output curves in least-squares principle. The simulation result also shows the proposed model is promising to describe the glucose metabolism. However, the model still requires further investigation to validate its efficiency by the dual tracer studies, which could measure the blood flow and metabolism.

Since the parameters of circulatory system are included in this model, it is potential to connect organ model with circulatory system and construct whole body model. The simulation is carried out only for parameters of brain at present. Whether this model could be applied to other organs is still under investigation. Further study will be achieved in this field and whole-body PET imaging will be applied to aid to evaluate the model.

5. ACKNOWLEDGEMENT

This work is supported by the National Natural Science Foundation of China, Grant # 60331010, and Australia-China Special Fund for S&T Cooperation. The authors thank Dr. Lingfeng Wen for his valuable comments at school of information technologies, the University of Sydney.

REFERENCES

Benedek, G. B. and F. M. H. Villars (1974). *Physics with Illustrative Examples from Medicine and Biology*. Addison-Wesley Publishing Company, New York.

Bertoldo, A., P. Peltoniemi, et al. (2001). Kinetic modeling of [18F]FDG in skeletal muscle by PET: a four-compartment five-rate-constant model. *Am J Physiol Endocrinol Metab*, **281**, E524-E536.

Chen, D.L., A.M. Mark and D. P. Schuster (2004). Comparison of Methods to Quantitate 18F-FDG Uptake with PET During Experimental Acute Lung Injury. *J. nucl. Med.*, **45**, 1583-1590.

Chen, S. and D. Feng (2004). Noninvasive Quantification of the Differential Portal and Arterial Contribution to the Liver Blood Supply From PET Measurements Using the ^{11}C-Acetate Kinetic model. *IEEE trans. Biomed. Eng.*, **51**, 1579-1585.

Chen, S., C. Ho and D. Feng (2004). Tracer Kinetic Modeling of ^{11}C-Acetate Applied in the Liver

With Positron Emission Tomography. *IEEE trans. Biomed. Eng.*, **23**, 426-432.

Chiari, L., G. Avanzolini and M.Ursino (1997). A Comprehensive Simulator of the Human Respiratory System: Validation with Experimental and Simulated Data. *Ann.biomed.eng.*, **25**, 985-999.

Feng, D., K. P. Wong, C. M. Wu, and W. C. Siu (1997). A technique for extracting Physiological parameters and the required input function simultaneously from PET image measurements: theory and simulation study. *IEEE transactions on information technology in biomedicine.*, **1**, 243-254.

Fang, Y.H., L. C. Wu and T. Kao (2001). A New Composite Technique to Estimate the Input Function for FDG-PET Brain Quantitative Analysis without any Blood Sample. *Ann. Rep. Res. React Inst Kyoto Univ.*, **3**, 2759-2762.

Goldman, D. (2001). Modeling the Effect of Biophysical Parameter on Mass Transport in Capillary Network. *J. theor. Boil.*, **209**, 189-199.

Hays, M. T. and G. M. Segall (1999). A Mathematical Model for the Distribution of Fluorodeoxyglucose in Humans. *J. nucl. Med.*, **40**, 1358-1366.

Huang, S. C., M. E. Phelps, E. J. Hoffman, et al. (1980). Noninvasive determination of local cerebral metabolic rate of glucose in man. *Am. J. physiol.*, **238**, E69-E82.

Laffon, E., M. Allard, R. Marthan, et al. (2005) A method to quantify at late imaging a release rate of 18F-FDG in tissues, *C. r. biologies.*, **328**, 767-772.

Lassen, N. A. and W. Perl (1979). *Tracer Kinetic method in Medical Physiology*, pp. 62-175. Raven Press, New York.

Munk, O. L., L. Bass, H. Feng, et al. (2003). Determination of Regional Flow by Use of Intravascular PET Tracers: Microvascular Theory and Experimental Validation for Pig Livers. *J. nucl. Med.*, **44**, 1862-1870.

Munk, O. L., L. Bass, K. Roelsgaard, et al. (2001). Liver Kinetics of Glucose Analogs Measured in Pigs by PET: Importance of Daul-Input Blood Sampling. *J. nucl. Med.*, **42**, 795-801

Muzic, R. F. and G. M. Saidel (2003) Distributed Versus compartment Models for PET Receptor Studies, *IEEE trans. med. Imag.*, **22**, 11-21.

Muzic, R. F. and S. Cornelius (2000) *Compartment Modeling Kinetic Analysis Tool System User Manual*. Departments of Radiology and Biomedical Engineering, Case Western Reserve University.

Muzic, R. F. and S. Cornelius (2001) COMKAT: Compartment Model Kinetic Analysis Tool, *J. nucl. Med.*, **42**, 636-645.

Sharan, M. and A. S. Popel (2002). A Compartmental Model for Oxygen Transport in Brain Microcirculation in the Presence of Blood Sbstitutes. *J. theor. Biol.*, **216**:479-500.

Sharan, M., M. P. Sing and B. Singh (1995). An Analytical Model for Oxygen Transport in Tissue Capillaries in a Hyperbaric Environment with First Order Metabolic Consumption. *Math. comput. Model.*, **22**, 99-111.

Truskey, G. A., F. Yuan and D. F. Katz (2004). *Transport phenomena in biological system*, pp. 427-446,718-742. Upper Saddle River, New Jersey.

NEUROMUSCULAR BLOCKADE ADVISORY SYSTEM RANDOMISED, CONTROLLED CLINICAL TRIAL: PRELIMINARY RESULTS

Terence J. Gilhuly [**,*] Alex Bouzane[*]
Stephan K.W. Schwarz[*] Bernard A. MacLeod[*]
Guy A. Dumont[**]

[*] Dept. Anesthesiology, Pharmacology & Therapeutics
[**] Dept. Electrical & Computer Engineering,
University of British Columbia
2176 Health Sciences Mall, Vancouver, BC, V6T 1Z4,
Canada
contact: terenceg@ece.ubc.ca

Abstract: In this paper, preliminary results of the Neuromuscular Blockade Advisory System (NMBAS) clinical trial comparing the safety and efficacy of NMBAS to standard care are presented. The NMBAS offers advice to the anesthesiologist on dosing of rocuronium based on measured patient response. The NMBAS is being compared against standard practice in a randomized, controlled clinical trial. The NMBAS uses a sixth order Laguerre model to approximate neuromuscular response and a extended horizon control scheme to predict future levels and needs for NMB agent. Thirty-six patients were tested, thirteen patients in the NMBAS group, eleven in the standard care group and twelve excluded. Patient health and demographics, procedures, drug use, and ability to maintain surgically useful conditions and with easy reversibility were equivalent between the two groups. The incidence of adverse events in the OR showed a marked improvement with the NMBAS. As well, responses measured at reversal and extubation were higher for the NMBAS indicating less chance of post-operative adverse events. Copyright © 2006 IFAC

Keywords: advisory system, automated drug delivery, computer controlled drug therapy, Laguerre model, neuromuscular blockade, pharmacokinetics, rocuronium

1. INTRODUCTION

Automatic drug delivery can potentially improve drug therapy by allowing for more efficient delivery, reducing drug usage and costs; permitting health care staff to work more efficiently, providing better care; and allowing the safe use of drugs that are difficult to administer manually.

The authors of this paper have been working in automatic drug delivery, with the development of models and controllers specifically for automated neuromuscular blockade (NMB). NMB drugs produce paralysis to prevent motion, permit tracheal intubation and allow access to deep structures with smaller incisions.

As NMB drugs have high therapeutic indices in hospital settings, they are often used in excess of minimal effective requirements. A strategy for administration is to provide an overdose to prolong paralysis, monitor for returning muscle function and, once it returns, overdose again [Linkens et al. (1982)]. The large dose delivers rapid onset of paralysis, quicker surgical conditions, and avoids titration to a precise anesthetic setpoint and regulation once there [Miller et al. (1984)].

Unfortunately this approach eliminates fine control and increases the possibility of toxicity. Fine control is crucial during surgeries where knowledge of the patient's state is important for safety. For example, in Harrington rod insertion for reshaping the spine, the surgeon assesses whether or not the rods have impinged nerves by the ability of the patient to respond physically. Testing can be performed only after the return of muscle function. Automatic control could keep the patient minimally paralysed until a test is required, reduce drug administration to allow function to return, and then re-paralyse for continued work with minimal waiting time by the surgical staff.

The overdosing strategy is also a source of inconvenience should complications arise and the surgical conditions change, which is not uncommon. An example of this was seen in the study used to collect data for the NMBAS starting model, [Gilhuly et al. (2005)]. After paralysis and induction had taken place, examination of the patient revealed extensive invasive carcinoma. The procedure was cancelled, and the anesthesiologist and attending nurses had to monitor the patient until the drug wore off enough that the patient could be reversed (more below on irreversibility).

Computerized NMB has been attempted previously. Researchers have been able to deliver blockade at a near-constant controlled, setable level compared to conventional practice, while using less drug [Linkens et al. (1982); MacLeod et al. (1989)]. However, the controllers developed have not been stable or robust enough to handle the intra- and interpatient variability present. Representative efforts include bang-bang [Wait et al. (1987)], PID/Smith predictor [Linkens et al. (1985)] and fuzzy logic control [Mason et al. (1999)].

As an intermediate step towards the control of NMB and other anesthetic and pharmaceutical agents, an advisory system for the administration of rocuronium has been developed. This system - the neuromuscular blockade advisory system (NMBAS) - makes dosing recommendations for the NMB agent rocuronium, to the attending anesthesiologist based on measured patient response and an internal model of the patient. The initial dose is determined by manufacturer's recommendations. Subsequent doses are adjusted to adapt to the individual's response to the drug and ability to eliminate it.

The patient's rocuronium response is represented by a sixth order Laguerre model. This model structure was selected as optimal based on simulation against polynomial, autoregressive exogenous and Laguerre models with more filters, as described in [Gilhuly et al. (2005)]. The initial patient model is an average model constructed from a prior study of dose response measurements for rocuronium used in prostate brachytherapy cases. This model is adapted in real-time using recursive least squares estimation with an exponential forgetting and resetting scheme. An extended horizon controller (an algorithm using a state-space model to calculate inputs based on predicted response at a defined length of time into the future) uses the model to predict future response levels as affected by the predicted elimination of the drug. These levels are then used to make predictions on what drug would be required to arrive at the chosen setpoint of a Train-of-Four (To4) measurement of 10% in 20 minutes and at the end of the case. This setpoint was chosen as it is at the most responsive end of the range of surgically useful and easily reversible levels of NMB.

The To4 is a form of electrical stimulation used to measure muscle strength and thereby level of paralysis. The To4 consists of four electrical pulses of up to $300 \mu s$ duration and up to $70 mA$ current spaced at $0.5s$ intervals, that stimulate a nerve (the *ulnar nerve* here) to produce muscle (the *adductor pollicis*) twitches which are measured by EMG. As NMB drug is administered the twitches decrease in magnitude starting with the last. Thus, the ratio of the fourth twitch to the first indicates muscle strength and is clinically useful as known values predict such things as ability to move and to breath spontaneously, and when reversal agents will be effective.

Reversal agents block acetylcholinesterase, the enzyme that breaks down acetylcholine (ACh), the neurotransmitter used at the neuromuscular junction. Reversants thus permit more ACh to accumulate, increasing transmission and muscle function. However, as rocuronium is a competitive antagonist of the ACh receptor (AChR), if there is too much rocuronium, the ACh cannot access the AChR, and the patient cannot be reversed. Reversibility is possible when a To4 showing two twitches appears.

The authors of this paper have been testing the NMBAS in a randomized, double-blinded clinical trial. The clinical trial is now at a pre-determined point where safety and efficacy are being judged to determine whether or not the trial should be completed. The results of this evaluation are presented here.

For this trial, informed consent has been obtained from all patients, and the protocol has been approved by the UBC/Providence Health Care Research Ethics Board.

2. METHODS

The objective of this portion of the NMBAS clinical trial was to demonstrate safety and effectiveness enough to justify continuing the trial. The hypotheses being tested are that NMBAS will be as safe as or more so than standard care, and that it will provide better care. Safety was judged by the incidence of intra- and post-anesthetic clinically relevant events. Comparative effectiveness is judged based on quantified deviation of the neuromuscular response from a surgically useful and easily reversible level of blockade, levels of neuromuscular blocker and anesthetic drug use, and timing of clinically significant events.

The trial is a double-blinded trial. Although the anesthesiologist will be aware of the treatment as they will or will not be receiving advice, the patient and analysis procedure are unaware of the grouping. Analysis of the results is done blindly by computer with the patient identified only by the number they are assigned for the trial.

The sample size for this pre-trial analysis was chosen to provide enough data for an initial estimate of the effectiveness of the NMBAS versus standard care. This was judged to be ten patients under each treatment.

Patient eligibility was determined by examination of the patient charts and through a patient interview. Inclusion criteria were:

- Male or female, aged 18 years or older
- ASA physical status I-III (E)
- Scheduled for surgery under general anesthesia requiring NMB
- NMB agent to be used is rocuronium
- Anesthesia is predicted to last at least one and a half hours

Exclusion criteria were:

- History of hypersensitivity or allergy to rocuronium or any component of its formulation or other neuromuscular blocking agents
- Liver failure
- Renal failure
- Severe obesity
- Pregnancy
- History of neuromuscular disease
- Decreased/low neuromuscular response in forearm, low/non-responsive to NMT/EMG measurement (e.g. peripheral neuropathy)

- Inability to communicate or provide informed consent
- Receiving drugs interfering with neuromuscular transmission
- Epidural scheduled for administration of anesthetic in the operating room

During the patient interview patient demographic and health status details were obtained. Demographic data obtained included sex, age, weight, height and ASA Physical Status. Body Mass Index was calculated. Significant health conditions were polled for. These included: coronary artery disease, heart failure, hypertension, liver disease, kidney disease, neuromuscular disease, respiratory disease, diabetes, abnormal lab results and smoking history. Medications currently used were also enquired for.

Patients were randomly assigned to one of two groups, standard care and care with advice from NMBAS. This was done in lines of four patients; two each of standard and advisor care in a random sequence. The computer program was run for both groups to capture the response data. Calculations and advice were reported to the anesthetist for the NMBAS group only. Control group anesthesiologists were left alone.

All surgeries were conducted as normal. Neuromuscular stimulation was used to determine the drug effect throughout the procedure. Standard stimulation protocols available to the anesthesia monitors (Datex-Ohmeda) were used. A computer (portable IBM PC, Intel Pentium 3 processor) was interfaced to the anesthesia monitor for recording and analysis of the measured electromyography (EMG) response.

All drugs administered were recorded.

The timing of the following events was recorded: the patient entering the operating room, starting anesthetic induction, intubation of the patient, starting surgery, completion of surgery requiring NMB, the presence of two twitches following completion of the NMB dependent surgery, the patient reaching a To4 of 100% without reversant, the patient being reversed pharmacologically, extubation of the patient, and admission of the patient to the post-anesthesia care unit.

Significant clinical events were recorded for comparison between the treatment groups. Intraoperative events watched for were: patient motion, breathing against the ventilator, bucking on the ventilator, and inadequate surgical relaxation as judged by surgeon requests for more relaxation. Post-operative events included inadequate reversal.

Incidence of anesthesiologist non-compliance with NMBAS was recorded.

Post-operative actions included the recording of medications administered, and adverse events and corrective actions taken.

Data analysis of the collected and measured data was done for patient demographics and health conditions, drug use, timing of the procedure, intra- and post-anesthetic clinical events, and deviation from the desired setpoint or error. The patient demographics and health data were compared to show the equivalency of the two groups. The record of procedure events was used to ensure that the procedures in each group were comparable. Drug use, clinical event and error information were compared to judge benefit. Due to the limited size of the dataset, comparison was made between the two groups by Wilcoxon rank order testing. To aid comprehension these results are presented along with mean and standard deviation data.

Neuromuscular response was quantified for the purposes of assessing the performance of the two approaches to care by measuring the deviation from the desired condition of reversibility with adequate relaxation for surgery. At each timestep of the procedure, error is assessed as a score based on the measured NMT response according to the scheme displayed in Table 1. This scheme has been set up to penalize for under- and over-paralysis, with a range around the To4 measurement of 10% considered to be optimal. The overall performance measurement for the case is the sum of the error scores at each timestep, normalized for the length of the case.

Table 1. Quantization of NMB error.

NMT Measurement Range	Score
To4 > 50%	2
To4 ≤ 50% and To4 > 20%	1
To4 ≤ 20% and number of twitches = 2 or 3	0
Number of twitches = 1	1
Number of twitches = 0	2

The two groups were also compared for incidence of the worst performances (scores of two) normalized by the length of the case to see if either of the methods is more likely to produce over-paralysis or under-paralysis.

3. RESULTS

Thirty-six patients were included in the trial. Twelve were excluded from data analysis for reasons of sensor failures and disconnected leads, failing to meet inclusion criteria, and inadequate application of proper clinical control at the beginning of the trial. There were ten women and one man in the standard care group and twelve women and one man in the NMBAS group. Surgeries were predominantly gynecological in nature.

Representative cases demonstrating the data that was measured and the process undertaken are shown in Figure 1. The standard care case on the top is for a woman during a hysterectomy. The NMBAS case on the bottom is for a woman during a cholecystectomy. Both cases start with large intubation doses to paralyse the patient and are followed by small maintenance doses. The standard care response falls to a To4 of 50% before the first maintenance dose and then to 65% for the second. A To4 of 50% indicates muscle tone will be present and may have triggered a complaint from the surgeon. The second dose occurred after noticing the patient breathing against the ventilator. The NMBAS response shows an initial decrease to approximately 65% as well (the initial spikes occur during a saturated time and are due to titanic stimulation). From there, the adaptive nature of the NMBAS commences and To4 recovery is limited to smaller and smaller levels, eventually maintaining it above 80%, with short periods of saturation (approximately 15 minutes).

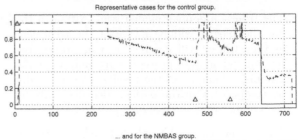

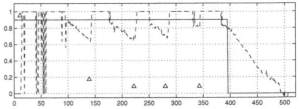

Fig. 1. Representative cases for the standard care and NMBAS treatments. Setpoint (solid line) and measured To4 response (broken line) are displayed in terms of relaxation (To4 ratio subtracted from one). The triangles indicate administrations of NMB agents and the normalized amount of drug given. The ordinate axis is time in units of $20s$ timesteps.

The patient parameters showed that the groups were statistically equivalent. This data is displayed in Table 2. The only significant health conditions were two cases of hypertension, one per group.

Table 2. Patient demographics.

Group	Age yrs.	Weight kg	Height cm	ASA I/II/III Class
standard	46±8	63±8	157±9	3/8/0
NMBAS	52±15	63±12	163±6	3/9/1

Neuromuscular related drug use throughout the case also showed no real differences between the groups. This is shown in Table 3. Propofol and inhalational anesthetic use were analysed to determine if a reduction in rocuronium could be attributed to an increase in anesthetic drug use. Inhalational anesthetic values for both groups had a mean of 1.4 MAC.

Table 3. Intra-operative drug use. RocNorm, Neo, Edro and Prop are rocuronium normalized for weight and length of case, neostigmine, edrophonium and propofol, respectively.

Group	RocNorm mg/kg/min	Neo mg	Edro mg	Prop mg
standard	$(6.0\pm2) \times 10^{-3}$	1.0 ± 1.5	16 ± 30	197 ± 84
NMBAS	$(6.2\pm1) \times 10^{-3}$	2.6 ± 1.4	10 ± 19	180 ± 71

The time course of the operations was statistically similar for each group. On average, patients were induced, intubated and surgery began for each group at ten, fifteen and thirty-one minutes, respectively. Surgeries for the standard care group required 165 ± 46 minutes versus 147 ± 39 for the NMBAS group. Similarly, admissions to the post-anesthesia recovery room (PAR) were delayed for the standard care group. However, the difference in time measured from the finish of surgery to the admission to the PAR was similar for the two groups.

Prior to reversal, To4 measurements were lower on average for the standard care group at approximately 3% versus 18% for the NMBAS group. As well, at the time of extubation, To4 response was also lower for the standard care group at 55% versus 73% for the NMBAS.

The incidence of clinically significant adverse events showed a marked difference between the two groups, with the standard care group have twice as many as the NMBAS group. The details of this appear in Table 4.

Table 4. Clinical event incidence: intra-operative motion, breathing against and bucking on the ventilator, inadequate surgical relaxation and inadequate post-operative reversal.

Group	Motion	Breath -ing	Buck -ing	Inad Surg Relax	Inad PostOp Rev
standard	5	9	2	8	0
NMBAS	4	5	2	1	0

Anesthesiologist non-compliance with the NMBAS recommendations occurred seven times. Four times, the anesthesiologist refused to dose due to the proximity of the end of the case. Two non-compliances were recommendations of clinically insignificant amounts of drug. These were ignored until the dose became significant. The last non-compliance was a suggestion to dose while the patient was paralysed.

Post-operative administrations and incidents were similar for both groups. In eight of the standard care and ten of the NMBAS cases, post-operative drugs for pain (e.g. morphine) and non-NMB related conditions were administered. In two cases for each group, nausea and vomiting were experienced.

Total error normalized for time was 1.27 ± 0.29 and 1.30 ± 0.40 for the standard care and NMBAS groups respectively. The incidence of the extremes of errors (scores of two) was 0.71 ± 0.18 and 0.71 ± 0.24.

4. DISCUSSION

In the NMBAS trial to this point, twenty-four patients have been admitted, treated and their results analysed. Although the results are not statistically significant, it can be seen that there is some merit to the hypotheses proposed and merit in following the clinical trial to completion. Equivalent performance to standard care was seen and safety was demonstrated.

The first hypothesis was that the NMBAS was as safe as or more so than standard care as judged by the incidence of intra- and post-anesthetic clinically relevant events. NMBAS showed itself to be safer by having half the number of clinically significant events in the OR. In terms of post-operative administrations and post-operative incidences the two groups were similar: near equivalent numbers of patients received post-operative medications: eight of eleven patients for the standard care group and ten of thirteen of the NMBAS cases; and incidences of post-operative nausea and vomiting were identical at two happenings each.

On a further note of safety the To4 measurements taken at reversal and at extubation were higher for the NMBAS group. This indicates that the level of blockade was better maintained and response was quicker to return for the NMBAS group. Although extubation was possible in all cases, this is a matter of concern. The lesser the neuromuscular response, the greater the patient's muscle weakness, impaired hypoxic ventilatory response, pharyngeal dysfunction, and risk of aspiration, hypoxemia and delays of emergence from anesthesia. Problems start at To4 measurements between 70 and 90% [Murphy (2004)]. The larger responses recorded with the NMBAS hint that the NMBAS may be the safer treatment.

The second hypothesis was that the NMBAS provided better care as judged by maintenance of an easily reversible level of blockade with adequate relaxation for surgery, by amounts of NMB and anesthetic drug use, and timing of clinically significant events. Equivalent care may be argued but better care was not witnessed.

The ability to maintain appropriate levels was roughly equivalent with the standard care group performing slightly better for total error and near identically for incidence of error extremes. This may be due to these cases being long with the vast proportion of time spent in a saturated condition. Any advantage seen by one treatment might not have a large enough effect to overcome the time averaging that occurs in summing the error.

Overall neuromuscular related drug use was similar for the two groups. For an unknown reason each group seemed to prefer a certain drug: standard care tended to use edrophonium; the NMBAS group used more neostigmine. However, on the whole difference in usage was not statistically significant.

Propofol and inhalational anesthetic were analysed to investigate the use of these drugs as substitutes for NMB agents. Towards the end of the case, the anesthesiologist might elect to use more anesthetic to dampen patient sensitivity and thereby avoid administering some NMB agent. This might have unfairly biased the trial towards the standard care group in terms of NMB consumption. This practice did happen in the trial, however its effect was not noticeable in the data.

From the analysis of the patient demographics and health data the two groups were shown to be equivalent. As well, the timing of events in the procedures demonstrated that comparable procedures and conditions in the operating room were seen by each group of patients. Surgeries for the standard care group required slightly more time than for the NMBAS group. However, that apparent trend is most likely a random coincidence and cannot be attributed to the treatments. The similarity in times from the end of the surgery to the admission to the PAR suggests that the difference is not to do with the NMB protocol employed by the two groups. Once surgery is completed, the delay is in closing the patient and getting them to an acceptable state for extubation.

From the similarity of patient and procedure profiles, it can be said that equivalent representation was found in each group, equivalent procedures were had for the two groups, and a lack of bias can be assumed.

5. CONCLUSIONS

The clinical trial of the NMBAS is underway. Preliminary results from approximately the half-way point have been obtained. Trends are starting to emerge revealing the NMBAS to be as safe or safer than the current standard of care, however more patients are required before substantial claims on the effectiveness of the project can be made. The trial will proceed until completion. The authors hope that this will be accomplished by the time that this paper is presented at MCBMS2006.

ACKNOWLEDGMENT

The authors thank the staff of St. Paul's Hospital for their interest, enthusiasm, accommodation and patience in this clinical trial.

REFERENCES

T. Gilhuly, G. Dumont, and B. MacLeod. Modelling for Computer Controlled Neuromuscular Blockade. In *Proceedings of the 27th Annual International Conference of the IEEE Engineering in Medicine and Biology Society*, Shanghai, China, September 2005.

D.A. Linkens, A.J. Asbury, S.J. Rimmer, and M. Menad. Identification and control of muscle-relaxant anaesthesia. *IEE Proceedings–D*, 129 (4):136–141, 1982.

D.A. Linkens, M. Menad, and A.J. Asbury. Smith predictor and self-tuning control of muscle-relaxant drug administration. *IEE Proceedings–D*, 132(5):212–218, 1985.

A.D. MacLeod, A.J. Asbury, W.M.Gray, and D.A. Linkens. Automatic control of neuromuscular block with atracurium. *British Journal of Anaesthesia*, 63:31–35, 1989.

D.G. Mason, J.J. Ross, N.D. Edwards, D.A. Linkens, and C.S. Reilly. Self-Learning Fuzzy Control with Temporal Knowledge for Atracurium-Induced Neuromuscular Block during Surgery. *Computers and Biomedical Research*, 32:187–197, 1999.

R. Miller, C. Prys-Roberts (editor), and C. Hug Jr. (editor). *"Pharmacokinetics of Muscle Relaxants and their Antagonists"*, chapter 11 of Pharmacokinetics of Anaesthesia. Blackwell Scientific Publications, 1984.

G.S. Murphy. Postanesthesia Care Unit Recovery Times and Neuromuscular Blocking Drugs: A Prospective Study of Orthopedic Surgical Patients Randomized to Receive Pancuronium or Rocuronium. *Anesthesia and Analgesia*, 98: 193–200, 2004.

C.M. Wait, V.A. Goat, and C.E. Blogg. Feedback control of neuromuscular blockade: A simple system for infusion of atracurium. *Anaesthesia*, 42:1212–1217, 1987.

Copyright © IFAC Modelling and Control in Biomedical Systems
Reims, France, 2006

DETERMINISTIC MODELING OF
INTERFERON-BETA SIGNALING PATHWAY

Jaroslaw Smieja [*,1] Mohammad Jamaluddin [**]
Allan Brasier [**] Marek Kimmel [***]

* *Silesian University of Technology, Gliwice, Poland*
** *UTMB, Galveston, TX, USA*
*** *Rice University, Houston, TX, USA*

Abstract: The paper is concerned with dynamical modeling of early and late gene expression in one of Interferon-β induced signaling pathways. First, the biological background is given. Subsequently, the importance of stochastic nature of biological processes is addressed. Then, the assumptions underlying their deterministic modeling are presented and the mathematical model is introduced. Finally, the methodology for identification of model parameters is briefly described, followed by the presentation of experimental and simulation results. In addition to analysis of the particular regulatory network, this work also builds a framework for modeling of other signalling pathways whose not all components are known. *Copyright © 2006 IFAC*

Keywords: Biocybernetics, Biomedical systems, feedback systems, dynamic modelling

1. INTRODUCTION

Following rapid developments in new experimental techniques, mathematical modeling of regulatory pathways that control intracellular biological and chemical processes is gaining increasing interest in the biomedical research. However, so far much more knowledge has been gained concerning pathways structure than their dynamics. Despite a lot of efforts, relatively small number of models has been hitherto tested against experimental data, and therefore a lot of their parameters remain unknown. Moreover, due to their complexity, intertwining and lack of detailed knowledge of the mechanisms at each step of the pathways, it is impossible to build precise mathematical descrip-

tion of entire pathways and take into account all factors playing a role in a realistic system. Therefore, analysis is always constrained to several most important processes and only a part of the whole pathway, which is also the case in this paper. Nevertheless, the resulting models provide valuable insights into complex behavior on the cellular level (Tyson *et al.*, 2003), into kinetics of the involved proteins and their complexes and gives the predictions of the possible responses of whole system to the change in the level of a given activator or inhibitor. Thus, even simplified models can significantly contribute to the biological field. First, they can imply the need for search of additional mechanisms if those already known do not allow obtaining particular dynamics characteristics (such as oscillation periods, amplitude, damping or time constants). Secondly, they can indicate time points at which the experimental measurements should be made to gain maximum

[1] Partially supported by NHLBI Contract N01-HV-28184, Proteomic technologies in airway inflammation (A. Kurosky, P.I.) and by KBN (Polish Committee for Scientific Research) Grant No. 3T11 A02928

knowledge about processes involved, making the experimental work much more efficient.

2. BIOLOGICAL BACKGROUND

Interferons (IFNs) are very important components of the immunodefense system. Their role and elements of interferon-induced signaling pathways are subjects of ongoing research (see e.g. reviews (Kalvakolanu, 2003; Bekisz *et al.*, 2004)). However, except for a model of initial response to the IFNγ (Yamada *et al.*, 2003; Zi *et al.*, 2005), there exist no known dynamical models of pathways of interferon activated pathways.

Interferon family of proteins is divided into two classes of molecules: type I, comprising IFN-α and IFN-β and type II, to which IFN-γ belongs. This work presents the dynamical model of a signaling pathway induced by IFN-β produced by most cell types in response to viral infection.

It has been found that the class IFN-β upregulates a large number of genes (Der *et al.*, 1998; Pfeffer *et al.*, 2004). This paper concentrates on a particular pathway whose aim is to induce cell surface display of intracellular peptides in the context of Major Histocompatibility Complex (MHC) I. This involves production of peptides from intracellular proteins by inducible members of the 26S proteasome (Low Molecular Mass Protein 2 - LMP2), and Transporter of Antigenic Peptides (TAP1 and TAP2) to display the presence of intracellular pathogens (Janeway, 2001).

The most important molecules mediating cell responses after IFN (both type I and II) stimulation are STAT (Signal Transducer and Activator of Transcription) proteins. In particular, two members of this family of proteins, STAT1 and STAT2, mediate the responses taken into account in the analyzed pathway.

Binding of IFN-β to a cell receptor results in phosphorylation of STAT proteins. Subsequently, phosphorylated STATs form hetero- and homodimers (for the sake of simplicity, the terms homodimer and heterodimer refer to dimers of phosphorylated STATs in this paper). In cytoplasm, $STAT1|STAT2$ heterodimers form a complex with IRF9, called ISGF3 Both STAT1 dimers and ISGF3 complex are very rapidly transported into the nucleus where they serve as active transcription factors. STATs are dephosphorylated by phosphatases both in the nucleus and in cytoplasm. Dephosphorylation results in dissociation of complexes leading to nuclear export of STATs and making them available to subsequent phosphorylation/dephosphorylation cycles. For more detailed information about this pathway see recent reviews (Levy and Darnell, 2002; Shuai and Liu, 2003). One of the phosphatases is inactive in resting cells and activated in the course of IFN stimulation, constituting a mechanism of a negative feedback.

One of the genes transcribed early in response to IFN stimulation is IRF1. The newly synthesized IRF1 protein undergoes posttranslational modifications making it active and is imported into the nucleus. Once there, it plays an important role in initiating transcription of late genes. LMP2 and TAP1 are among the genes activated by a complex of unphosphorylated STAT1 and IRF1. Moreover, $IRF1|CBP$ complex is the transcription factor for STAT1 gene, thus creating a positive feedback loop.

3. DETERMINISTIC MODELING OF SIGNALING PATHWAYS

While stochastic effects undoubtedly play a great role in any signaling pathway, deterministic modeling seems to be justifiable, at least in some cases. First and foremost, in multicellular organisms cell responses must be synchronized (and, therefore, stochastic effects must be reduced) to benefit the whole organism. Second, even if this synchronicity is lost, deterministic description of an "average" cell can reflect true dynamics of a real system (see more detailed discussion in section 3.3 of this paper). However, the choice of deterministic approach should be always preceded by rigorous analysis of its applicability. In particular, three underlying assumptions must be tested: applicability of the law of mass action, homogeneity of cell populations and, finally, stochastic effects in gene expression.

3.1 Applicability of the law of mass action

Most deterministic approaches to modeling of complexes formation are based on the law of mass action with cells usually represented as one- or two-compartmental (in the latter case two compartments represent cytoplasm and nucleus) chemical reactors. Taking into account that in the analyzed pathway the number of proteins of each species is large and the gene expression model is not based on individual interactions of transcription factors and their corresponding promoter regions in DNA, it is reasonable to base the model on the law of mass action.

3.2 Homogeneity assumption and its consequences

The general concept of deterministic modeling and fitting model parameters into data coming from Western Blots, EMSA blots, Real-Time

PCR, etc., is based on the notion of homogeneity of cell populations used in experiments. In fact, even if all cells are cloned from the same ancestor, they are not homogenous in the sense of dynamics of intracellular processes. The heterogeneity can be attributed to stochastic distribution of initial conditions, which, in turn, result in different dynamics of intracellular processes. This can lead to deceptive artifacts, considering that experimental procedures consist in growing cell cultures on different plates each of which is subsequently used to get measurement for one time point. Moreover, if there are large oscillations in actual single cells, the data gathered during the experiments does not reflect real dynamics at all (Lipniacki et al., 2005).

Though the short analysis presented above indicates that assumption of cell homogeneity is an oversimplification, this approach can be used to show average behavior of a cell. There seem to be two fundamental conditions that should be satisfied, however: 1) lack of significant oscillations in single cells, and 2) very clear trends in experimental data (in terms of increasing or decreasing levels of essential pathway components). Both of them are met in the pathway analyzed here.

3.3 Stochastic effects in gene transcription

The other aspect of stochastic effects is in regulation of gene transcription. Since a single event of binding of active transcription factor (TF) to the promoter region can result in a burst of mRNA level and, consequently, newly synthesized proteins, transcription is a process where stochastic effects are the most apparent (Paszek et al., 2005).

Importance of stochastic effects on gene transcription depends on two factors 1) the stability of DNA binding by TFs and 2) the number of cofactors needed to start the transcription.

There are basically two ways in which transcription process can be explained in terms of TF binding (the complex process of assembling polymerase complex is not the subject of this discussion). In the first one, when TF is bound to a promoter region of a given gene, it initiates transcription that proceeds until a repressor is bound to a respective regulatory sequence (or actively unbinds the TF from the promoter region). In this case, stochastic modeling would be more appropriate. Alternatively, induced gene transcription might consist in frequent, successive binding and unbinding of TF to the promoter region, in which case deterministic approach tying transcription rate to the concentration of TF would be an acceptable approximation. However, if in order to start transcription a complex of several TFs must be created on the promoter region, formed by

subsequent binding of cofactors in a determined order, a simple deterministic approach, tying transcription rate to one known TF, is not sufficient to model transcription process, even if the model is used to estimate average levels of mRNA in a homogenous population of cells.

Taking into account instability of binding of TFs containing STAT1 proteins (Vinkemeier et al., 1996), modeling of early gene transcription in the analyzed pathway can be realized in a deterministic manner. The rate for IRF1 gene transcription is proportional to STAT1 homodimer concentration in the nucleus. In contrast, transcription of STAT1 gene must be dealt with in a different way. The apparent delay between the peak of nuclear concentration of IRF1 protein (Fig. 2d), being a member of complexes activating the process, and the peak of transcription for each of the three late genes in the pathway (Fig. 1), suggests that, in addition to binding of the known TFs, other processes must take place in order to initiate transcription.

3.4 Using simple 1st order dynamical elements to model late gene expression

It can be safely assumed that the molecules required to start transcription of the late genes are predominantly members of the transcriptional apparatus needed to perform specific tasks, such as, for example, chromatine remodeling and attracting subsequent parts of polII complex. They are constitutively present in the nucleus and their concentration can be assumed to be constant. Therefore, their binding to DNA or to regulatory complex being formed on the promoter region can be described as a Poisson process and the binding times are exponentially distributed random variables. In terms of deterministic modeling, the binding of a single molecule can be represented as a first order time–lag element.

This approach allows including unknown processes in the model. Moreover, only a couple of such elements need to be included, regardless of the number of processes that take place in transcription initiation. The reason for that lies in the theory of system dynamics. If the time constants significantly differ, and only the final output of the system is of interest, faster processes can be neglected, reducing the model order. Alternatively, if they are similar, introducing new elements beyond the first couple of them, does not affect the output significantly, at least for the type of input that is possible in analyzed system (meaning no high frequency oscillations). In practice, 3-4 elements are sufficient to reproduce system responses. In the model that is presented in this paper, the input for STAT1 gene has its own preceding dynamical fourth order element.

4. DETERMINISTIC VS STOCHASTIC MODELS - SIMPLISTIC COMPARISON

An interesting observation can be made when the two approaches, based on apparently different assumptions, are compared.

Denoting activator concentration, transcript concentration, transcript degradation constant and maximum possible transcription rate by (TF), $(mRNA)$, k_{deg} and v_{max}, respectively, the equation describing transcript dynamics in the deterministic model is as follows:

$$\frac{d(mRNA)}{dt} = -k_{deg}(mRNA) + v_{max}k \cdot (TF)\ (1)$$

where the first term represents transcript degradation, and the second - gene expression actively induced in a given signaling pathway ($k < 1$).

The expected values in stochastic modelling, in turn, can be calculated as (Paszek et al., 2005)

$$\frac{dE[(mRNA)]}{dt} = -k_{deg}E[(mRNA)] + v_{max}E[g(t,A,R)]\ (2)$$

where

$$g(t,A,R) = \begin{cases} 0 \ for & t < A \\ 1 \ for & A < t < A+R \\ 0 \ for & t > A+R \end{cases} \quad (3)$$

i.e., $g = 1$ when activator (and no repressor) is bound to the promoter region, 0 otherwise. Binding of both an activator and a repressor are Markov processes and A and R are random moments of those events, correspondingly.

To show the relation between deterministic and stochastic models it is sufficient to concentrate on transcription rates represented by $v_{max}k \cdot (TF)$ in (1) and $v_{max}E[g(t,A,R)]$ in (2).

First, let us investigate a deterministic model. Let us assume that n transcription factors are required to bind in an orderly manner to the promoter region of a gene activated in a given pathway. Furthermore, let us assume that the first transcription factor is a signalling molecule, whose concentration first increases and then decreases (as it is often the case in a stimulated cell), while others are members of transcription apparatus that are at steady level in the nucleus. In that case, usually the time profile of the first transcription factor level can be roughly approximated by

$$(TF_1) = k_0(\exp(-\mu_1 t) - \exp(-\mu_2 t)), \mu_1 > \mu_2\ (4)$$

This concentration is an input to the n-th order inertial element representing unknown processes that must take place before transcription starts. Output of this element is the input (TF) used in (1). Then, the Laplace transform of the transcription rate in the deterministic model is given by

$$F(s) = k_2 \frac{\mu_2 - \mu_1}{\prod_{i=1}^{n} T_i} \cdot$$

$$\cdot \frac{1}{(s+\mu_1)(s+\mu_2)\prod_{i=1}^{n}(s+1/T_i)} \quad (5)$$

On the other hand, let us assume that a simple stochastic model is based on the assumptions presented in (Paszek et al., 2005). There, n activators are needed to start gene transcription and repressor binding is required to stop it. All those molecules are assumed to be at steady level in the nucleus. Binding of both an activator and a repressor are Markov processes with parameters λ_i and λ_0 for i-th activator and repressor, respectively.

The expected gene activity in stochastic modeling is given then by

$$E[g(t,A,R)] = \sum_{k=0}^{k=n} \left[\left(\frac{\prod_{i=1}^{n} \lambda_i}{\prod_{i=0,i\neq k}^{n}(\lambda_i - \lambda_k)} e^{-\lambda_k t} \right) \right] (6)$$

Having calculated inverse Laplace transform of (5), it is easy to notice that, assuming $\mu_2 = \lambda_0$, $\mu_1 = \lambda_1$, $1/T_i = \lambda_{i+2}$ ($i = 1,...,n$) and $k_2 = \mu_1/(\mu_2 - \mu_1)$, the transcription rates in stochastic and deterministic modeling are the same.

5. MODEL OF IFN-β PATHWAY

Basic processes taken into account in the model include formation and dissociation of protein complexes, phosphorylation and dephosphorylation of molecules, gene transcription, translation of mRNA nuclear import and export and degradation of molecules. Variables denote nuclear and cytoplasmic molar concentrations of molecules. Parameters have been fitted to experimental data.

Due to limited space, the full model is not shown here. Instead, the general concepts forming its basis are presented.

5.1 Formation of complexes

Formation of complexes is based on law of mass action (Segel, 1991). The model comprises the following complexes: $IRF1|STAT1$ complexes, STAT1 homodimers and $STAT1|STAT2$ heterodimers.

5.2 Phosphorylation and dephosphorylation

The phosphorylation of STAT1 and STAT2 proteins takes place after IFN bind to a specific receptor. The actual process involves several sequential

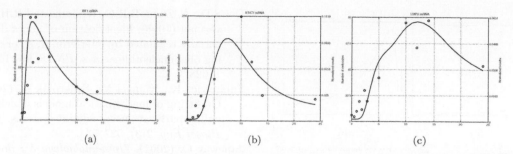

Fig. 1. Comparison of simulation (solid line) and Real-Time PCR experimental results (circles) for the following mRNA: (a) IRF1; (b) STAT1; (c) LMP2.

steps but in order to simplify the model it is represented as a single process.

The experimental results (not shown here) suggest, however, that a simple first order process is not sufficient to model STAT phosphorylation, since the level of phosphorylated STATs does not follow with dramatic increase in total STAT concentration. Therefore, saturation has been introduced to the equation describing this process.

Dephosphorylation is mediated by various phosphatases, both in cytoplasm and in nucleus. However, following the line of reasoning applied to phosphorylation description, intermediate steps are not explicitly modelled. Instead, dephosphorylation rate is assumed to be proportional to concentration of a given substrate. This approach, is justified not only by need to simplify the model, but also by availability of experimental procedures that allowed measuring levels of phosphorylated proteins but not tracking interactions with individual phosphatases.

If (A) and (A_p) denote the cytoplasmic concentration of unphosphorylated and phosphorylated protein, phosphorylation and dephosphorylation are included in the model in the following way:

$$\begin{cases} \dfrac{d(A)}{dt} = -Activation \cdot \dfrac{k_{phos} \cdot (A)}{1 + k_{sat} \cdot (A)} + k_{deph}(A_p) \\ \dfrac{d(A_p)}{dt} = Activation \cdot \dfrac{k_{phos} \cdot (A)}{1 + k_{sat} \cdot (A)} - k_{deph}(A_p) \end{cases} \quad (7)$$

where k_{phos} is the rate constant for the process, k_{deph} - rate constant for dephosphorylation k_{sat} - saturation parameter, $Activation$ - logical variable, equal to 1 if IFN activation is on, 0 otherwise.

The model includes phosphorylation of STAT1 and STAT2 proteins. Prior to activation of the signaling pathway there are no phosphorylated proteins.

5.3 Gene transcription

The transcription rate is assumed to be proportional to the concentration of the active transcription factors:

$$\frac{d(mRNA)}{dt} = k_{const} + k_t \cdot (TF) \quad (8)$$

where (TF) denotes concentration of an active transcription factor (for IRF1, LMP2 and TAP1 genes), $(mRNA)$ is transcript concentration, k_t is the transcription constant (calculated per cytoplasmic volume) and k_{const} is constitutive production rate. For STAT1 gene (TF) denotes the output of an inertial element excited by free nuclear IRF1, as described in the preceeding section.

5.4 Other processes

Translation rate is assumed to be proportional to the mRNA concentration in the cytoplasm. Nuclear import and export rates are assumed to be proportional to concentrations of molecules.

6. IDENTIFICATION OF MODEL PARAMETERS

For identification of model parameters a generalized backpropagation through time (GBPTT) algorithm has been used. It was designed for training continuous-time neural networks based on discrete-time measurements (Fujarewicz *et al.*, 2005).

However, to avoid identification of scaling weights and to reduce influence of noisy or poorly quantified experimental data, all output values have been scaled to the area below respective plots. Therefore, the performance index was defined as follows:

$$J = 0.5 \sum_{i=1}^{I} \sum_{n=1}^{N} \left[\frac{y_i(t_n)}{S_{yi}} - \frac{m_i(t_n)}{S_{mi}} \right]^2 \quad (9)$$

where I and N denote the number of measured outputs and the number of measurements, respectively, $y_i(t_n)$ and $m_i(t_n)$ denote simulation and experimental result for the i-th output at time t_n, respectively. S_{yi} and S_{mi} denote the area below y_i and m_i plots, respectively.

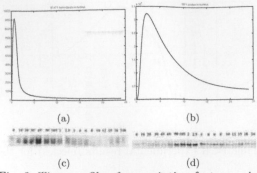

(a)　　　　　　　　(b)

(c)　　　　　　　　(d)

Fig. 2. Time profile of tanscription factors - simulaton and Western Blot data: (a) and (c) homodimer of phosphorylated STAT1; (b) and (d)- IRF1; time points up to 120 are in [minutes], the remaining are in [hours]

6.1 Results

Fig. 2 illustrates concentrations of TFs required for transcription of target genes in the analyzed pathway. Levels of mRNA are presented in the Fig. 1. Both in terms of actual number of molecules, and comparison of normalized values, those results are satisfactory. Other simulation results, not shown here due to the lack of space are also concordant with experimental data.

7. CONCLUSIONS

Usually, mathematical modeling is confined to early system response, often only a couple of hours long. The rationale behind this constraint is twofold. First, analysis of late responses is confounded by a crosstalk from other pathways, rendering isolating of a given pathway almost impossible. Secondly, complexity of the pathway increases as more and more processes are involved in the course of time, many of them not investigated yet or involving unknown intermediaries. Nonetheless, approximation of unknown processes by inertial elements made modeling of late system response possible, providing means for mathematical description of other pathways, whose structure has not been completeley defined yet.

Using a relatively simple deterministic approach, it was possible to build a mathematical model of IFN-β stimulated pathway that mirrors the pathway dynamics reasonably well.

REFERENCES

Bekisz J., H. Schmeisser, J. Hernandez, N.D. Goldman and K.C. Zoon (2004). Human Interferons Alpha, Beta and Omega. *Growth Factors*, **22**(4), 243-251.

Der S.D., A. Zhou, B.R.G. Williams and R.H. Silverman (1998). Identification of genes differentially regulated by interferon α, β, or γ using oligonucleotide arrays. *PNAS*, **95**, 15623-15628.

Fujarewicz K., Kimmel M., Swierniak A. (2005). On fitting of mathematical models of cell signaling pathways using adjoint systems. *Math Biosci Eng*, **2**(3), 527-534.

Janeway C. (2001). *"Immunobiology 5 : the immune system in health and disease"*, Garland Pub. New York.

Kalvakolanu D.V. (2003). Alternate interferon signaling pathways. *Pharm. & Therap.*, **100**, 1-29.

Levy D.E. and J. Darnell Jr. (2002). STATs: transcriptional control and biological impact. *Nat Rev Moll Cell Biol*, **3**, 651-662.

Lipniacki T., P. Paszek, A.R. Brasier, B. Tian, H.-Q. Wang, B.Luxon and M. Kimmel (2005). Stochastic regulation in early immune response. *Biophys J*, (in press).

Paszek P., T. Lipniacki, A.R. Brasier, B. Tian, D.E. Nowak and M. Kimmel (2005). Stochastic effects of multiple regulators on expression profiles in eukaryotes. *J Theor Biol* **233**(3), 423-33.

Pfeffer L.M., J.-G. Kim, S.R. Pfeffer, D.J. Carrigan, D.P. Baker, L. Wei and R. Homayouni (2004). Role of Nuclear Factor-κB in the Antiviral Action of Interferon and Interferon-regulated Gene Expression. *J Biol Chem*, **279**(30), 31304-31311.

Segel L.A. (ed.) (1991). *"Biological kinetics"*, Cambridge University Press, Cambridge.

Shuai K. and B. Liu (2003). Regulation of JAK-STAT signalling in the immune system. *Nat Rev Immun*, **3**, 900-911.

Tyson J.J., K.C. Chen and B. Novak (2003). Sniffers, buzzers, toggles and blinkers: dynamics of regulatory and signaling pathways in the cell. *Curr Op Cell Biol*, **15**, 221-231.

Vinkemeier U., S.L.Cohen, I. Moarefi, B.T.Chait, J. Kuriyan and J.E. Darnell Jr. (1996). DNA binding of in vitro activated Stat1α, Stat1β and truncated Stat1: interaction between NH2-terminal domains stabilizes binding of two dimers to tandem DNA sites. *EMBO J*, **15**(20), 5616-5626.

Yamada S., S. Shiono, A. Joo and A. Yoshimura (2003). Control mechanism of JAK/STAT signal transduction pathway. *FEBS Letters*, **534**, 190-196.

Zi Z., K.-H. Cho, M.-H. Sung, X. Xia, J. Zheng and Z. Sun (2005). In silico identification of the key components and steps in IFN-γ induced JAK-STAT signaling pathway. *FEBS Letters*, **579**, 1101-1108.

PHYSIOLOGICAL MODELLING AND ANALYSIS OF THE PULMONARY MICROCIRCULATION IN SEPTIC PATIENTS

M.A Denaï [1], M. Mahfouf [1], O. King [1], J.J. Ross [2]

[1] *Dept of Automatic Control & Systems Engineering, University of Sheffield, UK.*
[2] *Dept of Anaesthetics, Northern General Hospital, Sheffield, UK.*

Abstract: A physiological model integrating a pulsatile cardiovascular system model with a model of the pulmonary capillary fluid exchange based on the Starling's equations is proposed in order to analyse the micro-circulatory physiological alterations which occur during the evolution of sepsis. Sepsis-induced acute lung injury is typically characterized by an increased microvascular permeability and interstitial edema. Pulmonary edema occurs because the capillary filtration capacity increases and the reflection coefficient to proteins decreases causing fluid leak across the capillary barrier. Patients with severe sepsis may develop respiratory failure and hence requiring ventilatory support. These signs represent the clinical expression of the acute respiratory distress syndrome (ARDS) and are associated with high mortality in medical intensive care units (ICU). The proposed model is used to simulate the cardiovascular hemodynamics under these complex pathophysiological conditions. *Copyright © 2006 IFAC*

Keywords: Septic shock, capillary leak, microvascular permeability, pulmonary edema, Starling's force, cardiovascular system.

1. INTRODUCTION

The syndrome of septic shock is characterized by several physiological abnormalities such as: (1) peripheral arteriolar vasodilation which results in low systemic vascular resistance causing hypotension (2) increased heart-rate (2) increased vascular leakage and fluid loss from the intravascular space causing hypovolaemia and (3) myocardial depression with decreased myocardial compliance due to dilated and poorly contractile ventricles (Parillo, 1989; Bridges and Dukes, 2005).

Clinical observations indicate that, in a severe sepsis case, the primary injured target is most often the pulmonary microcirculation. Patients with these clinical complications develop an increased microvascular permeability of the endothelial barrier and interstitial edema. Pulmonary edema diminishes the compliance of the respiratory system and may lead to respiratory failure.

According to Starling's equation, capillary fluid filtration is determined by the hydrostatic and osmotic pressures gradient across the capillary wall. To facilitate gas exchange, the lungs should stay dry

and consequently the balance in Starling's forces is generally in favour of fluid reabsorption. Pulmonary edema occurs when there is fluid accumulation in the interstitial space. This may be caused by an increased capillary pressure (heart failure, arteriolar dilation), increased vascular permeability (sepsis, traumatic injury), decreased plasma oncotic pressure (liver, kidney, nutrition) and eventually lymphatic blockage (lymphedema). This paper is concerned with the analysis of micro-circulatory alterations which are known to occur in the lungs of patients developing severe sepsis. The physiological model used here combines a pulsatile model of the human cardiovascular system with a compartmental model of the pulmonary microvascular exchange. The model is parameterized to simulate the hemodynamic response of a patient under three different stages of sepsis. Quantitative descriptions of the relevant changes in the physiological model parameters are based on the clinician's experiential knowledge.

This paper is organized as follows: First, the physiological model describing the cardiovascular system and the pulmonary microcirculation are presented. The model is then used to simulate the dynamics of the microvascular exchange of fluid and proteins during the evolution of sepsis. The filtration capacity (K_f) and the reflection coefficient (σ_F) of the lung capillary barrier are gradually increased and decreased respectively to simulate different stages of sepsis.

2. PHYSIOLOGICAL MODEL DESCRIBING THE CARIOVASCULAR SYSTEM AND THE PULMONARY MICROCIRCULATION

2.1 Cardiovascular system model

The cardiovascular system (CVS) model consists of fourteen compartments including the systemic, pulmonary, coronary and cerebral circulations (Denaï et al., 2005).
Each compartment consists of a compliant element (C) and a resistance (R) as shown in Fig. 1.

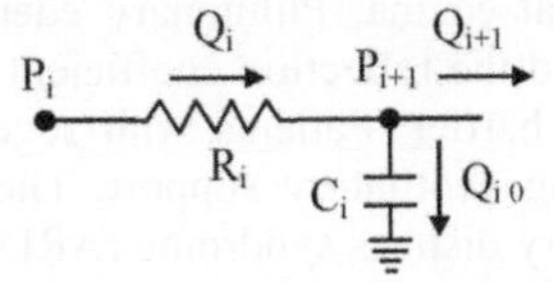

Fig. 1. Electric analog model of a compartment.

The relationships between pressure (P), flow (Q) and volume (V) in a compartment are given as follows:

$$P_i = (V_i - V_{i0})/C_i$$
$$Q_i = (P_i - P_{i+1})/R_i \qquad (1)$$
$$dV_i/dt = Q_i - Q_{i+1}$$

Each ventricle is modelled as time-varying elastance E(t) using the following double Hill equation :

$$E(t) = E_{min} + E_{max} \left[\frac{\left(\frac{t_n}{\alpha_1 T}\right)^{n_1}}{1 + \left(\frac{t_n}{\alpha_1 T}\right)^{n_1}} \right] \left[\frac{1}{1 + \left(\frac{t_n}{\alpha_2 T}\right)^{n_2}} \right] \qquad (2)$$

The parameters n_1, n_1, $\alpha_1 T$ and $\alpha_2 T$ are obtained from experimentally observed elastance curve.

2.2 Mathematical model of the pulmonary microcirculation

The model describing the lung microcirculation consists of three compartments (Bert et al, 1984): circulation, lung tissue and lymph as shown in Fig. 2.

The basic model has been modified so that it can interact with cardiovascular system model.
In the microcirculation, fluid and protein balance is maintained by hydrostatic and oncotic pressures existing on either sides of the capillary barrier.

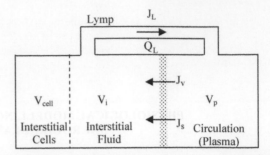

Fig. 2. Compartmental model describing the microvascular exchange.

Filtration takes place at the arteriolar side where hydrostatic pressure is higher than plasma proteins oncotic pressure whereas re-absorption occurs at the venous side as hydrostatic pressure drops along the capillary bed. The lymphatic system regulates this transcapillary exchange by constantly draining fluid and proteins from the interstitium back to the circulation.
The coupling Starling equations describing the transcapillary fluid and protein (k denotes albumin and globulins) exchanges are given as follows

$$J_V = K_f [(P_c - P_i) - \sigma_d (\pi_p - \pi_i)]$$
$$J_{s,k} = PS_a (C_{p,k} - C_{AV,k}) + (1 - \sigma_{F,k}) \overline{C}_{s,k} J_V \qquad (3)$$

Where PS_a is the permeability-surface product (the diffuse capacity of the membrane), σ_F is the protein reflection coefficient and $\overline{C}_{s,k} = (C_{p,k} + C_{AV,k})/2$. The total tissue volume of fluid (interstitial and cellular) is the difference between the input and output fluxes such that

$$dV_{tot}/dt = J_V - J_L \qquad (4)$$

The protein concentrations of fluid leaving the tissue and that forming the lymph are assumed identical. Hence the rate of protein transfer through the lymph is expressed as follows

$$dQ_{L,k}/dt = J_L C_{i,k} \qquad (5)$$

The tissue protein content is calculated as follows

$$dQ_k/dt = \dot{Q}_{s,k} - \dot{Q}_{L,k} \qquad (6)$$

and the tissue fluid volume available to a protein is given by the following expression

$$V_{AV,k} = V_i - V_{E,k} \qquad (7)$$

Where $V_i = V_{tot} - V_{cell}$ and V_E is the excluded volume which depends on protein size. The protein concentration in lymph which has been approximated

to the protein concentration in the interstitial compartment is given by the following equation:

$$C_{L,k} = C_{i,k} = Q_k/V_i \qquad (8)$$

The effective concentration of protein which is responsible for generating the oncotic pressure in the interstitial compartment is based on the tissue volume which is available to proteins and is expressed as follows

$$C_{AV,k} = Q_k / V_{AV,k} \qquad (9)$$

This pressure is given as a function of the sum of the concentrations of albumin and globulins (Bert and Pinder, 1984).

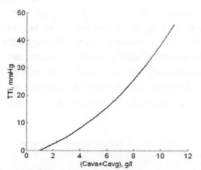

Fig. 3. Oncotic pressure versus plasma protein content: $\pi_i = f(C_{AVa} + C_{AVg})$.

The interstitial compliance is defined by the relationship $P_i = f(V_{tot})$ and is plotted in Fig. 4 (Bert and Pinder, 1984).

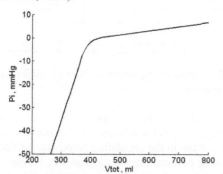

Fig. 4. Interstitial compliance curve: $P_i = f(V_{tot})$.

The plasma protein concentrations are calculated using a similar relationship $\pi_p = f(C_{pa} + C_{pg})$. Where

$$C_{pa} = \frac{Q_{pa}}{V_p} \qquad C_{pg} = \frac{Q_{pg}}{V_p} \qquad (10)$$

The plasma volume and protein contents in the plasma are updated using mass balance principle.

$$\frac{dV_p}{dt} = -\frac{dV_{tot}}{dt} \qquad (11)$$

$$\frac{dQ_{pa}}{dt} = -\frac{dQ_{ia}}{dt} \qquad \frac{dQ_{pg}}{dt} = -\frac{dQ_{ig}}{dt} \qquad (12)$$

Finally, the total blood volume in the circulation is $V_{blood} = V_p + V_{rbc}$, V_{rbc} denotes the volume of red blood cells. The proportions of plasma and red blood cells volumes have been set to $V_p = 3400$ ml and $V_{rbc} = 2200$ ml respectively in order to have a total blood

volume in the circulation of 5600 ml. The two models are linked via the pulmonary capillary pressure and through the circulation compartment

3. PHYSIOLOGICAL MODELING OF SEPSIS

Most of septic shock patients undergo alterations in the cardiac function (ventricles contractility (E_{max}) and heart rate (HR)) and peripheral vascular tone (SVR) which directly affect the patient cardiovascular hemodynamics. Furthermore, clinical observations revealed that patients with septic shock have a significantly higher filtration coefficient K_f which may increase up to 6-fold during their stay in ICU (Chris et al., 1998). In addition to increased fluid permeability, microcirculatory dysfunction is also associated with an increased leakage of proteins into the interstitial space (Staub, 1981; Chris et al., 1998). The transcapillary transport of proteins is described by equation (3). The reflection coefficients σ_{Fa}, σ_{Fg} and the permeability-surface product are the main parameters which characterize the protein permeability of the capillary barrier.

The assumed changes in the underlying physiological model parameters are summarized in Tables 1 and 2.

Table 1 Quantitative description of the circulatory parameters in sepsis

	Mild	Moderate	Severe
HR	80	90	110
Emax	normal	↓ 30 %	↓ 30 %
SVR	↓ 20 %	↓ 35 %	↓ 50 %

Table 1 Quantitative description of the microvascular parameters in sepsis

	Mild	Moderate	Severe
K_f	normal	↑ 50 %	↑ 100 %
σ_{Fa}	normal	↓ 25 %	↓ 50 %
σ_{Fg}	normal	↓ 20 %	↓ 40 %

4. SIMULATION RESULTS

The cardiovascular system model parameters correspond to a human subject of 75 Kg, a total blood volume of 5600 ml and a heart rate of 75 beats/min have been adapted from (Masuzawa et al., 1992). The values of the parameters corresponding to normal human lungs are listed in the Appendix (Bert and Pinder, 1984). An integration step size of 0.005 sec was used throughout.

4.1 Simulation under normal conditions

All the parameters are set to their nominal values. Fig. 5 shows the simulated left and right ventricle pressures and the aortic and pulmonary pressures related to a normal subject.

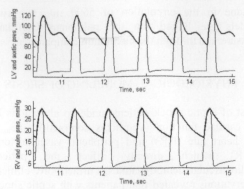

Fig. 5. Simulated left and right ventricles, aortic and pulmonary pressures of a normal subject.

The oncotic model describing the dynamics of the pulmonary microcirculation requires initial values for the extravascular volume and proteins contents which are set to V_{tot} = 300 ml, Q_a = 5.93 g and Q_g = 2.48 g respectively. Fig. 6 and 7 show the transient response of the volume, oncotic pressure, hydrostatic pressure and protein concentration in the plasma and the interstitial space respectively.

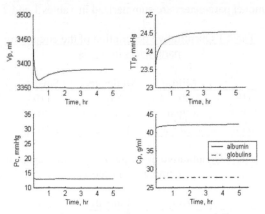

Fig. 6. Transient responses of V_p, π_p, P_c and C_p.

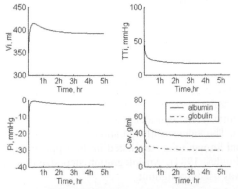

Fig. 7. Transient responses of V_i, π_i, P_i and C_{av}.

The steady-state normal values of the parameters are listed in Table 3. All the values compare favourably

with published data for human lungs (Bert and Pinder, 1984; Roselli et al., 1984).

Table 3 Steady-state oncotic model parameter values

π_p	=	25 mmHg	π_i =	16.8mmHg
C_{pa}	=	42 g/ml	C_{ava} =	36.5 g/ml
C_{pg}	=	27.8 g/ml	C_{avg} =	20 g/ml
P_c	=	13 mmHg	P_i =	-2.8 mmHg
V_p	=	3390 ml	V_i =	392 ml

4.2 Simulation under septic conditions

The physiological model parameters are varied according to Fig. 8 to simulate the hemodynamic alterations in a patient going through the three different stages of sepsis. Similar patterns are applied to the pulmonary oncotic model parameters K_f, σ_{Fa} and σ_{Fg}. All these parameters changes are allowed to occur simultaneously throughout the assumed septic stages.

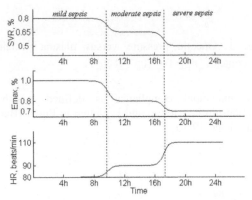

Fig. 8. Simulated parameters changes under sepsis conditions.

The hemodynamic responses to these pathophysiological conditions are shown in Fig. 9. There is a fall in the circulating blood volume due the increasing permeability of the capillary barrier. This contributes to the marked increase in the cardiac output (CO). A decrease in arteriolar and venous tones results in a systemic hypotension and increased venous capacity respectively. In reality, these alterations may vary at different vascular beds, which lead to a maldistribution of blood flow in the circulation and subsequent cascaded organs dysfunction at a later stage.

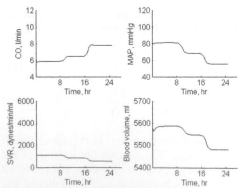

Fig. 9. Cardiovascular hemodynamic reponses under sepsis.

The steady-state hemodynamic data for simulated non-septic and septic patients are listed in Table 4.

Table 4 Hemodynamic data for simulated non-septic and septic patients.

| | | Non-septic | Septic | | |
			Mild	Moderate	Severe
CO	l/min	5.2	5.8	6.5	7.8
MAP	mmHg	94.0	81.0	68.0	55.4
HR	beats/min	75.0	80.0	90.0	110.0
MPAP	mmHg	22.4	23.8	23.8	23.5
CVP	mmHg	7.1	7.7	8.5	8.9
PCP	mmHg	13.0	13.4	13.7	13.6
SVR	dyn.s.cm^{-5}	1409.5	1105.3	842.9	566.9

Microvascular changes in the pulmonary circulation are shown in Fig. 10 and 11. As the capillary barrier becomes more permeable to plasma fluid and proteins, hydrostatic and oncotic pressures in the interstitial compartment are expected to increase. The gained fluid volume and proteins in the interstitial space contribute to an expansion of the extracellular volume (Fig. 11). There is a slight increase in the pulmonary capillary hydrostatic pressure due to the increase in the cardiac output.

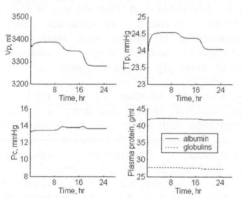

Fig. 10. Transient responses of V_p, π_p, P_c and C_p under sepsis.

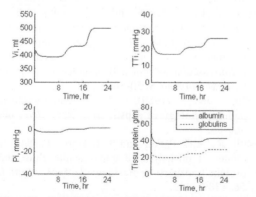

Fig. 11. Transient responses of V_i, π_i, P_i and C_{av} under sepsis.

Lung fluid balance is determined by the net fluid flow ($J_V - J_L$) which should be equal to zero so that a tissue fluid volume is maintained constant. As filtration flow J_V increases, the flow of the lung's lymphatic system J_L will increase to conserve a zero net fluid flow. As shown in Fig. 12, there is a time

lag between J_V and J_L which causes fluid to accumulate in the lungs (Drake *et al.*, 1987). However, if the filtration rate exceeds the transport capacity of the lymphatic system, fluid accumulation in the interstitial compartment is increased and leads to pulmonary edema.

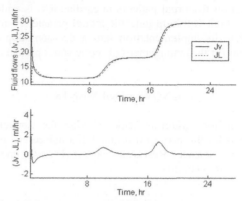

Fig. 12. Inter-compartmental fluid flows

4.3 Severe sepsis with lymphedema

Other physiological conditions can be simulated such as changes in lymph flow characteristics to characterize different forms of lymphedema. The lymphatic pumping capacity is modulated by Vtot through the linear relationship given in the Appendix. Fig. 13 shows the effects of decreasing the lymphatic flow by 10% and 20% respectively. The model parameters are those related to severe sepsis conditions. There is an increased interstitial volume expansion due to the decreased lymphatic pumping capacity and this contributes to edema accumulation.

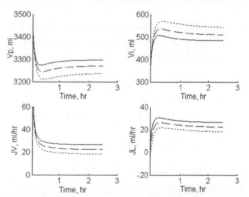

Fig. 13 Effect of decreased lymph flow : normal (solid), -10% (dashed), -20% (dotted)

5. CONCLUSIONS

The modelling and simulation studies presented in this paper aimed at analyzing the mechanisms which affect the pulmonary microcirculation during different stage of sepsis. The physiological model structure proposed herein represents a useful approach for understanding sepsis-induced organ dysfunctions and their effects on the cardiovascular hemodynamics.

The present investigation concentrated on those factors characterizing the permeability of the lung microcirculation during the evolution of severe sepsis. The model simulated successfully the contribution of these factors to the development of clinical symptoms of severe sepsis such as capillary leakage, pulmonary edema and hypovolemia. Data collection from real patients in cardiac ICU is under way which will help tune the model parameters and validate its implementation into a decision support system for the management of septic shock patients.

ACKNOWLEDGEMENTS

The authors gratefully acknowledge the financial support for this project from the UK Engineering and Physical Sciences Research Council (EPSRC) under Grant GR/S94636/1.

APPENDIX

Nomenclature

CO   cardiac output
HR   heart-rate
MAP   mean arterial pressure
MPAP mean pulmonary arterial pressure
CVP   central venous pressure
PCP   pulmonary capillary pressure
SVR   systemic vascular resistance

P_c capillary hydrostatic pressure
P_i interstitial hydrostatic pressure
π_c capillary oncotic pressure
π_I interstitial oncotic pressure

J_v fluid flux from plasma into tissue (ml/hr)
J_s protein flux from plasma into tissue(g/hr)
J_L lymph flow (ml/hr)

V_{tot} total extravascular volume (ml)
V_i interstitial fluid volume (ml)
V_{AV} interstitial volume available to protein (ml)
V_E excluded volume (ml)
V_{cell} cellular volume (ml)

Q   protein content of interstitial fluid (g)
dQ/dt   rate of protein transfer (g/hr)
Q_L protein flux from tissue to lymph

C_p protein concentration in plasma
C_i protein concentration in tissue
C_{AV} protein concentration in tissu based on V_{AV}
C_L protein concentration in lymph

K_f fluid filtration coefficient (ml/hr.mmHg)
σ_d fluid reflection coefficient
σ_F protein reflection coefficient
PS   permeability surface area

Parameter values for normal human lungs.

K_f	1.12 ml/hr.mmHg
σ_d	0.75
V_{cell}	150 ml
J_L	$0.17V_{tot} - 55.6$
PS_a	3.0 ml/hr
σ_{Fa}	0.4
V_{Ea}	73.5 ml
PS_g	1.0 ml/hr
σ_{Fg}	0.6
V_{Eg}	115.5 ml

REFERENCES

Auckland K., R.K. Reed (1993), Interstitial-lymphatic mechanisms in the control of extracellular fluid volume, *Physiol Rev*, **73**, 1-78.

Bert, J.L., K.L. Pinder (1984). Pulmonary microvascular exchange: An analog computer simulation, *Microvascular Research*, **27**, 51-70.

Bridges E.J., M.S. Dukes, Cardiovascular aspects of septic shock: Pathophysiology, monitoring and treatment, *Critical Care Nurs*, **25**, 2005, 14-40.

Chris E., J. Gamble, L.B. Gartside and W.J. Kox (1998). Increased microvascular water permeability in patients with septic shock, assessed with venous congestion plethysmography (VCP), *Intensive Care Med.* **24**, 18-27.

Denaï M.A., M. Mahfouf, J.J. Ross (2005). A physiological model describing dobutamine interaction with septic patients: A simulation study, Proceedings of 3rd European Medical and Biological Engineering Conference (EMBEC'05), 20-25 Nov. 2005, Prague.

Drake R.E., G.A. Laine, S.J. Allen, J. Katz and J.C. Gable (1987), A model of the lung interstitial-lymphatic system, *Microvascular Research*, **34**, 96-107.

Masuzawa T., Y. Fukui and N.T. Smith (1992). Cardiovascular simulation using a multiple modeling method on a digital computer – simulation of interaction between the cardiovascular system and angiotensin II, *J. of Clin. Monitoring*, **8**, 50-58.

Parillo, J.E. (1989). The cardiovascular pathophysiology of sepsis, *Ann. Rev. Med.*, **40**, 469-85.

Roselli, R., R.E. Parker and T.R. Harris (1984), A model of unstedy-state transvascular fluid and protein transport in the lung, *J. Appl. Physiol*, **56**, 1389-1402.

Staub, N.C. (1981). Pulmonary oedema due to increased microvascular permeability, *Ann. Rev. Med.*, **32**, 291-312.

Wiederhielm, C.A. (1979). Dynamics of capillary fluid exchange: A nonlinear computer simulation, *Microvascular Research*, **18**, 48-82.

Xie, S.L., R.K. Reed, B.D. Bowen and J.L. Bert (1995). A model of human microvascular exchange, *Microvascular Research*, **49**, 141-162.

MODELING AN ENZYMATIC DIFFUSION-REACTION PROCESS IN ONE DIMENSIONAL SPACE

J. Santos and R. Lozano [*,1] A. Friboulet [**]
E. Castellanos and S. Mondié [***]

[*] *Heuristique et Diagnostic des Systèmes Complexes -
UTC, France*
[**] *Génie Enzymatique et Cellulaire - UTC, France*
[***] *Departamento de Control Automático
(CINVESTAV-IPN) , México*

Abstract: In this paper a nonlinear model of a spatially distributed biological system representing the interaction between diffusion and reaction in living cells is proposed and analyzed. The model is derived from a kinetic study of the enzyme Acetylcholinesterase immobilized within an artificial membrane. The formulated system represents a model of three different chemical species that interact with each other to produce Acetate and Choline. Numerical results employing the Method of Lines make possible to assess the concentration profile of each specie involved in the enzymatic reaction on space and time, what is not directly observable by biochemists. Copyright (C) 2006 IFAC.

Keywords: Immobilized Enzymes, Reaction and Diffusion System, One Dimensional System

1. INTRODUCTION

Reaction-diffusion equations are used to describe the behavior of a wide range of applied areas. In this work we propose a model for the Acetylcholinestersase (*AChE*) immobilized into an artificial membrane. The model is inspired on a previous work of (Santos *et al.*, 2005) on *AChE* immobilization via zero dimensional approach for modelling multiple steady states in a system involving the diffusion of substrate through an artificial membrane. They proposed a model into which the reactor containing the enzyme perfectly agitated

[1] Supported by the Programme Alban, the European Union Programme of High Level Scholarships for Latin America under the reference number E04D047796MX and by Laboratoire Franco-Mexicain d'Automatique Appliquée (LAFMAA). These supports are gratefully acknowledged.

and homogeneous and verified that the results presented by (Friboulet and Thomas, 1982) can be interpreted in terms of a coupling between the diffusion and reaction. However, a distributed system is more realistic than the one based on zero dimensional approach. In fact, enzyme molecules are mostly located within cell membranes and organelles, i.e., those regions where diffuse resistance to mass transfer is concentrated (Kernevez, 1980). Despite several works concerning this subject in the literature, only a few are available on parabolic Partial Differential Equations (PDEs) applied to systems with more than two species involved in the biochemical reaction.

This paper is organized as follows. In section 2 a mathematical development of the kinetic reaction based on the scheme of hydrolysis regulation for *AChE* and of the diffusion equations is presented.

The model formulation of this enzymatic process (section 3) is based on a one dimensional approach by considering the coupling between diffusion and reaction equations. The particularity of the model is that two continuous independent variables, the space and time, i.e., (x, t) in the PDEs are used to characterize the states of the physical system. The Finite Element Method (FEM) used to discretize the PDEs is briefly summarized in section 4. The system of parabolic PDEs is discretized and converted to a set of nonlinear Ordinary Differential Equations (ODEs) used to model three different chemical species. The FEM involves approximating the solutions at successive time steps, each approximation requiring the solution of the system. Numerical simulation results are presented in section 5.

2. THE REACTION-DIFFUSION COUPLING

The approach introduced in this section describes the interaction of diffusion and reaction in the $AChE$ active membrane. The distributed system is defined by a series of parabolic PDEs of second order describing the mass diffusion that combined with the kinetic reaction result in a system with initial-boundary value problem in one dimensional space. On one hand the reaction term is obtained from a mathematical development of the kinetic mechanism for hydrolysis of ACh by $AChE$ taking into account electroneutrality condition and the acid-base chemical equilibria. On the other hand the Fick's equation of diffusion is used to determine the flux of the three different chemical species through the active membrane.

2.1 The reaction term

The formation of an intermediary acetyl-enzyme complex in the kinetic model presented in Figure 1 is inhibited by excess of substrate. It takes into account the high concentration of Choline (Ch) that may appear during the reaction and exert a negative feedback control by inhibiting the $AChE$. Moreover, the pH effect is considered because the reaction produces Acetate (Ac), which rapidly dissociates in Ac and protons at pH values higher than 5. From Figure 1 we obtain the equation (1) corresponding to the chemical reaction rate. The ACh^+ is represented by s, the inhibition by Ch is represented by p and the pH-dependence is represented by h. By considering the K_m value as the natural unit of concentration, the description of the reaction rate in a dimensionless form is given by

$$R(s, p, h) = \frac{sF(h)}{1 + \frac{p}{K_P} + s(1 + \frac{p}{K_P'}) + k_i s^2} F(h) \tag{1}$$

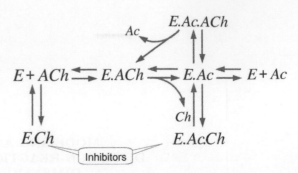

Fig. 1. Representation of the immobilized enzymatic model described by (Krupka and Laidler, 1983). The reaction includes a rapid binding of the substrate to yield the Michaelis-Menten complex (ES) and the formation of an intermediary acetyl-enzyme complex ($E.Ac$) with concomitant elimination of Ch. The inhibition by excess of substrate (ACh^+) is explained by the binding of an additional substrate molecule to the intermediary complex to form the dead-end ternary complex ($E.Ac.ACh$).

where $F(h)$ describes the pH-dependence given by

$$F(h) = 1/(1 + \frac{h}{C_{H1}} + \frac{C_{H2}}{h}), \tag{2}$$

where $\mathbf{s} = (s_1, ..., s_n)$, $p = (p_1, ..., p_n)$, $a = (a_1, ..., a_n)$ are vectors of chemical concentrations; $k_i = \frac{k_i^*}{(1 + \frac{h}{C_{Hss}})}$ is the inhibition by excess of substrate; $k_P = k_P^*(1 + \frac{h}{C_{Hp}})$ and $k_P' = k_P'^*(1 + \frac{h}{C_{Hp}})$ represent the effect of pH on Ch.

The parameters $C_{H1} = \frac{C_{H1}}{K_m}$, $C_{H2} = \frac{C_{H2}}{K_m}$, $C_{Hss} = \frac{C_{Hss}}{K_m}$ and $C_{Hp} = \frac{C_{Hp}}{K_m}$ are constants which values are given in table I. See (Santos et al., 2005). In order to solve the equation (2) we must calculate the local pH resulting from Ac dissociation. It is assumed that the different ionic equilibria related to electroneutrality are fast when compared to the diffusion of hydronium ions. The local concentration of free H^+ results from the dissociation of Ac and buffer $\left(\frac{[B^-][Na^+]}{[BH]} \right)$ by taking into account the two next considerations: First the **electroneutrality condition** ($[H^+] + [Na^+] = [OH^-] + [B^-] + [A^-]$) and second the **acid-base chemical equilibria**. These considerations yield the dimensionless form

$$a = \left(1 + \frac{h}{k_a}\right)\left(xb + \frac{bk_b}{(h + k_b)}\right) \tag{3}$$

where $a = \frac{[A]_T}{K_M}$, $b = \frac{[B]_T}{K_M}$, $k_w = \frac{K_W}{K_{M2}}$, $k_a = \frac{K_A}{K_M}$ and $k_b = \frac{K_B}{K_M}$ are given in table I. The h value is solved iteratively as follows

$$h^2(\frac{bx}{k_a}) + h(bx + b(x-1)\frac{k_b}{k_a} - a) + bk_b(x-1) - ak_b = 0 \tag{4}$$

2.2 Fick's equation of diffusion

Diffusion is the mechanism by which an assemblage of chemical particles of a mixture are transported randomly back and forward throughout *AChE* membrane by means of random molecular motion of each one of the three species in the two compartments. The particles reside in a region called $\Omega \in \mathbb{R}^n$ (the $n - th$ dimensional space with Cartesian coordinate system) with $n = 1$ corresponding to one dimensional space.

The chemical particles along the enzyme membrane are determined in fixed steps Δx that are taken in a fixed time Δt. The transport of molecules across the permeable membrane is passive because it does not require any active role for the membrane. In life science this transport corresponds to a flux which is proportional to the gradient concentration (Okubo, 1980) characterized by the Fick's Second Law as follows

$$J_x = -D\frac{\partial c}{\partial x}, \ x \in \mathbb{R} \qquad (5)$$

where J_x is the flux of material, $c(x,t)$ is the concentration gradient of the different species and $D > 0$ is the diffusion coefficient [2] concentration. The minus sign indicates that diffusion transport occurs from a high to a low concentration. We are interested in how the function $c(x,t)$ changes as time t evolves and as the distance x varies. According to (Murray, 1977) the amount of material in a region $x_0 \leq x \leq x_1$ is given by

$$\frac{\partial}{\partial t}\int_{x_0}^{x_1} c(x,t)dx = J(x_0,t) - J(x_1,t)$$

By using (5) and evaluating the upper limit $x_1 = x_0 + \Delta x$ and for $\Delta x \to 0$ we get the following classical diffusion equation in one dimensional space

$$\frac{\partial c}{\partial t} = -\frac{\partial J}{\partial x} = \frac{\partial\left(D\frac{\partial c}{\partial t}\right)}{\partial x} \qquad (6)$$

From (6) the Fick's equation of diffusion is

$$\frac{\partial c}{\partial t} = D\frac{\partial^2 c}{\partial x^2} \qquad (7)$$

---

[2] More detailed treatments might consider that D depends on the temperature, etc. of the solvent and also on the existing concentration, even for dilute concentrations. As earlier, these effects are insignificant for the situations considered, so that D is constant and is defined in (8).

3. THE ONE-DIMENSIONAL SYSTEM

The one dimensional approach is based on the scheme of hydrolysis regulation for *AChE* as illustrated in Figures 1 and 2. The dynamics are represented by a set of ODEs that arises in the reaction kinetics through application of the **Law of Mass Action** that gives the equation (1) and the **Fick's Second Law** that results the equation (7). The three chemical species are based on the *AChE* kinetics in an heterogeneous phase. It means that the catalyst is in a different phase to the reactants, characterizing a distributed parameter system governed by parabolic PDEs so that the states, for each t are a function of position in the spatial region Ω.

The diffusion and reaction phenomena take place into the same physical space (the enzymatically active membrane) and not separately as in the case of zero dimensional approach. Both compartments (reservoir and reactor) contain well mixed solution of substrate s and the membrane is initially empty, i.e., no substrate or product. By considering the diffusion equation for the substrate concentration and for the reaction's products, the Ch and Ac represented by s, p, a respectively, we obtain the following nondimensional model that governs the system's dynamics

$$\left.\begin{aligned}
\frac{\partial s(x,t)}{\partial t} &= Ds\frac{\partial^2 s(x,t)}{\partial x^2} - \sigma F(s,p,h(a)) \\[6pt]
\frac{\partial p(x,t)}{\partial t} &= \frac{D_p}{D_s}\frac{\partial^2 p(x,t)}{\partial x^2} + \sigma F(s,p,h(a)) \\[6pt]
\frac{\partial a(x,t)}{\partial t} &= \frac{D_a}{D_s}\frac{\partial^2 a(x,t)}{\partial x^2} + \sigma F(s,p,h(a))
\end{aligned}\right\} \qquad (8)$$

$Ds = 1$, $\frac{D_p}{D_s} = 1$ and $\frac{D_a}{D_s} = \beta$ are the diffusion constants of flux concentrations for the three species, i.e., $s(x,t)$ for the substrate, $p(x,t)$ for Choline and $a(x,t)$ for Acetate at a given point x and time t respectively; $F(s,p,h(a))$ is a non-linear function describing the reaction term or interaction among the different chemical species obtained in (1). $\sigma = \frac{V_M}{K_S}\frac{L^2}{D_S}$ is the Thiele modulus (nondimensional constant) corresponding to the ratio between the maximum rate of reaction and the maximum rate of diffusion of the three reactants; $x = L \in [0,1]$ is the membrane thickness.

4. METHOD FOR SPATIAL DISCRETIZATION OF FLUXES

4.1 The Finite Element Method

For diffusion-reaction problems there exist several methods to prove the existence and uniqueness of a positive solution and asymptotic stability of

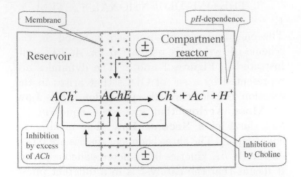

Fig. 2. Active membrane. Diffusion and reaction take place into the same space. The $AChE$-catalyzed reaction can be inhibited by ACh^+ as well as by the high concentration of Ch. The pH acts either as a inhibitor or accelerator, directly on the $AChE$ as well as indirectly by means of ACh and Ch, what characterizes the pH−dependence as a controller in the reaction.

a steady state. Here is applied the FEM, traditionally called **Method of Lines** for solving the PDEs by using finite difference relationships for the spatial derivatives and ODEs for the time derivative, i.e., one variable is chosen to be the temporal continuous variable t and the other is chosen to be the spatial variable x which is discretized, resulting in a system of ODEs. This method can be adapted to problems of great complexity and unusual geometry. Furthermore, the availability of fast and inexpensive computers allows to face problems that are intractable using analytic methods.

The procedure used by this method consists in dividing the spatial interval $L = \{x \in [0,1]\}$ into N equal intervals and define a time step $k = \Delta t$ to obtain a discretization in time-space by rewriting the PDEs in terms of finite difference approximation given by

$$\left.\frac{\partial u}{\partial t}\right|_{i,n} = \frac{u_i^{n+1} - u_i^n}{\Delta t}$$

$$\left.\frac{\partial^2 u}{\partial x^2}\right|_{i,n} = \frac{u_{i+1}^n - 2u_i^n + u_{i-1}^n}{\Delta x^2}$$

$$\underbrace{\frac{u_i^{n+1} - u_i^n}{\Delta t} - \frac{u_{i+1}^n - 2u_i^n + u_{i-1}^n}{\Delta x^2} = 0}_{\text{Diffusion equation}} \quad (9)$$

For a particular $n \geqslant 0$ and $1 \leq i \leq N-1$ we compute the values of s, p and a for all i, and we can solve equation (9) to find u_i^{n+1} for each i with the following explicit [3] Euler aproximation

$$u_i^{n+1} = u_i^n + \frac{\Delta t}{\Delta x^2}(u_{i+1}^n - 2u_i^n + u_{i-1}^n) \quad (10)$$

---

[3] Numerical solution schemes are often referred to as being explicit or implicit. When a direct computation of the dependent variables can be made in terms of known quantities, the computation is said to be explicit.

where u corresponds to the state variables $s(x,t)$, $p(x,t)$, $a(x,t)$ of the system (8) with $x \in [0,1]$ and $t \in [0,\infty)$. The Method of Lines is appropriate when we are interested in the qualitative nature of the solutions rather than a quantitative analysis. For this reason its application to (8) makes possible the study of the system's behavior for $0 \leq x \leq 1$ with Dirichlet boundary conditions and the analysis of the concentration profile for each chemical specie, which is not directly observable by biochemists.

5. NUMERICAL SOLUTION OF THE DIFFUSION-RECTION COUPLING IN THE $ACHE$ ACTIVE MEMBRANE

The algorithm is implemented via the Method of Lines and computed with the PDE solver in Matlab®, although this technique is not restricted to any program. The advantage of this explicit method is that it provides greater accuracy with less computational effort than implicit methods. The diffusion-reaction system as well as the initial and boundary conditions in the form of the parabolic equation expected by PDE solver is given by (Skeel and M., 1990) as follows

$$\mathbf{c}(x, t, u, \frac{\partial u}{\partial x})\frac{\partial u}{\partial t} =$$

$$x^{-m}\frac{\partial}{\partial x}(x^m f(x, t, u, \frac{\partial u}{\partial x})) + R(x, t, u, \frac{\partial u}{\partial x}) \quad (11)$$

The PDEs hold for $t_0 \leq t \leq t_f$ and $0 \leq x \leq 1$, where x is the spatial variable, $m = 0$ corresponds to slab geometry of the enzyme membrane depicted in Figure 2, $f(x, t, u, \partial u/\partial x)$ is the flux term of the diffusion equation and $R(x, t, u, \partial u/\partial x)$ is a reaction term. $\mathbf{c}$ is a diagonal matrix that restricts the coupling of the partial derivatives with respect to t. The diagonal elements of $\mathbf{c}$ are either identically zero or positive. An element in $\mathbf{c}$ equal to zero corresponds to an elliptic equation, otherwise to a parabolic equation. Then we rewrite (8) according to (11) as follows

$$\begin{bmatrix} 1 \\ 1 \\ 1 \end{bmatrix} .* \frac{\partial}{\partial t}\begin{bmatrix} s \\ p \\ a \end{bmatrix} = \frac{\partial}{\partial x}\begin{bmatrix} \left(\frac{\partial s}{\partial x}\right) \\ \left(\frac{\partial p}{\partial x}\right) \\ \beta\left(\frac{\partial a}{\partial x}\right) \end{bmatrix} +$$

$$+ \begin{bmatrix} -\sigma F(s,p,h) \\ \sigma F(s,p,h) \\ \sigma F(s,p,h) \end{bmatrix} \quad (12)$$

5.1 Initial-boundary value problem

The boundary and initial conditions must be specified and added to complete the physical description of the system, since the conditions in the reactor can vary with time and position (also called distance or space). At the initial time $t = t_0$ and $0 \le x \le 1$ the initial conditions that specify the states of the system at time $t = 0$ are

$$s(x, t_0) = s_0(x) = 853$$

$$p(x, t_0) = p_0(x) = 0$$

$$a(x, t_0) = a_0(x) = 0$$

The Dirichlet boundary conditions are required so that the second order parabolic PDEs take the form of and boundary value problem. They denote the concentration of the different chemical species $s(x,t), p(x,t), a(x,t)$ in the one-dimensional membrane. The variable x is defined in the interval $[0, L]$, with $L = 1$. The ODEs resulting from discretization in x space are integrated to obtain approximate solutions in t. The Matlab solver function returns values of the solution on a mesh provided in x. By applying the integral to the left hand side of (11) we obtain

$$c \int_0^t \frac{\partial u}{\partial \tau} d\tau = cu(x,t) - cu(x,0)$$

On the other hand, by integrating the right hand side of (11) we get

$$\int_0^t \frac{\partial}{\partial x} \left(f(x) \frac{\partial u(x,\tau)}{\partial x} \right) d\tau \Big|_{0=x}^{x=1}$$

$$+ \int_0^t R\left(x, \tau, u, \frac{\partial u}{\partial x} \right) d\tau$$

where the first integral with respect to t is known as the Dirichlet boundary condition and its boundedness is

$$\int_0^t f(x) \frac{\partial u(x,\tau)}{\partial x} d\tau =$$

$$f(x) \frac{\partial}{\partial x} [n(x,t) - u(x,0)]$$

where $\lim_{t \to \infty} \int_{0+}^t u(x,\tau) d\tau = n(x,t) < \infty$ converges to initial conditions. Then, for $0 \le x \le 1$ we have

$$q(L,t) - p(L,0) - q(0,t) + p(0,0) = 0$$

Therefore

$$\int_0^1 f(x) \frac{\partial}{\partial x} [q(x,t) - p(x,0)] dx = 0$$

Finally, the Dirichlet boundary condition is the following

$$q(0,t) = p(0,0) - p(1,0) = p(x,0)$$

$$q(1,t) = 0$$

The general equation to define boundary conditions to PDEs of the form (11) must satisfy the terms of the flux f of the form

$$p^i(x,t,u) + q^i(x,t) f^i \left(x,t,u, \frac{\partial u}{\partial x} \right) = 0 \quad (13)$$

By applying (13) to the system (12) we obtain the left boundary conditions $\partial s / \partial x = 853$, $\partial p / \partial x = 0$, $\partial a / \partial x = 0$ that written in the form (11) are

$$\underbrace{\begin{bmatrix} 0 \\ p \\ a \end{bmatrix}}_{p(0,t,u)} + \underbrace{\begin{bmatrix} s - 853 \\ 0 \\ 0 \end{bmatrix}}_{q(0,t)} . * \underbrace{\begin{bmatrix} \left(\frac{\partial s}{\partial x} \right) \\ \left(\frac{\partial p}{\partial x} \right) \\ \beta \left(\frac{\partial a}{\partial x} \right) \end{bmatrix}}_{f(x,\, t,\, u,\, \partial u / \partial x)} = \begin{bmatrix} 0 \\ 0 \\ 0 \end{bmatrix}$$

Similarly the right boundary conditions $\partial s / \partial x = 0$, $\partial p / \partial x = 0$, $\partial a / \partial x = 0$ are

$$\underbrace{\begin{bmatrix} s \\ p \\ a \end{bmatrix}}_{p(1,t,u)} + \underbrace{\begin{bmatrix} 0 \\ 0 \\ 0 \end{bmatrix}}_{q(1,t)} . * \underbrace{\begin{bmatrix} \left(\frac{\partial s}{\partial x} \right) \\ \left(\frac{\partial p}{\partial x} \right) \\ \beta \left(\frac{\partial a}{\partial x} \right) \end{bmatrix}}_{f(x,\, t,\, u,\, \partial u / \partial x)} = \begin{bmatrix} 0 \\ 0 \\ 0 \end{bmatrix}$$

The solutions of (12) readily obtained are presented in Figures 3, 4, 5, 6 and show the evolution of the concentration profile in the $AChE$ membrane for the different species. All plots were generated with $N = 75$ in the intervals $(0, L)$, $L = 1$ and $(0,t)$, $t = 2.5$.

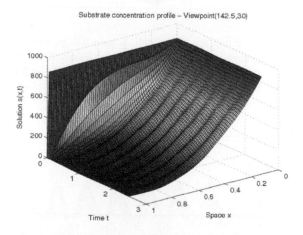

Fig. 3. The solution $s(x,t)$ changes rapidly for small t. Substrate concentration tends to zero as t tends to ∞.

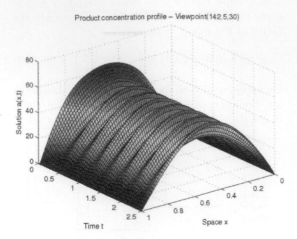

Product concentration profile – Viewpoint(142.5,30)

Fig. 4. Effect of the Dirichlet boundary conditions in the production of Ac is observed in the evolution equation $a(x,t)$ on $0 \leq x \leq 1$.

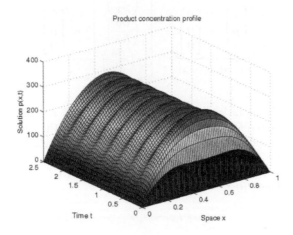

Product concentration profile

Fig. 5. Fine spatial mesh is needed to obtain accuracy in the solution of the PDEs. The Ch concentration profile is limited by Dirichlet boundary conditions.

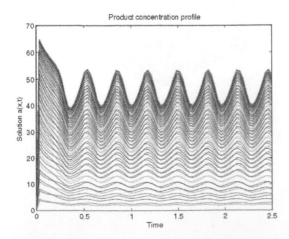

Product concentration profile

Fig. 6. Oscillations observed in the formation of Ac.

6. CONCLUSIONS AND FURTHER WORK

A mathematical model describing the $AChE$ immobilized into an artificial membrane was introduced. The model represents the biochemical phenomena that occur when the ACh is combined with the $AChE$ to form the products Ch and Ac. As immediate benefits, the proposed model makes possible to compute and directly analyze the concentration profile of the three chemical species involved in the reaction.

Because the $AChE$ is immobilized in an homogeneous way into the artificial membrane where the diffusion and reaction take place, a more realistic model is conceived and as consequence the system's behavior in time and space is more representative of a real experimentation. The numerical results reported in this paper can be considered a valuable tool in the comprehension of the biological complexity present in the $AChE$ immobilization, provided that enough information about the process can be obtained.

Further numerical simulations are now in progress to study of the system's behavior for different values of the Thiele modulus, characterizing a phenomenon of hysteresis that describes the $AChE$ activity and permits to determine the quantity of substrate consumed within the active membrane. An extension of this technique to describe a multienzymatique system is also expected.

REFERENCES

Friboulet, A. and D. Thomas (1982). Electrical excitability of artificial enzyme membranes. *Biophysical Cheministry* **16**, 153–157.

Kernevez, J.P. (1980). *Enzyme Mathematics*. North-Holland. New York.

Krupka, R.M. and K.J. Laidler (1983). Molecular mechanisms for hydrolytic enzyme action. i. apparent non-competitive inhibition, with special reference to acetylcholinesterase. *J. Am. Chem. Soc.* pp. 1448–1454.

Murray, J.D. (1977). *Lectures on Nonlinear Differential-Equation Models in Biology*. Claredon Press Oxford.

Okubo, A. (1980). *Diffusion and Ecological Problems: Mathematical Models*. Vol. 10. Springer-Verlag Berlin Heidelberg New York.

Santos, J., A.Friboulet, R.Lozano, S.Mondié and E.Castellanos (2005). Computer simulation of qualitative behavior resulting from the immobilization of acetylcholinesterase-ache. *MGMS International Meeting - Biomolecular Simulation. Trinity College Dublin*.

Skeel, R.D. and Berzins M. (1990). A method for the spatial discretization of parabolic equations in one space variable. *SIAM Journal on Scientific and Statistical Computing* **11**, 1–32.

GARCH MODELS FOR DRUG EFFECTS ON PATIENT HEART RATE, DURING GENERAL ANAESTHESIA

Susana Brás * **Catarina S. Nunes** *,[1]
Pedro Amorim **

* *Departamento de Matemática Aplicada, Faculdade de Ciências da Universidade do Porto, Portugal*
** *Serviço de Anestesiologia do Hospital Geral de Santo António, Porto, Portugal*

Abstract: A model that can describe the effect of anaesthetic drugs on patient's heart rate (HR) is of great importance when considering haemodynamic stability under surgery. A Generalized Autoregressive Conditional Heteroscedasticity (GARCH) model was used to model HR considering the effect concentrations of the anaesthetic propofol and the analgesic remifentanil, using the clinical data of 16 patients. The model was able to capture the HR trend in all 16 patients with very small errors throughout the surgical time. A correlation was found between the GARCH parameters and patient baseline characteristics, leading to the possibility a patient adjusted adaptive model. *Copyright © 2006 IFAC*

Keywords: Biomedical systems, stochastic modelling, modelling errors, pharmacokinetic data

1. INTRODUCTION

Anaesthesia can be defined as the lack of response and recall to noxious stimuli, involving the use of three drugs, a muscle relaxant, an anaesthetic (hypnotic) and an analgesic. The analgesic drug is of great importance since it affects the pharmacodynamics of the anaesthetic drug and there is no clear indicator of the degree of pain. The analgesic and anaesthetic drugs are interconnected, since they interact with each other so as to achieve an adequate level of depth of anaesthesia (DOA) and analgesia (Vuyk, 1999). The possibility of consciousness during surgery is a factor that affects

clinicians and patients. The brain signals (e.g. electroencephalogram EEG) are used to indicate the level of DOA, measuring the depression in the central nervous system. But, haemodynamic signals indicate the level of analgesia and stability (McGregor *et al.*, 1998)(O'Hare *et al.*, 1999). The heart rate (HR) (i.e. the number of heart beats per unit of time) is an haemodynamic signal, which as normal values around 72 beat/min. Overall, general anaesthesia consists of both loss of consciousness through the acting of the anaesthetic drugs, and the inhibition of noxious stimuli reaching the brain through the acting of the analgesics. The intravenous anaesthetic drug propofol is used in combination with the analgesic remifentanil.

Propofol and remifentanil have a synergistic relationship. The effect of the combination of these two drugs is greater than that expected as based on the concentration-effect relationships of the in-

[1] Corresponding author: Dr. Catarina S. Nunes, Departamento de Matemática Aplicada, FCUP, Rua do Campo Alegre 687, 4169-007 Porto, Portugal (ccnunes@fc.up.pt) Financial support: Portuguese Foundation for Science and Technology POSC/EEA-SRI/57607/2004.

dividual agents (Vuyk *et al.*, 1997). The properties of remifentanil make it a suitable analgesic for use with propofol, and adequate for control in anaesthesia.

A model for heart rate can be very useful to understand the effect of different drugs and drugs' interactions. This model could have in consideration only the effect of remifentanil or remifentanil and propofol. Since remifentanil has a stronger effect than propofol on the haemodynamic signals (McAtamney *et al.*, 1998)(Prakash *et al.*, 2001). However, drug interactions can influence HR. The aim of this study is to develop a model that can describe the characteristics and trend of patient HR under general anaesthesia.

The Generalized Autoregressive Conditional Heteroscedasticity (GARCH) model structure was used, since it is a good model for processes without seasonality and with high variability. Heart rate variability increases in the presence of pain (Toweill *et al.*, 2003).

In this work, a comparative study will be performed on a wide group of patients to evaluate the effectiveness of GARCH models with different input variables (effect concentration of remifentanil or remifentanil and propofol). The clinical data are presented in section 2. Section 3 describes the model that was applied to the clinical data, for the concentration-effect relationship on HR. The results are presented in section 4. And sections 5 and 6 present the discussion and conclusions.

2. CLINICAL DATA

Data collected during 16 neurosurgical interventions were used in this study. All 16 patients were subject to general anaesthesia using the anaesthetic drug propofol and the analgesic drug remifentanil. The level of unconsciousness (DOA) was manually controlled by the anaesthetist using as reference the patient's vital signs and the bispectral index of the EEG (BIS) monitor. The following clinical signs were recorded during the surgery every 5 seconds: BIS, infusion rate of propofol and remifentanil, haemodynamic parameters. The infusion rates were used to calculate the plasma and effect concentration of both drugs, as described in the following subsections. The 16 patients studied were Glasgow 15, ASA 1/2, 46.3±15 years, 64±14 kg, 164±8 cm, 10 female. Anaesthesia started with a constant infusion 200 ml/hr of propofol until loss of consciousness (LOC), thereafter propofol was changed according to the BIS value. The remifentanil infusion started at LOC. The mean duration of surgery was 482.2±195.4 minutes (245.0 - 972.2).

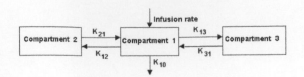

Fig. 1. 3-compartment pharmacokinetic model. The plasma concentration is defined as the concentration in compartment 1.

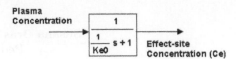

Fig. 2. Effect compartment model

2.1 Pharmacokinetic (PK) Models

The PK models of the two drugs use a 3-compartment model (figure 1). For propofol, the PK parameters from Schnider (Schnider *et al.*, 1998) were used, whereas for remifentanil, the parameters from Minto (Minto *et al.*, 1997a) were used. The PK models have its parameters adjusted to age, gender, weight and height of the patients.

2.2 Effect Compartment

The effect compartment is a hypothetical compartment describing the delay between the plasma concentration and the effect concentration. Figure 2 shows the diagram of the effect compartment relationship. The pharmacodynamic parameters $ke0$ used were described by Schnider (Schnider *et al.*, 1999) for propofol, and for remifentanil by Minto (Minto *et al.*, 1997b).

2.3 Average Patient

The data of an average patient was constructed using the average values of all 16 patients (i.e. their signals, figure 3). This average patient was used to determine the fixed structure of the model for HR.

3. GARCH MODEL

Figure 4 shows the block diagram of the HR model. The objective is to describe the relationship between the drugs effect concentrations and its effect.

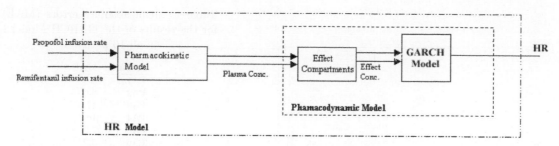

Fig. 4. Block diagram of the HR model.

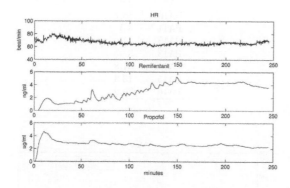

Fig. 3. Average patient mean arterial pressure (MAP), heart rate (HR), and effect concentrations of propofol and remifentanil.

3.1 Model Structure

The Generalized Autoregressive Conditional Heteroscedasticity (GARCH) is a model that predicts the data (time series) and its variance. The change in variability is very important when describing the HR signal. A variance that changes with time has implications in the validity and efficiency of the statistical inference of the parameters that describe HR (y_t) (Hamilton *et al.*, 1994).

A process u_t, that satisfies equation 1 is described by an ARCH(q) model.

$$u_t^2 = \xi + \alpha_1 u_{t-1}^2 + \alpha_2 u_{t-2}^2 + ... + \alpha_m u_{t-q}^2 + \omega_t \quad (1)$$

A generalized model GARCH(p,q) is:

$$u_t = \sigma_t v_t \quad (2)$$

where v_t is an independent random sequence with zero mean and unit variance. And σ_t^2 is the conditional variance of u_t (conditional on all the information up to time $t-1$):

$$\sigma_t^2 = k + \beta_1 \sigma_{t-1}^2 + \beta_2 \sigma_{t-2}^2 + ... \\ + \beta_p \sigma_{t-p} + \alpha_1 u_{t-1}^2 + \alpha_2 u_{t-2}^2 + ... \quad (3) \\ + \alpha_q u_{t-q}^2$$

where $k \equiv [1 - \beta_1 - \beta_2 - ... - \beta_p]\xi$, $\alpha_i \geq 0$ $i = 1,...q$, and $\beta_i \geq 0$ $i = 1,...,p$.

3.2 Implementation

To develop a model it is necessary to specify inputs and outputs, estimation parameters with any optimization technique, evaluate errors and validate the model.

Each patient reacts to pain in a different way. Two GARCH models were implemented: GARCH Model 1 using just the effect concentration of remifentanil; and GARCH Model 2 using the effect concentrations of remifentanil and propofol. A basic fixed structure (equation 4) given by the average patient data was used for the GARCH models.

$$y_t = 70.12 + u_t \\ \sigma_t^2 = 0.2059 + 0.66922\sigma_{t-1}^2 + 0.30416u_{t-1}^2 \quad (4)$$

The HR signal was initially filtered with a moving average filter (6 samples) to remove outliers and then filtered with a lowpass second order Butterworth filter, so as to remove the electrical interference.

The parameters of the GARCH models were individually adjusted to each patient data, so as to capture the interindividual variability. A log-likelihood objective function was used to optimize the parameters, using the software MATLAB 6.5.1

4. RESULTS

The two models (GARCH model 1 using just the effect concentration of remifentanil and GARCH model 2 using the effect concentrations of remifentanil and propofol) were fitted to the data of the 16 patients. The mean absolute errors were calculated for the results of the two models and for each of the 16 patients.

4.1 Results with the GARCH Model 1

The results of GARCH model 1 are good, however in some patients there seems to be constant error between the model result and the real HR (figures

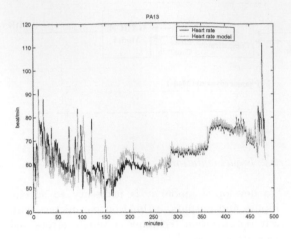

Fig. 5. Results of the GARCH Model 1 for the data of patient PA13.

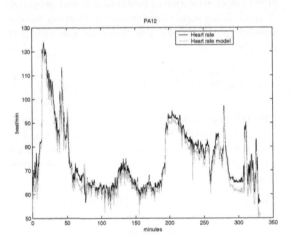

Fig. 6. Results of the GARCH Model 1 for the data of patient PA12.

5 and 6). This constant error, or shift in scale could be the influence of the other drug (i.e. propofol), for which this model does not account for.

The mean absolute error of GARCH Model 1 for the 16 patients was 10.9±9.3. The individual mean absolute errors of the model in all 16 patients are presented in table 1.

4.2 Results with the GARCH Model 2

The results of GARCH Model 2 are good, following the HR trend in all patients. Figures 7 and 8 show the model results for patient PA13 and PA12. The amplitude shift that was present in the

Table 1. Mean absolute errors (MAE) for the results of the GARCH Model 1 in all 16 patients.

Patient	MAE
PA1	5.9
PA2	8.6
PA3	17.0
PA4	16.3
PA5	7.9
PA6	5.2
PA7	5.7
PA8	3.5
PA9	2.9
PA10	16.7
PA11	4.3
PA12	3.0
PA13	3.0
PA14	31.8
PA15	13.3
PA16	30.2

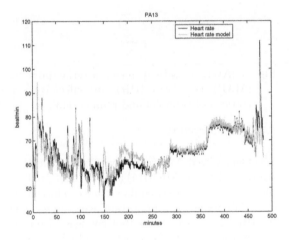

Fig. 7. Results of the GARCH Model 2 for the data of patient PA13.

results of GARCH Model 1 are not present when using GARCH Model 2.

The mean absolute error of GARCH Model 2 for the 16 patients was 11.2±9. The individual absolute errors of the model in all 16 patients are presented in table 2.

5. DISCUSSION

Analyzing the figures, the results of GARCH Model 2 do not have any scale shift from the real data. However, the mean absolute error shows that on average a smaller error is associated with GARCH Model 1, which only takes into consideration the effect concentration of remifentanil. Remifentanil is a drug that directly affects the haemodynamic signals (Vuyk, 1999).

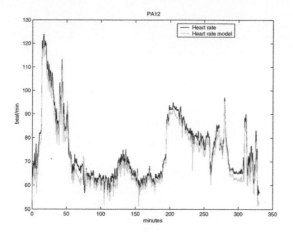

Fig. 8. Results of the GARCH Model 2 for the data of patient PA12.

Table 2. Mean absolute errors (MAE) for the results of the GARCH Model 2 in all 16 patients.

Patient	MAE
PA1	4.6
PA2	8.1
PA3	17.1
PA4	15.2
PA5	10.7
PA6	5.1
PA7	5.2
PA8	10.0
PA9	3.7
PA10	14.7
PA11	4.3
PA12	3.0
PA13	2.4
PA14	31.6
PA15	15.1
PA16	30.2

A correlation analysis was performed between the GARCH Model 1 parameters and the patients' individual characteristics (i.e. age, weight, baseline HR value) (table 3). A high correlation was found between patient's weight and K, GARCH and ARCH parameters. In addition, baseline HR is strongly correlated with the GARCH and ARCH parameters. This high correlation between patients' characteristics and the model parameters can be further used to adapt the model online based on the initial fixed structure.

Table 3. Correlation coefficients between GARCH parameters and patients' individual characteristics.

	K	GARCH	ARCH
Age	-0.1904	0.3982	-0.3982
Weight	-0.5255	0.5385	-0.5385
Baseline HR	0.2937	-0.5581	0.5581

6. CONCLUSIONS

The heamodynamic stability under surgery depends on the patient's individual response to the drugs. The degree of sensitivity/resistance of the patient to the drugs has a great influence on the amount of drugs necessary during surgery, to maintain an adequate level of unconsciousness and analgesia. Information extracted from models can be used to adapt the infusion rates of both drugs, avoiding cases of overdosage or pain. The control system parameters could be adjusted or adapted to individual patient requirements.

The two GARCH models tested in this study proved to be efficient in modeling the HR variation according to the concentrations of the anaesthetic drugs. These models can be used in the operating theatre to predict the HR trend according to the drug concentrations used by the anaesthesiologist, i.e. as an advisor system.

Haemodynamic stability as measured by the HR its clinically important, specially under surgery. HR variations are associated with the level of pain, and depend on the individual patient.

In the future, this model can be automatically adjusted to the patient, identify the degree of pain and subsequently help to adjust the dose of the analgesic, improving the patients' comfort and safety

REFERENCES

Vuyk, J. (1999). Drug interactions in anaesthesia. *Minerva Anestesiologica* **65**, 215–8.

McGregor, R.R., L.G. Allan, R.M. Sharpe, C. Thornton and D.E. Newton (1998). Effect of remifentanil on the auditory evoked response and haemodynamic changes after intubation and surgical incision. *British Journal of Anaesthesia* **81**, 785–6.

O'Hare, R., D. McAtamney, R.K. Mirakhur, D. Hughes and U. Carabine (1999). Bolus dose remifentanil for control of haemodynamic response to tracheal intubation during rapid sequence induction of anaesthesia. *British Journal of Anaesthesia* **82**, 283–5.

Vuyk, J., M.Mertens, E. Olofsen, A. Burn and J. Bovill (1997). Propofol anesthesia and rational opioid selection: determination of optimal EC50-EC95 propofol-opioid concentrations that assure adequate anesthesia and a rapid return of consciousness. *Anesthesiology* **87**, 1549–62.

McAtamney, D., R. O'Hare, D. Hughes, U. Carabine and R. Mirakhur (1998). Evaluation of remifentanil for control of haemodynamic response to tracheal intubation. *Anaesthesia* **53**, 1223–7.

Prakash, N., T. McLeod and F. Gao Smith (2001). The effects of remifentanil on haemodynamic stability during rigid bronchoscopy. *Anaesthesia* **56**, 576–80.

Toweill, D.L., W. D. Kovarik, R. Carr, D. Kaplan, S. Lai, S. Bratton and B. Goldstein (2003). Linear and nonlinear analysis of heart rate variability during propofol anesthesia for short-duration procedures in children. *Pediatric Critical Care Medicine* **4**, 308–14.

Schnider, T., C. Minto, P. Gambus, C. Andersen, D. Goodale, S. Shafer and E. Youngs (1998). The influence of method of administration and covariances on the pharmacokinetics of propofol in adult volunteers. *Anesthesiology* **88**, 1170–82.

Minto, C., T. Schnider, T. Egan, E. Youngs, H. Lemmens, P. Gambus, V. Billard, J. Hoke, K. Moore, D. Hermann, K. Muir and S. Shafer (1997a). Influence of age and gender on the pharmacokinetics and pharmacodynamics of remifentanil. I. Model development. *Anesthesiology* **86**, 10–23.

Schnider, T., C. Minto, S. Shafer, P. Gambus, C. Andersen, D. Goodale and E. Youngs (1999). The influence of age on propofol pharmacodynamics. *Anesthesiology* **90**, 1502–16.

Minto, C., T. Schnider and S. Shafer (1997b). Pharmacokinetics and pharmacodynamics of remifentanil. II. Model application. *Anesthesiology* **86**, 24–33.

Hamilton, J.D.(1994). *Time series analysis*. Princeton University Press, New Jersey USA.

MODELLING DRUGS' PHARMACODYNAMIC INTERACTION DURING GENERAL ANAESTHESIA: THE CHOICE OF PHARMACOKINETIC MODEL

Catarina S. Nunes [*,1] Teresa F. Mendonça [*]
Luís Antunes [**] David A. Ferreira [**]
Francisco Lobo [***] Pedro Amorim [***]

[*] *Departamento de Matemática Aplicada, Faculdade de
Ciências da Universidade do Porto, Portugal*
[**] *CECAV, Universidade de Trás-os-Montes e Alto Douro,
Vila Real, Portugal*
[***] *Serviço de Anestesiologia do Hospital Geral de Santo
António, Porto, Portugal*

Abstract: The effect of drugs' interaction on the brain signal Bispectral Index (BIS) is of great importance for an anaesthesia control drug infusion system. In this study, two renowned pharmacokinetic (PK) models for propofol are compared, in order to evaluate its influence on the performance/predictably of a drug interaction model for BIS, considering data of 45 patients. The model was fitted per patient during anaesthesia induction, and tested for prediction under surgery. The results showed that the choice of PK model had influence on the overall performance. In the prediction phase, only one PK model presented good results with small errors. *Copyright © 2006 IFAC*

Keywords: Pharmacokinetic data, modelling, biomedical systems, prediction

1. INTRODUCTION

Anaesthesia can be defined as the lack of response and recall to noxious stimuli, involving the use of three drugs, a muscle relaxant, an anaesthetic (hypnotic) and an analgesic. The analgesic drug is of great importance since it affects the pharmaco-dynamics of the anaesthetic drug and there is no clear indicator of the degree of pain. The analgesic and anaesthetic drugs are interconnected, since they interact with each other so as to achieve

an adequate level of depth of anaesthesia (DOA) and analgesia (Vuyk, 1999). The bispectral index of the EEG (BIS) is a numerical processed, clinically-validated EEG parameter, used as an indicator of the level of DOA, measuring the degree of depression in the central nervous system. The BIS is a number between 0 and 100, where values near 100 represent an "awake" clinical state while 0 denotes the maximal EEG effect possible (i.e., an isoelectric EEG) (Schaarg *et al.*, 1999). Overall, general anaesthesia consists of both loss of consciousness through the action of anaesthetic drugs, and the inhibition of noxious stimuli reaching the brain through the acting of the analgesics. The intravenous anaesthetic drug propofol is used in combination with the analgesic remifentanil.

[1] Corresponding author: Dr. Catarina S. Nunes, Departamento de Matemática Aplicada, FCUP, Rua do Campo Alegre 687, 4169-007 Porto, Portugal (ccnunes@fc.up.pt) Financial support: Portuguese Foundation for Science and Technology POSC/EEA-SRI/57607/2004.

Propofol and remifentanil have a synergistic relationship. The effect of the combination of these two drugs is greater than that expected as based on the concentration-effect relationships of the individual agents (Vuyk et al., 1997). A model for anaesthetic drug interactions can prove to be very useful in understanding the full relationship between the concentrations of the two drugs and drug effects. This model should take into consideration the interactions between drugs and variability between patients.

In this study, two well known and commercialised pharmacokinetic (PK) models were used for the plasma and effect concentrations of propofol, Marsh (Marsh et al., 1991) (PK Model 1) and Schnider (Schnider et al., 1998) (PK Model 2). The interaction model (Bruhn et al., 2003)(Minto et al., 2000) was fitted to the data of each patient in the induction phase (first 15 min). The individual patient models were then used to predict BIS during maintenance of anaesthesia (surgery), considering the drugs' concentrations. Since the interaction model is based on the modelled effect concentrations its results could be greatly influenced by the choice of PK model. Therefore, a comparative study will be performed on a wide group of patients to evaluate the influence of PK model on the overall performance of the interaction model and its prediction ability.

The clinical data, the two PK models for propofol (PK Model 1 (Marsh et al., 1991) and PK Model 2 (Schnider et al., 1998)), and the remifentanil PK model are presented in section 2. Section 3 describes the interaction model (Bruhn et al., 2003) for the concentration-effect relationship on BIS, while section 4 presents the results on the data. Sections 5 and 6 present the discussion and the conclusion, respectively.

2. CLINICAL DATA

Data collected during 45 neurosurgical interventions were used in this study. All 45 patients were subject to general anaesthesia using propofol and remifentanil. The level of unconsciousness (DOA) was manually controlled by the anaesthetist using as reference the patient's vital signs and BIS. The following data were recorded during the surgery every 5 seconds: BIS, infusion rate of propofol and remifentanil. The infusion rates were used to calculate the plasma and effect concentration of both drugs, as described in the following subsections. The patients studied were 51 ± 16 years, 70 ± 13 kg, 163 ± 9 cm, 28 female. Anaesthesia started with a constant infusion 200 ml/hr of propofol until loss of consciousness (LOC), thereafter propofol was changed according to the BIS value. The remifentanil infusion started at LOC.

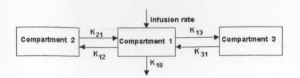

Fig. 1. 3-compartment pharmacokinetic model. The plasma concentration is defined as the concentration in compartment 1.

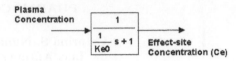

Fig. 2. Effect compartment model

2.1 Pharmacokinetic (PK) Models

The PK models of the two drugs use a 3-compartment model (Figure 1). For propofol, the PK parameters from Marsh (Marsh et al., 1991) (PK Model 1) and from Schnider (Schnider et al., 1998) (PK Model 2) were used, whereas for remifentanil, the parameters from Minto (Minto et al., 1997a) were used. PK Model 2 has its parameters adjusted to age, gender, weight and height of the patients, whereas PK Model 1 only takes into consideration the patient's weight.

2.2 Effect Compartment

The effect compartment is a hypothetical compartment describing the delay between the plasma concentration and the effect concentration. Figure 2 shows the diagram of the effect compartment relationship. The pharmacodynamic parameters $ke0$ used were described by Marsh (Marsh et al., 1991) (PK Model 1) and from Schnider (Schnider et al., 1999) (PK Model 2) for propofol, and for remifentanil by Minto (Minto et al., 1997b).

3. INTERACTION MODEL

Figure 3 shows the block diagram of the BIS model. The objective is to describe the relationship between the drugs effect concentrations and its effect.

Bruhn et al. (Bruhn et al., 2003) used an interaction model to relate the electroencephalographic parameter values (including BIS) to the effect concentrations of propofol and remifentanil. This model was developed by Minto et al. in a previous study (Minto et al., 2000).

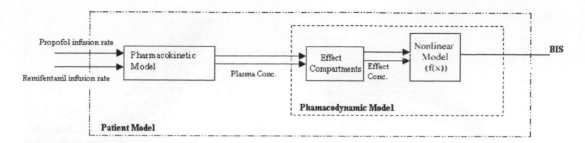

Fig. 3. Block diagram of BIS model.

First, the concentrations were normalised to their respective potencies (EC_{50p} and EC_{50r} for propofol and remifentanil, respectively), i.e. the effect concentration at half the maximal effect:

$$U_{remi} = \frac{Ce_r(t)}{EC_{50r}} \quad U_{prop} = \frac{Ce_p(t)}{EC_{50p}} \quad (1)$$

where Ce_r and Ce_p are the respective effect concentrations of remifentanil and propofol. For an additive interaction, the "effective" concentration is the sum of the individual concentrations normalised, so the effect (E, in this case the effect is BIS) can be described as equation 2.

$$E = E_0 \left(1 - \frac{U_{prop} + U_{remi}}{1 + U_{prop} + U_{remi}} \right) \quad (2)$$

where E_0 is the effect at zero concentrations (e.g. $BIS_0 = 97.7$ for the case of BIS - monitor restriction). Deviation from a purely additive interaction is modelled by changing the potency of the drug mixture depending on the ratio of the interacting drugs (equation 3).

$$\theta = \frac{U_{prop}}{U_{prop} + U_{remi}} \quad (3)$$

By definition, θ ranges from 0 (remifentanil only) to 1 (propofol only). Thus, the concentration-response relationship for any ratio of the two drugs regardless of the type of interaction can be described as equation 4.

$$E = E_0 \left(1 - \frac{\left((U_{prop} + U_{remi}) / U_{50(\theta)} \right)^\gamma}{1 + \left((U_{prop} + U_{remi}) / U_{50(\theta)} \right)^\gamma} \right) (4)$$

where γ is the steepness of the concentration-response relation, and $U_{50(\theta)}$ is the number of units (U) associated with 50% of maximum effect at ratio θ. According to (Minto et $al.$, 2000) equation 3 can be simplified to a quadratic polynomial (equation 5).

$$U_{50(\theta)} = 1 - \beta_{2,U50}\theta + \beta_{2,U50}\theta^2 \quad (5)$$

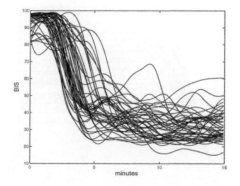

Fig. 4. Recorded BIS values of the 45 patients during the induction phase, i.e. the first 15 min.

4. RESULTS

Both models were fitted to the data of the 45 patients in the induction phase of anaesthesia (first 15 min). The interaction model parameters were fitted using nonlinear least squares with the software MATLAB 6.5.1. The BIS signal was pre-filtered with a lowpass second order Butterworth filter. For the interaction model, the parameters EC_{50p}, EC_{50r}, γ and $\beta_{2,U50}$ were obtained for each patient. The mean absolute error was calculated for the results of the two models (interaction model using the PK Model 1 and the interaction model using the PK Model 2) and for each patient. Figure 4 shows the BIS trends for the 45 patients during the induction phase. Figure 5 shows the effect concentrations of propofol using PK Model 1 and PK Model 2. Figure 6 shows the remifentanil effect concentrations.

4.1 Results with PK Model 1

Figure 7 shows the results of the interaction model when the PK Model 1 is used for the propofol effect concentrations. The mean absolute errors for the induction of anaesthesia (fitting phase) and for the maintenance phase (from 15 min until the end of surgery - prediction results) are presented in Figure 8. Only in 6 patients, the fitting model errors were statistically different from zero (t-$test$, P<0.05). However, for 2 patients the prediction

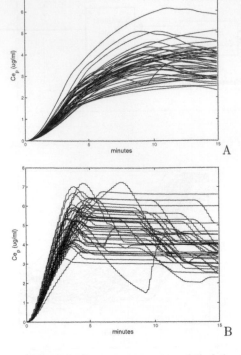

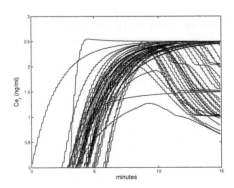

Fig. 5. Propofol effect concentration (Ce_p) for the 45 patients during the induction phase (i.e. the first 15 min) using: **A**- PK Model 1; **B**- PK Model 2

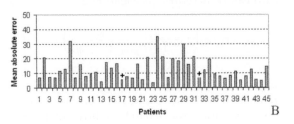

Fig. 6. Remifentanil effect concentration (Ce_r) for the 45 patients during the induction phase, i.e. the first 15 min.

errors were not statistically different from zero (*t-test*, P<0.05).

4.2 Results with PK Model 2

Figure 9 shows the results of the interaction model using the PK Model 2 for the propofol effect concentration, for the 45 patients. The model had a good performance in the induction phase (fitting phase) with statistical zero error (*t-test*, P<0.05) in some patients. The mean absolute errors for the fitting and prediction phases are presented in Figure 10. In 13 patients, the fitting model

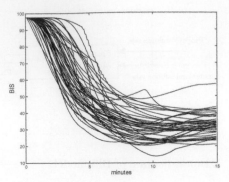

Fig. 7. Modelled BIS values for the interaction model using PK Model 1 for the propofol effect concentration, for the 45 patients during the induction phase, i.e. the first 15 min.

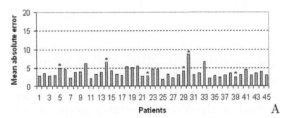

Fig. 8. Mean of absolute errors for the interaction model using PK Model 1 in: **A**- induction phase (fitting phase). * errors are statistically different from zero (*t-test*, P<0.05); **B**- maintenance phase (prediction phase). + errors that are not statistically different from zero (*t-test*, P<0.05).

errors were statistically different from zero (*t-test*, P<0.05). The prediction results were not good.

5. DISCUSSION

Comparing the results of the two models at its best and worst case, it is possible to analyse the performance of the two techniques. In the fitting phase, the result of the interaction model using PK Model 1 had smaller errors than when using PK Model 2, but both models follow the BIS trend. However, it is in the maintenance phase (prediction phase - from 15 min until the end of surgery) that the difference is clearer.

The interaction model using PK Model 2 did not capture the BIS trend. Figure 11 shows the pre-

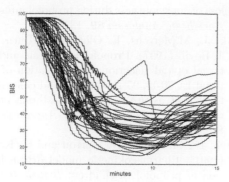

Fig. 9. Modelled BIS values for the interaction model using PK Model 2 for the propofol effect concentration, for the 45 patients during the induction phase, i.e. the first 15 min.

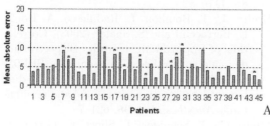

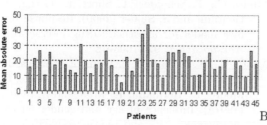

Fig. 10. Mean of absolute errors for the interaction model using PK Model 2 in: **A**- induction phase (fitting phase). * errors are statistically different from zero (*t-test*, P<0.05); **B**- maintenance phase (prediction phase).

diction results with both models for Patient 23, which had the smallest prediction error with PK Model 1. Figure 12 shows the prediction results for the patient with the smallest prediction error with PK Model 2 (Patient 19). The mean absolute error with PK Model 2 is smaller than with PK Model 1 for Patient 19 (5.85 and 6.86, respectively), however the results present a greater oscillation around the BIS value. Figure 13 shows the results of both models for Patient 17, which had prediction errors statistically not different from zero, and a small mean absolute prediction error when using PK Model 1.

The patient with the worst model performance in the prediction phase was Patient 24, which had the biggest mean absolute prediction error using both PK models. Maybe one could be in the presence of an extreme case.

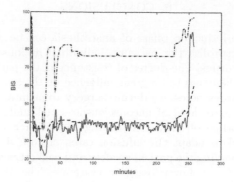

Fig. 11. Recorded BIS (solid line) versus modelled BIS using PK Model 1(dashed line) and PK Model 2 (dashed dot line) in the prediction phase (from 15 min until end of surgery), for Patient 23 which had the smallest mean absolute prediction error with PK Model 1

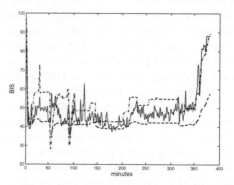

Fig. 12. Recorded BIS (solid line) versus modelled BIS using PK Model 1(dashed line) and PK Model 2 (dashed dot line) in the prediction phase (from 15 min until end of surgery), for Patient 19 which had the smallest mean absolute prediction error with PK Model 2.

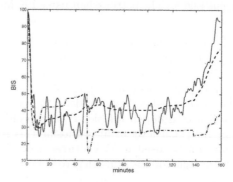

Fig. 13. Recorded BIS (solid line) versus modelled BIS using PK Model 1(dashed line) and PK Model 2 (dashed dot line) in the prediction phase (from 15 min until end of surgery), for Patient 17 which had prediction errors statistically not different from zero, and a small mean absolute prediction error when using PK Model 1.

6. CONCLUSIONS

The induction phase of anaesthesia can be used to establish the patient's individual response to the drugs. The degree of resistance of the patient to the drugs has a great influence on the amount of drugs necessary during surgery to maintain an adequate level of unconsciousness and analgesia. Information extracted during induction can be used to adapt the infusion rates of both drugs, improving the patient's safety and comfort, avoiding cases of overdosage or awareness. The control system parameters can be adjusted or adapted to individual patient requirements.

The two models tested in this study are already credited and published models. In addition, both models are currently commercialised in Target Controlled Infusion (TCI) devices for propofol.

The interaction model described by Bruhn et al. (Bruhn et al., 2003) and previously developed by Minto et al. (Minto et al., 2000), uses a drug interaction model based on a Hill equation structure. This model proved to be effective by adequately modelling the induction BIS trend in all 45 patients with both PK models. However, the use of PK Model 1 improves the results of the interaction model for BIS. In addition, when using PK Model 1, the interaction model can capture the BIS trend during the prediction phase in many patients. Therefore, the performance of the interaction model is greatly influenced by the choice of PK models. Bruhn et al. tested the interaction model considering steady state conditions in volunteers, and when Minto et al. first presented it, they used the PK Model 2 for propofol. This study has proved that the model could be used in non-steady state conditions (i.e. induction) and also used to predict. In addition, the results were very different and for the better when using PK Model 1.

In conclusion, the model can capture the individual patient response during induction identifying unique characteristics (EC_{50p}, EC_{50p}, γ and $\beta_{2,U50}$), e.g. patients that respond slower or faster to the same infusion dose (sensitive or resistant), and will need different infusion control profiles to obtain the same level of anaesthesia. This information can be used in the future to develop a control system for the infusion rate of both drugs.

REFERENCES

Vuyk, J. (1999). Drug interactions in anaesthesia. *Minerva Anestesiologica* **65**, 215–8.

Schraag, S., U. Bothner, R. Gajraj, G. Kenny and M. Georgieff (1999). The performance of electroencephalogram bispectral index and auditory evoked potential index to predict loss of consciousness during propofol infusion. *Anesthesia Analgesia* **89**, 1311–5.

Vuyk, J., M.Mertens, E. Olofsen, A. Burn and J. Bovill (1997). Propofol anesthesia and rational opioid selection: determination of optimal EC50-EC95 propofol-opioid concentrations that assure adequate anesthesia and a rapid return of consciousness. *Anesthesiology* **87**, 1549–62.

Marsh, B., M. White, N. Morton and G. Kenny (1991). Pharmacokinetic model driven infusion of propofol in children. *British Journal of Anaesthesia* **67**, 41–8.

Schnider, T., C. Minto, P. Gambus, C. Andersen, D. Goodale, S. Shafer and E. Youngs (1998). The influence of method of administration and covariances on the pharmacokinetics of propofol in adult volunteers. *Anesthesiology* **88**, 1170–82.

Bruhn, J., T. Bouillon, L. Radulesco, A. Hoeft, E. Bertaccini and S. Shafer (2003). Correlation of approximate entropy, Bispectral index, and spectral edge frequency 95 (SEF95) with clinical signs of "anesthetic depth" during coadministration of propofol and remifentanil. *Anesthesiology* **98**, 621–7.

Minto, C., T. Schnider, T. Short, K. Gregg, A. Gentilini and S. Shafer (2000). Response surface model for anesthetic drug interactions. *Anesthesiology* **92**, 1603–16.

Minto, C., T. Schnider, T. Egan, E. Youngs, H. Lemmens, P. Gambus, V. Billard, J. Hoke, K. Moore, D. Hermann, K. Muir and S. Shafer (1997a). Influence of age and gender on the pharmacokinetics and pharmacodynamics of remifentanil. I. Model development. *Anesthesiology* **86**, 10–23.

Schnider, T., C. Minto, S. Shafer, P. Gambus, C. Andersen, D. Goodale and E. Youngs (1999). The influence of age on propofol pharmacodynamics. *Anesthesiology* **90**, 1502–16.

Minto, C., T. Schnider and S. Shafer (1997b). Pharmacokinetics and pharmacodynamics of remifentanil. II. Model application. *Anesthesiology* **86**, 24–33.

Copyright © IFAC Modelling and Control in Biomedical Systems
Reims, France, 2006

CARDIOVASCULAR SYSTEM MODELLING OF HEART-LUNG INTERACTION DURING MECHANICAL VENTILATION

**Bram W. Smith[1], Steen Andreassen[1], Geoffrey M. Shaw[2],
Stephen E. Rees[1] and J. Geoffrey Chase[3]**

[1] *Centre for Model-based Medical Decision Support, Aalborg University,
Aalborg, Denmark*
[2] *Centre for Bio-Engineering, Christchurch Hospital Dept of Intensive Care,
Christchurch, New Zealand*
[3] *Centre for Bio-Engineering, Department of Mechanical Engineering, University of
Canterbury, Christchurch, New Zealand*

Abstract: Choosing suitable ventilation strategies for critically ill patients with lung disorders involves considering the difficult and poorly understood trade-off between achieving adequate ventilation, while maintaining suitable perfusion. This study presents a minimal cardiovascular system model that includes variations in pulmonary vascular resistance during mechanical ventilation. The model is shown to capture transient haemodynamics from experimentally measured data. It also enables investigation into the effects of time varying resistance on pulmonary haemodynamics. The study shows the potential usefulness of this model in a tool to assist clinical staff in optimising ventilation pressures while maintaining adequate pulmonary perfusion. *Copyright © 2006 IFAC*

Keywords: Biomedical systems, Physiological models, Dynamic modelling, Dynamic models, Lumped constant models.

1 INTRODUCTION

Although the lungs and the circulation system are usually simulated independently, the interaction between them has significant consequences for both systems. One important example of this is the interaction between lung pressures and pulmonary haemodynamics in critically ill patients with lung disorders. For example, patients suffering from acute respiratory distress syndrome (ARDS), or post cardiac surgery patients, require ventilation at high pressures to increase lung ventilation and improve gas exchange (Claxton *et al.*, 2003; Dyhr *et al.* 2002). However, these high pressures can also cause a reduction in pulmonary perfusion, which can have a negative impact on gas exchange, as well as reducing cardiac output (Parrillo and Dellinger, 2002). The trade-off between achieving adequate ventilation, while maintaining adequate pulmonary perfusion, is an important consideration when treating intensive care patients.

High ventilator pressures affect circulation in a number of ways (West, 2005; Parrillo and Dellinger, 2002). Increased pressure acting on the outside of the heart limits ventricle filling. Increased pressure on the large pulmonary arteries and veins causes a reduction in the pulmonary circulation blood volume. Increased pleural pressure and lung volume impedes blood flow through the capillaries, increasing the pulmonary vascular resistance.

Pulmonary vascular resistance (R_{pul}) is generally defined as:

$$R_{pul} = \frac{P_{pa} - P_{pu}}{CO} \qquad (1)$$

where the pressure drop across the pulmonary circulation is defined as the pulmonary artery pressure (P_{pa}) minus the pulmonary venous pressure (P_{pu}), and cardiac output (CO) represents the average blood flow through the pulmonary circulation. This resistance can vary during both the cardiac cycle and the respiratory cycle by two main mechanisms (West, 2005). Firstly, the cross-sectional area of a capillary, and thus the resistance, is dependent on the pressure drop across the capillary wall. A decreased blood pressure in the capillary, or a reduced pleural pressure acting on the outside of the capillary, will cause the capillary to expand and its resistance to be reduced. Secondly, due to hydrostatic effects, the blood pressure in the capillaries is lower at the highest point in the lungs than at the lowest point. A pressure increase in the pulmonary artery can cause capillaries to become recruited, thus reducing the total pulmonary resistance. Both of these effects are largely dependent on the pressure difference between the pulmonary artery and the pleural pressure.

There are many models of the circulation system and the respiratory system in the literature (Beyar *et al.* 1987; Ursino, 1999; Barbini *et al.*, 2003). However, there are very few models that simulate the impact of changes in lung pressure and volume on haemodynamics, especially relating to pulmonary vascular resistance. Probably the most comprehensive compartmental cardiopulmonary interaction models are described by Liu *et al.* (1998) and Lu *et al.* (2001). Both these models combine detailed circulation system and respiratory system models. Liu *et al.* (1998) divides the pulmonary vascular resistance into three different resistances that are dependent on pleural pressure, alveolar volume and capillary volumes. Lu *et al.* (2001) uses a much simpler definition where pulmonary resistance is dependent on lung volume. However, in both cases, these models are not verified against experimentally measured pulmonary artery pressure, which is an important factor in pulmonary perfusion.

Scharf *et al.* (1980) have carried out experimental studies where they measured pulmonary and systemic artery pressures and flow rates simultaneously with pleural pressure variations during mechanical ventilation. If the respiratory drive has been suppressed, it can be assumed that thoracic cavity compliance remains constant during mechanical ventilation. Under these conditions, according to West (2005), pleural pressure, lung volume and pulmonary vascular resistance should all vary proportionally to one another. So during the mechanical inspiration, pulmonary vascular resistance will increase as pleural pressure increases and visa versa.

This research presents a model based investigation into the affect of mechanical ventilation on pulmonary haemodynamics. All of the interaction mechanisms discussed above are considered, with specific focus on the effects of variations in pulmonary vascular resistance during respiration. A minimal cardiovascular system model, described by Smith *et al.* (2004a), is used to simulate experimentally measured haemodynamic changes during mechanical ventilation (Scharf *et al.* 1980). A simple proportional relationship is defined between the pleural pressure and the pulmonary vascular resistance. The investigation focuses on the importance of including a time varying pulmonary vascular resistance and the ability of this simple model to capture the measured haemodynamic trends in the experimental data.

2 METHOD

2.1 The cardiovascular system model

The minimal cardiovascular system model used in this study, shown schematically in Figure 1, is defined in detail in Smith et al (2004a). The systemic circulation is made up of two chambers representing the vena-cava (vc) and the aorta (ao), connected by a resistor to simulate the net systemic resistance (R_{sys}). Similarly, the pulmonary circulation is simulated as the pulmonary artery (pa) chamber connected to the pulmonary vein (pu) chamber by the pulmonary vascular resistance (R_{pul}).

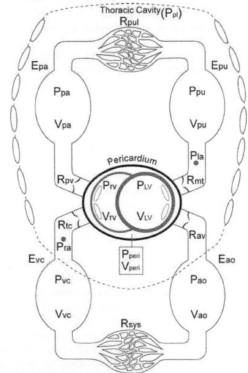

Fig. 1. Diagram of the cardiovascular system model used in this study.

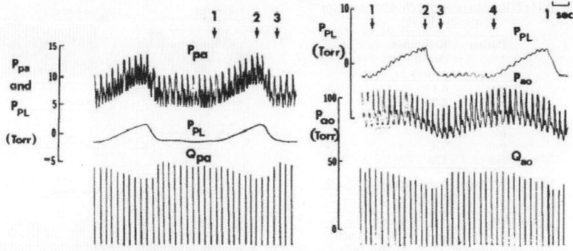

Fig. 2. Experimentally measured pulmonary and systemic artery pressures (P_{pa} and P_{ao}) and flow rates (Q_{pa} and Q_{ao}) during mechanical ventilation, as shown by the variations in pleural pressure (P_{pl}) (Scharf *et al.*, 1980).

The two central chambers represent the left and right ventricles (lv and rv). The atria are not included in the model for simplicity. Resistances at the inlet and exit of the right ventricle account for pressure drops of blood flow entering from the systemic circulation through the tricuspid valve (tc) and exiting through the pulmonary valve (pv) into the pulmonary circulation. For the left ventricle, resistances are simulated acting on blood flow entering from the pulmonary circulation through the mitral valve (mt) and exiting through the aortic valve (av) into the systemic circulation. The pleural (pl) pressure defines the pressure inside the thoracic cavity and acts on the outside of the heart and pulmonary circulation. Respiration is simulated by cyclically varying the pleural pressure (P_{pl}).

Tables 1, 2 and 3 list the generic model parameters used by Smith (2004b). The 2 ventricles are divided into 3 walls, the left ventricle wall (lvf), the right ventricle wall (rvf) and the septum wall (spt). During ventricle relaxation, the pressure volume relationships of these walls are defined by elastance (P_0), the non-linearity (λ) and the volume at zero pressure (V_0). During ventricular contraction, the pressure volume relationships of these walls are defined by the contractility (E_{es}) and the volume at zero pressure (V_d). The same non-linear pressure volume relationship used for the relaxed ventricles is used for the pericardium (pcd).

2.2 The experimental data

The experiments by Scharf *et al.* (1980) were carried out on anaesthetized dogs on positive pressure ventilation. Systemic arterial pressure (P_{ao}) was measured in the thoracic aorta using a femoral artery catheter. A pulmonary artery catheter was used to get the pulmonary artery pressure (P_{pa}). Square wave electromagnetic flow

probes were placed around the ascending aorta and the main pulmonary artery to measure the systemic arterial and pulmonary arterial flow rates (Q_{ao} and Q_{pa}) respectively. Pleural pressure was measured using a 0.25 inch diameter cannula placed into the right hemothorax at the midaxillary line. Figure 2 shows the experimentally measured variations in these values during 2 mechanical ventilation breaths.

Very little information about the cardiovascular system mechanical properties of the studied dogs can be gained from the publication (Scharf *et al.*, 1980). It is known that the heart rate remained relatively constant during the procedure at approximately 160 beats per minute. The respiration rate was held at 10 breaths per minute and tidal volume was constant at 300ml. To verify that the minimal model captures the experimental dynamics, despite the lack of specific information, the generic model parameter values listed in Tables 1, 2 and 3, from Smith (2004b), are used. The simulated heart rate is set to 160 beats per minute and pleural pressure is varied cyclically at 10 breaths per minute.

Table 1. Mechanical properties of the heart and circulation system (Smith, 2004b).

Param	E_{es} Pa/m^3 ($\times 10^6$)	V_d m^3 ($\times 10^{-6}$)	V_0 m^3 ($\times 10^{-6}$)	λ m^{-3} ($\times 10^3$)	P_0 Pa
lvf	100	0	0	33	10
rvf	54	0	0	23	10
spt	6500	2	2	435	148
pcd	-	-	-	30	66.7
vc	1.3	2830	-	-	-
pa	72	160	-	-	-
pu	1.9	200	-	-	-
ao	98	800	-	-	-

Table 2. Resistances in the circulation system (Smith, 2004b).

Param	Resistance Pa.s/m^3 ($\times 10^{-6}$)
mt	6.1
av	2.75
tc	1
pv	1
pul	9.4
sys	170

Table 3. Additional model parameters (Smith, 2004b).

Parameter	Value
Heart rate (HR)	160 beats/min
Blood volume (V_{tot})	5.5×10^{-3} m^3
Pleural pressure (P_{pl})	-1mmHg

The magnitude and contour of the variation in pleural pressure used in the model simulation was estimated by eye from Figure 2. The pleural pressure is set to vary between -1mmHg and 1mmHg. The variation in pulmonary vascular resistance used in the model is defined by the following simple linear relationship:

$$R_{pul}(t) = C_R \times P_{pl}(t) + R_{pul,0} \qquad (2)$$

where $R_{pul,0}$ defines the resistance at zero pleural pressure and C_R defines the gain of the relationship between pleural pressure and pulmonary resistance. For these simulations C_R is set to 7×10^6Pa.s/m^3 and $R_{pul,0}$ is set to 16.5×10^6Pa.s/m^3. This definition means that at end expiration, when the pleural pressure is -1mmHg, $R_{pul}(t)$ is equal to the base value in Table 2. When the pleural pressure increases to a maximum value of 1mmHg, $R_{pul}(t)$ increases to 2.5 times the base value. These values were chosen by manually increasing the variation in $R_{pul}(t)$ until the simulated profile of P_{pa} was similar to the experimental results in Figure 2.

3   RESULTS

Figure 3 shows the results using the cardiovascular system model to simulate the experiment carried out by Scharf *et al.*, (1980). Figure 4 shows the same simulation results, but with the pulmonary vascular resistance (R_{pul}) held constant. Values of pleural pressure (P_{pl}), systemic artery pressure (P_{ao}) and pulmonary artery pressure (P_{pa}) are labeled in the same way in Figures 2, 3 and 4. The measured flow in the pulmonary artery (Q_{pa}) in Figure 2 correlates to the simulated flow through the pulmonary valve (Q_{pv}) in Figures 3 and 4. Likewise, the measured flow in the aorta (Q_{ao}) in Figure 2. correlates to the simulated flow through the aortic valve (Q_{ao}) in Figures 3 and 4.

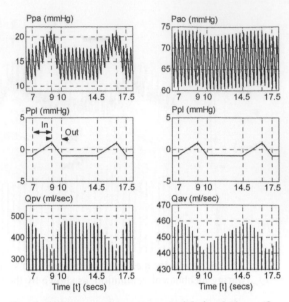

Fig. 3. Cardiovascular system model simulations of mechanical ventilation with time varying pulmonary vascular resistance.

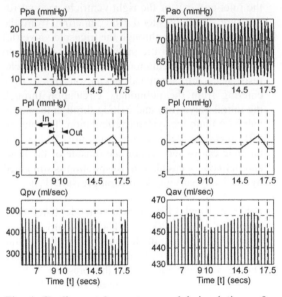

Fig. 4. Cardiovascular system model simulations of mechanical ventilation with constant pulmonary vascular resistance.

The simulation results with time varying pulmonary vascular resistance, shown in Figure 3, capture all of the main trends in the experimental results, shown in Figure 2. However, it was not possible to produce quantitative comparisons between the simulations and the experimental data, since there was not enough data available about the experiments. For example, the magnitudes of the flow rates in Figure 2 are not shown. Figure 4 shows that with resistance held constant, the cardiovascular system is not longer capable of capturing the variations in pulmonary artery pressure (P_{pa}). However, if the pulmonary artery pressure variations are ignored, the trends in the remaining variables for both simulations roughly match the experimental data.

Figure 5 shows an enlarged view of the second breath in Figure 3 to more clearly show how the flow rate through the pulmonary artery (Q_{pv}) and the aorta (Q_{av}) vary during a positive pressure inspiration. The pulmonary artery flow is seen to respond immediately at the start of inspiration (t=14.5secs) and reach a minimum at the end of inspiration (t=16.5secs). However, the effect of the inspiration on the flow through the aorta is not seen immediately, with an approximately 0.5 seconds lag behind the pulmonary artery response. This immediate response in pulmonary artery flow, and delayed response of aortic flow, can also be seen in the experimental measurements in Figure 2.

4   DISCUSSION

The results show the ability of the model to simulate the variety of different mechanisms by which lung pressures affect haemodynamics. Although the experimental results used to validate the simulations are poor in quality, they clearly show the model captures the main trends. Increased pleural pressure during mechanical ventilation is shown to cause a reduction in the flows through both the pulmonary and systemic arteries as well as a drop in blood pressure (P_{ao}).

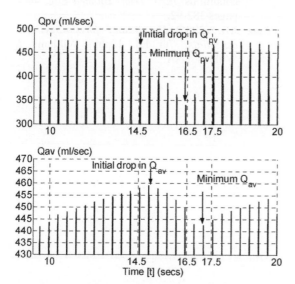

Fig. 5. Enlarged view of the second breath in Figure 3 showing that the variations in Q_{av} due to inspiration lag behind those of Q_{pv} by about 0.5 seconds.

The reduction in pulmonary artery flow (Q_{pv}) is due to the increased pleural pressure during inspiration. This compresses the heart, causing a reduction in right ventricle filling and therefore an immediate reduction in flow into the pulmonary artery. This effect is reversed during expiration, where the pulmonary artery flow rapidly recovers to its initial value.

The reduction in systemic artery flow (Q_{av}) is slightly delayed relative to the reduction in Q_{pv}, as shown in Figure 5. This delay occurs because the increase in pleural pressure actually causes a small rise in flow through the systemic artery as blood is pushed out of the pulmonary circulation. However, this rise is quickly overcome by the reduction in blood flow due to restrictions on pulmonary perfusion and the drop in pulmonary filling (Q_{pv}). The flow rate in the aorta begins to increase again during expiration, but once again Figure 5 shows there is a delay between the onset of expiration and the beginning of an increase in flow rate.

In particular the results show the importance of including time varying pulmonary vascular resistance when simulating cardiopulmonary interaction. With time varying pulmonary vascular resistance included in the simulations, the increased pleural pressure during inspiration causes the pulmonary artery pressure to increase, as shown in Figure 3. This result could be misinterpreted as the pleural pressure simply compressing the pulmonary artery. However, if the pulmonary vascular resistance is held constant, Figure 4 shows that the pulmonary artery pressure actually decreases. This means that the rise in pulmonary artery pressure, seen in the experimental data during inspiration, is actually due to a rise in pulmonary vascular resistance during inspiration. The reduction in pulmonary artery pressure with constant resistance, as shown in Figure 4, is most likely due to the reduced flow rate into the pulmonary artery (Q_{pv}).

This is the first illustration known to the authors of a cardiovascular system model simulating transient changes in pulmonary artery pressure during mechanical ventilation. Although measuring pulmonary artery pressure is a relatively invasive procedure, requiring insertion of a pulmonary artery catheter (PAC), this procedure is currently carried out in many clinical institutions on critically ill patients. Other models were found to focus on simulating the dynamics of pressures and flow in the systemic artery. However, the simulations in Figures 3 and 4 show little difference in systemic artery dynamics between constant and time varying pulmonary resistance. These results show the importance of considering the pulmonary artery pressure changes when verifying a cardiopulmonary interaction model.

These results are achieved using a relatively small scale model compared to others in the literature. The presented model uses only two elastic chambers and one time varying resistance to define the pulmonary circulation. This is important when considering application of these models to the clinical setting where parameter identification techniques may be needed to create patient specific models (Hann et al., 2004). The number of parameters must be minimised to reduce the complexity of fitting to specific patient data.

5 CONCLUSIONS

The minimal cardiovascular system model presented is shown to accurately simulate experimentally measured transient haemodynamics due to cardiopulmonary interaction during mechanical ventilation. Previous models are more complex and have not been shown to simulate pulmonary artery pressure fluctuations. This study highlights an important link between variations in pulmonary vascular resistance and fluctuations in pulmonary artery pressure during respiration. The model shows potential for implementation in a diagnostics tool where it is necessary to simulate the effects of changes in respiratory pressures on a patient's circulation system.

REFERENCES

Barbini P., G. Cevenini and G. Avanzolini (2003) Nonlinear Mechanisms Determining Expiratory Flow Limitation in Mechanical Ventilation: A Model-Based Interpretation, *Annals of Biomedical Engineering*, **31**(8), pages 908-916

Beyar, R., M.J. Hausknecht, H.R. Halperin, F.C.P. Yin and M.L. Weisfeldt, (1987). Interaction between cardiac chambers and thoracic pressure in intact circulation. *Am. J. Physiol.* **22**(253), H1240-H1252.

Claxton B.A., P. Morgan, H. Mckeague, A. Mulpur and J. Berridge (2003) Alveolar recruitment strategy improves arterial oxygenation after cardiopulmonary bypass. *Anaesthesia.* **58**(2), page 111.

Dyhr T., N. Laursen and A. Larsson (2002) Effects of lung recruitment maneuver and positive end-expiratory pressure on lung volume, respiratory mechanics and alveolar gas mixing in patients ventilated after cardiac surgery. *Acta Anaesthesiologica Scandinavica.* **46**(6) page 717.

Hann, C.E., J.G. Chase, G.M. Shaw, and B.W. Smith (2004) Identification Of Patient Specific Parameters For A Minimal Cardiac Model. *Proc 26th International Conf of IEEE Engineering in Med and Biology Society.* San Francisco, CA, pages 813-816.

Lu K, J.W. Clark, F.H. Ghorbel, D.L. Ware and A. Bidani (2001) A human cardiopulmonary system model applied to the analysis of the Valsalva maneuver. *Am J Physiol Heart Circ Physiol.* **281**(6) pages H2661-79.

Liu C.H., S.C. Niranjan, J.W. Clark, K.Y. San, J.B. Zwischenberger and A. Bidani (1998) Airway mechanics, gas exchange, and blood flow in a nonlinear model of the normal human lung. *J Appl Physiol.* **84** pages 1447-1469.

Parrillo, J.E. and R.P. Dellinger (2002) *Critical Care Medicine, Principles Of Diagnosis And Management In The Adult*, 2nd Ed. St. Louis, Missouri, Mosby.

Scharf, S.M., R. Brown, N. Saunders and L.H. Gren (1980) Hemodynamic effects of positive-pressure inflation. *J. Appl. Physiol.* **49**(1) pages 124-31.

Smith B.W., J.G. Chase, R.I. Nokes, G.M. Shaw and G. Wake (2004a) Minimal haemodynamic system model including ventricular interaction and valve dynamics. *Medical Engineering and Physics* **26** pages 131-139

Smith B W (2004b) Minimal Haemodynamic Modelling of the Heart and Circulation for Clinical Application. PhD Thesis, Canterbury University, Christchurch, New Zealand.

Ursino, M. (1999). A mathematical model of the carotid baroregulation in pulsating conditions. *IEEE Trans Biomed Eng,* **46**(4) pages 382-92.

West J.B. (2005) *Respiratory physiology, The essentials*. 7th Ed. Lippin Williams & Wilkins, USA.

A DIFFERENTIAL MODEL OF CONTROLLED CARDIAC PACEMAKER CELL

Karima Djabella* Michel Sorine*

*INRIA Rocquencourt / B.P.105.78153 Le Chesnay Cedex,
France

Abstract: A differential model of a cardiac pacemaker cell with only ten state variables is proposed. It is intended for 0D or 3D simulation of the heart under the vagal control of the autonomous nervous system. Three variables are used to describe the membrane (membrane potential and two gate variables of ionic channels), taking into account the dynamics of the main ionic currents (inward sodium, L-type calcium and outward potassium), Na^+/Ca^{2+} exchangers and Na^+/K^+ pumps. The remaining seven variables are associated with the fluid compartment model that includes Ca^{2+} binding by myoplasmic proteins, and the intracellular concentrations of free Calcium, Sodium and Potassium. Despite its moderate number of state variables, this model includes the main processes thought to be important in pacemaking on the cell scale and predicts the experimentally observed ionic concentration of calcium, sodium and potassium, action potential and membrane currents. The control by the calcium of the pacemaking activity is also considered. Copyright © 2006 IFAC

Keywords: Electrical activity, Nonlinear systems, Dynamic modelling, Frequency control.

1. INTRODUCTION

There are many mathematical models of the electrophysiology of the different types of cardiac cells. For models of human ventricular or atrial cells, see e.g. (ten Tusscher et al., 2004; Nygren et al., 1998) and the references herein. The sinoatrial node cells and their pacemaker activity, considered here, have been studied in (Demir et al., 1994; Dokos et al., 1996; Dokos et al., 1998; Zhang et al., 2000; Kurata et al., 2002). These models result from iterations between mathematics and experimentation on the cell scale where detailed characteristics of isolated ion channels can now be measured. They are based on the ionic current model of (Hodgkin and Huxley, 1952), but the cardiac myocytes being far more complex than the squid giant axon considered by this first model,

their complexity is high with e.g. 28 state variables for the model in (Kurata et al., 2002).

Recently, model-based image and signal processing on the heart scale has become an important goal as in (CardioSense3D, 2006). In such project, models are not only needed in direct computations to gain insights and for their predictive capabilities, but also in inverse problems to estimate state and parameters from measurements. In that case it is necessary to predict the shape of action potential (AP) for electrocardiogram interpretation, as well as the concentration of calcium bound on Troponin C, responsible for electromechanical coupling at the origin of heart deformations seen in the images. It is then necessary to represent also some intracellular calcium buffering, as will be done here, a special attention being paid to model complexity in order to have a good tradeoff between the descriptive power of the model and the well-posedness of associated inverse problems.

In this paper, a model for a cardiac pacemaker cell is proposed. It is realistic enough to exhibit many of the characteristics of larger pacemaker cell models, and yet, is simple enough with only ten state variables. It has furthermore a sound asymptotic behaviour without drifts of the state, a useful property for multi-beat simulations. The same model structure has been used in (Djabella and Sorine, 2005) to represent excitation–contraction coupling in a ventricular cell. It consists of two parts: 1) a cell membrane with capacitance, voltage-dependent ion channels, electrogenic pump and exchanger, the ionic currents model being derived using conservation laws as in (Endresen et al., 2000), and 2) a lumped compartmental model that accounts for intracellular changes in concentrations of Na^+, K^+ (Hund et al., 2001) and the main processes that regulate intracellular calcium concentration: release and uptake by the sarcoplasmic reticulum (SR), buffering in the SR (ten Tusscher et al., 2004) and in the bulk cytosol (Shannon et al., 2004).

The ionic currents that control membrane depolarization during diastole and then the heart rate, are still a matter of debate. (DiFrancesco, 1993) argues that the hyperpolarization activated current (i_f) is the only current that can generate and control the slow depolarization of pacemaker cells. This current is normally carried by Na^+ and K^+. (Guo et al., 1995) reported another current, called the sustained inward current i_{st}, where the major charge carrier is believed to be Na^+. Also a Ca^{2+} "window" current has been observed in rabbit sinoatrial node cells (Denyer and Brown, 1995). It is possible that any of these currents, or a combination of them, is responsible for membrane depolarization during diastole.

During diastole the electrochemical driving forces produce outward K^+ currents and inward Na^+ and Ca^{2+} currents, and the driving force for Ca^{2+} is much larger than that for Na^+ (Endresen et al., 2000). This implies that a significant background influx of Ca^{2+} is possible during diastole, and that this current might be responsible for pacemaking activity in sinoatrial node cells (Boyett et al., 2001). The conductance for this current is denoted $\bar{I}_{b,Ca}$ and used in the proposed model to control the voltage-dependent calcium current $I_{Ca,t}$. $\bar{I}_{b,Ca}$ is responsible for the slow diastolic depolarization, and appears to have control capability of the pacemaker activity. In fact, changes in the AP pacemaker frequency will be observed in an almost linear relationship with $\bar{I}_{b,Ca}$. Then, we conclude that the autonomous nervous system interacts

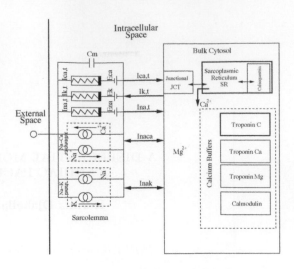

Fig. 1. A representation of the model of a cardiac pacemaker cell: electrical equivalent circuit for the sarcolemma and fluid compartment

almost linearly in the regulation of heart rate as assumed in (Warner and Russell, 1969).

The paper is organized as follows: the model is described in Section 2. Section 3 shows some simulation results. A discussion and conclusions are presented in Sections 4 and 5 respectively.

2. MODEL DESCRIPTION

The mathematical model is a nonlinear system of ten first order ordinary differential equations. The detailed equations, parameters values and abbreviations used are presented in the APPENDIX.

Figure 1 shows the lumped electrical equivalent circuit for the sarcolemma and the fluid compartment system of a single pacemaker cardiac cell. The membrane model includes both the potential–mediated ion channels responsible for the dynamic aspects of the membrane AP (inward sodium, L-type calcium and outward potassium) and Na^+/Ca^{2+} exchangers, Na^+/K^+ pumps. The fluid compartment is modelled by seven differential equations, three of them describing the intracellular concentrations of free Calcium, Sodium and Potassium. The remaining four equations describe the binding of Ca^{2+} to specific sites on the myoplasmic troponin and calmodulin proteins, taking into account the competition between Ca^{2+} and Mg^{2+}. The Ca^{2+} buffering system is very important for the regulation and limitation of free intracellular Ca^{2+} concentration transients.

3. RESULTS

The dynamic behavior of the cell model was computed by solving the system of nonlinear ordinary

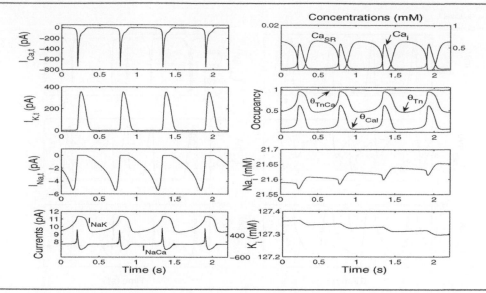

Fig. 2. Computed spontaneous AP and ionic currents (left) and intracellular Ca^{2+} dynamics (right)

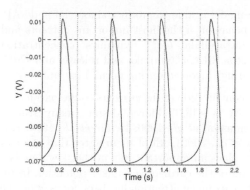

Fig. 3. Spontaneous action potential

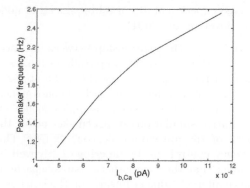

Fig. 5. The relationship between the pacemaker frequency and the amplitude of the pacemaker current: the control effect

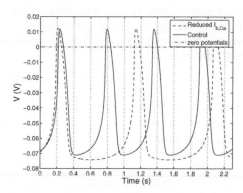

Fig. 4. Effect of a reduced $\bar{I}_{b,Ca}$ on action potential

differential equations with a second order modified Rosenbrock method with variable steplength. The initial conditions are listed in the table 1.

Figure 3 shows the computed AP that had a cycle length, amplitude, duration (measured at -30 mV) and maximal diastolic potential of $550ms$, $85mV$, $120ms$ and $-71mV$, respectively. This simulated pacemaker AP has a reasonable shape

compared with those recorded experimentally. Figure 2 shows, on the left, the computed temporal behaviour of sarcolemmal ionic currents. On the right, it shows the intracellular Ca^{2+} dynamics including the changes in Ca^{2+} concentration in the SR, the associated changes in the occupancy ratio of Ca^{2+} buffers and the changes in Na_i and K_i during pacemaker activity. These computed waveform changes during spontaneous AP are very similar to those recorded experimentally (Demir *et al.*, 1994).

In Fig. 4, the AP computed under control conditions is compared with that computed when the pacemaker current $\bar{I}_{b,Ca}$ was affected. It shows:
- a cycle length increase from 550 to $900ms$,
- an AP amplitude slight change from 85 to $88mV$,
- an AP duration increase, at $-30mV$, from 120 to $130ms$, and
- a maximal diastolic potential decrease of $5mV$.
These changes are qualitatively similar to those

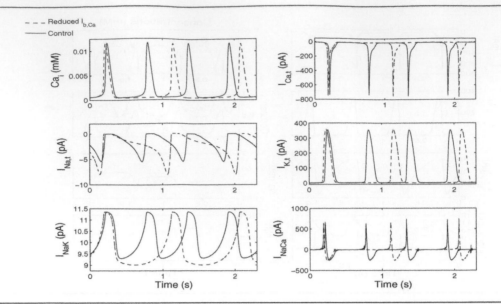

Fig. 6. Ca^{2+} transients and ionic currents computed under control conditions and for a reduced $\bar{I}_{b,Ca}$

observed experimentally in rabbit sinoatrial node cells (Boyett *et al.*, 2001).

Figure 5 shows the relationship between the pacemaker frequency and the amplitude of the pacemaker current $\bar{I}_{b,Ca}$: it appears to be approximately linear. This has an important consequence: there is no need for a more complex model for quantitative simulations of pacemaker under the control of the autonomic nervous system. This frequency control can be described fairly well by assuming that the sympathetic–parasympathetic balance interacts almost linearly on the heart rate as assumed in (Warner and Russell, 1969).

Figure 6 shows the effect of a reduced pacemaker current $\bar{I}_{b,Ca}$ on the simulated intracellular calcium concentration and ionic currents. In this case, there is no slight change in the Ca^{2+} transients shapes or in transmembrane ionic currents waveforms (there is a small decrease in the $I_{Na,t}$ current amplitude): they were only shifted. In conclusion, only pacemaking rate was affected. In the present paper $I_{Ca,t}$ means $I_{Ca,L}$ (Djabella and Sorine, 2005) and the $\bar{I}_{b,Ca}$ affects this current (eq. 6), therefore, the simulations are consistent with the experimental data (Boyett *et al.*, 2001).

4. DISCUSSION

A simple model for a cardiac pacemaker cell has been presented. It involves only Na^+, K^+ and Ca^{2+} ions, their respective channels, the Na^+/Ca^{2+} exchanger, and the Na^+/K^+ pump. It also includes a description of the dynamics of the main calcium buffers in the bulk cytosol and in the SR, and it takes into account the calcium uptake and release from SR.

The model is able to produce sinoatrial node AP, the behavior of the most important currents and the intracellular Ca^{2+} dynamics (concentration changes, SR Ca^{2+} uptake and release, and Ca^{2+} buffering) involved during normal pacemaking.

The contribution of the currents to the pacemaker activity is still ill known despite many studies (Rasmusson *et al.*, 1990; Demir *et al.*, 1994; Kurata *et al.*, 2002). All of them agree that the calcium plays an important role in the slow depolarization of the cardiac pacemaker potential. In recent years much attention has been focused on the possibility that Ca^{2+} can control the pacemaker activity of the sinoatrial node. In this article, using computer simulations, it has been shown that a significant background influx of Ca^{2+} may be important in the changes in the AP and pacemaker activity (Boyett *et al.*, 2001).

The proposed model and simulations can provide guidance for future developments of more realistic controlled cardiac pacemaker cell for use in models of the intact sinoatrial node or in whole heart models in three dimensions.

5. CONCLUSION

A differential model of cardiac pacemaker cell has been presented. Simulations of the electrical pacemaker activity and associated cytosolic ion concentration changes appear realistic. They demonstrate the control of the pacemaker activity by the calcium, so that the modulation of this activity by the autonomous nervous system can be explained fairly well by assuming that the sympathetic–parasympathetic system interacts linearly on the heart rate via a calcium input.

Due to its sound asymptotic behavior without drifts of the state and to its medium complexity, this model can provide guidance for future modelling work on the controlled cardiac pacemaker cells in multi-beat simulations from the cell to the heart scales.

6. APPENDIX

The proposed model of cardiac pacemaker cell is the following system of differential equations (where the function $|x|_+ = max(x,0)$):

$$\frac{dV}{dt} = -\frac{I_{K,t}+I_{Na,t}+I_{Ca,t}+I_{NaK}+I_{NaCa}}{C_m}$$

$$\frac{dK_i}{dt} = \frac{2I_{NaK}-I_{K,t}}{FV_C}$$

$$\frac{dNa_i}{dt} = -\frac{I_{Na,t}+3I_{NaK}+3I_{NaCa}}{FV_C}$$

$$\frac{dCa_i}{dt} = \frac{2I_{NaCa}-I_{Ca,t}}{2FV_C}+J_{leak}+J_{rel}-J_{up}$$

$$-\sum_{b\in I_B} B_b\frac{d\theta_b}{dt}, \quad I_B=\{Tn, Cal, TnCa\}$$

$$\frac{dg_X}{dt} = \frac{g_{X\infty}-g_X}{\tau_{gx}}, \quad X\in\{Na, K\} \tag{1}$$

$$\frac{d\theta_{Tn}}{dt} = k_{Tn}^{on}|Ca_i|_+(1-\theta_{Tn})-k_{Tn}^{off}\theta_{Tn}$$

$$\frac{d\theta_{Cal}}{dt} = k_{Cal}^{on}|Ca_i|_+(1-\theta_{Cal})-k_{Cal}^{off}\theta_{Cal}$$

$$\frac{d\theta_{TnCa}}{dt} = k_{TnCa}^{on}|Ca_i|_+(1-\theta_{TnCa}-\theta_{TnMg})$$
$$-k_{TnCa}^{off}\theta_{TnCa}$$

$$\frac{d\theta_{TnMg}}{dt} = k_{TnMg}^{on}|Mg_i|_+(1-\theta_{TnCa}-\theta_{TnMg})$$
$$-k_{TnMg}^{off}\theta_{TnMg}$$

The gate dynamics are defined by

$$g_{X\infty} = \frac{1}{2}\left[1+\tanh\left(\frac{V-V_{gX}}{RT/2F}\right)\right],$$
$$\tau_{gx} = \frac{\tau_X}{\cosh\left(\frac{V-V_{gX}}{RT/2F}\right)}, \quad X\in\{Na, K, d, m\} \tag{2}$$

where $X=d, m$ represent fast Ca, Na activation gating, denoted as usual $d_\infty = g_{d\infty}$, $m_\infty = g_{m\infty}$. Setting

$$V_X = \frac{RT}{z_XF}\log\left|\frac{X_e}{X_i}\right|, \quad X\in\{Ca, Na, K\}, \tag{3}$$

the currents through the membrane are then:

$$I_{K,t} = \bar{I}_K g_K \sinh\left(\frac{V-V_K}{2RT/F}\right) \tag{4}$$

$$I_{Na,t} = \bar{I}_{Na}g_{Na}m_\infty \sinh\left(\frac{V-V_{Na}}{2RT/F}\right) \tag{5}$$

$$I_{Ca,t} = [\bar{I}_{Ca}(1-g_K)d_\infty + \bar{I}_{b,Ca}]\sinh\left(\frac{V-V_{Ca}}{RT/F}\right) \tag{6}$$

$$I_{NaK} = \bar{I}_{NaK}\tanh\left(\frac{V+2V_K-3V_{Na}-V_{ATP}}{2RT/F}\right) \tag{7}$$

$$I_{NaCa} = \bar{I}_{NaCa}\sinh\left(\frac{V+2V_{Ca}-3V_{Na}}{2RT/F}\right) \tag{8}$$

Finally, the CICR mechanism is described using

$$J_{up} = Q_{up}J_{max}\frac{\left|\frac{Ca_i}{K_{mf}}\right|^H - \left|\frac{Ca_{SR}}{K_{mr}}\right|^H}{1+\left|\frac{Ca_i}{K_{mf}}\right|^H+\left|\frac{Ca_{SR}}{K_{mr}}\right|^H} \tag{9}$$

$$J_{rel} = K_{rel}d_\infty(Ca_{SR}-Ca_{iJCT}) \tag{10}$$

$$J_{leak} = K_{leak}(Ca_{SR}-Ca_{iJCT}) \tag{11}$$

$$Ca_{iJCT} = \frac{B_{JCT}|Ca_i|_+}{|Ca_i|_+ + K_{JCT}} \tag{12}$$

$$Ca_{SR} + \frac{B_{SR}|Ca_{SR}|_+}{|Ca_{SR}|_+ + K_{SR}} =$$
$$\frac{V_C}{V_{SR}}\left(Ca_T-Ca_i-\sum_{b\in I_B}B_b\theta_b-Ca_{iJCT}\right) \tag{13}$$

$$Ca_T = \frac{1}{2}\left(\frac{C_m}{FV_C}(V-V_{ext})-Na_i-K_i\right) \tag{14}$$

$$V_{ext} = -\frac{FV_C}{C_m}(Na_e+K_e+2Ca_e) \tag{15}$$

REFERENCES

Boyett, M. R., H. Zhang, A. Garny and A. V. Holden (2001). Control of the pacemaker activity of the sinoatrial node by intracellular ca^{2+}. experiments and modelling. *Phil. Trans. The Royal Society* **359**, 1091–1110.

Table 1 Initial conditions

Variables	Initial values	Units
V_0	$-51.4\,10^{-3}$	V
K_{i0}	127.8	mM
Na_{i0}	20.7	mM
Ca_{i0}	0.001	mM
θ_{Tn0}	0.0451	
θ_{TnCa0}	0.139	
θ_{TnMg0}	0.0003	
θ_{Cal0}	0.0031	
g_{K0}	0.074	
g_{Na0}	0.029	

Table 2 Abbreviations used in the text

Abbrev.	Definitions
V	Action potential
V_{ext}	External stimulus voltage
$I_{X,t}$	Total X current through all channels
I_{NaCa}	$Na^+ - Ca^{2+}$ exchanger current
I_{NaK}	$Na^+ - K^+$ pump current
g_K	Potassium activation gating
g_{Na}	Sodium activation gating
d_∞	Fast Calcium activation gating
m_∞	Fast Sodium activation gating
J_{rel}	Calcium-Induced Calcium Release current
J_{up}	Pump current taking up calcium in the SR
J_{leak}	Leakage current from SR to the cytoplasm
X_i	Intracellular concentration of the free ion X
X_e	External concentration of the ion free X
Ca_T	Total calcium concentration in the cell
Ca_{SR}	Free calcium concentration in the SR
θ_{Tn}	Fraction of Troponin–C sites bound with Ca
θ_{TnCa}	Fraction of Troponin (Ca) sites bound with Ca
θ_{TnMg}	Fraction of Troponin (Mg) sites bound with Mg
θ_{Cal}	Fraction of Calmodulin sites bound with Ca
Ca_{iJCT}	SR Calcium buffered in the junction

Table 3 Model parameters

Parameter	Value	Unit
V_C	16.404	pL
V_{SR}	1.094	pL
F	96.486	$Cmmol^{-1}$
V_m	$-56.86\,10^{-3}$	V
V_d	$-5\,10^{-3}$	V
V_{g_K}	$-26\,10^{-3}$	V
$V_{g_{Na}}$	$-71.55\,10^{-3}$	V
$\tau_{Na} = \tau_K$	0.2	s
V_{ATP}	$-450\,10^{-3}$	V
C_m	22	pF
R	$8.314\,10^{-3}$	$Jmmol^{-1}K^{-1}$
T	310	K
$z_{Na} = z_K$	1	
z_{Ca}	2	
$\bar{I}_{Na}$	11.27	pA
$\bar{I}_K$	164.5	pA
$\bar{I}_{Ca}$	131	pA
$\bar{I}_{b,Ca}$	0.0074	pA
$\bar{I}_{NaK}$	11.46	pA
$\bar{I}_{NaCa}$	7000	pA
K_e	5.4	mM
Na_e	140	mM
Ca_e	2	mM
Mg_i	1	mM
K_{leak}	$5\,10^{-8}$	s^{-1}
H	1.787	
K_{mf}	$0.246\,10^{-3}$	mM
K_{mr}	1.7	mM
J_{max}	$286\,10^{-3}$	mMs^{-1}
Q_{up}	$2.6\,10^{-5}$	
K_{rel}	$25\,10^{-2}$	s^{-1}
k^{on}_{Tn}	$32.7\,10^{3}$	$mM^{-1}s^{-1}$
k^{off}_{Tn}	19.6	s^{-1}
B_{Tn}	$70\,10^{-8}$	mM
k^{on}_{TpCa}	$2.37\,10^{3}$	$mM^{-1}s^{-1}$
k^{off}_{TnCa}	0.032	s^{-1}
B_{TnCa}	$140\,10^{-8}$	mM
k^{on}_{TnMg}	$0.003\,10^{3}$	$mM^{-1}s^{-1}$
k^{off}_{TnMg}	3.33	s^{-1}
B_{TnMg}	$140\,10^{-3}$	mM
k^{on}_{Cal}	$34\,10^{3}$	$mM^{-1}s^{-1}$
k^{off}_{Cal}	238	s^{-1}
B_{Cal}	$24\,10^{-8}$	mM
K_{JCT}	$13\,10^{-3}$	mM
B_{JCT}	$4.6\,10^{-3}$	mM
K_{SR}	0.0065	mM
B_{SR}	0.14	mM

CardioSense3D (2006). An INRIA Large Initiative Action. //www-sop.inria.fr/CardioSense3D.

Demir, S. S., J. W. Clark, C. R. Murphey and W. R. Gilles (1994). A mathematical model of a rabbit sinoatrial node cell. *Am J Physiol Heart Cell Physiol* **266(35)**, C832–C852.

Denyer, J. C. and H. F. Brown (1995). Calcium 'window' current in rabbit sino-atrial node cells. *Journal of Physiol.* **429**, 405–424.

DiFrancesco, D. (1993). Pacemaker mechanisms in cardiac tissue. *Annual Review of Physiol.* **55**, 455–472.

Djabella, K. and M. Sorine (2005). Differential model of the excitation–contraction coupling in a cardiac cell for multicycle simulations. In: *EMBEC'05*. Prague.

Dokos, S., B. G. Celler and N. H. Lovell (1996). Ion currents underlying sinoatrial node pacemaker activity: a new single cell mathematical model. *Journal of Theoretical Biology* **181**, 245–272.

Dokos, S., N. H. Lovell and B. G. Celler (1998). Review of ionic models of vagal–cardiac pacemaker control. *Journal of Theoretical Biology* **192(3–7)**, 265–274.

Endresen, L. P., K. Hall, J. S. Hoye and J. Myrheim (2000). A theory for the membrane potential of living cells. *Eur Biophys J* **29**, 90–103.

Guo, J., K. Ono and A. Noma (1995). A sustained inward current activated at the diastolic potential range in rabbit sinoatrial node cells. *Journal of Physiol.* **483**, 1–13.

Hodgkin, A. L. and A. F. Huxley (1952). A quantitative description of membrane current and its application to conduction and excitation in nerve. *Journal of physiology* **117**, 500–544.

Hund, T. J., J. P. Kucera, N. F. Otani and Y. Rudy (2001). Ionic charge conservation and long–term steady state in the Luo-Rudy dynamic cell model. *Biophys. Journal* **81**, 3324–3331.

Kurata, Y., I. Hisatome, S. Imanishi and T. Shibamoto (2002). Dynamical description of sinoatrial node pacemaking: improved mathematical model for primacy pacemaker cell. *Am J Physiol Heart Circ Physiol* **283**, H2074–H2101.

Nygren, A., C. Fiset, L. Firek, J. W. Clark, D. S. Lindblad, R. B. Clark and W. R. Giles (1998). Mathematical Model of an Adult Human Atrial Cell : The Role of K+ Currents in Repolarization. *Circ Res* **82**(1), 63–81.

Rasmusson, R. L., J. W. Clark, W. R. Giles, E. F. Shibata and D. L. Campbell (1990). A mathematical model of a bullfrog cardiac pacemaker cell. *Am J Physiol Heart Circ Physiol* **259(28)**, H352–H369.

Shannon, T. R., F. Wang, J. Puglisi, C. Weber and D. M. Bers (2004). A mathematical treatment of integrated ca dynamics within the ventricular myocyte. *Biophys J* **87**, 3351–3371.

ten Tusscher, K. H. W. J., D. Noble, P. J. Noble and A. V. Panfilov (2004). A model for human ventricular tissue. *Am J Physiol Heart Circ Physiol* **286**, 1573–1589.

Warner, H. R. and R. O. Russell (1969). Effect of combined sympathetic and vagal stimulation on heart rate in the dog. *Circ. Res.* **24(4)**, 567–573.

Zhang, H., A. V. Holden, I. Kodama, H. Honjo, M. Lei, T. Varghese and M. R. Boyett (2000). Mathematical models of action potentials in the periphery and center of the rabbit sinoatrial node. *Am J Physiol Heart Circ Physiol* **279**, H397–H421.

MODELLING LIGHT AND MODERATE EXERCISE IN TYPE 1 DIABETIC PATIENTS WITH GLYCOGEN DEPLETION AND REPLENISHMENT

M. Hernández-Ordoñez [*,1] **D.U. Campos-Delgado** [**]

* CIEP, Fac. de Ing., UASLP, S.L.P., México,
mar@uaslp.mx
** Fac. de Ciencias, UASLP, S.L.P., México,
ducd@fciencias.uaslp.mx

Abstract: The purpose of this paper is to present the main interactions promoted by the exercise in a type 1 diabetic mellitus patient. These dynamics are synthesized into mathematical equations to describe them analytically. It is intended to extend the ability of the compartmental model introduced by Sorensen (1985) to reproduce the variations in the blood glucose induced by the exercise. Solely the short–term consequences of exercise are incorporated in this work. The hepatic glycogen reservoir limits the peripheral glucose uptake for prolonged exercise. Therefore, the depletion and replenishment of the hepatic glycogen are modelled, looking to reproduce the blood glucose levels for a diabetic patient in a normal day, with three-meals, insulin infusions and an exercise regime. *Copyright © 2006 IFAC.*

Keywords: Biomedical, Diabetes, Modelling Exercise

1. INTRODUCTION

The insulin is a hormone in charge of promoting the processing of glucose (energy) by the body cells. As a result, this hormone has a regulatory effect in the blood glucose concentration. The absence of this regulatory effect can produce severe variations in the glucose concentration beyond the euglycemic (normal) level $70 - 120\ mg/dL$, resulting in the tendency of low (hypoglycemia) or high (hyperglycemia) blood glucose scenarios. The type 1 diabetes mellitus is a desease characterized by the destruction of the β-cells in the pancreatic islets of Langerhans. The β-cells produce the insulin in the pancreas, and consequently external insulin infusions are needed by the patient in order to maintain regulated his/her blood glucose. These glucose variations can produce short and long term illnesses in a diabetic patient (nephropathy, retinopathy, and other tissue damage) (DCCT, 1993). On the other hand, the exercise can have a positive effect in reducing the evolution of the diabetes complications. A daily exercise routine improves the insulin sensitivity, and increase the glucose reception and utilization by the muscles (Ruderman et al., 2002). However, in some cases, it cannot be advised, due to vascular problems, hypertension, and tendency to present hypoglycemia.

Some research efforts in the treatment of diabetes have focused on modeling the insulin–glucose dynamics (Sorensen, 1985), these models can also be used as educational simulators for demonstration and self-learning (Lehmann and Deutsch, 1992).

[1] Acknowledges the support provided by CONACYT (No.158330) through a doctoral scholarship

Due to the positive effects of the exercise, it is important to describe it in a quantitative way. In (Derouich and Boutayeb, 2002), the minimal glucose-insulin model derived by Bergman *et al.* (Bergman et al., 1981) was modified to introduce parameters that can be related to the physiological consequences of exercise. Recently, in (Lenart and Parker, 2002) and (Parker et al., 2002), the implications of exercise were studied in the compartmental glucose–insulin model proposed by Sorensen. All of these efforts with the ultimate goal of providing a complete model that could reproduce a normal day in the patient's life: meal intakes, insulin infusions and exercise routines. Hence, control algorithms could be tested in a more realistic way. In this context, this research pretends to extend the work by (Lenart and Parker, 2002) and (Parker et al., 2002) analyzing the blood flow redistribution after the exercise, and presenting a depletion and replenishment scheme of the hepatic glycogen, which restricts the hepatic glucose production during prolonged exercise. In this work, the effects of the long–term exercise (e.g. the improvement of subcutaneous insulin absorption, carbohydrate metabolism, cardiorespiratory performance) are not analyzed, neither the metabolism of glycogen in the skeletal muscle nor lipids in adipose tissue are studied which are important part of the exercise physiology. Since these interactions are difficult to quantify analytically and the compartamental model derived by Sorensen does not incorporate this information.

The paper is organized as follows. Section 2 introduces the physiological changes induced by exercise and their mathematical interpretations. The glycogen depletion and replenishment dynamics are illustrated in Section 3. Finally, in Section 4, simulations with the compartmental glucose-insulin model are presented, and some concluding remarks are given in Section 5.

1.1 COMPARTMENTAL DIABETIC MODEL

The short–term implications of exercise are now incorporated into the insulin–glucose compartmental model for a type 1 diabetic patient. This model departs from experimental evidence to formulate and validate metabolic processes of the compartmental model on the whole organ and tissue level including counter-regulatory effects. Thus, the insulin–glucose model is governed by 19 nonlinear ordinary differential equations, and is divided into three subsystems: glucose, insulin, and glucagon. The first two subsystems were modelled for the brain, arterial system (heart/lungs), liver, gut, kidney, and periphery compartments. The glucagon was modelled as a single blood pool

compartment. The system output is the arterial glucose concentration, that permits to obtain accurate glucose levels. The system has three possible inputs: subcutaneous insulin infusion (Belazzi et al., 2001), intravenous insulin infusion (Parker et al., 2001) and glucose input via gastric emptying by a meal (Lehmann and Deutsch, 1992). As a result, the induced changes by exercise (see Figure 1) represent modifications into the dynamics of the heart/lungs, kidney, gut, liver and periphery compartments for the glucose subsystem; and only periphery for the insulin subsystem.

2. EXERCISE MODELLING

The first step in the exercise modelling is to determine a quantification measure that can be general, in the sense that it could represent different persons with an equivalent working load. First note that the exercise produce an increment in the oxygen consumption and cardiac rate (Chapman and Mitchell, 1965), (Patton et al., 1989). The oxygen is necessary to promote the utilization of the energy sources by the working tissue. Moreover, there is a direct relation between the exercise working load and the oxygen consumption. As a result, a percentage of the maximum oxygen consumption rate (PVO_2^{max}) is selected as an appropriate measure for the exercise intensity. In the basal state, the average PVO_2^{max} is 8 %. Hence the PVO_2^{max} will vary from the 8 % to a maximum of 100 %. On the other hand, besides the exercise intensity, the type of exercise will determine the amount of muscular mass involved. If it is considered that an average person (man of 70 kg) has 28 kg of muscular mass, a new measure, the percentage of active muscular mass ($PAMM$) (Lenart and Parker, 2002) is defined as:

$$PAMM = \frac{x \; kg \; active \; muscular \; mass}{28 \; kg \; total \; muscular \; mass} \qquad (1)$$

Note that in basal state $PAMM = 0$, and when the total muscular mass is active during the exercise period $PAMM = 1.0$. Consequently, in this study, the exercise will be quantified by PVO_2^{max} and $PAMM$ as shown in Figure 1. Now the onset of the exercise produces a re-distribution of the blood flows per organ (Chapman and Mitchell, 1965), (Patton et al., 1989):

- An increment in the blood flow of the heart/lungs and peripheral tissue.
- A decrement in the flow for the kidneys and splanchnic organs.

However, the flow at the brain remains constant. The re-distribution of the blood flows as a function of PVO_2^{max} is presented in Table 1 following the notation used by the compartmental model of Sorensen.

Remark 1. In the previous studies about exercise modelling (Lenart and Parker, 2002), (Parker et al., 2002), it is not considered a re-distribution

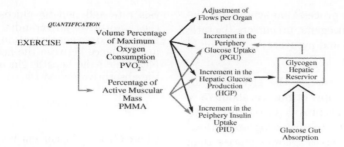

Fig. 1. Exercise Effects in the Body.

Table 1. Re-distributions of Blood Flows (dL/min) as a Function of PVO_2^{max}.

Tissue	PVO_2^{max}		
	8 %	30 %	60 %
Brain	5.9	5.9	5.9
Heart/Lungs	43.7	74.2	115.4
Liver	12.6	9.8	6.1
Gut	(12.6)	(9.8)	(6.1)
Kidneys	10.1	8.1	4.3
Periphery	15.1	50.6	99.1

in the heart/lungs compartment and gut blood flows. However, by using the original reference in (Chapman and Mitchell, 1965) and (Patton et al., 1989), it is found important to adjust also these parameters. Moreover, during the simulation testing of the modified compartmental model of Sorensen, the lack of adjustment could lead to numerical unstability of the solutions. Note that the flow in heart/lungs compartment is distributed in the others compartments, *i.e.*, there is a balance of flow in the model. In the same way that in (Sorensen, 1985), those entries in parentheses represent redundant flows, *i.e.*, it is the flow in the splanchnic bed (Liver, Stomach and guts), thus these terms are excluded in the flows balance.

In addition, the exercise produces two phenomena in the periphery compartment where the working load is performed. Since the involved tissue will require more energy to meet the required load, the peripheral glucose and insulin uptakes rates (*PGU* and *PIU* respectively) are raised (Lavoie et al., 1997). These dynamics are modelled following the ideas in (Lenart and Parker, 2002):

- The total *PGU* in basal state is 35 mg/min, but this rate can be modified by the actual insulin and glucose at the periphery (Sorensen, 1985). Now, the *PGU* at the active tissue (PGU_A) is considered as a new variable, which is a function of the PVO_2^{max} and *PAMM*. Its is proposed that the PGU_A has a characteristic time of 60 min to reach its steady state value. As a result, the *PGU* is modelled by dimensionless multipliers M^i:

$$PGU = M^I \times M^G \times M^E \times 35 \, mg/min \quad (2)$$

where the superscript i denotes insulin, glucose and exercise respectively. M^E is then a function of PVO_2^{max}, *PAMM* and PGU_A with $0 \leq M^E \leq 1$.

- The *PIU* is assumed to be also related to the actual insulin concentration at the periphery. In (Kalant et al., 1978), it was observed that the *PIU* at the active tissue could be increased by 3.4 times the basal rate. Moreover, the amount of active tissue involved should change this proportion. So, the *PIU* is modelled as a function only of the *PAMM*.

In order to satisfy the increment in the peripheral glucose uptake, the liver raises its glucose production (*HGP*) (Ahlborg et al., 1974), (Ahlborg and Felig, 1982). For short periods of exercise, the liver can compensate the increased periphery uptake by the glycogenolosis process (Radziuk and Pie, 2001). However, as the hepatic glycogen reservoir is depleted, the periphery demand cannot be compensated (this behavior will be described in more detail in the next section). Similarly, *HGP* is also modelled by dimensionless multipliers, where the actual insulin, glucose and glucagon concentrations determine the *HGP* (Sorensen, 1985). In the basal state, *HGP* is 155 mg/min. An exercise multiplier M^E is added that depends on the PVO_2^{max} and *PAMM*, by defining a extra variable, the hepatic glucose production due to the active tissue (HPG_A), which balances the PGU_A, *i.e.*

$$HGP = M^I \times M^G \times M^\Gamma \times M^E \times 155 \, mg/min \quad (3)$$

where the superscript Γ denotes the glucagon contribution.

3. GLYCOGEN DEPLETION AND REPLENISHMENT

The liver is the organ responsable of the glucose homeostasis for human beings and others species. The glucose stored as glycogen within the liver is the main source of energy. Commonly, there is $75 - 90 \, g$ of glycogen in the liver for a man of $70 \, kg$ (corporal mass) (Wahren et al., 1971). There are two major pathways which mobilizes the glucose throughout the body:

- *Glycogenolysis*: process which breaks down the glycogen into glucose.

- *Glyconeogenesis*: process that synthesizes glucose from gluconeogenic precursors (lactate, alanine, glycerol and pyruvate) circulating in the bloodstream.

At the beginning of exercise, the glycogenolysis process is the major supply of glucose, about 75 % of the glucose demand is provided from this mechanism and 25 % is due to glyconeogenesis. However, the glyconeogenesis is a slower process than the glycogenolysis. During moderate and short-term exercises, the liver provides enough glucose to maintain the blood concentration regulated, at the same time the glycogen in the muscles is metabolized with the purpose of becoming the main source of energy for the working tissue (Radziuk and Pie, 2001), but this reservoir is rapidly exhausted, and the liver provides then the main source of glucose. The finite liver's glycogen reservoir limits the hepatic glucose production, and the effect of depletion is presented during long-term exercise. Moreover, the relative contributions of glycogenolysis and glyconeogenesis in the total glucose production change according with the duration of the exercise. Once the exercise is ended, the liver's glycogen reservoir waits to be replenished during the next absorptive postprandial period. This repletion is accomplished by three factors (Radziuk and Pie, 2001):

(1) An increment in the hepatic glucose uptake from the liver,
(2) The information of the metabolic and hormonal signals in the portal vein,
(3) An increment in the gluconeogenic flux (glyconeogenesis).

The physiologic requirement of exercise results in adaptations that gradually are normalized in the recovery period from exercise. As a result, the hepatic glucose uptake is increased, approximately 25 % of the total glucose absorbed postprandially is taken by the liver. On the other hand, the dynamics of the glycogen depletion effect can be represented as a function of current glycogen concentration. The net glycogenolysis rate can then be expressed as a function of the exercise intensity (Parker et al., 2002), this dependence is shown in the Table 2. The value for 30 PVO_2^{max} was obtained considering the time to achieve a 75 % glycogen depletion.

Table 2. Net Glycogenolysis Rate in the Liver as a Function of PVO_2^{max}.

PVO_2^{max} (%)	Net glycogenolysis rate (mg/min)
8	0
30	250
60	333

The repletion glycogen concentration rate is formulated considering two effects: the net glycogenolysis rate and hepatic glucose uptake rate from the absorptive postprandial period. Thus, the liver's glycogen concentration rate is proposed as a mass balance between the net glycogenolysis rate ($\Phi(\cdot)$), and the hepatic glucose uptake rate from the absorptive period ($\Psi(\cdot)$):

$$\frac{dGLY}{dt} = -\Phi\left(PVO_2^{max}, GLY\right) + \Psi\left(G_{abs}, GLY\right) \quad (4)$$

where GLY is the current liver's glycogen concentration and G_{abs} represent the amount of glucose uptake by the liver from the glucose absorbed by the gut. Thus, it is proposed that the function Ψ depends on the gastric glucose absorption G_{abs} and the status of glycogen reservoir GLY. If there is a postprandial period, then the liver uptakes 25 % of the absorbed glucose from the gut after a meal G_{meal} (Lehmann and Deutsch, 1992), until the glycogen reservoir is filled, or until the postprandial period is ended. That is $G_{abs} = G_{meal}/4$ if $GLY < GLY^{max}$.

Figure 2 shows both depletion and repletion effects for an exercise period of 250 min with $PVO_2^{max} = 30$ % and a meal intake of 50 g of carbohydrates after 20 min. It is easy to see that the glycogen regeneration is not complete, this is due to the large storage capacity by the liver, *i.e.*, a single meal usually cannot fill the liver's reservoir. Moreover, the depletion function Φ is just considered a constant rate that depends on the, day PVO_2^{max} according with Table 2, and the glycogen stored in the liver. The net glycogenolysis rates were calculated based on the time to obtain a 75 % glycogen depletion as observed in (Ahlborg et al., 1974) and (Ahlborg and Felig, 1982). Consequently, hepatic glucose

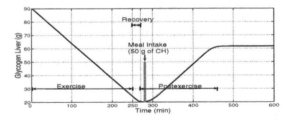

Fig. 2. Effect of Depletion during Long–Term Exercise (30 PVO_2^{max}) and Replenishment due to Meal Intake.

production can be extended by incorporating the depletion and repletion effects induced by the glycogen concentration. The depletion effect is directly included in (3), and it is given by:

$$HGP = M^I \times M^G \times M^\Gamma \times M^E \times M^D \times 155 \ mg/min \quad (5)$$

where M^D is related to the glycogen reservoir expressed as:

$$M^D = 0.7 + 0.3 \cdot \tanh\left[7 \times 10^{-5} \cdot (GLY - 36000)\right] \quad (6)$$

A hyperbolic tangent function was taken to reproduce the dynamic depletion as in (Parker et al., 2002). As a result, if there is a high glycogen concentration then the depletion effect over the hepatic glucose production is null. For the opposite, if there is a low glycogen concentration, then the multiplier depletion will affect largely the production. The parameters values were updated from the original work in (Parker et al., 2002), considering the degree of depletion of hepatic glucose production observed in the literature data (Ahlborg et al., 1974), (Ahlborg and Felig, 1982) and the depletion effect after 90 min of exercise.

4. SIMULATIONS RESULTS

Two scenarios were tested. First, the validation of the extended model is carried out, and finally a simulation throughout a complete day incorporating meals, intravenous insulin, and short–long term light–moderate intensity exercise are illustrated.

4.1 MODEL VALIDATION

The simulation of the patient model corresponds to short and long–term legged exercise with a step from 8 to 30 and 60 PVO_2^{max} at 30 min. It was considered a 25 % of active muscular mass ($PAMM = 0.25$) due to the exercise. The patient is subjected to a continuous intravenous insulin infusion of 24 mU/min, with the purpose to emulate the basal pancreatic insulin rate throughout the simulation. At the beginning of

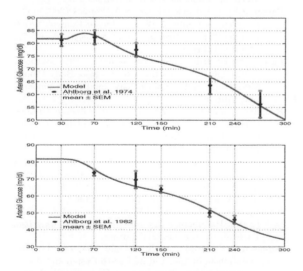

Fig. 3. Model versus Literature Data. Glucose concentration as a function of time in response to 30 (top) and 60 (bottom) PVO_2^{max}.

light exercise, there is a trend of increasing the arterial glucose concentration as shown in Figure 3 (top). This behavior is due to liver's response motivated by the exercise. After that, the glucose concentration falls due to the finite reserve of

glycogen, which cannot compensate the peripheral glucose uptake by the exercised muscle. Once the exercise is prolonged (more that 90 min), the depletion effect predominates the behavior of glucose concentration. At the beginning of moderate exercise (bottom), the arterial glucose concentration rapidly falls due to exercise intensity, *i.e.*, the uptake of glucose overcomes the production. After that, the long–term behavior is similar to the light exercise, however the dropping rate is greater. The simulations show a good agreement with the experimental data in (Ahlborg et al., 1974) and (Ahlborg and Felig, 1982). As a result, the arterial glucose concentration profiles observed in exercising patients at both exercise intensities are captured in this model. In previous

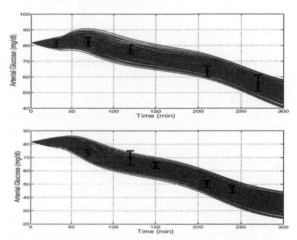

Fig. 4. Experimental Data versus Variation on Parameters of the extended Model. The Simulations Correspond to 30 PVO_2^{max} (top) and 60 PVO_2^{max} (bottom).

studies (Ramprasad et al., 2004), it was shown that the parameters related to the hepatic and peripheral glucose uptake, and fractional hepatic insulin clearance presented the largest impact in the blood glucose concentration. Thus, in order to analyze this scenario, these parameters were perturbed ±10 % and ±5 % respectively, in order to achieve the largest sensitivity, 125 combinations of parameters were simulated (see Figure 4). Note that the original references presented 6 (30 PVO_2^{max}) and 20 (60 PVO_2^{max}) individuals in their studies. So, the simulation in Figure 4 present a good agreement with the experimental data for 125 virtual patients.

4.2 SIMULATION THROUGHOUT A DAY

Once again, the patient is subjected to a continuous insulin infusion of 24 mU/min. However, the exercise duration is 90 min with a recovery period of 20 min at 30 and 60 PVO_2^{max}. It is considered that the glycogen reservoir is full (90 g) at the

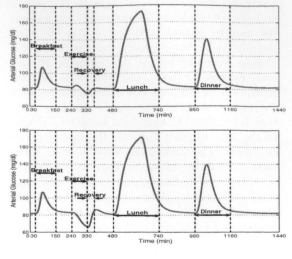

Fig. 5. 24 *hrs* Simulation with Three–Meals, Constant Intravenous Insulin Infusion and light(Top)–Moderate(Bottom) Exercise Routine.

beginning of the simulation. Three major meals are taken per day: breakfast with 5 *g*, lunch with 22 *g* and dinner with 10 *g* of carbohydrates. The results are presented in Figure 5, where there is a fast increment in the arterial glucose after meals, breakfast at $t = 30 \ min$, lunch at $t = 480 \ min$ and dinner at $t = 950 \ min$, which are proportional to the carbohydrates intakes. Also, there is a raise in the arterial glucose concentration at $t = 240 \ min$ due to the light exercise. However, in general the arterial glucose concentration falls, but it is not enough to cause a hypoglycemic scenario, since the exercise is not prolonged and the intensities are light (top) and moderated (bottom).

5. CONCLUSIONS

In this research, the short–term effects of light and moderate exercise were revised and extended for the compartmental model of a type 1 diabetic patient proposed by Sorensen (1985). The exercise induces several key effects in the body: a re-distribution of the blood-flows per organ, an increment in the peripheral glucose and insulin uptakes, and an increment in the hepatic glucose production. The hepatic glycogen reservoir limits the glucose production in long–term exercise. The depletion effect of the glycogen was modelled as a function of the PVO_2^{max}. Meanwhile, the replenishment was considered a function of the actual glycogen value and the glucose gastric absorption. All these interactions were first validated through a comparison with experimental data (Ahlborg et al., 1974) and (Ahlborg and Felig, 1982). Finally, a whole period of a 24 *hrs* was simulated including meals and a light and moderate exercise routine.

REFERENCES

Ahlborg G., P. Felig, L. Hagenfeldt, R. Hendler and J. Wahren (1974). Substrate Turnover during Prolonged Exercise in Man. *J. Clin. Invest.*, 53, 1080–1090.

Ahlborg G., P. Felig (1982). Lactate and glucose exchange across the forearm, legs and splanchnic bed during and after prolonged leg exercise. *J. Clin. Invest.*, 69(1), 45–54.

Bergman R.N., L.S. Phillips and C. Cobelli (1981). Physiologic Evaluation of Factors Controlling Glucose Tolerance in Man. *Journal Clinical Investigation*, 68, 1456–1467.

Belazzi R., G. Nucci and G. Cobelli (2001). The Subcutaneous Route to Insulin-Dependent Diabetes Therapy. *IEEE Engineering in Medicine and Biology*, 20, 54–64, January/February.

Chapman C.B. and J.H. Mitchell (1965). The Physiology of Exercise. *Sci. Am.*, 212, 88–96.

Derouich M. and A. Boutayeb (2002). The Effect of Physical Exercise on the Dynamics of Glucose and Insulin. *Journal of Biomechanics*, 35, 911–917.

Kalant N., T. Leibovici, I. Rahan and K. McNeill (1978). Effect of Exercise on Glucose and Insulin Utilization in the Forearm. *Metabolism*, 27, 333–340.

Lavoie C., F. Ducros, J. Bourque, H. Langelier and J.L. Chiasson (1997). Glucose Metabolism During Exercise in Man: the Role of Insulin in the Regulation of Glucose Utilization, *Can. J. Physiol. Pharmacol.*, 75, 36–43.

Lehmann E.D. and T. Deutsch (1992). A Physiological Model of Glucose-Insulin in Type I Diabetes Mellitus. *Journal of Biomedical Engineering*, 14, 235–242.

Lenart P.J. and R.S. Parker (2002). Modeling Exercise Effects in Type I Diabetic Patients. *Proceedings of the 15th Triennial World Congress*, Barcelona, Spain, June.

Parker R.S. , P.J. Lenart and L.N. DiMascio (2002). Modeling Glycogen-Exercise Interactions in Type I Diabetic Patients. *Proceedings of the AIChE Annual Meeting*, Indianapolis, IN, November 3–8, .

Parker R.S., F.J. Doyle III and N.A. Peppas (2001). The Intravenous Route to Blood Glucose Control. *IEEE Engineering in Medicine and Biology*, 20, 65–73, January/February.

Patton, Fuchs, Hille, Scher and Steiner (1989). Textbook of Physiology: Circulation, Respiration, Body Fluids, Metabolism and Endocrinology. *Saunders Company*, 21st Edition.

Radziuk J. and S. Pie (2001). Hepatic Glucose Uptake, Gluconeogenesis and the Regulation of Glycogen Synthesis. *Diabetes Metabolism, Research and Reviews*, 17, 250–272.

Ramprasad Y., G.P. Rangaiah, and S. Lakshminarayanan (2004). Robust PID Controller for Blood Glucose Regulation in Type I Diabetics. *Industrial Engineering Chemistry Research*, 43, 8257–8268.

Ruderman N., J.T. Devlin, S.H. Schneider and A. Kriska (2002). Handbook of Exercise in Diabetes. *American Diabetes Association*, 2nd Edition.

Sorensen J.T. (1985). A Physiologic Model of Glucose Metabolism in Man and its Use to Design and Assess Improved Insulin Therapies for Diabetes. Ph.D. Dissertation, Chemical Engineering Department, MIT, Cambridge.

The Diabetes Control and Complications Trial Reserach Group (1993). The Effect of Intensive Treatment of Diabetes on the Development and Progression of Long-term Complications in Insulin-dependent Diabetes Mellitus. *N. Engl. J. Med.*, 329, 977–986.

Wahren J., P. Felig, G. Ahlborg and L. Jorfeldt (1971). Glucose Metabolism During Leg Exercise in Man. *J. Clin. Invest*, 50, 2715–2725.

Copyright © IFAC Modelling and Control in Biomedical Systems
Reims, France, 2006

A NONLINEAR MATHEMATICAL MODEL OF AN IMMUNOTHERAPY TREATMENT OF PARATHYROID CARCINOMA

J. Hattersley * M.J. Chappell * N.D. Evans *
G.P. Mead ** A.R. Bradwell **

*School of Engineering, University of
Warwick, Coventry, CV4 7AL, England
** The Binding Site, Warstock Road, Kings
Heath, Birmingham, B14 4RT, England

Abstract: A mathematical model has been developed that describes the competitive binding process present in an immunotherapy treatment for parathyroid carcinoma. Compartmental analysis was employed to relate the flow and interaction of parathyroid hormone (PTH) and antibodies during the treatment. The model indicates a mechanism of how the antibody response effectively reduces the levels of free PTH. The results suggest that a maximum immune response occurs at approximately 13 weeks after the initial treatment. The immunotherapy treatment used injections of PTH hormone to induce an immune response; it was found that these injections had no negative effect on the PTH levels in the system. Additionally, the model allowed several conclusions to be drawn relating to optimal parameter choices with respect to treatment. For antibody binding the optimal level of effect was around $10^9 s^{-1}$, this is within the published *in vivo* range of 10^8-$10^{10} s^{-1}$. It was also established that the concentrations of parathyroid receptors are crucial in determining the pharmacodynamic effects of the treatment. Copyright © IFAC 2006

Keywords: Hypercalcemia, antibodies; parathyroid hormone; immunotherapy; compartmental models; nonlinear models; receptor binding kinetics.

1. INTRODUCTION

Parathyroid hormone (PTH) is a peptide hormone secreted by the parathyroid glands. It controls the concentration of calcium in the plasma by promoting intestinal absorption, renal reabsorption and release of calcium from the bones. Secretion of PTH from the glands is controlled by direct feedback from the concentration of calcium in the plasma. Parathyroid tumours are not common but overproduction of PTH by the tumours cause hypercalcaemia which, if untreated, can be fatal. A novel treatment for this condition was proposed by Bradwell and Harvey (1999) that utilized im-

munotherapy to affect a cure. The treatment used a combination of human and bovine PTH to force the patient's immune system to create antibodies (Ab) that would attach to PTH in plasma and prevent it from binding to PTH receptors (PTHr).

This paper proposes a mathematical model that describes the complex chemical interactions that take place during the auto-immune treatment described above. The model was simulated with published values to replicate possible treatment scenarios. The model facilitates understanding of the immunotherapy treatment, whilst also providing data on important features that may not be measurable by clinicians.

2. THE MODEL

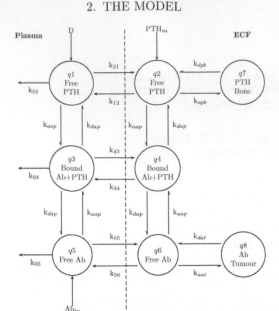

Fig. 1. Full Model containing PTH, Ab, PTH/Ab binding in plasma and ECF, including PTH and Ab tumour receptor binding

The model was developed using compartmental techniques, there are many excellent text books covering this subject (Godfrey, 1983; Jaquez, 1985). As can be seen in Figure 1 the compartmental model separates the process into three distinct components:

- PTH in plasma, ECF and bound to PTHr receptors.
- Bound PTH/Ab in plasma and ECF
- Ab in plasma, ECF and bound in close proximity to the PTH producing tumours.

This separation allowed the maximum use of available clinical data whilst maintaining an acceptable level of generalization.

The model incorporates the flow of material (free Ab, PTH and bound complexes of PTH/Ab) across the plasma/ECF membrane and the kinetic binding of the substances to receptors. It is assumed that no additional binding takes place and the flow of material across the plasma/ECF barrier is characterised solely by molecular size. In accordance with Thomas et al. (1989) PTH and Immunoglobulin G (IgG) molecules are able to pass freely between the two pools; whilst Immunoglobulin M (IgM), either free or bound, is unable to cross barrier. Due to the relative volumes of the two pools the rate constant of flow from ECF to plasma is considered to be approximately a fifth of that in plasma (Thomas et al., 1989). In addition,

the excretion rate of material is assumed to be equal to the flow from plasma to ECF as it is believed the substance must traverse the same biological path.

The reaction of Ab on PTH, and binding to relevant receptors, is modelled through simple binding kinetics (Foreman and Johansen, 2002). As shown in Chappell et al. (1991), if the receptor concentration is considered constant it is possible to remove the free receptor compartments from the model. This was possible in terms of PTHr and Ab tumour sites. However, as Ab and PTH is created and destroyed continuously the total number of receptors must be considered dynamic and therefore modelled as a compartment. The system of equations defining this model is given by:

$$\frac{dq_1}{dt} = k_{dap}q_{3p} - k_{aap}q_1q_5 + k_{12}q_2$$
$$- (k_{01} + k_{21})q_1 + D\delta(t)$$

$$\frac{dq_2}{dt} = k_{dap}q_{4p} - k_{aap}q_2q_6 + k_{dpb}q_7$$
$$- k_{apb}q_2[(C_{PTHRec} \cdot V_e) - q_7)]$$
$$- k_{12}q_2 + k_{21}q_1 + PTH_{in}$$

$$\frac{dq_{3a}}{dt} = k_{aap}q_1q_5 - k_{dap}q_{3a} - q_{3a}k_{03}$$
$$- q_{3a}k_{43} + q_{4a}k_{34}$$

$$\frac{dq_{3p}}{dt} = k_{aap}q_1q_5 - k_{dap}q_{3p} - q_{3p}k_{03}$$
$$- q_{3p}k_{43} + q_{4p}k_{34}$$

$$\frac{dq_{4a}}{dt} = k_{dap}q_{4a} - k_{aap}q_1q_6 - q_{4a}k_{34}$$
$$+ q_{3a}k_{43}$$

$$\frac{dq_{4p}}{dt} = k_{dap}q_{4p} - k_{aap}q_1q_2 - q_{4p}k_{34}$$
$$+ q_{3p}k_{43}$$

$$\frac{dq_5}{dt} = k_{dap}q_{3a} - k_{aap}q_1q_5 + k_{56}q_6$$
$$- (k_{05} + k_{65})q_5 + Ab_{in}$$

$$\frac{dq_6}{dt} = k_{dap}q_{4a} - k_{aap}q_2q_6 + k_{dat}q_8$$
$$- k_{aat}q_8[(C_{AbRec} \cdot V_t) - q_8]$$
$$- k_{56}q_6 + k_{65}q_5$$

$$\frac{dq_7}{dt} = k_{apb}q_2[(C_{AbRec} \cdot V_t) - q_7] - k_{dpb}q_7$$

$$\frac{dq_8}{dt} = k_{aat}q_6[(C_{PTHRec} \cdot V_e) - q_8]$$

(1)

$$y_1 = c_1 q_1 + c_3 q_{3p}$$
$$y_2 = c_5 q_5$$

(2)

See Table 1 for a description of the variables and parameters. As can be seen above (eqn. 1), sub-compartments are used to represent the kinetic binding of PTH and Ab. Both compartments 3 and 4 have been divided into two sub-compartments: q_{3a} and q_{4a}, which represent the bound Ab during treatment, with q_{3p} and q_{4p} describing the PTH that has been bound to Ab. The reason for the sub-compartments is two-fold: the sub-compartments maintain the mass balance relationship necessary for compartmental modelling, whilst allowing analysis of the PTH and Ab complexes during simulation.

The following initial conditions were used:

$$\begin{aligned}
q_1(0^+) &= q_{1ss} & q_2(0^+) &= q_{2ss} \\
q_{3a}(0^+) &= 0 & q_{3p}(0^+) &= 0 \\
q_{4a}(0^+) &= 0 & q_{4p}(0^+) &= 0 \\
q_5(0^+) &= 0 & q_6(0^+) &= 0 \\
q_7(0^+) &= q_{7ss} & q_8(0^+) &= 0
\end{aligned}$$

where q_{1ss}, q_{2ss} and q_{7ss} represent the steady state values calculated for the relevant compartments. The steady state conditions are used to represent the fact that, prior to treatment, the patient's plasma and ECF pools are saturated with excess PTH. As the recorded PTH levels constantly remain high this seems feasible. An assumption is therefore made that as the calcium concentrations are also extremely high, the PTH receptors on osteoblast cells are also saturated to force maximal transferal of calcium from the bone matrix into ECF. This is described by the steady state value in compartment 7. For details on how the steady state conditions are determined refer to Section 2.1.1.

The above model contains two observations: PTH and Ab concentrations in plasma. PTH concentrations were measured by a *two-site immunoradiometric assay* (Bradwell and Harvey, 1999). Unfortunately, neither treatment produced full data relating to the Ab concentrations in response to the PTH injections, so whilst this is a feasible observation it is only provided here for completeness. The model contains two parameters related to receptor concentration. Compartment 7 represents the PTHr sites in ECF, whilst compartment 8 donates possible binding sites of Ab close to the secondary tumours. It is assumed that both these remain constant throughout the procedure. The parameter values used during simulation are listed in Table 1.

2.1 System Inputs

The system as defined has three inputs: PTH injections administered during the treatment, PTH production and Ab production.

2.1.1. PTH Inputs The input via PTH injections is defined by the treatment schedules (Bradwell

Table 1. Model parameters.

Variable	Description	Range
PTH_{in}	Production rate of PTH (s^{-1})	see section 2.1.1
Ab_{in}	Production rate of PTH antibodies (s^{-1})	see section 2.1.2
D	Injected Dose of PTH ($200\mu g$ human + $50\mu g$ bovine) injection (mol)	2.7×10^{-8}
q_i	Quantity free in compartment i (mol) - x_i denotes the equivalent concentration	
$q_{i,j}$	Quantity bound from compartments i and j (mol)	
y_i	Observation of compartment i, c_i will be used as observation gain	
k_{21}	Rate Constant of unbound PTH from plasma to ECF (s^{-1})	1×10^{-3}
k_{12}	Rate Constant of unbound PTH from ECF to plasma (s^{-1})	2×10^{-4}
k_{43}	Rate Constant of bound PTH/antibody complexes from plasma to ECF (s^{-1})	8×10^{-7}
k_{34}	Rate Constant of bound PTH/antibody complexes from ECF to plasma (s^{-1})	16×10^{-8}
k_{65}	Rate Constant of unbound antibody from plasma to ECF (s^{-1})	1×10^{-6}
k_{56}	Rate Constant of unbound antibody from ECF to plasma (s^{-1})	2×10^{-7}
k_{01}	Excretion of unbound PTH from plasma (s^{-1})	1×10^{-3}
k_{03}	Excretion of bound PTH/antibody complexes from plasma (s^{-1})	8×10^{-7}
k_{05}	Excretion of unbound antibody from plasma (s^{-1})	1×10^{-6}
k_{apa}	Association rate of PTH and antibody ($mol^{-1} s^{-1}$)	1×10^{6}
k_{dpa}	Dissociation rate of PTH and antibody (s^{-1})	1×10^{-2}
k_{apb}	Association rate of PTH and PTH receptors on bone ($mol^{-1}s^{-1}$)	1×10^{6}
k_{dpb}	Dissociation rate of PTH and PTH receptors on bone (s^{-1})	1×10^{-2}
k_{aat}	Association rate of antibody and tumour receptors ($mol^{-1}s^{-1}$)	1×10^{6}
k_{dat}	Dissociation rate of antibody and tumour receptors (s^{-1})	1×10^{-2}
C_{PTHRec}	Concentration of PTH Receptors in ECF (mol/litre)	2×10^{-10}
C_{AbRec}	Concentration of antibody receptors on the tumour (mol/litre)	2×10^{-8}
V_p	Volume of Plasma (litre)	2.5L
V_e	Volume of ECF (litre)	12L
V_t	Volume of Tumour (litre)	3.27mL
V_b	Volume of Body (litre)	70L

and Harvey, 1999; Betea *et al.*, 2004). The PTH injected was a combination of human and bovine PTH hormone; however, in the model it is assumed that the two types of PTH (human and bovine) and the peptide combinations are indistinguishable and therefore the kinetic binding and flow-rates are identical. In both treatments $250\mu g$ was injected periodically to ensure an immune response throughout the treatment durations. Due to rapid distribution of PTH throughout the blood-stream the injection was modelled as periodic instantaneous increase in the value of compartment 1.

$$\frac{dq_1}{dt} = k_{12}q_2 - (k_{01} + k_{21})q_1$$
$$\frac{dq_2}{dt} = -k_{12}q_2 + k_{21}q_1 + PTH_{in} \qquad (3)$$

A value for PTH production (PTH_{in}) could not be found in the available literature. However, as the PTH level before treatment was available it was possible to estimate a PTH production that would attain the known steady state level of PTH within plasma (compartment 1). For a patient with normal PTH production the concentration in plasma should be approximately 10ng/L, whilst for a patient with severe Hypercalcemia it is much higher, around 755ng/L (Bradwell and Harvey, 1999; Betea *et al.*, 2004).

In order to calculate the rate at which PTH is produced *in vivo* a simplified two compartmental model was (eqn. 3) used that excluded all compartments except 1 and 2, PTH in plasma and in ECF. If the system input is assumed to be constant and the system in steady-state ($\dot{q}_1 = \dot{q}_2 = 0$) it is possible to calculate the PTH production by equation 4.

$$PTH_{in} = k_{01}\tilde{q}_1 \qquad (4)$$

Where $\tilde{q}_1$ is the steady-state quantity of PTH in plasma.

The values calculated for PTH production under normal and hypercalcemic conditions can be seen in Table 2.

Table 2. PTH Production - mol. weight 9.4KDa (Bradwell and Harvey, 1999; Betea *et al.*, 2004), PTH excretion $1 \times 10^{-3}s^{-1}$

	Normal	Hypercalcemic
q_1 steady state	2×10^{-12} mol	2×10^{-10} mol
PTH_{in}	2×10^{-15} mol/s	2×10^{-13} mol/s

2.1.2. Antibody Inputs The final input to the system is the immuno-response, Ab_{in}, to the PTH

injections. As with the PTH model a steady state concentration of Ab in plasma is reported by Bradwell and Harvey (1999) as between 100-200mg/L. By reducing the model to Ab quantities only (compartments 5 and 6) and assuming a steady state concentration of 100mg/L, using default values for the excretion rate established from Thomas *et al.* (1989) a value of $1.7 \times 10^{-11}s^{-1}$ was calculated. Additionally, the Binding Site Ltd have carried out tests regarding the production of Ab in response to PTH antigens in sheep. Although the data have not been officially published the response can be characterised as:

(1) 0.5 - 1 g/L of specific antibody produced over an 8 week immunisation schedule,
(2) 95% or more of this production takes place after the second immunisation, at 6 weeks
(3) Antibody titres tend to decline slowly over months.

Models have been suggested for Ab production (Tarakanov and Dasgupta, 2000; Dibrov *et al.*, 1977; Bell, 1973), these models are complex and would introduce additional unknown parameters. Therefore a simplified model for the Ab production was sought. Three basic inputs that were derived from the above characteristics: constant, ramped and step. Of these the ramp input (eqn. 5) appeared to be the most feasible, as it emulated the primary (< 6 weeks) and secondary phase (> 6 weeks) of the immune response [1].

$$Ab_{in}(t) = \begin{cases} 1.5 \times 10^{-18} \cdot t & 0 < t < 6 \text{ weeks} \\ 6.6 \times 10^{-12} & t \geq 6 \text{ weeks} \end{cases}$$
$$(5)$$

3. RESULTS

During simulation it is assumed that the compartments representing free PTH (compartments 1,2 and 7) are at steady state, i.e. completely saturated with PTH. The following steady state molar quantities were generated assuming zero Ab input:

$$q_{ss1}(0^+) = 2.0 \times 10^{-10} \text{mol}$$
$$q_{ss2}(0^+) = 2.0 \times 10^{-9} \text{mol}$$
$$q_{ss7}(0^+) = 1.6 \times 10^{-9} \text{mol}$$

In the results shown in Figure 2 the mechanics of the auto-immune treatment can be clearly recognised. At the beginning of the treatment the system is completely saturated with PTH in plasma, ECF and bound to PTHr; this is evident from the steady state values attained. However, as the Ab levels begin to increase, the binding

---

[1] For brevity the definition of the step and constant input function have been omitted.

between PTH and Ab reduces the level of free PTH available to move between plasma and ECF. Reducing the total quantity of PTH in both pools. Figure 3 shows the bound PTH within the system. If compared to Figure 2, it can clearly been seen that as the free PTH is reduced the bound increases, thus indicating that the free PTH is being successful taken up by the Ab. Ultimately preventing free PTH from binding to PTHr sites, and thus restricting the calcium released. The large 'spikes' seen in both figures occur due to the injections of PTH administered.

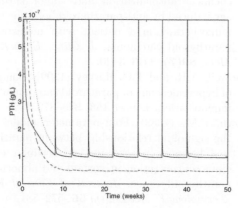

Fig. 2. Free PTH Simulation results using Betea *et al.* (2004) injection scheduling PTH levels: plasma (solid), ECF (dashed) and PTHr (dotted)

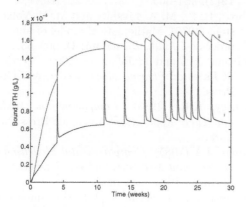

Fig. 3. Bound PTH Simulation results using Betea *et al.* (2004) injection scheduling PTH levels: i) plasma ii) ECF

If the Ab production is assumed to occur immediately after the first PTH injection the simulation attained good steady-state approximation with the real-world data. However, the steady-state was reached within the first 2 weeks. This would indicate the maximum Ab production was not reached until later on in the treatment. It was estimated that the maximum response would be more likely to occur within week 13 of the treatment.

To validate the model it is possible to compare the simulation results with the values measured during the treatments by clinicians. In Betea *et*

al. (2004) PTH levels were measured throughout the duration of the treatment. A comparison of the simulated results against the Betea *et al.* (2004) treatment data can be seen in Figure 3. Bradwell and Harvey (1999) only provided data relating to the calcium levels during the treatment, not PTH levels. Unless the PTH/Ab model incorporated an effect compartment that describes the pharmacodynamic impact of PTH on calcium production, a comparison cannot be provided.

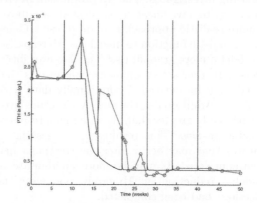

Fig. 4. Comparison of simulated PTH levels (solid) with measured results obtained from Betea *et al.* (2004) (dashed/circles)

A series of simulations were executed to identify the binding kinetic affinities and receptor concentrations that would optimise the hypercalcemia treatment. As would be expected the model showed marked sensitivity to the changes in all three binding affinities. The optimal results seen in all three cases occurred with a high association rate (e.g. $10^6 \mathrm{mol}^{-1} s^{-1}$) and a low dissociation (e.g. $10^{-2} s^{-1}$), which would equate to the antigen binding quickly to its receptors and released extremely quickly, indicating a high turnover but with a maximum saturation being maintained. Interestingly the optimal value for each of the affinities appears to be within the quoted values of between 10^8-$10^{10} \mathrm{mol}^{-1}$ (Betea *et al.*, 2004; Bradwell and Harvey, 1999).

4. CONCLUSION

The relationship between parathyroid hormone and its antibody is complex and there are numerous factors that must be taken into account during the parathyroid carcinoma treatment. However, two key parameters that are not available through published literature are:

- The rate at which PTH is produced by the body.
- The rate, and characteristics, of the immune response to the PTH hormone antigens.

From the investigations undertaken it has been possible to estimate characteristic functions for both these inputs. It has been shown that the PTH production can be successfully modelled by a constant input, calculated from observations of PTH in plasma. Whilst a ramp function provides a suitable estimate of the Ab production, enabling the primary and secondary response of the immune system to be modelled.

Several improvements to the modelled Ab input are being investigated. The Ab production *in vivo* is unlikely to have linear response as shown above. A more realistic approach may be to use a Gaussian or logistic function to model the Ab response, to model a more gradual rise. This however introduces a further set of unknown parameters that would may be derived if additionally data were available. Additionally, the final Ab level achieved was probably greater than the maximum response possible *in-vivo*. This resulted in a masking of features that may occur after the treatment had been completed. It may be more appropriate to model a reduction in Ab production after the injections had been completed.

The simulation results shown above were conducted using established parameter values. However, these may vary between patient resulting in unknown parameters. In such cases it would be beneficial to employ parameters estimation techniques to improve accuracy. Prior to parameter estimation it is important to know the structural identifiability of a model, that is, whether the unknown parameters can be uniquely determined from the model output (Godfrey, 1983; Jaquez, 1985). Unfortunately, due to the nonlinearity and complexity of the model the structural indentifiabily has not been completed, a software based approach is currently being investigated.

The PTH/Ab model provides a first step in modelling the kinetics of the immunotherapy treatment. A natural progression from this is to determine the pharmacodynamic effects of the system. For the parathyroid carcinoma treatment this would focus up the relationship between PTH, PTHr and calcium. PTH-calcium curves have been documented by Malberti *et al.* (1999) and Brown (1983) that could be incorporated into the model through an effect compartments (Godfrey, 1983). This would enable additional real-world data to be used when validating the model.

In conclusion, with limited knowledge of the parathyroid carcinoma immunotherapy treatment the model is capable of providing insight into the mechanics of the biological process involved. The model suggests how the treatment is able to effectively reduce calcium levels in plasma, through a reduction in PTH binding to PTHr. This reduc-

tion can be directly attributed to the uptake of free PTH by the PTH antibody.

REFERENCES

Bell, G.I. (1973). Predator-prey equations simulating an immune response. *Math. Biosci.* **16**, 291–314.

Betea, D., A.R. Bradwell, T.C. Harvey, G.P. Mead, H. Schmidt-Gayk, B. Ghaye, A.F. Daly and A. Beckers (2004). Hormonal and biochemical normalization and tumor shrinkage induced by anti-parathyroid hormone immunotherapy in a patient with metastatic parathyroid carcinoma. *J. Clinc. Endocrino Meta.* **89(7)**, 3413–3420.

Bradwell, A.R. and T.C. Harvey (1999). Control of hypercalcaemia of parathroid carcinoma by immunisation. *Lancet* **353**, 370–373.

Brown, E.M. (1983). Four-parameter model of the sigmoidal relationship between parathyroid hormone release and extracellular calcium concentration in normal and abnormal parathyroid tissue. *Journal of Clinical Endocrinology & Metabolism* **56**, 572–581.

Chappell, M.J., G.D. Thomas, K.R. Godfrey and A.R. Bradwell (1991). Optimal tumour targeting by antibodies: Development of a mathematical model. *J. Pharma. Bioparma* **19**(2), 364–365.

Dibrov, B. F., M. A. Livshits and M. V. Volkenstein (1977). Mathematical model of immune processes. *Math. Biosci.* **65(4)**, 609–631.

Foreman, J.C. and T. Johansen (2002). *Textbook of Receptor Pharmacology*. second ed.. CRC Press.

Godfrey, K.R. (1983). *Compartmental Models and Their Application*. Academic Press. New York.

Jaquez, J.A (1985). *Compartmental Modelling in Biology and Medicine*. 2nd ed.. University of Michigan Press. Michigan.

Malberti, F., M. Farina and Enrico Imbasciati (1999). The pth-calcium curve and the set point of calcium in primary and secondary hyperparathyroidism. *Nephrol Dial Transplant* **14**, 2398–2406.

Tarakanov, A. and D. Dasgupta (2000). A formal model of an artificial immune system. *Biosystems* **55(1-3)**, 151–158.

Thomas, G.D., M.J. Chappell, P.W. Dykes, D.B. Ramsden, K.R. Godfrey, J.R.M Ellis and A.R. Bradwell (1989). Effect of dose, molecular size, affinity and protein binding on tumour uptake of antibody ligand: A biomathematical model. *Cancer Research* **49**, 3290–3296.

A PK-PD MODEL OF CELL CYCLE RESPONSE TO TOPOTECAN

R. Ali* L. Campbell** N. D. Evans*
R. J. Errington*** K. R. Godfrey* P. J. Smith**
M. J. Chappell*

* School of Engineering, University of Warwick, Coventry
CV4 7AL, U.K.
** Department of Pathology, Wales College of Medicine,
Cardiff University, Cardiff CF14 4XN, U.K.
*** Department of Medical Biochemistry, Wales College of
Medicine, Cardiff University, Cardiff CF14 4XN, U.K.

Abstract: A model describing the response of the growth of single human cells in the absence and presence of the anti-cancer agent, topotecan, is presented. The model is a result of linking the pharmacokinetic (pK) and pharmacodynamic (pD) responses. By linking the models in this way, rather than using separate (static) approaches, it is possible to illustrate how the drug perturbs the cell cycle. The model is validated for a range of drug concentrations with experimental data. Copyright ©2006 IFAC

Keywords: Pharmacodynamics, pharmacokinetics, compartmental models, topotecan, drug kinetics.

1. INTRODUCTION

A mathematical model which is capable of describing the *in vitro* kinetics of toptecan on human osteosarcoma cells has been developed. It addresses the targeting of the agent topotecan (pK) to the biological (pD) response. In this way, it is possible to show the dynamic and temporal interactions of the drug with its molecular target, and how these can be affected by the delivery of the agent and its impact on cell growth and death. The relationships between the pK and pD outcomes are extremely complicated, especially for discrete events within a heterogeneous population.

The linking of pK to pD models to describe drug kinetics on hetergenous cell populations is relatively new. (A recent model, developed independently by Alarcòn *et al.* (2004) consider a similar approach.) A drawback of the current models is

that there appears to be little or no validation with experimental data. In this paper, this is addressed by making use of live-cell data generated from new experimental procedures developed at the Wales College of Medicine (Errington *et al.*, 2003). They have developed a series of robust quantative laboratory assays to track and measure time-integrated events at single cell level. These data are used in the present model and to further investigate the interactions of the drug with its target and possible routes for cellular evasion of drug action (i.e. drug resistance). Ultimately, an aim of the model is to design and predict the consequences of tailored drug treatments for individuals. With this in mind, a highly flexible generic model has been developed, which is capable of predicting cell response pathways that may be used in drug discovery.

2. ACTION OF THE DRUG

The anti-cancer agent considered here is topotecan (TPT). Clinical evidence for its cytotoxic activity against lung, breast and ovarian cancers is well known (Bailly, 2000). TPT is a water-soluble derivative of Camptothecin (CPT), an alkaloid isolated from the tree *Camptotheca acimunata*, and acts as a topoisomerase I, (topo I), inhibitor (Wang, 1996). Topo-I is a nuclear enzyme involved in DNA replication and repair. The enzyme unwinds the supercoiled double stranded DNA (dsDNA) by temporally binding to and cleaving one of the strands, forming a 'cleavable complex'. DNA cleavage and ligation reactions catalysed by the enzyme are tightly controlled and barely detectable. The cleavage is coupled with religation to restore continuity to the DNA complex (Figure 1(a)). In the presence of TPT, the cleaved DNA-topo I complex is stabilised, effectively inhibiting religation (Figure 1(b)). The drug-induced single-strand breaks are reversible and considered non-toxic as they can be easily repaired. However, as replication proceeds double-strand breaks result which are responsible for the cytotoxic effects of TPT.

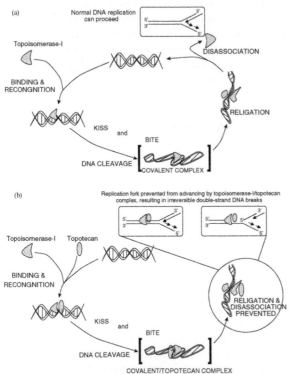

Fig. 1. Behaviour of Topoisomerase I in (a), the absence and (b), the presence of TPT. (After Bailly (2000).)

Of interest is where TPT is active in terms of the events describing the (regulated) growth and division of a single cell, the so-called cell cycle (Figure 2). The cell cycle comprises four phases. In G1,

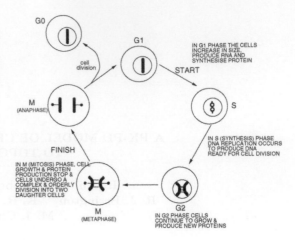

Fig. 2. Schematic of the cell cycle. (After Tyson *et al.* (2001).)

the chromosomes are unreplicated and the cell uncomitted to division. During transition from this phase to S phase the cell commits to replication. DNA is then replicated and two chromatids form. This is followed by the G2 phase where the chromatids are separated so each daughter cell receives a copy of each chromosome. Nuclei form around the replicated material and the daughter cells are separated. This is the M-phase. The processes are distinct and tightly regulated temporally and (to a degree) spatially (Thomas and Goodyear, 2003).

The cell cycle may be thought of as two alternative states: G1 and S-G2-M separated by irreversible Start and Finish transitions, as defined by Tyson and Novak (2001). Start is defined as where the cell begins replication and Finish where the DNA replication is complete. Finish cannot occur if there have been any problems with DNA replication or chromosome alignment. With this in mind, TPT is believed to be S-phase specific: the cleavable complexes lead to dsDNA breaks. As a result many cells resist the effect of TPT by failing to enter S phase or replicate DNA during exposure (Feeney *et al.*, 2003). By blocking entry to S-phase it is possible to halt the growth of cells.

3. PK-PD MODEL

Figure 3 describes the pK-pD model. Separate models have been developed for the cell cycle and drug kinetics. These contain the relevant basic physiology and chemistry and are coupled together. The TPT model describes the chemical reactions when the drug moves from the medium to extracellular region to cytoplasm and then to the nucleus. The active, closed-ring, (lactone), form of TPT (TPT-L) undergoes reversible hydrolysis to

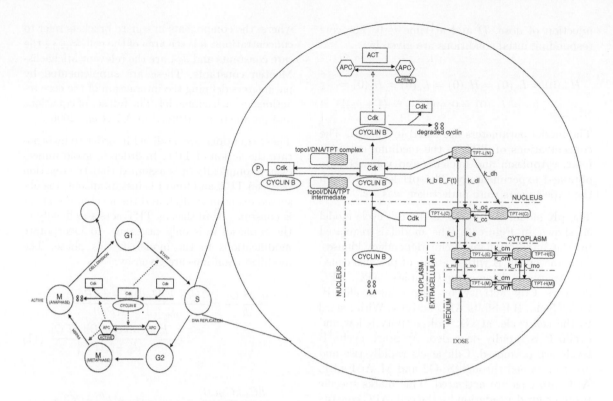

Fig. 3. Schematic of cell cycle model with inset describing the drug kinetic model within S-phase.

an open-ring, (hydroxy acid) form (TPT-H). This reaction is pH-dependent: the active and inactive form predominates at high pH (>10) and low pH (<4) respectively (Lakowicz *et al.*, 1999). The same notation as Evans *et al.* (2005) is adopted, where concentrations of TPT-L and TPT-H are defined as L and H with subscripts, m, e, c and n defining the medium, extracellular, cellular and nucleic regions respectively. It is assumed that (i) all the drug in the nucleus is bound and only TPT-L binds to DNA, and (ii) elsewhere reversible, pH-dependent hydrolysis occurs. The latter is modelled using a straightforward linear two-compartment model, where rate constants, k_{om} define the ring opening TPT-L and k_{cm} the ring closing TPT-H. In the cytoplasm this is k_{oc} and k_{cc}. The mixing between the medium and extracellular region is modelled by first-order flows. k_{mi} refers to the flow rate into the extracellular region from the medium and k_{mo}, the flow out of extracellular region into the medium. The flow between the extracellular and cytoplasm is also modelled as first-order. Note that only TPT-L crosses the plasma membrane (as observed experimentally). The rate at which TPT-L binds to DNA is assumed proportional (with rate constant, k_b), to the product of the concentration of TPT-L in the cytoplasm, $L_c(t)$ and free binding sites $B_F(t)$. B_T is the total concentration of avaliable DNA binding sites, $B_F(t)$. The concentration of free sites is given as $B_F(t)=B_T-L_N(t)$, where L_N

is the concentration of bound drug. Dissocation of bound drug is assumed as first-order with either TPT-L (k_{dl}) or TPT-H (k_{dh}). The system of ODEs describing the system is given by:

$$\frac{dL_m}{dt} = -(k_{om} + k_{mu})L_m + k_{cm}H_m + k_{mo}\frac{V_e}{V_m}L_e \quad (1)$$

$$\frac{dH_m}{dt} = k_{om}L_m - (k_{cm} + k_{mi})H_m + k_{mo}\frac{V_e}{V_m}H_e \quad (2)$$

$$\frac{dL_e}{dt} = \frac{k_{mi}V_m}{V_e}L_m - (k_{mo} + k_{om} + k_i)L_e +$$
$$+ k_{cm}H_e + \frac{k_eV_c}{V_e}L_c \quad (3)$$

$$\frac{dH_e}{dt} = \frac{k_{mi}V_m}{V_e}H_m + k_{om}L_e - (k_{cm} + k_{mo})H_e \quad (4)$$

$$\frac{dL_c}{dt} = k_i\frac{V_e}{V_c}L_e - (k_e + k_{oc})L_c + k_{cc}H_c +$$
$$+ k_{dl}\frac{V_n}{V_c}L_n - k_b(B_T - Ln)Lc \quad (5)$$

$$\frac{dH_c}{dt} = k_{oc}L_c - k_{cc}H_c + k_{dh}\frac{V_n}{V_c}L_n \quad (6)$$

$$\frac{dL_n}{dt} = \frac{k_bV_c}{V_n}(B_T - Ln)L_c - (k_{dl} + k_{dh})L_n \quad (7)$$

where V_m, V_e, V_c and V_n denote the volumes of compartments. The drug is injected as a bolus injection of dose, D and at time $t=0$. The corresponding intial conditions are given by:

$$H_m(0) = L_e(0) = H_e(0) = L_c(0) = H_c(0) =$$
$$= L_n(0) = 0; \text{ and } L_m = (1 + \nu_0)D$$

The model parameters are listed in Table 1. The concentrations of TPT in the medium, extracellular, cytoplasm and nucleus, and volumes were obtained experimentally. The pH level at which the experiments were undertaken was 7.2.

The pK model is coupled to the cell cycle model as shown in Figure 3. The model is regulated by the interaction of cyclin dependent kinases, Cdk and cyclin B with a group of proteins called the Anaphase Promoting Complex, APC. APC destroys Cdk activity by degrading cyclin B; Cdk/Cyclin B inhibits APC activity. With regard to the cell cycle, at G1, Cdk activity is low and cyclin B is rapidly degraded. At Start, cyclin B levels are promoted. Cdk levels rapidly rise and are maintained through S, G2 and M. At Finish, APC proteins are activated. This marks specific proteins for degradation by the cell. APC consists of polypeptides and auxiliary proteins: Cdc20 and Cdh1 which are key to targeting and marking those proteins that are to be degraded at the end of M to allow the system to return to G1. Cdc20 and Cdh1 are controlled differently by cyclin B which activates other features in the model.

In the interests of brevity we will avoid lengthy description of our model. A full description can be found in Ali *et al.* (2006). The cell cycle model consists of four sub-models governing G1, S, G2 and M phases, with separate governing equations or switches defining the next event. (Unlike this model, most other models are based on mechanisms occuring in yeast cells.) At the core of the overall model are the equations governing the behaviour of Cdk/Cyclin B with APC. The core model is essentially a modified version of the approach taken by Tyson and Novak (2001). The core equations governing interaction of Cdk/CyclinB with APC are given by:

$$\frac{d[APC]}{dt} = \frac{(k_3' + k_3''A)(1 - [APC])}{J_3 + 1 - [APC]} -$$
$$- \frac{k_4 a[CdkCycB][APC]}{J_4 + [APC]} \quad (8)$$

$$\frac{d[CdkCycB]}{dt} = -k_1 - (k_2' + k_3''[APC])$$
$$[CdkCycB] \quad (9)$$

$$\frac{da}{dt} = ga\left(1 - \frac{a}{a_*}\right) \quad (10)$$

where, the components in square brackets refer to concentrations, a is the area of the cell, $k_{1,2,3,4}$ the rate constants and $J_{3,4}$ are the relevant Michaelis-Menten constants. These are supplemented by parameters defining the interaction of the core reactions in each submodel. The full set of equations and parameters is defined in Ali *et al.* (2006).

These equations are modified in order to incorporate the action of TPT. In order to avoid unnecessary complexity, it is assumed that the reaction between TPT and topo-I is instantaneous, (as observed experimentally), and the level of the latter is constant. Note that as TPT acts specifically in the S-phase, it is only necessary to incorporate modifications to the model in this phase. The modified equations are given by:

$$\frac{d[APC]}{dt} = \frac{(k_3' + k_3''[L_n])(1 - [APC])}{J_3 + 1 - [APC]} -$$
$$- \frac{k_4 a[CdkCycB][APC]}{J_4 + [APC]} \quad (11)$$

$$\frac{d[CdkCycB]}{dt} = -k_1 - (k_2' + k_2''[APC] +$$
$$+ k_3'''[L_n])[CdkCycB] \quad (12)$$

$$\frac{dV}{dt} = gV\left(1 - \frac{V}{V_*}\right) \quad (13)$$

The equation for the cell area has been replaced with the volume, V, (which is obtained experimentally). Note that V^*, (and a^*), define the maximum size to which a cell can grow and are defined experimentally. Values for the parameters are defined in Table 1. They are initially based on

Table 1. Table of Parameters.

Dose level:	0μM TPT	1μM TPT	10μM TPT
k_{om} (1/s)	1.545×10^{-4}	1.341×10^{-4}	1.301×10^{-4}
k_{cm} (1/s)	2.753×10^{-4}	2.431×10^{-4}	2.378×10^{-4}
k_{oc} (1/s)	1.545×10^{-4}	1.341×10^{-4}	1.301×10^{-4}
k_{cc} (1/s)	2.753×10^{-4}	2.431×10^{-4}	2.378×10^{-4}
k_{mi} (1/s)	1.374×10^{-6}	1.095×10^{-6}	1.062×10^{-6}
k_{mo} (1/s)	8.175×10^{-2}	7.489×10^{-2}	7.372×10^{-2}
k_b (1/sμM)	3.411×10^{-4}	3.041×10^{-4}	3.241×10^{-4}
k_i (1/s)	2.112×10^{-2}	1.876×10^{-2}	1.849×10^{-2}
k_e (1/s)	7.821×10^{-3}	7.341×10^{-3}	7.251×10^{-3}
k_{dl} (1/s)	4.468×10^{-2}	4.061×10^{-2}	3.951×10^{-2}
k_{dh} (1/s)	2.521×10^{-7}	2.012×10^{-7}	2.003×10^{-7}
B_T (μM)	9.991×10^{-1}	9.091×10^{-1}	9.101×10^{-1}
k_1 (1/s)	7.5×10^{-4}	7.67×10^{-4}	7.68×10^{-4}
k_2 (1/s)	1.63×10^{-2}	1.62×10^{-2}	1.58×10^{-2}
k_2' (1/s)	1.68×10^{-2}	1.74×10^{-2}	1.78×10^{-2}
k_2'' (1/s)	1.67×10^{-1}	1.75×10^{-1}	1.81×10^{-1}
k_3 (1/s)	2.83×10^{-3}	3.17×10^{-3}	3.51×10^{-3}
k_3'' (1/s)	2.80×10^{-2}	3.10×10^{-2}	3.53×10^{-2}
k_3''' (1/s)	2.83×10^{-1}	3.12×10^{-1}	3.58×10^{-1}
k_4 (1/s)	0.0035	0.0037	0.0038
J_3	0.034	0.036	0.036
J_4	0.034	0.036	0.036
g	0.012	0.014	0.014

those given in Tyson and Novak (2001) and have been fine-tuned according to the live-cell data provided from our experiments. It is important to bear in mind that, due to the nature of the cell cycle, these parameters are constantly changing and are varied slightly according to a simple first-order relationship.

4. RESULTS & DISCUSSION

A series of experiments has been conducted were live-cell, time-series, data are collected describing the cell cycle phases. U-20S human osteosarcoma cells where treated with 0.1, 1 and 10μM concentrations of TPT for one hour at 37°C, 5%CO_2. The drug is then washed out. The cells are tagged with a green flourescent protein, (GFP), which acts as a cyclin B reporter. This reveals the behaviour of the cell. The change in flouresence is tracked with a specially designed time-lapse instrument, every twenty minutes for a period of 48 hours. From the resulting movie, a number of cells are tracked individually and the time to a cell event is recorded. The levels of cyclin B reported are also recorded. The movement of the cell was compensated for, and background flourescence was subtracted from the original intensity readout and normalised against basal levels of cyclin B. See Campbell *et al.* (2006) and Marquez *et al.* (2003) for full details regarding the experimental procedure and data processing techniques.

The model is solved numerically using a modified ode23t MATLAB routine, with the initial conditions and parameters defined in Table 1. This returned results which are comparable to when the equations are solved using the Facsimile package (UES Software, Dorset, UK).

Figures 4, 5 and 6 show three typical traces for the growth of a cell in the absence and presence of 1 and 10μM TPT. The live-cell data are denoted by the solid line and experimental data by the dash-dot curve. It is possible to deduce the Start and Finish transitions of the cell cycle. These transitions are marked on Figure 5. Whilst the G2 phase is not clear, due to the low signal-to-noise ratio in the experimental data, it is possible to deduce the start and finish of the other phases. As the cell divides, indicated by the spike, the growth of either one of its daughter cells can be monitored. The corresponding simulation shows a reasonable approximation to the experiment. The model is capable of predicting the Start and Finish transitions, and cell cycle phases. This is partly due to incorporating the fact that the parameter values are constantly altering from phase to phase and cell-to-cell. For the case where TPT has been adminstered, (Figures 5 and 6), the model outputs compare very well with the experimental data. It

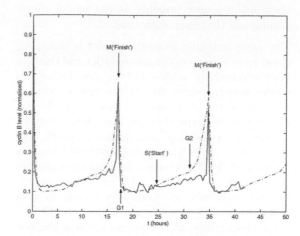

Fig. 4. Variation of cyclin B with time, (t), in the absence of TPT. (Legend: (-) and (--) denote experimental and model output respectively.)

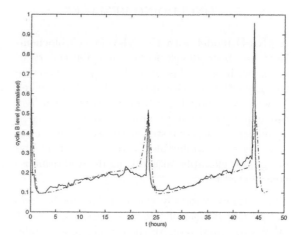

Fig. 5. Variation of cyclin B with time, (t), in presence of 1μM TPT. (Legend: Refer to Figure 4.)

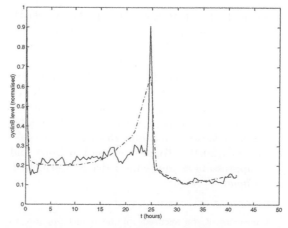

Fig. 6. Variation of cyclin B with time, (t), in presence of 10μM TPT. (Legend: Refer to Figure 4.)

can be seen that the drug extends S-phase and hence the overall time between mitotis. Again, these fits are only possible as the model allows parameters that vary with time. [1]

The main outcome from the model is obtaining the correct time-event characteristics and this has been successfully achieved. It is noted that the model underpredicts the M/G1 spikes. This is a result of the experimental procedure. As the cell grows, its shape changes. Just before the cell divides, it 'rounds up' and becomes spherical in shape. As it does so, the light reflected back, a measure of the flourescence, is at its most intense resulting in a false peak. The model takes this into account, as it allows for the change in area and volume and predicts peaks that are 30-40% lower. Experimental observations where the cell has been collapsed to its original size agrees with this (Campbell *et al.*, 2006).

5. CONCLUDING REMARKS

A pK-pD model with the relevant cell biochemistry has been developed to describe cell regulation with time. The model is able to describe the effect that varying doses of TPT have on cell growth. The model has been validated with live-cell experimental data and found to give good agreement. The next step is to use the model to test scenarios applicable for drug treatment and design, for example, introducing delayed response characteristics.

The authors gratefully acknowledge the *Biotechnology and Biological Sciences Research Council*, (EPS subcommittee), for their kind support under Grant No. 88/E19305.

REFERENCES

Alarcòn, T., H. M. Byrne and P. K. Maini (2004). A mathematical model of the effects of hypoxia on the cell cycle of normal and cancer cells. *J. Theor. Biol.*, **229**, 395–411.

Ali, R., N. D. Evans, L. Campbell, M. J. Chappell, R. J. Errington, P.J. Smith and K. R. Godfrey (2006). A pK-pD model of single cell cycle response to anti-cancer agent, topotecan. *Submitted to Math. Biosci.*

Bailly, C. (2000). Topoisomerase-I poisons and suppressors as anti-cancer drugs. *Curr. Med. Chem.*, **7**, 39–58.

Campbell, L., R. J. Errington, N. D. Evans, I. Khan, C. Headley, M. J. Chappell, S.C. Chappell, K. R. Godfrey, R. Ali and P. J. Smith (2006). Single cell tracking of the complex pharmacodynamic response to topotecan and the routes for evasion of drug action of human osteosarcoma cells. *Submitted to Cancer Res.*

Errington, R. J., S. M. Ameer-Beg, B. Vojaovic, L. H. Patterson, M. Zloh and P. J. Smith (2003). Advanced microscopy solutions for monitoring the kinetics and dynamics of drug-DNA damage-activated G2 checkpoint. *Adv. Drug Deliv. Rev.*, **57**, 153–167.

Evans, N. D., R. J. Errington, M. J. Chapman, P. J. Smith, M. J. Chappell and K. R. Godfrey (2005). Compartmental modelling of the uptake kinetics of the anti-cancer agent topotecan in human breast cancer cells. *Int. J. Adapt. Control Signal Process.*, **19**, 395–417.

Feeney, G. P., R. J. Errington, M. Wiltshire, N. Marquez, S. C. Chappell and P. J. Smith (2003). Tracking the cell cycle origins for escape from topotecan action by breast cancer cells. *Br. J. Cancer*, **88**, 1310–1317.

Lakowicz, J. R., I. D. Fang, Z. Gryczynski, I. Gryczynski and T. G. Burke (1999). Flouresence spectral properties of the anti-cancer drug topotecan by steady-state and frequency domain fluorometry with one-photon and multi-photon excitation. *Photochemistry & Photobiology*, **69**, 421–428.

Marquez, N., S. C. Chappell, O. J., Sansom, A. R. Clarke J. Court and P. J.Smith (2003). Single cell tracking reveals that Msh2 is a key component of an early-acting DNA damage-activated G2 checkpoint. *Oncogene*, **22**, 7642–7648.

Thomas, N. and I. D. Goodyear (2003). Stealth sensors: real-time monitoring of the cell cycle. *Targets*, **2**, 26–33.

Tyson, J. J. and B. Novak (2001). Regulation of the eukaryotic cell cycle: molecular anatagonism, hysteresis and irreversible transitions. *J.Theor. Biol.*, **61**, 759–778.

Wang, J. C. (1996). DNA topoisomerases. *Annu. Rev. Biochem.*, **65**, 635–692.

---

[1] A measure of the accuracy of the model response to the experimental data can be found by calculating the coefficient of determination, or r^2 values. The closer to the value of r^2 is to 1 the better the fit. For the control data shown, $r^2=0.86$ which is viewed as a good fit (Figure 4). Good agreement in the presence of 1μM and 10μM TPT shown here are found, with r^2 values are 0.91 and 0.76 respectively (Figures 5 and 6).

INTERPOLATED MAPS OF BIOMECHANICAL CHARACTERISTICS OF HUMAN SKULL

F.Rambaud*, A.Pinti*, P.Drazetic*, R. Delille*, L.Soufflet**

* LAMIH – CNRS UMR 8530
Université de Valenciennes - Le Mont Houy
59313 Valenciennes Cedex 9, France

** FORENAP
27, rue du 4ₑ-RSM
68250 Rouffach, France

Abstract: Each year, thousands of fatalities result from head injuries, of which the majority are sustained in motor vehicle accidents. Within the framework of the PREDIT PROTEUS (Head protection of vulnerable users) project, the aim of our researches consists on the study and prediction of the headbones' tolerance to impacts. Biomechanical characteristics have been extracted from 20 human skulls. This work presents a method of Dm Spline interpolation, which allows us to create maps of the various parameters. Results show the distribution of the various mechanical variables extracted from the measurement protocol. *Copyright © 2006 IFAC*

Keywords: Skull, interpolation, map, biomechanics, injury

1. INTRODUCTION

Each year, thousands of fatalities result from head injuries; the majority are sustained in motor vehicle accidents. In frontal collisions, the sources of injury are the steering wheel, pillar and roof, glazing impacts, instrument panel, and exterior objects. In lateral motor vehicle impacts, because of the proximity of the impact vector to the head, contacts involve the temporo-parietal (side) region of the human head (Thomas and Bradford, 1995). Housing the brain, the skull bone protects the soft tissue from deformations secondary to external forces.

Because the skull is a vital component that encloses the brain, it is necessary to understand its biomechanical role and its tolerance to impacts. In recent years, owing to increased public awareness of occupant safety, the consequences of impacts on skull are being examined in detail by epidemiologists, clinicians, biomechanical investigators...(Yoganandan and Pintar, 2004)

A number of different techniques and approaches have been used in order to study head injury mechanisms (Yoganandan and Pintar, 2004). These approaches and techniques can be classified as experimental, analytical or numerical. In these studies, a variety of variables have been included in experimental protocols, such as local anatomic data, peak force, deflection, energy, stiffness, acceleration...

Concerning the experimental techniques, the impact conditions could be quasi-static compression, dropping specimens onto a surface, impacted specimens with padded and unpadded strikers, bending tests, and at varying velocities. Models have used intact cadavers, isolated heads with intact brain, and pieces of skull specimens, using unembalmed, partially embalmed, and fully embalmed conditions (Johnson and Young, 2005; Thali, *et al*, 2002; Fujita, *et al*, 1999).

Numerical models, such as finite element models, can be generated from the use of a Magnetic Resonance

Imaging (MRI) system, or X-Ray Computerized Tomography (CT Scanners). These models allow the reconstruction of the geometry and the structure of the human skull (Delille, *et al*, 2003).

Physical models, like rapid prototyped skull models, can be generated from these data too (Johnson and Young, 2005).

All these approaches, their various techniques, have multiple results.

The purpose of our researches is to predict and analyse the effect of a crash landing, and to facilitate the improvement of vehicles and materials protection for the users. The aim of this work is to improve the prediction of wounds on human skulls in impact situations. To this end, experimental tests have been made on 20 human skulls. The protocol was defined with unembalmed subjects, whose age is lower than 80. Maps in 2D have been worked out for the virtual analysis of distribution of biomechanical characteristics. An algorithm for the interpolation of data using a 3D Dm spline method has been implemented.

2. MATERIALS AND METHODS

2.1 Measurement protocol

The protocol was defined with 20 unembalmed subjects (18 males, 2 females), whose average age is 71 (+/- 8). Seventeen fragments have been extracted from each human skull.(Delille, *et al*, 2005)

The human skull is composed of many bones; the specimens are taken away the skull, following a precise cartography (Figure 1) :

- 5 specimens from the frontal bone (yellow coloured)
- 8 specimens from the parietal bone (green coloured)
- 2 specimens from the temporal bone (blue coloured)
- 2 specimens on the coronal suture (yellow coloured, named EP13 and EP14)

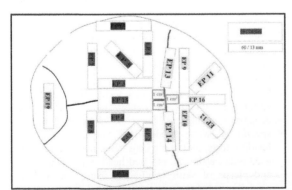

Fig. 1. Map of skull's fragments

Extraction of characteristics

The mechanical characteristics are then extracted from each specimen. Because of the high time varying of mechanical charateristics after death, the measured values have been extracted quickly after death on unembalmed cadavers. The time between death and measurement is on the order of 12.8 days, with a standard deviatio of 4.6 days.

First, the entire skull and each specimen are scanned using a digitalisation machine without contact, with a resolution of a tenth of a millimetre. The extracted data are morphometric and anatomical data. The geometry of the specimens is then reconstructed using Rapidform software.

Then, in order to obtain their mechanical characteristics, such as peak force, each specimen is loaded in three points bending at 10mm/min (Figure 2).

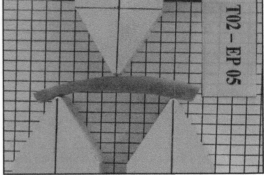

Fig. 2. Sample on bending system

The peak force, shown on Figure 3, is the value of the force (in Newtons) at the moment of the sample's breakpoint.

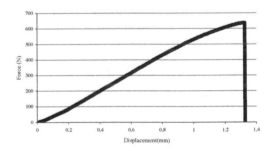

Fig. 3. Sample of peak force

Finally, densitometry and mineralization tests are performed. Densitometry tests provide the weights of the specimens (here calculated in air and in water); mineralization tests provide the mineral content in the bone, expressed as a percentage. For that, each specimen is burned at a temperature of 600°C during 40 minutes. The ashes are then weighed; the weight of ashes corresponds to the mineral quality of the bones of each subject.

The thickness and width are measured from each specimen.

2.2 Method

Interpolated maps

The specimens are first characterized by the position of their centre of gravity, calculated from the numerical images. They are placed on a hemisphere, used as a simplified model of the human skull.

A 3D Dm spline interpolation of order 2 was used to estimate the distribution of the values on the skull, resulting in a top view 2D map encoded with an optimized colour scale. The Dm spline interpolation originates from the theory of surface splines (Duchon, 1976). Splines are known to give smooth interpolations with exact values at the locations of the measurement points. It also typically produces extrema values at locations which differ from those of the measurement points, contrary to linear interpolations for instance (Soufflet, *et al.*, 1991). The amplitude of the extrema is controlled by means of the order of the Dm spline function. A second order interpolation generates extrema values close to the values at the measurement points.

Our interpolated maps were based on interpolations at the 3D locations on the hemisphere corresponding to the 2D locations of the pixels.

3D Dm Spline Interpolation

Let n be the total number of measurement points, v_i the measured value at the ith point of measure (x_i, y_i, z_i), and m an integer ≥ 2. The 3D Dm spline function of order m at the location (x, y, z) of the 3D space is defined as follows:

$$Dm(x, y, z) = p(x, y, z) + \sum_{i=1}^{n} c_i \, n(x - x_i, y - y_i, z - z_i) \quad (1)$$

where $p(x, y, z)$ is a polynomial of order m-1:

$$p(x, y, z) = \sum_{L=0}^{m-1} \sum_{i+j+k=L} a_{ijk} x_i y_j z_k \quad (2)$$

and

$$n(s, t, v) = (s^2 + t^2 + v^2)^{(2m-3)/2} \quad (3)$$

Let us denote A the vector of the a_{ijk} coefficients, C the vector of the c_i coefficients and V the vector of the measured values v_i:

$$A = (a_{000}, a_{100}, a_{010}, a_{001}, \ldots)^T \quad (4)$$

$$C = (c_1, c_2, \ldots, c_n)^T \quad (5)$$

$$V = (v_1, v_2, \ldots, v_n)^T \quad (6)$$

Vectors A and C are solutions of the following matrix equations:

$$N\,C + E\,A = V \quad (7)$$

$$E^T\,C = 0 \quad (8)$$

$N = (n_{ij})$ being an n×n matrix with

$$n_{ij} = n(x_i - x_j, y_i - y_j, z_i - z_j) \quad (9)$$

and

$$E = \begin{pmatrix} 1 & x_1 & y_1 & z_1 & \ldots \\ 1 & x_2 & y_2 & z_2 & \ldots \\ & & \ldots\ldots\ldots \\ 1 & x_n & y_n & z_n & \ldots \end{pmatrix} \quad (10)$$

3. RESULTS

The following maps illustrate the various variables calculated at the time of the experimental tests. For each sample, the position of the centre of gravity is calculated, which is symbolized by the points on the maps. A coloured scale represents the values of the variables, with the colour blue for the minima, and the colour pink for the maxima.

For this article, the data used for the maps which are showed here, are the average data of the 20 skulls. In fact, it is impossible here to show the results for all the skulls. Moreover, there is no abnormal measurement, and the standard deviation is low for the variables.

Eight variables are used here for each sample : the bone mineral content, density, force, thickness, width, weight, and weight of burned fragment (Figure 4 to Figure 10).

The assumption for the design of the map of the force is that the data are isotropic.

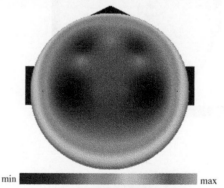

min ◼◼◼◼◼◼◼◼◼◼ max

Fig. 4. Bone mineral content (%)

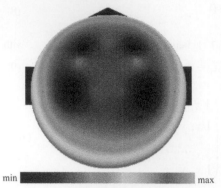

Fig. 5. Density

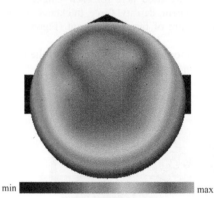

Fig. 6. Force

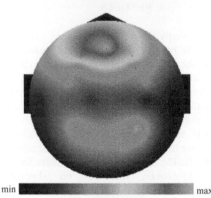

Fig. 7.Thickness

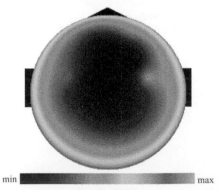

Fig. 8. Width

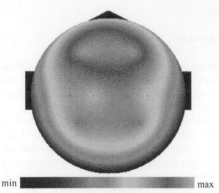

Fig. 9. Weight

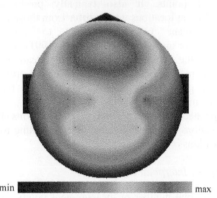

Fig. 10. Weight of burned specimen

The maps provide much information on the variables, such as the distribution of data.

Resemblances between variables are detected; for example we can conclude that density and mineral content in the bone have the same distribution (with a correlation of 98.6%), then a later analysis, such as linear regression, will be made. Also, the thickness and the weight of samples seem to have a similar distribution (with a correlation of 80.3%).

Symmetry between the left side and the right side of the human skull is observed, especially for the mineral content and the density.

Moreover, we can observe a distinction from the distribution by osseous zones. For example, the thickness (and weight) of the skull bone demonstrates regional variations : the temporal region is thinner compared to the parietal and frontal counterparts. In fact, the thickness grows gradually from the parietal bone to the centre of the skull (sagittal suture), with a maximal value at the coronal suture. The parietal bones have less mineral content than the other skull bones. Concerning the peak force, its values are bigger on the frontal bone.

4. CONCLUSION

Software has been developed, which maps in 2 dimensions the biomechanical properties of the human skull. The algorithm, using interpolation with

Dm Spline, has been used in order to determine the values on the whole surface of the skull.

This software allows us to visualize the distribution of the values of each variable, and the symmetry between the left side and the right side of the skull. It also highlights differences between the various bones on the human skull. From these observations, the scientist would elaborate thorough analysis, such as linear regression analysis; then, some indices could be employed to predict and show these resemblances.

Mapping is a technique of visualisation from surface data. This technique is usually used in analysis of electrophysiological signals, with the aim of representing the electric activity of the brain, and proved reliable in the field of electroencephalography. However, this type of representation is not used in human biomechanics, and is a new method in this research topic. In fact, this work could allow putting forth this hypothesis as for the behaviour of the samples after a loading shock according to their characteristics. This work has improved our knowledge about the skull bones mechanical behaviour; in fact, from the observation of the previous maps, we could conclude that the frontal bone, with a maximal value of the peak force, is the most solid bone of the skull, in contrast to the temporal bone, which is supposedly the most fragile bone of the skull. Moreover, there is a correlation between the peak force, and the weight and thickness of the sample, which are lower on the temporal bone. Then we can conclude that there are zones of weaknesses on the human skull (and particularly the temporal bone), due to parameters such as thickness of bones.

Finally, it could be a step in the development of the design of realistic numerical prototype.

Future work will involve developing maps for each bone of the human skull, with the representation and analysis of the sutures of headbones (Oota, *et al*, 2006), in 3 dimensions. We also propose the development of a map including directional characteristics. Development of differentiated maps according to various morphological types could also be useful; in fact, the results presented here are for an 'average head', however the skull form is different for each one.

ACKNOWLEDGEMENTS

The authors thank all the teams who finance the PREDIT PROTEUS (Head Protection of Vulnerable Users) programme, Pr Vallancien and Pr Gagey (René Descartes University), as well as persons who donated their bodies to the science.

REFERENCES

Delille, C., S. Baivier, C. Masson, P. Drazétic (2003). Identification des lois de comportement du crâne à partir d'essais de flexion. *Mécaniques et Industries*, **4**, pp 119-123.

Delille, R., D. Lesueur, P. Potier, F. Rambaud, P. Drazétic, E. Markiewicz (2005). Identification protocol of skull human bone using a mono-layer law. *Computer Methods in Biomechanics and Biomedical Engineering*, **supplement 1**, pp 69-70.

Duchon, J. (1976). Interpolation des fonctions de deux variables suivant le principe de flexion des plaques minces. *R.A.I.R.O. Anal. Num.*, **10**, pp 5–12.

Fujita, T., Y. Fujii, T. Morishita, T. Inoue (1999). Changes of regional distribution of bone mineral according to age, gender, and activity. *Journal of Bone and Mineral Metabolism*, **17**, pp 217-223.

Johnson, E.A.C., Young P.G. (2005). On the use of a patient-specific rapid-prototyped model to simulate the response of the human head to impact and comparison with analytical and finite element models, Journal *of Biomechanics*, **38**, pp 39-45.

Oota, Y., K. Ono, S. Miyazima (2006). 3D sagital suture. *Physica A : statistical mechanics and its applications*, **359**, pp. 538-546.

Soufflet, L., M. Toussaint, R. Luthringer, J. Gresser, R. Minot and J-P. Macher (1991). A statistical evaluation of the main interpolation methods applied to 3-dimensional EEG mapping. *Electroenceph. Clin. Neurophysiol.*, **79**, pp 393–402.

Thali, M.J., B.P. Kneubuehl, U. Zollinger, R. Dirnhofer (2002). The "skin-skull-brain model" : a new instrument for the study of gunshot effects. *Forensic Science International*, **125**, pp 178-189.

Thomas, P., M. Bradford (1995). The nature and source of the head injuries sustained by restrained front-seat car occupants in frontal collisions. *Accid. Anal. and Prev.* , **27 (no4)**, pp 561-570.

Yoganandan, N., F.A. Pintar (2004). Biomechanics of temporo-parietal skull fracture. *Clinical Biomechanics*, **19**, pp 225-239.

ELSEVIER

IFAC

PUBLICATIONS

A CONTINUOUSLY UPDATED HYBRID BLOOD GAS MODEL FOR VENTILATED PATIENTS

A.Wang[a], M.Mahfouf[a], G.H.Mills[b]

[a]Department of Automatic Control and Systems Engineering, University of Sheffield ,
Mappin Street, Sheffield, S1 3JD
[b]Intensive Care Unit, Royal Hallamshire Hospital, Glossop Road, Sheffield, S10 2JF, UK

Abstract: SOPAVent (Simulation of Patients under Artificial Ventilation) is a blood gas model for ventilated patients in intensive care units. In this paper, a continuously updated blood gas model based on SOPAVent is developed and extended to simulate patients' states from a stable to an unstable status. The changes in the patient's physiological state are simulated by updating the shunt and relative dead space in the patient model. The model was validated against blood gas measurements from real patients during a 7-hour period and with changes to the ventilator settings. Results show that, with a selector based on a time criterion, the autonomous model can represent the real patient with a changing physiological state and give good blood gas predictions. Copyright © 2006 IFAC

Keywords: Intensive Care Unit; Autonomous; Dynamics; Hybrid; Modelling; Simulation;

1. INTRODUCTION

Mechanical ventilation is an important part of intensive care therapy. The aim of mechanical ventilation is to ensure that there is enough oxygen in the blood to support the metabolism of the patient and to prevent the build-up of excessive carbon dioxide, which can cause acidosis and impair the bodily functions of the patient. In the management of ventilatory therapy, the clinical team adjusts the ventilator settings according to the patient's general condition, blood gases (mainly arterial oxygen and carbon dioxide pressure), respiratory parameters, and the cardiovascular parameters. Among the many parameters, the arterial blood gas measurement is one of the most important measurements.

The need for a ventilated patient's blood gas model has long been recognized. Such a model can be used to predict the patient's blood gas subjected to ventilator setting changes and help clinicians choose the optimal ventilator settings (Hinds *et al.* 1984; Hardman *et al.* 1998). It can be used outside intensive care units (ICU) as a teaching and training tool (Hinds *et al.* 1982). Also, such a model can be used to develop decision support systems for ventilator management (Thomsen and Sheiner 1989; Kwok *et al.* 2004b).

Although most of the hitherto developed models show reasonable blood gas predictions, they require either invasive measurements or a time-consuming algorithm to obtain all the model parameters before it is able to provide reliable predictions. Recently, our group developed a totally non-invasive blood gas hybrid model (Wang *et al.* 2006). Furthermore, All of the current models are limited to only represent stable patients, i.e. those patients' physiological states which do not change. However, the patient's state often changes with time during ventilation. Therefore, if a blood gas model could be developed to simulate unstable patients by continuously updating its internal parameters, the model's application scope will be improved further and it will be more beneficial in terms of clinical and educational exploitations.

In this paper, a continuously updated blood gas hybrid model for ventilated patients is described. The word 'hybrid' refers to a model which includes mathematical equations from physiology knowledge in combination with elicited neuro-fuzzy formulations. The paper is organized as follows: Section 2 introduces the current SOPAVent model and reviews its development. Section 3 describes the method and validation results for the autonomous blood gas model while Section 4 gives the discussion. Finally, Section 5 draws conclusions in relation to the overall study.

2. THE SOPAVENT MODEL

SOPAVent v.1 (Simulation of Patients under Artificial Ventilation) was developed to provide simulated closed-loop validation of a prototype expert system (Goode 2001). The model represents the exchange of O2 and CO2 in the lungs and tissues together with their transport through the circulatory system based on respiratory physiology and mass balance equations. The model used a compartmental structure (see Figure 1), where the circulatory system is represented by lumped arterial, tissue, venous and pulmonary compartments. The lung is sub-divided into three compartments; (1) an ideal alveolus, where all gas exchange takes place with a perfusion-diffusion ratio of unity; (2) a dead space representing lung areas that are ventilated but not perfused, and (3) a shunt that is a fraction of cardiac output, representing both anatomical shunts and lung areas that are perfused but not ventilated. The details of the model equations can be seen in the Appendix of this paper.

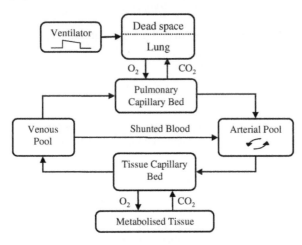

Figure 1: Schematic overview of the patient model.

The inputs of the model are the ventilator settings and the outputs are the arterial PO2 and PCO2. In order to evaluate the model, a set of parameters is required, such as body temperature, patient's age, gender, weight, and height, haemoglobin level (Hb), cardiac output (CO), oxygen consumption (VO2), carbon dioxide production (VCO2), shunt and dead space. Some of the parameters are readily available as part of the routine clinical measurements. However, the last five parameters are not part of the routine measurements. CO, VO2, VCO2 are obtained from invasive cardiovascular measurements while the shunt and dead space are derived by tuning the model using a numerical algorithm, the secant

method (Ewans 1993). The model was implemented using MATLAB® and SIMULINK® and tested clinically using data collected from ICU.

The main limitations of SOPAVent v.1 had been identified by Kwok et al (2004a) and they include the need for invasive measurements and a model tuning algorithm. Invasive measurements are not available for every patient. The secant algorithm for parameter estimation is slow and occasionally no solution can be found for shunt and dead space. Therefore, new non-invasive methods should be developed for shunt, dead space, CO, VO2 and VCO2 estimation.

A non-invasive model for shunt estimation based on the respiratory index (RI) had been developed by Kowk et al. (2004a) using a non-linear adaptive neuro-fuzzy inference system (ANFIS) (Jang 1993). The respiratory index is expressed as equation 2.1.

$$RI = \frac{P_A O_2 - P_a O_2}{P_a O_2} \qquad (2.1)$$

Where the alveolar partial pressure of oxygen (PAO2) is given by:

$$P_A O_2 = FiO_2 (P_B - P_{H_2O}) - PaCO_2 (FiO_2 + (1 - FiO_2)RQ) \qquad (2.2)$$

Therefore, if the FiO2 and PaCO2 are known, PAO2 can be estimated using (2.2) assuming RQ=0.85 and $(P_B - P_{H_2O}) = 95kPa$. Respiratory index can be estimated with FiO2, PaO2, PaCO2, which are all routinely measured in ICU. The shunt data derived from the secant tuning method were used to train the ANFIS model. The model structure is shown in Figure 2.

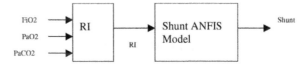

Figure 2: The shunt model structure.

Recently, a non-invasive relative dead space model was developed (Wang et al. 2006). The latest type of ventilator (Drager EvitaXL) used in our hospital can provide the relative dead space measurements. Therefore, a dead space model based on the patient data was developed. The model inputs were identified by conducting correlation analysis between the dead space and other routine ICU measurements. The results showed that PaCO2, tidal volume (VT), respiratory rate (RR), inspiratory pressure (Pinsp) and positive end-expiratory pressure (PEEP) have the most significant correlation with relative dead space. Therefore, they were used as model inputs and a relative dead space model was developed using ANFIS (Figure 3).

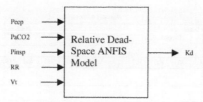

Figure 3: The relative dead space mode structure.

The CO, VO2, VCO2 were also derived non-invasively using a mean population (Kwok *et al.* 2004a).As a result, the current SOPAVent is totally independent of any invasive measurement and the secant method for parameter estimation. The model's application scope and speed are significantly improved.

3. A CONTINUOUSLY UPDATED MODEL FOR BLOOD GAS PREDICTIONS

The SOPAVent model was developed to give steady-state blood gas predictions for stable patients. With further improvements, the model became totally independent of any invasive measurements. However, SOPAVent's applications are still limited to stable patients and if one wishes to simulate a real patient for a period of time (i.e. the patient's state might change), one must collect real patient data frequently then update the model parameters; this, obviously, limits the model's application scope. In this section, the method and results for a continuously updated patient model based on SOPAVent is presented.

3.1 Data

Two patients from the previously studied group (Wang *et al.* 2006) were selected. Their data were collected from the patient data management system (PDMS) located in the Royal Hallamshire Hospital ICU, Sheffield, UK. The local medical research ethics committee was consulted and the use of the patient data was approved. The two patients were admitted between April 2005 and August 2005. The periods when they were mechanically ventilated without spontaneous breathing and had regular ventilator setting changes were identified. Their ventilator settings and blood gas measurements (PaO2, PaCO2, PH, SaO2) were collected continuously for the whole periods. At the first blood gas sample of each patient, the patient's demographic information, ventilator settings (FiO2, PEEP, PIP, RR I:E ratio), tidal volume (Vt), body temperature, blood pressure (BPs, BPd), Hb and HCO3 were collected.

3.2. Method

In the SOPAVent model parameters sensitivity analysis (Kwok 2003), it was noted that the shunt and the relative dead space are the most sensitive patient parameters that affect PaO2 and PaCO2 respectively. In clinical practice, shunt and dead space are also viewed as important indicators of

pulmonary disease severity and progression (Hardman and Bedforth 1999; Moppett *et al.* 2005). Therefore, the patient physiological state changes are represented by shunt and dead space changes in our model. Based on this simplification, a blood gas model with updated shunt and dead space is hence developed as follows:

1. Within the chosen period, use the first blood gas sample data to construct the initial patient model. For those parameters that are not directly measured, such as shunt, dead space, CO, VO2, VCO2, they were derived using the non-invasive estimation methods described in Section 2 respectively. The blood gas measurements during this period are used as the validation data.

2. Change the ventilator settings of the initial patient model as they are on the real patient and predict the blood gas. The blood gas prediction results are referred to as PaO2_instant and PaCO2_instant.

3. Based on the instant blood gas predictions and the changed ventilator settings, the shunt and relative dead space are re-estimated using the ANFIS model respectively, then the updated shunt and dead space are used in the model to give a new blood gas prediction. The blood gases results are referred to as PaO2_updated and PaCO2_updated.

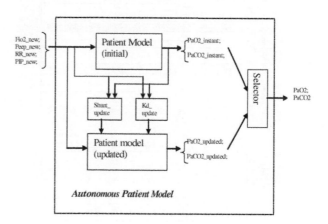

Figure 4: The structure for the new patient model.

4. As shown in Figure 4, there are two sets of blood gas predictions for one new ventilator setting, 'instant' and 'updated'. A time criterion was used to decide the final model output. When the blood gas predictions are required within 1 hour after the ventilator setting change, the 'instant' blood gases results are selected. This indicates that the patient state is not changed. The model parameters are kept constant for the next ventilator settings. When the blood gas predictions are required after 1 hour of ventilator setting change, the patient state might be changed and the 'updated' blood gas results are used as the model outputs. The patient model parameters are also replaced by the updated patient model parameters for the next simulation.

Finally, the whole procedure is repeated with every change of ventilator settings until all the validation data have been compared.

3.3 Results

The model predictions were compared with the real data from the patient database using the model of section 3.2. The results are shown in Figures 5 and 6. The time between each validation data and the corresponding ventilator setting change is shown in the figure. If the validation data were measured within 60 minutes of the new ventilator setting, they were compared with the 'instant' blood gas predictions from the model. If the validation data were measured after 60 minutes of the new settings, then they were compared with the 'updated' blood gas predictions. The shunt and relative dead space were also shown in the figure. It can be seen that the instant predictions are based on the same shunt and dead space value while the updated blood gas predictions are based on the updated shunt and dead space value. From the results, it can be seen that, using the new model architecture, the model predictions are matched with the real measurements based on our method.

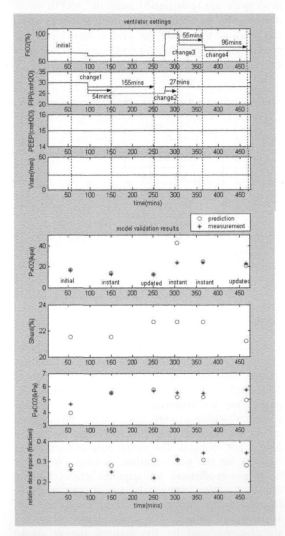

Figure 5: The ventilator settings and model validation results for patient 1 during approximately a 7-hour simulation.

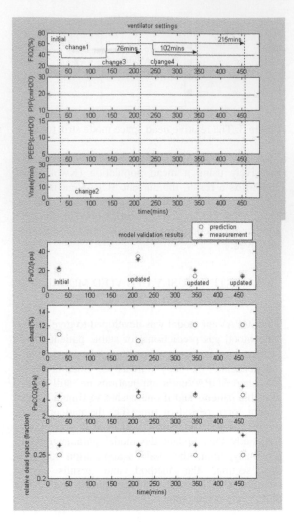

Figure 6: The ventilator settings and model validation results for patient 2 during approximately a 7-hour simulation.

4. DISCUSSION

In clinical practice, the ventilated patient's physiological states are very complex and highly interactive. Shunt and dead space are often regarded as reliable indicators of patient's states.

Currently, the shunt value is predicted using an ANFIS model with one input: the respiratory index (RI) based on PaO2, PaCO2 and FiO2. The relative dead space (Kd) is predicted using an ANFIS model with five inputs: PaCO2, VT, RR, Pinsp and PEEP. It can be seen from the inputs that both the shunt and Kd are affected by the ventilator settings. Although the oxygen index is widely accepted as a good estimator of shunt, several investigators have pointed out that this index may also be misleading because of its dependence on FiO2, especially when FiO2 is changed (Gould *et al.* 1997; Maulen-Radovan *et al.* 1999). Therefore, the use of RI as a shunt model input may not be reliable in this current application, which is the dynamical prediction of shunt with ventilator settings changes. However, the RI did have a close correlation with the shunt data in our previous study (Kwok *et al.* 2004a) and several studies also showed that the oxygen indices correlated closely with the measured shunt (Zetterstrom 1988), especially in hemodynamically stable patients. Therefore, it is fair to consider that the shunt prediction from the ANFIS model represents the shunt value when the patient with the current ventilator settings reaches a stable state. In Figure 7, the dashed line represents the real shunt with time but the prediction by our current shunt model after the change of ventilator setting is given to be the steady-state shunt value directly (the straight line). Hence, the shunt model cannot provide the shunt dynamical information between the two steady states. The relative dead space model has the similar limitation because its modelling data were collected at the blood gas samples when the patient's states were usually stable.

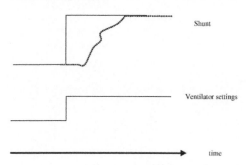

Figure 7: Diagram illustrating the limitation of the shunt model.

Based on this understanding, a selector for shunt and Kd predictions and model outputs using 'time' as a criterion has been included. A 1-hour time period was deemed sufficient for updating the model and hence the predictions.

Due to the retrospective nature of this study, the validation data size is limited by the infrequent blood gas measurements. The blood gases are usually measured every one or two hours. There is often more than one ventilator setting change between two continuous blood gas measurements. The validation data quality is also uncertain because it is not known where there were any medical or nursing interventions before the measurements were taken.

5. CONCLUSION

A continuously updated blood gas hybrid dynamic model for ventilated patients in general ICU was developed based on an earlier mathematical model called SOPAVent. The features of the new model architecture include the fact that it relies on non-invasive measurements and uses frequently updated values of the shunt and relative dead space to provide reliable predictions of blood gas variables such as PaO2 and PaCO2. Validation results obtained from two 7-hour real patients data sets showed that the model can provide reliable output predictions for stable and unstable patient states. Future work will consider validating the model further using more patient data and also investigating the influence of shunt and relative dead space on the predictions in order to generalise the model. The ultimate aims of the model are to act as a patient simulator for junior doctors and ICU medical staff and to design a decision support system for optimal settings of the ventilator.

APPENDIX

The mass transport of O2 was described by the following 5 linked differential equations (Thomsen and Sheiner 1989);

$$\frac{\partial CaO_2}{\partial t} \cdot Va = \dot{Q}_t \cdot [X \cdot CvO_2 + (1-X) \cdot CpO_2 - CaO_2] \quad (1)$$

$$\frac{\partial CtO_2}{\partial t} \cdot Vt = \dot{Q}_t \cdot [CaO_2 - CtO_2] - \dot{V}o_2 \quad (2)$$

$$\frac{\partial CvO_2}{\partial t} \cdot Vv = \dot{Q}_t \cdot [CtO_2 - CvO_2] \quad (3)$$

$$\frac{\partial CpO_2}{\partial t} \cdot Vp = \dot{Q}_t \cdot (1-X) \cdot [(CvO_2 - CpO_2) + O_2 Diff] \quad (4)$$

$$\frac{\partial CAO_2}{\partial t} \cdot VA = RR \cdot (VT - VD) \cdot (FIO_2 - CAO_2 / 1000) \quad (5)$$
$$- \dot{Q}_t \cdot (1-X) \cdot O_2 Diff$$

Where VA, Va, Vt, Vv, Vp indicate volumes of alveolar, arterial, tissue, venous, and pulmonary compartments respectively (litres); $\dot{Q}_t$, cardiac output (ml blood/min); X, Fraction of blood shunted past lungs; VO2, O2 consumption by tissues (ml O2/min); VD, Alveolar dead space volume (ml); VT, Tidal volume (ml); RR, Respiratory rate (breath/min); CAO2, Alveolar O2 content (ml O2/l gas) ; CxO2, where x=a, t, v, p – arterial, tissue, venous and pulmonary O2 content respectively (ml O2/l blood) ; t, Time (min) ; FiO2, Inspired O2 gas fraction.

The gas exchange between the ideal alveolus and the pulmonary compartment is driven by the pressure gradient across the different boundary for each gas (equ. 6);

$$O_2 Diff = BO_2 \cdot (PB \cdot (CAO_2 / 1000) - PpO_2)$$
$$[ml\ O_2/l\ blood] \quad (6)$$

where, PpO2, Pulmonary partial pressure of O2 (kPa); PB, Barometric pressure (kPa); and BO2 is the diffusion coefficient expressed in terms of ml O2/kPa/l blood and is derived from the O2 diffusion capacity of the lung (DO2 in ml/min/kPa) and the non-shunted blood flow rate in l/min (equ. 7);

$$BO_2 = \frac{DO_2}{\dot{Q}_t(1-X)} \quad [ml\ O_2/kPa/l\ blood] \quad (7)$$

Whilst only equations pertaining to the diffusion and circulation of O2 are presented here, there exists within the model a set of similar equations for CO2.

REFERENCES

Ewans, C. W. (1993). Engineering Mathematics - A Programmed Approach. London UK, Chapman & Hall.

Goode, K. M. (2001). Model-based development of a fuzzy logic advisor for artificially ventilated patients. Ph.D. thesis. University of Sheffield.

Gould, M. K., Ruoss, S. J., Rizk, N. W., Doyle, R. L. and Raffin, T. A. (1997). "Indices of hypoxemia in patients with acute respiratory distress syndrome: Reliability, validity, and clinical usefulness." Critical Care Medicine 25(1): 6-8.

Hardman, J. G. and Bedforth, N. M. (1999). "Estimating venous admixture using a physiological simulator." British Journal of Anaesthesia 82(3): 346-349.

Hardman, J. G., Bedforth, N. M., Ahmed, A. B., Mahajan, R. P. and Aitkenhead, A. R. (1998). "A physiology simulator: validation of its respiratory components and its ability to predict the patient's response to changes in mechanical ventilation." British Journal of Anaesthesia 81(3): 327-332.

Hinds, C. J., Ingram, D. and Dickinson, C. J. (1982). "Self-instruction and assessment in techniques of intensive-care using a computer-model of the respiratory system." Intensive Care Medicine 8(3): 115-123.

Hinds, C. J., Roberts, M. J., Ingram, D. and Dickinson, C. J. (1984). "Computer-Simulation to Predict Patient Responses to Alterations in the Ventilation Regime." Intensive Care Medicine 10(1): 13-22.

Jang, J. (1993). "ANFIS: Adaptive-network-based fuzzy inference system." IEEE Transactions on System, Man, and Cybernetics 23(3): 665-685.

Kwok, H. F. (2003). SIVA: An Intelligent Advisory System for Intensive Care Ventilators. PhD thesis. The University of Sheffield.

Kwok, H. F., Linkens, D. A., Mahfouf, M. and Mills, G. H. (2004a). "Adaptive ventilator FiO(2) advisor: use of non-invasive estimations of shunt." Artificial Intelligence in Medicine 32(3): 157-169.

Kwok, H. F., Linkens, D. A., Mahfouf, M. and Mills, G. H. (2004b). "SIVA: A hybrid knowledge-and-model-based advisory system for intensive care ventilators." IEEE Transactions on Information Technology in Biomedicine 8(2): 161-172.

Maulen-Radovan, I., Castrellon, P. G., Ochoa, E. C. and Aguirre, M. M. (1999). "Are oxygen indices effective for predicting pathological intrapulmonary shunt in mechanically ventilated children?" Archives of Medical Research 30(3): 179-185.

Moppett, I. K., Gornall, C. B. and Hardman, J. G. (2005). "The dependence of measured alveolar deadspace on anatomical deadspace volume." British Journal of Anaesthesia 95(3): 400-405.

Thomsen, G. and Sheiner, L. (1989). "SIMV: An application of mathematical modelling in ventilator management". In: 13th Ann. Symp. on Computer Applications in Medical Care., Washington DC. IEEE Computer Society.

Wang, A., Mahfouf, M. and Mills, G. H. (2006). "A Blood Gas Hybrid Model For Ventilated Patients In ICU With New Formulations For Dead Space And Tidal Volume." In: The 4th IASTED International Conference on Biomedical Engineering, Austria.

Zetterstrom, H. (1988). "Assessment of the efficiency of pulmonary oxygenaton: the choice of oxygen index." Acta. Anaesthesiologica Scandinavica 32: 579-584.

ANALYSIS OF RUPTURE OF INTRACRANIAL SACCULAR ANEURYSMS

Krzysztof Szafrański

Department of Electricity, Szczecin University of Technology

Abstract: The factors leading to the rupture of intracranial saccular aneurysms are presented in this paper. The mathematical models based on the Legendre functions are presented, moreover minimisation of difference between actual and calculated radius of aneurysm is shown. The impact was put on the new approach towards estimation of rupture, which is more dependent on curvature and shape of an aneurysm than its size. *Copyright © 2006 IFAC*

Keywords: biomedical systems, curves, modelling, polynomials, scalar, shapes, variable.

1. GENERAL DESCRIPTION OF RUPTURE OF INTRACRANIAL ANEURYSMS

Intracranial saccular aneurysm (ISA) is a localised distended sac affecting only a part of the circumference of the artery wall. About 2-5 % of the population can have ISA (The International Study of Unruptured Intracranial Aneurysms Inverstigation, Unruptured intracranial aneurysms, 1998) but in case of a rupture 50-60 % of people with an aneurysm may die (Van Gijn and Rinkel, 2001). Treatments used for saccular aneurysms have a mortality rate reaching 18 %, hence it is critical to determine the risk of the aneurysm's rupture very quickly.

The main point of the investigations and tests is to determine the critical parameters for the risk of rupture. Mathematical models of aneurysms are typically based on Laplace's law which defines a linear relation between the circumferential tension and the radius. However, since the aneurysm wall is viscoelastic, a nonlinear model was developed to characterise the development and rupture of intracranial spherical aneurysms within an arterial bifurcation and the model describes the aneurysm in terms of biophysical and geometric variables at static equilibrium. A comparison is made between mathematical models of a spherical aneurysm based on linear and nonlinear forms of Laplace's law. The first form is the standard Laplace's law which states that a linear relation exists between the circumferential tension, T, and the radius, R, of the aneurysm given by $T = PR/2t$ where P is the systolic pressure. The second is a 'modified' Laplace's law which describes a nonlinear power relation between the tension and the radius defined by $T = ARP/2At$ where A is the elastic modulus for collagen and t is the wall thickness. Differential expressions of these two relations were used to describe the critical radius or the radius prior to aneurysm rupture. Using the standard Laplace's law, the critical radius was derived to be $Rc = 2Et/P$ where E is the elastic modulus of the aneurysm. The critical radius from the modified Laplace's law was $R = [2Et/P]2At/P$. Substituting typical values of E = 1.0 MPa, t = 40 microns, P = 150 mmHg, and A = 2.8 MPa, the critical radius is 4.0 mm for the standard Laplace's law and 4.8 mm for the modified Laplace's law (Hademenos, et al., 1994).

Hence, the size is the primary parameter used for the prediction of rupture of an aneurysm. Reasearches prove that treatment is necessary for aneurysms larger than 10 mm, however, some small aneurysms less than 4 mm are not stable and can rupture more often than the bigger ones. Geometry of saccular aneurysms is not well explored, and as the main predictor the height-to width of an aneurysm (also called aspect ratio) is used (Parlea, et al., 1999). One of the most important parameters used for prediction of rupture is also stress which is measured in the fundus and neck, and then compared to check the difference (84 % of ruptures are located in the fundus and only 2 % ruptures are located in the neck). Moreover, the stretch ratio as the ratio of radius in the pressurised and unloaded configuration is calculated in accordance with data obtained from MRA.

According to tests performed by some scientists, the surface of the aneurysm has properties alike membrane, and it makes the curvature of a lesion a very important parameter leading to rupture. Following this assumption, it is necessary to calculate the curvatures in a precise and quick way. Calculations of curvatures have not been performed so far apart from some work done by Sacks, et al. (1999) on abdominal aortic aneurysms, which included method for calculation of curvatures based on MRA. The new method of calculation of curvatures by the means of Legendre functions is proposed in the following section, and it makes it possible to provide an almost real aneurysm geometry.

Another aspect of modelling of saccular aneurysms is determination of blood and lesion interactions. Therefore it is essential to compare the Newtonian fluid model, which mimics shear-thinning blood behaviour and the non-Newtonian fluid model. The choice of the model is necessary for determination of relationship between the aspect ratio and the wall shear stress.

Finally, the impact of stent on the inflow in the aneurysm should be taken into account. This impact is described by the blocking ratio (C_α) and it facilitates determination of rupture of an aneurysm for any stent location (Burleson, et al., 1995).

2. MODELLING BASED ON THE LEGENDRE FUNCTIONS

The computation of boundaries for aneurysms, which data are received in the form of MRA films, by the usage of splines and some modelling packages is pretty time-consuming and it is rather impractical for application during patient's test. The aneurysms are not ideal spheres, therefore the best solution is the usage of spheroidal functions (Legendre functions), which guarantee calculation accuracy and the possibility of alteration of shape.

2.1 The concept of modelling and transformation into Cartesian coordinates.

Legendre functions can be described by:

$$P_n^m(x) = (-1)^m (1-x^2)^{m/2} \frac{d}{dx^m} P_n(x) \qquad (1)$$

where m and n are integer values, $P_n(x)$ is a Legendre polynomial and x is any argument. The boundary of the lesion can be described by:

$$r = \beta(1 + c \cdot P_n^m(\cos\phi) \cdot \cos(m\theta)) \qquad (2)$$

where r is the radius, ϕ is from $[0,\pi]$ and θ is from $[0,2\pi]$. ϕ and θ are angles in spherical coordinates, P_n^m is the Legendre function of the first kind, and β, c, n and m are shape parameters. The shape can be defined for any value of ϕ and θ, if the center point and the equation for radius are determined.

The variation of β changes the overall size of the figure and the variation of c changes the shape of the figure. Therefore the higher value of c, the bigger distortion of an aneurysm from a spherical geometry. The exemplary shapes of aneurysms were presented below:

Fig. 1. Shape of an aneurysm based on Legendre functions with n=3 and m=0 and c=0.4.

Firstly, the Legendre polynomials are transformed from spherical (r, ϕ, θ) into Cartesian (x, y, z) coordinates,

$$R = xi + yj + zk \qquad (3)$$

and

$$
\begin{aligned}
x &= r\cos\theta\sin\phi \\
y &= r\sin\theta\sin\phi \\
z &= r\cos\phi
\end{aligned}
\qquad (4)
$$

and then every component is multiplied by a scalar $(\alpha x, \gamma y, \delta z)$,

$$R = \alpha x i + \gamma y j + \delta z k \qquad (5)$$

This operation stretches the spheroid in three directions.

2.2 The optimisation based on the Marquardt-Levenberg regression code.

The difference between the actual radius and radius of an aneurysm calculated from the Legendre functions shall be minimised. The Marquardt-Levenberg regression code was used in order to determine parameters that minimise the sum of squares error (SSE), defined as:

$$SSE = \sum (r - r_{th})^2 \qquad (6)$$

These parameters m, n, c, α, γ, δ, β, $x0$, $y0$, $z0$, $rot1$, $rot2$, $rot3$. α, γ, δ are the stretches in the x, y and z

directions, $x0$, $y0$ and $z0$ define the center of the spheroid, and rot1, rot2 and rot3 define the Euler angles for the rigid rotation of an aneurysm shape.

The root mean squared error (RMS) is used as the error criterion and is given in milimeters (mm),

$$RMS = \sqrt{MSE} \qquad (7)$$

where

$$MSE = \frac{SSE}{N} \qquad (8)$$

The main point of the tests is the calculation of curvatures. The calculations of curvatures for Legendre spheroids are performed in MATLAB, while curvature maps are presented in Maple.

2.3 Calculation of curvatures.

According to the previously defined conditions the following can be determined:

$$R = r\sin\phi\cos\theta \cdot i + r\sin\phi\sin\theta \cdot j + r\cos\phi \cdot k \qquad (9)$$

The infitesimal movement on the surface is defined by:

$$dR = R_{,\theta}\, d\theta + R_{,\phi}\, d\phi \qquad (10)$$

where $R_{,\theta}$ and $R_{,\phi}$ are the base vectors:

$$R_{,\theta} = \frac{\partial R}{\partial \theta}$$

$$R_{,\phi} = \frac{\partial R}{\partial \phi} \qquad (11)$$

The curvatures are calculated as the maximal and minimal values of K_n, which is called the normal curvature and is strictly related to the curvature vector k:

$$k_n = -K_n n \qquad (12)$$

where k_n is the normal component of the curvature vector, defined by:

$$k = \frac{dt}{dS} = k_n + k_t \qquad (13)$$

The impact of k_t is not taken into account in this paper.

n and t are perpendicular, and after taking the derivative with respect to S, the following is obtained:

$$\frac{dn}{dS} \cdot t + \frac{dt}{dS} \cdot n = 0 \qquad (14)$$

K_n can be defined as:

$$K_n = \frac{dR \cdot dn}{dR \cdot dR} \qquad (15)$$

where:

$$dn = n_{,\theta}\, d\theta + n_{,\phi}\, d\phi$$

$$dR = R_{,\theta}\, d\theta + R_{,\phi}\, d\phi \qquad (16)$$

Finally K_n can be expressed as (Kraus, 1967):

$$K_n = \frac{L(d\theta)^2 + 2M d\theta d\phi + N(d\phi)^2}{E(d\theta)^2 + 2F d\theta d\phi + G(d\phi)^2} \qquad (17)$$

where E, F and G are defined as:

$$E = R_{,\theta} \cdot R_{,\theta}$$

$$F = R_{,\theta} \cdot R_{,\phi} \qquad (18)$$

$$G = R_{,\phi} \cdot R_{,\phi}$$

and L, M and N are second fundamental magnitudes:

$$L = R_{,\theta} \cdot n_{,\theta} = -R_{,\theta\theta} \cdot n$$

$$M = \frac{1}{2}(R_{,\theta} \cdot n_{,\phi} + R_{,\phi} \cdot n_{,\theta}) = -R_{,\theta\phi} \cdot n \qquad (19)$$

$$N = R_{,\phi} \cdot n_{,\phi} = -R_{,\phi\phi} \cdot n$$

The formula for K_n can be modified by defining direction λ as $\lambda = d\o/d\theta$:

$$K_n(\lambda) = \frac{L + 2M\lambda + N\lambda^2}{E + 2F\lambda + G\lambda^2} \qquad (20)$$

The maximal (η_1) and minimal (η_2) values of the normal curvature were received upon calculation of $dK_n/d\lambda = 0$ as follows:

$$\eta_1 = (K_n)_1 = \frac{L + 2M\lambda_1 + N\lambda_1^2}{E + 2F\lambda_1 + G\lambda_1^2}$$

$$\eta_2 = (K_n)_2 = \frac{L + 2M\lambda_2 + N\lambda_2^2}{E + 2F\lambda_2 + G\lambda_2^2} \qquad (21)$$

where λ_1 and λ_2 are the directions of the maximal and minimal curvatures.

$$\{\lambda_1, \lambda_2\} = \frac{-(LG - NE)}{2(MG - NF)} \pm$$

$$\frac{\sqrt{(LG - NE)^2 - 4(MG - NF)(LF - ME)}}{2(MG - NF)} \qquad (22)$$

Modelling of aneurysms with more complicated shapes by usage of Legendre spheroids makes it possible to estimate curvatures at any location of a lesion and risk of rupture for any direction of curvature. η_1 and η_2 are the values pointing such locations of aneurysms, where stretches tend to be bigger, which may induce an aneurysm to rupture in case of larger stresses. Therefore the maximal value η_1 is the critical value for curvature of an aneurysm indicating a high rupture risk.

2.4 Modification of the Legendre spheroids

Modelling of aneurysm by the usage of Legendre functions makes it possible to improve on RMS values. The average RMS values for five aneurysms, which data were taken for calculation from MRA films, were 0.45 mm for the standard Legendre function, and 0.77 mm for the sphere. Therefore the general improvement is about 42 %. The further improvement of 2 to 12 % was achieved thanks to the modification of the Legendre function by scalar multiplies. The results of optimisation are presented in the following table by the comparison of RMS values for unmodified Legendre spheroid (values were obtained by the Marquardt-Levenberg search algorithm) and modified (by scalar multiplies) Legendre spheroid. According to the above given formulas curvatures are strictly related to boundary (radius) of a lesion, and it is a very complicated task to compare directly curvature obtained from CT or MRA data and calculated curvature, but it has been proved that it is possible to perform comparison indirectly by calculation of difference between the actual radius and radius of the Legendre-shaped aneurysm. Thanks to minimisation of error by the use of Marquardt-Levenberg regression code the value of calculated radius is close to the actual radius and therefore the calculated curvature is close to the real curvature.

Table 1 Comparison of RMS values for two kinds of Legendre spheroids (modified and unmodified).

Parameter	Unmodified	Modified
c	0.29	0.0099
beta	4.01	2.1185
m	1	2
n	2	4
alpha	1	1.71
gamma	1	2.63
delta	1	1.17
x_0	0.08	0.03
y_0	0.09	-0.1044
z_0	0.06	0.0476
rot1	-1.3	0.7055
rot2	-1.47	0.025
rot3	-1.15	-1.75
RMS (mm)	0.4015	0.3667
Improvement over unmodified		8.67 %

2.5 Characteristics of curvatures

The modified Legendre spheroids are shown in the figures below, and the minimal and maximal values of curvatures are bordered by different colours by the means of Maple.

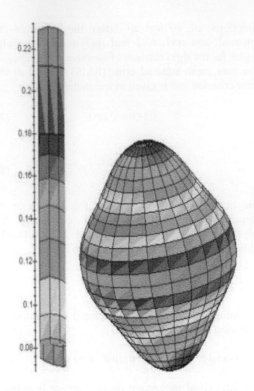

Fig. 2. Maximal curvature values η_1 for the exemplary aneurysm.

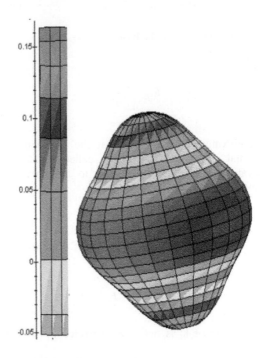

Fig. 3: Minimal curvature values η_2 for the exemplary aneurysm.

2.6 Calculation of stress in relation to curvatures

The principal stress resultants T_1 and T_2 can be calculated upon maximal and minimal curvature η_1 and η_2.

$$T_1 = \frac{P}{2\eta_2}$$

$$T_2 = \frac{P}{\eta_2}(1 - \frac{\eta_1}{2\eta_2}) \qquad (23)$$

It shows that stress resultants can be calculated independent of the properties of the material. Finally the principal stress resultants for geometry of ellipse are as follows:

$$T_1 = \frac{Pa^2}{2(a^2 \sin^2 \phi + b^2 \cos^2 \phi)^{1/2}}$$

$$T_2 = [\frac{Pa^2}{(a^2 \sin^2 \phi + b^2 \cos^2 \phi)^{1/2}}] \cdot$$

$$\cdot (1 - \frac{a^2 \cdot \sin^2 \phi + b^2 \cdot \cos^2 \phi}{2b^2})$$

$$(24)$$

where a and b are the deformed major and minor dimension, and $\varnothing$ is from $[0,\pi]$, which is the angle between the axis of symmetry and the line connecting the origin and the point of interest. The result for a sphere is received, if a=b. Therefore the stress resultants can be calculated on the basis of spherical or ellipsoidal geometry.

3. SUMMARY

Modelling of saccular aneurysms is an important basis for the future treatment and rupture prevention of aneurysms. Therefore the proper shape shall be assumed, as the sphere is the too simplified curvature.

According to international researches on intracranial saccular aneurysms the size cannot be used for prediction of risk of rupture in aneurysms of diameter less than 10 mm (Wiebers, 1998). Thanks to the usage of Legendre spheroids it is possible to evaluate curvatures at any location of an aneurysm. As it was stated in the section of results, the general improvement of RMS values for the standard Legendre function is about 42 % in relation to the sphere. The average improvement rate of RMS value in case of modification of Legendre spheroid was 2 to 12 %, however the maximal improvement of η was 37 %. The model of an aneurysm based on Legendre function can be still modified, as RMS values for the modified Legendre spheroid are as big as 0.85 mm comparing to 0.2 mm resolution of MR and 0.4 mm of SOMATOM Sensation 64 CT scanner.

The main fault of the Legendre spheroid is the smoothing effect of the surface of a lesion, hence the curvature values of the Legendre spheroid do not differ too much. Although splines can be used for evaluation of curvatures, they increase computation time to 9-10 hours, which makes it an almost impractical method. The computation time for the Legendre spheroid is about 3 minutes, while for the modified Legendre spheroid amounts to about 40 minutes. More complex functions than Legendre

functions will be tested in the future in order to eliminate smoothing effect and decrease RMS.

Since vascular changes are sensitive to minor changes in the environment, these changes can be controlled by modelling of saccular aneurysms. Aneurysms resemble membranes and their stresses can be managed by local curvatures. The shapes are not ideal spheroids, therefore the application of Legendre function is the correct solution. Thanks to the usage of Legendre spheroids the RMS values can be reduced of up to 40 % and even more. The Marquardt-Levenberg search algorithm was also used. The computation time is reasonable for the Legendre spheroids, which predispose them to modelling of lesions. Nevertheless the size of aneurysm shall be taken into account as well, as there is relationship between the aspect ratio (AR) and normalised wall shear stress (Ujie, et al., 1999). Such a relationship makes it possible to classify aneurysms which are more prone to ruptures.

The choice of the initial conditions is essential for simplification of further calculations, especially if blood flow is analysed. Finally, the impact of stents used to harbour aneurysms on blood flow and wall shear stress inside the aneurysm is worth testing. The critical value for which the probability of aneurysmal rupture is slight was found and there is a need to look for critical relationships between stent, vortical flow and wall shear stress for different shapes of stent.

REFERENCES

Burleson A.C., Strother C.M., and Turitto V.T. (1995). *Computer Modelling of Intracranial Saccular and Lateral Aneurysms for the Study of their Hemodynamics.* Journal of Neurosurgery, 37, 774-784.

Hademenos G.J., Massoud T., Valentino D.J., Duckwiler G., Vinuela F. (1994). *A nonlinear mathematical model for the development and rupture of intracranial saccular aneurysms.* Neurol. Res.; 16(5):376-84.

Kraus H. (1967). *Thin elastic shells an introduction to the theoretical foundations and the analysis of their static and dynamic behavior.* John Wiley & Sons, New York.

Parlea L., Fahrig R., Holdsworth D.W., and Lownie S.P. (1999). *An analysis of the geometry of saccular intracranial aneurysm.* Am J. Neuroradiol, 1079-1089.

Sacks M.S., Vorp D.A., Raghavan M.L., Federle M.P., Webster M.W. (1999). *In vivo three-dimensional surface geometry of abdominal aortic aneurysm.* Annals of Biomedical Engineering 27, 469-479.

The International Study of Unruptured Intracranial Aneurysms Inverstigation, Unruptured intracranial aneurysms (1998). *Risk of rupture and risks of surgical intervention.* New England Journal of Medicine; 339: 1725-1733.

Ujie H., Tachibana H., Hiramatsu O., et al. (1999). *Effects of size and shape (aspect ratio) on the hemodynamics of saccular aneurysms: a possible index for surgical treatment of intracranial aneurysms.* Neurosurgery 45, 119-129.

Van Gijn J. and Rinkel G. (2001). *Subarachnoid hemorrhage: diagnosis, causes and management.* Brain; 124:249-278.

Wiebers D.O. (1998). *Unruptured intracranial aneurysms – risk of rupture and risks of surgical intervention.* The New England Journal of Medicine 339, 1725-1733.

MODELLING AND CONTROL OF HIV DYNAMICS

Alberto Landi[*], Alberto Mazzoldi[°], Chiara Andreoni[°], Matteo Bianchi[°],
Andrea Cavallini[°], Leonardo Ricotti[°], Luca Ceccherini Nelli[#], Riccardo Iapoce[§]

Department of Electrical Systems and Automation, University of Pisa,
via Diotisalvi 2, 56126, Pisa, Italy. e-mail: landi@ieee.org
° Interdepartmental Research Center E.Piaggio, University of Pisa,
Via Diotisalvi 2, 56126, Pisa, Italy
 # Department of Virology, Via San Zeno, University of Pisa
§ U.O. Malattie Infettive, Ospedale Cisanello – Azienda Ospedaliera Pisana,
Via Paradisa 2–56100, Pisa, Italy

Abstract: Various models have been considered in literature for modelling HIV infection
and evolution. This paper considers a modification of the Wodarz and Nowak model, in
order to obtain a simple, but effective mathematical model useful to predict the effects of
a therapeutic drug regimen. After presenting several simulations for illustrating the
effectiveness of the considered model, an accurate analysis of the results and some new
ideas for future studies are discussed. *Copyright © 2006 IFAC*

Keywords: Physiological models, HIV, Biomedical system, Differential equations,
Numerical simulations.

1. INTRODUCTION

Over the last years HIV dynamical models have been
the objects of an intensive research. Nevertheless
"Human Immunodeficiency Virus," (HIV) still
continues to be not completely modelled. Several
aspects of the pathology have been identified and
modelled in an effective way, but unfortunately other
aspects (especially correlated to therapeutic effects)
are under research activity and require more accurate
experimental and theoretical evaluations. Dynamic
interactions between viral infection and immune
system are particularly complex (Wodarz and
Nowak, 2000). Although the immune responsiveness
is potentially able to attack the virus, HIV infection
causes the depletion of the cell Helper T CD4[+],
which has a primary role in the generation of
immune response. Moreover, HIV infection attacks
other immune cells, as macrophages, dendrites cell,
etc. Therefore, in the initial acute phase of this
pathology, there is an immune response, which is
sub-optimal for the intrinsic viral activity reducing

ability of the immune systems. This peculiar viral
activity contributes to the permanence of the virus
and to its very high mutation rate (Vergu, Mallet and
Golmard, 2005). Some days after the burst of the
viral aggression, there is a high increase of number of
virus cells at lymph-nodes, with a peak of viremia.
In the following 12 weeks the immune response is
completed and the viremia decreases up to low
values, which can be also below the measurement
threshold (Zurakowski, and Teel, 2006). After the
initial phase characterized by a strong reduction, also
CD4[+] cells come back to acceptable values. It starts a
new phase of the infection, with a "clinical latency":
in the lymph-nodes and spleen there is a continuous
replication of the virus, with destruction of immune
cells. In this phase, the immune system is apparently
able to control the situation and to oppose its action
of virus and of other opportunistic microbes, such
that there is no particular evidence of the presence of
the virus in the patients. Only after few years, a new
acute phase bursts, with re-increasing of viremia and
CD4[+] decreasing. Primarily viral reservoirs (in which

virus cells are conserved without possibility to be destruct by immune system or by external drugs) cause re-emergence of the virus upon cessation of therapy, even after many years of suppression (D. Finzi et al, 1999). Modelling of reservoirs (Ortega and Landrove, 2000), (Di Mascio et al, 2004), at the moment is one of the more difficult aspects to be implemented in the mathematical models. In this context, the pharmacology therapy offers several interesting results to an increasing of the quality and of expectation of life for the patient. Two main classes of drugs are used to reduce the replication of the virus and to delay the progression of the pathology (see Adams et al. and references therein, 2005). The so-called highly active anti-retroviral therapy (HAART), is a combination therapy including
- reverse transcriptase inhibitors, to stop the process of inverse transcription and to avoid to permit to the virus to infect other cells,
- protease inhibitors, to stop the production of precursors of viral proteins avoid the assembling the productions of virions by infected cells.
Some plain comments on the HAART can be introduced: infected cells have a half-life short (from less than one month to 6 month), but hidden reservoirs of virus contribute to an even slower disease phase (Brandt and Chen, 2001). These long lasting time phases of infection make complete eradication of the virus from the body impossible with current therapies. In addition, genetic modifications of the virus and its ability to change its response to drugs com-plicate the problem. Therefore possible mathematical model have to consider and quantify the 'force' of the virus and its response to the drugs.
In this context a mathematical model able to balance the model complexity with a simple description of the viral dynamics is a difficult task to satisfy: low order models are usually too simple to be useful, on the other hand high order models are too complex for simulation purposes and have too many unknown parameters to be identified. Some interesting models have been proposed by Wodarz and Nowak (2000), they include state variables representing both the viral dynamics and the immune responses, in terms of precursors of cytotoxic T-lymphocytes (CTLp), responsible of the development of an immune memory, and effectors of cytotoxic T-lymphocytes (CTLe).
This paper has the primary goal to improve the Wodarz and Novak model, in the ambitious attempt to add new information to the results of simulation useful to physicians for comparing different treatment policies such as when to start or to switch therapy. More in detail the main equations of the model are analyzed and discussed in various cases (healthy patients, HIV patients without and with drug treatments, evaluated on short and long times). With respect to other models, a new variable, denoted as "aggressiveness," is considered for a best evaluation of therapeutic protocols. In order to obtain simulation results coherent with the medical practice, a strict cooperation with clinical researchers expert in HIV therapies was successfully considered.

2. MODELS OF WODARZ AND NOWAK

The first model presented [9] considers three state variables (expressed as cell counts in blood per cubic millimetre) inside a whole body model. The model is mathematically described by:

$$\begin{cases} \dot{x} = \lambda - dx - \beta xv \\ \dot{y} = \beta xv - ay \\ \dot{v} = ky - uv \end{cases} \quad (1)$$

The first equation represents the dynamics of the concentration of healthy CD4$^+$ cells (x); λ represents the rate (supposed constant) at which new CD4$^+$ T-cells are generated. The death rate of healthy cells is d. In case of active HIV infection the concentration of healthy cells decreases proportionally to the product βxv, where β represents a coefficient depending to various factors, as the velocity of penetration of virus into the cells, frequency of encounters between uninfected cells free virus, etc.
The second equation describes the dynamics of the concentration of infected CD4$^+$ cells (y); β is the rate of infection, a is the death rate of infected cells.
The last equation describes the concentration of free virions (v), they are produced by the infected cells at a rate k, u is the death rate of the virions.
The therapy is considered with the following policy: reverse transcriptase inhibitors stop the infection in cells still healthy. If the drug efficacy is maximum and equal to 100%, and if the system is at equilibrium before the drug treatment, β is set to zero in the model. If the drug efficacy is imperfect, β is substituted by $\beta^* = s\,\beta$, with $s<1$.
Protease inhibitors need a different modelling, since they reduce infection of new cells but do not block production of viruses from cells already infected and model (1) must be suitably modified (Craig, and Xia, 2005).
A more complex model was presented in (Wodarz, and Nowak, 1999) and augmented in (Wodarz and Nowak, 2000): it offers important theoretical insights into immune control of virus based on treatment strategies, which can be viewed as a fast subsystem of the dynamics of HIV infection.

The final model of Wodarz and Nowak is mathematically described by:

$$\begin{cases} \dot{x} = \lambda - dx - \beta xv \\ \dot{y} = \beta xv - ay - pyz \\ \dot{v} = ky - uv \\ \dot{w} = cxyw - cqyw - bw \\ \dot{z} = cqyw - hz \end{cases} \quad (2)$$

Two differential equations are added to (1) for describing the dynamics of precursors of cytotoxic T-lymphocytes CTLp (w), responsible of the development of an immune memory, and effectors of cytotoxic T-lymphocytes CTLe (z). This model can discriminate the trend of the infection as a function of the rate of viral replication: if the rate is high a successful immune memory cannot establish, on the other hand if the replication rate is slow, a immune memory CTL helps the patient to successfully fight against the infection. A more detailed description of this model can be found both in the original papers and in the description of a modified model (2) in (Zurakowski, and Teel, 2006).

3. MODELS PROPOSED

The model developed at our university is developed starting from the model (2), in order to reach the following objectives: the first one (not innovative) was to develop a model able to qualitatively describe experimental data existing in literature and synthesized in Fig. 1. The second one was to manage a model directly devoted for studying and predicting the effects of the therapies.
The proposed model is:

$$\begin{cases} \dot{x} = \lambda - dx - rxy \\ \dot{y} = rxy - ay - pyz \\ \dot{w} = cxyw - cqyw - bw \\ \dot{z} = cqyw - hz \\ \dot{r} = r_0 - \mu_1 f_1 - \mu_2 f_2 \end{cases} \quad (3)$$

The proposed model, based on the final model of Wodarz and Nowak, considers the new state variable r as the intrinsic virulence of the virus; the constant β is substituted with the adimensional state variable r, index of the aggressiveness of the virus. This new equation increases linearly in case of an untreated HIV-infected individual, with a growth rate depending on the constant r_0 (higher is r_0, higher is the virulence growth rate). This equation has the typical structure:

$$\dot{r} = r_0 - \sum_i \mu_i f_i \quad (4)$$

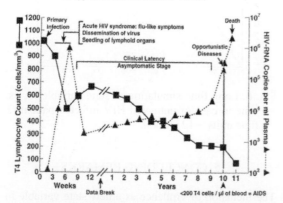

The typical clinical course of HIV disease.

Fig. 1. Clinical behavior of HIV infection. Virus concentration and CD4$^+$ concentration, in the case of an untreated HIV-infected individual (Abbas, Lichtman and Pober, 2005).

where μ_i represents a drug efficacy coefficient for the specific drug f_i. In the following simulation tests the initial condition of the state variable r_0 is set to 10, the different f_i's (drug concentrations in arbitrary units) are set to 1 (treated patients) or 0 (untreated patients). The equation

$$\dot{v} = ky - uv \quad (5)$$

can be added to model (3), although in the hypothesis of a constant coefficient k and since usually k>>u, the time response of viremia is almost proportional to the concentration of infected CD4$^+$ cells.
An advantage of the proposed model is its direct and simple interpretation in terms of the drug efficacy: it shows limitations due to its simplicity with respect to more complex equations presented in (e.g.) in Zurakowski and Teel (2006), or in Adams et al (2005), but it shows a good agreement with the results of HIV clinical researchers.

4. RESULTS OF SIMULATION TESTS

All the simulations have been performed using the Simulink environment of Matlab™. Chosen parameters are the same considered in Wodarz and Nowak models, unknown parameters are selected from heuristic considerations, in order to obtain time responses of the state variables physiologically consistent and respecting the findings of medical literature (e.g., the time responses shown in Fig.1). Simulations in different cases have been performed using adimensional values reported in Wodarz (1999):
$\lambda = 1$, $d = 0.1$, $\beta = 0.5$, $a = 0.2$, $p = 1$,
$c = 0.1$, $b = 0.01$, $q = 0.5$, $h = 0.1$, $s = 0.042$).
Consider now the simulation tests in the cases of:
- untreated HIV-infected individual
- treated HIV-infected individual

In the following figures cases of untreated (from Fig. 2 to Fig. 6) and poorly treated patients ($\mu_1 = \mu_2 = 0.1$) (from Fig. 7 to Fig. 11) are shown. If coefficients μ_i increase (e.g., $\mu_i = 0.8$) therapeutic action becomes more and more efficient (from Fig. 12 to Fig. 16).
Modelling simulation hypotheses are the following:
-the initial burst of the viral infection is simulated with a short impulse, acting as an external input on y and z variables.
- the existence of an additional reservoir of CD4$^+$ cells, produced by the bone marrow, has been considered as an external input added to the variable x (T-lymphocytes), which permits to have a fast recovering of CD4$^+$ cells after the minimum value typical after the first 12 weeks of infection (this 'reservoir effect' allows the physiological rebound observed in the experimental studies).

4.1 Untreated HIV-infected individuals

– T CD4$^+$ healthy cells show a *rebound* typical of the acute infection phase, followed by a constant quasi-homeostatic condition in the latency period. After the latency period the viral burst leads to almost total cell depletion during the last phase of the infection;

− viremia shows a peak, corresponding to the initial infection, followed by a reduction during the clinical latency. A long time simulation shows a continuous increasing of viremia, often associated to opportunistic infections;

− CTLp cells increase up to a maximum value, followed by a decreasing dynamics;

− CTLe cells have the same dynamics of CTLp's, but delayed.

4.2 Treated HIV-infected individuals

Two combined drugs are considered.

− T CD4$^+$ healthy cells after the rebound phase tend to increase as in the physiological case (healthy people) when the therapy inhibits the viral replication;

− viremia shows again the initial peak, corresponding to the initial infection, followed by a reduction near zero in case of a perfect (ideal) efficacy of the drugs;

− CTLp and CTLe cells increase as in healthy people.

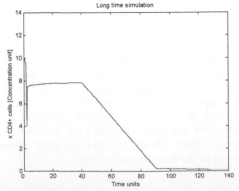

Fig. 2. Short time simulation of state variables x, vs. time in case of untreated HIV-infected patient (5 time units = 12 weeks).

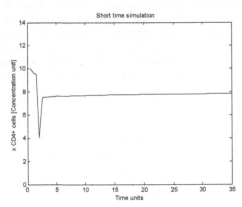

Fig. 3. Long time simulation of state variables x, vs. time in case of untreated HIV-infected patient (5 time units = 12 weeks).

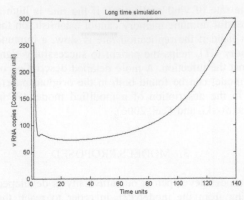

Fig. 4. Long time simulation of state variables v, vs. time in case of untreated HIV-infected patient (5 time units = 12 weeks).

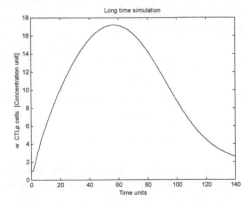

Fig. 5. Long time simulation of state variables w, vs. time in case of untreated HIV-infected patient (5 time units = 12 weeks).

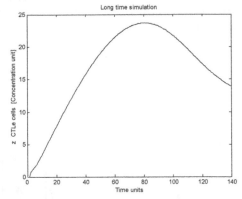

Fig. 6. Long time simulation of state variables z, vs. time in case of untreated HIV-infected patient (5 time units = 12 weeks).

5. CONCLUDING REMARKS

The inclusion of virulence as a new state variable in the Wodarz and Nowak model allows an easy evaluation both in terms of the definition of a variable representing an index of the aggressiveness of the virus and the introduction of the drugs in a simple and direct way.

A simplified simulation model may be a useful starting tool for the analysis and prediction of a therapy, especially in a complex case as the HAART, where the therapy needs to be optimized for reducing side effects, toxicity and resistance to medications.

Future work will be devoted to a further testing phase of the model proposed in cooperation with clinical researchers, along with the attempt to adapt the coefficient of the model to single patients.

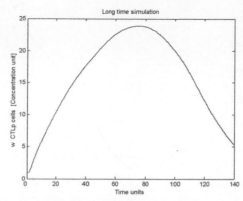

Fig. 10. Long time simulation of state variables w, vs. time in case of poorly treated ($\mu_1=\mu_2=0.1$) HIV-infected patient (5 time units = 12 weeks).

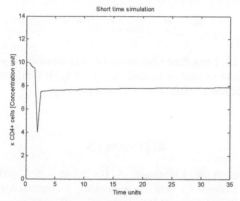

Fig. 7. Short time simulation of state variables x, vs. time in case of poorly treated ($\mu_1=\mu_2=0.1$) HIV-infected patient (5 time units = 12 weeks).

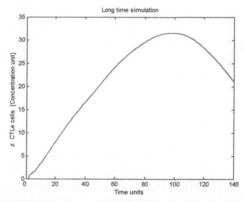

Fig. 11. Long time simulation of state variables z, vs. time in case of poorly treated ($\mu_1=\mu_2=0.1$) HIV-infected patient (5 time units = 12 weeks).

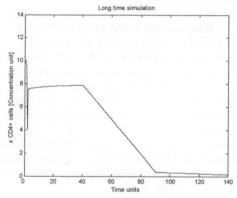

Fig. 8. Long time simulation of state variables x, vs. time in case of poorly treated ($\mu_1=\mu_2=0.1$) HIV-infected patient (5 time units = 12 weeks).

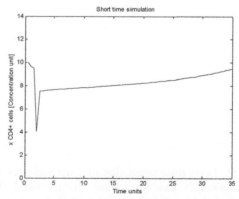

Fig. 12. Short time simulation of state variables x, vs. time in case of treated ($\mu_1=\mu_2=0.8$) HIV-infected patient (5 time units = 12 weeks).

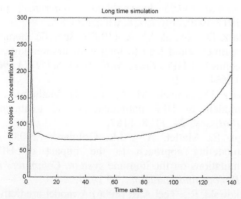

Fig. 9. Long time simulation of state variables v, vs. time in case of poorly treated ($\mu_1=\mu_2=0.1$) HIV-infected patient (5 time units = 12 weeks).

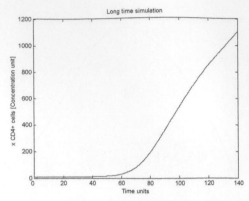

Fig. 13. Long time simulation of state variables x, vs. time in case of treated ($\mu_1=\mu_2=0.8$) HIV-infected patient (5 time units = 12 weeks).

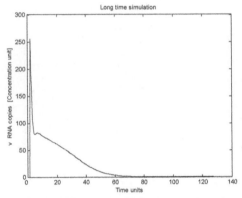

Fig. 14. Long time simulation of state variables v, vs. time in case of treated ($\mu_1=\mu_2=0.8$) HIV-infected patient (5 time units = 12 weeks).

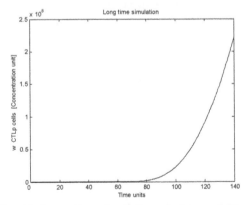

Fig. 15. Long time simulation of state variables w, vs. time in case of treated ($\mu_1=\mu_2=0.8$) HIV-infected patient (5 time units = 12 weeks).

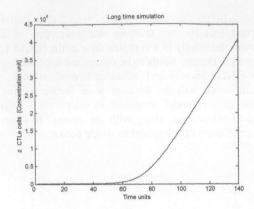

Fig. 16. Long time simulation of state variables z, vs. time in case of treated ($\mu_1=\mu_2=0.8$) HIV-infected patient (5 time units = 12 weeks).

REFERENCES

Abbas, A. K., Lichtman, A. H., Pober, J. S. (2005). *Cellular and molecular immunology.* Philadelphia: WB Saunders Co., IV Edition.

Adams B.M. et al. (2005) HIV dynamics: modeling, data analysis, and optimal treatment protocols. *Journal of Computational and Applied Mathematics*, **184**, 10-49.

Brandt, M. E., Chen, G. , (2001). Feedback Control of a Biodynamical Model of HIV-1. *IEEE Trans. on Biomedical Engineering*, **48**, 754,759.

Craig, I., Xia, X. (2005). Can HIV/AIDS Be Controlled? *IEEE Control Systems Magazine*, 80-83.

Finzi, D. et al. (1999). Latent infection of CD4+ T cells provides a mechanism for lifelong persistence of HIV-1, even in patients on effective combination therapy. *Nat. Med.* **5**, 512–517.

Di Mascio M. et al. (2004). Modeling the long-term control of viremia in HIV-1 infected patients treated with antiretroviral therapy. *Mathematical Biosciences* **188**, 47–62.

Nowak, M.A. Bangham , C.R.M. (1996). Population dynamics of immune responses to persistent viruses. *Science*, **272**, 74–79.

Ortega, H., Landrove, M. M. (2000). A Model for Continuously Mutant HIV-1. *Proc. of the 22nd Annual EMBS International Conference*, pp. 1917-1920, July 23-28, Chicago USA.

Wodarz, D., Nowak M. A. (1999). Specific therapy regimes could lead to long-term immunological control of HIV. *Proc. Natl. Acad. Sci. USA* **96**, 14464–14469.

Wodarz, D., Nowak, M. A. (2000). Mathematical models of HIV pathogenesis and treatment. *BioEssays* **24**, 1178–1187.

Vergu, E., Mallet, A. , J.L. Golmard. (2005) A modeling approach to the impact of HIV mutations on the immune system. *Computers in Biology and Medicine*, **35** 1–24.

Zurakowski, R., Teel A.R. (2006) A model predictive control based scheduling method for HIV therapy. *Journal of Theoretical Biology*, **238**, 368-382.

IN SILICO ANALYSIS OF P53 RESPONSE TO DNA DAMAGE

Gabriele Lillacci* Mauro Boccadoro* Paolo Valigi*

* [lillacci, boccadoro, valigi]@diei.unipg.it
*Dipartimento di Ingegneria Elettronica e
dell'Informazione, Università degli Studi di Perugia,
Via G. Duranti 93, 06125 Perugia – Italy*

Abstract: p53 gene and its protein product play a key role in the cell's response to DNA damage. Approximately 50% of all human cancers displays p53 mutations, and in the vast majority of the other cases the gene's functionality is otherwise impaired. In this paper a new dynamic model of p53 activation in response to double strand brakes damage (DSB) is developed. Proteins that have been left behind by other works (such as ARF) are found to be important for the dynamics of this process, which is characterized by an oscillatory behavior. A technique for assessing the system's period is also proposed. *Copyright © 2006 IFAC*

Keywords: Gene Networks, DNA damage, Double Strand Brakes, p53 Oscillator, ARF, Periodic Behavior

1. INTRODUCTION

Every living being is uniquely characterized by the code in its DNA. Such precious data must be guarded against several types of damage. Among these, double strand brakes (DSB) are particularly serious and can be lethal if left unrepaired. DSBs are thought to be the main type of lesion through which ionizing radiation (IR) induces cancer and hereditary diseases.

Cells react to DNA damage in three basic ways. If the damage level is very low it is *tolerated*: the cell has specific structures to operate DNA replication and transcription even in presence of lesions. If the damage is more serious it is *repaired*: several mechanisms have been described, among which homologous recombination (HR) and non-homologous end joining (NHEJ). If the damage level is too high to be effectively treated, *apoptosis* is started: this is a programmed death through which the cell eliminates itself from a population that might otherwise suffer the serious pathological consequences of the transmission of disrupted genetic material.

Unfortunately, criteria that regulate the cell's decision among tolerance, repair and apoptosis are poorly understood. An in-depth knowledge of them could be exploited to artificially trigger apoptosis in irreparably damaged cells, thus opening new paths toward a more effective cancer therapy. Initial experiments in this direction have been already carried out (Surendran (2004), Vassilev et al. (2004)).

p53 plays a key role in cell's response to DNA damage. When first discovered in 1979, this gene was incorrectly identified as an oncogene. Later studies revealed its tumor suppressing function, and since then the gene, and the protein it codes for, have been intensely investigated to determine their function in apoptosis induction. Approximately 50% of all human cancers displays p53 mutations, and in the vast majority of the other cases the gene's functionality is otherwise impaired. In this paper, a dynamic model of the main interactions among p53 protein and other proteins involved in its activation after DNA damage is developed, analyzed and simulated under various conditions, both healthy and pathological.

2. LITERATURE REVIEW

The basic components of the p53 network are two genes and their protein products, namely p53 and MDM2. Since p53 can induce cell cycle arrest and apoptosis, its levels must be kept low when no stress is present: MDM2 is the protein in charge of doing so. MDM2 is an *ubiquitin ligase*, which means that it can attach ubiquitin molecules to p53. These act as labels that target p53 for destruction through a pathway known as *proteolytic degradation*. p53, on the other hand, can enhance MDM2 gene transcription, thus promoting production of its own negative regulator. The two form a feedback loop: if p53 levels go up, more MDM2 is produced and excess p53 is destroyed, thus restoring equilibrium. When DNA damage is detected, this equilibrium is broken, p53 is phosphorylated and stabilized and its levels are allowed to rise. During the last five years, several models of this phenomenon at molecular level have been proposed.

The first one is by Lev Bar-Or et al. (2000). It models three substances: p53, MDM2 and a hypothetical intermediate state of p53 called I. This is used to introduce a delay between activation of p53 and p53-dependent MDM2 transcription enhancement. The key result obtained is that p53 and MDM2 concentrations under certain conditions undergo *damped* oscillations. This behavior depends on several factors, the most important of which are the presence of the delay and the presence of a sufficiently strong DNA damage signal. The authors speculate that the cell's decision to start apoptosis could depend on the presence or absence of oscillations. Later studies showed that the delay is given by the time the cell takes to transcribe and translate MDM2 under the effect of active p53 and failed to detect a biological counterpart for state I.

Similar results can be found in Mihalas et al. (2000). A more explicit delay term is used and p53-dependent MDM2 transcription enhancement is modeled using stepwise or Hill kinetics. Modeled substances are p53 and MDM2 proteins and p53 and MDM2 mRNAs. The fundamental result obtained is the discovery that the models could also show *sustained* oscillations. Oscillations are not found to be triggered without accounting for the delay. Only the free evolution of the system is studied: no explicit input signal which could switch oscillations on or off is included.

Another work is the one by Brewer (2002). Three new components are introduced into the models: ARF, E2F1 and ATM which is explicitly considered as the p53 activating component. The obtained conclusions deal mainly with presence or absence of oscillations, with the parameters on which they depend most and with criteria proposed to limit parameters' values. The models' behavior is examined at increasing ATM concentration levels and no important variation is detected. This leads to the conclusion that if Lev Bar-Or's hypothesis is true, the decision about starting apoptosis or not must be taken outside the p53 network. ATM is considered as a state variable and the presence of damage is modeled as a non-zero initial ATM concentration, which exponentially decays as time goes by and the cell starts to repair damage. Later investigation showed that ATM concentration is better characterized by a "digital" on-off signal (see below). No time delay is included and only damped oscillations are observed.

The importance of time delay in the p53 network is addressed in Tiana et al. (2002). The authors build a model including p53, MDM2 and a p53-MDM2 complex needed for the MDM2-induced degradation of p53. A non-zero time delay is found to be required to get an oscillatory behavior from the model. The other key finding is that oscillations are triggered only if the dissociation constant between active (phosphorylated) p53 and MDM2 is greater than the one between inactive (unphosphorylated) p53 and MDM2. This means that active p53 binds *more tightly* to MDM2 than inactive p53 does, and this result could be counterintuitive. However, we know that direct binding of p53 to MDM2 is not the prevalent mechanism leading to p53 degradation: p53 ubiquitination is much more important, and the kinetics of this process has been deeply investigated by Lai et al. (2001). They show that MDM2-mediated ubiquitination of p53 can fit two reaction mechanisms, called *modified Ping-Pong* and *Rapid Equilibrium Random Bi-Bi (RERBB)*: this process is thought to be better modeled using one of them.

The work by Monk (2003) is a general study about the importance of including transcriptional time delays (both deterministic and stochastic) in models of oscillating gene regulation networks. Together with Hes1 and NF-κB, the p53 network is also considered. The modeled substances are p53 protein, MDM2 protein and MDM2 mRNA. Cooperative kinetics is used. Results are much like the ones by Mihalas et al. (2000). Again, there is no explicit description of what triggers oscillations: growing evidence supports the idea that they should be only present when important DNA damage exists.

The most recent work on the p53 network is the one by Ma et al. (2005). It is based on the fundamental experimental observations by Lahav et al. (2004) that p53 and MDM2 oscillations are *not damped* at single cell level. Single cells show a "digital" behavior: it is the *number* of oscillations that shows dependence with damage amount, not their *amplitude*. Ma et al. (2005) build a three-module model. In the first one, a group of repair proteins interact with DSBs. This complexes (indicating the presence of an unrepaired damage) are sensed by the second module, represented by ATM kinase. Activation of ATM switches on the third module, the p53-MDM2 feedback loop, which starts oscillating. This model can replicate experimental results by Lahav et al. (2004) to a high degree of accuracy. It does not include ARF because this component is thought not to have important effects on p53 and MDM2 dynamics. This is somehow controversial, as other results indicate that ARF failure leads to serious consequences.

3. BIOLOGICAL ANALYSIS

The p53 network includes many proteins, genes and transcription factors. We will consider only the main known components and fundamental interactions among them. These are summarized in Figure 1.

ATM kinase is the sensor protein of the network. It is a big protein made of 3056 amino acids. When inactive, ATM exists in the form of dimers or higher order multimers. Bakkenist and Kastan (2003) have shown that in response to IR doses as low as 0.5 Gy most of ATM molecules in the cell are rapidly phosphorylated at serine 1981. This event activates ATM causing dimer (or multimer) dissociation and initiates cellular response to DSBs. Although earlier studies (Smith et al. (1999)) suggested that ATM could directly bind to DSBs, Bakkenist and Kastan (2003) show that ATM activation is caused by intermolecular autophosphorylation and propose that this may result from changes in the structure of chromatin induced by DSBs. Defective ATM functionality is associated with the hereditary disease *ataxia telangiectasia*, characterized by a strong predisposition to cancer and extreme cellular sensitivity to radiation.

Active ATM phosphorylates *p53 protein*. It also phosphorylates *MDM2 protein* at serine 395. These modifications alter the p53-MDM2 equilibrium described in Section 2. p53 becomes more stable and MDM2 becomes less effective in promoting p53 degradation, so p53 levels are allowed

to rise and induce cell cycle arrest and apoptosis. There is more than one mechanism through which MDM2 hinders p53 functionality, but we will consider ubiquitin-mediated proteolysis only, since the others are thought to be much less important. Impaired p53 and MDM2 functionality is associated with serious consequences: Li-Fraumeni syndrome (lack of p53) and MDM2 overexpression are both associated with the onset cancer, while MDM2 elimination in mice results in early embryonic lethality.

Other components of the p53 network include CHK2, E2F1 and ARF. *CHK2* is an important protein with cell cycle control functions. It is activated through phosphorylation by ATM. Active CHK2, in turn, phosphorylates p53 at serine 20. This modification further hinders MDM2 effectiveness and has a positive effect on p53 levels. *E2F1* is a transcription factor phosphorylated and stabilized by active ATM. Its action is not clearly understood: it has been suggested that E2F1 can enhance ARF transcription. *ARF* is a small protein called $p14^{ARF}$ in man and $p19^{ARF}$ in mice. ARF is rather important in the p53 network: mice without ARF display almost the same predisposition to cancer as the ones without p53 (Kamijo et al. (1997)). In man, ARF deletion is associated with the onset of breast, brain and lung cancer (Vogelstein et al. (2000)). ARF directly binds to MDM2, blocking its ability to ubiquitinate p53. ARF is also a negative regulator of E2F1: the two form a feedback loop. ARF, just like p53, is expressed at very low levels when no stress in present.

4. THE DYNAMIC MODEL

Translation of biological and biochemical information into differential equations requires a great deal of approximation. In order to set up a mathematical model for the p53 network, all processes are treated as if they *happen is a homogeneous chemical solution*. This allows us to consider mean concentrations rather than single molecules, but completely ignores the cell's spatial structure.

The model is restricted to *fundamental networks components* and, when two components interact through more than one mechanism, *only the main one* is considered. This step has been already carried out at a biological level in Section 3.

Another important step is the *choice of state variables and input signals*. Every component of the p53 network is present in the cell under many different biochemical states, such as phosphorylated, unphosphorylated, acetylated, etc. In our model, we only consider two possible forms, called "active" and "inactive". "Active" is the form in

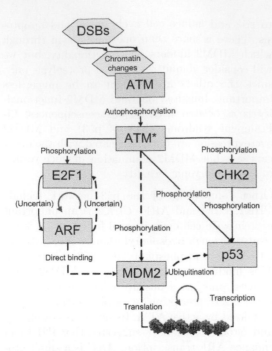

Fig. 1. Main interactions in the p53 network. Continuous lines mean positive actions, dashed lines negative actions, circular arrows feedback loops.

which a component can take part in the p53 network's reactions and interact with other components. For example, phosphorylated p53 is active p53, because in this state it can affect MDM2 transcription. Phosphorylated MDM2, as well as MDM2 bound with ARF, are inactive MDM2, because in these states MDM2 cannot ubiquitinate p53. Active components are marked with *. We choose as state variables the concentrations of the main components described in Section 3 *in the forms we are interested in*. These are $[p53]$, $[p53^*]$, $[MDM2^*]$, $[ARF^*]$ and $[E2F1^*]$. $[ATM^*]$ is considered as the input signal.

The final step is to *remove redundant pathways* and incorporate their action into other pathways. If we look again at Figure 1, we see that ATM* produces the same effect on p53 both directly and through CHK2. Since we do not require from the model information on CHK2, we choose to remove the CHK2 arc and consider p53 activation only by means of ATM*.

We are now able to translate the processes described in Section 3 into differential equations. Phosphorylations can be described by classical Michaelis-Menten kinetics. MDM2-dependent p53 ubiquitination is modeled by the RERBB reaction mechanism (Lai et al. (2001)). Direct bindings, as well as uncertain interactions, are assumed to follow first order kinetics described by the law of mass action. In addition to these, components may exhibit an independent production term, which is the basal rate of their transcription and

translation from DNA, and an independent degradation term, which is the rate of their spontaneous degradation.

The complete model is reported in Table 1. Some remarks are needed. The RERBB mechanism equation includes the concentration of an intermediate product of the reaction, denoted by AX. Since no information about intermediated products in the MDM2-dependent ubiquitination of p53 is available, AX concentration has been replaced with the constant parameter k_6 in the RERBB terms. p53* acts as a transcription factor to enhance MDM2 gene transcription: the resulting change in the MDM2 protein concentration appears after the transcriptional time delay τ. So the MDM2 protein concentration at time t depends on the p53* concentration a time $t - \tau$. E2F1* activation by ATM* is described by the term $k_3[ATM^*]$, because we suppose that inactive E2F1 concentration is much greater than the others considered: this is done to avoid adding an extra equation to the model. In the Michaelis-Menten equation, if we let inactive E2F1 concentration tend to infinity we get:

$$\lim_{[E2F1]\to\infty} \frac{k_3[ATM^*][E2F1]}{k_{M3} + [E2F1]} = k_3[ATM^*].$$

5. ANALYSES AND SIMULATIONS

5.1 Input signal and parameters

Since most of ATM molecules in the cell are rapidly autophosphorylated in response to DSB damage, ATM* input signal exhibits a "digital" behavior: ATM* concentration quickly switches from 0% ("off") to 100% ("on") when DSBs are detected and from 100% to 0% when the damage is repaired. It has been modeled with a signal similar to a square wave, resulting from the difference of two sigmoid curves.

Determining plausible values for the many parameters of the model represents a challenging task. Since in most cases it is not feasible to measure them directly, one has to refer to the literature to obtain indications about the correctness of the solution. Some examples are reported below.

- In response to a damage signal, p53* concentration must rise.
- MDM2* concentration must decrease (because inactivated by ATM*) and then increase under the action of p53* (after the transcriptional delay τ).
- Since the model refers to a single cell, the system must show sustained oscillations, that persist until the input signal is on.
- The system must return to the initial equilibrium state when the input signal goes off.

$$\frac{d[p53]}{dt} = \lambda_{p53} - \mu_{p53}[p53] + \nu_{p53}[p53^*] - \frac{k_6 k_{cat}[MDM2^*][p53]}{\alpha K_{AX} K_B + \alpha k_6 K_B + \alpha K_{AX}[p53] + k_6[p53]} - \frac{k_1[ATM^*][p53]}{k_{M1} + [p53]}$$

$$\frac{d[p53^*]}{dt} = -\nu_{p53}[p53^*] - \frac{k_6 k_{cat}[MDM2^*][p53^*]}{\alpha K_{AX} K_B + \alpha k_6 K_B + \alpha K_{AX}[p53^*] + k_6[p53^*]} + \frac{k_1[ATM^*][p53]}{k_{M1} + [p53]}$$

$$\frac{d[MDM2^*]}{dt} = \lambda_{MDM2} - \mu_{MDM2}[MDM2^*] + k_4[p53^*](t - \tau) - \frac{k_2[ATM^*][MDM2^*]}{k_{M2} + [MDM2^*]} - k_7[ARF^*][MDM2^*]$$

$$\frac{d[ARF^*]}{dt} = \lambda_{ARF} - \mu_{ARF}[ARF^*] + k_5[E2F1^*] - k_7[ARF^*][MDM2^*] - k_8[ARF^*][E2F1^*]$$

$$\frac{d[E2F1^*]}{dt} = -\nu_{E2F1}[E2F1^*] + k_3[ATM^*] - k_8[ARF^*][E2F1^*]$$

Table 1. Dynamic model of the p53 network.

- Oscillations' period must be about 7 hours (420 minutes).

Whenever applicable, values of parameters have been taken from other publications. Independent production terms λ_{p53}, λ_{MDM2} and λ_{ARF} have been computed from expression of the equilibrium state imposing reasonable values for p53, MDM2* and ARF* basal concentrations. Reference values for totally unknown parameters have been determined on a trial basis, selecting from a big number of automatically run simulations the one that fitted best the above criteria.

Results of a typical model simulation are shown in Figure 2.

5.2 Period detection

A rigorous measure of the system's period cannot rely on a single state variable. This problem can be solved using a visualization tool firstly introduced by Eckmann et al. (1987) called *recurrence plot*. A recurrence plot can show the behavior of a system with any number of state variables in a bidimensional graph. It can be defined as:

$$R_{t_1, t_2} = u_{-1}(\epsilon - \|\mathbf{x}(t_1) - \mathbf{x}(t_2)\|),$$

where u_{-1} is the unit step function, $\mathbf{x}$ is the system's state vector, t_1 and t_2 are time instants, $\|\cdot\|$ is a norm and ϵ is an arbitrarily chosen real number, which serves as a threshold. The recurrence plot shows the time instants when the system state assumes a value "near" (closer than ϵ) to the one assumed in a past instant. We use a slightly modified version of recurrence plot, where different gray tones mean different values of ϵ. Figure 3(a) shows the recurrence plot of the simulation reported in Figure 2 computed using this method.

Presence of such a repetitive and regular pattern in a recurrence plot means that the system has a periodic behavior. Figure 3(b) shows the bidimensional normalized autocorrelation of the recurrence plot in Figure 3(a). Autocorrelation maxima

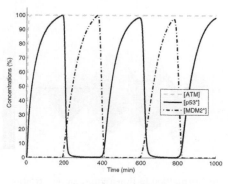

(a) p53* and MDM2*

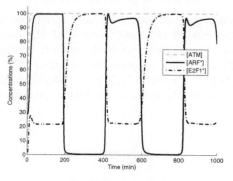

(b) ARF* and E2F1*

Fig. 2. Results of a typical model simulation. Concentrations are normalized to their maximum values.

correspond to time instants when state values are *exactly* the same. The system's period can thus be determined through the *distance between two consecutive maxima*. This yields a period of 408 minutes.

5.3 Pathological conditions

An increasing number of studies supports the idea that a healthy operation of the p53 network relies on its periodic behavior. To reproduce the situation of the Li-Fraumeni syndrome some simulations have been run imposing $\lambda_{p53} = 0$: the periodic behavior of the network is always lost.

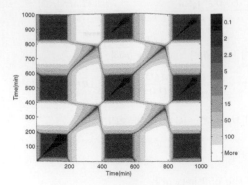

(a) Recurrence plot of the system

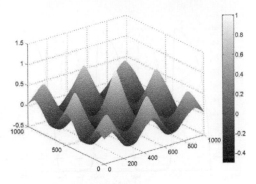

(b) Normalized bidimensional autocorrelation

Fig. 3. Plots used of period detection.

A subsystem without ARF and E2F1 has been also simulated to assess the role of this components. Again, their removal resulted in loss of oscillations. This supports the idea that ARF and E2F1 play an essential role in the p53 network, as also indicated by evidence on ARF cited in Section 3.

6. CONCLUSIONS

A new dynamic model of the p53 network has been developed. Unlike most of the previous ones, it also includes ARF and E2F1. Our simulations indicate that this components are essential for the oscillatory dynamics of the network and they should be carefully considered for further investigation.

A technique for period assessment is also proposed. It uses basic image processing tecniques to extract quantitative data from recurrence plots, so it can be applied to non-linear dynamic systems with any number of state variables.

REFERENCES

C. J. Bakkenist and M. B. Kastan. DNA damage activates ATM through intermolecular autophosphorylation and dimer dissociation. *Nature*, 421(6922):499–506, 2003.

D. Brewer. Investigations of the p53 protein DNA damage network using mathematical models. http://dan.complex.ucl.ac.uk, 2002.

J. P. Eckmann, S. O. Kamphorst, and D. Ruelle. Recurrence Plots of Dynamical Systems. *Europhys. Lett.*, 4(9):973–977, 1987.

T. Kamijo, F. Zindy, M. F. Roussel, D. E. Quelle, J. R. Downing, R. A. Ashmun, G. Grosveld, and C. J. Sherr. Tumor suppression at the mouse INK4a locus mediated by the alternative reading frame product p19ARF. *Cell*, 91(5):649–659, 1997.

G. Lahav, N. Rosenfeld, A. Sigal, N. Geva-Zatorsky, A. J. Levine, M. B. Elowitz, and U. Alon. Dynamics of the p53-MDM2 feedback loop in individual cells. *Nat. Genet.*, 36(2):147–150, 2004.

Z. Lai, K. V. Ferry, M. A. Diamond, K. E. Wee, Y. B. Kim, J. Ma, T. Yang, P. A. Benfield, R. A. Copeland, and K. R. Auger. Human mdm2 mediates multiple mono-ubiquitination of p53 by a mechanism requiring enzyme isomerization. *J. Biol. Chem.*, 276(33):31357–31367, 2001.

R. Lev Bar-Or, R. Maya, L. A. Segel, U. Alon, A. J. Levine, and M. Oren. Generation of oscillations by the p53-MDM2 feedback loop: a theoretical and experimental study. *P. Natl. Acad. Sci. USA*, 97(21):11250–11255, 2000.

L. Ma, J. Wagner, J. J. Rice, W. Hu, A. J. Levine, and G. A. Stolovitzky. A plausible model for the digital response of p53 to DNA damage. *P. Natl. Acad. Sci. USA*, 102(40):14266–14271, 2005.

G. I. Mihalas, Z. Simon, G. Balea, and E. Popa. Possible oscillatory behavior in p53-MDM2 interaction computer simulation. *J. Biol. Syst.*, 8(1):21–29, 2000.

N. A. Monk. Oscillatory expression of Hes1, p53, and NF-κB driven by transcriptional time delays. *Curr. Biol.*, 13(16):1409–1413, 2003.

G. C. M. Smith, R. B. Cary, N. D. Lakin, B. C. Hann, S. H. Teo, D. J. Chen, and S. P. Jackson. Purification and DNA binding properties of the ataxia-telangiectasia gene product ATM. *P. Natl. Acad. Sci. USA*, 96(20):11134–11139, 1999.

A. Surendran. The virtuous virus. *Nat. Med.*, 10(8):767–768, 2004.

G. Tiana, M.H. Jensen, and K. Sneppen. Time delay as a key to apoptosis induction in the p53 network. *Eur. Phys. J. B*, 29(1):135–140, 2002.

L. T. Vassilev, B. T. Vu, B. Graves, D. Carvajal, F. Podlaski, Z. Filipovic, N. Kong, U. Kammlott, C. Lukacs, C. Klein, N. Fotouhi, and E. A. Liu. In vivo activation of the p53 pathway by small-molecule antagonists of MDM2. *Science*, 303(5659):844–848, 2004.

B. Vogelstein, D. Lane, and A. J. Levine. Surfing the p53 network. *Nature*, 408(6810):307–310, 2000.

MODEL ANALYSIS OF THE CHOKE POINTS ARRANGEMENT
DURING FORCED EXPIRATION

Adam G. Polak and Janusz Mroczka

*Chair of Electronic and Photonic Metrology, Wroclaw University of Technology
ul. B. Prusa 53/55, 50-317 Wroclaw, Poland*

Abstract: Flow limitation in the airways, seen as the choke points, plays a fundamental role in constituting the maximal expiratory flow-volume curve. A computational model with asymmetrical airways was used to analyse the choke points arrangement. We conclude that flow limitation begins at similar time in every branch of the bronchial tree (developing a parallel arrangement of the choke points) and may prolong to the end of expiration. A serial configuration of the choke points is possible for short time periods in case of increased airway heterogeneity. The most probable locations of the choke points are the regions of airway junctions. *Copyright © 2006 IFAC*

Keywords: Biomedical systems, Physiology, Modelling, System analysis, Simulation.

1. INTRODUCTION

Flow limitation in the airways can be seen as independence of airflow on driving pressure, well presented by isovolume flow-pressure curves (Fry, *et al.*, 1954). It plays a crucial role in determining the shape of the maximum expiration flow-volume (MEFV) curve (Hyatt, *et al.*, 1958; Hyatt, 1983) registered during a forced expiration – a standard test of lung function. Limitation of flow is caused by airway wall collapsing which follows the drop of transmural pressure, i.e. the difference between internal and external pressure, along a bronchus. When flow velocity approaches wave-speed of pressure disturbance propagation along the airway wall (Dawson, and Elliott, 1977; Shapiro, 1977), the loss of pressure is strongly amplified and the airway narrows much quicker. In effect, any growth of flow produces faster airway collapsing, overcoming the expansion of pressure, and finally the flow remains constant. The wave-speed theory predicts flow limitation during the forced expiration over most of vital capacity (VC).

One of primary questions concerns locations of the flow limiting sites (the so-called choke points) inside the airways, and the character of their movement during the VC manoeuvre. The problem is fairly clear in case of the symmetrical bronchial tree. In this instance, flow limitation is present in all the airways of a given generation (a parallel arrangement) (Solway, *et al.*, 1987). On the contrary, in the heterogeneous bronchial tree, the mechanism of movement of the choke points is more complex. A theoretical analysis (McNamara, *et al.*, 1987) suggests that the choke points can exist in series if a downstream (i.e. lying towards the mouth) flow-limiting airway is fed both through an upstream (i.e. lying towards the alveoli) flow-limiting bronchus and a branch without limitation. In such circumstances the non-limiting pathway will supplement the difference between maximal flows in the downstream and upstream airways. The serial choke points could not be observed during forced deflation from the excited lungs (Mink, *et al*, 1988), however they were found in the experiment with steady deflation within excited central airways (Solway, 1988).

In the present study, a model for the forced expiration from the multi-compartmental inhomogeneous lung (Polak, and Lutchen, 2003) was used to track positions of the choke points, and to investigate the arrangement of these flow-limiting sites. The model, used formerly to analyse expiratory flow from a normal asymmetrical lung, is well suited to investigate the mechanisms of heterogeneous flow limitation. First, a short description of the computational model is given. Then the methods for the flow limitation tracking and simulation of airway heterogeneity are described. In section 3 the main results concerning the choke-points locations and arrangement are presented. Simulation outcomes are discussed and the main conclusions are drawn in section 4.

2. METHODS

2.1 Computational model

The computational model including an asymmetric structure of the bronchial tree has been described elsewhere (Polak, and Lutchen, 2003), but will be summarised here. The airway structure follows the description by Horsfield, et al. (1971) and is presented as a branching pattern of the distinct airway orders. The highest order (35) is the trachea. Each order is characterized by its own mechanical properties, and the orders of two daughter airways are established through a set of order-specific recursion indexes. The bronchial tree includes over 6 million airways that may possess distinct features at any given time during expiration. Solving such a problem is computationally unrealistic. A reasonable simplification is achieved by replacing peripheral parts of the Horsfield tree with symmetrical Weibel's ones (Weibel, 1963). Therefore, airway branching from the trachea follows the Horsfield asymmetry down to a designated order in the bronchial tree (order 32 in Fig. 1). Then branches with airways of smaller orders are replaced with the symmetric structures. The dimension of each peripheral tree depends on the order of the mother airway. The peripheral trees lead to identical alveoli of the same properties (volume, pressure, recoil). Hence, all the alveoli subtended by a given branch are treated as a single alveolar compartment. Consequently, the lungs are divided into a number of the alveolar regions which empty non-uniformly with own compartmental flows. Each region is characterized by its own alveolar pressure producing individual driving pressure.

Drops of pressure (ΔP) along distinct airways are computed by numerical integration of the equation for the pressure gradient (dP/dx) in a flexible tube proposed by Lambert, et al. (1982):

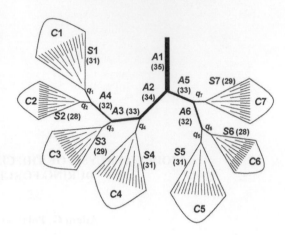

Fig. 1. Asymmetric structure of the bronchial tree: A – separate airways (numbers in parentheses denote Horsfield's orders), S – symmetric peripheral trees (numbers in parentheses denote Horsfield's orders of "mother" airways), C – alveolar compartments, and q – airflows from the compartments.

$$\frac{dP}{dx} = \frac{-f}{1 - S^2} = \frac{-f}{1 - \frac{\rho q^2}{A^3}\left(\frac{\partial A}{\partial P_{tm}}\right)}, \quad (1)$$

where f is the elementary dissipative pressure loss (Reynolds, 1982), $S=u/c$ is the local speed index equal to the ratio between flow (u) and wave (c) speed, q is volume flow in the bronchus, A is the cross-sectional area, and $\partial A/\partial P_{tm}$ is elementary compliance of the airway wall dependent on transmural pressurre P_{tm}. Considering flows through the airways and pressures at their connections (Fig. 1), one is able to write an equation for each pathway. The pressure losses ΔP_i of the succeeding airways belonging to the given branch are added and equalled to driving pressure P_{dk} of the kth lung compartment. These losses of pressure are computed for the actual lung volume and airflow which is a sum of flows coming from the compartmental branches leading to the airway given. This approach yields the following system of nonlinear equations:

$$\sum_i \Delta P_i(q_1, q_2, ..., q_k) = P_{d1},$$

$$\sum_j \Delta P_j(q_1, q_2, ..., q_k) = P_{d2},$$

$$\vdots \quad (2)$$

$$\sum_l \Delta P_l(q_1, q_2, ..., q_k) = P_{dk}.$$

Solving it for the input data consisting of mechanical properties of the airways and lung tissue allows determination of k unknown compartmental flows (seven in our simulations) as well as node pressures for a given time and lung volume. A sum of peripheral flows q_k gives the expiratory flow measured at the airway opening (i.e. the MEFV curve). All calculations are made for the time instants increasing by 0.01 s (i.e., flow sampling at 100 Hz), and then compartmental volumes are calculated by the integration of flows. During calculations related to a given time instant (or lung volume) flow is treated as quasi-steady. In effect, the forced expiration characterized by VC=5.5 dm³, forced expiratory volume in 1 second ratio to VC equal to 80.4% and peak expiratory flow (PEF) of 8 dm³s⁻¹ is simulated.

2.2 Tracking flow limitation

Limitation of flow exists when the denominator of Eq. 1 tends to zero, i.e. for the speed index S approaching unity. Flow speed reaches then wave speed, and the critical flow Q_{ws} equals:

$$Q_{ws} = \sqrt{\frac{A^3}{\rho\left(\dfrac{\partial A}{\partial P_{tm}}\right)}} . \qquad (3)$$

Then $S=u/c=q/Q_{ws}$. The speed ratio S indicates the degree of flow limitation.

The largest value of S is reached at the downstream end of a uniform bronchus (Shapiro, 1977), so S has been tracked at these locations for every separate airway, or airway generation in the symmetric trees, during the first 3 seconds of expiration (99% of normal VC). Thus, choke points can be detected by finding airways with S approaching unity at a given time instant.

2.3 Simulation studies

Simulations with 7 peripheral compartments (as in Fig. 1) yielding the system of 7 nonlinear equations to be solved at each time instant, applying normal values of the respiratory system parameters (Polak, and Lutchen, 2003), were used as a baseline in the present study. Besides, augmented heterogeneity was simulated by the increase (bronchus dilation) or decrease (bronchus constriction) of the areas of some central airways shown in Fig. 1 as the separate bronchi.

To check the hypothesis concerning the possibility of a serial arrangement of the choke points, a suitable change of airway properties was introduced. Airway narrowing was imitated by a proportional change of the airway cross-sectional area for every transmural pressure (specifying, the maximal airway area, one of parameters describing the tube law (Lambert, et al.,

1982)). This approach simulated also stiffening of airways caused *in vivo* by smooth muscle constriction. Cross-sectional areas of the airways A2 and A4 (see Fig. 1) were decreased 2.5 and 6 times, respectively, to enable development of the serial choke points in these bronchi. Furthermore, values of the shape coefficient of the tube law for negative transmural pressures (Lambert, et al., 1982) were set equal to 1 in all central airways to make them more compliant and to ensure the possibility of wave speed limitation within them (Lambert, 1989). It could be suspected that the highly constricted airway A4 would limit flow to its own critical value and remaining, not restricted flows from the segments S3 and S4 would produce collapsing of the narrowed airway A2. Further effort was put to prolong the time of the serial arrangement of the choke points in the airways A2 and A4. Cross-sectional areas of the order 29 and 27 bronchi in the segment S3 (the largest airways of this segment), and order 31 and 30 bronchi in the segment S4 (the largest airways of that segment) were enlarged twice to enable faster airflows from the compartments C3 and C4, whereas constriction of the airway A4 was enlarged to 10 times.

Additionally, conditions of flow limitation in the "left" and "right" lung were compared by recording speed indexes S and transmural pressures at the downstream ends of the airways A2 and A5, and the segments S5, S6 and S7.

3. RESULTS

3.1 Location of flow limitation

Simulated MEFV curves of the normal lung (solid line) and of the lung with the constricted airways A2 and A4 (dashed line) are shown in Fig. 2. Despite partial obstruction of only two airways belonging to the same branch, the total flow from the constricted lung is suppressed in the whole range of VC, comparing to the normal case.

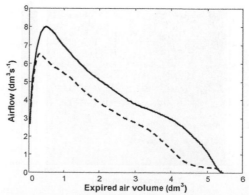

Fig. 2. Simulated MEFV curves for normal (solid line) and constricted airways (dashed line).

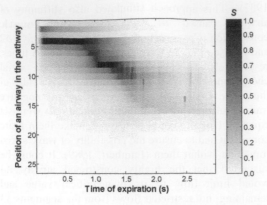

Fig. 3. Index of wave-speed flow limitation S (value given by the greyscale) in airways belonging to the pathway leading to the alveolar compartment $C1$ (airways $A1$, $A2$, $A4$, $A6$ and 22 successive airway generations from segment $S1$, see Fig. 1).

A typical pattern of flow limitation is presented in Fig. 3. It shows the change of the flow limitation index S in the pathway leading from the alveolar compartment $C1$ to the mouth (see Fig. 1). This pathway includes the following airways: $A1$ (1st position), $A2$, $A3$, $A4$ and the 22 successive airway generations in the segment $S1$. Wave-speed limitation appears in the airway $A4$ (4th position) of the order 32 after about 0.1 s of expiration and then the choke point moves upstream to the order 27 airway (inside segment $S1$) at about 1 second of expiration (in both locations S is close to 1). Finally, wave-speed flow limitation vanishes after 1.5 s which corresponds to about 94% of VC.

Comparing the maximal values of the flow limitation indexes achieved inside each of the seven pathways (Fig. 1), it is evident that flow limitation begins at the similar time in every branch of the bronchial tree, forming a parallel pattern of the choke points (Fig. 4). In the first phase, the maximal values are approximately equal to 1, and, depending on a branch, between 1.2 and 1.5 s they drop to values within the range of 0.6 – 0.7.

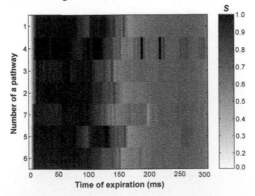

Fig. 4. Maximal values of the flow limitation index in the seven pathways shown in Fig. 1.

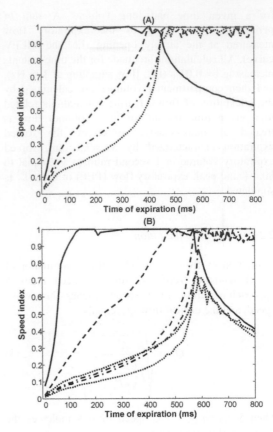

Fig. 5. A: Heterogeneous constriction case (airways $A2$ and $A4$ decreased 2.5 and 6 times, respectively) – the maximal speed indexes S of airways $A2$ (—) and $A4$ (---), 31 order airway in the segment $S4$ (–·–) and 29 order airway in the segment $S3$ (····). B: Increased heterogeneity case (airways $A2$ and $A4$ decreased 2.5 and 10 times, respectively, and 29 and 27 order bronchi in segment $S3$, and 31 and 30 order bronchi in segment $S4$ enlarged twice) – the maximal speed indexes S of airways $A2$ (—) and $A4$ (---), 31 and 29 order airways in segments $S3$ and $S4$ (····), and 25 order airways in segments $S3$ and $S4$ (–·–·).

3.2 Arrangement of the choke points

Simulations performed in the case of airway constriction (Fig. 5A) indicated the possibility of the choke points arrangement in series. In fact, flow limitation (the speed index close to 1) was achieved in the airway $A2$ first, solid line (at 120 ms of expiration), and after that in the airway $A4$, dashed line (at about 400 ms). Thus, the choke points existed in series between 400 and 450 ms of expiration and then flow in the airway $A2$ became non-limited. This choke point moved to the order 29 and 31 airways of the segments $S3$ and $S4$, dash-dotted and dotted lines, creating three flow-limiting sites in parallel. In the conditions of increased heterogeneity (Fig. 5B), the phenomenon existed between 460 and 580 ms of the maximum expiration.

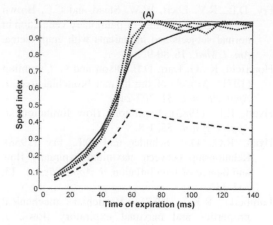

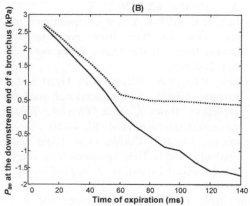

Fig. 6. Heterogeneous constriction case – airway $A2$ constricted 2.5 times, and $A4$ and $A6$ constricted 6 times. A: Maximal speed indexes S of airways $A2$ (—), $A5$ (---), and segments $S5$, $S6$ and $S7$ (····). B: Transmural pressures (P_{tm}) at the downstream ends of airways $A2$ and $A5$ (—), and segments $S5$ and $S6$ (····).

Fig. 6A shows a fundamental difference between flow limitation in the "left" and "right" lung. Whereas the speed index S of the constricted airway $A2$ (solid line) grows systematically and finally flow is choked within it, S of the airway $A5$ (dotted line) presents a rapid change in the slope at about 60 ms and the choke point does not appear inside it. On the contrary, parallel choke points arise in the "mother" airways of the segments $S5$, $S6$ and $S7$ at this time instant. It is also worth noticing that the parallel choke points in the segments $S5$ and $S6$ exist at positive transmural pressure at their downstream ends (Fig. 6B).

4. DISCUSSION AND CONCLUSIONS

The speed index has been used to track the location and degree of flow limitation. It has been found that the maximal value of the speed index S is reached at the downstream ends of bronchi, as stated by Shapiro

(1977) and Lambert (1987). This implies that limitation due to wave-speed is reached at the outlet of the bronchus. It has been shown previously that the drop of lateral pressure at airway junctions, following convective gas acceleration, may also induce flow limitation (Polak, 1998). The above supports the hypothesis that the most probable locations of the choke points in the central part of the bronchial tree are regions of the airway junctions.

The choke point in Fig. 3 appears in the central airway ($A4$) at about 0.1 s (0.6 dm^3), and moves upstream along the segment $S1$ during expiration. At the moment when flow limitation begins, the total airflow reaches its maximal value (Fig. 2). Since this time instant, the flow is effort-independent, whereas the lung recoil systematically lessens following the decrease of lung volume. This causes narrowing of the small airways and enlarges the pressure losses between the alveoli and the central bronchi. In effect, transmural pressure gets smaller and smaller, entailing upstream shift of the choke points.

The choke points are produced by the wave-speed mechanism in the central airways (Fig. 3). It also steams from Fig. 3 that flow limitation does not need to move from a given bronchus directly to the daughter airways – it can shift to a more peripheral bronchi. For example, in the pathway leading from the compartment $C1$, the choke point existed in the airway $A4$ up to about 0.8 s of expiration (4.0 dm^3), and the next airways with the speed index approximately equal to 1 were 27 order bronchi in the symmetric segment $S1$ (8th position in Fig. 3) from about 1 s (4.4 dm^3) of expiration.

Comparison of maximal values of the speed indexes in the seven bronchial branches (Fig. 4) reveals that flow limitation begins at the similar time in every pathway. Increased effort cannot produce faster flow in anyone of them, thus the total airflow measured at the airway outlet cannot be also changed. Simultaneous arising and existence of flow limitation in all of the pathways must result from the increasing number of the choke points in parallel that move upstream during expiration and double during transition between succeeding generations.

A general feature of the speed index behaviour is that S starts to drop down when flow limitation is reached upstream of a given bronchus (e.g. the airway $A5$ in Fig. 6A). This is accompanied by a rapid change in the slope of the speed index trajectory, both in the airways $A2$ and $A5$. From Fig. 6B it is clear that the modification of the speed index slope of the airway $A2$ follows the change of transmural pressure sign (about 60 ms of expiration) from positive to negative, whereas the slope related to the airway $A3$ is controlled by a parallel flow limitation arising in the upstream airways of the segments $S5$, $S6$ and $S7$ (also at 60 ms). Positive transmural pressure at the downstream ends of the segments S6 and S7 during flow limitation (compare Fig. 6A and 6B) indicate that the airways do not need to collapse during flow limitation when it is produced purely by the wave-speed mechanism.

Though first experimental attempts to induce and observe the choke points in series failed (Mink, et al., 1988), other studies on lung deflation, which in comparison with the forced expiration favours serial location of the flow limiting sides, demonstrated such an arrangement (Solway, 1988). Simulations performed in this study confirm that the choke points can be placed in series, also during a maximal expiration. However, despite favourable conditions for their serial arrangement in the airways A2 and A4, this phenomenon did not last long – after a few dozen of ms the serial pattern was replaced by the parallel one (Fig. 5A). The explanation is that the transition to the critical flows in the segments S2 and S3, with the simultaneous choke point in the airway A4 and decreasing driving pressures, make the entire flow in the airway A2 smaller than the critical value. In case of increased heterogeneity, the drop of the speed index in the bronchus A2 (after 580 ms) is caused not by the order 31 and 30 airways, which have been dilated, but by flow limitation in the upstream generations of order 25 in both segments S2 and S3 (Fig. 5B). It means that allowing faster flow in the dilated airways induces flow limitation in the upstream airways of smaller calibre quickly, and finishes flow control by the downstream segments. The above results suggest that the parallel formation of the choke points is more probable and common than their arrangement in series.

The results presented here show that the wave-speed mechanism is responsible for flow limitation for the most of VC. The serial configuration of the choke points is possible for short time periods in case of increased airway heterogeneity, however their parallel formation is more common. Finally, the most probable locations of the choke points are the regions of the airway junctions.

REFERENCES

Dawson, S.D. and E.A. Elliott (1977). Wave-speed limitation on expiratory flow – a unifying concept. J. Appl. Physiol.: Respirat. Environ. Exercise Physiol., 43, 498-515.

Fry, D.L., R.V. Ebert, W.W. Stead and C.C. Brown (1954). The mechanics of pulmonary ventilation in normal subjects and in patients with emphysema. Am. J. Med., 16, 80-97.

Horsfield, K., G. Dart, D.E. Olson and G. Cumming (1971). Models of the human bronchial tree. J. Appl. Physiol., 31, 207-217.

Hyatt, R.E. (1983). Expiratory flow limitation. J. Appl. Physiol., 55, 1-8.

Hyatt, R.C., D.P. Schilder and D.L. Fry (1958). Relationship between maximum expiratory flow and degree of lung inflation. J. Appl. Physiol., 13, 331-336.

Lambert, R.K. (1987). Bronchial mechanical properties and maximal expiratory flows. J. Appl. Physiol., 62, 2426-2435.

Lambert, R.K. (1989). A new computational model for expiratory flow from nonhomogeneous human lungs. ASME Trans. J. Biomech. Eng., 111, 200-205.

Lambert, R.K., T.A. Wilson, R.E. Hyatt and J.R. Rodarte (1982). A computational model for expiratory flow. J. Appl. Physiol.: Respirat. Environ. Exercise Physiol., 52, 44-56.

McNamara, J.J., R.G. Castile, G.M. Glass and J.J. Fredberg (1987). Heterogeneous lung emptying during forced expiration. J. Appl. Physiol., 63, 1648-1657.

Mink, S.N., H. Greville, A. Gomez and J. Eng. (1988). Expiratory flow limitation in dogs with regional changes in lung mechanical properties. J. Appl. Physiol., 64, 162-173.

Polak, A.G. (1998). A forward model for maximum expiration. Comput. Biol. Med., 28, 613-625.

Polak, A.G. and K.R. Lutchen (2003). Computational model for forced expiration from asymmetric normal lungs. Ann. Biomed. Eng., 31, 891-907.

Reynolds, D.B. (1982). Steady expiratory flow-pressure relationship of a model of the human bronchial tree. J. Biomech. Eng., 104, 153-158.

Shapiro, A.H. (1977). Steady flow in collapsible tubes. J. Biomech. Eng., 99, 126-147.

Solway, J. (1988). Properties of steady maximal expiratory flow within excised canine central airways. J. Appl. Physiol., 64, 1650-1658.

Solway, J., J.J. Fredberg, R.H. Ingram, Jr., O.F. Pedersen and J.M. Drazen. (1987). Interdependent regional lung emptying during forced expiration: a transistor model. J. Appl. Physiol., 62, 2013-1025.

Weibel, E.R. (1963). Morphometry of the Human Lung. Springer, Berlin.

A FUZZY CLASSIFIER FOR DRUG SENSITIVITY IN SEPTIC PATIENTS DURING CARDIOPULMONARY BYPASS

O.K. King*, M. Mahfouf*, J.J. Ross**, M. Denai*

*Department of Automatic Control and Systems Engineering, The University of Sheffield, Sheffield, UK
**Department of Surgical and Anaesthetic Sciences, Royal Hallamshire Hospital, The University of Sheffield, Sheffield, UK

Abstract: A compartmental model is modified to simulate the capillary leak associated with Sepsis and Cardiopulmonary Bypass (CPB). This involves continuously updating the oncotic pressures with regard to the flows in and out of each compartment. As a result, it is possible to model the effects of administering fluids with different oncotic pressures on filtration. The model allows for simulated infusions of vasoactive and inotropic drugs with a range of sensitivities to these drugs, giving a comprehensive platform for testing various control strategies. Furthermore, a fuzzy logic based system is designed to classify drug responses according to sensitivity, using the drug input and mean arterial pressure (MAP) signals from the model. This can be used as part of a comprehensive drug decision support system to estimate initial sensitivity and/or detect long-term changes in drug sensitivity. *Copyright © 2006 IFAC*

Keywords: Sepsis, Capillary leak, Fuzzy inference, Medical applications, Simulation, Decision support, Discrimination.

1. INTRODUCTION

Starling's hypothesis states that the fluid movement due to filtration across a capillary wall is dependent on the balance between the hydrostatic pressure gradient and the oncotic pressure gradient across the capillary (Klabunde, 2005). This is summarised by the Starling equation (1), where the net fluid movement (J_v) is dependent on the filtration coefficient (K_f), the reflection coefficient (σ) and the hydrostatic (P_x) and oncotic pressures (π_x) on either side of the capillary.

$$J_v = K_f[(P_c - P_i) - \sigma(\pi_c - \pi_i)] \qquad (1)$$

During and after Cardio-pulmonary bypass (CPB) however, this balance is disrupted and there may be a net 'capillary leak' into the interstitial compartment. Capillary leak is one of the symptoms associated with sepsis, which affects a significant proportion of CPB patients. Sepsis is also characterised by

increased heart rate and cardiac output, as well as persistent hypotension and hypoperfusion (Astiz and Rackow, 1998).

There are several published circulatory models of various levels of complexity, designed to simulate different conditions. However, only a few of these deal with specifically with capillary leak in a physiological sense. The objective here was to develop a physiologically based model, capable of simulating the key haemodynamic variables used by medical staff during and after CPB.

Model development combined ideas and equations from two previous models by Randall (1986) and Xie *et al* (1995). Randall's model is a lumped parameter, steady flow model representing commonly measured haemodynamic parameters (see Figure 1). It uses simple elements to describe parts of the circulation. Capacitors represent the veins and arteries, a steady flow pump represents the left and right ventricles and variable resistors represent the systemic and pulmonary vascular resistance. Subscript 'p' denotes pulmonary, 's' systemic, 'a' arterial and 'v' venous. CO_l and CO_r are the left and right cardiac outputs respectively, described by a non-linear function 'f'.

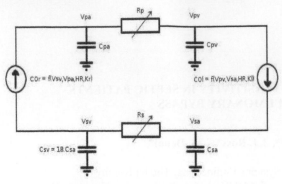

Figure 1: The electrical analogue circuit of the circulatory model where frequency, voltage current and charge are analogues of heart rate, blood pressure, flow rate and volume respectively.

Xie and co-workers developed a compartmental microcirculation model, which describes the transport and distribution of fluid and plasma proteins according to physiologically based, mathematical equations such as the Starling equation (1) and the lymph equation (2) as shown in Figure 2.

$$J_l = J_{l0} + LS\,(P_l - P_{l0}) \qquad (2)$$

Where P_l is the current interstitial pressure, P_{l0} is the nominal interstitial pressure, and LS and J_{l0} are constants determined from their simulations.

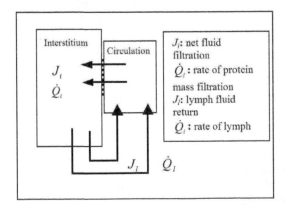

Figure 2: A Schematic of the fluid and protein exchange model by Xie et al [4].

The new model has an additional circulatory compartment, the capillaries, to act as the site of exchange between the circulation and the interstitium (Figure 3). The capillary pressure in this new compartment takes the place of the 'circulation' pressure in Xie's model. Each compartment has a continuously updated oncotic pressure. It was assumed that all capillary leak took place in the systemic circulation. All compartments were assumed to be well mixed, i.e., all properties were considered uniform throughout each compartment. As in Xie's model, at steady state, the transcapillary exchange rate of protein is equal to its removal rate via the lymph.

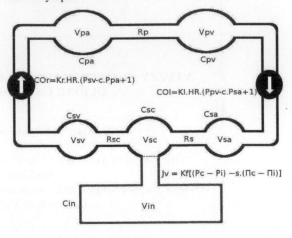

Figure 3: A Schematic diagram of the modified cardiovascular model

Mason (1989) has modelled the effects of vasoactive and inotropic drugs on systemic vascular resistance (SVR) and ventricular function (Rs and Kl/Kr respectively in Figure 3). A transport delay of 30 seconds was assumed for all drugs, representing the average time for the blood flow to transport the drug to its action sites. This was followed by an exponential change in ventricular function or SVR towards the dose-response curve. Based on his clinical experience, the time constant for vasodilator effects was set at 1 minute, and that for inotropic and vasoconstrictive agents to 2 minutes. The gain of the drug effects was adjusted until a response was produced which agreed with clinical experience and data presented by Greenway (1982). However, patients may show a wide range of responses to drugs. These differences can be simulated by adjusting the dose-response curve for each drug. Mason's piecewise linear dose-response curve was replaced with a sigmoidal one, while keeping the slope at the median effect the same.

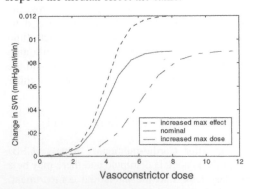

Figure 4: Dose response curve for vasoconstrictor on SVR, altered using max effect and max dose.

Dose response curves are typically sigmoidal, as there are a finite number of receptors for many drugs, and drugs reach their maximum effect as these become occupied. The drug response can be altered in the model by adjusting the maximum effect or the maximum dose as shown in Fig 4.

2. ANALYSIS OF CAPILLARY LEAK SIMULATIONS

Grocott and Mythen (2000) state that during sepsis induced capillary leak, σ decreases in the Starling equation, due to damage to the capillary endothelial structure through the inflammatory process. In the simulation depicted in Figure 7, σ was reduced by 50%. This caused a net fluid shift from the circulation to the interstitium of 0.5L. This also caused a drop in CO from 6.2 to 4.2 L/min and MAP fell from 95 to 61 mmHg, which meets the criterion for shock.

To simulate the management of this condition, an iso-oncotic fluid bolus of 250ml was added to the venous compartment. Figure 8 shows that most of the added fluid is lost to the interstitial compartment within an hour. When followed by 5 µg/kg per min of noradrenaline (Figure 9), the MAP is restored to above 80 mmHg. However, if the patient is also insensitive to noradrenaline, a larger dose would be needed (Figure 10). As noradrenaline is modelled here as a pure vasoconstrictor, this raises the afterload and lowers the cardiac output.

3. DESIGN OF THE FUZZY LOGIC BASED CLASSIFIER

A fuzzy logic based system was designed to classify drug responses according to sensitivity, using the drug input and mean arterial pressure (MAP) signals. The aim of this project was to design a system for estimating drug sensitivity which:-

- Can be used from any initial state.
- Uses commonly measured inputs.
- Chooses most conservative option where ambiguity exists
- Can work even if inputs cannot be changed arbitrarily.

The decision was taken to use the change in drug input divided by the change in MAP after 3 minutes (i.e. the local drug gain) as an input. Three minutes was chosen because it is longer than the combined lag and time constant for the vasoconstrictor simulation chosen, noradrenaline. This figure can be adapted for other drugs. The gains were calculated and plotted against the drug input for different drug sensitivities in Fig 5 and 6.

As shown, the gain of a highly sensitive system will be the same as an insensitive system at a certain point. Therefore the gradient data is needed to

conclusively distinguish between the two, assuming the simulation has just started and nothing is known about the previous state of the system. However, because of the lag and time constant associated with the drugs, gains can only be produced a minimum of three minutes after a change in drug input in this simulation.

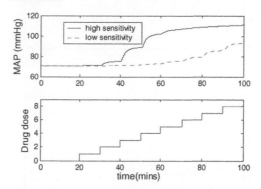

Figure 5: Change in mean arterial pressure with step increases in noradrenaline (ug/min) for two different drug sensitivities.

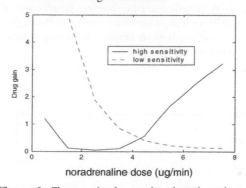

Figure 6: Changes in drug gain plotted against drug dose for two different drug sensitivities.

Furthermore, as two points are needed to calculate a slope, there is a minimum of 6 minutes needed in some cases for a definitive classification. A conservative estimate can be made with one point however. In many cases this will mean assuming the system is more sensitive rather than less sensitive in the face of ambiguity.

The fuzzy system is a three input, one output Mamdani type inference system, with and method 'min', or method 'max' and 'centroid' defuzzification method. It takes the drug gain, the slope of the gain and the current drug does as inputs, and outputs a crisp value between 0 and 1. Where 0 is very sensitive and 1 is insensitive. The gain input is fuzzified using 6 membership functions (MFs), the gain slope using 2 MFs and the dose using 4 MFs (Fig. 11). A rulebase of 34 if:then rules was generated, using a mixture of trial and error and the authors experience of using the simulation (Table 1). In the rulebase, 's', 'n' and 'i' denote the sensitive, nominal and insensitive MFs respectively. 'S' denotes the sensitive MF only when the gain slope is positive. The fuzzy output was mapped to a crisp value using centroid defuzzification of 3 output MFs.

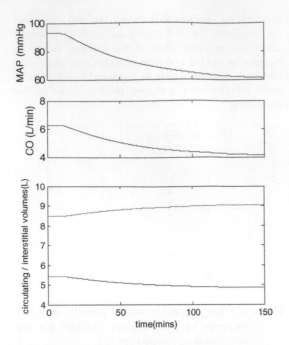

Figure 7: A Simulation run showing progression of capillary leak. Interstitial volume is the higher line on the bottom graph. Circulating volume is below.

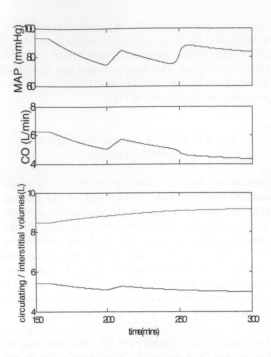

Figure 9: A Simulation run showing capillary leak treated with iso-oncotic fluid and vasoconstrictor noradrenaline.

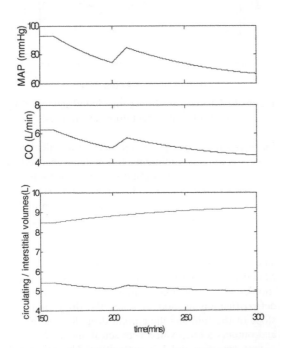

Figure 8: A Simulation run showing capillary leak treated with iso-oncotic fluid.

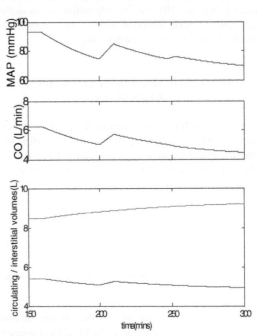

Figure 10: A Simulation run showing capillary leak treated with iso-oncotic fluid and vasoconstrictor on hyposensitive patient.

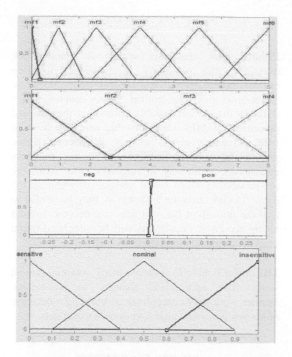

Figure 11: Fuzzy classifier membership functions. Drug gain, drug dose, gain slope and sensitivity output are ordered from top to bottom.

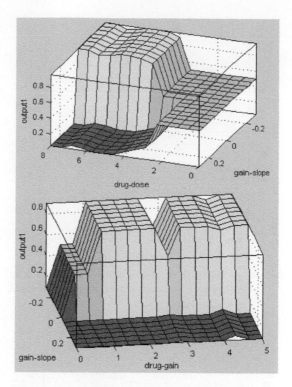

Figure 12: Control surfaces for three-input drug sensitivity classifier.

Table 1: Rule base for three-input drug sensitivity estimator

		Drug gain				
		MF1	MF2	MF3	MF4	MF5	MF6
Drug dose	MF1	s	s	n	n	i	n
	MF2	s	n	n	n	i	i
	MF3	s	n	i	i	i	i
		S	S	S	S	S
	MF4	s	i	i	i	i	i
		S	S	S	S	S

The control surface for the fuzzy logic based classifier is non-linear and it classifies the responses into three clear categories (Fig. 12). As there are four dimensions to the surface and only three can be displayed at once, the missing variable is assumed to be zero in each case.

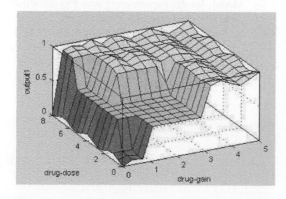

4. APPLICATION OF THE FUZZY LOGIC BASED CLASSIFIER

The fuzzy based system was able to distinguish between low, medium and high sensitivity responses in the majority of cases. Fig 13-15 shows the results of stepping from 0 to 8 units of vasoconstrictor at 3 different levels of sensitivity.

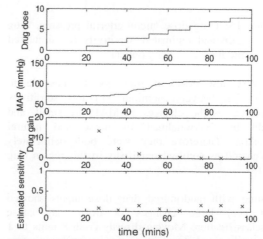

Figure 13: Drug dose, mean arterial pressure, drug gain and estimated sensitivity for simulated high sensitivity patient.

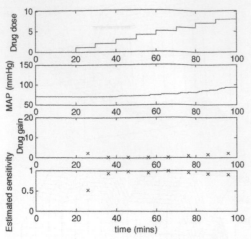

Figure 14: Drug dose, mean arterial pressure, drug gain and estimated sensitivity for simulated low sensitivity patient.

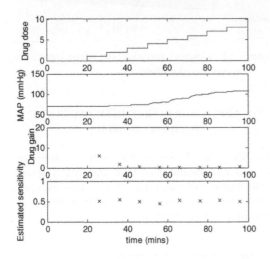

Figure 15: Drug dose, mean arterial pressure, drug gain and estimated sensitivity for simulated medium sensitivity patient.

At very low doses it may not be possible to distinguish between nominal and low sensitivity responses as the changes in MAP are small, and could be overwhelmed by noise and natural variation. Therefore they were both deliberately designated as nominal sensitivity in this region (Fig 14,15).

Testing with randomised drug dose inputs showed that very large changes of dose may cause misclassification. Moving directly from 8 units to 1 unit while simulating high sensitivity produces a gain of 0.17 and a classification of 'nominal' sensitivity with the current rule base. Changes of less than 5 units are correctly identified. If two equal sensitivity results in a row are required, this kind of error would be largely eliminated.

5. CONCLUSION

Results show that this system is suitable for estimating the sensitivity of responses to drug changes in simulation. Further work may concentrate on testing this on clinical data, adaptation for different drugs, and possibly optimising the size and placement of MFs. Currently this can only be used with vasoactive drugs, as not all haemodynamic parameters such as cardiac output are routinely measured continuously in intensive care. Also, the pre-processing stage could include de-trending the data. As time may be a factor, it may be useful to find out how short the wait time can become without losing accuracy. Finally this will be integrated into a drug decision support system.

The model is able to simulate many potential patient states with appropriate changes to parameters. Further work may concentrate on building a database of known states and their appropriate treatments.

ACKNOWLEDGEMENTS
The authors gratefully acknowledge the financial support for this project from the UK Engineering & Physical Research Council (EPSRC) and in particular the support falling under grant GR/S94636/1.

REFERENCES

Astiz M.E., Rackow E.C. (1998): 'Septic shock', *Lancet,* **351**, pp.1501-1505.

Grocott M.P.W., Mythen M.G. (2000): 'Fluid Administration in Septic Shock', *Sepsis*, **4**, pp.111-124.

Klabunde R.E. (2005): Exchange Function of the Microcirculation, In: *Cardiovascular Physiology Concepts*, Chapter 8, Lippincott Williams & Wilkins.

Mason D. G. (1989), Comprehensive Circulatory Management of Seriously Ill patients with a Closed-loop System, Ph.D Thesis for Dept of Electrical and Electronic Engineering, University of Melbourne

Randall J.E. (1986), A Cardiovascular System Model, In: *Microcomputers and Physiological Simulation*, Chapter 14, Raven Press.

Xie S.L., Reed R.K., Bowen B.D., Bert J.L. (1995): 'A model of human microvascular exchange', *Microvasc Res.*, **49(2)**, pp.141-62.

A MODEL OF THE VENTRICULAR ACTIVITY USING BOND GRAPHS

V. Le Rolle [1][2], **A. Hernández** [2], **P-Y. Richard** [1], **J. Buisson** [1], **G. Carrault** [2]

[1] *Supelec IETR, avenue de la Boulaie, B.P. 81127, 35511 Cesson-Sévigné cedex, France*
[2] *Laboratoire Traitement du Signal et de l'Image, InsermU 642, Université Rennes1*
35042 Rennes cedex, France

Abstract: A model of the ventricular activity using the Bond Graph formalism is presented. This model considers a simplified description of the ventricular geometry and the electromechanical phenomena occurring during cardiac contraction. Besides the interactions between the mechanical structure and the blood flow are considered. Finally the simulations obtained with the model are compared with real data. *Copyright © 2006 IFAC*

Keywords: Biomedical systems, Bond Graphs, Medical applications, Physiological models, Simulation

1. INTRODUCTION

Heart diseases are the first cause of death in western countries (about 30%). The understanding of cardiovascular diseases can help to elaborate methods that allow early detection of risky events. Modelling in medicine plays more and more a major role. In fact, models could lead to a better comprehension of cardiac pathologies. It can also help to analyse non-invasive signals to determine indicators that help to diagnosis. This work presents a model of the left ventricular activity that takes into account several energy domains, especially the structure-fluid interaction.

Many models of the left ventricle have been already published. Some of them are based on a global description of the cardiac activity as a single elastance model that has often been used in the literature (Guarini *et al*, 1998 ; Palladino *et al*, 2002). Although these kinds of models give pretty good results, they are not able to consider the geometrical characteristics that influence the ventricular performance. The cardiac fibre function has also been described (Montevecchi,, 1987), allowing the definition of whole heart models by means of differential equations (Redaelli *et al*,1997). The finite-element method (FEM) is also often used as

computational method for ventricular models simulations (May-Newman K.,1998, Vetter, 2000, Kerckoffs, 2003). This kind of representation gives broadly good results as precise indications on the mechanical behaviour. However, the FEM requires big computational resources, the model modification is difficult and, as a consequence, their clinical applicability is limited. Besides, the interactions between energy domains are difficult to consider. Bond Graphs appear as a good approach since one formalism can be used for all energy domains. Bond Graph models of the ventricle have already been presented (Lefebvre, 1999; Diaz-Zuccarini, 2003, Fakri, 2005). The interest resides in the fact that the cardiac fibre contraction is described using Bond Graph properties. However, in the above mentioned works, the electrical activation is not realistic enough to study some cardiac pathologies, and the interaction between the hydraulic and mechanical activity and the spatial variations of the mechanical and hydraulic properties are completely ignored.

Cardiac geometry of models can be based on real data (Nash, 1998). This approach is interesting but the flexibility is considerably reduced. In this work, the ventricular shape is described analytically. The size and the shape can be changed easily. It is also possible to study the influence of these parameters (shape, size) on cardiac performance. Cylindrical models have been used in the literature, by Redaelli *et al* (1997) to study the influence of cardiac performance on coronary circulation, by Taber *et al* (1996) to analyse the ventricular torsion. Although the cylindrical model is a good approximation, the ellipsoidal geometry is closer to the anatomical structure. This geometry has been also largely used in the literature to analyse the electrical propagation during contraction (Szathmary *et al*, 1994 Franzone *et al*,1998) or ventricular torsion (Taber *et al*, 1996).

This paper shows how Bond Graph method can be used to model and simulate a physiological system. The ventricular activity is first presented. Then, the model is described: the mechanical and the hydraulic aspects. Finally, the simulation results are reported and compared with real data.

2. THE MECHANICAL ACTIVITY OF THE HEART

The heart is a muscular pump system that pushes blood to all parts of the body. It is divided into four chambers: the two top chambers are called atria, and the lower chambers are called ventricles (figure 1). The atria collect the blood that enters the heart and push it to the ventricles, which eject blood out of the heart into the arteries. These heart chambers alternate periods of relaxation called diastole and periods of contraction called systole. The mechanical activity of the heart is controlled by a preceding electrical activity. This process is called the cardiac excitation-contraction coupling.

The cardiac muscle (or myocardium) is composed of cardiac myocytes, which are specialized muscle cells. These myocytes are made of myofibrils that contain sarcomeres, which are the elementary contractile elements. Sarcomeres can contract only if there is enough intracellular calcium available. This concentration rises during the action potential, which is produced through changes in membrane ion permeabilities. The calcium entrance into the cell increases the intracellular calcium concentration and lead to the sarcomeres contraction that converts electrical energy into mechanical energy.

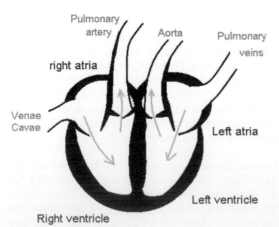

Fig. 1: Heart Physiology

3. A MODEL OF THE LEFT VENTRICLE

The ventricular model should take into account the interactions between the hydraulic and mechanical activities. This last one is activated by the cardiac electrical activity as seen previously.

3.1 Mechanical description.

The mechanical ventricular activity is classically divided into active and passive properties. Active properties are related to force development in the contractile elements of cardiac cells, which is due to the intracellular calcium concentration; whereas, passive ones are due to myocardium organisation (fibres, collagen…)

3.1.1 Passive properties

The ventricle is assimilated to a thick-wall structure. A wall segment that is under the influence of large deformations is first considered. The deformation is supposed to be exclusively radial. So, supposing that, in spherical coordinates, a material particle in the undeformed state (R,Θ,Ψ) goes to (r,θ,φ) in the deformed state, we have:

$$r = r(R); \qquad \theta = \Theta; \qquad \varphi = \Psi \quad (1)$$

Then deformation gradient tensor F and the left and right Cauchy-Green tensor (B,C) can be obtained. As the deformation is known, the strain in the principal direction can be expressed. Moreover, wall segment is assumed to be incompressible:

$$\lambda = \lambda_\theta = \lambda_\varphi = \frac{r}{R} \quad (2)$$

and the material is supposed to be hyperelastic. So, it is possible to determine the relation between stress and strain:

$$\sigma = -pI + 2F \frac{\partial W}{\partial C} F^T, \quad (3)$$

where p is the hydrostatic pressure, I is the identity matrix, C is the Cauchy-Green tensor, F deformation gradient tensor and W is the strain energy function. Different functions W have been proposed and enumerated in the literature (Munteanu *et al*, 2002, Mourad, 2003). Most of them are based on knowledge on the ventricle structure and have been measured experimentally on myocardial tissues. The greater part of these models takes into account cardiac fibre orientation, so the material is supposed to have an anisotropic behaviour. For example, some models are based on the hypothesis of orthotropy. Hunter *et al* (1998) propose a law called "pole-zero" that is based on a laminar description of the myocardium. Guiccione *et al* (1995) introduce an exponential law. However, the preceding formulation is complex and utilization is difficult because the strain energy function is defined in the fibre coordinates. The material can be also considered to be transversely isotropic. For example, Lin (1998) proposes a law that describes the passive state by an exponential function and the active state by a polynomial function. Humphrey *et al* (1990) define the energy function as a polynomial energy function, which has been used in a number of works (Taber et al, 1996, Chaudhry *et al*, 1996):

$$W = c1.(\alpha-1)^2 - c2.(\alpha-1)^3 + c3(I1-3) + c4(I1-3)(\alpha-1) + c5(I1-3)^2 \quad (4)$$

with $I1 = tr(C)$, $I4 = N^t.C.N$ and $\alpha = \sqrt{I4}$

Here, the energy function of Humphrey *et al* has been chosen, as the hypothesis of the transversely isotropic behaviour seems to be judicious to take into account the cardiac fibre orientation. Moreover the polynomial form of the function is easier to use. It is then possible to express the stress-strain relation:

$$\sigma = -pI + 2W_1 B + 2W_4 FN \times NF^t \quad (5)$$

with $W_1 = \dfrac{\partial W}{\partial I1}$ and $W_4 = \dfrac{\partial W}{\partial I4}$

where N is a unitary vector in the fibre direction, ψ is the fibre angle. As described previously, the stress tensor expression can be obtained from the strain λ and the properties of each myocardial segment concerned. The passive stress in the longitudinal and the latitudinal directions is then:

$$\sigma_{\theta\theta\_pass} = -p + 2.W_1.\lambda^2 + 2.W_4.\lambda^2.\cos^2(\psi) \quad (6)$$

$$\sigma_{\varphi\varphi\_pass} = -p + 2.W_1.\lambda^2 + 2.W_4.\lambda^2.\sin^2(\psi) \quad (7)$$

3.1.2 Active properties

The description of electro-mechanical interactions taking place during the action potential is essential to model the ventricular activity, because this phenomenon is at the origin of ventricular contraction. This complex mechanism has been described precisely in several works (Rice *et al*, 1999; Hunter *et al*, 1998). However, less precise descriptions can be used as we attempt to model the whole ventricle. An empirical relation between the calcium concentration and the fibre tension is often used (Nash, 1998):

$$T = T_{max} \frac{[Ca^{2+}]_i^n}{[Ca^{2+}]_i^n + Ca_{50}^n} [1 + \beta(\lambda - 1)] \quad (8)$$

Where *Tref* is the referred tension at $\lambda = 1$, Ca_{50} is the calcium concentration at 50% of the isometric tension, n is the Hill coefficient determining the shape of the curve, β is a the myofilament "cooperativity". Then, it is possible to express the Cauchy stress as the sum of the passive stress and the active stress:

$$\sigma = \sigma_p + \sigma_a \quad (9)$$

with $\sigma_a = T.(FN).(FN)^T$ and N a unitary vector in the fibre direction. So, the active stress in the longitudinal and the latitudinal directions can be expressed as:

$$\sigma_{\theta\theta\_act} = T.\lambda^2.\cos^2(\psi) \quad (10)$$

$$\sigma_{\varphi\varphi\_act} = T.\lambda^2.\sin^2(\psi) \quad (11)$$

Where ψ is the fibre angle. To describe the influence of the electrical activity on the fibre mechanical performance, the well-known Beeler and Reuter (1977) model (BR model) has been chosen. It presents a basic description of the intracellular Ca2+ dynamics, while keeping a low level of complexity. It is based on a Hodgkin-Huxley type membrane potential model. The intracellular calcium concentration variable of the BR model modulates T (equation 8)

3.2 Coupling

The stress in the longitudinal and the latitudinal directions ($\sigma_{\theta\theta}$, $\sigma_{\varphi\varphi}$) are defined as:

$$\sigma_{\theta\theta} = \sigma_{\theta\theta\_pas} + \sigma_{\theta\theta\_act} \quad (12)$$

$$\sigma_{\varphi\varphi} = \sigma_{\varphi\varphi\_pas} + \sigma_{\varphi\varphi\_act} \quad (13)$$

Then, it is possible to obtain the radial stress from a well-known relation, called the Laplace Relation that has been demonstrated by Back (1977).

$$-\sigma_{rr} = \frac{\sigma_{\theta\theta} \times e}{R_p} + \frac{\sigma_{\varphi\varphi} \times e}{R_m} \quad (14)$$

where R_m and R_p are the radii of curvature in the principal directions and e is the wall thickness. The influences of shear stress and wall acceleration have been neglected. By integrating the Laplace relation, the force developed by the wall segment is defined as:

$$F = \int (\frac{\sigma_{\theta\theta} \times e}{R_p} + \frac{\sigma_{\varphi\varphi} \times e}{R_m}) dS \quad (15)$$

The pressure at the wall surface can be express as:

$$P = \frac{F}{S} \quad (16)$$

and the integration on the surface represents no difficulties because the ventricle is assimilated to an ellipsoid.

3.3 Hydraulic description.

A thick wall segment has first been described to take into account the mechanical characteristics of the structure. The force development and the wall size variation lead to the pressure variation at the structure surface. So the influence of the fluid in contact with the wall has to be considered. The fluid is assumed to be inside a pipe.

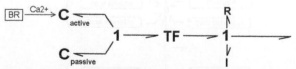

Fig.2: Bond Graph Model of a wall segment

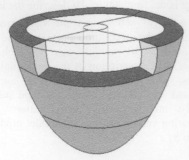

Fig.3: Segmentation of the ventricle model

To describe the fluid hydraulic behaviour, some energy phenomenon can be identified on each pipe. In fact, the fluid mass brings inertial effects. Moreover, for a laminar flow, the pressure difference is proportional to the flow, so resistive effects that represent the losses due to the cavity can be shown.

3.3 Bond Graph model

The equations (6), (7), (10) and (11) show the material elastic properties. As a relation between the stress and the strain can be written, a capacitive element can be defined in the Bond Graph formalism. The capacity is deduced by the relations defined previously, integrated on the volume of the material. Equation (16) defined a relation that allows the mechanical-hydraulic conversion and can be represented by a Bond Graph transformer. Hydraulic aspects are modelled by resistive and inertial elements (figure 2).

3.4 The whole ventricle Model

The ventricle is assumed to be composed of several mechano-hydraulic sub-systems. The myocardium is first divided into three layers (called layer1, layer 2 and layer 3). Then, each layer is separated into 4 components: septal, lateral, anterior and inferior wall. So the myocardial wall is divided into 12 segments that interact with the hydraulic part of the intra-ventricular cavity (figure 3). The Bond Graph model described previously represents each mechano-hydraulic part.

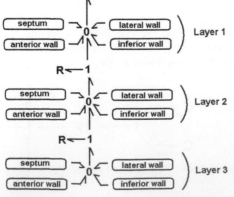

Fig. 4: Bond Graph model of the whole ventricle

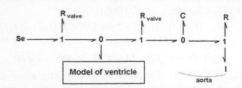

Fig.5: Simulation Model

To connect each segment, the boundary conditions have to be defined. At the center of each layer, the pressures of each segment are equal and the flow is the sum of the flows generated by each segment. This effect can be represented in Bond Graphs by a junction 0 (figure 4). The mechanical interaction between each part is taken into account through the hemodynamic domain.

3.5 Simulation Model

The ventricle is assimilated to a truncated ellipsoid of revolution that is defined by a minor and a major axis and by the wall thickness (Grossman, 1980). The basal plane position can be defined in function of the ellipsoid major radius (Streeter, 1973).

To simulate the model behaviour without the preload influence, the ventricular filling is modelled by a constant effort source. A parallel capacitance, a resistance and an inertance in series describe the aortic resistance. The heart valves are modelled by modulated resistances (figure 5).

The mechanical activity is under the influence of the electrical activity. The action potential propagation in the myocardial tissues is at the origin of the global cardiac contraction. To reproduce the ventricular behaviour, a discrete formalism is usually used. To simulate the asynchronously ventricular contraction, the well-known isochrones of cardiac activation are used (Malmivuo, 1995).

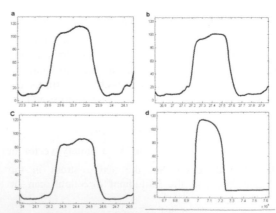

Fig. 6: Ventricular pressure (mmHg): experimental results (a),(b) and (c); and simulations (d)

4. RESULTS

4.1 Experimental protocol

Experimentations have been realised on 3 pigs to obtain the intra-ventricular and the intra-myocardial pressures. A left lateral thoracotomy was performed before the acquisition. The intra-ventricular pressure is obtained by the insertion of a catheter (Millar Instrument, SPR-350, 5F) by the right carotid artery. The intra-myocardial pressure acquisition is done by a needle-type catheter (Millar Instrument, SPR-477, 2F) that is inserted inside the myocardial wall. The signals obtained are analysed for different afterload. The afterload augmentation and the afterload diminution are made by the aorta coarctation and by sodium nitroprussiate injection (Lavigne, 2001).

4.2 Comparison between simulation and real Data

The 20-sim software is used to simulate the proposed model with the Runge-Kunta numerical method. In this work, only the intra-ventricular pressure signal is analysed because the model is not yet able to give the intra-myocardial pressure. It is then possible to compare the simulated and experimental ventricular pressure (figure 6).

The model simulations have been realised with different afterload conditions. To model the aortic obstacle augmentation, the aorta resistance is increased (figure 7). As the afterload grows, the systolic ventricular pressure increases.

The afterload effect on ventricular performance can be best understood using the Pressure-volume (PV) loop. It can be generated by simulating the model and plotting the ventricular pressure against the ventricular volume (figure 8). We recognize the characteristic phases of the cardiac cycle: ventricular filling, iso-volumetric contraction, ejection and iso-volumetric relaxation. When the afterload increases, the ventricle has to generate a higher pressure before the opening of the aortic valve. Besides, the quantity of blood ejected decreases. This effect describes an important physiological behaviour of the heart. It is possible to observe the end-systolic pressure linearity that is characteristic of the ventricular behaviour (Suga, 2003).

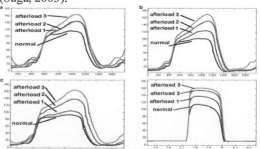

Fig. 7: Ventricular pressure augmentation (mmHg) during afterload variation: experimental results (a),(b) and (c); and simulations (d)

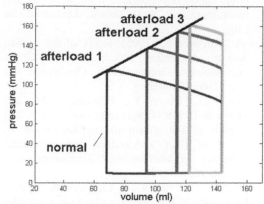

Fig. 8: Simulated pressure-volume loop with different afterload conditions.

5. CONCLUSION

In this work, a model of the mechanical ventricular activity based on the Bond Graph formalism has been proposed. The Bond Graph approach is attractive since one single formalism can be used for all energy domains. This model takes into account a simplified geometrical description of the ventricle, keeping a low level of complexity. In fact, the ventricular shape is described analytically and an adapted model to each patient can be envisaged in our future works. Simulations require low computational resources and the parameters adaptation to specific systems is easier than in complex models.

Results are encouraging and further works will be focused on the clinical application of the model on different pathologies such as cardiac ischemia or heart failure. In this perspective, the future developments should take into account several layers in the thickness of the myocardium, so that the influence of electrical desynchronisation can be analysed.

REFERENCES

Back L. (1977) Left ventricular wall and fluid dynamics of cardiac contraction. Math. Biosci. 36, 257-297

Beeler, G.W. and Reuter H. (1977). Reconstruction of the action potential of ventricular myocardial fibres. In: *Journal of Physiology*, 268 : 177-210.

Bestel, J. (2000). *Modèle différentiel de la contractrion musculaire contrôlée : Application au système cardiovasculaire*, PhD thesis, University Paris 9

Chaudhry, H. R., Bukiet, B. and Findley, T. (1996), Stresses and Strains in the Passive Left Ventricle, in *Journal of Biological Systems,* , Vol. 4, No. 4, pp. 535-554.

Diaz-Insua, M., Delgado, M. (1996). Modeling and Simulation of the human cardiovascular system with Bond Graph : a basic development. In: *Computer In Cardiology*, 393-396

Diaz-Zuccarini, V.A. (2003). Etude des conditions d'efficacité du ventricule gauche par optimisation téléonomique d'un model de son fonctionnement. PhD thesis, Université de Lille.

Fakri A., Rocaries F. (2005), Study of the cardiac muscle dynamics utilising Bond Graph methodology, International Conference on Bond Graph Modeling

Franzone P.C., Guerri L., Pennacchio M. and Taccardi. B. (1998) Spread of excitation in 3-D Models of the anisotropic cardiac tissue. II. Effect of fiber architecture and ventricular geometry, in *Mathematical Biosciences*, 147, Issue 2, 15, 131-171

Guarini M. , Urzua J. , Cipriano A. (1998) Estimation of Cardiac Function from Computer Analysis of the Arterial Pressure Waveform, In : *IEEE Transactions on Biomedical Engineering* , Vol. 45 , 1420-8.

Guccione M., K. D. Costa, and A. D. McCulloch. (1995) Finite element stress analysis of left ventricular mechanics in the beating dog heart. In : *J. Biomechanics*, Vol 28 :1167-1177

Grossman W. (1980) Cardiac hypertrophy: useful adaptation or pathologic process?, Am. J. Med, 69 : 576

J.D. Humphrey, R.K. Strumpf and F.C.P. Yin (1990) determination of a constitutive relation for passive myocardium: II. Parameter estimation In *J. Biomech.* , 112 : 340-346.

Hunter, P.J., McCulloch A.D. and ter Keurs H.E.D.J. (1998) Modelling the mechanical properties of cardiac muscle. In: *Progress in Biophysics & Molecular Biology* ,69 , 289-331

Kerckoffs R.C.P., Bovendeerd P.H.M., Prinzen F.W., et al (2003) Intra- and interventricular asynchrony of electromechanics in the ventricularly paced heart, in: Journal Of Engineering Mathematics, 47: 201-216

Lavigne D. (2001) Etude temps-fr equence de la relation entre la fréquence instantanee du premier son cardiaque et la contraction du ventricule gauche. *Rapport technique interne*, Laboratoire de Génie biomédical, Institut de Recherches Cliniques de Montréal

LeFèvre J., Lefèvre L. and Couteiro B. (1999), A bond graph model of chemo-mechanical transduction in the mammalian left ventricle, In : *Simulation Practice and Theory*, Volume 7, Issues 5-6, 531-552

Lin D.H.S. and Yin F.C.P. (1998) Amultiaxial constitutive law for mammalian left ventricular myocardium in steady-state barium contracture or tetanus., 1998, ASME, J. Biomech. Engng Verla, Vol 120 : 504-517

Malmivuo J. and Plonsey R. (1995) Bioelectromagnetism: Principles and Applications of Bioelectric and Biomagnetism Fields, Oxford University Press, New York

May-Newman K.,. McCulloch A.D (1998) Homogenization moeling for the mechanics of perfused myocardium, in Progress in Biophysic & Molecular Biology, 69 463-481.

Mourad A. (2003) Description topologique de l'architecture fibreuse et modélisation mécanique du myocarde, PhD thesis, University of Grenoble

Munteanu L., Chiroiu C. and Chiroiu V. (2002) Nonlinear dynamics of the left ventricle, in Physiol. Meas. , 23: 417-435

Montevecchi, FM and Pietrabissa, R, (1987) A model of multicomponent cardiac fiber, J. Biomechanics, 20, 365-370

Nash, M., (1998) Mechanics and Material Properties of the Heart using an Anatomically Accurate Mathematical Model. PhD thesis, University of Auckland.

Palladino J.L. , Noordergraaf A. (2002) A paradigm for quantifying ventricular contraction. In : *Cell. Mole. Biol.* Letters 7(2) : 331-335.

Redaelli A, Pietrabissa R. (1997) A structural model of the left ventricle including muscle fibres and coronary vessels : mechanical behaviour in normal conditions, Meccanica 32: 53-70

Rice J.J. , Winslow R.L. and Hunter W.C. (1999) Comparison of putative cooperative mechanisms in cardiac muscle: length dependence and dynamic responses. In : *Am J Physiol.* ; 276 : H1734-54.

Streeter DD Jr, Hanna WT (1973) Engineering mechanics for successive states in canine left ventricular myocardium: I. Cavity and wall geometry, Circ. Res 33: 639

Suga H. (2003), Cardiac Energetics : from Emax to pressure-volume area. In: *Clinical and Experimental Pharmacology and Physiology*, Volume 30, Issue 8, pp. 580

Szathmary V. and R.Osvald (1994) An interactive Computer Model of propagated activation with analytically defined geometry of ventricles., in computer and biomedical research, , 27, 27-38

Taber L.A., Yang M. and Podszus W. (1996) mechanics of ventricular torsion, J.Biomechanics, , Vol 29, 745-752.

Vetter R.J. and McCulloch A.D. (2000) Three-dimensional Stress and Strain in Passive Rabbit Left Ventricle: A Model Study, in Annals of Biomedical Engineering, Vol 28, pp. 781-792.

MODEL OF THE KNEE FOR UNDERSTANDING THE SQUAT MOVEMENT BIOMECHANICS

Guillaume Agnesina, Redha Taïar, William Bertucci, Alain Lodini

Laboratoire d'Analyse des Contraintes Mécaniques (LACM – EA 3304)
UFR STAPS
Université de Reims, Moulin de la Housse
51100 Reims, France

Abstract: By means of MSC Adams- BRG LifeMOD software, a three dimensional lower extremity model has been developed in this study. This model take into account 16 muscles, 4 ligaments, 2 tendons in order to quantify forces and contacts (patello-femoral and tibio-femoral) during muscular training movement (e.g. a squat) with various raised loads (0, 20 and 30 kg). The first results showed the importance of the relationships between muscle activations (e.g. Quadriceps, Hamstrings) and ligament forces (e.g. Anterior and Posterior Cruciate Ligaments). *Copyright © 2006 IFAC*

Keywords: Model, Human Reliability, Estimation, Force, Knee.

1. INTRODUCTION

The means whereby we can understand and predict the normal knee motion is by reconstructing and modelling this joint taking into account the ligaments and tendons.

There have been many studies about the relationships between knee loading and ligament tension or strain (Ahmed et al., 1992, Markolf et al., 1993, Renstrom et al., 1986, Takai et al., 1993, Wascher et al. 1993, Bendjaballah et al. 1995). Furthermore, numerous studies have investigated the effects of muscle forces on ligament loading (Draganisch and Vahey, 1990, Kurosawa et al., 1991, Pandy and Shelburne, 1997, Hsieh and Draganich, 1997, Shelburne and Pandy, 1997, Abdel-Rahman and Hefzy, 1998). All the studies as mentioned above are very complete and the different models developed integrate well the complete knee motion. For instance those of Pandy and Shelburne in 1997. Even if it is a two-dimensional model (sagittal plane), they were be able to estimate the anterior cruciate ligament (ACL) and the posterior cruciate ligament (PCL) tensions according to the flexion-extension movements of the knee. They estimate also the patellar-tendon force

and the tibiofemoral-contact force with the aim to minimize ACL force.

In order to study the knee movement, we developed a new three dimensional model joint. The aim of our study can be divided in two parts. In the first one, we studied the forces of the muscles, ligaments and contacts (patello-femoral and tibio-femoral) during movement of muscular training (e.g. a squat) with various raised loads. In the second one, we predicted ACL and PCL forces, lateral collateral ligament (LCL) and medial collateral ligament (MCL) forces as a function of loads, knee flexion and muscular contribution. The results obtained can help us to limit injuries bound to this joint.

2. METHODS

In this study, MSC ADAMS - BRG LifeMOD 2005 software was used in order to create the new model.

A healthy subject was chosen with the physical conditions: a man, 40 years old, 1.74 m height and 85 kg weight. The leg model is created for simulation. The model consists of a single leg, adding masses at the hip location (It represents the mass of the upper body more the mass of the raised loads).

Contact ellipsoids are created to describe the tibio-femoral and patello-femoral contact elements. They are installed on the distal end of the femur to provide contact between the femur and the tibia. Thus, contact forces can be predicted between these condyles and the tibial plateau. To create these segments, we used a value of 1400 kg/m^3 for the osseous density. Also, the patella is created as a separate segment with the aim to predict contact forces between this segment and the condyles of the femur (Fig. 1).

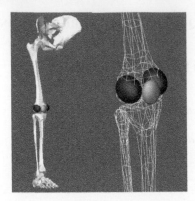

Fig 1. Location of the patella and condyles ellipsoids. In blue, there are lateral and medial condyles segments, in red, there is the patella condyle segment.

The joint is stabilized by adding ligaments and patellar tendon. In this study, four ligaments are represented: MCL, LCL, ACL and the LCL. (Fig. 2) Mechanical ligament properties are provided from the studies of Woo et al. (1982) and Wilson et al. (1988).

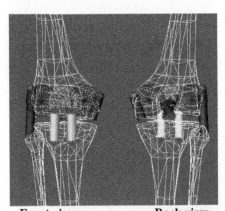

Front view　　　　**Back view**

Fig 2. Insertion of ligaments and tendons. In blue, the four ligaments (MCL, LCL, ACL, LCL), in yellow, the tendon.

To model muscles, LifeMOD uses a force in order to replicate the desired body motion, while staying within each muscle's physiological limits. The calculation muscle forces uses the physiological cross sectional area (pCSA). The muscle geometry data (pCSA) was developed by amongst others Eycleshymer et al. (1970). The upper limit of the muscle force (F_{max}) is generated by multiplying pCSA for each muscle to a maximum tissue stress (M_{stress}) value derived from Hatze (1981).

In our study, 16 muscles have been generated. There are: Gluteus Maximus 1 and 2, Gluteus Medius 1 and 2, Adductor Magnus, Semitendinosus, Vastus Medialis, Vastus Lateralis, Biceps Femoris 1 and 2, Rectus Femoris, Iliacus, Gastrocnemius 1 and 2, Soleus and Tibialis Anterior. (Fig. 3)

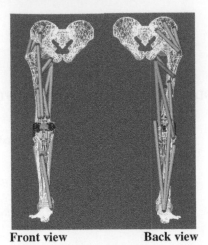

Front view　　　　**Back view**

Fig 3. Insertion of muscles (in red).

To create the flexion movement of the knee, a motion agent (Fig. 4) is added to the lower leg model. This motion agent is removed for the inverse-dynamics simulation (the muscle contraction histories has been recorded). We can now use the active muscle formulation to produce a force to recreate the motion history.

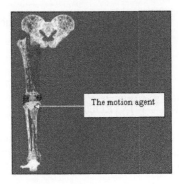

Fig 4. Insertion of a motion agent. This motion agent allows the flexion of the knee.

To simulate the movement of a squat in muscular training we applied two different masses on the lower torso (Pelvis) to have three analyses and results. In the calculation, we divided these masses by two, because we have one leg. We made an analysis with:
-   no mass, the squat movement is made without load.
-   with a mass of 20 kg,
-   with a mass of 30 kg.

3. RESULTS

We made the analysis and we obtained the following results. Firstly, we can analyze the ACL behaviour. At 1.8 seconds, we have the maximal knee flexion (90°).

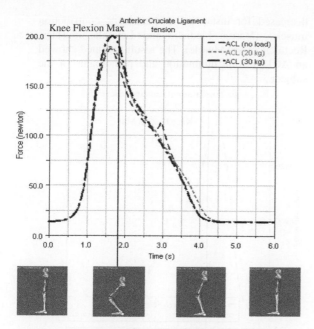

Fig 5. Anterior Cruciate Ligament behaviour

We have the ACL maximal tension just before the bottom dead centre (when the model is still moving). For a 30 kg load, the ACL tension is maximal compared to without load and 20 kg load. (Fig 5)

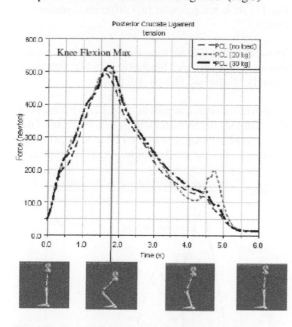

Fig 6. Posterior Cruciate Ligament behaviour

For the PCL tension (Fig. 6), we can make the same diagnostic findings. The major difference is in the tension value (in Newton). We see the PCL is more solicited than the ACL.

The very interesting result that we can see is the behaviour of some muscles. For instance, we analyzed the Vastus Medialis (which is a part of the quadriceps muscle), the Biceps Femoris (which is a part of the hamstrings muscle) and the gastrocnemius muscle.

For the gastrocnemius muscle, its activity is maximal when the knee flexion is about 90°. (Fig. 7) Furthermore, for a 30 kg load, this muscle has a tension less significant than with a 20 kg load.

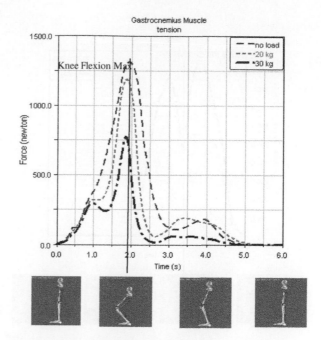

Fig 7. Gastrocnemius Muscle behaviour

This result can be explained by examining the equilibration of the forces of the model. Indeed, for a squat movement without load, the model can directly pick up on the gastrocnemius muscle but with a load (20 or 30 kg) this muscle is not sufficient. With the action of the others muscles (e.g. Vastus Medialis, Biceps Femoris), the activity of the gastrocnemius muscle decreases.

When we compare one agonist and antagonist muscle we see how the movement is made. (Fig 8 and 9) For two muscles of the thigh (the Biceps Femoris and the Vastus Medialis), we can explain this movement of a squat (muscular training). For instance, when the Vastus Medialis tension is lower, the Biceps Femoris tension is higher (during the downward phase). Furthermore, when we are at the dead centre the tension in each muscle is roughly equilibrated (For a 30 kg load, at the dead centre we have 490 N for the Biceps Femoris muscle and 440 N for the Vastus Medialis muscle).

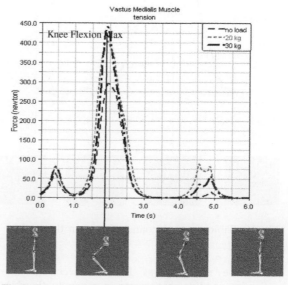

Fig 8. Vastus Medialis Muscle behaviour

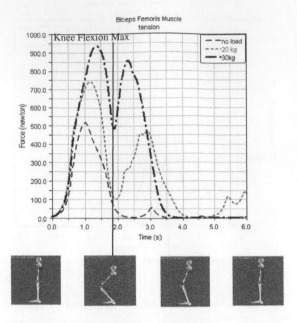

Fig 9. Biceps Femoris Muscle behaviour

What is very interesting is to analyze the tibio-femoral contact forces in the vertical axis (Fig. 10).

This figure showed the relationships between forces and knee angle during flexion and extension. We observed during the first phase (until 1.83s) the high force values in function to the raised loads. In the second phase (until 3.5s) the force values decreased as a function of the no load movement. In addition these values increased for the other raised loads.
During flexion and extension, we observed a link between the contact forces and the PCL (or ACL) tension. Indeed, if this contact is high, the PCL (or ACL) tension becomes higher.

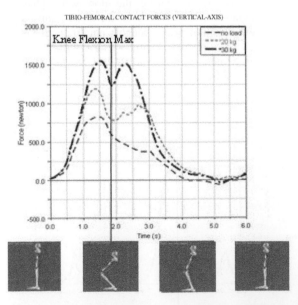

Fig 10. Tibio-femoral contact forces in the vertical axis

The same relation was found between muscle activation and ligament tension in our study. (Fig 11) For the same movement with no load, and taking into account the possibilities of our software, we

decreased for instance the quadriceps contribution muscles (Vastus Medialis and Lateralis muscles, Rectus Femoris Muscle). The result obtained showed an ACL tension diminution and pathologies of the subject .

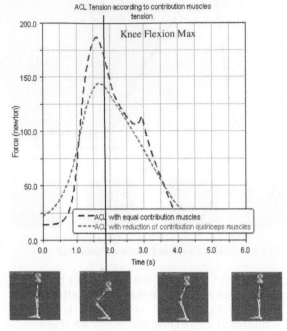

Fig 11. ACL tension with two different contribution muscles

These observations are in agreement with the results shown by Pandy and Shelburne (1997) and more recently Mesfar and Shirazi-Adl (2005).

In the horizontal component (Fig.12) we observed the similarity of the forces values as a function of the raised loads during extension (2.5 and 3.2s). This result indicates the good equilibrium of the subject.

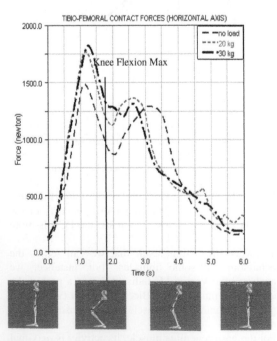

Fig 12. Tibio-femoral contact forces in the horizontal axis

4. DISCUSSION

The objectives of this first study were to determine the behaviour of the knee joint: more precisely the ligaments and the muscles of the lower extremity and the contact forces in the knee during muscular training activity (the squat). The results are in good agreement with other studies covering the same subject. We have found, for instance, the interest to interpret the quadriceps or hamstring tensions in the aim of limiting cruciate ligament forces. Moreover, the contact forces allowed us to appreciate these cruciate ligament forces. The originality of our study is to take for first time into account the real weight of the subject and the various raised loads representing the movement. The model developed in this study made possible the estimation of the knee movement for high level athletes or a pathological subject and permit a good estimation for muscle coordination during movement.

For this first approach, there are some limitations: The menisci are not integrated in our model and the condylar surfaces have been simplified by ellipsoids. In the future we will integrate twelve ligament bundles in Abdel-Rahman and Hefzy's study (1998) in comparison to the fourth created in our study and will study the shear contact forces between Tibia and Femur. All the results that we can obtain permit a better knee joint understanding in order to decrease the pathologies of subjects.

REFERENCES

Abdel-Rahman EM, Hefzy MS. (1998) Three-dimensional dynamic behaviour of the human knee joint under impact loading. *Medical Engineering and Physics.* 20: 276-290

Ahmed AM, Burke DL, Duncan NA, Chan KH. (1992) Ligament tension pattern in the flexed knee in combined passive anterior translation and axial rotation. *Journal of Orthopaedic Research.* 10: 854-867.

Bendjaballah MZ, Shirazi-Adi A, Zukor DJ. (1995) Biomechanics of the human knee joint in compression: reconstruction, mesh generation and finite element analysis. *The Knee Vol.* 2.2: 69-79.

Draganisch LF, Vahey JW. (1990) An in-vitro study of anterior cruciate ligament strain induced by quadriceps and hamstrings forces. *Journal of Orthopaedic Research.* 8: 57-63

Eycleshymer AC, Shoemaker D.M. (1970). A cross-section anatomy. *New York: Appleton-Century-Crofts*

Hatze H, (1981). Estimation of myodynamics parameter values from observations on isometrically contracting muscle groups. *European Journal of Applied Physiology and Occupational Physiology.* 46: 325-338.

Hsieh YF, Draganich LF. (1997) Knee kinematics and ligament lengths during physiologic levels of isometric quadriceps loads. *The Knee.* 4: 145-154

Kurosawa H, Yamakoshi KI, Yasuda K, Sasaki T. (1991) Simultaneous measurement of changes in length of the cruciate ligaments during knee motion. *Clin Orthop.* 265: 233-240.

Mesfar W and Shirazi-Adl A. (2005) Biomechanics of the knee joint in flexion under various quadriceps forces *The Knee.* 12(6): 424-434.

Markolf KL, Wascher DC, Finerman GAR. (1993) Direct in vitro measurement of forces in the cruciate ligaments. Part II: The effects of section of the posterolateral structure. *Journal of bone and joint surgery.* 75A: 387-394.

Pandy MG, Shelburne KB. (1997) Dependence of cruciate-ligament loading on muscle forces and external load. *Journal of biomechanics.* 30: 1015-1024

Renstrom P, Arms SW, Stanwyck TS, Johnson RJ, Pope MH. (1986) Strain within the anterior cruciate ligament during hamstring and quadriceps activity. *American journal of sports medicine.* 14: 83-87.

Shelburne KB, Pandy MG. (1997) A musculoskeletal model of the knee for evaluating ligament forces during isometric contractions. *Journal of Biomechanics.* 30: 163-176.

Takai S, Adams DJ, Livesay GA, Woo SL-Y. (1993) Determination of the in situ loads on the human anterior cruciate ligament. *Journal of Orthopaedic Research.* 11: 686-695.

Washer DC, Markolf KL, Shapiro MS, Finerman GAR. (1993) Direct in vitro measurement forces in the cruciate ligaments of the knee. Part I: The effects of multiplane loading in the intact knee. *Journal of bone and joint surgery.* 75: 377-386.

Wilson C.J, Dahners LE. (1988) An examination of the mechanisms of ligament contracture. *Clinical Orthopaedics and Related Research,* 227: 286-291.

Woo SLY, Gomez MA, Woo YK., Akeson WH. (1982) Mechanical properties of tendons and ligaments. II:The relationships of immobilization and exercise on tissue remodeling. *Biorheology.* 19(3): 397-408.

GENERIC PROBABILISTIC NETWORKS IN MEDICAL DECISION SUPPORT

K. Jensen S. Andreassen

Center for Model-based Medical Decision Support, Aalborg University, Denmark

Abstract: Causal probabilistic networks provide a natural framework for representation of medical knowledge, allowing clinical experts to encode assumptions about dependencies between stochastic variables. Application in medical decision support has produced promising results. However, model parameters may vary between patient groups or over time. Therefore methods are needed that allow for easy calibration of the model to a change in conditions. A solution to this problem is presented and illustrated with an example from a medical decision support system. *Copyright ©2006 IFAC*

Keywords: Probabilistic network, Calibration, Databases, Decision support systems, Medical applications

1. INTRODUCTION

Causal probabilistic networks (CPN), also known as Bayesian networks or belief networks, have been applied in construction of a number of medical decision support systems. A lesson learned from construction of such large scale models is that a model of a complex medical domain may contain a number of variables that vary between different localities or patient groups or over time. This implies that a model must be calibrated to particular demands for the model to be applicable to a specific hospital or patient group at a given point in time.

An example is TREAT, a decision support system for antibiotic treatment (Andreassen *et al.*, 2005). The conditional probabilities in TREAT can be divided into two groups.

(1) The largest group, by far, consists of conditional probabilities that are considered to be independent of time and space. An example is the conditional probabilities required to assess the state of sepsis from a set of symptoms.

(2) The smaller group are conditional probabilities that are assumed to be specific for a given hospital, and they may change over time. The most important example in this group is conditional probability distributions representing the local susceptibility of pathogens to antibiotics.

To handle the different conditional probabilities for each hospital the TREAT system has a number of calibration databases (Andreassen *et al.*, 2005). The calibration databases contain conditional probabilities that are specific to each hospital using the system. When asked for advice the system will make a search in the calibration database and insert the correct conditional probabilities. This implies that advices from the system to a given input may vary from one hospital to another.

While this solution works well for TREAT, it has some limitations. Prior to inference a CPN must be compiled into a secondary structure, a junction tree (Jensen, 2001). Once that has happened both the state space and structure of the model is fixed. In TREAT calibration data are inserted into the junction tree, meaning that the solution used in TREAT does not apply to cases where the calibration data imply changes in the state space of one or more variables, or manipulation of the structure of the CPN.

This is the case in MUNIN, a diagnostic decision support system for neurophysiology (Andreassen *et al.*, 2005). Here the more general calibration problem outlined above occurs naturally. A part of the solution has been to specify MUNIN generically, and then create special instances of the generic model where structure, state space and conditional probabilities have been created from a particular set of calibration data. In the present paper this method for generic representation of a CPN is presented and the applicability of the method to handle variations in state space, between different instances of the CPN, is illustrated with an example from MUNIN. Finally it is argued that the method represents an improvement over state of the art technology in generic CPN modeling (Koller and Pfeffer, 1997).

2. A METHOD FOR GENERIC REPRESENTATION OF CPN'S

A CPN is a directed acyclic graph representing a joint probability distribution over the variables represented by the nodes of the graph (Jensen, 2001). If there is a directed arc from node A to node B this arc may be interpreted as a causal link and node A is called the parent of node B. Specification of a CPN involves three major steps:

(1) Selection of a set of stochastic state variables, that adequately represents the problem domain. Some of these variables might relate to observables, while others can represent unobservable features or concepts.
(2) Encoding of a number of assumptions into the structure, defined by nodes and links of the network.
(3) Specification of conditional probability tables for each node in the graph.

Before describing how to represent a CPN generically, and use this representation to solve the general calibration problem, a few definitions are needed.

Definition 1. An **invariant clause** is a set of attributes $A_1, ..., A_n$ of a CPN. A **construction protocol**, is a procedure, that will create an instance of a CPN. A construction protocol can be parameterized. A **class declaration** is a composition of an invariant clause and a construction protocol.

Definition 2. A **class** is a set of instances of a CPN, all sharing the same class declaration.

To represent a CPN generically the following two steps are taken:

(1) Define a list of invariants that are common to all instances of a CPN.
(2) Define a construction protocol that will create an instance of a CPN given a set of calibration data as parameters.

To exemplify the method of generic representation, consider the following example from MUNIN.

3. A GENERIC REPRESENTATION OF MUNIN

MUNIN represents the pathophysiological concepts related to muscles and nerves that are necessary to interpret electromyographic and neurographic findings in terms of neuromuscular system disorders.

3.1 Specification of the MUNIN CPN structure

Figure 1 shows some relevant anatomical and physiological coordinates for a nerve conduction study. In a nerve conduction study the nerve is stimulated electrically at certain points, and action potentials are recorded at an endpoint. The stimulation points and the endpoint logically divide the nerve into a number of nerve segments.

CTS: Carpal Tunnel Syndrome
l_{ns}: Length of nerve segment
CV_{normal}: Conduction Velocity of nerve signal in a normal subject

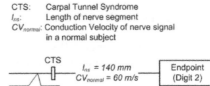

Fig. 1. The median nerve is stimulated electrically at the wrist and an action potential is recorded at digit 2. A demyelinating local nerve lesion, for example the Carpal Tunnel Syndrome (CPT), will decrease the conduction velocity of the nerve signal. To detect a local nerve lesion from the measured conduction velocity, the length of the nerve segment, l_{ns}, and the mean conduction velocity of the nerve signal in a normal subject, CV_{normal}, must be specified.

Examples of assumptions that are hardwired into the topology of MUNIN include:

- A demyelinating local nerve lesion may cause a delay of the nerve signal in the demyelinated nerve segment.

- A local delay in a nerve segment will decrease the conduction velocity of a nerve signal induced electrically proximally to the nerve lesion and measured distally to the nerve lesion.

Figure 2 shows four variables in a CPN representing the potential slowing of a nerve signal, due to demyelination.

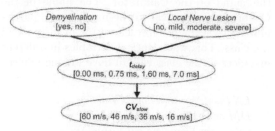

Fig. 2. Assumptions related to causal interaction between a set of stochastic variables are represented by the structure of the CPN. The connected variables represent the mapping of a time delay (t_{delay}), caused by a demyelinating local nerve lesion, into the observed conduction velocity (CV_{slow}). The values in brackets are the state space of the variables.

3.2 Specification of conditional probabilities in MUNIN

As with TREAT the conditional probabilities of MUNIN can be divided into two groups. Some are assumed constant over time and space and some are known to change. Among those from the latter group are a set of conditional probability distributions that are derived from a description of a particular nerve conduction study.

To represent a nerve conduction study in MUNIN a number of parameters must be specified for each nerve segment (see figure 1), including:

- The length of a nerve segment, l_{ns}.
- The mean value of the conduction velocity of the nerve signal in a normal subject, CV_{normal}.

Now, the values of these physiological parameters may vary between different neurophysiologic laboratories, because each laboratory may have their own guidelines for specification of nerve conduction studies, including a unique set of reference values for the normal population (Kimura, 2001). Also they may vary between different patient groups, e.g. child and adult. Finally the parameter values for a particular nerve conduction study will vary between different parts of the anatomy. This is an analogy to the calibration problem as it occurs in TREAT, with the extra condition that the specification of a particular nerve conduction study may have an impact on the state space

of the model. To clarify this proposition it is necessary to consider the specification of conditional probabilities for a nerve conduction study in greater detail.

The physiological parameters are utilized in models that describe the interaction between variables in the network. The purpose of these models is to simplify the specification of conditional probability tables and to handle potential discrepancies between variables that are discrete and variables that are continuous by nature. An example is the variable, CV_{slow}, representing the measured conduction velocity of a nerve signal in a demyelinated nerve segment (figure 2). The mean values this variable can assume are calculated as follows:

$$\mathbf{CV_{slow}} = \frac{l_{ns}}{\mathbf{t_{delay}} + \frac{l_{ns}}{CV_{normal}}}, \qquad (1)$$

where l_{ns} is the length of a given nerve segment and CV_{normal} is the mean value of the conduction velocity of the nerve signal in a normal population (figure 1). $\mathbf{t_{delay}}$ is a state vector representing different degrees of delay of the nerve signal, due to demyelination of the nerve (figure 2).

The outcome of equation 1 is used to generate a conditional probability table for the node representing the variable $\mathbf{CV_{slow}}$. For a thorough description of the utilization of this kind of models the reader is referred to (Andreassen, 1992). The intention here is simply to illustrate that the specification of conditional probability tables in MUNIN for some nodes depends on physiological variables.

To illustrate how the state space of $\mathbf{CV_{slow}}$ depends on l_{ns} and CV_{normal}, consider the following two examples.

(1) A nerve conduction study with $l_{ns} = 270$ mm and $CV_{normal} = 64$ m/s. In this case the state space of $\mathbf{CV_{slow}}$ becomes [64 m/s, 54 m/s, 46 m/s, 24 m/s].
(2) A nerve conduction study where $l_{ns} = 140$ mm and $CV_{normal} = 60$ m/s. In this case the state space of $\mathbf{CV_{slow}}$ becomes [60 m/s, 46 m/s, 36 m/s, 15 m/s].

To summarize, the conditional probability table for the variable $\mathbf{CV_{slow}}$ in the MUNIN CPN depends on the parameters l_{ns} and CV_{normal} that are specified for any particular nerve conduction study (figure 1). In addition it depends on the state space of the parent node, $\mathbf{t_{delay}}$. As a consequence the state variable $\mathbf{CV_{slow}}$ must have a state space that is calibrated to any particular nerve conduction study.

3.3 Implementation of a generic model of MUNIN

The generic model of a MUNIN is implemented as a compositional hierarchy of Java classes and the Java constructor serves as a construction protocol. The prototype generic model represents a subset of the MUNIN CPN, and is created using the Java API of Hugin Expert, a commercially available shell for construction of CPN's (Hugin, 2004). Using the Java API it is possible to generate a CPN from a set of Java operations or to load and manipulate an already specified CPN. Note that the following code examples are pseudocode. Furthermore the model has been modified to simplify the description.

3.3.1. The invariant clause

The model of a nerve conduction study in a single nerve segment is represented by a Java class, NerveSegment. The class NerveSegment declares the invariant attributes needed to represent all nerve segments. In the present example the structure of the network in figure 2 is an invariant for all nerve segments, so it must be declared in the invariant clause.

$Node\ LNL$;
$Node\ DM$;
$Node\ \mathbf{t_{delay}}$;
$Node\ \mathbf{CV_{slow}}$;
$\mathbf{t_{delay}}.parents = \{LNL, DM\}$;
$\mathbf{CV_{slow}}.parents = \{\mathbf{t_{delay}}\}$;

LNL and DM are abbreviations for *Local Nerve Lesion* and *Demyelination*.

3.3.2. The construction protocol

The construction protocol of the class contains the operations necessary to create an instance of the CPN. The constructor protocol is a parametric creator function, meaning that a set of calibration data can be passed as a parameters.

$NerveSegment(\ Calibrator\ ns)$

The Calibrator is an internal representation of the part of the calibration database representing attributes of a particular nerve segment. It contains the calibration data and provides the methods needed to retrieve them. Among the calibration data are conditional probability tables (CPT's) and anatomical and physiological coordinates needed to generate a CPT.

The CPT defines the state space of a node and associates a probability distribution over the states of the node with each configuration of states in the parent nodes. A CPT must be given as a parameter for each instantiated node.

The body of the constructor must name the variables and insert the proper CPT's.

3.3.2.1. Naming of variables and insertion of CPT's

The following set of operations will name the variables. The method $setName(String\ name)$ will concatenate the variable name with the name of the Calibrator. The name of the Calibrator is identical to the name of the particular nerve segment represented by an instance of the class. This way identical variables in different instances of the class will all have unique names.

$LNL.setName(ns.getName())$;
$DM.setName(ns.getName())$;
$\mathbf{t_{delay}}.setName(ns.getName())$;
$\mathbf{CV_{slow}}.setName(ns.getName())$;

When retrieving the CPT's two different types of situations must be handled. In the simplest cases the CPT's are retrieved from the Calibrator passing the name of the CPT as a parameter. For example the CPT representing the prevalence of the Carpal Tunnel Syndrome (see figure 1) is stored in the Calibrator under the name "LNL".

$LNL.setTable(ns.getTable("LNL"))$;

In more complicated cases the CPT must be generated by a parameterized model. For example the table for $\mathbf{CV_{slow}}$ must be generated using the parameters l_{ns} and CV_{normal} (figure 1 and equation 1). This type of cases adds another level of complexity to the construction of the model since the parameters to the model now becomes parameterized. A detailed account of how to handle this kind of problem, will be given in a future publication.

3.3.3. Composition of objects

The approach to generic modeling taken here is object-oriented. The object-orientation implies that an object can be composed of other objects. In figure 3 an example is shown, where a model of a nerve conduction study is composed of objects representing nerve conduction studies of individual nerve segments. Each nerve segment object contains its own unique state space and set of conditional probabilities.

Object composition implicates a number of issues that must be handled, when formulating a generic model. Algorithms must be designed to combine components, when the number of components is not known in advance. As the number of conditional probabilities in a node is exponential in the number of parent nodes, measures must be taken to control the number of parents to any given node

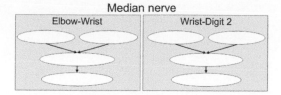

Fig. 3. An object of a class SensoryNerve can be composed of objects of the class NerveSegment.

(Olesen *et al.*, 1989). Also the Calibrator must be designed carefully to match the structure of the compositional hierarchy. A detailed account of these issues cannot be given here due to space limitations.

4. DISCUSSION

The method for generic representation of CPN's described in the present paper is object-oriented. An object-oriented approach to representation of CPN's, has already been described in the litterature (Koller and Pfeffer, 1997). However, the method presented here is more general in several ways.

In (Koller and Pfeffer, 1997) a class represents a *unique* joint probability distribution over the set of variables contained in the class. An instance of a class is simply a copy of that joint probability distribution. Thus the framework introduced by (Koller and Pfeffer, 1997), does not represent a solution to the calibration problem described in the introduction. In the framework presented here a class is a *set* of joint probability distributions, all sharing the same *class declaration*. A class declaration is composed of an *invariant clause* and a *construction protocol*. If the invariant clause contains a complete CPN and the construction protocol consists of a single operation, that will copy the CPN, then this special case is equivalent to a class as defined by (Koller and Pfeffer, 1997).

Another difference relates to the object composition described above. In (Koller and Pfeffer, 1997) a class definition contains a specification of a set of input nodes to each instance of a class. These input nodes are *placeholders* and are replaced by so called output nodes from other objects, when the objects are combined into a composite object. Thus the interaction between objects is determined *statically* in the definition of the class, and the number of parents to an object of the class is identical for all instances. In the method presented here the interaction between objects is determined *dynamically*, after the objects have been instantiated, and the number of inputs and outputs may vary between different instances of the same class. The cost of this extra flexibility is that special algorithms are needed to control the number of parents to any given node, as mentioned briefly above.

One can compare the method presented here to the solution of the calibration problem used in the TREAT system, as described in the introduction. In the TREAT system all hospitals are interacting with the same CPN, but calibration data are inserted into the CPN prior to inference. If the method of generic representation was used, all hospitals would be interacting through the same *interface*, but the inference would be done in different CPN's, each one generated from a particular set of calibration data. This solution would imply a slight reduction of inference time, since a search in the calibration database is no longer necessary.

It should be mentioned that in its present form the modeling technique is quite complex. It requires the participation of a knowledge engineer trained in object-oriented programming. Also for the method to be fully general, an editor for the Calibrator must be designed. Alternatively a Calibrator must be designed specifically for each problem domain. However, once the model has been formulated it can easily be calibrated to particular settings.

Finally it must be emphasized, that the line of research presented here, is still in an exploratory phase and more work is needed to produce results that allows for a precise assessment of the methodological approach.

5. CONCLUSION

In conclusion a preliminary method for generic representation of CPN's has been described and application of the theory has been illustrated with an example from the medical domain. The method is object-oriented allowing multiple users to interact with different instances of the model through the same model interface. Also a model can be composed out of generic model elements. The modeling technique is quite complex, but as far as the authors are informed, it is the first of its kind to allow CPN's to be easily calibrated to a change in conditions affecting the state space and the structure of the model. The authors believe that the method, when it is fully developed, will be well suited for the medical domain, where this kind of dynamics in their experience often occurs.

REFERENCES

Andreassen, S. (1992). Knowledge representation by extended linear model. In: *Deep Models for Medical Knowledge Engineering* (E. Keravnou, Ed.). pp. 129–145. Elsevier. Amsterdam.

Andreassen, S., L. Leibovici, M. Paul, A.D. Nielsen, A. Zalounina, L.E. Kristensen, K. Falborg, B. Kristensen, U. Frank and H.C. Schønheyder (2005). A probabilistic network for fusion of data and knowledge in clinical microbiology. In: *Probabilistic Modeling in Bioinformatics and Medical Informatics* (D. Husmeier, R. Dybowsky and S. Roberts, Eds.). pp. 451–452. Springer. London.

Hugin (2004). Hugin expert, white paper.

Jensen, F.V. (2001). *Bayesian Networks and Decision Graphs.* Springer Verlag. New York.

Kimura, J. (2001). *Electrodiagnosis in Diseases of Nerve and Muscle: Principles and Praxis.* Oxford University Press. Oxford.

Koller, D. and A. Pfeffer (1997). Object-oriented bayesian networks. In: *Proceedings of the Thirteenth Annual Conference on Uncertainty in Artificial Intelligence* (D. Geiger and P.P. Shenoy, Eds.). pp. 302–313.

Olesen, K.G., U. Kjærulff, F. Jensen, F.V. Jensen, B. Falck, S. Andreassen and S.K. Andersen (1989). A munin network for the median nerve - a case study on loops. *Applied Artificial Intelligence* **3**, 385–403.

GENERALIZED CELLULAR AUTOMATA FOR STUDYING THE BEHAVIOR OF CELL POPULATIONS

Noël Bonnet [1,2] and Jean-Marie Zahm [1]

[1] *Inserm, U514, IFR53, Hôpital Maison Blanche,*
45, rue Cognacq Jay, F-51092 Reims Cedex, France
[2] *CReSTIC-LERI, University of Reims, France.*

Abstract: Cellular automata are generalized to handle non-local rules, i.e. rules taking into account the states of the whole set of objects present in the array. Considering a binary state (presence/absence of objects), evolution rules are defined as a function of the local density of objects, estimated according to the Parzen method. This allows tackling problems found in the field of cellular sociology, such as cell clustering or cell sorting. *Copyright © 2006 IFAC*

Keywords: Automata. Simulation. Dynamical behavior. Biomedical. Social.

1. INTRODUCTION

In the framework of cancer invasion and metastasis, we are interested in the collective behavior of cell populations in culture conditions. In order to study this behavior, we have often to simulate it, according to the present knowledge of the model that governs this behavior. Our simulation approach is within the framework of cellular automata.

A cellular automaton is usually defined as an array of cells[1]. Each cell represents an object having a finite number of states. This state is updated in discrete time[2] as a function of the states of its closest neighbors. One famous example of cellular automata can be found in the John Conway's game of life (Gardner, 1970).

In the specific case of a mono-layer of a biological cell population, the geometrical cell represents a possible position for one of the biological cells. Thus, the state of any biological cell evolves as a function

of the states of the biological cells within a small neighborhood (a 3x3 neighborhood is generally considered).

In cell biology, after the pioneering work of Bard Ermentrout and Edelstein-Keshet (1993), cellular automata have been considered to tackle the following problems, among others:

- Modeling the proliferation of a human breast cancer cell line (Palmari, et al., 1994)
- Aggregation (Bussemaker, et al., 1997; Deutsch, 2000; Alber and Kiskowski, 2001)
- Swarm systems (Adamatsky and Holland, 1998)
- Neurogenesis in *Drosophila* (Luthi, et al., 1998)
- Modeling gliding and aggregation of Myxobacteria (Stevens, 2000)
- Simulating brain tumor growth dynamics (Kansal, et al., 2000)
- Analysis of cellular lesions in tissue sections (Luebeck and de Gunst, 2001)
- Simulation of medication-induced autoimmune diseases (Stauffer and Proykova, 2004)

However, we believe that many problems in biology of cell populations cannot be solved within the framework of cellular automata with evolution rules considering small neighborhoods only. Instead, we do think that many cell behaviors are the

---

[1] Called geometrical cells in the sequel.
[2] Thus, a cellular automaton is a discrete-state discrete-time system.

consequence of large-scale interactions where the states of the whole set of cells govern the evolution of any individual cell.

As an example for such large-scale interactions, let us assume that certain type of cells produce some chemical substance and that the same cells are attracted by this substance (chemotaxis).

For these problems, generalized cellular automata (GCA) must be defined, where the state evolution rules depend on the whole set of states and not on the state of objects in a small neighborhood only.

As an example of such GCA, we consider in this contribution the case of rules that depend on the local density of cells, this local density depending on the presence/absence of biological cells on the geometrical cells constituting the array. Of course, GCA are not restricted to this simple approach with a single binary state. More sophisticated GCA can be defined where the multi-valued states of all the objects are used to define an evolution rule for the multi-valued state of any individual object.

The simple density-based cellular automata will be used to tackle the following problems:
a)   Considering one single population of undifferentiated cells, we would like to simulate and quantify the behavior of a cell population according to different rules:
  - Cells attract each other: in this case, any individual cell will move in the direction of the highest local cell density. Thus, cell clusters are formed. The process of cluster formation can be studied more deeply using this approach.
  - Cells repel each other: in this situation, not only clusters are not formed, but the ultimate cell distribution may even become more regular than random.
  - Cells neither attract nor repel each other.

This problem of cluster formation is one of the problems raised by the differential behavior of invasive and non-invasive cells, in the context of cancer metastasis [Nawrocki-Raby et al. 2001].

b)   Considering two (or more) cell populations, where the different populations display a different behavior in terms of cell attraction/repulsion, we will show that the GCA approach can also be used to reconsider the problem of cell sorting.

2.   DENSITY-BASED CELLULAR AUTOMATA

Since we consider the specific case of evolution rules depending on the local density of objects, we will first explain how this can be computed within the framework of cellular automata.

We start with the distribution of cells within the two-dimensional array:

$X(i,j)$ = 1 for a geometrical cell at position (i,j) filled by a biological cell

= 0 for an empty geometrical cell

(1)

The local density of cells is computed according to the (kernel) Parzen approach (Parzen, 1962; Silverman, 1986):

$$D(i,j) = \sum_{i',j'} \ker(i-i', j-j').X(i',j') \quad (2)$$

where the kernel function $\ker(.)$ is chosen as a Gaussian function, for instance:

$$\ker(i,j) = \frac{1}{\sqrt{2\sigma^2}} \exp\left(-\frac{i^2+j^2}{2\sigma^2}\right) \quad (3)$$

and σ is the standard deviation of the kernel.

Figure 1 illustrates the concept of local cell density.

In the specific case we are considering here, the state

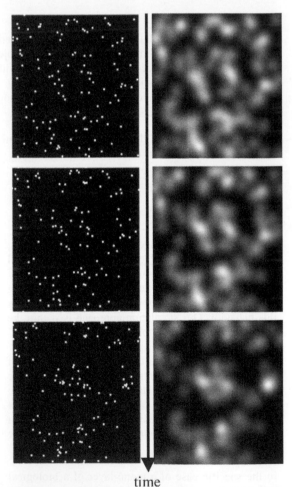

time

Figure 1: Illustration of the concept of local cell density:
Three snapshots of a simulated temporal image series
(where cells attract each other and thus form clusters) and the corresponding local cell density:
Left: Positions of cells
Right: Local cell density

of any biological cell is its position (i,j) within the array. So, the next state is a new position: (i',j'). This new position is computed according to the chosen model.

For a single population of biological cells:

- for a random walk model: the cells move in a random direction, chosen among eight. The amount of displacement is chosen randomly between 0 and a maximum value, chosen by the user. If the final computed position is already occupied by a biological cell, a new random shot is performed, until the maximum number of shots is attained.

- for an attraction model: any cell moves in the direction of the largest local density.

- for a repulsion model: any cell moves in the direction of the lowest cell density.

For a two-population model:
The local cell density of the two cell populations is computed at each iteration. Then, any biological cell moves according to the model (random, attraction or repulsion model) and to the local density of cells that belong to the same population.

Note that the same approach can be applied to cell populations in three dimensions (3D) as well.

3. EXAMPLES OF APPLICATION

3.1 A single population model: study of clustering and non clustering by non-invasive and invasive cells

Our purpose here was to simulate the behavior of cell

populations in culture, with the aim of checking that we were able to quantify this behavior using specifically developed tools. For instance, a tool was developed to assess the amount of attraction (or repulsion) exerted by a cell on all the other ones (Bonnet, et al., 2004). This index of attraction/repulsion should be close to 1 for a purely attractive model, close to −1 for a purely repulsive model and close to 0 when neither attraction nor repulsion governs cell migration.

Figure 2 displays the values of the attraction/repulsion index computed from a series of images simulated with the generalized cellular automaton model described above, for an attractive model and a repulsive model. It also displays the values of the attraction/repulsion index computed from series of real images recorded by video microscopy, with invasive (BZR) and non invasive (16HBE) cell lines. One can see that the behavior of cell populations in culture neither correspond to an attraction model nor to a repulsion model. This specific result allowed us to deduce that, despite non-invasive cells form clusters as a function of time and invasive cells do not (Nawrocki-Raby, et al., 2001), this difference cannot be explained by a global attraction/repulsion potential.

As a more specific study reported here, we tried to see whether the range of attraction (or repulsion) can be determined in the case of an attraction (or repulsion) model. Within our approach, the range of attraction is coded by the standard deviation σ of the Parzen kernel used to estimate the local cell density.

Figure 3 displays the results of a simulation (according to the GCA approach) where the range of attraction of an attraction model is modified and the variation in the number of objects is evaluated as a

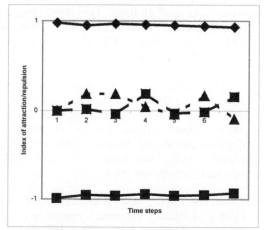

Figure 2: Index of attraction/repulsion computed, as a function of time (time step =100 min) for two simulations and two real experiments. The top curve represents the result corresponding to the simulation of an attraction model. The bottom curve represents the simulation with a repulsion model. The two intermediate curves correspond to real experiments, cultures of invasive and non invasive cells (BZR and 16HBE, respectively).

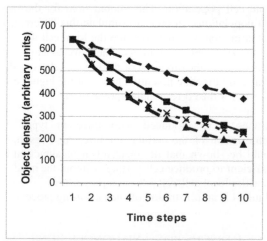

Figure 3: Evolution of the object (cell) density for a cell attraction-clustering model, computed for four values of the parameter describing the range of attraction. This parameter increases from the top curve to the bottom curve. This is reflected by the fact that the number of objects (individual cells + cell clusters) decreases faster when the range of attraction increases.

function of time, for the different values of the parameter describing the range of attraction. (The number of objects, individual cells and cell clusters, is evaluated according to a new method based on the auto-correlation of the local cell density (Bonnet, et al., submitted)). The result shows that different values of the range of attraction lead to a more or less fast decrease of the number of objects as a function of time (corresponding to cluster formation and growth), as expected. These curves obtained from simulations could serve to calibrate the results obtained from real experiments.

3.2 A two-population model: study of cell sorting

It is generally admitted that cell-cell and cell-substrate adhesion properties govern the capabilities of cells to perform sorting without the need for any external agent. For instance, Hobmayer et al. (2001) demonstrated that inside-outside sorting of two cell types A and B occurs when the strength of the adhesive force between the different cells A-B is intermediate between the two homotypic strengths A-A and B-B. In contrast, separation of the two cell types occurs when the adhesive strength of A-B is lower than the two adhesive strength A-A and B-B. Also, Graner and Glazier (1992) demonstrated that differences in contact energies between cells of different types (differential adhesion) cause cell motion that reduces the pattern's energy and lead to cell sorting.

In the context of our work on generalized cellular automata, we tried to demonstrate that cell-cell adhesion properties are not a requisite to cell sorting, although it is certainly involved.
For this, we consider a mixture of two cell types, constituting two cell populations. Then, we assume that any cell attracts all the cells that belong to the same cell population. This should hold for the two cell populations. In order to simulate this differential cell attraction, we first compute the local cell density for the two cell populations. Then, we assume that cells move in the direction of the higher values of the local cell attractive potential, hence of the higher cell density for the corresponding population.

Movies were produced with different types of initialization of the cellular mixture. As a result, it could be shown that the mechanism of attraction is sufficient to produce cell sorting, without the need to consider local cell-cell adhesion properties.
Figure 4 is an illustration of such a sorting process.

4. DISCUSSION AND CONCLUSIONS

Modeling in Biology can be performed according to different approaches, among which systems of differential equations and cellular automata play a highly significant role. Systems of differential equations are non-spatial models, but space can also be treated explicitly, through reaction-diffusion equations for instance. Although local concepts are generally considered, non-local concepts can be used as well (Lee, et al., 2001). In the cellular automata framework, local concepts are mostly considered, the evolution rules being generally defined in a very small neighborhood. In this work, we attempted to define generalized cellular automata, where the evolution rules depend on the states of the whole set of objects present in the field. As a starting point, we considered a binary state (presence/absence) only, but the approach is not limited to this specific case.

This simple approach already allowed us to tackle several problems related to the simulation of the behavior of cell populations in culture. As a first example, GCA were used to simulate the behavior of cell populations in the presence of an attractive (or repulsive) potential, where each cell attracts the other ones like a pheromone. It could be shown that GCA can be used to simulate the strength, or the range, of attraction or repulsion. As a second example, GCA was used to simulate cell sorting. It could be shown that cellular adhesion (cell-cell or cell-substrate) is not a pre-requisite to cell sorting. Cell sorting can be observed in the presence of local attractive potentials associated to the cell densities for the two cell populations. This does not mean that cellular adhesion does not play a role in cell sorting, but that another mechanism may eventually cooperate with cell adhesion.

In the future, less simple approaches may be incorporated in GCA, with multiple state objects, to solve more complex simulation problems in the field of cellular sociology, such as cell differentiation for instance.

REFERENCES

Adamatsky, A., and Holland, O. (1998) Phenomenology of excitation in 2-D cellular automata and swarm systems. *Chaos, Solitons and Fractals* **9**, 1253-1265.

Alber, M.S., Kiskowski, M.A., Glazier, J.A., and Jiang, Y. (2002) On cellular automaton approaches to modeling biological cells. In: *Mathematical Systems Theory in Biology, Communication and Finance*, IMA vol. 132, (Arnold, D.N., and Santosa, F., eds) 1-40. Springer-Verlag, New York.

Bard Ermentrout, G., and Edelstein-Keshet, L. (1993) Cellular automata approaches to biological modeling. *J. theor. Biol.* **160**, 97-133.

Bonnet, N., Matos, M., Polette, M., Zahm, J-M., Nawrocki-Raby, B., and Birembaut, P. (2004) A density-based cellular automaton for studying the clustering of noninvasive cells. *IEEE Trans. Biomed. Eng.* **51**, 1274-1276.

Bussemaker, H.J., Deutsch, A., and Geigant, E. (1997) Mean-field analysis of a dynamical phase transition in a cellular automaton model for collective motion. *Phys. Rev. Lett.* **78**, 5018-5021.

Deutsch, A. (2000) A new mechanism of aggregation in a lattice-gas cellular automaton model. *Math. Comp. Modeling* **31**, 35-40.

Gardner, M. (1970) Mathematical games. *Scientific American* **223**, 120-123.

Graner, F., and Glazier, J.A. (1992) Simulation of biological cell sorting using a two-dimensional extended Potts model. *Phys. Rev. Lett.* **69**, 2013-2017.

Hobmayer, B., Snyder, P., Alt, D., Happel, C., and Holstein, T. (2001) Quantitative analysis of epithelial cell aggregation in the simple metazoan Hydra reveals a switch from homotypic to heterotypic cell interactions. *Cell Tissue Res.* **304**, 147-157.

Kansal, A.R., Torquato, S., Harsh, G.R., Chiocca, E.A., and Deisboeck, T.S. (2000) Simulated brain tumor growth dynamics using a three-dimensional cellular automaton. *J. theor. Biol.* **203**, 367-382.

Lee, C.T., Hoopes, M.F., Diehl, J., Gilliland, W., Huxel, G., Leaver, E.V., McCann, K., Umbanhowar, J., and Mogilner, A. (2001) Non-local concepts and models in Biology. *J. theor. Biol.* **210**, 201-219.

Luebeck, E.G., and de Gunst, M.C. (2001) A stereological method for the analysis of cellular lesions in tissue sections using three-dimensional cellular automata. *Math. Comp. Modeling* **33**, 1387-1400.

Luthi, P., Chopard, B., Preiss, A., and Ramsden, J. (1998) A cellular automation model for neurogenesis in *Drosophila*. *Physica D* **118**, 151-160.

Nawrocki-Raby, B., Polette, M., Gilles, C., Clavel, C., Strumane, K., Matos, M., Zahm, J-M., Van Roy, F., Bonnet, N. and Birembaut, P. (2001) Quantitative cell dispersion analysis: new test to measure cell aggressiveness. *Int. J. Cancer* **93**, 644-652.

Palmari, J., André, J., Martin, P., Dussert, C. (1994) Cellular automaton model of proliferation of a human breast cancer cell line. *Proc. SPIE* **2168**, 408-415.

Parzen, E. (1962) Estimation of a probability density function and mode. *Ann. Math. Stat.* **33**, 1065-1076.

Silverman, B.W. (1986) *Density estimation for statistics and data analysis*. Chapman & Hill, London.

Stauffer, D., and Proykova, A. (2004) Cellular automata simulation of medication-induced autoimmune diseases. *Physica A* **331**, 545-551.

Stevens, A. (2000) A stochastic cellular automaton modeling gliding and aggregation of Myxobacteria. *Siam J. Appl. Math.* **61**, 172-182.

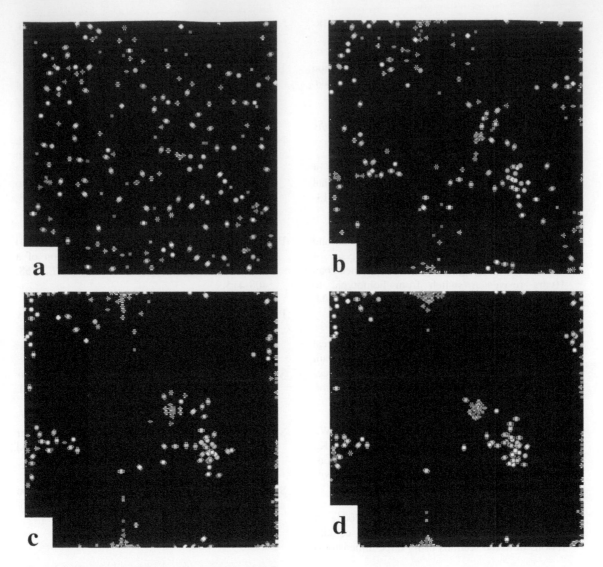

Figure 4: Illustration of the two-population model:
Starting from a mixture of two cell populations (a) (two different symbols for the two types of cells), we observe a progressive unmixing of these two populations and the appearance of clusters with mainly one type of cells. (b) after 15 iterations (c) after 30 iterations (d) after 45 iterations.

PATIENT VARIABILITY AND UNCERTAINTY QUANTIFICATION IN ANESTHESIA: PART I - PKPD MODELING AND IDENTIFICATION

Stéphane Bibian * **Guy A. Dumont** **
Mihai Huzmezan *** **Craig R. Ries** ****

* *Cleveland Medical Devices, NeuroWave Division,*
Cleveland, OH, USA
** *University of British Columbia, Department of Electrical and*
Computer Engineering, Vancouver, BC, Canada
*** *United Technologies Research Center, East Hartford, CT, USA*
**** *University of British Columbia, Department of Anesthesiology,*
Vancouver, BC, Canada

Abstract: The outcome of any surgery is particularly dependent on the adequate delivery of anesthetic drugs. Not surprisingly, clinical researchers have been trying to automatize their delivery in order to provide anesthesiologists with titration tools that can target the exact needs of each individual patient. As compared to today's population-normed drug delivery strategy, closed-loop drug delivery systems would provide patients with customized pharmacological action, thereby improving surgery outcome. While some anesthesia closed-loop designs have already shown promising results within controlled clinical protocols, the pharmacological variability that exists between patients needs to be addressed within a mathematical framework to prove the stability of the control laws, and gain faster and wider acceptance of these systems by the clinical community and regulatory committees. This paper is the first of a series of 2 papers addressing the issue of pharmacological variability, and how this variability translates into quantifiable system uncertainty. In this work, we focus essentially on deriving patient-specific models to assess inter-patient variability. These models will serve as basis for illustrating the uncertainty quantification approach proposed in the accompanying paper. Copyright ©2006 IFAC

Keywords: Anesthesia closed-loop control, Pharmacokinetic modeling, Pharmacodynamic modeling, Uncertainty, Propofol.

1. INTRODUCTION

Surgical acts are usually accompanied by the activation of both Central and Autonomic Nervous Systems (CNS and ANS). This CNS/ANS activation usually results in hypertension, tachycardia, arousal, hormonal discharge, *etc.* Clinical anesthesia consists of limiting this activation through the administration of CNS/ANS depressant drugs (*i.e.*, anesthetics). One of the anesthesiologist's role is to constantly adjust the drug titration in order to maintain an adequate activation *vs.* depression balance throughout the surgery, such that to avoid both under- and over-dosing. The driving idea in anesthesia closed-loop control is the automatic delivery of anesthetic drugs based on a quantitative feedback measure of the CNS/ANS activity.

Automation in clinical anesthesia has been suggested since the early 1950s (Bickford, 1950). While many attempts have been documented over the last 60 years, automated anesthesia has not yet found its way into mainstream practice, even though the clinical utility of such systems has been demonstrated (Liu *et al.*, 2005; Locher *et al.*, 2004).

One argument brought forth by detractors of automated anesthesia delivery is the potential for titration errors due to the pharmacological variability that exists between patients with respect to drug effect *vs.* drug administration. This variability introduces significant system uncertainty, which can yield instable dynamic behaviors. Some prior attempts at closed-loop anesthesia have indeed shown instability even in a limited healthy adult patient population (Absalom *et al.*, 2002). The consequence of system uncertainty onto the behavior of the closed-loop system is therefore an issue that needs to be addressed in order to gain acceptance and regulatory approval of such systems.

This paper and the accompanying article (Bibian *et al.*, 2006) focus on expressing patient variability into quantified system uncertainty. This quantification can then be readily used in the control design to prove the stability of the closed-loop system for a given population of patients.

In order to illustrate our approach, we first derive patient-specific pharmacokinetic-pharmacodynamic (PKPD) models that express the dynamic behavior of the anesthetic drug effect with respect to the infusion rate. In particular, this paper focuses on the modeling of propofol, a widely used anesthetic for the depression of cortical activity. A total of 44 propofol PKPD models are derived from adult patients undergoing elective surgery. These models are fully disclosed in this paper.

Our PKPD modeling approach is described in Section II. The identification procedure and the resulting models are the subject of Section III. These models are further used to illustrate inter-patient variability.

2. PROPOFOL PKPD MODEL

Combined pharmacokinetic-pharmacodynamic models (PKPD) are used to express the dynamic behavior of the drug effect with respect to the infusion rate. To model the effect of propofol – a CNS depressant drug – we use the PKPD model structure summarized in the block diagram of Fig. 1.a. This model has three distinct parts detailed in the following paragraphs.

2.1 Propofol Pharmacokinetics

The pharmacokinetic model describes the evolution of the drug concentration in the blood following the administration of the drug:

$$PK(s) = \frac{C_p(s)}{I(s)}, \qquad (1)$$

where $PK(s)$ is the pharmacokinetic model, $C_p(s)$ is the drug plasma concentration and $I(s)$ is the administered dose. For most anesthetic drugs, the mathematical model $PK(s)$ governing drug pharmacokinetics can be expressed as a third order transfer function:

$$PK(s) = \frac{1}{V_1} \cdot \frac{(s + k_{21}) \cdot (s + k_{31})}{(s + \pi) \cdot (s + \alpha) \cdot (s + \beta)}, \qquad (2)$$

where V_1 is the central compartment volume and π, α, β, k_{21}, and k_{31} are the pharmacokinetic distribution time constants. These PK parameters have been found to be mostly dependent on the patient's age, weight, lean body mass, *etc.*, as well as the method of drug administration. Drugs delivered through boluses (large doses over very short amount of time) have different kinetics as compared to the same drugs delivered with a slower infusion rate.

Note that the notation used in (2) has the advantage of clearly expressing each one of the system dynamic modes, hence allowing a trained observer to readily identify the frequency response of the system. However, pharmacologists usually prefer the use of clearances and compartmental volumes rather than that of poles and zeros. Some simple mathematical manipulations are therefore needed in order to express the PK sets published in the literature into the notation of (2).

2.2 Propofol Pharmacodynamics

The pharmacodynamic model expresses the relationship between the blood plasma concentration of a given drug, and its corresponding clinical effect. This model usually comprises of a Linear Time Invariant (LTI) element $PD(s)$, followed by a non-linear element.

The LTI element is typically given by the following generic relationship:

$$PD(s) = \mathrm{e}^{-T_d \cdot s} \cdot \frac{\sum_{k=1}^{m} b_k \cdot s^k + b_0}{s^n + \sum_{k=0}^{n-1} a_k \cdot s^k} \cdot \frac{1}{2EC_{50}}, \quad (3)$$

where $m \leq n$, T_d is the time delay corresponding to the arm-to-brain travel time of the drug, and EC_{50} is the concentration of drug which yields 50% of the maximal effect. Note that no *a priori* decision should be made as to the structure of $PD(s)$. The exact order of $PD(s)$ must be determined based on the analysis of the identification

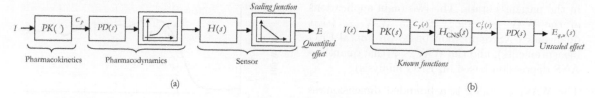

Fig. 1. Combined pharmacokinetic-pharmacodynamic model. (a) Overall block diagram. (b) Simplified block diagram used in stage #3: the non-linear element is omitted and the sensor filter is used as an input filter.

residuals. It is usually good practice to select a model order that is large enough to yield white residuals and limited cross-correlation between the input signal and the residuals. If the model order is insufficient, some linear dynamics might not be accounted for. This is often the case in classical pharmacology where $PD(s)$ is most of the time a delay-free first order function.

Another aspect accounted for in the pharmacodynamic model is the inherent saturation of the effect *vs.* drug dosage. The non-linear sigmoid characteristic of the dose *vs.* response is usually captured using the Hill equation:

$$\overline{E} = \frac{\overline{C}_p^{\gamma}}{EC_{50}^{\gamma} + \overline{C}_p^{\gamma}} \qquad (4)$$

where $\overline{E}$ is the steady state effect, and $\overline{C}_p$ is the steady state plasma concentration. The parameter γ is a measure of the steepness of the dose-response curve. Finally, E_0 and E_{max} are the minimum and maximum effects. When used in conjunction with the LTI element $PD(s)$, (4) must be rewritten as:

$$\overline{E} = \frac{\overline{E}_{LTI}^{\gamma}}{0.5^{\gamma} + \overline{E}_{LTI}^{\gamma}}. \qquad (5)$$

$\overline{E}_{LTI}$ is the steady state effect calculated using (3): $\overline{E}_{LTI} = \overline{C}_p(s)/(2 \cdot EC_{50})$, where $\overline{C}_p$ is the steady state plasma concentration.

2.3 Feedback Sensor Model

Most studies in pharmacology do not account for the sensor dynamics. As a result, the modelled effect usually corresponds to the effect measured by the sensor instead of the true physiological effect. PD time constants published in the literature are therefore often dependent on the sensor/monitor used during the clinical study. Models derived based on two different sensors cannot be readily compared for consistency, as some discrepancy might be due to the technical characteristics of the sensors.

As compared to the traditional approach, our model clearly separates the dynamics of the physiological effect from the quantified drug effect obtained from the sensor. This is done by considering the sensor dynamics $H(s)$ and its eventual scaling.

This approach makes it easier to substitute new sensors with different dynamics, as well as to study the effect of the sensors dynamics on the limitation of the closed-loop performance.

3. APPLICATION TO PROPOFOL PKPD MODELING

In this section, we derive an integrated PKPD model for propofol using the modeling approach presented in Section 2.

3.1 Clinical Data

To identify the pharmacodynamic model of propofol, we are using induction data collected during a clinical study involving 76 patients undergoing elective surgery. This study was conducted after obtaining the approval of our Ethic Review Board, as well as the patients' consent.

Protocol. Prior to induction, a 2-channel EEG recording was initiated using a Crystal Monitor 16 (Cleveland Medical Devices Inc., Cleveland, OH). The electrode positions were F_{p1}-AT_1 (channel 1) and F_{p2}-AT_2 (channel 2). F_{pz} was used as the ground electrode for the two bipolar montages. The two signals were acquired at a sampling rate of 480 S/s, and resolution of 16 bits.

Each patient first received a bolus of fentanyl (0.5-1.5 μg/kg) followed by a bolus of propofol (2-3 mg/kg). Both the start and end of the propofol syringe push were recorded by the study monitor. Forty seconds after loss of consciousness, a Laryngeal Mask Airway [1] (LMA) was inserted. During the LMA insertion, any movement from the patient was logged in. The EEG recording was discontinued after the start of the surgery.

The sensor used for measuring the propofol drug effect is based on the WAV (Wavelet-based Anesthetic Value) technology developed by our research group (Zikov *et al.*, 2006). This technology is used to characterize non-stationary electrophysiological signals in order to capture changes

---

[1] A tube and air-filled cuff that sits above the voice-box to ensure proper ventilation during the surgery.

in the patient's state. The two main applications of the WAV technology is the WAV$_\text{CNS}$ (that quantifies CNS depression based on frontal EEG measurements), and the WAV$_\text{ANS}$ (that quantifies ANS depression based on EKG analysis).

The WAV$_\text{CNS}$ index is a bounded dimensionless number scaled between 100 (conscious patient) and 0 (electro-cortical silence). As the cortical depression (*i.e.*, anesthetic drug effect) increases, the index value decreases. During surgery, it is recommended to keep the WAV$_\text{CNS}$ value between 40 and 60 in order to prevent both overdosing and intra-operative awareness.

Clinical Data for PKPD Modeling. The LMA insertion by itself can provoke the activation of the CNS. Hence, the LMA insertion can be considered to be a typical output disturbance. Among the 76 patients of the study, 22 patients elicited a reaction to the insertion. To avoid having the LMA reaction acting as a disturbance for identification purposes, these 22 cases were rejected from the identification procedure.

Both the start and end of the propofol injection were recorded. The identification window was chosen to start at the beginning of the propofol injection, and to stop 90 seconds after LMA insertion. Three cases had insufficient data to cover this identification time window. These cases were withdrawn from the analysis.

In order to keep consistent results, it was further decided to eliminate all cases whose WAV$_\text{CNS}$ during induction reached values lower than 10. It is indeed possible that a saturation phenomenon can affect the WAV$_\text{CNS}$ time course in the lower WAV$_\text{CNS}$ values, which in turn would result in a significantly different dynamics. Two cases were excluded based on this criteria. Finally, 2 more cases were withdrawn from the study due to a large EMG activation observed after the LMA insertion. These cases were characterized by strong extremity movements, but no airway reaction.

A total of 44 cases were thus compiled for the identification procedure. These cases were further subdivided into 4 age groups (18-29 yrs; 30-39 yrs; 40-49 yrs and 50-60 yrs). The demographics of the study population are detailed in Table 1.

3.2 Feedback Sensor

As compared to similar technologies (*e.g.*, the bispectral index), the WAV$_\text{CNS}$ makes use of the time-frequency localization property of wavelets in order to capture subtle phase and frequency shifts in the electroencephalogram (EEG), which

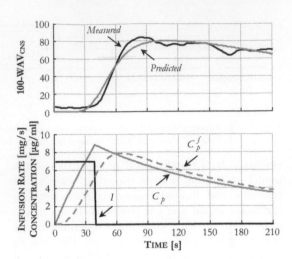

Fig. 2. PD identification illustrative example (patient #52).

are indicative of a change in the patient's cortical activity. The low computational complexity of wavelet decomposition further allowed a per second refreshing rate. To limit the measurement noise to acceptable levels, a post-processing trending 2nd order IIR filter was added. The overall sensor model is given by:

$$H_{CNS}(s) = \frac{1}{(8 \cdot s + 1)^2} \cdot \frac{1 - e^{-s}}{s} \qquad (6)$$

Note that the WAV$_\text{CNS}$ index is the only cortical index that can be fully modelled by a LTI transfer functions across its whole operating range. Other available cortical indexes are based on decisional schemes which make them inherently non-linear, in particular during large transients. Also, the WAVCNS does not add additional computational delays, which makes it particularly fast in detecting changes in the patient's state. The WAV$_\text{CNS}$ is currently being integrated into the NeuroSENSE Monitor (CleveMed NeuroWAVE, Cleveland, OH), a dedicated cortical monitor specifically designed for use in the operating room.

3.3 PKPD Identification

The PKPD identification is carried out in 3 distinct steps, see Fig. 2.

The first step consists of calculating the drug plasma concentration using the well-defined propofol PK model published by Schüttler and Ihmsen (Schüttler and Ihmsen, 2000). The time course of the plasma concentration can be easily calculated assuming that the infusion profile of the drug follows that of an impulse function whose duration is that of the syringe push.

With the sensor filter $H_{CNS}(s)$ being defined, the block diagram of Fig. 1.a is rewritten as in Fig. 1.b, where the non-linear function is omitted.

The only unknown element is the transfer function $PD(s)$, which can be identified using the filtered plasma concentration $C_p^f = H_{CNS}(s) \cdot C_p(s)$ as input, and the WAV_{CNS} output that is re-scaled between 0 (no effect) and 1 (maximal effect). The analysis of the identification residuals show that a first order plus delay is sufficient to yield white residuals. Therefore, the structure of $PD(s)$ can be written as:

$$PD(s) = e^{-T_d \cdot s} \cdot \frac{k_d}{s + k_d} \cdot \frac{1}{2 \cdot EC_{50}}, \qquad (7)$$

where T_d, k_d and EC_{50} are calculated using standard least square estimation.

Finally, the Hill parameter γ is determined by minimizing the identification residuals.

3.4 Results

The result of the identification procedure is presented in Table 1. The PK parameters can be easily calculated based on Schüttler's published PK sets, and on the age and weight of each patient.

The models presented in Table 1 were obtained specifically for each patient. In order to expand on this result, we derive population-normed nominal models that can be used to predict the WAV_{CNS} time course for any surgical patient. A usual approach would be to calculate the nominal model parameters by averaging the PD parameters over the whole study population. However, we found that age is a statistically significant covariate[2] of the PD parameters. Using a basic linear fit, the nominal PD parameters were derived for the proposed approach using age as a covariate:

$$\begin{cases} T_d = 26 - 0.3 \cdot \text{age} & k_d = 81 - 0.99 \cdot \text{age} \\ EC_{50} = 1.9 + 0.043 \cdot \text{age} & \gamma = 3.0 - 0.027 \cdot \text{age} \end{cases} \qquad (8)$$

The inter-patient variability can be illustrated by considering the frequency response of the 44 individual models. The frequency response can be obtained by linearizing the Hill function for a given operating range (*e.g.*, $20 \leq \text{WAV}_{CNS} \leq 80$). The non-linear Hill element is therefore reduced to a gain K that is dependent on the operating point of the system. This gain is bounded between a minimum and maximum values ($K_{\min} < K < K_{\max}$). We can therefore associate for each PKPD model in the Table 1 two frequency responses corresponding to $K_{\max}$ and $K_{\min}$. It is also important to consider two distinct $PK(s)$ functions,

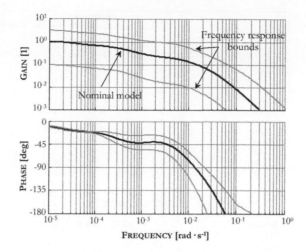

Fig. 3. Frequency response of the normalized PKPD nominal model, and the associated uncertainty bounds.

depending on whether the drug is given as a bolus or infusion. The envelope containing all possible individual frequency responses captures the inherent inter-patient variability present in the system, see Fig. 3. We found that the system uncertainty is particularly large (*e.g.*, the ratio between the maximum and minimum dc gain in the system is about 30).

4. CONCLUSION

In this paper, we used a new PKPD modeling approach to model the dynamic behavior of the propofol effect following its administration during induction of anesthesia. As compared to traditional PKPD modeling, our approach incorporates the sensor dynamics (a second order LTI function in this case), and makes no *a priori* assumption as *per* the structure of the pharmacodynamic LTI element $PD(s)$. During our identification of propofol, we found that white residuals can be obtained when $PD(s)$ is a first order LTI function that includes a time delay. The overall PKPD model is thus a 6th order plus delay transfer function, as compared to the usual 4th order found in most pharmacological PKPD studies.

The 44 models identified in this study can serve as basis to capture the inter-patient variability present in propofol PKPD. We show in (Bibian *et al.*, 2006) how this uncertainty can be quantified using the unstructured multiplicative uncertainty framework.

---

[2] All of the parameters obtained from this identification have shown a similar dependence. In particular the EC_{50} parameter was shown to increase with age, *i.e.*, we found that older patients actually require *more* propofol than younger patients. This is consistent with the results published by Kazama *et al.* (Kazama *et al.*, 1999).

REFERENCES

Absalom, A.R., N. Sutcliffe and G.N.C. Kenny (2002). Closed-loop control of anesthesia using bispectral index. *Anesth.* **96**, 67–73.

PATIENT #	DEMOGRAPHICS					PD PARAMETERS				
	ASA	Age	Weight	Height	Gender	LTI			Hill	
						T_d	k_d	EC_{50}	E_0	γ
		[yrs]	[kg]	[cm]		[s]	[$s^{-1} \cdot 10^{-3}$]	[$\mu g/ml$]		
G1: $\geq$18 - <30 yrs										
007	nc	21	100	178	M	22	133.5	3.2	98.3	4.7
008	nc	28	59	168	F	4	44.4	3.1	99.7	2.5
010	2	26	90	190	M	44	25.0	2.4	96.1	2.0
015	2	21	53	157	F	45	51.5	3.8	100.0	1.2
016	2	19	90	185	M	39	85.7	3.8	98.4	2.3
023	1	28	60	162	F	18	82.5	3.9	100.0	2.1
030	1	24	78	170	M	32	44.4	2.9	97.5	2.7
035	2	19	68	164	F	12	26.7	1.9	93.8	2.1
038	2	25	70	170	M	7	35.2	3.4	98.0	1.9
046	1	23	81	180	M	9	32.8	2.8	97.5	2.8
048	1	18	83	178	M	17	46.4	2.8	99.8	2.3
053	2	21	67	163	F	4	26.2	2.4	100.0	2.5
058	1	22	88	183	M	9	50.4	2.5	96.1	2.6
066	1	21	59	162	M	18	160.5	3.6	100.0	4.1
071	1	19	72	176	M	20	75.0	2.5	99.6	1.9
Mean		**22.3**	**74.5**	**172**		**20.0**	**61.4**	**3.0**	**98.3**	**2.5**
G2: $\geq$30 - <40 yrs										
006	nc	34	73	180	M	44	54.8	3.2	99.6	2.6
009	nc	34	71	178	M	29	83.1	4.0	94.5	2.3
029	1	35	91	189	M	18	34.4	3.7	99.5	2.1
036	1	38	85	180	M	1	29.6	3.3	80.2	1.9
047	1	33	86	168	F	1	24.9	3.1	98.3	1.5
049	2	38	75	176	M	12	35.2	3.9	98.9	1.8
051	1	39	91	178	M	4	24.8	2.7	91.4	2.0
061	1	34	78	178	M	12	28.7	2.8	99.0	2.3
063	1	36	65	163	F	5	27.0	2.8	96.2	2.1
065	1	34	58	157	F	4	67.2	3.6	98.5	2.0
068	2	33	77	180	M	12	29.3	3.1	98.7	1.8
074	2	39	105	185	M	13	29.1	3.7	93.4	1.9
Mean		**35.6**	**79.6**	**176**		**12.9**	**39.0**	**3.3**	**95.7**	**2.0**
G3: $\geq$40 - <50 yrs										
004	nc	49	80	177	M	35	38.0	3.3	99.0	1.8
025	1	46	66	168	F	11	36.6	6.1	99.4	1.3
027	2	45	99	182	M	2	32.6	4.7	98.1	1.3
040	1	48	77	173	M	12	35.0	4.5	97.0	1.4
042	1	47	98	189	M	10	28.7	3.9	96.3	2.1
043	1	46	79	172	M	12	34.8	3.9	96.9	1.8
052	1	40	96	193	M	9	36.6	3.2	95.4	2.0
069	2	40	77	176	M	8	35.6	3.4	94.3	2.5
072	1	48	97	190	M	13	30.0	3.0	95.0	2.0
Mean		**45.4**	**85.4**	**180**		**12.4**	**34.2**	**4.0**	**96.8**	**1.8**
G4: $\geq$50 - $\leq$60 yrs										
018	2	60	63	165	F	3	31.5	3.5	95.8	2.4
033	3	52	91	185	M	29	42.0	4.4	88.8	2.5
041	2	52	100	182	M	2	21.8	4.7	89.5	1.7
057	1	52	97	176	M	16	28.8	3.7	89.4	1.4
060	1	50	95	183	M	10	26.4	4.0	97.5	2.0
064	2	52	56	173	F	6	58.0	5.0	91.5	1.9
070	2	54	100	180	M	6	32.2	4.2	99.0	1.5
075	3	60	95	176	M	12	24.3	3.1	98.6	1.8
Mean		**54.0**	**87.1**	**177**		**10.5**	**33.1**	**4.1**	**93.8**	**1.9**

Table 1. Study demographics and Propofol PD models.

Bibian, S., G.A. Dumont, M. Huzmezan and C.R. Ries (2006). Patient variability and uncertainty quantification in clinical anesthesia: PART II - PKPD uncertainty. In: *Proc. of the 2006 IFAC Symposium on Modelling and Control in Biomedical Systems.*

Bickford, R.G. (1950). Automatic electroencephalographic control of general anesthesia. *Electro. and Clin. Neurophys.* **2**, 93–96.

Kazama, T., K. Ikeda, K. Morita, M. Kikura, M. Doi, T. Ikeda, T. Kurita and Y. Nakajima (1999). Comparison of the effect-site k_{e0}s of propofol for blood pressure and EEG bispectral index in elderly and younger patients. *Anesth.* **90**, 1517–1527.

Liu, N., A. Genty, A. Landais, T. Chazot and M. Fischler (2005). Titration of propofol guided by the bispectral index (BIS): Closed-loop versus manual target controlled infusion. In: *Proc. of the 2005 American Anesth. Soc. Conf.*

Locher, S., K.S. Stadler, T. Boehlen, T. Bouillon, D. Leibundgut, P.M. Schumacher, R. Wymann and A.M. Zbinden (2004). A new closed-loop control system for isoflurane using bispectral index outperforms manual control. *Anesth.* **101**, 591–602.

Schüttler, J. and H. Ihmsen (2000). Population pharmacokinetics of propofol: a multicenter study. *Anesth.* **92**(3), 727–738.

Zikov, T., S. Bibian, G.A. Dumont, M. Huzmezan and C.R. Ries (2006). Quantifying decrease in cortical activity during general anesthesia using wavelet analysis. *IEEE Trans. on Biomed. Eng.* **53**, 617–632.

PATIENT VARIABILITY AND UNCERTAINTY QUANTIFICATION IN ANESTHESIA: PART II - PKPD UNCERTAINTY

Stéphane Bibian* Guy A. Dumont**
Mihai Huzmezan*** Craig R. Ries****

* Cleveland Medical Devices, NeuroWave Division,
Cleveland, OH, USA
** University of British Columbia, Department of Electrical and
Computer Engineering, Vancouver, BC, Canada
*** United Technologies Research Center, East Hartford, CT, USA
**** University of British Columbia, Department of Anesthesiology,
Vancouver, BC, Canada

Abstract: The outcome of any surgery is particularly dependent on the adequate delivery of anesthetic drugs. Not surprisingly, clinical researchers have been trying to automatize their delivery in order to provide anesthesiologists with titration tools that can target the exact needs of each individual patient. As compared to today's population-normed drug delivery strategy, close loop drug delivery systems would provide patients with customized pharmacological action, thereby improving surgery outcome. While some anesthesia close loop designs have already shown promising results within controlled clinical protocols, the pharmacological variability that exists between patients needs to be addressed within a mathematical framework to prove the stability of the control laws, and gain faster and wider acceptance of these systems by the clinical community and regulatory committees. This paper is the second of a series of 2 papers addressing the issue of pharmacological variability and PKPD uncertainty. In the first paper, we presented our own drug modeling approach, which we applied towards the identification of 44 adult patient models for propofol, a central nervous system depressant drug. The individual patient models have shown a large inter-patient variability. In this paper, we further expand on our previous result in order to derive an uncertainty metrics that can be used in the control design to ensure stability and assess performances. *Copyright © 2006 IFAC*

Keywords: Anesthesia closed-loop control, Pharmacodynamic modeling, Uncertainty, Propofol.

1. INTRODUCTION

In our accompanying paper (Bibian *et al.*, 2006), we derived PKPD propofol models for 44 patients undergoing elective surgery. These models were obtained using a modified PKPD approach, and

our WAV$_{CNS}$ sensor designed for quantifying cortical activity. In this paper, we use the information obtained during the identification procedure in order to quantify the pharmacological variability into system uncertainty. This is achieved by considering the uncertainty of the PKPD model in the frequency domain, and using a unstructured multiplicative uncertainty framework to translate the frequency response uncertainty into a mathematical expression suitable for control design.

In Section 2, we discuss the origin of pharmacological variability in terms of inter- and intra-patient variability. In Section 3, we present our uncertainty characterization approach. In Section 4, we apply our methodology to the PKPD models derived in the accompanying paper. In particular, we show that system uncertainty can be particularly large and may be difficult to manage in the controller design. However, we show how the uncertainty can be reduced satisfactorily by simply limiting the operating range of the controller.

2. ORIGIN OF PKPD UNCERTAINTY

Before characterizing PKPD uncertainty into a quantitative metrics, it is useful to first consider the origin and mechanism of pharmacological variability.

It is customary to distinguish between two different types of uncertainty: the uncertainty caused by inter-patient variability (*i.e.*, the variability observed between different individuals), and the uncertainty originating from intra-patient variability (*i.e.*, the variability observed within one particular individual).

2.1 Inter-patient Variability

Inter-patient variability affects both the pharmacokinetics and pharmacodynamics of any given drug. For instance, it has been shown that age as well as weight, lean body mass, ethnicity, *etc.*, are all factors of PKPD variability in humans. Co-existing illnesses involving either the liver and/or kidneys may also significantly alter the way drugs are metabolized and eliminated from the body. In general, 2 patients with similar physiological characteristics (age, weight, lean body mass, *etc.*) may have largely different PKPD parameters. For instance, patient #15 (female, 21 yrs old, 53 kg, 157 cm) in Table 1 (from (Bibian *et al.*, 2006)), and patient #53 (female, 21 yrs old, 67 kg, 163 cm) have significantly different time delay (45 sec *vs.* 4 sec), EC$_{50}$ parameter (3.8 μg/ml *vs.* 2.3 μg/ml), and saturation characteristics (Hill steepness of 1.2 *vs.* 2.5).

Inter-patient variability can be easily characterized by considering the differences between PKPD models obtained over a large population of patients. In particular, our previous study on 44 adult patients spanning the 18-60 yrs age groups provides a good representative sample of an adult population.

2.2 Intra-patient Variability

Intra-patient variability expresses the variability observed in the drug response within one particular subject. This variability originates from different factors.

Drug administration. It is a well-documented fact that the pharmacokinetics of intravenous agents differ depending on the method of administration of the drug. Even though bolus and infusion PK models have the same steady state gain, the initial peak plasma concentration following a bolus administration is significantly over-predicted by the corresponding infusion model.

During steady state (and for small setpoint changes and/or disturbances), it is likely that the controller will administer propofol at an infusion rate inferior to 0.5 mg·min^{-1}·kg^{-1}. In this range, it is expected that the propofol pharmacokinetics will be accurately described by the infusion model. However, during large transients, the controller may have to output large infusion rates ($>$1 mg·min^{-1}·kg^{-1}), in which case the propofol uptake and distribution may follow the behavior observed for bolus regimen. Therefore, the controller design must account for the difference in dynamics between the bolus and infusion PK models. This difference in models can be expressed as system uncertainty by associating to each case presented in Table 1 (from (Bibian *et al.*, 2006)) the 2 possible PK frequency responses.

Controller Setpoint. The Hill saturation can be viewed as a gain dependent on the operating point of the system. In terms of the closed-loop application, it is desired to maintain control over a wide range of WAV$_{CNS}$ values (*e.g.*, from 80 to 20). As a result, for each PKPD model, we can linearize the Hill equation as a gain K bounded between two values K_{max} and K_{min}, and defined as:

$$\begin{cases} K_{max} = \max\{K_{\overline{x}}, & \overline{x}_{min} \le \overline{x} \le \overline{x}_{max}\} \\ K_{min} = \min\{K_{\overline{x}}, & \overline{x}_{min} \le \overline{x} \le \overline{x}_{max}\}, \end{cases} \quad (1)$$

where:

$$\overline{x}_{min} = \frac{1}{2} \cdot \sqrt[\gamma]{\frac{E_{min}}{1 - E_{min}}} \quad (2)$$

and where $E_{min} = 0.2$ corresponds to the smallest desired effect (shallow sedation: WAV$_{CNS}$=80). $\overline{x}_{max}$ is obtained in a similar fashion with $E_{max} = 0.8$, corresponding to the strongest desired control setpoint (very deep anesthetic sleep where WAV$_{CNS}$=20).

The Hill saturation being simplified as a bounded gain $K \in [K_{min}; K_{max}]$, we can associate for each case in Table 1 (from (Bibian *et al.*, 2006)) 2 frequency responses corresponding to the minimum and maximum Hill gains.

Physiological Time Variance. All physiological processes evolve in time (*e.g.*, circadian rhythms, hemodynamic changes, hormonal fluctuations, *etc.*). Alterations in these processes can affect drug distribution, elimination, and effect, which in turn can result in large intra-patient PKPD parameter variability. The time variance of the PKPD parameters cannot be predicted, and therefore should be accounted for as uncertainty. Our study protocol did not allow for the characterization of this phenomenon. However, in a previous work carried out for thiopental (Bibian *et al.*, 2004), we found that intra-patient variability due to physiological time variance was significantly limited as compared to the inter-patient variability.

3. QUANTIFYING UNCERTAINTY

When considering PKPD models, only the overall uncertainty in terms of the gain and phase of the system is defined. Consequently, the unstructured uncertainty approach is the preferred approach since the uncertainty cannot be readily expressed as parametric uncertainty. In this section, we present the multiplicative unstructured uncertainty approach discussed in detail in (Skogestad and Postlethwaite, 2005).

3.1 The Relative Uncertainty Framework

Let us consider a system $G(s)$ for which some uncertainty bounds exist. A common approach is to model the uncertainty using the following:

$$G(j\omega) = G_0 \cdot \tilde{G}_0(j\omega) \cdot (1 + w(j\omega) \cdot \Delta_u(j\omega)), \quad (3)$$

where $||\Delta_u(j\omega)|| \leq 1$, $\tilde{G}_0(j\omega)$ is the normalized nominal model of the system, and $G_0 = ||G_0(j\omega = 0)||$ is the steady state gain of the system. The weight function $w(j\omega)$ quantifies the magnitude of the unstructured uncertainty, while $\Delta_u(j\omega)$ expresses this uncertainty as a unity disk in the Nyquist plot. The multiplicative uncertainty gain $w(j\omega)$ is also referred to as *relative uncertainty*.

To better understand this concept, let us consider the example of Fig. 1.a-b. We assume that the uncertainty bounds of $G(j\omega)$ are defined in the frequency domain and that a nominal model $G_0(j\omega)$ exists. If we map the frequency domain information into the complex Nyquist plane, the uncertainty at each frequency ω can be represented as the section of a ring centered at the origin. The outer and inner radii of the ring are defined by the uncertainty magnitudes $\tilde{G}_{\text{MIN}} = G_{\text{MIN}}/G_0$ and $\tilde{G}_{\text{MAX}} = G_{\text{MAX}}/G_0$, while the section is defined by the uncertainty angles φ_{MIN} and φ_{MAX}. To quantify the uncertainty according to the framework of (3), we define the disk $\mathcal{D}$ centered on $\tilde{G}_0(j\omega)$ and of radius $l(\omega)$. This circle is the smallest circle centered on $\tilde{G}_0(j\omega)$ and which contains

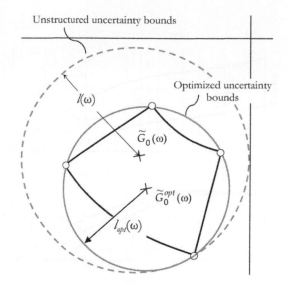

Fig. 2. Effect of the nominal model Nyquist path with respect to the uncertainty radius: note that nominal models which are close to the uncertainty edges can significantly increase the unstructured uncertainty radius.

all of the original uncertainty surface. Following (3), the multiplicative weighting function $w(j\omega)$ is defined as:

$$||w(j\omega)|| = \frac{l(\omega)}{||\tilde{G}_0(j\omega)||}. \quad (4)$$

3.2 Selection of an Optimal Nominal Model

It is important to note that the uncertainty quantified by (3) considers a larger uncertainty surface than the one originally defined from the frequency domain. A limitation of the method is therefore that its representation of the frequency domain uncertainty can be very conservative, mostly if the center of the disk $\tilde{G}_0(j\omega)$ is located close to one of edges of the ring section. A control design based on the uncertainty defined by the disk $\mathcal{D}(l(\omega), \tilde{G}_0(j\omega))$ may thus be unnecessarily conservative.

A simple way to reducing the conservativeness introduced by this method is to minimize $l(\omega)$ by selecting the best location for the center of the uncertainty disk. In other words, this leads to the optimization of the nominal model $\tilde{G}_0$, see Figure 2. This can be done simply by considering the 4 corners of the ring section and finding the center of the circumscribing circle which goes through all 4 points. Note that if $\pi < (\varphi_{\text{MAX}} - \varphi_{\text{MAX}}) < 2\pi$, the center of the smallest circle is simply the middle point between the two outer corners. If $(\varphi_{\text{MAX}} - \varphi_{\text{MAX}}) > 2\pi$, the center of the circle can be located anywhere on the inner edge of the ring.

The search for the optimal circle center must be iterated for each frequency ω, which in turn defines the optimal Nyquist path for the nominal model

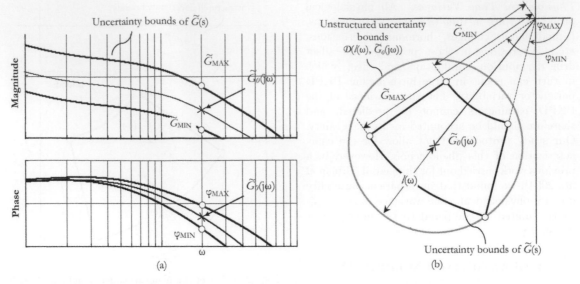

Fig. 1. Quantifying uncertainty. (a) Uncertainty expressed in the frequency domain via Bode plots. (b) Nyquist mapping of the uncertainty at the given frequency ω.

of the system. At this point, the optimal Nyquist path is just a geometrical construct without a formal mathematical expression. It is then necessary to express this path into a LTI transfer function which can be used in the design process. In most cases, it is not possible to find a rational LTI function that exactly describes the selected Nyquist path. Instead, a frequency domain identification can be carried out to determine a 'near optimal' solution $\tilde{G}_0^{opt}(j\omega)$. One attractive solution is to define a LTI function $w_{nom}(j\omega)$ that is tuned specifically such that $\tilde{G}_0^{opt}(j\omega) = w_{nom}(j\omega) \cdot \tilde{G}_0(j\omega)$ is as close as possible from the optimal Nyquist path. Note that this approach yields a nominal model whose order is greater than that of the initial model.

3.2.1. Realization of the Uncertainty Weight
Once the near optimal nominal model is identified, the new uncertainty radius $l(\omega)$ can be easily calculated as:

$$l(\omega) = \sqrt{(x_0^{opt}(\omega) - x_1(\omega))^2 + (y_0^{opt}(\omega) - y_1(\omega))^2},$$
(5)

where:

$$\begin{cases} x_0^{opt}(\omega) = \|\tilde{G}_0^{opt}(\omega)\| \cdot \cos\big(\arg(\tilde{G}_0^{opt}(\omega))\big) \\ y_0^{opt}(\omega) = \|\tilde{G}_0^{opt}(\omega)\| \cdot \sin\big(\arg(\tilde{G}_0^{opt}(\omega))\big) \\ x_1(\omega) = \tilde{G}_{MAX} \cdot \cos(\varphi_{MIN}) \\ y_1(\omega) = \tilde{G}_{MAX} \cdot \sin(\varphi_{MIN}) \end{cases}$$
(6)

The resulting uncertainty weight magnitude is directly calculated as the ratio between $l(\omega)$ and the new nominal model $\tilde{G}_0^{opt}(j\omega)$. Once $\|w(j\omega)\|$ is determined, an identification procedure is once again carried out to express $w(j\omega)$ as a rational linear transfer function $\hat{w}(j\omega)$. This transfer function will be used in the design process to optimize

the stability of the controller. The parameters of $\hat{w}(j\omega)$ are estimated by minimizing the criteria $\mathcal{J}_w$:

$$\mathcal{J}_w^2 = \int_0^\infty \left[1 + \lambda_w(\omega) \cdot \text{sign}(\epsilon(\omega)) \right] \cdot \epsilon(\omega)^2 d\omega,$$
(7)

where $\epsilon(\omega) = \|w(j\omega)\| - \|\hat{w}(j\omega)\|$, $\lambda_w \gg 1$, and:

$$\begin{cases} \text{sign}(\epsilon(\omega)) = 0 & \text{if } \epsilon(\omega) \leq 0 \\ \text{sign}(\epsilon(\omega)) = 1 & \text{if } \epsilon(\omega) > 0 \end{cases}$$
(8)

Equation (7) represents essentially a least square minimization criterion. Note that the phase of $\hat{w}(j\omega)$ does not bear any relevance. The parameter $\lambda_w(\omega)$ simply adds a penalty weight on the realizations $\hat{w}(j\omega)$ whose magnitude at some frequency ω is less than $\|w(j\omega)\|$.

3.2.2. Comparing Uncertainty Between Systems
Note that any system presenting a relative uncertainty gain above 1 cannot be tightly controlled since the uncertainty disk contains the Nyquist origin [1]. More generally, it can be shown that Robust Stability (RS) is guaranteed if:

$$(\text{RS}) \Leftrightarrow \|\hat{w}(j\omega) \cdot T(j\omega)\| < 1$$
(9)

where S and T are the sensitivity and complimentary sensitivity functions of the close loop system. Clearly, low $\|\hat{w}(j\omega)\|$ values will benefit to the overall performance of the system. Hence, we can compare the effect of system uncertainty between two systems S1 and S2 by comparing directly their relative uncertainty weight: a system S1 presents less uncertainty than a system S2 in a frequency bandwidth BW if $\|\hat{w}_{S1}(j\omega)\| < \|\hat{w}_{S2}(j\omega)\|$, for $\omega \in$ BW.

---

[1] Therefore, there exists a particular plant for which the open loop gain can be 0, meaning that no control action can have any effect on the output.

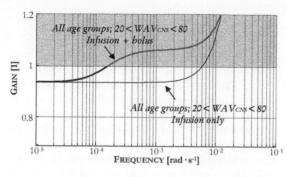

Fig. 3. Uncertainty weights corresponding to the whole adult population and an effect spanning light sedation (WAV$_{CNS}$ = 80) to deep anesthesia (WAV$_{CNS}$=20).

4. PROPOFOL PKPD UNCERTAINTY

In this section, we apply the uncertainty quantification approach discussed previously to the propofol PKPD models derived in (Bibian *et al.*, 2006).

4.1 Initial Uncertainty

In order to apply the proposed methodology, it is first necessary to derive the uncertainty bounds in the frequency domain. Following what was presented in Section 2, we derive for each patient 4 frequency responses corresponding to both infusion and bolus PK models, and the two Hill gains K_{min} and K_{max}. Once all patient models are plotted, the minimum and maximum gain and phase uncertainty bounds can be easily extracted by simply considering the envelope containing each individual model, as shown in Fig. 3 in (Bibian *et al.*, 2006). The frequency response bounds are then used to define the uncertainty in the Nyquist plane in order to re-tune the nominal PKPD model, as described in Section 3.2. With the nominal weight $w_{nom}(j\omega)$ defined, the uncertainty weight can be easily calculated using (5). A LTI realization $\hat{w}(j\omega)$ of the uncertainty weight can be then determined.

When this methodology is applied to the 44 patient models of our previous study, we find that the uncertainty weight $\hat{w}(j\omega)$ is particularly large, see Fig. 3. The magnitude of the uncertainty weight is only less than 1 in the low frequency range, which thereby imposes a significant limitation in the achievable closed-loop bandwidth.

4.2 Uncertainty Reduction

System uncertainty leads to conservative control designs, which usually translates in limited closed-loop performances. In particular, the results presented in Fig. 3 emphasize the need to investigate methods to reduce the uncertainty to more manageable levels.

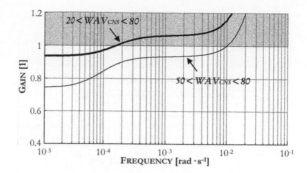

Fig. 4. The reduction in the controller target range significantly reduces the system uncertainty, mainly when considering the sedation range.

In that respect, we present here simple methods which can bring immediate benefits without adding significant complexity to the control design. These methods aim at reducing the uncertainty by limiting the validity of the models to a particular population subset, or operating conditions.

Infusion vs. *Bolus Administration*. In our initial PKPD uncertainty characterization, we included both bolus and infusion-type administrations. However, we can reasonably expect that the controller action will remain constrained to a lower range of infusion rates for safety reasons. The controller may therefore not be able to deliver boluses. Consequently, we can limit the intrapatient variability by considering only infusion-type pharmacokinetics. Such a limitation of the PKPD model directly results in a smaller uncertainty weight, see Fig. 3. In particular, the uncertainty 'bump' observed in the lower frequency range and due to differences in the drug distribution and redistribution dynamics is now eliminated.

Limiting the Control Range. Another effective way of minimizing intra-patient variability, and thus uncertainty, is to consider a more limited operating range. In particular, the results presented in Fig. 3 were derived assuming that the controller may target any WAV$_{CNS}$ level from 80 to 20 (from light sedation to deep anesthesia). It is likely that controllers tuned specifically for sedation (WAV$_{CNS}$ range: 80-50), general anesthesia (WAV$_{CNS}$ range: 60-30), and deep anesthesia (WAV$_{CNS}$ range: 40-20) may have to account for less uncertainty than a general purpose controller.

This assumption was evaluated. In particular, we found that the uncertainty is significantly reduced when considering the 80-50 sedation range, see Fig. 4. This stems form the fact that the slope of the Hill saturation is quasi-constant within this range. Conversely, as the effect nears the end of the observable range, the slope of the saturation reduces considerably, which yields a

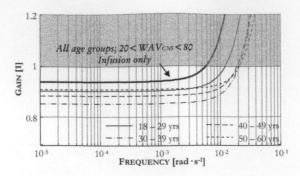

Fig. 5. Effect of age onto the uncertainty weight magnitude.

large K_{max}/K_{min} ratio, a major component in gain uncertainty.

This observation indicates that an application targeting specifically sedation in the ICU is more robust with respect to propofol administration than general anesthesia applications. Consequently, it may be preferable to first develop controller for sedation rather than general purpose controllers. This observation also warns researchers against validating an anesthesia controller based on performance obtained solely from sedated patients.

Using Covariates   Finally, another very simple and effective way of minimizing inter-patient variability is to consider covariates. In particular, age has been shown to be both a PK and PD covariate. As such, considering a limited age bracket should reduce patient variability, and thus, system uncertainty. In that respect, we present in Fig. 5 the uncertainty weights derived from the four different age groups. Each of these weights does indeed present a lower magnitude than that of the weight obtained from the whole adult population. More importantly, the uncertainty weights now cross the unity line in a higher frequency range, which in turn allows for a more aggressive stable control design. Hence, by simply considering the age of the patient, a specific nominal model can be chosen and used to derive a controller that is specific for that age group. Note that in this analysis we selected a 10 years age bracket. It is expected that further reduction of this bracket will provide reduction in uncertainty.

5. CONCLUSION

Pharmacological variability can be a major hurdle towards the development of automated drug delivery systems in anesthesia. In this paper, we proposed an approach to quantify this variability into uncertainty weights which can be readily used in the control design process to tune the controller parameters in order to guarantee stability. The design of robust controllers for automated anesthetic drug delivery will thus be far less likely to undergo numerous iterations in order to yield a satisfactory stable output.

Our results suggest that general purpose controllers designed for the whole adult population (18-60 yrs) and a wide range of drug administration (from slow infusions to fast boluses) cannot be robustly stable, while achieving adequate performance. In order to solve the limitations introduced by the system uncertainty, we therefore investigated simple methods aimed at limiting the controller operating conditions and/or target patient population. We found that limiting the controller to infusion-type administration provides significant improvements. Further tuning of the controller parameters to account for the patient's age group provides additional benefits. Finally, another particularly interesting result is the fact that a closed-loop application targeting the sedation range may be easier to design and implement due to the larger robustness of the PKPD models in that particular output range.

Note that the uncertainty quantification proposed in this paper is conservative, mostly when considering that PKPD models represent positive systems. In that respect, a less conservative approach is to consider the non-negativity of these models, see for instance (Haddad et al., 2003). However, a PKPD model is a mathematical construct of a system which may not be positive. For instance, clinicians often observe an inverse response following propofol administration (EEG activation corresponding to an excitation phase), and propofol elimination (some patients also go into a deeper anesthetic state just before waking up during emergence). The added conservatism imposed by the unstructured framework appears necessary to account for eventual right-hand-plane zeros not modelled in the PKPD structure.

REFERENCES

Bibian, S., G.A. Dumont, M. Huzmezan and C.R. Ries (2006). Patient variability and uncertainty quantification in clinical anesthesia: PART I - PKPD modeling and identification. In: *Proc. of the 2006 IFAC Symposium on Modelling and Control in Biomedical Systems*.

Bibian, S., T. Zikov, C.R. Ries, D.M. Voltz, G.A. Dumont and M. Huzmezan (2004). Pharmacodynamic intra- and inter-patient variability of processed electroencephalography variable during thiopental induction for ECT. In: *Proc. of the 58th Post Grad. Assembly of the New York State Society of Anesthesiologists*. pp. P–9145.

Haddad, W.M., T. Hayakawa and J.M. Bailey (2003). Adaptive control for nonnegative and compartmental dynamical systems with applications to general anesthesia. *Int. J. Adapt. Control Signal Process.* **17**, 209–235.

Skogestad, S. and I. Postlethwaite (2005). *Multivariable Feedback Control : Analysis and Design*. Wiley.

AUTHOR INDEX

Printed and bound by CPI Group (UK) Ltd, Croydon, CR0 4YY

03/10/2024

01040315-0014